Introductory Algebra

Second Edition

To the memory of my mother,
Jeanene Tussy,
and to my dad, Bill Tussy

To my parents,
Roy and Lois Gustafson,
with love and affection

Books in the Tussy and Gustafson Series

In paperback:

Basic Mathematics for College Students Second Edition
Student edition: ISBN 0-534-37643-6
Instructor's edition: ISBN 0-534-38585-0

Prealgebra Second Edition
Student edition: ISBN 0-534-37642-8
Instructor's edition: ISBN 0-534-38309-2

Developmental Mathematics
Student edition: ISBN 0-534-38031-X
Instructor's edition: ISBN 0-534-38584-2

Introductory Algebra Second Edition
Student edition: ISBN 0-534-37641-X
Instructor's edition: ISBN 0-534-38571-0

Intermediate Algebra Second Edition
Student edition: ISBN 0-534-37640-1
Instructor's edition: ISBN 0-534-38586-9

In hardcover:

Elementary Algebra Second Edition
Student edition: ISBN 0-534-38629-6
Instructor's edition: ISBN 0-534-39119-2

Intermediate Algebra Second Edition
Student edition: ISBN 0-534-38628-8
Instructor's edition: ISBN 0-534-39120-6

Elementary and Intermediate Algebra Second Edition
Student edition: ISBN 0-534-38627-X
Instructor's edition: ISBN 0-534-39118-4

Introductory Algebra

Second Edition

Alan S. Tussy
Citrus College

R. David Gustafson
Rock Valley College

BROOKS/COLE

THOMSON LEARNING

Australia • Canada • Mexico • Singapore • Spain • United Kingdom • United States

BROOKS/COLE
THOMSON LEARNING™

Sponsoring Editor: *Jennifer Huber*
Assistant Editor: *Rachael Sturgeon*
Editorial Assistant: *Lisa Jones*
Marketing: *Leah Thomson*
Marketing Communications: *Samantha Cabaluna*
Marketing Assistant: *Maria Salinas*
Production Editor: *Ellen Brownstein*
Production Service: *Hoyt Publishing Services*
Manuscript Editor: *Penelope Suess*
Permissions Editor: *Sue Ewing*

Interior Design: *Vernon T. Boes* and *John Edeen*
Cover Design: *Roy R. Neuhaus*
Cover Illustration: *George Abe*
Interior Illustration: *Lori Heckelman*
Print Buyer: *Vena Dyer*
Typesetting: *The Clarinda Company*
Cover Printing: *Phoenix Color Corp.*
Printing and Binding: *Quebecor World Book*
   Services–Versailles

For more information about this or any other Brooks/Cole product, contact:
BROOKS/COLE
511 Forest Lodge Road
Pacific Grove, CA 93950 USA
www.brookscole.com
1-800-423-0563 (Thomson Learning Academic Resource Center)

For permission to use material from this work, contact us at
www.thomsonrights.com
fax: 1-800-730-2215
phone: 1-800-730-2214

All products named herein are used for identification purposes only
and may be trademarks or registered trademarks of their respective owners.

Printed in the United States of America

10 9 8 7 6 5 4 3 2 1

Images provided by PhotoDisc © 2000

All products used herein are used for identification purposes only
and may be trademarks or registered trademarks of their respective owners.

Library of Congress Cataloging-in-Publication Data
Tussy, Alan S., [date]
    Introductory algebra / Alan S. Tussy, R. David Gustafson.—2nd ed.
      p. cm.
    Includes index.
    ISBN 0-534-37641-X (pbk. : alk. paper)
    1. Algebra.   I. Gustafson, R. David (Roy David), [date]   II. Title.
QA152.3 T87 2002
512.9—dc21
                                  2001025897

CONTENTS

6 *Rational Expressions and Equations* *391*

7 *Solving Systems of Equations and Inequalities* *464*

8 *Roots and Radicals* *529*

For the Instructor

Algebra is a language in its own right. The purpose of this textbook is to teach students how to read, write, speak, and think mathematically using the language of algebra. It presents all the topics associated with a first course in algebra. We have used a variety of instructional approaches, reflecting the recommendations of NCTM and AMATYC. You will find the vocabulary, practice, and well-defined pedagogy of a traditional approach. You will also find that we emphasize the reasoning, modeling, communicating, and technological skills that are such a big part of today's reform movement.

Introductory Algebra expands the students' mathematical reasoning abilities and gives them a set of mathematical survival skills that will help them succeed in a world that increasingly requires that every person become a better analytical thinker.

The second edition retains the basic philosophy and organization of the highly successful first edition. However, we have made several improvements as a direct result of the comments and suggestions we received from instructors and students who have used the first edition. To make the book more enjoyable to read, easier to understand, and more relevant, we have

- added additional examples and problems involving real-life data to make this text more relevant to students, and to show how algebra is used in a wide variety of vocations.

- used a more spacious design, in conjunction with more art and diagrams, to provide stronger support for the visual learner.

- revised Chapter 1 to include a review of fractions and decimals. Operations with signed numbers are now introduced in Chapter 1.

- written a new, more extensive chapter on factoring. This material now appears earlier in the text, as part of Chapter 5.

- reorganized the Table of Contents. Rational Expressions and Equations has been moved to Chapter 6, Systems of Equations to Chapter 7, Roots and Radicals to Chapter 8, and Quadratic Equations (the quadratic formula) to Chapter 9.

- included keystroke instructions for graphing calculators in the Accent on Technology features.

- inserted Cumulative Review Exercises at the end of each chapter (except Chapter 1).

Features of the text

Interactivity

Most worked examples in the text are accompanied by Self Checks. This feature allows students to practice skills discussed in the example by working a similar problem.

Because the Self Check problems are adjacent to the worked examples, students can easily refer to the solution and author's notes of the example as they solve the Self Check. Author's notes are used to explain the steps in the solutions of examples. The notes are extensive so as to increase the student's ability to read and write mathematics.

Example titles highlight the ▶
concept being discussed.

Author's notes explain the steps ▶
in the solution process.

Most examples have Self ▶
Checks. The answers are
provided.

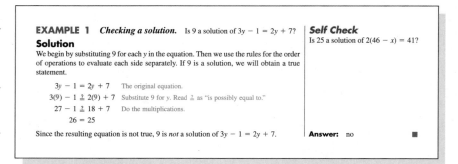

EXAMPLE 1 *Checking a solution.* Is 9 a solution of $3y - 1 = 2y + 7$?

Solution
We begin by substituting 9 for each y in the equation. Then we use the rules for the order of operations to evaluate each side separately. If 9 is a solution, we will obtain a true statement.

$3y - 1 = 2y + 7$ The original equation.
$3(9) - 1 \stackrel{?}{=} 2(9) + 7$ Substitute 9 for y. Read $\stackrel{?}{=}$ as "is possibly equal to."
$27 - 1 \stackrel{?}{=} 18 + 7$ Do the multiplications.
$26 = 25$

Since the resulting equation is not true, 9 is *not* a solution of $3y - 1 = 2y + 7$.

Self Check
Is 25 a solution of $2(46 - x) = 41$?

Answer: no ■

Study Sets—More Than Just Exercises

The problems at the end of each section are called Study Sets. Each Study Set includes Vocabulary, Notation, and Writing problems designed to help students improve their ability to read, write, and communicate mathematical ideas. The problems in the Concepts section of the Study Sets encourage students to engage in independent thinking and reinforce major ideas through exploration. In the Practice section, students get the drill necessary to master the material. In the Applications section, students deal with real-life situations that involve the topics being studied. Each Study Set concludes with a Review section consisting of problems based on material from previous sections.

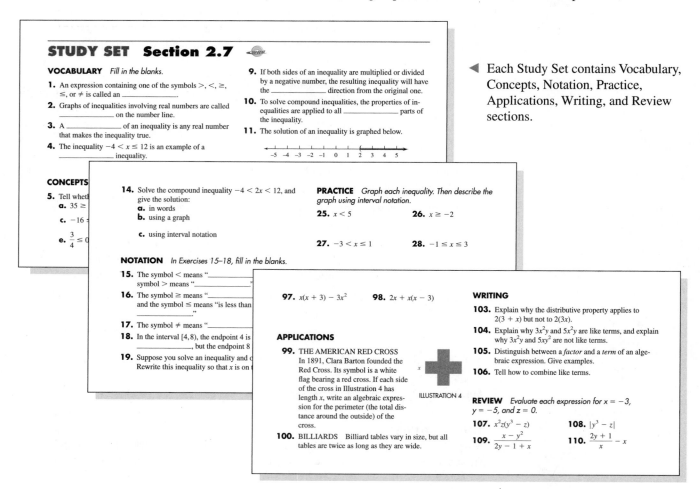

◀ Each Study Set contains Vocabulary, Concepts, Notation, Practice, Applications, Writing, and Review sections.

STUDY SET Section 2.7

VOCABULARY *Fill in the blanks.*

1. An expression containing one of the symbols $>$, $<$, $\geq$, $\leq$, or $\neq$ is called an _____.

2. Graphs of inequalities involving real numbers are called _____ on the number line.

3. A _____ of an inequality is any real number that makes the inequality true.

4. The inequality $-4 < x \leq 12$ is an example of a _____ inequality.

9. If both sides of an inequality are multiplied or divided by a negative number, the resulting inequality will have the _____ direction from the original one.

10. To solve compound inequalities, the properties of inequalities are applied to all _____ parts of the inequality.

11. The solution of an inequality is graphed below.

$$-5 \quad -4 \quad -3 \quad -2 \quad -1 \quad 0 \quad 1 \quad 2 \quad 3 \quad 4 \quad 5$$

CONCEPTS

5. Tell whet[h]
  a. $35 \geq$
  c. -16
  e. $\frac{3}{4} \leq 0$

14. Solve the compound inequality $-4 < 2x < 12$, and give the solution:
  a. in words
  b. using a graph
  c. using interval notation

NOTATION *In Exercises 15–18, fill in the blanks.*

15. The symbol $<$ means "_____"
  symbol $>$ means "_____"

16. The symbol $\geq$ means "_____"
  and the symbol $\leq$ means "is less than _____"

17. The symbol $\neq$ means "_____"

18. In the interval $[4, 8)$, the endpoint 4 is _____, but the endpoint 8 is _____.

19. Suppose you solve an inequality and o[btain]
  Rewrite this inequality so that x is on [the]

PRACTICE *Graph each inequality. Then describe the graph using interval notation.*

25. $x < 5$

26. $x \geq -2$

27. $-3 < x \leq 1$

28. $-1 \leq x \leq 3$

97. $x(x + 3) - 3x^2$

98. $2x + x(x - 3)$

APPLICATIONS

99. THE AMERICAN RED CROSS In 1891, Clara Barton founded the Red Cross. Its symbol is a white flag bearing a red cross. If each side of the cross in Illustration 4 has length x, write an algebraic expression for the perimeter (the total distance around the outside) of the cross.

ILLUSTRATION 4

100. BILLIARDS Billiard tables vary in size, but all tables are twice as long as they are wide.

WRITING

103. Explain why the distributive property applies to $2(3 + x)$ but not to $2(3x)$.

104. Explain why $3x^2y$ and $5x^2y$ are like terms, and explain why $3x^2y$ and $5xy^2$ are not like terms.

105. Distinguish between a *factor* and a *term* of an algebraic expression. Give examples.

106. Tell how to combine like terms.

REVIEW *Evaluate each expression for $x = -3$, $y = -5$, and $z = 0$.*

107. $x^2 z(y^3 - z)$

108. $|y^3 - z|$

109. $\dfrac{x - y^2}{2y - 1 + x}$

110. $\dfrac{2y + 1}{x} - x$

In-Depth Coverage of Geometry

Perimeter, area, and volume, as well as many other geometry concepts, are used in a variety of contexts throughout the book. We have included many drawings to help students improve their ability to spot visual patterns in their everyday lives.

Geometry topics are presented in a practical setting. ▶

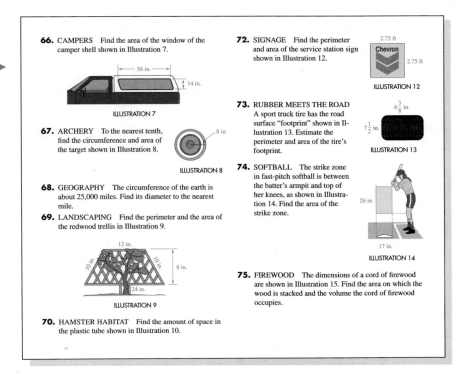

66. CAMPERS   Find the area of the window of the camper shell shown in Illustration 7.

ILLUSTRATION 7

67. ARCHERY   To the nearest tenth, find the circumference and area of the target shown in Illustration 8.

ILLUSTRATION 8

68. GEOGRAPHY   The circumference of the earth is about 25,000 miles. Find its diameter to the nearest mile.

69. LANDSCAPING   Find the perimeter and the area of the redwood trellis in Illustration 9.

ILLUSTRATION 9

70. HAMSTER HABITAT   Find the amount of space in the plastic tube shown in Illustration 10.

72. SIGNAGE   Find the perimeter and area of the service station sign shown in Illustration 12.

ILLUSTRATION 12

73. RUBBER MEETS THE ROAD   A sport truck tire has the road surface "footprint" shown in Illustration 13. Estimate the perimeter and area of the tire's footprint.

ILLUSTRATION 13

74. SOFTBALL   The strike zone in fast-pitch softball is between the batter's armpit and top of her knees, as shown in Illustration 14. Find the area of the strike zone.

ILLUSTRATION 14

75. FIREWOOD   The dimensions of a cord of firewood are shown in Illustration 15. Find the area on which the wood is stacked and the volume the cord of firewood occupies.

Coordinate Graphing Appears Early

The foundation for coordinate graphing is laid in Chapter 1, where the students graph many different types of real numbers on the number line. In Chapter 3, students learn how to graph lines. They quickly learn that the graph of an equation in two variables is not always a straight line.

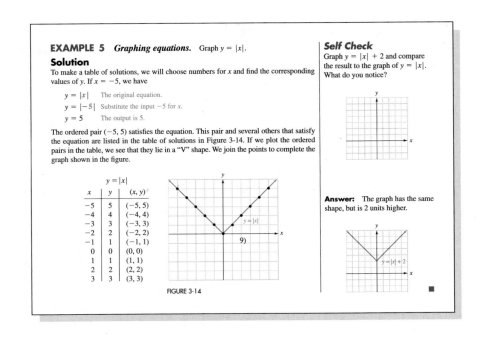

EXAMPLE 5   *Graphing equations.*   Graph $y = |x|$.

Solution

To make a table of solutions, we will choose numbers for x and find the corresponding values of y. If $x = -5$, we have

$y = |x|$ The original equation.

$y = |-5|$ Substitute the input -5 for x.

$y = 5$ The output is 5.

The ordered pair $(-5, 5)$ satisfies the equation. This pair and several others that satisfy the equation are listed in the table of solutions in Figure 3-14. If we plot the ordered pairs in the table, we see that they lie in a "V" shape. We join the points to complete the graph shown in the figure.

$y = |x|$

x	y	(x, y)
-5	5	$(-5, 5)$
-4	4	$(-4, 4)$
-3	3	$(-3, 3)$
-2	2	$(-2, 2)$
-1	1	$(-1, 1)$
0	0	$(0, 0)$
1	1	$(1, 1)$
2	2	$(2, 2)$
3	3	$(3, 3)$

FIGURE 3-14

Self Check

Graph $y = |x| + 2$ and compare the result to the graph of $y = |x|$. What do you notice?

Answer: The graph has the same shape, but is 2 units higher.

Problem-Solving Strategy

One of the major objectives of this textbook is to make students better problem solvers. To this end, we use a five-step problem-solving strategy throughout the book.

The steps of the problem-solving strategy are labeled. ▶

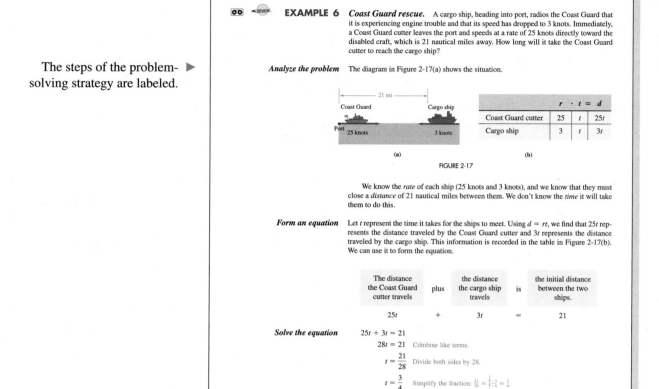

EXAMPLE 6   *Coast Guard rescue.*   A cargo ship, heading into port, radios the Coast Guard that it is experiencing engine trouble and that its speed has dropped to 3 knots. Immediately, a Coast Guard cutter leaves the port and speeds at a rate of 25 knots directly toward the disabled craft, which is 21 nautical miles away. How long will it take the Coast Guard cutter to reach the cargo ship?

Analyze the problem   The diagram in Figure 2-17(a) shows the situation.

	r	$\cdot$ t	$=$ d
Coast Guard cutter	25	t	$25t$
Cargo ship	3	t	$3t$

(a)   (b)

FIGURE 2-17

We know the *rate* of each ship (25 knots and 3 knots), and we know that they must close a *distance* of 21 nautical miles between them. We don't know the *time* it will take them to do this.

Form an equation   Let t represent the time it takes for the ships to meet. Using $d = rt$, we find that $25t$ represents the distance traveled by the Coast Guard cutter and $3t$ represents the distance traveled by the cargo ship. This information is recorded in the table in Figure 2-17(b). We can use it to form the equation.

The distance the Coast Guard cutter travels	plus	the distance the cargo ship travels	is	the initial distance between the two ships.
$25t$	$+$	$3t$	$=$	21

Solve the equation
$$25t + 3t = 21$$
$$28t = 21 \quad \text{Combine like terms.}$$
$$t = \frac{21}{28} \quad \text{Divide both sides by 28.}$$
$$t = \frac{3}{4} \quad \text{Simplify the fraction: } \tfrac{21}{28} = \tfrac{\overset{1}{\cancel{7}} \cdot 3}{\underset{1}{\cancel{7}} \cdot 4} = \tfrac{3}{4}.$$

State the conclusion   The ships will meet in three-quarters of an hour, or 45 minutes.

Check the result   In three-quarters of an hour, the Coast Guard cutter travels $25 \cdot \tfrac{3}{4} = \tfrac{75}{4}$ nautical miles, and the cargo ship travels $3 \cdot \tfrac{3}{4} = \tfrac{9}{4}$ nautical miles. Together, they travel $\tfrac{75}{4} + \tfrac{9}{4} = \tfrac{84}{4} = 21$ nautical miles. Since this is the initial distance between the ships, the solution checks. ∎

Statistics

The concept of arithmetic mean (average) is discussed in Chapter 1. An in-depth study of the mean, the median, and the mode appears in Appendix I.

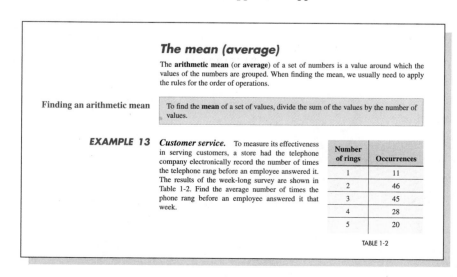

The mean (average)

The **arithmetic mean** (or **average**) of a set of numbers is a value around which the values of the numbers are grouped. When finding the mean, we usually need to apply the rules for the order of operations.

Finding an arithmetic mean   To find the **mean** of a set of values, divide the sum of the values by the number of values.

EXAMPLE 13   *Customer service.*   To measure its effectiveness in serving customers, a store had the telephone company electronically record the number of times the telephone rang before an employee answered it. The results of the week-long survey are shown in Table 1-2. Find the average number of times the phone rang before an employee answered it that week.

Number of rings	Occurrences
1	11
2	46
3	45
4	28
5	20

TABLE 1-2

Group Work

A one-page feature called Accent on Teamwork appears near the end of each chapter. It gives the instructor a set of problems that can be assigned as group work or to individual students as outside-of-class projects.

Key Concepts

Nine key algebraic concepts are highlighted in one-page Key Concept features, appearing near the end of each chapter. Each Key Concept page summarizes a concept and gives students an opportunity to review its importance in the course.

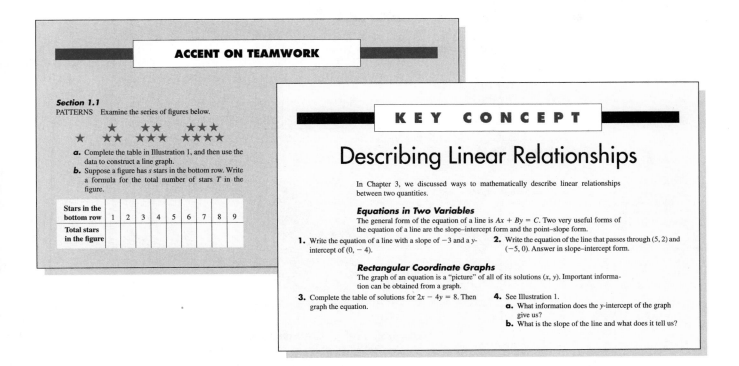

ACCENT ON TEAMWORK

Section 1.1
PATTERNS   Examine the series of figures below.

a. Complete the table in Illustration 1, and then use the data to construct a line graph.
b. Suppose a figure has *s* stars in the bottom row. Write a formula for the total number of stars *T* in the figure.

Stars in the bottom row	1	2	3	4	5	6	7	8	9
Total stars in the figure									

KEY CONCEPT

Describing Linear Relationships

In Chapter 3, we discussed ways to mathematically describe linear relationships between two quantities.

Equations in Two Variables
The general form of the equation of a line is $Ax + By = C$. Two very useful forms of the equation of a line are the slope–intercept form and the point–slope form.

1. Write the equation of a line with a slope of -3 and a y-intercept of $(0, -4)$.

2. Write the equation of the line that passes through $(5, 2)$ and $(-5, 0)$. Answer in slope–intercept form.

Rectangular Coordinate Graphs
The graph of an equation is a "picture" of all of its solutions (x, y). Important information can be obtained from a graph.

3. Complete the table of solutions for $2x - 4y = 8$. Then graph the equation.

4. See Illustration 1.
 a. What information does the y-intercept of the graph give us?
 b. What is the slope of the line and what does it tell us?

Analyzing Real Data

There are many problems that require students to use newly learned algebraic skills to interpret real data that appears in the form of tables, graphs, and diagrams.

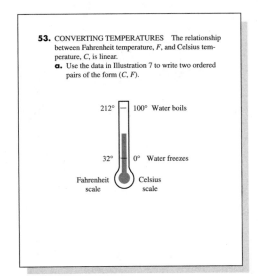

53. CONVERTING TEMPERATURES   The relationship between Fahrenheit temperature, F, and Celsius temperature, C, is linear.
 a. Use the data in Illustration 7 to write two ordered pairs of the form (C, F).

$212°$ — $100°$ Water boils

$32°$ — $0°$ Water freezes

Fahrenheit scale   Celsius scale

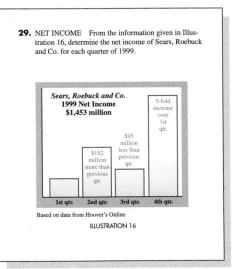

29. NET INCOME   From the information given in Illustration 16, determine the net income of Sears, Roebuck and Co. for each quarter of 1999.

Sears, Roebuck and Co.
1999 Net Income
$1,453 million

5-fold increase over 1st qtr.

$95 million less than previous qtr.

$182 million more than previous qtr.

1st qtr. 2nd qtr. 3rd qtr. 4th qtr.

Based on data from Hoover's Online
ILLUSTRATION 16

Systematic Review

Each Study Set ends with a Review section that contains problems similar to those in previous sections. Each chapter ends with a Chapter Review and a Chapter Test. The chapter reviews have been designed to be "user friendly." In a unique format, the reviews list the important concepts of each section of the chapter in one column, with appropriate review problems running parallel in a second column. In addition, Cumulative Review Exercises appear at the end of each chapter (except Chapter 1).

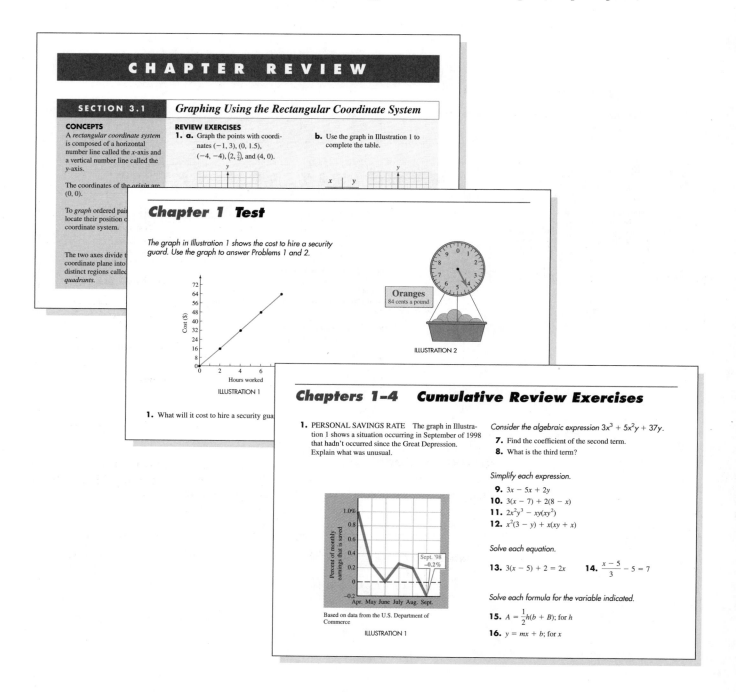

CHAPTER REVIEW

SECTION 3.1 — Graphing Using the Rectangular Coordinate System

CONCEPTS

A *rectangular coordinate system* is composed of a horizontal number line called the *x*-axis and a vertical number line called the *y*-axis.

The coordinates of the *origin* are (0, 0).

To *graph* ordered pair locate their position coordinate system.

The two axes divide coordinate plane into distinct regions called *quadrants*.

REVIEW EXERCISES

1. a. Graph the points with coordinates $(-1, 3)$, $(0, 1.5)$, $(-4, -4)$, $(2, \frac{7}{2})$, and $(4, 0)$.

b. Use the graph in Illustration 1 to complete the table.

x	y

Chapter 1 Test

The graph in Illustration 1 shows the cost to hire a security guard. Use the graph to answer Problems 1 and 2.

Cost ($) vs. Hours worked

ILLUSTRATION 1

Oranges
84 cents a pound

ILLUSTRATION 2

1. What will it cost to hire a security gua

Chapters 1–4   Cumulative Review Exercises

1. PERSONAL SAVINGS RATE   The graph in Illustration 1 shows a situation occurring in September of 1998 that hadn't occurred since the Great Depression. Explain what was unusual.

Percent of monthly earnings that is saved

Sept. '98
−0.2%

Apr. May June July Aug. Sept.

Based on data from the U.S. Department of Commerce

ILLUSTRATION 1

Consider the algebraic expression $3x^3 + 5x^2y + 37y$.

7. Find the coefficient of the second term.

8. What is the third term?

Simplify each expression.

9. $3x - 5x + 2y$

10. $3(x - 7) + 2(8 - x)$

11. $2x^2y^3 - xy(xy^2)$

12. $x^2(3 - y) + x(xy + x)$

Solve each equation.

13. $3(x - 5) + 2 = 2x$ **14.** $\frac{x - 5}{3} - 5 = 7$

Solve each formula for the variable indicated.

15. $A = \frac{1}{2}h(b + B)$; for h

16. $y = mx + b$; for x

Calculators

For instructors who wish to use calculators as part of the instruction in this course, the text includes an Accent on Technology feature that introduces keystrokes and shows how scientific calculators and graphing calculators can be used to solve problems. The Study Sets display a logo 🖩 to denote problems that require a scientific calculator. In Chapter 3, graphing calculators are introduced as a means of checking students' graphs.

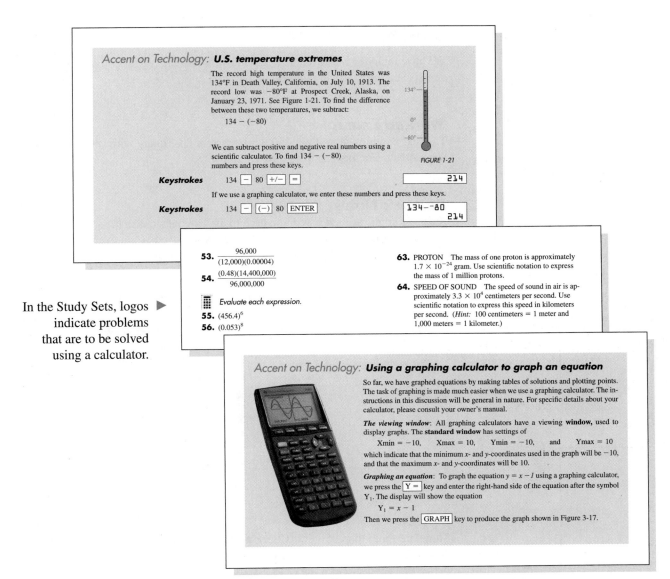

Accent on Technology: **U.S. temperature extremes**

The record high temperature in the United States was 134°F in Death Valley, California, on July 10, 1913. The record low was −80°F at Prospect Creek, Alaska, on January 23, 1971. See Figure 1-21. To find the difference between these two temperatures, we subtract:

$$134 - (-80)$$

We can subtract positive and negative real numbers using a scientific calculator. To find $134 - (-80)$ numbers and press these keys.

FIGURE 1-21

Keystrokes   134 [−] 80 [+/−] [=]   `214`

If we use a graphing calculator, we enter these numbers and press these keys.

Keystrokes   134 [−] [(−)] 80 [ENTER]   `134--80`
                                               `214`

In the Study Sets, logos ▶ indicate problems that are to be solved using a calculator.

53. $\dfrac{96{,}000}{(12{,}000)(0.00004)}$

54. $\dfrac{(0.48)(14{,}400{,}000)}{96{,}000{,}000}$

▦ *Evaluate each expression.*

55. $(456.4)^6$

56. $(0.053)^8$

63. PROTON   The mass of one proton is approximately 1.7×10^{-24} gram. Use scientific notation to express the mass of 1 million protons.

64. SPEED OF SOUND   The speed of sound in air is approximately 3.3×10^4 centimeters per second. Use scientific notation to express this speed in kilometers per second. (*Hint:* 100 centimeters = 1 meter and 1,000 meters = 1 kilometer.)

Accent on Technology: **Using a graphing calculator to graph an equation**

So far, we have graphed equations by making tables of solutions and plotting points. The task of graphing is made much easier when we use a graphing calculator. The instructions in this discussion will be general in nature. For specific details about your calculator, please consult your owner's manual.

The viewing window: All graphing calculators have a viewing **window,** used to display graphs. The **standard window** has settings of

   Xmin = −10,   Xmax = 10,   Ymin = −10,   and   Ymax = 10

which indicate that the minimum *x*- and *y*-coordinates used in the graph will be −10, and that the maximum *x*- and *y*-coordinates will be 10.

Graphing an equation: To graph the equation $y = x - 1$ using a graphing calculator, we press the [Y =] key and enter the right-hand side of the equation after the symbol Y_1. The display will show the equation

   $Y_1 = x - 1$

Then we press the [GRAPH] key to produce the graph shown in Figure 3-17.

Connections to Other Disciplines

A distinguishing feature of this book is its wealth of application problems We have included numerous applications from disciplines such as science, economics, business, manufacturing, history, and entertainment, as well as mathematics.

Every application problem ▶ has a title.

99. PHYSICS   An oscilloscope is an instrument that displays electrical signals, which appear as wavy lines on a fluorescent screen. (See Illustration 4.) By switching the magnification setting (MAGNIFN.) to × 2, for example, the "height" of the crest and the "depth" of the trough of a graph will be doubled. Use signed numbers to indicate the crest height and the trough depth for each setting of the magnification dial.
a. normal   **b.** × 0.5
c. × 1.5   **d.** × 2

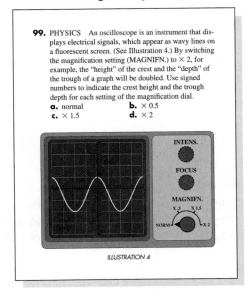

ILLUSTRATION 4

129. SCRABBLE   Illustration 6(a) shows a portion of the game board before and Illustration 6(b) shows it after the word *QUARTZY* is played. Determine the score. (The number on each tile gives the point value of the letter.)

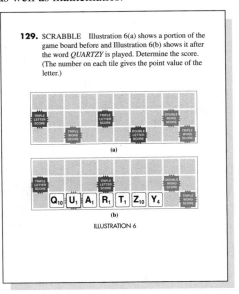

ILLUSTRATION 6

Student support

We have included many features that make *Introductory Algebra* very accessible to students. (See the examples starting on page x.)

Worked Examples

The text contains more than 450 worked examples, many with several parts. Explanatory notes make the examples easy to follow.

Author's Notes

Author's notes, printed in red, are used to explain the steps in the solutions of examples. The notes are extensive; complete sentences are used so as to increase the students' ability to read and write mathematics.

Special logos show which ▸
examples are included in the CD
and the videotape series.

Each step is explained using ▸
detailed author's notes.

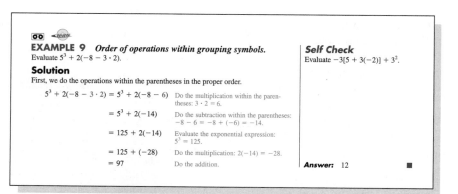

Self Checks

There are more than 350 Self Check problems that allow students to practice the skills demonstrated in the worked examples.

Comments

Throughout the text, Comments call attention to common mistakes and how to avoid them.

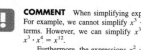

COMMENT When simplifying expressions, note the operations that are involved. For example, we cannot simplify $x^3 + x^4$ or $x^3 - x^4$, because x^3 and x^4 are not like terms. However, we can simplify $x^3 \cdot x^4$, because x^3 and x^4 have the same base: $x^3 \cdot x^4 = x^{12}$.

Furthermore, the expressions $x^2 + y^3$ and $x^2 - y^3$ cannot be simplified, because they do not contain like terms; neither can the expression $x^2 y^3$, because x^2 and y^3 have different bases.

Videotapes

The videotape series that accompanies this book shows students the steps in solving many examples in the text. A video logo 🆗 placed next to an example indicates that the example is taught on tape. In addition, the tapes present the solutions of some of the Study Set problems from each section.

Functional Use of Color

For easy reference, definitions, strategies, and properties are printed in blue boxes. In addition, color is used in some multi-step solutions to aid student understanding.

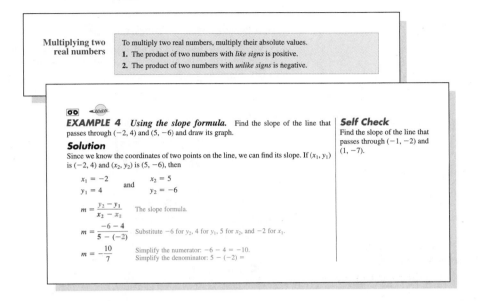

| Multiplying two real numbers | To multiply two real numbers, multiply their absolute values.
 1. The product of two numbers with *like signs* is positive.
 2. The product of two numbers with *unlike signs* is negative. |

EXAMPLE 4 *Using the slope formula.* Find the slope of the line that passes through $(-2, 4)$ and $(5, -6)$ and draw its graph.

Solution

Since we know the coordinates of two points on the line, we can find its slope. If (x_1, y_1) is $(-2, 4)$ and (x_2, y_2) is $(5, -6)$, then

$$x_1 = -2 \quad \text{and} \quad x_2 = 5$$
$$y_1 = 4 \qquad\qquad y_2 = -6$$

$$m = \frac{y_2 - y_1}{x_2 - x_3} \quad \text{The slope formula.}$$

$$m = \frac{-6 - 4}{5 - (-2)} \quad \text{Substitute } -6 \text{ for } y_2, 4 \text{ for } y_1, 5 \text{ for } x_2, \text{ and } -2 \text{ for } x_1.$$

$$m = -\frac{10}{7} \quad \text{Simplify the numerator: } -6 - 4 = -10.$$
$$\qquad\qquad \text{Simplify the denominator: } 5 - (-2) =$$

Self Check

Find the slope of the line that passes through $(-1, -2)$ and $(1, -7)$.

Problems and Answers

The book includes thousands of carefully graded exercises. Appendix III provides the answers to most of the odd-numbered exercises in the Study Sets as well as all the answers to the Chapter Review, Chapter Test, and Cumulative Review problems.

Reading and Writing Mathematics

Also included (on pages xxi-xxii) are two features to help students improve their ability to read and write mathematics. "Reading Mathematics" helps students get the most out of the examples in this book by showing them how to read the solutions properly. "Writing Mathematics" highlights the characteristics of a well-written solution.

Study Skills and Math Anxiety

These two topics are discussed in detail in the section entitled "For the Student" beginning on page xx. In "Success in Algebra," students are asked to design a strategy for studying and learning the material. "Taking a Math Test," on page 84, helps students prepare for a test and then gives suggestions for improving their performance.

Ancillaries for the instructor

Annotated Instructor's Edition

This is a special version of the complete student text, with all answers printed in blue next to the respective exercises.

Complete Solutions Manual

The *Complete Solutions Manual* provides worked-out solutions to all the exercises.

BCA Testing

Brooks/Cole Assessment is a text-specific, Internet-ready testing suite that allows instructions to customize exams and track student progress in a browser-based format.

BCA offers full algorithmic generation of problems and free-response questions. The testing and course-management components simplify routine tasks. Test results flow automatically into the gradebook, and the instructor can easily communicate with individuals, sections, or entire courses.

Text-Specific Videotapes

A set of videotapes is available free upon adoption of the text. Each tape covers one chapter of the text, broken into problem-solving sessions of 10 to 20 minutes. Examples from each section of the chapter are covered, as well as exercises from each Student Set. Where an example is taught on tape, a special logo [oo] is printed next to the example in the text.

Ancillaries for the student

Student Solutions Manual

The *Student Solutions Manual* provides worked-out solutions to the odd-numbered exercises in the text.

BCA Tutorial

This text-specific interactive software is delivered via the Web (at http://bca.brookscole.com). It is offered in both student's and instructor's versions. Because it is browser-based, it can serve as an intuitive guide even for students who have little technological proficiency. BCA Tutorial allows students to work with real math notation in real time, providing instant analysis and feedback. In the instructor's version, a built-in tracking program enables instructors to monitor student progress.

Interactive Video Skillbuilder CD

Packaged with each book, this single CD-ROM contains more than eight hours of video instruction. The problems worked during each video lesson are listed next to the viewing screen, so that students can work them ahead of time if they choose. To help students evaluate their progress, each section contains a 10-question WEB quiz, and there is a chapter test, with answers provided, for each chapter.

Acknowledgments

We are grateful to the instructors who have reviewed the text at various stages of its development. Their comments and suggestions have proven invaluable in making this a better book. We sincerely thank all of them for lending their time and talent to this project.

Linda Beattie
Western New Mexico University

Julia Brown
Atlantic Community College

Linda Clay
Albuquerque TVI

John Coburn
Saint Louis Community College–Florissant Valley

Sally Copeland
Johnson County Community College

Ben Cornelius
Oregon Institute of Technology

James Edmondson
Santa Barbara Community College

David L. Fama
Germanna Community College

Barbara Gentry
Parkland College

Laurie Hoecherl
Kishwaukee College

Judith Jones
Valencia Community College

Therese Jones
Amarillo College

Joanne Juedes
University of Wisconsin–Marathon County

Dennis Kimzey
Rogue Community College

Sally Lesik
Holyoke Community College

Elizabth Morrison
Valencia Community College

Jan Alicia Nettler
Holyoke Community College

Scott Perkins
Lake–Sumter Community College

Angela Peterson
Portland Community College

J. Doug Richey
Northeast Texas Community College

Angelo Segalla
Orange Coast College

June Strohm
Pennsylvania State Community College–DuBois

Rita Sturgeon
San Bernardino Valley College

Jo Anne Temple
Texas Technical University

Sharon Testone
Onondaga Community College

Marilyn Treder
Rochester Community College

Thomas Vanden Eynden
Thomas More College

We want to express our gratitude to Karl Hunsicker, Cathy Gong, Dave Ryba, Terry Damron, Marion Hammond, Lin Humphrey, Doug Keebaugh, Robin Carter, Tanja Rinkel, Bob Billups, Liz Tussy, and the Citrus College Library staff (including Barbara Rugeley) for their help with some of the application problems in the textbook.

Without the talents and dedication of the editorial, marketing, and production staff of Brooks/Cole, this revision of *Introductory Algebra* could not have been so well accomplished. We express our sincere appreciation for the hard work of Bob Pirtle, Jennifer Huber, Rachael Sturgeon, Leah Thomson, Samantha Cabaluna, Ellen Brownstein, Vernon Boes, Micky Lawler, and Vena Dyer, as well as the freelance talents of David Hoyt, Lori Heckelman, John Edeen, and Roy Neuhaus and the superb typesetting of the Clarinda Company.

Alan S. Tussy
R. David Gustafson

For the Student

Success in algebra

To be successful in mathematics, you need to know how to study it. The following checklist will help you develop your own personal strategy to study and learn the material. The suggestions listed below require some time and self-discipline on your part, but it will be worth the effort. This will help you get the most out of this course.

As you read each of the following statements, place a check mark in the box if you can truthfully answer Yes. If you can't answer Yes, think of what you might do to make the suggestion part of your personal study plan. You should go over this checklist several times during the semester to be sure you are following it.

Preparing for the Class

☐ I have made a commitment to myself to give this course my best effort.

☐ I have the proper materials: a pencil with an eraser, paper, a notebook, a ruler, a calculator, and a calendar or day planner.

☐ I am willing to spend a minimum of two hours doing homework for every hour of class.

☐ I will try to work on this subject every day.

☐ I have a copy of the class syllabus. I understand the requirements of the course and how I will be graded.

☐ I have scheduled a free hour after the class to give me time to review my notes and begin the homework assignment.

Class Participation

☐ I know my instructor's name.

☐ I will regularly attend the class sessions and be on time.

☐ When I am absent, I will find out what the class studied, get a copy of any notes or handouts, and make up the work that was assigned when I was gone.

☐ I will sit where I can hear the instructor and see the chalkboard.

☐ I will pay attention in class and take careful notes.

☐ I will ask the instructor questions when I don't understand the material.

☐ When tests, quizzes, or homework papers are passed back and discussed in class, I will write down the correct solutions for the problems I missed so that I can learn from my mistakes.

Study Sessions

☐ I will find a comfortable and quiet place to study.

☐ I realize that reading a math book is different from reading a newspaper or a novel. Quite often, it will take more than one reading to understand the material.

☐ After studying an example in the textbook, I will work the accompanying Self Check.

☐ I will begin the homework assignment only after reading the assigned section.

☐ I will try to use the mathematical vocabulary mentioned in the book and used by my instructor when I am writing or talking about the topics studied in this course.

☐ I will look for opportunities to explain the material to others.

☐ I will check all my answers to the problems with those provided in the back of the book (or with the *Student Solutions Manual*) and resolve any differences.

☐ My homework will be organized and neat. My solutions will show all the necessary steps.

☐ I will work some review problems every day.

☐ After completing the homework assignment, I will read the next section to prepare for the coming class session.

☐ I will keep a notebook containing my class notes, homework papers, quizzes, tests, and any handouts—all in order by date.

Special Help

☐ I know my instructor's office hours and am willing to go in to ask for help.

☐ I have formed a study group with classmates that meets regularly to discuss the material and work on problems.

☐ When I need additional explanation of a topic, I use the tutorial videos and the interactive CD, as well as the website.

☐ I make use of extra tutorial assistance that my school offers for mathematics courses.

☐ I have purchased the *Student Solutions Manual* that accompanies this text, and I use it.

To follow each of these suggestions will take time. It takes a lot of practice to learn mathematics, just as with any other skill.

No doubt, you will sometimes become frustrated along the way. This is natural. When it occurs, take a break and come back to the material after you have had time to clear your thoughts. Keep in mind that the skills and discipline you learn in this course will help make for a brighter future. Good luck!

Reading mathematics

To get the most out of this book, you need to learn how to read it correctly. A mathematics textbook must be read differently than a novel or a newspaper. For one thing, you need to read it slowly and carefully. At times, you will have to reread a section to understand its content. You should also have pencil and paper, so that you can work along with the text to understand the concepts presented.

Perhaps the most informative parts of a mathematics book are its examples. Each example in this textbook consists of a problem and its corresponding solution. One form of solution that is used many times in this book is shown in the diagram on the next page. It is important that you follow the "flow" of its steps if you are to understand the mathematics involved. For this solution form, the basic idea is this:

- A property, rule, or procedure is applied to the original expression to obtain an equivalent expression. We show that the two expressions are equivalent by writing an equals sign between them. The property, rule, or procedure that was used is then listed next to the equivalent expression in the form of an author's note, printed in red.

- The process of writing equivalent expressions and explaining the reasons behind them continues, step by step, until the final result is obtained.

The solution in the following diagram consists of three steps, but solutions have varying lengths.

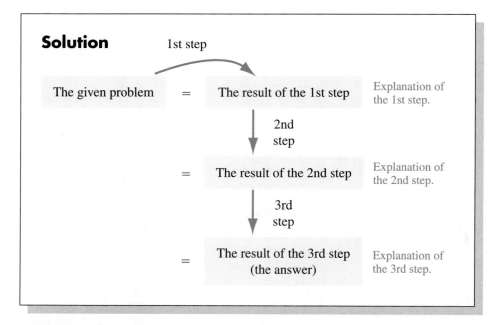

Solution   1st step

The given problem $=$ The result of the 1st step   Explanation of the 1st step.

2nd step

$=$ The result of the 2nd step   Explanation of the 2nd step.

3rd step

$=$ The result of the 3rd step (the answer)   Explanation of the 3rd step.

Writing mathematics

One of the major objectives of this course is for you to learn how to write solutions to problems properly. A written solution to a problem should explain your thinking in a series of neat and organized mathematical steps. Think of a solution as a mathematical essay—one that your instructor and other students should be able to read and understand. Some solutions will be longer than others, but they must all be in the proper format and use the correct notation. To learn how to do this will take time and practice.

To give you an idea of what will be expected, let's look at two samples of student work. In the first, we have highlighted some important characteristics of a well-written solution. The second sample is poorly done and would not be acceptable.

Evaluate $35 - 2^2 \cdot 3$.

A well-written solution:

The problem has been ▶ copied from the textbook.

$$35 - 2^2 \cdot 3 = 35 - 4 \cdot 3$$
$$= 35 - 12$$
$$= 23$$

◀ The first step of the solution is written here.

◀ The steps are written under each other in a neat, organized manner.

The equals signs are lined up vertically.

A poorly written solution:

The problem has not ▶ been copied from the text.

$2^2 = 4 = 35 - 4 \cdot 3$
$\underbrace{}$
12

SUB: 35
$\underline{-12}$
$23 \longrightarrow = \boxed{23}$

◀ An equals sign is improperly used.

◀ The work is disorganized and difficult to follow.

An Introduction to Algebra

1

ALGEBRA IS A MATHEMATICAL LANGUAGE THAT CAN BE USED TO SOLVE MANY TYPES OF PROBLEMS.

1.1 *Describing Numerical Relationships*

In this section, you will learn about

- Tables • Graphs • Vocabulary • Symbols and notation
- Variables, algebraic expressions, and equations • Constructing tables

INTRODUCTION. Algebra is the result of contributions from many cultures over thousands of years. The word *algebra* comes from the title of the book *Ihm Al-jabr wa'l muqābalah,* written by the Arabian mathematician al-Khwarizmi around A.D. 800. Using the vocabulary, symbols, and notation of algebra, we can mathematically describe (or **model**) the real world. In this section, we begin to explore the language of algebra by introducing four algebraic methods that are used to describe numerical relationships: tables, graphs, words, and equations.

Tables

Two-column **tables** are often used to describe numerical relationships. For example, Figure 1-1 lists the number of bicycle tires a production planner must order when a given number of bicycles are to be manufactured. For a production run of, say, 300 bikes, we locate 300 in the left-hand column and then scan across the table to see that the company must order 600 tires.

Bicycles to be manufactured	Tires to order
100	200
200	400
300	600
400	800

FIGURE 1-1

Graphs

The information in the table can also be presented graphically. The **bar graph** in Figure 1-2 has a **horizontal axis** labeled "Number of bicycles to be manufactured" and has been scaled in units of 100 bicycles. The **vertical axis,** labeled "Number of tires to be ordered," is scaled in units of 100 tires. The bars directly over each of the production amounts extend to a height indicating the corresponding number of tires to order. For example, if 200 bikes are to be manufactured, the height of the bar indicates that 400 tires should be ordered.

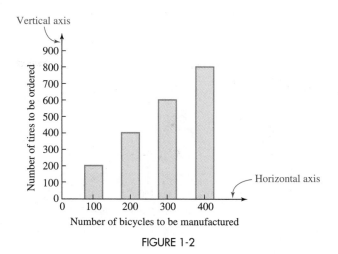

FIGURE 1-2

Another way to present the information in Figure 1-1 is with a **line graph.** Instead of using a bar to denote the number of tires to order for a production run of a given size, we use a dot drawn at the correct height. See Figure 1-3(a). After drawing the four data points for 100, 200, 300, and 400 bicycles, we connect them with line segments to create the line graph shown in Figure 1-3(b).

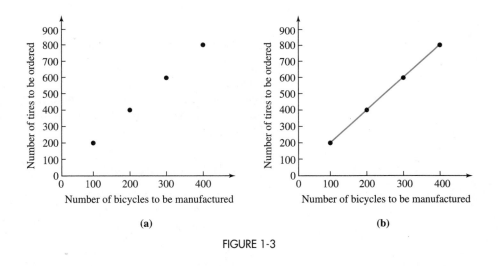

FIGURE 1-3

The line graph not only presents all the information contained in the table and the bar graph; it provides additional information that they do not. We can use the line graph to find the number of tires to order for a production run of a size not shown in the table or the bar graph.

EXAMPLE 1 *Reading a line graph.* Use the graph in Figure 1-3(b) to find the number of tires needed when 250 bicycles are to be manufactured.

Solution

First, locate 250 (between 200 and 300) on the horizontal axis. Then draw a line straight up to intersect the graph. (See Figure 1-4 on the next page.) From the point of intersection, draw a horizontal line to the left that intersects the vertical axis. We see that the number of tires to order is 500.

Self Check

Use the graph in Figure 1-4 to find the number of tires needed when 350 bicycles are to be manufactured.

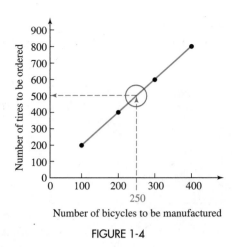

FIGURE 1-4

Answer: 700   ■

Vocabulary

After working with the table, the bar graph, and the line graph, it is evident that there is a relationship between the number of tires to order and the number of bicycles to be manufactured. Using words, we can express this relationship as follows:

"The number of tires to order is two times the number of bicycles to be manufactured."

Since the word **product** is used to indicate the answer to a multiplication, we can restate the relationship this way:

"The number of tires to order is the product of 2 and the number of bicycles to be manufactured."

To indicate other arithmetic operations, we will use the following words. A **sum** is the result of an addition: The sum of 5 and 6 is 11. A **difference** is the result of a subtraction: The difference of 3 and 2 is 1. A **quotient** is the result of a division: The quotient of 6 and 3 is 2.

Symbols and notation

The + sign is used to indicate addition, and the − sign is used to indicate subtraction. Because the letter *x* is often used in algebra and could be confused with the multiplication sign ×, we normally write multiplication in another form.

Symbols that are used for multiplication

Symbol	Name	Examples
×	times sign	$6 \times 4 = 24$
·	raised dot	$6 \cdot 4 = 24$
( )	parentheses	$(6)4 = 24$ or $6(4) = 24$ or $(6)(4) = 24$

There are several ways to indicate division. In algebra, the form most often used involves a fraction bar.

Symbols that are used for division

Symbol	Name	Examples
÷	division sign	$24 \div 4 = 6$
$)\overline{}$	long division	$4\overline{)24}$ with quotient 6
—	fraction bar	$\dfrac{24}{4} = 6$

EXAMPLE 2   *Vocabulary.*   Express each statement in words, using one of the words *sum, product, difference,* or *quotient:*   **a.** 22 ÷ 11 = 2   and
b. 22 + 11 = 33.

Solution
a. The quotient of 22 and 11 is 2.

b. The sum of 22 and 11 is 33.

Self Check

Express the following statement in words.

$$22 - 11 = 11$$

Answer: The difference of 22 and 11 is 11.   ■

Variables, algebraic expressions, and equations

Another way to describe the relationship between the number of tires to order and the number of bicycles being manufactured uses *variables.* **Variables** are letters that stand for numbers. If we let the letter *t* stand for the number of tires to be ordered and *b* for the number of bicycles to be manufactured, we can translate the **verbal model** to mathematical symbols.

The number of tires to order	is	two	times	the number of bicycles to be manufactured.
t	$=$	2	$\cdot$	b

The statement $t = 2 \cdot b$ is called an **equation.** An equation is a mathematical sentence that contains an = sign. Some examples of equations are

$$3 + 5 = 8 \qquad x + 5 = 20 \qquad 17 - t = 14 - t \qquad p = 100 - d$$

In the equation $t = 2 \cdot b$, the variable *b* is multiplied by 2. When we multiply a variable by another number or multiply a variable by another variable, we can omit the symbol for multiplication.

$$2b \text{ means } 2 \cdot b \qquad xy \text{ means } x \cdot y \qquad abc \text{ means } a \cdot b \cdot c$$

Using this form, we can write the equation $t = 2 \cdot b$ as $t = 2b$. The notation $2b$ on the right-hand side of the equation is called an **algebraic expression.**

Algebraic expressions

> Variables and/or numbers can be combined with the operations of addition, subtraction, multiplication, and division to create **algebraic expressions.**

Here are some examples of algebraic expressions.

$2a + 7$ This algebraic expression is a combination of the numbers 2 and 7, the variable *a*, and the operations of multiplication and addition.

$\dfrac{10 - y}{3}$ This algebraic expression is a combination of the numbers 10 and 3, the variable *y*, and the operations of subtraction and division.

$15mn(2m)$ This algebraic expression is a combination of the numbers 15 and 2, the variables *m* and *n*, and the operation of multiplication.

In the bicycle-manufacturing example, using the equation $t = 2b$ to describe the relationship has one major advantage over the other methods we have discussed. It can be used to determine the exact number of tires to order for a production run of *any* size.

EXAMPLE 3   *Using an equation.*   Find the number of tires needed for a production run of 178 bicycles.

Self Check

Use the equation $t = 2b$ to find the number of tires needed if 604 bicycles are to be manufactured.

Solution

To find the number of tires needed, we use the equation that describes this numerical relationship.

$t = 2b$	The describing equation.
$t = 2(178)$	Replace b, which stands for the number of bicycles, with 178. Use parentheses to show the multiplication.
$t = 356$	Do the multiplication: $2(178) = 356$.

To manufacture 178 bicycles, 356 tires will be needed.

Answer: 1,208   ■

Constructing tables

Equations such as $t = 2b$, which express a known relationship between two or more variables, are called **formulas.** Formulas are used in many fields, such as economics, biology, nursing, and construction. In the next example, we will see that the results found using the formula $t = 2b$ can be presented in table form.

EXAMPLE 4   *Constructing a table.*   Find the number of tires to order for production runs of 233 and 852 bicycles. Present the results in a table.

Solution

We begin by constructing a table with the appropriate column headings. The size of each production run (233 and 852) is entered in the left-hand column of the table.

Bicycles to be manufactured	Tires to order
233	
852	

Next, we use the formula $t = 2b$ to find the number of tires needed if 233 and 852 bikes are to be manufactured.

$t = 2b$	$t = 2b$
$t = 2(233)$ Replace b with 233.	$t = 2(852)$ Replace b with 852.
$t = 466$	$t = 1,704$

Finally, we enter these results in the right-hand column of the table: 466 tires for 233 bicycles to be manufactured and 1,704 tires for 852 bicycles to be manufactured.

Bicycles to be manufactured	Tires to order
233	466
852	1,704

Self Check

Find the number of tires to order for production runs of 87 and 487 bicycles. Present the results in a table.

Bicycles to be manufactured	Tires to order

Answers:

Bicycles to be manufactured	Tires to order
87	174
487	974

■

STUDY SET   Section 1.1

VOCABULARY   *Fill in the blanks.*

1. The answer to an addition problem is called the _____ sum _____. The answer to a subtraction problem is called the ___ difference ___.

2. The answer to a multiplication problem is called the _____ product _____. The answer to a division problem is called the ___ quotient ___.

3. _____Variables_____ are letters that stand for numbers.

4. Variables and numbers can be combined with the operations of addition, subtraction, multiplication, and division to create algebraic _____expressions_____.

5. An _____equation_____ is a mathematical sentence that contains an = sign.

6. An equation such as $t = 2b$, which expresses a known relationship between two or more variables, is called a _____formula_____.

7. In Illustration 1, a _____line_____ graph is shown.

8. In Illustration 1, the _____horizontal_____ axis of the graph has been scaled in units of 1 second. The _____vertical_____ axis of the graph has been scaled in units of 50 feet.

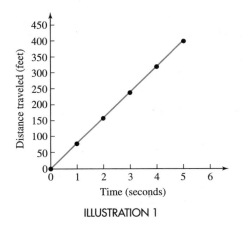

ILLUSTRATION 1

CONCEPTS *In Exercises 9–16, classify each item as either an algebraic expression or an equation.*

9. $18 + m = 23$
equation

10. $18 + m$
algebraic expression

11. $y - 1$
algebraic expression

12. $y - 1 = 2$
equation

13. $30x$ algebraic expression

14. $t = 16b$ equation

15. $r = \dfrac{2}{3}$
equation

16. $\dfrac{c - 7}{5}$
algebraic expression

17. a. What operations does the expression $5x - 16$ contain?   multiplication, subtraction
b. What variable does the expression contain? x

18. a. What operations does the expression $\frac{12 + t}{25}$ contain?
addition, division
b. What variable does the expression contain? t

19. a. What operations does the equation $4 + 1 = 20 - m$ contain?   addition, subtraction
b. What variable does it contain? m

20. a. What operations does the equation $y + 14 = 5(6)$ contain?   addition, multiplication
b. What variable does it contain? y

21. See Illustration 2. As the railroad crossing guard drops, the measure of angle 1 (denoted $\angle 1$) increases, while the measure of $\angle 2$ decreases. At any instant, the sum of the measures of the two angles is 90°.
a. Complete the table.

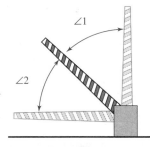

$\angle 1$	$\angle 2$
0°	90°
30°	60°
45°	45°
60°	30°
90°	0°

ILLUSTRATION 2

b. Use the data in the table to construct a line graph for values of $\angle 1$ from 0° to 90°.

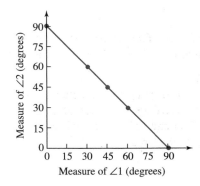

22. See Illustration 3. As the legs of the keyboard stand are widened, the measure of angle 1 (denoted $\angle 1$) will increase, and in turn, the measure of $\angle 2$ will decrease. For any position, the sum of the measures of the two angles is 180°.
a. Complete the table.

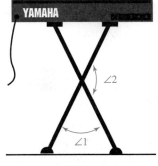

$\angle 1$	$\angle 2$
50°	130°
60°	120°
70°	110°
80°	100°
90°	90°

ILLUSTRATION 3

b. Use the data in the table to construct a line graph (see the next page) for values of $\angle 1$ from 50° to 90°.

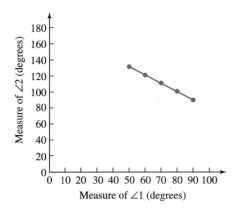

23. a. Explain what the dotted lines help us find in the graph in Illustration 4.

They help us determine that 15-year-old machinery is worth $35,000.

b. As the machinery ages, what happens to its value?

It decreases.

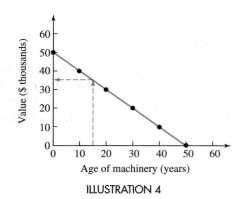

ILLUSTRATION 4

24. a. Use the line graph in Illustration 5 to find the income received from 30, 50, and 70 customers.

$250, $350, $450

b. As the number of customers increases, what happens to the income?   It increases.

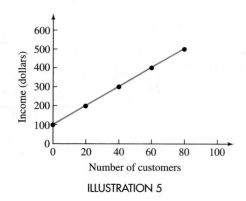

ILLUSTRATION 5

NOTATION   *Write each multiplication in two other ways: first using a raised dot · and then using parentheses ( ).*

25. 5 × 6   5 · 6, 5(6)   **26.** 4 × 7   4 · 7, 4(7)

27. 34 × 75   34 · 75, 34(75)   **28.** 90 × 12   90 · 12, 90(12)

Write each expression without using a multiplication symbol.

29. 4 · x   4x   **30.** 5 · y   5y

31. 3 · r · t   3rt   **32.** 22 · q · s   22qs

33. l · w   lw   **34.** b · h   bh

35. P · r · t   Prt   **36.** l · w · h   lwh

37. 2(w)   2w   **38.** 2(l)   2l

39. (x)(y)   xy   **40.** (r)(t)   rt

Write each division using a fraction bar.

41. $32 \div x$ $\frac{32}{x}$ **42.** $y \div 15$ $\frac{y}{15}$

43. $30\overline{)90}$ $\frac{90}{30}$ **44.** $20\overline{)80}$ $\frac{80}{20}$

PRACTICE   *Express each statement in words, using one of the words sum, difference, product, or quotient.*

45. 18(24)   **46.** 45 · 12

the product of 18 and 24   the product of 45 and 12

47. 11 − 9   **48.** 65 + 89

the difference of 11 and 9   the sum of 65 and 89

49. 2x   **50.** 16t

the product of 2 and x   the product of 16 and t

51. $\dfrac{66}{11}$ **52.** 12 ÷ 3

the quotient of 66 and 11   the quotient of 12 and 3

Translate each verbal model into an equation. (Hint: You will need to use variables. Answers may vary, depending on the variables chosen.)

53.

| The sale price | is | $100 | minus | the discount. |

$p = 100 - d$

54.

| The cost of dining out | equals | the cost of the meal | plus | $7 for parking. |

$c = m + 7$

55.

| 7 | times | the age of a dog in years | gives | the dog's equivalent human age. |

$7d = h$

56.

| The number of centuries | is | the number of years | divided by | 100. |

$c = \frac{y}{100}$

Translate each verbal model into an equation. (Hint: You will need to use variables. Answers may vary, depending on the variables chosen.)

57. The amount of sand that should be used is the product of 3 and the amount of cement used. $s = 3c$

58. The number of waiters needed is the quotient of the number of customers and 10. $w = \frac{c}{12}$

59. The weight of the truck is the sum of the weight of the engine and 1,200. $w = e + 1{,}200$

60. The number of classes that are still open is the difference of 150 and the number of classes that are closed. $n = 150 - c$

61. The profit is the difference of the revenue and 600. $p = r - 600$

62. The distance is the product of the rate and 3. $d = 3r$

63. The quotient of the number of laps run and 4 is the number of miles run. $\frac{l}{4} = m$

64. The sum of the tax and 35 is the total cost. $t + 35 = c$

Use the given formula to complete each table.

65. $d = 360 + l$

Lunch time (minutes)	School day (minutes)
30	390
40	400
45	405

66. $b = 1{,}024k$

Kilobytes	Bytes
1	1,024
5	5,120
10	10,240

67. $t = 1{,}500 - d$

Deductions	Take-home pay
200	1,300
300	1,200
400	1,100

68. $w = \dfrac{s}{12}$

Inches of snow	Inches of water
12	1
24	2
72	6

Use the data to find a formula that describes the relationship between the two quantities. Then state the relationship in words.

69.

Eggs	Dozen
24	2
36	3
48	4

$d = \frac{e}{12}$; the number of dozen eggs is the quotient of the number of eggs and 12.

70.

Couples	Individuals
20	40
100	200
200	400

$I = 2c$; the number of individuals is the product of 2 and the number of couples.

APPLICATIONS

71. CHAIR PRODUCTION   Use the diagram shown in Illustration 6 to write six formulas that planners could use to order the necessary number of legs l, arms a, seats S, backs b, arm pads p, and screws s for a production run of c chairs.

$l = 4c,\ a = 2c,\ S = c,\ b = c,\ p = 2c,\ s = 20c$

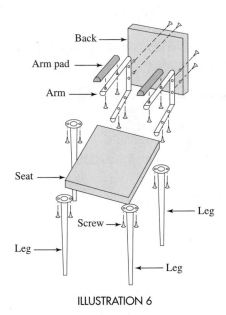

Back

Arm pad

Arm

Seat

Screw

Leg

Leg

Leg

ILLUSTRATION 6

72. STAIRCASE PRODUCTION   Write four formulas that could be used by the job superintendent to order the necessary number of staircase parts for a tract of h homes, each of which will have a staircase as shown in Illustration 7 (next page).

$b = 16h,\ p = 3h,\ r = 2h,\ t = 8h$

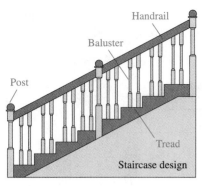

ILLUSTRATION 7

73. RELIGIOUS BOOKS   Illustration 8 shows the annual sales of books on religion, sprituality, and inspiration for the years 1991–1998. Graph the data using a bar graph. Then describe any trend that is apparent. On the horizontal axis, use the label 1 to represent the year 1991, 2 to represent 1992, and so on. (The symbol ⚡ indicates a break in the vertical scale.)

Sales have steadily increased.

Year	Book sales
1991	36,651,000
1992	50,104,000
1993	60,449,000
1994	70,541,000
1995	74,794,000
1996	78,022,000
1997	91,627,000
1998	100,295,000

Based on data from
www.BookWeb.org

ILLUSTRATION 8

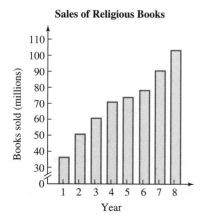

74. U.S. CRIME STATISTICS   Property crimes include burglary, theft, and motor vehicle theft. Graph the property crime rates listed in Illustration 9 using a bar graph. Is an overall trend apparent? (The symbol ⚡ indicates a break in the vertical scale.)

Property crime rates steadily declined.

Year	Victimizations per 1,000 households
1991	354
1992	325
1993	319
1994	310
1995	291
1996	266
1997	248
1998	217

Based on data from the Bureau of Justice Statistics

ILLUSTRATION 9

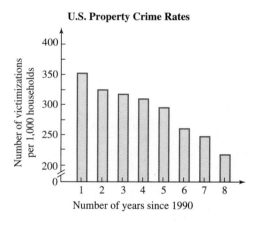

WRITING

75. Many people misuse the word *equation* when discussing mathematics. What is an equation? Give an example.

76. Explain the difference between an algebraic expression and an equation. Give an example of each.

77. Which do you think is more informative, a bar graph or a line graph? Explain your reasoning.

78. Create a bar graph that shows, on average, how many hours of television you watch each day of the week. Let Sunday be day 1, Monday day 2, and so on.

1.2 Fractions and Decimals

In this section, you will learn about

- Fractions • Simplifying fractions • Multiplying and dividing fractions
- Adding and subtracting fractions • Mixed numbers • Decimals
- Writing fractions as decimals

INTRODUCTION. It is often said, "A building is only as strong as its foundation." The same is true of studying mathematics. A thorough understanding of arithmetic is essential to your success in algebra.

In arithmetic, we learned how to add, subtract, multiply, and divide with **whole numbers:** 0, 1, 2, 3, 4 5, 6, 7, ... (The dots indicate that the numbers continue indefinitely in the same pattern.) Assuming that you have mastered those skills, we will now strengthen your mathematical foundation by reviewing the rules for arithmetic operations with fractions and decimals.

Fractions

In the **fractions**

$$\frac{1}{2}, \quad \frac{3}{5}, \quad \frac{2}{17}, \quad \text{and} \quad \frac{37}{7}$$

the number above the bar is called the **numerator,** and the number below it is called the **denominator.**

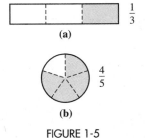

(a)

(b)

FIGURE 1-5

$\frac{1}{3}$

$\frac{4}{5}$

Fractions can be used to indicate parts of a whole. In Figure 1-5(a), a rectangle has been divided into 3 equal parts, with 1 of the parts shaded. The fraction $\frac{1}{3}$ indicates how much of the figure is shaded. In Figure 1-5(b), $\frac{4}{5}$ of the circle is shaded. In either example, the denominator of the fraction shows the total number of equal parts into which the whole is divided, and the numerator shows the number of these equal parts that are shaded.

Fractions with a numerator that is less than the denominator, such as $\frac{1}{3}$ and $\frac{4}{5}$, are called **proper fractions.** A proper fraction is less than 1. Fractions with a numerator that is equal to or greater than the denominator, such as $\frac{47}{47}$ and $\frac{5}{4}$, are called **improper fractions.** An improper fraction is greater than or equal to 1.

Fractions can also be used to indicate division. For example, the fraction $\frac{8}{2}$ indicates that 8 is to be divided by 2:

$$\frac{8}{2} = 8 \div 2 = 4$$

We note that $\frac{8}{2} = 4$, because $4 \cdot 2 = 8$, and that $\frac{0}{7} = 0$, because $0 \cdot 7 = 0$. However, the fraction $\frac{6}{0}$ is undefined, because no number multiplied by 0 gives 6. The fraction $\frac{0}{0}$ is indeterminate, because every number multiplied by 0 gives 0.

!

COMMENT   Remember that the denominator of a fraction cannot be zero.

Simplifying fractions

A fraction is in **lowest terms** when no natural number greater than 1 will divide both the numerator and the denominator exactly (with no remainder). The fraction $\frac{6}{11}$ is in lowest terms, because only 1 divides both 6 and 11 exactly. The fraction $\frac{6}{8}$ is not in lowest terms, because 2 divides both 6 and 8 exactly.

We can **simplify** (or **reduce**) a fraction that is not in lowest terms by dividing both its numerator and denominator by the same number. For example, to simplify the fraction $\frac{6}{8}$, we divide both numerator and denominator by 2:

$$\frac{6}{8} = \frac{6 \div 2}{8 \div 2} = \frac{3}{4}$$

From Figure 1-6, we see that $\frac{6}{8}$ and $\frac{3}{4}$ represent identical shaded amounts of the rectangle. Two fractions that represent the same number are called **equivalent fractions.** Equivalent fractions may look different, but they have the same value.

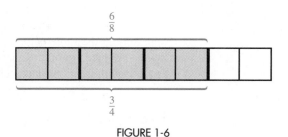

FIGURE 1-6

When simplifying a fraction, it is often helpful to write the numerator and denominator in factored form. To **factor** a number means to express it as the product of two or more numbers. For example, 8 can be written as

$$1 \cdot 8, \qquad 4 \cdot 2, \quad \text{and} \quad 2 \cdot 2 \cdot 2$$

In each case, we say that we have **factored** 8. The numbers 1, 2, 4, and 8 are called the **factors** of 8.

Some numbers have only two factors. For example, the only factors of 7 are 1 and 7, and the only factors of 23 are 1 and 23. We call such numbers **prime numbers.**

Prime numbers

> A **prime number** is a whole number greater than 1 that has only 1 and itself as factors. The prime numbers are 2, 3, 5, 7, 11, 13, 17, 19, 23, 29, 31, ...

When a number is written as the product of prime numbers, we say that it is written in **prime-factored** form.

EXAMPLE 1   *Prime factorization.*   Write 210 in prime-factored form.

Solution

We can write 210 as the product of 21 and 10 and proceed as follows:

$$210 = \mathbf{21 \cdot 10}$$
$$210 = \mathbf{3 \cdot 7 \cdot 2 \cdot 5} \quad \text{Factor 21 as } 3 \cdot 7 \text{ and factor 10 as } 2 \cdot 5.$$

The *factor tree* at the right shows an alternate way to prime factor 210.

Since 210 is now written as the product of prime numbers, its prime-factored form is $3 \cdot 7 \cdot 2 \cdot 5$.

Self Check

Write 189 in prime-factored form.

Answer: $7 \cdot 3 \cdot 3 \cdot 3$ ■

To simplify a fraction, we factor its numerator and denominator and then divide out all common factors that appear in both the numerator and denominator. To simplify the fractions $\frac{6}{8}$ and $\frac{189}{210}$, for example, we proceed as follows:

$$\frac{6}{8} = \frac{3 \cdot 2}{4 \cdot 2} = \frac{3 \cdot \overset{1}{\cancel{2}}}{4 \cdot \underset{1}{\cancel{2}}} = \frac{3}{4} \quad \text{and} \quad \frac{189}{210} = \frac{7 \cdot 3 \cdot 3 \cdot 3}{3 \cdot 7 \cdot 2 \cdot 5} = \frac{\overset{1}{\cancel{7}} \cdot \overset{1}{\cancel{3}} \cdot 3 \cdot 3}{\underset{1}{\cancel{3}} \cdot \underset{1}{\cancel{7}} \cdot 2 \cdot 5} = \frac{9}{10}$$

Slashes and small 1's are used to show that common factors of the numerator and denominator have been divided out.

COMMENT When working with fractions, you should always give your answers in lowest terms. Remember that a fraction is in lowest terms only when its numerator and denominator have no common factors other than 1.

EXAMPLE 2 *Simplifying fractions by factoring.* Simplify each fraction, if possible: **a.** $\frac{6}{30}$ and **b.** $\frac{33}{40}$.

Solution

a. To simplify $\frac{6}{30}$, we factor the numerator and denominator and divide out the common factor of 6.

$$\frac{6}{30} = \frac{6 \cdot 1}{6 \cdot 5} = \frac{\overset{1}{\cancel{6}} \cdot 1}{\underset{1}{\cancel{6}} \cdot 5} = \frac{1}{5} \qquad \text{Do the multiplications: } 1 \cdot 1 = 1 \text{ and } 1 \cdot 5 = 5.$$

b. To try to simplify $\frac{33}{40}$, we write the numerator and denominator in prime-factored form.

$$\frac{33}{40} = \frac{3 \cdot 11}{2 \cdot 2 \cdot 2 \cdot 5}$$

Since the numerator and denominator have no common factors, $\frac{33}{40}$ is in lowest terms.

Self Check

Simplify each fraction, if possible.

a. $\dfrac{24}{56}$

b. $\dfrac{16}{125}$

Answers: **a.** $\dfrac{3}{7}$, **b.** in lowest terms

The previous examples illustrate an important application of the **fundamental property of fractions.**

The fundamental property of fractions

Multiplying or dividing the numerator and the denominator of a fraction by the same nonzero number does not change the value of the fraction. In symbols, if a, b, and c represent numbers (and b and c are not zero),

$$\frac{a}{b} = \frac{a \cdot c}{b \cdot c} \qquad \text{and} \qquad \frac{a}{b} = \frac{a \div c}{b \div c}$$

Multiplying and dividing fractions

Multiplying fractions

To multiply two fractions, we multiply their numerators and multiply their denominators. In symbols, if a, b, c, and d represent numbers,

$$\frac{a}{b} \cdot \frac{c}{d} = \frac{a \cdot c}{b \cdot d} \qquad (b \neq 0 \text{ and } d \neq 0)$$

COMMENT After multiplying fractions, we should simplify the result, if possible.

EXAMPLE 3   *Multiplying fractions.*   Find **a.** $\dfrac{7}{8} \cdot \dfrac{3}{5}$ and **b.** $\dfrac{5}{8}\left(\dfrac{4}{5}\right)$.

Self Check

Find

a. $\dfrac{5}{9} \cdot \dfrac{2}{3}$

b. $\dfrac{6}{25}\left(\dfrac{5}{6}\right)$

Solution

a. $\dfrac{7}{8} \cdot \dfrac{3}{5} = \dfrac{7 \cdot 3}{8 \cdot 5}$ Multiply the numerators and multiply the denominators.

$\qquad = \dfrac{21}{40}$ Do the multiplications: $7 \cdot 3 = 21$ and $8 \cdot 5 = 40$.

This result cannot be simplified.

b. $\dfrac{5}{8}\left(\dfrac{4}{5}\right) = \dfrac{5 \cdot 4}{8 \cdot 5}$ Multiply the numerators and multiply the denominators.

Here, we can simplify the result by dividing out common factors. The numerator and denominator have a common factor of 5. Furthermore, if we factor 8 as $4 \cdot 2$, there will also be a common factor of 4.

$\dfrac{5}{8}\left(\dfrac{4}{5}\right) = \dfrac{5 \cdot 4}{4 \cdot 2 \cdot 5}$ Factor: $8 = 4 \cdot 2$.

$\qquad = \dfrac{\overset{1}{5} \cdot \overset{1}{4}}{\underset{1}{4} \cdot 2 \cdot \underset{1}{5}}$ Divide out the common factors of 4 and 5.

$\qquad = \dfrac{1}{2}$ Do the multiplications: $1 \cdot 1 = 1$ and $1 \cdot 2 \cdot 1 = 2$.

Answers: **a.** $\dfrac{10}{27}$,   **b.** $\dfrac{1}{5}$ ∎

One number is called the **reciprocal** of another if their product is 1. For example, $\frac{3}{5}$ is the reciprocal of $\frac{5}{3}$, because

$$\frac{3}{5} \cdot \frac{5}{3} = \frac{15}{15} = 1$$

Dividing fractions

To divide two fractions, we multiply the first fraction by the reciprocal of the second fraction. In symbols, if a, b, c, and d represent numbers,

$$\frac{a}{b} \div \frac{c}{d} = \frac{a}{b} \cdot \frac{d}{c} \quad (b \neq 0,\ c \neq 0,\ \text{and}\ d \neq 0)$$

EXAMPLE 4   *Dividing fractions.*   Find $\dfrac{1}{3} \div \dfrac{4}{5}$.

Self Check

Find $\dfrac{2}{3} \div \dfrac{7}{8}$.

Solution

$\dfrac{1}{3} \div \dfrac{4}{5} = \dfrac{1}{3} \cdot \dfrac{5}{4}$ Multiply $\frac{1}{3}$ by the reciprocal of $\frac{4}{5}$, which is $\frac{5}{4}$.

$\qquad = \dfrac{1 \cdot 5}{3 \cdot 4}$ Multiply the numerators and multiply the denominators.

$\qquad = \dfrac{5}{12}$ Multiply in the numerator and denominator.

Answer: $\dfrac{16}{21}$ ∎

Adding and subtracting fractions

Adding and subtracting fractions with like denominators

To add (or subtract) two fractions with the same denominator, we add (or subtract) the numerators and keep the common denominator. In symbols, if a, b, and d represent numbers,

$$\frac{a}{d} + \frac{b}{d} = \frac{a+b}{d} \quad \text{and} \quad \frac{a}{d} - \frac{b}{d} = \frac{a-b}{d} \quad \text{(provided } d \neq 0\text{)}$$

For example,

$$\frac{3}{7} + \frac{2}{7} = \frac{3+2}{7} \quad \text{and} \quad \frac{7}{9} - \frac{2}{9} = \frac{7-2}{9}$$

$$= \frac{5}{7} \qquad\qquad\qquad = \frac{5}{9}$$

 COMMENT Remember that only *factors* that are common to the entire numerator and the entire denominator can be divided out. To simplify $\frac{5+8}{5}$, it would be incorrect to divide out the 5. Doing so would give an incorrect answer of 9.

Correct

$$\frac{5+8}{5} = \frac{13}{5}$$

Incorrect

$$\frac{5+8}{5} = \frac{\overset{1}{\cancel{5}}+8}{\cancel{5}} = \frac{1+8}{1} = 9$$

To add fractions with unlike denominators, we rewrite the fractions so that they have a common denominator. The smallest common denominator, called the **least** or **lowest common denominator,** is usually the easiest common denominator to use.

Least common denominator

The **least common denominator (LCD)** for a set of fractions is the smallest number each denominator will divide exactly.

In the problem $\frac{3}{5} + \frac{1}{3}$, the denominators of the fractions are 5 and 3. The numbers 5 and 3 divide many numbers exactly (30, 45, and 60, to name a few), but the smallest number that 5 and 3 divide exactly is 15. Thus, 15 is the LCD for $\frac{3}{5}$ and $\frac{1}{3}$.

To find $\frac{3}{5} + \frac{1}{3}$, we express each fraction as an equivalent fraction with a denominator of 15. This process, known as **expressing a fraction in higher terms**, is an application of the fundamental property of fractions. To **build up** each fraction so that it has a denominator of 15, we multiply its numerator and denominator by the same number.

$$\frac{3}{5} + \frac{1}{3} \;=\; \frac{3 \cdot 3}{5 \cdot 3} \;+\; \frac{1 \cdot 5}{3 \cdot 5}$$

We need to multiply this denominator by 3 to obtain 15. We must also multiply the numerator by 3.

We need to multiply this denominator by 5 to obtain 15. We must also multiply the numerator by 5.

$$= \frac{9}{15} + \frac{5}{15}$$

Do the multiplications in the numerators and denominators. Note that the denominators are now the same.

$$= \frac{9+5}{15}$$

Add the numerators and write the sum over the common denominator 15.

$$= \frac{14}{15}$$

Do the addition: $9 + 5 = 14$.

EXAMPLE 5 *Using prime factorization to find the LCD.* Find $\dfrac{3}{10} - \dfrac{5}{28}$.

Solution

To find the LCD, we find the prime factorization of both denominators and use each prime factor the *greatest* number of times it appears in any one factorization:

$$\left.\begin{array}{l} 10 = 2 \cdot 5 \\ 28 = 2 \cdot 2 \cdot 7 \end{array}\right\} \quad \text{LCD} = 2 \cdot 2 \cdot 5 \cdot 7 = 140$$

2 appears twice in the factorization of 28.
5 appears once in the factorization of 10.
7 appears once in the factorization of 28.

Since 140 is the smallest number that 10 and 28 divide exactly, we write both fractions as fractions with the LCD of 140.

$$\dfrac{3}{10} - \dfrac{5}{28} = \dfrac{3 \cdot 14}{10 \cdot 14} - \dfrac{5 \cdot 5}{28 \cdot 5}$$ We must multiply 10 by 14 to obtain 140. We must multiply 28 by 5 to obtain 140.

$$= \dfrac{42}{140} - \dfrac{25}{140}$$ Do the four multiplications.

$$= \dfrac{42 - 25}{140}$$ Subtract the numerators and keep the common denominator.

$$= \dfrac{17}{140}$$ Do the subtraction.

Since 17 is a prime number, it has no common factor with 140. Thus, $\frac{17}{140}$ is in lowest terms and cannot be simplified.

■

Mixed numbers

A **mixed number** is the sum of a whole number and a proper fraction. For example, the mixed number $3\frac{3}{4}$ means $3 + \frac{3}{4}$.

EXAMPLE 6 *Division with mixed numbers.* Find $3\dfrac{3}{4} \div 2$.

Solution

To multiply or divide with mixed numbers, first we change the mixed numbers to improper fractions.

$$3\dfrac{3}{4} = \dfrac{3(4) + 3}{4} = \dfrac{15}{4}$$ To write a mixed number as an improper fraction, multiply the whole-number part by the denominator of the fraction and add the result to the numerator. Then write that sum over the denominator.

Now we replace $3\frac{3}{4}$ with $\frac{15}{4}$ and divide.

$$3\dfrac{3}{4} \div 2 = \dfrac{15}{4} \div \dfrac{2}{1}$$ Write $3\frac{3}{4}$ as $\frac{15}{4}$ and write 2 as $\frac{2}{1}$.

$$= \dfrac{15}{4} \cdot \dfrac{1}{2}$$ Multiply by the reciprocal of $\frac{2}{1}$, which is $\frac{1}{2}$.

$$= \dfrac{15}{8}$$ Multiply the numerators and multiply the denominators.

■

 COMMENT In studying algebra, you will see that it is usually preferable to work with an improper fraction rather than the equivalent mixed number.

EXAMPLE 7 *Adding mixed numbers.* Find $2\frac{1}{4} + 1\frac{1}{3}$. Write the answer as a mixed number.

Solution

We change the mixed numbers to improper fractions and proceed as follows.

$$2\frac{1}{4} + 1\frac{1}{3} = \frac{9}{4} + \frac{4}{3} \qquad \text{Write } 2\frac{1}{4} \text{ as } \frac{9}{4} \text{ and } 1\frac{1}{3} \text{ as } \frac{4}{3}.$$

$$= \frac{9 \cdot 3}{4 \cdot 3} + \frac{4 \cdot 4}{3 \cdot 4} \qquad \text{The LCD is 12.}$$

$$= \frac{27}{12} + \frac{16}{12} \qquad \text{Do the four multiplications.}$$

$$= \frac{43}{12} \qquad \text{Do the addition: } 27 + 16 = 43.$$

Finally, we change $\frac{43}{12}$ to a mixed number.

$$\begin{array}{r} 3 \\ 12\overline{)43} \\ -36 \\ \hline 7 \end{array}$$

To write an improper fraction as a mixed number, divide the numerator by the denominator to obtain the whole-number part. The remainder over the divisor is the fractional part.

$$\frac{43}{12} = 3\frac{7}{12}$$

Self Check

Find $4\frac{1}{6} + 1\frac{1}{5}$. Write the answer as a mixed number.

Answer: $5\frac{11}{30}$

Decimals

In the **decimal numeration system,** columns to the left of the decimal point have a value greater than or equal to 1. Columns to the right of the decimal point have a value less than 1. (See Figure 1-7.)

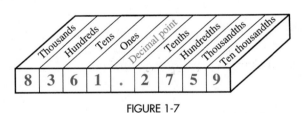

FIGURE 1-7

We can use a vertical column format to add or subtract decimals. For example,

$$\begin{array}{r} 25.568 \\ + \ 2.74 \\ \hline 28.308 \end{array} \qquad \begin{array}{r} 25.568 \\ - \ 2.74 \\ \hline 22.828 \end{array}$$

First, line up the decimal points. Then add (or subtract) the numbers as if they were whole numbers. Finally, write the decimal point in the result directly below the decimal points in the problem.

To multiply decimals, begin by multiplying the numbers as if they were whole numbers. Then we place the decimal point in the result so that the number of decimal places in the answer is equal to the sum of the decimal places in the factors.

$$\begin{array}{r} 3.453 \quad \leftarrow \text{ Here there are three decimal places.} \\ \times \ 9.25 \quad \leftarrow \text{ Here there are two decimal places.} \\ \hline 17265 \\ 6906 \\ 31077 \\ \hline 31.94025 \quad \leftarrow \text{ The product has } 3 + 2 = 5 \text{ decimal places.} \end{array}$$

To multiply a decimal by 10, 100, 1,000, and so on (such numbers are called **powers of 10**), we move the decimal point the same number of places to the right as the number of zeros in the power of 10.

One zero in 10

$8.675 \cdot 10 = 86.75$

Move the decimal point
1 place to the right.

Two zeros in 100

$8.675 \cdot 100 = 867.5$

Move the decimal point
2 places to the right.

To divide decimals, we move the decimal point in the divisor (the number that we are dividing by) to the right so that it becomes a whole number. We then move the decimal point in the dividend (the number being divided) the same number of places to the right.

$1.23\overline{)30.258}$ Move the decimal point in both the divisor and the dividend two places to the right.

We align the decimal point in the quotient with the repositioned decimal point in the dividend and use long division.

$$
\begin{array}{r}
24.6 \\
123\overline{)3025.8} \\
\underline{246} \\
565 \\
\underline{492} \\
73\,8 \\
\underline{73\,8} \\
0
\end{array}
$$

Writing fractions as decimals

To write a fraction as a decimal, we divide the numerator by the denominator. For example, to write $\frac{1}{4}$ and $\frac{5}{22}$ as decimals, we proceed as follows:

$$
\begin{array}{r}
0.25 \\
4\overline{)1.00} \\
\underline{8} \\
20 \\
\underline{20} \\
0
\end{array}
$$

$$
\begin{array}{r}
0.22727\ldots \\
22\overline{)5.00000} \\
\underline{4\,4} \\
60 \\
\underline{44} \\
160 \\
\underline{154} \\
60 \\
\underline{44} \\
160
\end{array}
$$

The decimal 0.25 is called a **terminating decimal** because it terminates, or ends. The decimal 0.227272727 . . . is called a **repeating decimal** because it repeats the block of digits 27 indefinitely. We can use an overbar to write repeating decimals in a more concise form: $0.227272727\ldots = 0.2\overline{27}$.

 COMMENT   When using an overbar to designate a repeating decimal, place the bar over the smallest repeating block of digits. For example, write 0.2272727 . . . as $0.2\overline{27}$, not $0.2\overline{727}$.

Terminating decimals	Repeating decimals
$\frac{1}{2} = 0.5$	$\frac{1}{6} = 0.16666\ldots$ or $0.1\overline{6}$
$\frac{5}{8} = 0.625$	$\frac{1}{3} = 0.3333\ldots$ or $0.\overline{3}$
$\frac{3}{4} = 0.75$	$\frac{2}{3} = 0.6666\ldots$ or $0.\overline{6}$

STUDY SET Section 1.2

VOCABULARY *Fill in the blanks.*

1. The ___numerator___ of the fraction $\frac{3}{4}$ is 3, and the ___denominator___ is 4.

2. When we express $\frac{6}{8}$ as $\frac{3}{4}$, we say that we have ___simplified or reduced___ $\frac{6}{8}$ to lowest terms. A fraction is in ___lowest___ terms when no whole number greater than 1 will divide its numerator and denominator exactly.

3. Two fractions that represent the same number, such as $\frac{1}{2}$ and $\frac{2}{4}$, are called ___equivalent___ fractions.

4. Numbers that have only 1 and themselves as factors, such as 23, 37, and 41, are called ___prime___ numbers.

5. When we write 60 as $20 \cdot 3$, we say that we have ___factored___ 60. When we write 60 as $5 \cdot 3 \cdot 2 \cdot 2$, we say that we have written 60 in ___prime-factored___ form.

6. The number $\frac{2}{3}$ is the ___reciprocal___ of the number $\frac{3}{2}$, because their product is 1.

7. The number 0.75 is called a ___terminating___ decimal, because it terminates, or ends. The number 0.111 . . . is called a ___repeating___ decimal.

8. The ___least or lowest___ common denominator for a set of fractions is the smallest number each denominator will divide exactly.

CONCEPTS

9. What equivalent fractions are shown in Illustration 1?
$\frac{4}{12} = \frac{1}{3}$

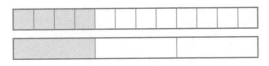

ILLUSTRATION 1

10. The prime factorization of a number is $2 \cdot 2 \cdot 3 \cdot 5$. What is the number? 60

11. To express $\frac{3}{8}$ as an equivalent fraction with a denominator of 40, by what number must we multiply the numerator and denominator? 5

12. a. Give three numbers that 4 and 6 divide exactly.
12, 24, 36 (Answers may vary.)
b. What is the smallest number that 4 and 6 divide exactly? 12

13. The prime factorizations of 24 and 36 are
$$24 = 2 \cdot 2 \cdot 2 \cdot 3$$
$$36 = 2 \cdot 2 \cdot 3 \cdot 3$$

a. What is the greatest number of times 2 appears in any one factorization? 3 times
b. What is the greatest number of times 3 appears in any one factorization? 2 times

14. a. Write $2\frac{15}{16}$ as an improper fraction. $\frac{47}{16}$
b. Write $\frac{49}{12}$ as a mixed number. $4\frac{1}{12}$

NOTATION

15. Consider
$$\frac{70}{175} = \frac{\overset{1}{\cancel{7}} \cdot \overset{1}{\cancel{5}} \cdot 2}{\underset{1}{\cancel{7}} \cdot \underset{1}{\cancel{5}} \cdot 5}$$

What do the slashes and the 1's show?
Common factors of 7 and 5 in the numerator and the denominator have been divided out.

16. Consider 2,345.6789.
a. What digit is in the thousands column? 2
b. What digit is in the thousandths column? 8

PRACTICE *List the factors of each number.*

17. 20   1, 2, 4, 5, 10, 20   **18.** 50   1, 2, 5, 10, 25, 50
19. 28   **20.** 36
   1, 2, 4, 7, 14, 28   1, 2, 3, 4, 6, 9, 12, 18, 36

Give the prime factorization of each number.

21. 75 $5 \cdot 5 \cdot 3$ **22.** 20 $5 \cdot 2 \cdot 2$
23. 28 $7 \cdot 2 \cdot 2$ **24.** 54 $3 \cdot 3 \cdot 3 \cdot 2$
25. 117 $13 \cdot 3 \cdot 3$ **26.** 147 $7 \cdot 7 \cdot 3$
27. 220 $11 \cdot 5 \cdot 2 \cdot 2$ **28.** 270 $5 \cdot 3 \cdot 3 \cdot 3 \cdot 2$

Build up each fraction or whole number to an equivalent fraction having the indicated denominator.

29. $\frac{1}{3}$, denominator 9 $\frac{3}{9}$ **30.** $\frac{3}{8}$, denominator 24 $\frac{9}{24}$

31. $\frac{4}{9}$, denominator 54 $\frac{24}{54}$ **32.** $\frac{9}{16}$, denominator 64 $\frac{36}{64}$

33. 7, denominator 5 $\frac{35}{5}$ **34.** 12, denominator 3 $\frac{36}{3}$

Write each fraction in lowest terms. If the fraction is already in lowest terms, so indicate.

35. $\frac{6}{12}$ $\frac{1}{2}$ **36.** $\frac{3}{9}$ $\frac{1}{3}$

37. $\frac{24}{18}$ $\frac{4}{3}$ **38.** $\frac{35}{14}$ $\frac{5}{2}$

39. $\dfrac{15}{20}$ $\frac{3}{4}$

40. $\dfrac{22}{77}$ $\frac{2}{7}$

41. $\dfrac{72}{64}$ $\frac{9}{8}$

42. $\dfrac{26}{21}$ in lowest terms

43. $\dfrac{36}{225}$ $\frac{4}{25}$

44. $\dfrac{175}{490}$ $\frac{5}{14}$

Do each multiplication. Simplify the result when possible.

45. $\dfrac{1}{2} \cdot \dfrac{3}{5}$ $\frac{3}{10}$

46. $\dfrac{3}{4} \cdot \dfrac{5}{7}$ $\frac{15}{28}$

47. $\dfrac{4}{3}\left(\dfrac{6}{5}\right)$ $\frac{8}{5}$

48. $\dfrac{7}{8}\left(\dfrac{6}{15}\right)$ $\frac{7}{20}$

49. $\dfrac{5}{12} \cdot \dfrac{18}{5}$ $\frac{3}{2}$

50. $\dfrac{5}{4} \cdot \dfrac{12}{10}$ $\frac{3}{2}$

51. $\dfrac{10}{21} \cdot 14$ $\frac{20}{3}$

52. $\dfrac{5}{24} \cdot 16$ $\frac{10}{3}$

53. $7\dfrac{1}{2} \cdot 1\dfrac{2}{5}$ $10\frac{1}{2}$

54. $3\dfrac{1}{4}\left(1\dfrac{1}{5}\right)$ $3\frac{9}{10}$

Do each division. Simplify the result when possible.

55. $\dfrac{3}{5} \div \dfrac{2}{3}$ $\frac{9}{10}$

56. $\dfrac{4}{5} \div \dfrac{3}{7}$ $\frac{28}{15}$

57. $\dfrac{3}{4} \div \dfrac{6}{5}$ $\frac{5}{8}$

58. $\dfrac{3}{8} \div \dfrac{15}{28}$ $\frac{7}{10}$

59. $\dfrac{21}{35} \div \dfrac{3}{14}$ $\frac{14}{5}$

60. $\dfrac{23}{25} \div \dfrac{46}{5}$ $\frac{1}{10}$

61. $6 \div \dfrac{3}{14}$ 28

62. $23 \div \dfrac{46}{5}$ $\frac{5}{2}$

63. $3\dfrac{1}{3} \div 1\dfrac{5}{6}$ $1\frac{9}{11}$

64. $2\dfrac{1}{2} \div 1\dfrac{5}{8}$ $1\frac{7}{13}$

Do each addition or subtraction. Simplify the result when possible.

65. $\dfrac{3}{5} + \dfrac{3}{5}$ $\frac{6}{5}$

66. $\dfrac{4}{13} - \dfrac{3}{13}$ $\frac{1}{13}$

67. $\dfrac{1}{6} + \dfrac{1}{24}$ $\frac{5}{24}$

68. $\dfrac{17}{25} - \dfrac{2}{5}$ $\frac{7}{25}$

69. $\dfrac{3}{5} + \dfrac{2}{3}$ $\frac{19}{15}$

70. $\dfrac{4}{3} + \dfrac{7}{2}$ $\frac{29}{6}$

71. $\dfrac{9}{4} - \dfrac{5}{6}$ $\frac{17}{12}$

72. $\dfrac{2}{15} + \dfrac{7}{9}$ $\frac{41}{45}$

73. $\dfrac{7}{10} - \dfrac{1}{14}$ $\frac{22}{35}$

74. $\dfrac{7}{25} + \dfrac{3}{10}$ $\frac{29}{50}$

75. $\dfrac{5}{14} - \dfrac{4}{21}$ $\frac{1}{6}$

76. $\dfrac{2}{33} + \dfrac{3}{22}$ $\frac{13}{66}$

77. $3 - \dfrac{3}{4}$ $\frac{9}{4}$

78. $\dfrac{17}{3} + 4$ $\frac{29}{3}$

79. $3\dfrac{3}{4} - 2\dfrac{1}{2}$ $1\frac{1}{4}$

80. $15\dfrac{5}{6} + 11\dfrac{5}{8}$ $27\frac{11}{24}$

81. $8\dfrac{2}{9} - 7\dfrac{2}{3}$ $\frac{5}{9}$

82. $3\dfrac{4}{5} - 3\dfrac{1}{10}$ $\frac{7}{10}$

Do each operation.

83. $23.45 + 135.2$
158.65

84. $345.213 - 27.35$
317.863

85. $67.235 - 22.45$
44.785

86. $12.17 + 3.457$
15.627

87. $3.4 \cdot 13.2$ 44.88

88. $4.21 \cdot 2.73$ 11.4933

89. $0.23\overline{)1.0465}$ 4.55

90. $4.7\overline{)10.857}$ 2.31

91. $2.9517(1{,}000)$ 2,951.7

92. $100(333.614)$ 33,361.4

93. $100 \cdot 0.05$ 5

94. $1{,}000 \cdot 0.085$ 85

Write each fraction as a decimal. If the result is a repeating decimal, use an overbar.

95. $\dfrac{5}{8}$ 0.625

96. $\dfrac{3}{32}$ 0.09375

97. $\dfrac{1}{30}$ $0.03\overline{3}$

98. $\dfrac{7}{9}$ $0.\overline{7}$

99. $\dfrac{21}{50}$ 0.42

100. $\dfrac{2}{125}$ 0.016

101. $\dfrac{5}{11}$ $0.\overline{45}$

102. $\dfrac{1}{60}$ $0.01\overline{6}$

APPLICATIONS

103. BOTANY   To assess the effects of smog on tree development, botanists cut down a pine tree and measured the width of the growth rings for the last two years. (See Illustration 2.)

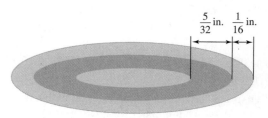

$\dfrac{5}{32}$ in. $\dfrac{1}{16}$ in.

ILLUSTRATION 2

a. What was the growth over this two-year period (in inches)? $\frac{7}{32}$ in.

b. What is the difference in the widths of the rings? $\frac{3}{32}$ in.

104. HARDWARE   See Illustration 3. To secure the bracket to the stock, a bolt and a nut are used. How long should the bolt be? $7\frac{9}{16}$ in.

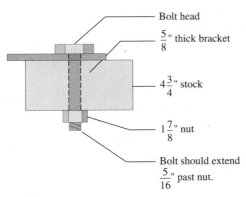

Bolt head

$\frac{5}{8}$" thick bracket

$4\frac{3}{4}$" stock

$1\frac{7}{8}$" nut

Bolt should extend $\frac{5}{16}$" past nut.

ILLUSTRATION 3

105. FRAMES   How much molding is needed to produce the square picture frame in Illustration 4? $40\frac{1}{2}$ in.

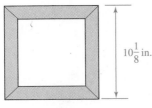

$10\frac{1}{8}$ in.

ILLUSTRATION 4

106. PRODUCTION PLANNING   The materials used to make a pillow are shown in Illustration 5. Examine the inventory list to decide how many pillows can be manufactured in one production run with the materials in stock.   147

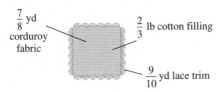

$\frac{7}{8}$ yd corduroy fabric

$\frac{2}{3}$ lb cotton filling

$\frac{9}{10}$ yd lace trim

Factory Inventory List

Materials	Amount in stock
Lace trim	135 yd
Corduroy fabric	154 yd
Cotton filling	98 lb

ILLUSTRATION 5

107. VEHICLE SPECIFICATIONS   Certain dimensions of a compact car are shown in Illustration 6. What is the wheelbase of the car?   103.4 in.

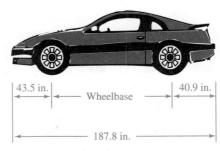

43.5 in.   Wheelbase   40.9 in.

187.8 in.

ILLUSTRATION 6

108. RETROFIT   Illustration 7 shows the width of the three columns of an existing freeway overpass. A computer analysis indicates that each column needs to be increased in width by a factor of 1.4 to ensure stability during an earthquake. According to the analysis, how wide should each of the columns be?
6.3 ft, 4.9 ft, 3.5 ft

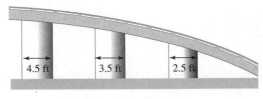

4.5 ft   3.5 ft   2.5 ft

ILLUSTRATION 7

WRITING

109. What does it mean to say that an employee is *terminated*?

110. What are equivalent fractions?

111. How does the set of factors of a number differ from the prime factorization of the number? Give an example.

112. Explain the error in the following work.

$$\frac{4}{3} + \frac{3}{2} = \frac{4}{\overset{1}{\cancel{3}}} + \frac{\overset{1}{\cancel{3}}}{5}$$

$$= \frac{4}{1} + \frac{1}{5}$$

$$= 4 + \frac{1}{5}$$

$$= 4\frac{1}{5}$$

REVIEW   *Express each statement in words, using one of the words* sum, difference, product, *or* quotient.

113. $7 - 5 = 2$ The difference of 7 and 5 is 2.

114. $5(6) = 30$ The product of 5 and 6 is 30.

115. $30 \div 15 = 2$ The quotient of 30 and 15 is 2.
116. $12 + 12 = 24$ The sum of 12 and 12 is 24.

Use the given formula to complete the table.

117. $T = 15g$

Number of gears	Number of teeth
10	150
12	180

118. $p = r - 200$

Revenue	Profit
1,000	800
5,000	4,800

1.3 The Real Numbers

In this section, you will learn about

- The integers • Order on the number line
- Rational numbers: fractions and mixed numbers • Rational numbers: decimals
- Irrational numbers • The real numbers • Absolute value

INTRODUCTION. We have previously discussed the set of whole numbers and the set of prime numbers. In this section, we define other sets of numbers that we will use in this course and show that they are part of a larger collection of numbers called the **real numbers.**

The integers

Table 1-1 shows the low temperatures for Rockford, IL during the first week of January. In the left column, we have used the numbers 1, 2, 3, 4, 5, 6, and 7 to denote the calendar days of the month. This collection of numbers is called a **set,** and the members (or **elements**) of the set can be listed within **braces** { }.

$$\{1, 2, 3, 4, 5, 6, 7\}$$

Day of the month	Low temperature (°F)
1	4
2	−5
3	−6
4	0
5	3
6	6
7	6

TABLE 1-1

Each of the numbers 1, 2, 3, 4, 5, 6, and 7 is a member of a basic set of numbers called the **natural numbers.** These are the numbers that we use for counting.

Natural numbers   The set of **natural numbers** is $\{1, 2, 3, 4, 5, 6, 7, 8, 9, 10, \ldots\}$.

The natural numbers together with 0 make up another important set of numbers called the **whole numbers.**

Whole numbers   The set of **whole numbers** is $\{0, 1, 2, 3, 4, 5, 6, 7, 8, 9, 10, \ldots\}$.

COMMENT Since every natural number is also a whole number, we say that the set of natural numbers is a **subset** of the set of whole numbers. However, not all whole numbers are natural numbers. Note that 0 is a whole number but not a natural number.

Table 1-1 contains positive and negative temperatures. For example, on the 2nd day of the month, the low temperature was $-5°$ (read as "negative 5 degrees"), and it means $5°$ below zero. On the 5th day, the low temperature was $3°$ ($3°$ above zero). The numbers used to represent the temperatures listed in the table are members of a set of numbers called the **integers.**

Integers | The set of **integers** is $\{\ldots, -4, -3, -2, -1, 0, 1, 2, 3, 4, \ldots\}$.

COMMENT Since every whole number is also an integer, we say that the set of whole numbers is a subset of the set of integers. The natural numbers are also a subset of the integers. However, not all integers are whole numbers, nor are they all natural numbers. For example, the integer -2 is neither a whole number nor a natural number.

Order on the number line

We can illustrate sets of numbers with a **number line.** Like a ruler, a number line is straight and has uniform markings, as in Figure 1-8. The arrowheads indicate that the number line continues forever to the left and to the right. Numbers to the right of 0 have values that are greater than 0; they are called **positive numbers.** Numbers to the left of 0 have values that are less than 0; they are called **negative numbers.** The number 0 is neither positive nor negative.

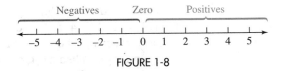

FIGURE 1-8

Positive numbers can be written with or without a $+$ sign. For example, $2 = +2$. Negative numbers are always written with a $-$ sign. They can be used to describe amounts that are less than 0, such as a checking account that is \$75 overdrawn ($-\$75$), an elevation of 200 feet below sea level (-200 ft), and a loss of 8 points (-8).

Using a process known as **graphing,** a single number or a set of numbers can be represented on a number line. The **graph of a number** is the point on the number line that corresponds to that number. *To graph a number* means to locate its position on the number line and then to highlight it by using a heavy dot.

EXAMPLE 1 *Graphing on the number line.* Graph the integers between -4 and 5.

Solution
The integers between -4 and 5 are $-3, -2, -1, 0, 1, 2, 3,$ and 4. To graph each integer, we locate its position on the number line and draw a dot.

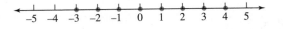

Self Check
Graph the integers between -2 and 2.

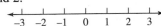

Answer:

As we move to the right on a number line, the values of the numbers increase. As we move to the left, the values of the numbers decrease. In Figure 1-9, we know that 5 is greater than -3 because the graph of 5 lies to the right of the graph of -3. We also know that -3 is less than 5 because its graph lies to the left of the graph of 5.

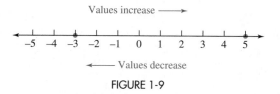

FIGURE 1-9

The **inequality symbol** $>$ ("is greater than") can be used to show that 5 is greater than -3, and the inequality symbol $<$ ("is less than") can be used to show that -3 is less than 5.

$5 > -3$ Read as "5 is greater than -3."

$-3 < 5$ Read as "-3 is less than 5."

To distinguish between these two inequality symbols, remember that each one points to the smaller of the two numbers involved.

$5 > -3$ $-3 < 5$

└─── Points to the smaller number. ───┘

EXAMPLE 2   *Inequality symbols.* Use one of the symbols $>$ or $<$ to make each of the following statements true: **a.** $-4 \quad\quad 4$ and   **b.** $-2 \quad\quad -3$.

Solution

a. Since -4 is to the left of 4 on the number line, we have $-4 < 4$.

b. Since -2 is to the right of -3 on the number line, we have $-2 > -3$.

Self Check

Use one of the symbols $>$ or $<$ to make each of the following statements true:

a. $1 \quad\quad -1$

b. $-5 \quad\quad -4$

Answers: a. $>$,   **b.** $<$ ■

By extending the number line to include negative numbers, we can represent more situations graphically. In Figure 1-10, the line graph illustrates the low temperatures listed in Table 1-1. The vertical axis is scaled in units of degrees Fahrenheit, and temperatures below zero (negative temperatures) are graphed. For example, for the third day of the month, the low was $-6°$ F.

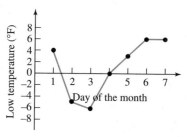

FIGURE 1-10

Rational numbers: fractions and mixed numbers

In this course, we will work with positive and negative fractions. For example, the time it takes a motorist to complete the commute home might be $\frac{3}{4}$ of an hour, or a surveyor might indicate that a building's foundation has fallen below finished grade by expressing its elevation as $-\frac{7}{8}$ of an inch.

We will also work with positive and negative mixed numbers. For example, a piece of fabric might be $12\frac{2}{3}$ yards long, or the time before a rocket launch might be expressed as "$-5\frac{1}{2}$ minutes and counting."

Fractions and mixed numbers belong to the set of **rational numbers,** so named because *ratio*nal numbers can be written as the *ratio* (or quotient) of two integers. This means that rational numbers can be written in the fractional form:

$\dfrac{\text{integer}}{\text{integer}}$ The numerator can be any integer.

The denominator can be any integer except 0.

Fractions such as $\frac{3}{4}$ and $\frac{25}{12}$ are rational numbers, because they have an integer numerator and a nonzero integer denominator. We can use the fact that

$$-\frac{a}{b} = \frac{-a}{b} = \frac{a}{-b} \qquad (b \neq 0)$$

to show that negative fractions are rational numbers. For example, $-\frac{7}{8}$ is a rational number because it can be written as $\frac{-7}{8}$ or as $\frac{7}{-8}$. Positive and negative mixed numbers such as $12\frac{2}{3}$ and $-5\frac{1}{2}$ are also rational numbers because they can be written as the ratios of two integers.

$$12\frac{2}{3} = \frac{38}{3} \qquad \text{and} \qquad -5\frac{1}{2} = \frac{-11}{2}$$

Rational numbers: decimals

In algebra, many numerical quantities are expressed in decimal notation. For example, a candy bar might cost $0.89, or a dragster might travel at 203.156 miles per hour, or the first-quarter loss of a business might be $-$2.7 million. Since these terminating decimals can be written as ratios of two integers, they are rational numbers.

$$0.89 = \frac{89}{100} \qquad 203.156 = 203\frac{156}{1,000} = \frac{203,156}{1,000} \qquad -2.7 = -2\frac{7}{10} = \frac{-27}{10}$$

Decimals such as $0.33333\ldots$ and $2.161616\ldots$ are repeating decimals. You have seen that $0.33333\ldots = \frac{1}{3}$. Although it is beyond the scope of this book, it can be shown that $2.161616\ldots = 2\frac{16}{99} = \frac{214}{99}$. In fact, *any* repeating decimal can be expressed as a ratio of two integers. For this reason, repeating decimals are also rational numbers.

 COMMENT   All terminating and repeating decimals are rational numbers.

The set of rational numbers is too extensive to be listed in the same way that we have listed other sets in this section. Instead, we use **set-builder notation** to describe it.

The set of rational numbers

$$\left\{ \frac{a}{b} \;\middle|\; a \text{ and } b \text{ are integers and } b \neq 0 \right\}$$

Read as "the set of all numbers of the form $\frac{a}{b}$, where a and b represent integers and $b \neq 0$."

Irrational numbers

The square root of 2 $\left(\text{denoted } \sqrt{2}\right)$ is the number that, when multiplied by itself, gives 2. That is, $\sqrt{2} \cdot \sqrt{2} = 2$. In Figure 1-11(a), the anchor wire is the diagonal of a square with sides of length 1 yard. It can be shown that the length of the wire is $\sqrt{2}$ yards.

The number represented by the Greek letter π (read as "pi") is often used in geometry. In Figure 1-11(b), the distance around the hula hoop (circumference) is found by multiplying the diameter of the hoop by π.

Expressed in decimal form,

$$\sqrt{2} = 1.414213562 \ldots \quad \text{and} \quad \pi = 3.141592654 \ldots$$

These **nonterminating, nonrepeating decimals** cannot be written as the ratio of two integers. Therefore, $\sqrt{2}$ and π are *not* rational numbers—they are called **irrational numbers.**

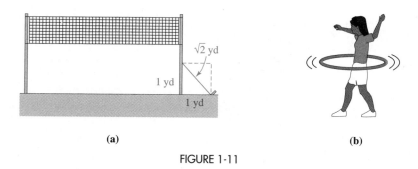

(a)   (b)

FIGURE 1-11

Irrational numbers

> An **irrational number** is a nonterminating, nonrepeating decimal.

Other examples of irrational numbers are $\sqrt{89}$, $-\sqrt{5}$, $-\pi$, and 3π (this means $3 \cdot \pi$). When doing calculations with irrational numbers, we often approximate them.

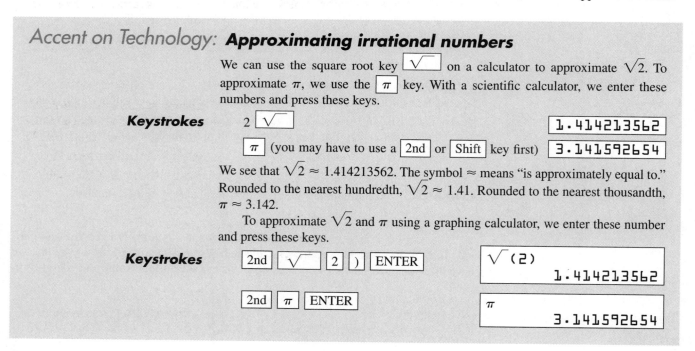

Accent on Technology: **Approximating irrational numbers**

We can use the square root key $\boxed{\sqrt{}}$ on a calculator to approximate $\sqrt{2}$. To approximate π, we use the $\boxed{\pi}$ key. With a scientific calculator, we enter these numbers and press these keys.

Keystrokes   2 $\boxed{\sqrt{}}$ $\boxed{1.414213562}$

$\boxed{\pi}$ (you may have to use a $\boxed{\text{2nd}}$ or $\boxed{\text{Shift}}$ key first) $\boxed{3.141592654}$

We see that $\sqrt{2} \approx 1.414213562$. The symbol $\approx$ means "is approximately equal to." Rounded to the nearest hundredth, $\sqrt{2} \approx 1.41$. Rounded to the nearest thousandth, $\pi \approx 3.142$.

To approximate $\sqrt{2}$ and π using a graphing calculator, we enter these number and press these keys.

Keystrokes $\boxed{\text{2nd}}$ $\boxed{\sqrt{}}$ $\boxed{2}$ $\boxed{)}$ $\boxed{\text{ENTER}}$ $\sqrt{(2)}$

                                                   1.414213562

$\boxed{\text{2nd}}$ $\boxed{\pi}$ $\boxed{\text{ENTER}}$ π

                                                    3.141592654

The real numbers

The set of rational numbers together with the set of irrational numbers form the set of **real numbers.** That is, a real number is either rational or irrational. All of the numbers that we have discussed in this section are real numbers.

The real numbers

> A **real number** is any number that is either a rational or an irrational number.

Figure 1-12 shows how the sets of numbers introduced in this section are related; it also gives some specific examples of each type of number. Note that a number can belong to more than one set. For example, -6 is an integer, a rational number, and a real number.

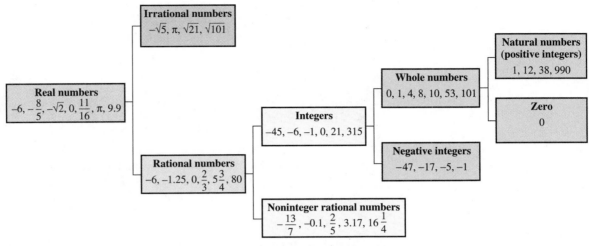

FIGURE 1-12

EXAMPLE 3   *Classifying real numbers.*   Tell which numbers in the following set are natural numbers, whole numbers, integers, rational numbers, irrational numbers, and real numbers: $\left\{-3.4, \frac{2}{5}, 0, -6, 1\frac{3}{4}, \pi, 16\right\}$.

Solution

Natural numbers: 16

Whole numbers: 0, 16

Integers: 0, -6, 16

Rational numbers: $-3.4, \frac{2}{5}, 0, -6, 1\frac{3}{4}, 16$ Rational numbers can be expressed as a
ratio of two integers: $-3.4 = \frac{-34}{10}, 0 = \frac{0}{1}$,
$-6 = \frac{-6}{1}, 1\frac{3}{4} = \frac{7}{4}$, and $16 = \frac{16}{1}$.

Irrational numbers: π

Real numbers: $-3.4, \frac{2}{5}, 0, -6, 1\frac{3}{4}, \pi, 16$

Self Check

Use the instructions for Example 3 with the set

$$\left\{0.4, \sqrt{2}, -\tfrac{2}{7}, 45, -2, \tfrac{13}{4}\right\}$$

Answers: natural numbers: 45; whole numbers: 45; integers: 45, -2; rational numbers: 0.4, $-\frac{2}{7}$, 45, -2, $\frac{13}{4}$; irrational numbers: $\sqrt{2}$; real numbers: 0.4, $\sqrt{2}$, $-\frac{2}{7}$, 45, $-2, \frac{13}{4}$ ■

The set of real numbers corresponds to all points on a number line. One and only one point on the number line corresponds to each real number.

EXAMPLE 4   *Graphing real numbers.*   Graph each number in the set $\left\{-3.25, -\frac{1}{5}, \sqrt{5}, 3\frac{7}{8}, 0.666. . ., -\frac{3}{2}\right\}$ on the number line.

Solution

We locate the position of each number on the number line and then draw a heavy dot. Recall that $0.25 = \frac{1}{4}$, so $-3.25 = -3\frac{1}{4}$. In mixed-number form, $-\frac{3}{2} = -1\frac{1}{2}$. Using a calculator, we see that $\sqrt{5} \approx 2.2$. The repeating decimal $0.666. . .$ is $\frac{2}{3}$.

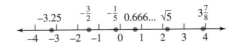

Self Check

Graph each number in the set

$$\left\{1.7, \pi, -1\tfrac{3}{4}, -0.333... , \tfrac{5}{2}\right\}$$

Answer:

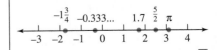

Absolute value

In Figure 1-13, we see that −4 and 4 are both a distance of 4 away from 0. Because of this, we say that −4 and 4 are **opposites.**

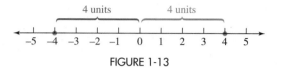

FIGURE 1-13

Opposites | Two numbers represented by points on a number line that are the same distance away from 0, but on opposite sides of it, are called **opposites.**

To write the opposite of a number, a − symbol can be used. For example, the opposite of 6 can be written as −6. The opposite of 0 is 0, so −0 = 0. Since the opposite of −6 is 6, we have −(−6) = 6. In general, if a represents any real number,

$$-(-a) = a$$

The **absolute value** of a number gives the distance between the number and 0 on a number line. To indicate absolute value, a number is inserted between two vertical bars. For the example shown in Figure 1-13, we would write $|-4| = 4$. This notation is read as "The absolute value of negative 4 is 4," and it tells us that the distance between −4 and 0 is 4 units. In Figure 1-13, we also see that $|4| = 4$.

Absolute value | The **absolute value** of a number is the distance on a number line between the number and 0.

> **COMMENT**   Since absolute value expresses distance, the absolute value of a number is always positive or zero—never negative.

EXAMPLE 5   *Evaluating absolute values.*   Evaluate   **a.** $|18|$,   **b.** $|-\frac{7}{8}|$, and   **c.** $|0|$.

Solution
a. Since 18 is a distance of 18 from 0 on the number line,

$$|18| = 18$$

b. Since $-\frac{7}{8}$ is a distance of $\frac{7}{8}$ from 0 on the number line,

$$|-\tfrac{7}{8}| = \tfrac{7}{8}$$

c. Since 0 is a distance of 0 from 0 on the number line, $|0| = 0$.

Self Check
Evaluate

a. $|100|$

b. $|-4.7|$

c. $|-\sqrt{2}|$

Answers: a. 100,   **b.** 4.7,
c. $\sqrt{2}$

EXAMPLE 6   *Comparing real numbers.*   Insert one of the symbols $>$, $<$, or = in the blank: **a.** $-(-3.9)$ ___ 3   and   **b.** $-|-\frac{4}{5}|$ ___ $|\sqrt{5}|$.

Solution
a. $-(-3.9)$ means the opposite of -3.9. Therefore, $-(-3.9) > 3$, because

$-(-3.9) = 3.9$ and $3.9 > 3$.

b. $-|-\frac{4}{5}|$ means the opposite of $|-\frac{4}{5}|$. Therefore, $-|-\frac{4}{5}| < |\sqrt{5}|$, because

$-|-\frac{4}{5}| = -\frac{4}{5}, |\sqrt{5}| = \sqrt{5} \approx 2.2$ and $-\frac{4}{5} < 2.2$.

Self Check
Insert one of the symbols $>$, $<$, or = in each blank:

a. $-(-7)$ ___ 12

b. $3\frac{3}{4}$ ___ $|-\frac{5}{4}|$

Answers: a. $<$,   **b.** $>$

STUDY SET Section 1.3

VOCABULARY *Fill in the blanks.*

1. The set of _____whole_____ numbers is {0, 1, 2, 3, 4, 5, . . .}.

2. The set of _____natural_____ numbers is {1, 2, 3, 4, 5, . . .}.

3. Numbers less than zero are _____negative_____, and numbers greater than zero are _____positive_____.

4. All numbers that can be represented by points on the number line are called _____real_____ numbers.

5. A _____rational_____ number can be written as a quotient (ratio) of two integers.

6. A decimal such as 0.25 is called a _____terminating_____ decimal, and 0.333. . . is called a _____repeating_____ decimal.

7. The set of _____integers_____ is {. . . , −2, −1, 0, 1, 2, . . .}.

8. The symbols < and > are _____inequality_____ symbols.

9. An irrational number is a nonterminating, nonrepeating _____decimal_____.

10. An _____irrational_____ number cannot be expressed as a quotient (ratio) of two integers.

11. The _____absolute value_____ of a number is the distance on a number line between the number and 0.

12. Two numbers represented by points on a number line that are the same distance away from 0, but on opposite sides of it, are called _____opposites_____.

CONCEPTS

13. Show that each of the following numbers is a rational number by expressing it as a fraction with an integer in its numerator and a nonzero integer in its denominator: $6, -9, -\frac{7}{8}, 3\frac{1}{2}, -0.3, 2.83.$ $\frac{6}{1}, \frac{-9}{1}, \frac{-7}{8}, \frac{7}{2}, \frac{-3}{10}, \frac{283}{100}$

14. Represent each situation using a signed number.
a. A loss of $15 million $-\$15$ million
b. A rainfall total 0.75 inch below average -0.75 in.
c. A score $12\frac{1}{2}$ points under the standard $-12\frac{1}{2}$ pts
d. A building foundation $\frac{5}{16}$ inch above grade $+\frac{5}{16}$ in.

15. What numbers are a distance of 8 away from 5 on the number line? 13 and −3

16. Suppose the variable m stands for a negative number. Use an inequality to state this fact. $m < 0$

17. The variables a and b represent real numbers. Use an inequality symbol, < or >, to make each statement true.

a. $a < b$ **b.** $b > a$
c. $b > 0$ and $a < 0$

18. What is the length of the diagonal of the square shown in Illustration 1? $\sqrt{2}$ in.

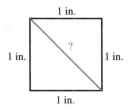

1 in.

ILLUSTRATION 1

19. The diagram in Illustration 2 can be used to show how the natural numbers, whole numbers, integers, rational numbers, and irrational numbers make up the set of real numbers. If the natural numbers are represented as shown, label each of the other sets.

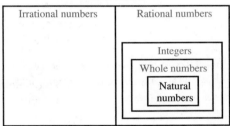

ILLUSTRATION 2

20. Which number graphed below has the largest absolute value? r

NOTATION *Fill in the blanks.*

21. $\sqrt{5}$ is read "the _____square root_____ of 5."

22. $|-15|$ is read "the _____absolute value_____ of −15."

23. The symbol ≈ means _____is approximately equal to_____.

24. The symbols { }, called _____braces_____, are used when writing a set.

25. In $\frac{3}{4}$, 3 is the _____numerator_____, and 4 is the _____denominator_____ of the fraction.

26. The symbol π is a letter from the _____Greek_____ alphabet.

Write each expression in simpler form.

27. The opposite of 5 -5 **28.** The opposite of −9 9

29. The opposite of $-\frac{7}{8}$ $\frac{7}{8}$ **30.** The opposite of 6.56 -6.56

31. $-(-10)$ 10

32. $-(-1)$ 1

33. $-(-2.3)$ 2.3

34. $-\left(-\frac{3}{4}\right)$ $\frac{3}{4}$

35. The opposite of the absolute value of 3. -3

36. $-|-5|$ -5

PRACTICE   *Insert one of the symbols* $>$, $<$, *or* $=$ *in the blank.*

37. $5 > 4$

38. $-5 < -4$

39. $-2 > -3$

40. $0 < 32$

41. $|3.4| > \sqrt{10}$

42. $0.08 > 0.079$

43. $-|-1.1| < -1$

44. $-(-5.5) = -\left(-5\frac{1}{2}\right)$

45. $-\left(-\frac{5}{8}\right) > -\left(-\frac{3}{8}\right)$

46. $-19\frac{2}{3} < -19\frac{1}{3}$

47. $\left|-\frac{15}{2}\right| = 7.5$

48. $\sqrt{2} < \pi$

49. $\frac{99}{100} = 0.99$

50. $|2| > -|-2|$

51. $0.333\ldots > 0.3$

52. $\left|-2\frac{2}{3}\right| > -\left(-\frac{3}{2}\right)$

53. $-(-1) > \left|-\frac{15}{16}\right|$

50. $-0.666\ldots < 0$

Tell which numbers in the given set are natural numbers, whole numbers, integers, rational numbers, irrational numbers, and real numbers.

55. $\left\{-\frac{5}{6}, 35.99, 0, 4\frac{3}{8}, \sqrt{2}, -50, \frac{17}{5}\right\}$

natural: none; whole: 0; integers: 0, -50; rational: $-\frac{5}{6}$, 35.99, 0, $4\frac{3}{8}$, -50, $\frac{17}{5}$; irrational: $\sqrt{2}$; real: all

56. $\left\{-0.001, 10\frac{1}{2}, 6, \pi, \sqrt{7}, -23, -5.6\right\}$

natural: 6; whole: 6; integers: 6, -23; rational: -0.001, $-10\frac{1}{2}$, 6, -23, -5.6; irrational: π, $\sqrt{7}$; real: all

Tell whether each statement is true or false.

57. a. Every whole number is an integer.   true

b. Every integer is a natural number.   false

c. Every integer is a whole number.   false

d. Irrational numbers are nonterminating, nonrepeating decimals.   true

58. a. Irrational numbers are real numbers.   true

b. Every whole number is a rational number.   true

c. Every rational number can be written as a fraction.   true

d. Every rational number is a whole number.   false

59. a. Write the statement $-6 < -5$ using an inequality symbol that points in the other direction. $-5 > -6$

b. Write the statement $16 > -25$ using an inequality symbol that points in the other direction. $-25 < 16$

60. If we begin with the number -4 and find its opposite, and then find the opposite of that result, what number do we obtain? -4

Graph each set of numbers on the number line.

61. $\left\{-\pi, 4.25, -1\frac{1}{2}, -0.333\ldots, \sqrt{2}, -\frac{35}{8}, 3\right\}$

62. $\left\{\pi, -2\frac{1}{8}, 2.75, -\sqrt{17}, \frac{17}{4}, -0.666\ldots, -3\right\}$

Approximate each irrational number to the nearest thousandth.

63. $\sqrt{5}$ 2.236

64. $\sqrt{19}$ 4.359

65. $\sqrt{99}$ 9.950

66. $\sqrt{42}$ 6.481

67. π 3.142

68. 2π 6.283

APPLICATIONS

69. BANKING   Later in this course, we will use a table such as the one in Illustration 3 to solve banking problems. Which numbers shown here are natural numbers, whole numbers, integers, rational numbers, irrational numbers, and real numbers?

natural, whole, integers: 750, 5,000; rational: all; irrational: none; real: all

Type of account	Principal	Rate	Time (years)	Interest
Checking	$135.75	0.0275	$\frac{31}{365}$	$0.32
Savings	$5,000	0.06	$2\frac{1}{2}$	$750

ILLUSTRATION 3

70. DRAFTING   The drawing in Illustration 4 shows the dimensions of an aluminum bracket.

a. Which numbers shown are natural numbers, whole numbers, integers, rational numbers, irrational numbers, and real numbers?

natural, whole, integers: 9; rational: 9, $\frac{15}{16}$, $3\frac{1}{8}$, 1.765; irrational: 2π, 3π, $\sqrt{89}$; real: all

b. Approximate all the irrational numbers in the drawing to the nearest thousandth.

$3\pi \approx 9.425$, $2\pi \approx 6.283$, $\sqrt{89} \approx 9.434$

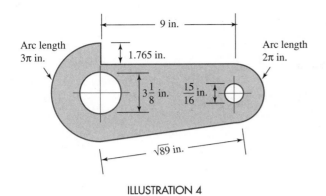

Arc length
3π in.

Arc length
2π in.

9 in.

1.765 in.

$3\frac{1}{8}$ in. $\frac{15}{16}$ in.

$\sqrt{89}$ in.

ILLUSTRATION 4

71. Each year from 1990 through 1999, the United States imported more goods and services from Japan than it exported to Japan. This caused trade *deficits*, which can be represented by negative numbers. See Illustration 5.

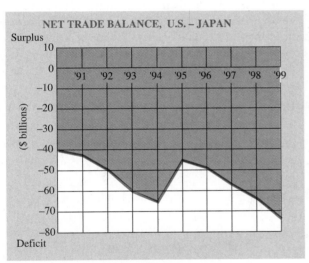

NET TRADE BALANCE, U.S. – JAPAN

Surplus

($ billions)

Deficit

Source: U.S. Bureau of the Census

ILLUSTRATION 5

a. In which three years was the deficit the worst? Estimate each of them.
'94: −$65 billion; '98: −$64 billion; '99: −$74 billion
b. In which year was the deficit the smallest? Estimate the deficit then.   '90; −$40 billion

72. GOVERNMENT DEBT   A budget *deficit* indicates that the government's outlays (expenditures) were more than the receipts (revenue) it took in that year. See Illustration 6.
a. For the years 1980–1999, when was the federal budget deficit the worst? Estimate the size of the deficit.   1992, −$290 billion
b. For the years 1980–1999, when did the first budget *surplus* occur? Estimate it. Explain what it means to have a budget surplus.
1998; $70 billion; the government takes in more money than it spends.

Federal Budget Deficit/Surplus

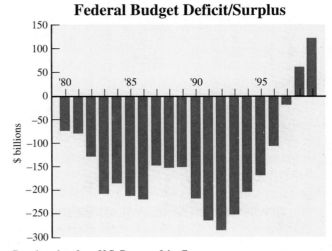

$ billions

Based on data from U.S. Bureau of the Census

ILLUSTRATION 6

73. TIRES   The distance a tire rolls in one revolution can be found by computing the circumference of the circular tire using the formula $C = \pi d$, where d is the diameter of the tire. How far will the tire shown in Illustration 7 roll in one revolution? Answer to the nearest tenth of an inch.   81.7 in.

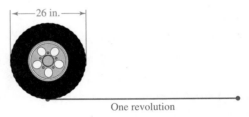

26 in.

One revolution

ILLUSTRATION 7

74. HULA HOOP   The length of plastic pipe needed to form a hula hoop can be found by computing the circumference of the circular hula hoop using the formula $C = \pi d$, where d is its diameter. Find the length of pipe needed to form the hula hoop shown in Illustration 8. Answer to the nearest tenth of an inch.   106.8 in.

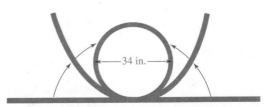

34 in.

A length of pipe is bent to form a Hula Hoop.

ILLUSTRATION 8

75. TARGET PRACTICE In Illustration 9, which artillery shell landed farther from the target? How can the concept of absolute value be applied to answer this question?   shell 1; $|-6| > |5|$

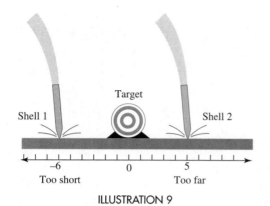

ILLUSTRATION 9

MAYA CIVILIZATION

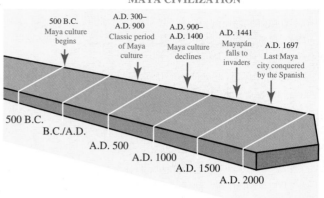

Based on data from *People in Time and Place, Western Hemisphere* (Silver Burdett & Ginn Inc., 1991), p. 129

ILLUSTRATION 10

76. Refer to the historical time line in Illustration 10.
  a. What basic unit was used to scale the time line?
    500 years
  b. On the time line, what symbolism is used to represent zero?   B.C./A.D.
  c. On the time line, what could be thought of as positive and what could be thought of as negative numbers?   pos: A.D.; neg: B.C.
  d. Express the dates for the Maya civilization using positive and negative numbers.   −500 to 1697

WRITING

77. Explain the difference between a rational and an irrational number.

78. Can two different numbers have the same absolute value? Explain.

79. Give two examples each of fractions, mixed numbers, decimals, and negative numbers that you use in your everyday life.

80. In writing courses, students are warned not to use double negatives in their compositions. Identify the double negative in the following sentence. Then rewrite the sentence so that it conveys the same idea without using a double negative. "No one didn't turn in the homework."

REVIEW

81. Simplify $\dfrac{24}{54}$.
    $\frac{4}{9}$

82. Prime factor 60.
    $5 \cdot 3 \cdot 2 \cdot 2$

83. Find: $\dfrac{3}{4}\left(\dfrac{8}{5}\right)$. $\frac{6}{5}$

84. Find: $5\dfrac{2}{3} \div 2\dfrac{5}{9}$. $2\frac{5}{23}$

85. Find: $\dfrac{3}{10} + \dfrac{2}{15}$. $\frac{13}{30}$

86. Write $\dfrac{4}{25}$ as a decimal.   0.16

1.4 Adding and Subtracting Real Numbers

In this section, you will learn about

- Adding two real numbers with the same sign
- Adding two real numbers with different signs • Properties of addition
- Subtracting real numbers

INTRODUCTION. Recall that all of the points on a number line represent the set of real numbers. Real numbers that are greater than zero are *positive real numbers*. (See Figure 1-14.) Positive numbers can be written with or without a + sign. For example, 2 = +2 and 4.75 = +4.75. Real numbers that are less than zero are *negative real numbers*. They are always written with a − sign. For example, negative 2 = −2 and negative 4.75 = −4.75. Positive and negative numbers are commonly referred to as **signed numbers.**

FIGURE 1-14

 COMMENT   Zero is neither positive nor negative.

We can use signed numbers to describe many real-world situations. Words such as *gain, above, up, to the right,* and *in the future* indicate positive numbers. Words such as *loss, below, down, to the left,* and *in the past* indicate negative numbers.

In words	In symbols	Meaning
16 degrees above 0	$+16°$	positive sixteen degrees
30 seconds after liftoff	30 sec	positive thirty seconds
$10.50 overdrawn	$−$10.50$	negative ten dollars and fifty cents
$5\frac{1}{2}$ feet below sea level	$−5\frac{1}{2}$ ft	negative five and one-half feet

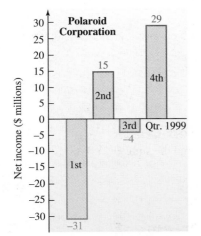

FIGURE 1-15

In Figure 1-15, signed numbers are used to denote the 1999 quarterly profits and losses of the Polaroid Corporation. The first-quarter loss of $31 million and the third-quarter loss of $4 million are represented by the negative numbers −31 and −4. The second-quarter profit of $15 million and the fourth-quarter profit of $29 million are represented by the positive numbers 15 and 29. To find Polaroid's 1999 net income, we must add these positive and negative numbers:

$$\text{Net income} = -31 + 15 + (-4) + 29$$

In this section, we will discuss how to perform such additions. We will also introduce a rule that is helpful when subtracting signed numbers.

Adding two real numbers with the same sign

We can use a number line to explain the addition of signed numbers. For example, Figure 1-16 shows the steps that are used to compute 5 + 2. We begin at the **origin** (the zero point) and draw an arrow 5 units long, pointing to the right; this represents 5. From that point, we draw an arrow 2 units long, also pointing to the right; this represents 2. We end up at 7; therefore, 5 + 2 = 7.

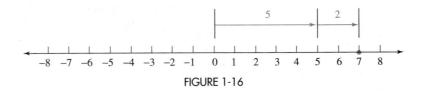

FIGURE 1-16

To compute −5 + (−2) on a number line, we begin at the origin and draw an arrow 5 units long, pointing to the left; this represents −5. From there, we draw an arrow 2 units long, also pointing to the left; this represents −2. We end up at −7, as shown in Figure 1-17 on the next page. Therefore, −5 + (−2) = −7.

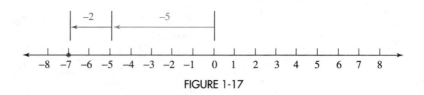

FIGURE 1-17

As a check, think of this problem in terms of money. If you had a debt of \$5 (-5) and incurred another debt of \$2 (-2), you would have a debt of \$7 (-7).

From these two examples, we observe that when we add two numbers with the same sign, the arrows point in the same direction and they build upon each other. Furthermore, the answer that they point to has the same sign as the numbers that are being added. If both numbers are positive, their sum is positive. If both numbers are negative, their sum is negative.

$$5 \quad + \quad 2 \quad = \quad 7$$
positive + positive = positive

and

$$-5 \quad + \quad (-2) \quad = \quad -7$$
negative + negative = negative

These observations suggest the following rule.

Adding two real numbers with the same sign

> To add two real numbers with the same sign, add their absolute values and attach their common sign to the sum.

EXAMPLE 1   *Adding numbers with the same sign.*   Find the sum: $-25 + (-18)$.

Solution

Since both numbers are negative, the answer will be negative.

$-25 + (-18) = -43$ Add their absolute values, 25 and 18, to get 43. Attach their common sign (which is a $-$ sign) to 43.

Self Check

Find the sum: $-45 + (-12)$.

Answer: -57 ∎

COMMENT   When writing an addition involving signed numbers, write negative numbers within parentheses to separate the negative sign $-$ from the plus sign $+$.

$$10 + (-1) \qquad\qquad -25 + (-18)$$
$$\cancel{10 + -1} \qquad\qquad \cancel{-25 + -18}$$

Adding two real numbers with different signs

To compute $5 + (-2)$ on a number line, we start at the origin and draw an arrow 5 units long, pointing to the right; this represents 5. From there, we draw an arrow 2 units long, pointing to the left; this represents -2. We end up at 3, as shown in Figure 1-18. Therefore, $5 + (-2) = 3$. In terms of money, if you had \$5 ($+5$) and lost \$2 (-2), you would have \$3 ($+3$) left.

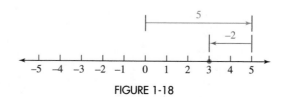

FIGURE 1-18

To compute $-5 + 2$ on a number line, we start at the origin and draw an arrow 5 units long, pointing to the left; this represents -5. From there, we draw an arrow 2 units long, pointing to the right; this represents 2. We end up at -3, as shown in Figure 1-19. Therefore, $-5 + 2 = -3$. In terms of money, if you owed a friend \$5 (-5) and paid back \$2 ($+2$), you would still owe your friend \$3 (-3).

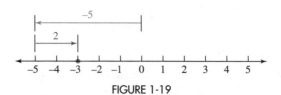

FIGURE 1-19

From these two examples, we observe that when we add two numbers with different signs, the arrows point in opposite directions. Furthermore, the longer arrow determines the sign of the answer. If the longer arrow represents a positive number, the sum is positive. If the longer arrow represents a negative number, the sum is negative.

$$5 + (-2) = 3 \qquad \text{and} \qquad -5 + 2 = -3$$

positive + negative = positive   negative + positive = negative

These observations suggest the following rule.

Adding two real numbers with different signs	To add two real numbers with different signs, subtract their absolute values (the smaller from the larger). To this result, attach the sign of the number with the larger absolute value.

EXAMPLE 2 *Adding numbers with different signs.* Find each sum: **a.** $-17 + 32$, **b.** $5.4 + (-7.7)$, and **c.** $\dfrac{3}{25} + \left(-\dfrac{19}{25}\right)$.

Solution

a. Since 32 has the larger absolute value, the answer will be positive.

$$-17 + 32 = 15 \quad \text{\small Subtract their absolute values, 17 from 32, to get 15.}$$

b. Since -7.7 has the larger absolute value, the answer will be negative.

$$5.4 + (-7.7) = -2.3 \quad \text{\small Subtract their absolute values, 5.4 from 7.7, to get 2.3.}$$
$$\text{\small Attach a} - \text{\small sign.}$$

c. Since the fractions have the same denominator, we add the numerators and keep the common denominator.

$$\frac{3}{25} + \left(-\frac{19}{25}\right) = \frac{3}{25} + \left(\frac{-19}{25}\right) \quad \text{\small Write } -\frac{19}{25} \text{ as } \frac{-19}{25}. \left(\text{Recall: } -\frac{a}{b} = \frac{-a}{b}.\right)$$

$$= -\frac{16}{25} \quad \text{\small Add the numerators: } 3 + (-19) = -16. \text{ Write}$$
$$\text{\small the sum over the common denominator 25,}$$
$$\text{\small putting the } - \text{ sign in front of the fraction.}$$

Self Check

Find each sum:

a. $63 + (-87)$

b. $-6.27 + 8$

c. $-\dfrac{1}{10} + \dfrac{1}{2}$

Answers: a. -24,
b. 1.73, **c.** $\frac{2}{5}$ ■

EXAMPLE 3 *Adding several signed numbers.* Find the 1999 net income of Polaroid Corporation from the data given in the graph in Figure 1-15 on page 33.

Solution

To find the annual net income, we add the 1999 quarterly profits and losses, performing the additions as they occur from left to right.

Self Check

Add $-7 + 13 + (-5) + 10$.

$$-31 + 15 + (-4) + 29 = -16 + (-4) + 29$$

Do the addition:
$-31 + 15 = -16$.

$$= -20 + 29$$

Do the addition:
$-16 + (-4) = -20$.

$$= 9$$

Do the addition.

In 1999, Polaroid's net income was $9 million.

Answer: 11   ■

Accent on Technology: **The sign change key**

A scientific calculator can be used to add the positive and negative numbers. For example, to do the addition $-31 + 15 + (-4) + 29$ from Example 3, we don't have to do anything special to enter the positive numbers. To enter negative 31 and negative 4, we must press the *opposite* or *sign change* key $\boxed{+/-}$ after entering 31 and after entering 4.

Keystrokes   31 $\boxed{+/-}$ $\boxed{+}$ 15 $\boxed{+}$ 4 $\boxed{+/-}$ $\boxed{+}$ 29 $\boxed{=}$ $\boxed{\qquad\qquad 9}$

Using a graphing calculator, we enter a negative number by first pressing the *negation* key $\boxed{(-)}$. To do the addition, we enter these numbers and press these keys.

Keystrokes $\boxed{(-)}$ 31 $\boxed{+}$ 15 $\boxed{+}$ $\boxed{(-)}$ 4 $\boxed{+}$ 29 $\boxed{\text{ENTER}}$

$\boxed{\begin{array}{l} -31 + 15 + {}^-4 + 29 \\ \qquad\qquad\qquad\qquad 9 \end{array}}$

The sum is 9. As we found in Example 3, Polaroid's 1999 net income was $9 million.

Properties of addition

A special property of addition, called the **commutative property,** states that two real numbers can be added in either order to get the same result. For example, when adding the numbers 10 and -25, we see that

$$10 + (-25) = -15 \qquad \text{and} \qquad -25 + 10 = -15$$

To state the **commutative property of addition** concisely, we use variables.

The commutative property of addition

If a and b represent real numbers, then
$$a + b = b + a$$

To find the sum of three numbers, we first add two of them and then add the third to that result. In the following example, we add $-3 + 7 + 5$ in two ways. We will use grouping symbols ( ), called **parentheses,** to show this. Standard practice requires that we do the operations within parentheses first.

Method 1: Group -3 and 7

$$(-3 + 7) + 5 = 4 + 5$$

Because of the parentheses, add -3 and 7 first to get 4.

$$= 9$$

Then add 4 and 5.

Method 2: Group 7 and 5

$$-3 + (7 + 5) = -3 + 12$$

Because of the parentheses, add 7 and 5 first to get 12.

$$= 9$$

Then add -3 and 12.

Either way, the sum is 9, which illustrates that it doesn't matter how we *group* or "associate" numbers in addition. This property is called the **associative property of addition.**

**The associative property
of addition**

> If a, b, and c represent real numbers, then
>
> $$(a + b) + c = a + (b + c)$$

EXAMPLE 4 *Adding the positives and negatives separately.* A contestant on the game show "Jeopardy!" answered the first question correctly to win $100, missed the second question to lose $200, answered the third question correctly to win $300, and answered the fourth question incorrectly to lose $400. Find her net gain or loss after four questions.

Solution "To win $100" can be represented by 100. "To lose $200" can be represented by -200. "To win $300" can be represented by 300, and "to lose $400" can be represented by -400. Her net gain or loss is the sum of these four numbers. We can find the sum by doing the additions from left to right. An alternate method, which uses the commutative and associative properties of addition, is to add the positives, then add the negatives, and finally add those results.

$$100 + (-200) + 300 + (-400) = \mathbf{100 + 300 + (-200) + (-400)} \qquad \text{Reorder the numbers.}$$

$$= \mathbf{(100 + 300) + [(-200) + (-400)]} \qquad \text{Group the positives together. Group the negatives together using brackets [\ \ ].}$$

$$= \mathbf{400 + (-600)} \qquad \text{Add the positives. Add the negatives.}$$

$$= -200$$

After four questions, she had a net loss of $200. ■

Whenever we add zero to a number, the number remains the same. For example,

$$0 + 8 = 8, \qquad 2.3 + 0 = 2.3, \qquad \text{and} \qquad -16 + 0 = -16$$

These examples illustrate the **addition property of zero.**

Addition property of zero

> If a represents a real number, then
>
> $$a + 0 = a \qquad \text{and} \qquad 0 + a = a$$

Two numbers that are the same distance away from the origin, but on opposite sides of it, are called **opposites** or **additive inverses.** For example, 10 is the additive inverse of -10, and -10 is the additive inverse of 10. Whenever we add opposites or additive inverses, the result is 0.

$$10 + (-10) = 0, \qquad -\frac{4}{5} + \frac{4}{5} = 0, \qquad 56.8 + (-56.8) = 0$$

**Adding opposites
(additive inverses)**

> If a represents a number, then
>
> $$a + (-a) = 0$$

Subtracting real numbers

The subtraction $5 - 2$ can be thought of as taking 2 away from 5. We can use the number line shown in Figure 1-20 (next page) to illustrate this. Beginning at the origin, we draw an arrow of length 5 units pointing to the right. From that point, we move back 2 units to the left. The result, 3, is called the **difference.**

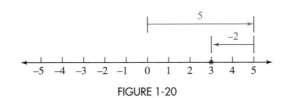

FIGURE 1-20

Figure 1-20 looks like the illustration for the addition problem $5 + (-2)$ shown in Figure 1-18. In the problem $5 - 2$, we subtracted 2 from 5. In the problem $5 + (-2)$, we added -2 (which is the opposite of 2) to 5. In each case, the result is 3.

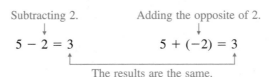

This observation suggests the following rule.

Subtracting real numbers	If a and b represent real numbers, then $$a - b = a + (-b)$$

This rule indicates that *subtraction is the same as adding the opposite of the number to be subtracted.* We won't need this rule for every subtraction problem. For example, $5 - 2$ is obviously 3. However, for more complicated problems such as $-8 - (-3)$, where the result is not obvious, the subtraction rule will be helpful.

$$-8 - (-3) = -8 + 3 \quad \text{To subtract } -3, \text{ add the opposite of } -3, \text{ which is 3.}$$
$$= -5 \qquad \text{Do the addition.}$$

EXAMPLE 5   *Adding the opposite.*   Find   **a.** $-13 - 18$,
b. $-45 - (-27)$,   and   **c.** $\dfrac{1}{4} - \left(-\dfrac{1}{8}\right)$.

Solution

a. In $-13 - 18$, the number to be subtracted is 18.

$$-13 - 18 = -13 + (-18) \quad \text{To subtract 18, add the opposite of 18, which is } -18.$$

$$= -31 \qquad \text{Add their absolute values, 13 and 18, to get 31. Keep their common sign.}$$

b. In $-45 - (-27)$, the number to be subtracted is -27.

$$-45 - (-27) = -45 + 27 \quad \text{To subtract } -27, \text{ add the opposite of } -27, \text{ which is 27.}$$

$$= -18 \qquad \text{Subtract their absolute values, 27 from 45, to get 18. Use the sign of the number with the greater absolute value, which is } -45.$$

c. The lowest common denominator (LCD) for the fractions is 8.

$$\frac{1}{4} - \left(-\frac{1}{8}\right) = \frac{2}{8} - \left(-\frac{1}{8}\right) \quad \text{Express } \tfrac{1}{4} \text{ in terms of eighths: } \tfrac{1}{4} = \tfrac{2}{8}.$$

$$= \frac{2}{8} + \frac{1}{8} \qquad \text{The number to be subtracted is } -\tfrac{1}{8}. \text{ Add the opposite of } -\tfrac{1}{8}, \text{ which is } \tfrac{1}{8}.$$

$$= \frac{3}{8} \qquad \text{Add the numerators: } 2 + 1 = 3. \text{ Write the sum over the common denominator, 8.}$$

Self Check

Find

a. $-32 - 25$

b. $1.7 - (-1.2)$

c. $-\dfrac{1}{2} - \dfrac{1}{8}$

Answers: **a.** -57,   **b.** 2.9,
c. $-\dfrac{5}{8}$

Accent on Technology: **U.S. temperature extremes**

The record high temperature in the United States was 134°F in Death Valley, California, on July 10, 1913. The record low was −80°F at Prospect Creek, Alaska, on January 23, 1971. See Figure 1-21. To find the difference between these two temperatures, we subtract:

$$134 - (-80)$$

We can subtract positive and negative real numbers using a scientific calculator. To find $134 - (-80)$, we enter these numbers and press these keys.

Keystrokes   134 $\boxed{-}$ 80 $\boxed{+/-}$ $\boxed{=}$ $\boxed{214}$

If we use a graphing calculator, we enter these numbers and press these keys.

Keystrokes   134 $\boxed{-}$ $\boxed{(-)}$ 80 $\boxed{\text{ENTER}}$ $\boxed{\begin{array}{r}134--80\\214\end{array}}$

The difference in the record high and low temperatures is 214°F.

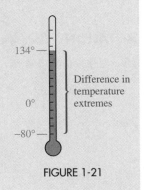

FIGURE 1-21

STUDY SET   Section 1.4

VOCABULARY   *Fill in the blanks.*

1. Real numbers that are greater than zero are called ___positive___ real numbers. Real numbers that are less than zero are called ___negative___ real numbers.

2. The only real number that is neither positive nor negative is ___zero___.

3. The ___commutative___ property of addition states that two numbers can be added in either order to get the same result.

4. The property that allows us to group numbers in addition in any way we want is called the ___associative___ property of addition.

5. The grouping symbols (   ) are called ___parentheses___.

6. Whenever we add ___opposites___, or additive ___inverses___, the result is 0.

CONCEPTS   *Use the number line in Illustration 1 to find each sum.*

7. $2 + 3$ 5   **8.** $-3 + (-2)$ −5

9. $4 + (-3)$ 1   **10.** $-5 + 3$ −2

ILLUSTRATION 1

In Exercises 11–12, fill in the blanks.

11. To add two real numbers, with the ___same___ sign, add their ___absolute___ values and attach their common sign to the sum.

12. To add two real numbers with different signs, ___subtract___ their absolute values, the ___smaller___ from the ___larger___, and attach the sign of the number with the ___larger___ absolute value.

13. Use the commutative property of addition to complete each statement.
   a. $-5 + 1 = $ ___$1 + (-5)$___
   b. $15 + (-80.5) = $ ___$-80.5 + 15$___
   c. $-20 + (4 + 20) = -20 + $ ___$(20 + 4)$___

14. Use the associative property of addition to complete each statement.
   a. $(-6 + 2) + 8 = $ ___$-6 + (2 + 8)$___
   b. $-7 + (7 + 3) = $ ___$(-7 + 7) + 3$___
   c. $-96 + (4 + 200) = $ ___$(-96 + (4)) + 200$___

15. Find each sum.
   a. $5 + (-5)$ 0   **b.** $-2.2 + 2.2$ 0
   c. $0 + (-6)$ −6   **d.** $\frac{-15}{16} + 0$ $-\frac{15}{16}$
   e. $-\frac{3}{4} + \frac{3}{4}$ 0   **f.** $19 + (-19)$ 0

16. To subtract b from a, add the ___opposite___ of b to a.

17. What is the opposite of 7? What is the opposite of −15?   −7, 15

18. a. Subtract 5 from -7. -12
 b. Subtract -7 from 5. 12

NOTATION Complete each solution.

19. $(-13 + 6) + 4 = -13 + (6 + 4)$
$= -13 + 10$
$= -3$

20. $-9 + (9 + 43) = (-9 + 9) + 43$
$= 0 + 43$
$= 43$

PRACTICE Find each sum.

21. $6 + (-8)$ -2
22. $4 + (-3)$ 1
23. $-6 + 8$ 2
24. $-21 + (-12)$ -33
25. $-65 + (-12)$ -77
26. $75 + (-13)$ 62
27. $15 + (-11)$ 4
28. $27 + (-30)$ -3
29. $300 + (-335)$ -35
30. $240 + (-340)$ -100
31. $-10.5 + 2.3$ -8.2
32. $-2.1 + 0.4$ -1.7
33. $-9.1 + (-11)$ -20.1
34. $-6.7 + (-7.1)$ -13.8
35. $-\dfrac{9}{16} + \dfrac{7}{16}$ $-\frac{1}{8}$
36. $-\dfrac{3}{4} + \dfrac{1}{4}$ $-\frac{1}{2}$
37. $-\dfrac{1}{4} + \dfrac{2}{3}$ $\frac{5}{12}$
38. $\dfrac{3}{16} + \left(-\dfrac{1}{2}\right)$ $-\frac{5}{16}$
39. $8 + (-5) + 13$ 16
40. $17 + (-12) + (-23)$ -18
41. $21 + (-27) + (-9)$ -15
42. $-32 + 12 + 17$ -3
43. $-27 + (-3) + (-13) + 22$ -21
44. $53 + (-27) + (-32) + (-7)$ -13
45. $-20 + (-16 + 10)$ -26
46. $-13 + (-16 + 4)$ -25

In Exercises 47–48, apply the associative property of addition, then find the sum.

47. $-99 + (99 + 215)$ 215
48. $67 + (-67 + 127)$ 127

⊞ Find each sum.

49. $3,718 + (-5,237)$ $-1,519$
50. $-5,235 + (-17,235)$ $-22,470$
51. $-237.37 + (-315.07) + (-27.4)$ -579.84
52. $-587.77 + (-1,732.13) + 687.39$ $-1,632.51$

Find each difference.

53. $8 - (-3)$ 11
54. $17 - (-21)$ 38
55. $-12 - 9$ -21
56. $-25 - 17$ -42

57. $-19 - (-17)$ -2
58. $-30 - (-11)$ -19
59. $-1.5 - 0.8$ -2.3
60. $-1.5 - (-0.8)$ -0.7
61. $2.8 - (-1.8)$ 4.6
62. $4.7 - (-1.9)$ 6.6
63. $-44 - 44$ -88
64. $-33 - 33$ -66
65. $0 - (-12)$ 12
66. $0 - 12$ -12
67. $-25 - (-25)$ 0
68. $13 - (-13)$ 0
69. $0 - 4$ -4
70. $0 - (-3)$ 3
71. $-\dfrac{1}{8} - \dfrac{3}{8}$ $-\frac{1}{2}$
72. $-\dfrac{3}{4} - \dfrac{1}{4}$ -1
73. $-\dfrac{9}{16} - \left(-\dfrac{1}{4}\right)$ $-\frac{5}{16}$
74. $-\dfrac{1}{2} - \left(-\dfrac{1}{4}\right)$ $-\frac{1}{4}$

⊞ Find each difference.

75. $8,713 - (-3,753)$ $12,466$
76. $-2,727 - 1,208$ $-3,935$
77. $-27,357.875 - 17,213.376$ $-44,571.251$
78. $-45,307.039 - (-27,592.47)$ $-17,714.569$

APPLICATIONS

79. MILITARY SCIENCE During a battle, an army retreated 1,500 meters, regrouped, and advanced 2,400 meters. The next day, it advanced another 1,250 meters. Find the army's net gain. $2,150\text{ m}$

80. MEDICAL QUESTIONNAIRE Determine the risk of contracting heart disease for the woman whose responses are shown in Illustration 2. 4%

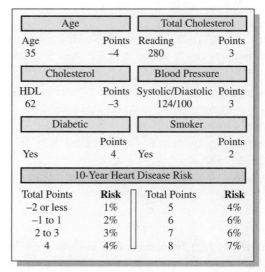

Age		Total Cholesterol	
Age	Points	Reading	Points
35	–4	280	3
Cholesterol		Blood Pressure	
HDL	Points	Systolic/Diastolic	Points
62	–3	124/100	3
Diabetic		Smoker	
	Points		Points
Yes	4	Yes	2
10-Year Heart Disease Risk			
Total Points	Risk	Total Points	Risk
–2 or less	1%	5	4%
–1 to 1	2%	6	6%
2 to 3	3%	7	6%
4	4%	8	7%

Source: National Heart, Lung, and Blood Institute

ILLUSTRATION 2

81. GOLF Illustration 3 shows the top four finishers from the 1997 Masters Golf Tournament. The scores for each round are related to *par*, the standard number of strokes deemed necessary to complete the course. A score of -2, for example, indicates that the golfer used two strokes less than par to complete the course. A score of +5 indicates the golfer used five strokes more than par.

a. Determine the tournament total for each golfer.

b. Tiger Woods won by the largest margin in the history of the Masters. What was the margin?
12 strokes

Leaderboard

	Round				
	1	**2**	**3**	**4**	**Total**
Tiger Woods	−2	−6	−7	−3	−18
Tom Kite	+5	−3	−6	−2	−6
Tommy Tolles	0	0	0	−5	−5
Tom Watson	+3	−4	−3	0	−4

ILLUSTRATION 3

82. CREDIT CARD STATEMENT

a. What amounts in the monthly credit card statement shown in Illustration 4 could be represented by negative numbers? 3,660.66, 1,408.78

b. What is the new balance? 1,242.86

Previous Balance	New Purchases, Fees, Advances & Debts	Payments & Credits	New Balance
3,660.66	1,408.78	3,826.58	

04/21/01 Billing Date	05/16/01 Date Payment Due	9,100 Credit Line

Periodic rates may vary.
See reverse for explanation and important information.
Please allow sufficient time for mail to reach us.

ILLUSTRATION 4

83. THE OLYMPICS   The ancient Greek Olympian Games, which eventually evolved into the modern Olympic Games, were first held in 776 B.C. How many years after this did the 1996 Olympic Games in Atlanta, Georgia, take place? 2,772

84. SUBMARINE   A submarine was cruising at a depth of 1,250 feet. The captain gave the order to climb 550 feet. Relative to sea level, find the new depth of the sub. −700 ft

85. TEMPERATURE RECORDS   Find the difference between the record high temperature of 108°F set in 1926 and the record low of −52°F set in 1979 for New York State. 160°F

86. LIE DETECTOR TEST   A burglar scored −18 on a lie detector test, a score that indicates deception. However, on a second test, he scored +3, a score that is inconclusive. Find the difference in the scores. 21

87. LAND ELEVATIONS   The elevation of Death Valley, California, is 282 feet below sea level. The elevation of the Dead Sea in Israel is 1,312 feet below sea level. Find the difference in their elevations. 1,030 ft

88. STOCK EXCHANGE   Many newspapers publish daily summaries of the stock market's activity. (See Illustration 5.) The last entry on the line for June 12 indicates that one share of Walt Disney Co. stock lost $0.81 in value that day. How much did the value of a share of Disney stock rise or fall over the five-day period shown? It fell $0.38.

June 12	43.88	23.38	Disney	.21	0.5	87	−43	40.75	−.81
June 13	43.88	23.38	Disney	.21	0.5	86	−15	40.19	−.56
June 14	43.88	23.38	Disney	.21	0.5	87	−50	41.00	+.81
June 15	43.88	23.38	Disney	.21	0.5	89	−28	41.81	+.81
June 16	43.88	23.38	Disney				−15	41.19	−.63

Based on data from the *Los Angeles Times*

ILLUSTRATION 5

89. VOTER INFORMATION   What will be the effect on state government if the ballot initiative shown in Illustration 6 passes? a gain of $2.2 million

212   **Campaign Spending Limits**   YES ☐   NO ☐

Limits contributions to $200 in state campaigns. Fiscal impact: Costs of $4.5 million for implementation and enforcement. Increases state revenue by $6.7 million by eliminating tax deductions for lobbying.

ILLUSTRATION 6

90. MOVIE LOSSES   According to the *Guinness Book of World Records 2000*, MGM's *Cutthroat Island* (1995), starring Geena Davis, cost about $100 million to produce, promote, and distribute. It has reportedly earned back just $11 million since being released. What dollar loss did the studio suffer on this film?
$89 million

In Exercises 91–94, use a calculator to help solve each problem.

91. SAHARA DESERT   From 1980 to 1990, a satellite was used to trace the expansion and contraction of the southern boundary of the Sahara Desert in Africa (see Illustration 7, next page). If movement southward is represented with a negative number and movement northward with a positive number, use the data in the table to determine the net movement of the Sahara Desert boundary over the 10-year period. southward, 132 km

Years	Distance/Direction
1980–1984	240 km/South
1984–1985	110 km/North
1985–1986	30 km/North
1986–1987	55 km/South
1987–1988	100 km/North
1988–1990	77 km/South

Based on data from A. Dolgoff, *Physical Geology*
(D. C. Heath, 1996), p. 496

ILLUSTRATION 7

92. BANKING   On February 1, Marta had $1,704.29 in a checking account. During the month, she made deposits of $713.87 and $1,245.57, wrote checks for $813.45, $937.49, and $1,532.79, and had a total of $500 in ATM withdrawals. Find her checking account balance at the end of the month.   −$120 (overdrawn $120)

93. CARD GAME   In the second hand of a card game, Gonzalo was the winner and earned 50 points. Matt and Hydecki had to deduct the value of each of the cards left in their hands from their running point totals. Use the information in Illustration 8 to update the score sheet. (Face cards are counted as 10 points and aces as 1 point.)

Matt   Hydecki

Running point total	Hand 1	Hand 2
Matt	+50	+29
Gonzalo	−15	+35
Hydecki	−2	−23

ILLUSTRATION 8

94. PROFITS AND LOSSES   The 1999 quarterly profits and losses of Greyhound Bus Lines are shown in the table. Losses are denoted using parentheses. Use the data to construct a line graph (using Illustration 9). Then calculate the company's total net income for 1999.   −$16 million

Quarter	1st	2nd	3rd	4th
Net income ($ million)	(24)	0	11	(3)

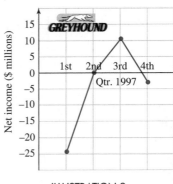

ILLUSTRATION 9

WRITING

95. Explain why the sum of two positive numbers is always positive and why the sum of two negative numbers is always negative.

96. Is subtracting 2 from 10 the same as subtracting 10 from 2? Explain.

97. Explain why we need to subtract when we add two real numbers with different signs.

98. Explain why we can subtract by adding the opposite.

REVIEW

99. True or false: Every real number can be expressed as a decimal.   true

100. True or false: Irrational numbers are nonterminating, nonrepeating decimals.   true

101. What two numbers are a distance of 6 away from −3 on the number line?   −9 and 3

102. Graph $\{-2.5, \sqrt{5}, \frac{11}{3}, -0.333\ldots, 0.75\}$.

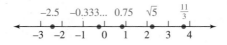

1.5 *Multiplying and Dividing Real Numbers*

In this section, you will learn about

- Multiplying signed numbers • Properties of multiplication
- Division of real numbers • Properties of division

INTRODUCTION. In this course, you will often need to multiply or divide positive and negative numbers. For example,

If the temperature drops 3° per hour for 4 hours, we can find the total drop in temperature by doing the multiplication $4(-3)$.

If the temperature uniformly drops 15° over a 5-hour period, we can find the number of degrees it drops each hour by doing the division $\frac{-15}{5}$.

In this section, we will show how to perform such multiplication and divisions.

Multiplying signed numbers

Multiplication represents repeated addition. For example, $4(3)$ equals the sum of four 3's.

$$4(3) = 3 + 3 + 3 + 3$$
$$= 12$$

This example illustrates that the product of two positive numbers is positive.

To develop a rule for multiplying a positive number and a negative number, we will find $4(-3)$. According to the definition of multiplication, $4(-3)$ means we are to add -3 four times.

$$4(-3) = -3 + (-3) + (-3) + (-3)$$
$$= -6 + (-3) + (-3) \qquad \text{Work from left to right.}$$
$$= -9 + (-3)$$
$$= -12 \qquad \text{The result is negative.}$$

This example illustrates that *the product of a positive number and a negative number is negative.*

In terms of money, if you lose $3 four times, you have lost a total of $12, which is denoted as $-\$12$.

EXAMPLE 1 *Multiplying two numbers with unlike signs.* Multiply **a.** $5(7)$, **b.** $8(-12)$, and **c.** $-15 \cdot 25$.

Solution

a. $5(7) = 35$ — The product of two positive numbers is positive.

b. $8(-12) = -96$ — Multiply the absolute values, 8 and 12, to get 96. Since one factor is positive and the other is negative, the answer is negative.

c. $-15 \cdot 25 = -375$ — Multiply the absolute values, 15 and 25, to get 375. Make the answer negative.

Self Check

Multiply:

a. $20(-30)$

b. $-0.4 \cdot 2$

Answers: **a.** -600, **b.** -0.8

To develop a rule for multiplying two negative numbers, we will find $-4(-3)$. Examine the following pattern, in which we multiply -4 and a series of factors that decrease by 1. After finding the first four products, we graph them on a number line, as shown in Figure 1-22 on the next page.

This factor decreases by 1 as   Look for a
you read down the column.   pattern here.

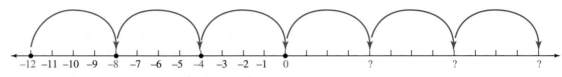

$$-4(3) \ = \ -12$$
$$-4(2) \ = \ -8$$
$$-4(1) \ = \ -4$$
$$-4(0) \ = \ 0$$
$$-4(-1) \ = \ ?$$
$$-4(-2) \ = \ ?$$
$$-4(-3) \ = \ ?$$

FIGURE 1-22

From the pattern, we see that the product increases by 4 each time Thus,

$$-4(-1) = 4, \qquad -4(-2) = 8, \quad \text{and} \quad -4(-3) = 12$$

These results illustrate that *the product of two negative numbers is positive.*

In terms of money, losing four debts of $3 is the same as gaining $12: $-4(-\$3) = \$12$.

EXAMPLE 2   *Multiplying two negative numbers.*   Multiply
a. $-5(-6)$ and   **b.** $\left(-\frac{1}{2}\right)\left(-\frac{5}{8}\right)$.

Solution

a. $-5(-6) = 30$ Multiply the absolute values, 5 and 6, to get 30. Since both factors are negative, the product is positive.

b. $\left(-\frac{1}{2}\right)\left(-\frac{5}{8}\right) = \frac{5}{16}$ Multiply the absolute values, $\frac{1}{2}$ and $\frac{5}{8}$, to get $\frac{5}{16}$. The product is positive.

Self Check

Multiply

a. $-15(-8)$

b. $-\frac{1}{4}\left(-\frac{1}{3}\right)$

Answers: a. 120,   **b.** $\frac{1}{12}$ ■

We now summarize the rules for multiplying two real numbers.

Multiplying two real numbers

To multiply two real numbers, multiply their absolute values.

1. The product of two numbers with *like signs* is positive.

2. The product of two numbers with *unlike signs* is negative.

Accent on Technology: **Bank promotion**

To attract business, a bank gave a clock radio to each customer who opened a checking account. The radios cost the bank $12.75 each, and 230 new accounts were opened. Each of the 230 radios was given away at a cost of $12.75, which can be expressed as -12.75. To find how much money the promotion cost the bank, we need to find the product of 230 and -12.75.

We can multiply positive and negative numbers with a scientific calculator. To find the product $(230)(-12.75)$, we enter these numbers and press these keys.

Keystrokes   230 $\boxed{\times}$ 12.75 $\boxed{+/-}$ $\boxed{=}$ $\boxed{-2932.5}$

Using a graphing calculator, we enter the following sequence:

Keystrokes   230 $\boxed{\times}$ $\boxed{(-)}$ 12.75 $\boxed{\text{ENTER}}$ $\boxed{\begin{matrix} 230*-12.75 \\ -2932.5 \end{matrix}}$

The promotion cost the bank $2,932.50.

Properties of multiplication

A special property of multiplication is that two real numbers can be multiplied in either order to get the same result. For example, when multiplying -6 and 5, we see that

$$-6(5) = -30 \qquad \text{and} \qquad 5(-6) = -30$$

This property is called the **commutative property of multiplication.**

The commutative property of multiplication	If a and b represent real numbers, then $ab = ba$

To find the product of three numbers, we first multiply two of them, and then we multiply the third by that result. In the following example, we multiply $-3 \cdot 7 \cdot 5$ in two ways. We will use parentheses (   ) to show this. Recall that we do the operations within parentheses first.

Method 1: Group -3 and 7

$(-3 \cdot 7)5 = (-21)5$ Because of the parentheses, multiply -3 and 7 first.

$= -105$ Then multiply -21 and 5.

Method 2: Group 7 and 5

$-3(7 \cdot 5) = -3(35)$ Because of the parentheses, multiply 7 and 5 first.

$= -105$ Then multiply -3 and 35.

Either way, the product is -105, which suggests that it doesn't matter how we *group* or "associate" numbers in multiplication. This property is called the **associative property of multiplication.**

The associative property of multiplication	If a, b, and c represent real numbers, then $(ab)c = a(bc)$

EXAMPLE 3 *Multiplying more than two numbers.* Multiply
a. $-5(-37)(2)$ and   **b.** $2(-3)(-2)(-3)$.

Solution

Using the commutative and associative properties of multiplication, we can reorder and regroup the factors to simplify the computations.

a. $-5(-37)(2) = -10(-37)$ Think of the problem as $-5(2)(-37)$, and then multiply -5 and 2 in your head.

$= 370$ The product of two negative numbers is positive.

b. $2(-3)(-2)(-3) = -6(6)$ Multiply the first two factors, and then multiply the last two factors.

$= -36$ The product of two numbers with unlike signs is negative.

Self Check

Multiply:

a. $-25(-3)(-4)$

b. $-1(-2)(-3)(-3)$

Answers: **a.** -300, **b.** 18

Whenever we multiply a number and 0, the product is 0. For example,

$$0 \cdot 8 = 0, \qquad 6.5(0) = 0, \quad \text{and} \quad 0(-12) = 0$$

We also see that whenever we multiply a number by 1, the number remains the same. For example,

$$6 \cdot 1 = 6, \qquad 4.53(1) = 4.53, \quad \text{and} \quad 1(-9) = -9$$

These examples illustrate the **multiplication properties of 0 and 1.**

Multiplication properties
of 0 and 1

If a represents a real number, then

$a \cdot 0 = 0$ and $0 \cdot a = 0$

$a \cdot 1 = a$ and $1 \cdot a = a$

Recall that if the product of two numbers is 1, the numbers are **reciprocals.** The numbers are also called **multiplicative inverses** of each other. For example, because $8 \cdot \frac{1}{8} = 1$, the numbers 8 and $\frac{1}{8}$ are reciprocals (or multiplicative inverses). Likewise, $-\frac{3}{4}$ and $-\frac{4}{3}$ are multiplicative inverses because $-\frac{3}{4}\left(-\frac{4}{3}\right) = 1$. All real numbers, except 0, have reciprocals (multiplicative inverses).

Reciprocals
(multiplicative inverses)

If a represents a nonzero number,

$$a\left(\frac{1}{a}\right) = 1$$

Division of real numbers

Every division fact containing three numbers can be written as an equivalent multiplication fact containing the same three numbers. For example,

$$\frac{15}{5} = 3 \quad \text{because} \quad 5(3) = 15$$

We will use this relationship between multiplication and division to develop the rules for dividing signed numbers. From the example $\frac{15}{5} = 3$, we see that *the quotient of two positive numbers is positive.*

To determine the quotient of two negative numbers, we consider the division $\frac{-15}{-5} = ?$. We can do the division by examining its related multiplication fact: $-5(?) = -15$. To find the number that should replace the question mark, we use the rules for multiplying signed numbers discussed earlier in this section.

Multiplication fact   **Division fact**

$-5(?) = -15$ $\dfrac{-15}{-5} = 3$

This must be
positive 3 if the
product is to be
negative 15.

So the quotient
is *positive* 3.

From this example, we see that *the quotient of two negative numbers is positive.*

To determine the quotient of a positive number and a negative number, we consider $\frac{15}{-5} = ?$ and its equivalent multiplication fact $-5(?) = 15$.

Multiplication fact   **Division fact**

$-5(?) = 15$ $\dfrac{15}{-5} = -3$

This must be
negative 3 if the
product is to be
positive 15.

So the quotient
is *negative* 3.

From this example, we see that *the quotient of a positive number and a negative number is negative.*

To determine the quotient of a negative number and a positive number, we consider $\frac{-15}{5} = ?$ and its equivalent multiplication fact $5(?) = -15$.

Multiplication fact   **Division fact**

$$5(?) = -15 \qquad\qquad \frac{-15}{5} = -3$$

This must be
negative 3 if the
product is to be
negative 15.

So the quotient
is *negative* 3.

From this example, we see that *the quotient of a negative number and a positive number is negative.*

We can now summarize the results from the previous discussion. Note that the rules for division are similar to those for multiplication.

Dividing two real numbers

To divide two real numbers, divide their absolute values.

1. The quotient of two numbers with *like signs* is positive.
2. The quotient of two numbers with *unlike signs* is negative.

EXAMPLE 4 *Dividing signed numbers.* Find each quotient:

a. $\frac{66}{11}$, **b.** $\frac{-81}{-9}$, **c.** $\frac{-45}{9}$, and **d.** $\frac{28}{-7}$.

Solution
To divide numbers with like signs, we find the quotient of their absolute values and make the quotient positive.

a. $\frac{66}{11} = 6$ Divide the absolute values, 66 by 11, to get 6. The answer is positive.

b. $\frac{-81}{-9} = 9$ Divide the absolute values, 81 by 9, to get 9. The answer is positive.

To divide numbers with unlike signs, we find the quotient of their absolute values and make the quotient negative.

c. $\frac{-45}{9} = -5$ Divide the absolute values, 45 by 9, to get 5. The answer is negative.

d. $\frac{28}{-7} = -4$ Divide the absolute values, 28 by 7, to get 4. The answer is negative.

Self Check
Find each quotient:

a. $\frac{48}{12}$

b. $\frac{-63}{-9}$

c. $\frac{40}{-8}$

d. $\frac{-49}{7}$

Answers: **a.** 4, **b.** 7, **c.** −5, **d.** −7

Properties of division

The examples

$$\frac{12}{1} = 12, \qquad \frac{-80}{1} = -80, \quad \text{and} \quad \frac{7.75}{1} = 7.75$$

illustrate that *any number divided by 1 is the number itself.* The examples

$$\frac{35}{35} = 1, \qquad \frac{-4}{-4} = 1, \quad \text{and} \quad \frac{0.9}{0.9} = 1$$

illustrate that *any number (except 0) divided by itself is 1.*

Division properties

> If a represents a real number, then
>
> $$\frac{a}{1} = a \quad \text{and} \quad \frac{a}{a} = 1 \quad (a \neq 0)$$

We will now consider three types of division that involve zero. In the first case, we will examine a division of zero; in the second, a division by zero; in the third case, a division of zero by zero.

Division statement	Related multiplication statement	Result
$\frac{0}{2} = ?$	$2(?) = 0$	$\frac{0}{2} = 0$
	↑ This must be 0 if the product is to be 0.	
$\frac{2}{0} = ?$	$0(?) = 2$	There is no quotient.
	↑ There is no number that gives 2 when multiplied by 0.	
$\frac{0}{0} = ?$	$0(?) = 0$	Any number can be the quotient.
	↑ Any number times 0 is 0.	

We see that $\frac{0}{2} = 0$. Since $\frac{2}{0}$ does not have a quotient, we say that division of 2 by 0 is *undefined*. Since $\frac{0}{0}$ can be any number, we say that $\frac{0}{0}$ is *undetermined*. These results suggest the following division facts.

Division involving 0

> **1.** If a represents a nonzero number, $\dfrac{0}{a} = 0$.
>
> **2.** If a represents a nonzero number, $\dfrac{a}{0}$ is undefined.
>
> **3.** $\dfrac{0}{0}$ is undetermined.

EXAMPLE 5 *Division involving zero.* Find each quotient, if possible: **a.** $\dfrac{0}{13}$ and **b.** $\dfrac{-13}{0}$.

Solution

a. $\dfrac{0}{13} = 0$ Because $13(0) = 0$.

b. Since $\dfrac{-13}{0}$ involves division by zero, the division is undefined.

Self Check

Find each quotient, if possible:

a. $\dfrac{4}{0}$

b. $\dfrac{0}{17}$

Answers: **a.** undefined, **b.** 0

■

Accent on Technology: **Depreciation of a house**

Over a 17.5-year period, the value of a $124,930 house fell at a uniform rate to $97,105. To find how much the house depreciated per year, we must first find the change in its value by subtracting $124,930 from $97,105. To compute this difference, we enter these numbers and press these keys on a scientific calculator.

Keystrokes   97105 $-$ 124930 $=$ $\boxed{-27825}$

-27825 represents a drop in value of $27,825. Since this depreciation occurred in 17.5 years, we divide $-27,825$ by 17.5 to find the amount of depreciation per year. With $-27,825$ on the display, we then enter these numbers and press these keys.

Keystrokes $\div$ 17.5 $=$ $\boxed{-1590}$

If we use a graphing calculator, we enter these numbers and press these keys.

Keystrokes   97105 $-$ 124930 $\boxed{\text{ENTER}}$ $\div$ 17.5 $\boxed{\text{ENTER}}$

```
97105-124930
            -27825
Ans/17.5
            -1590
```

The amount of depreciation per year was $1,590.

STUDY SET   Section 1.5   ◄www►

VOCABULARY   *Fill in the blanks.*

1. The answer to a multiplication problem is called a _____product_____. The answer to a division problem is called a ____quotient____.

2. The numbers -4 and -6 are said to have _____like_____ signs. The numbers -10 and 12 are said to have _____unlike_____ signs.

3. The ____commutative____ property of multiplication states that two numbers can be multiplied in either order to get the same result.

4. The statement $(ab)c = a(bc)$ expresses the _____associative_____ property of multiplication.

5. Division of a nonzero number by zero is _____undefined_____.

6. If the product of two numbers is 1, the numbers are called ____reciprocals____ or ____multiplicative____ inverses.

CONCEPTS   *In Exercises 7–12, fill in the blanks.*

7. The expression $-5 + (-5) + (-5) + (-5)$ can be represented by the multiplication statement $4(-5)$.

8. The quotient of two numbers with _____unlike_____ signs is negative.

9. The product of two negative numbers is _____positive_____.

10. The product of zero and any number is 0 .

11. The product of 1 and any number is that number.

12. The division fact $\frac{25}{-5} = -5$ is related to the multiplication fact $-5(-5) = 25$.

13. Draw a number line from -6 to 6. Graph each of these products on the number line. What is the distance between each product?   3

$$-3(2), \quad -3(1), \quad -3(0), \quad -3(-1), \quad -3(-2)$$

14. a. If we multiply two different numbers and the answer is 0, what must be true about one of the numbers?   One of the numbers is 0.

b. If we multiply two different numbers and the answer is 1, what must be true about the numbers?
They are reciprocals (multiplicative inverses).

c. If we divide two numbers and the answer is 1, what must be true about the numbers?
The numbers are the same.

d. If we divide two numbers and the answer is 0, what must be true about the numbers?
The number being divided is 0, the number we are dividing by is not 0.

15. Which property justifies each statement?
   a. $-5(2 \cdot 17) = (-5 \cdot 2)17$
   associative property of multiplication
   b. $-5\left(\frac{1}{5}\right) = 1$ multiplicative inverse
   c. $-5 \cdot 2 = 2(-5)$
   commutative property of multiplication
   d. $-5(1) = -5$ multiplication property of 1

16. a. Find $-1(8)$. In general, what is the result when a number is multiplied by -1?
   -8; the opposite of that number
   b. Find $\frac{8}{-1}$. In general, what is the result when a number is divided by -1?
   -8; the opposite of that number

In Exercises 17–18, POS stands for a positive number and NEG stands for a negative number. Determine the sign of each result, if possible.

17. a. POS $\cdot$ NEG   **b.** POS $+$ NEG
   NEG   not possible to tell
   c. POS $-$ NEG   POS   **d.** $\dfrac{\text{POS}}{\text{NEG}}$ NEG

18. a. NEG $\cdot$ NEG   POS   **b.** NEG $+$ NEG   NEG
   c. NEG $-$ NEG   **d.** $\dfrac{\text{NEG}}{\text{NEG}}$
   not possible to tell   POS

19. What is wrong with the following statement?
   A negative and a positive is a negative.
   If we are multiplying or dividing, this is true. If we are adding, the sum of a negative number and a positive number could be positive: For example, $-6 + 7 = 1$.

20. Give the opposite (additive inverse) and the reciprocal (multiplicative inverse) of each number.
   a. 2 $-2, \frac{1}{2}$ **b.** $-\dfrac{4}{5}$ $\frac{4}{5}, -\frac{5}{4}$
   c. 1.75 $-1.75, \frac{4}{7}$ **d.** -5 $5, -\frac{1}{5}$

21. When a calculator was used to compute $16 \div 0$, the message shown in Illustration 1 appeared on the display screen. Explain what the message means.
   Since division by 0 is undefined, the calculator was unable to do the division.

```
Error
```

ILLUSTRATION 1

22. a. Is 80 divided by -5 the same as -5 divided by 80?
   no
   b. Is 80 times -5 the same as -5 times 80?   yes

NOTATION   *Complete each solution.*

23. $(-37 \cdot 5)2 = -37(\boxed{5} \cdot 2)$
   $= -37(\boxed{10})$
   $= -370$

24. $-20(5 \cdot 79) = (-20 \cdot 5) \cdot 79$
   $= \boxed{-100} \cdot 79$
   $= -7,900$

PRACTICE   *Do each operation.*

25. $(-6)(-9)$ 54   **26.** $(-8)(-7)$ 56
27. $12(-5)$ -60 **28.** $(-9)(11)$ -99
29. $-6 \cdot 4$ -24 **30.** $-8 \cdot 9$ -72
31. $-20(40)$ -800 **32.** $-10(10)$ -100
33. $(-6)(-6)$ 36   **34.** $(-1)(-1)$ 1
35. $-0.6(-4)$ 2.4   **36.** $-0.7(-8)$ 5.6
37. $1.2(-0.4)$ -0.48 **38.** $0(-0.2)$ 0
39. $\dfrac{1}{2}\left(-\dfrac{3}{4}\right)$ $-\frac{3}{8}$ **40.** $\dfrac{1}{3}\left(-\dfrac{5}{16}\right)$ $-\frac{5}{48}$
41. $-1\dfrac{1}{4}\left(-\dfrac{3}{4}\right)$ $\frac{15}{16}$ **42.** $-1\dfrac{1}{8}\left(-\dfrac{3}{8}\right)$ $\frac{27}{64}$
43. $-5.2 \cdot 100$ -520 **44.** $-1.17 \cdot 1,000$ $-1,170$
45. $0(-22)$ 0   **46.** $-8 \cdot 0$ 0
47. $-3(-4)(0)$ 0   **48.** $15(0)(-22)$ 0
49. $3(-4)(-5)$ 60   **50.** $(-2)(-4)(-5)$ -40
51. $(-4)(3)(-7)$ 84   **52.** $5(-3)(-4)$ 60
53. $(-2)(-3)(-4)(-5)$ **54.** $(-3)(-4)(5)(-6)$
   120   -360
55. $-30 \div (-3)$ 10   **56.** $-12 \div (-2)$ 6
57. $\dfrac{-6}{-2}$ 3   **58.** $\dfrac{-36}{9}$ -4
59. $\dfrac{4}{-2}$ -2 **60.** $\dfrac{-9}{3}$ -3
61. $\dfrac{80}{-20}$ -4 **62.** $\dfrac{-66}{33}$ -2
63. $\dfrac{17}{-17}$ -1 **64.** $\dfrac{-24}{24}$ -1
65. $\dfrac{-110}{-110}$ 1   **66.** $\dfrac{-200}{-200}$ 1
67. $\dfrac{-160}{40}$ -4 **68.** $\dfrac{-250}{-50}$ 5
69. $\dfrac{320}{-16}$ -20 **70.** $\dfrac{-180}{36}$ -5
71. $\dfrac{0.5}{-100}$ -0.005 **72.** $\dfrac{-1.7}{10}$ -0.17
73. $\dfrac{0}{150}$ 0   **74.** $\dfrac{225}{0}$ undefined
75. $\dfrac{-17}{0}$ undefined   **76.** $\dfrac{0}{-12}$ 0

77. $-\dfrac{1}{3} \div \dfrac{4}{5}$ $-\frac{5}{12}$ **78.** $-\dfrac{1}{8} \div \dfrac{2}{3}$ $-\frac{3}{16}$

79. $-\dfrac{3}{16} \div \left(-\dfrac{2}{3}\right)$ $\frac{9}{32}$ **80.** $-\dfrac{3}{25} \div \left(-\dfrac{2}{3}\right)$ $\frac{9}{50}$

In Exercises 81–82, apply the associative property of multiplication. Then find the product.

81. $-5(2 \cdot 67)$ -670 **82.** $\left(-\dfrac{5}{16} \cdot \dfrac{1}{7}\right)7$ $-\frac{5}{16}$

🔢 *Do each operation.*

83. $(-23.5)(47.2)$ $-1,109.2$

84. $(-435.7)(-37.8)$ $16,469.46$

85. $(-6.37)(-7.2)(-9.1)$ -417.3624

86. $(5.2)(-8.2)(7.75)$ -330.46

87. $\dfrac{204.6}{-37.2}$ -5.5 **88.** $\dfrac{-30.56625}{-4.875}$ 6.27

APPLICATIONS

89. TEMPERATURE CHANGE   In a lab, the temperature of a fluid was decreased 6° per hour for 12 hours. What signed number indicates the change in temperature? $-72°$

90. BACTERIAL GROWTH   To slowly warm a bacterial culture, biologists programmed a heating pad under the culture to increase the temperature 4° every hour for 6 hours. What signed number indicates the change in the temperature of the pad? $+24°$

91. GAMBLING   A gambler places a $40 bet and loses. He then decides to go "double or nothing" and loses again. Feeling that his luck has to change, he goes "double or nothing" once more and, for the third time, loses. What signed number indicates his gambling losses? $-\$160$

92. REAL ESTATE   A house has depreciated $1,250 each year for 8 years. What signed number indicates its change in value over that time period? $-\$10,000$

93. PLANETS   The temperature on Pluto gets as low as $-386°$ F. This is twice as low as the lowest temperature reached on Jupiter. What is the lowest temperature on Jupiter? $-193°$ F

94. CAR RADIATOR   The instructions on the back of a container of antifreeze state, "A 50/50 mixture of antifreeze and water protects against freeze-ups down to $-34°$ F, while a 60/40 mix protects against freeze-ups down to one and one-half times that temperature." To what temperature does the 60/40 mixture protect? $-51°$ F

95. TWA   For 1998, the total net income of Trans World Airlines was $-\$120.5$ million. The company's losses for 1999 were even worse, by a factor of about 2.9. What signed number indicates the company's total net income that year? $-\$349.45$ million

96. ACCOUNTING   Illustration 2 shows the quarterly income statement for Converse Inc., the sports shoe company. Numbers in parentheses represent negative numbers, which indicate a loss of money. The fourth-quarter loss was about 3 times worse than that of the third quarter. About how much money did the company lose in the third quarter of 1999? about $8,737,667

Converse Inc.	INCOME STATEMENT			
All dollar amounts in thousands	1st Qtr **1999**	2nd Qtr **1999**	3rd Qtr **1999**	4th Qtr **1999**
Total Net Income	(3,239)	(5,580)	(?)	(26,213)

Based on information from Hoover's Online

ILLUSTRATION 2

97. QUEEN MARY   The ocean liner Queen Mary was commissioned in 1936 and cost $22,500,000 to build. In 1967, the ship was purchased by the city of Long Beach, California for $3,450,000 and now serves as a hotel and convention center. What signed number indicates the annual average depreciation of the Queen Mary over the 31-year period from 1936 to 1967? Round to the nearest dollar. $-\$614,516$

98. COMPUTER SPREADSHEET   The "formula" = A1*B1*C1 in cell D1 of the spreadsheet shown in Illustration 3 instructs the computer to multiply the values in cells A1, B1, and C1 and to print the result *in place of the formula* in cell D1. What values will the computer print in the cells D1, D2, and D3? $340, -9,240, 40,800$

	Microsoft Excel-Book 1			
	File Edit View Insert Format Tools			
	A	B	C	D
1	4	–5	–17	= A1*B1*C1
2	22	–30	14	= A2*B2*C2
3	–60	–20	–34	= A3*B3*C3
4				

Sheet 1 / Sheet 2 / Sheet 3 / Sheet 4 / Sheet 5

ILLUSTRATION 3

99. PHYSICS   An oscilloscope is an instrument that displays electrical signals, which appear as wavy lines on a fluorescent screen. (See Illustration 4.) By switching the magnification setting (MAGNIFN.) to × 2, for example, the "height" of the crest and the "depth" of the trough of a graph will be doubled. Use signed numbers to indicate the crest height and the trough depth for each setting of the magnification dial.

a. normal   5, −10   **b.** × 0.5   2.5, −5
c. × 1.5   7.5, −15   **d.** × 2   10, −20

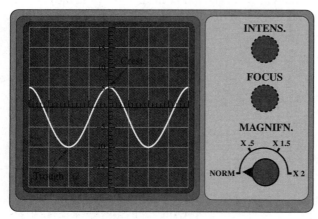

ILLUSTRATION 4

100. LIGHT   Water acts as a selective filter of light. As shown in Illustration 5, red light waves penetrate water only to a depth of about 5 meters. How many times deeper does

a. yellow light penetrate than red light?
6 times deeper

b. green light penetrate than orange light?
4 times deeper

c. blue light penetrate than yellow light?
2.5 times deeper

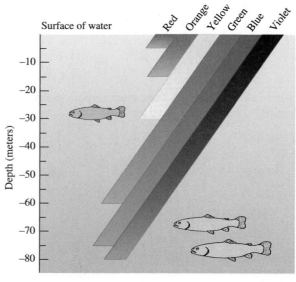

ILLUSTRATION 5

WRITING

101. Explain how you would decide whether the product of several numbers is positive or negative.

102. If the product of five numbers is negative, how many of them could be negative? Explain.

REVIEW

103. Is every integer a rational number?   yes

104. Write the subtraction statement $-3 - (-5)$ as addition of the opposite. $-3 + 5$

105. Find $\frac{1}{2} + \frac{1}{4} + \frac{1}{3}$ and express the result as a decimal.
$1.08\overline{3}$

106. Describe the balance in a checking account that is overdrawn $65 using a signed number.   −$65

107. Find 0.475(1,000).   475

108. Give two examples of irrational numbers.
$\sqrt{2}, \pi$ (answers may vary)

1.6 Exponents and Order of Operations

In this section, you will learn about

• Exponents • Powers of real numbers • Order of operations
• Evaluating expressions with no grouping symbols
• Evaluating expressions containing grouping symbols • The mean (average)

INTRODUCTION. In this course, we will perform six operations with real numbers: addition, subtraction, multiplication, division, raising to a power, and finding a root. Quite often, we will have to **evaluate** (find the value of) expressions containing more than one operation. In that case, we need to know the order in which the operations are to be performed. That is the focus of this section.

Exponents

In the expression $3 \cdot 3 \cdot 3 \cdot 3 \cdot 3$, the number 3 is used as a factor five times. We call 3 a *repeated factor.* To express a repeated factor, we can use an **exponent.**

Exponent and base	An **exponent** is used to indicate repeated multiplication. It tells how many times the **base** is used as a factor.

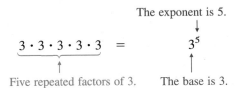

The exponent is 5.

$$\underbrace{3 \cdot 3 \cdot 3 \cdot 3 \cdot 3}_{\text{Five repeated factors of 3.}} = 3^5$$

The base is 3.

In the **exponential expression** a^n, a is the base, and n is the exponent. The expression a^n is called a **power of a.** Some examples of powers are

5^2 Read as "5 to the second power" or "5 squared." Here, $a = 5$ and $n = 2$.

9^3 Read as "9 to the third power" or "9 cubed." Here, $a = 9$ and $n = 3$.

$(-2)^5$ Read as "-2 to the fifth power." Here, $a = -2$ and $n = 5$.

EXAMPLE 1   *Repeated factors.*   Write each expression using exponents:
a. $4 \cdot 4 \cdot 4$,   **b.** $(-5)(-5)(-5)(-5)(-5)$,   **c.** sixteen cubed,   and
d. $8 \cdot 8 \cdot 15 \cdot 15 \cdot 15 \cdot 15$.

Solution

a. The factor 4 is repeated three times. We can represent this repeated multiplication with an exponential expression having a base of 4 and an exponent of 3: $4 \cdot 4 \cdot 4 = 4^3$.

b. The factor -5 is repeated five times: $(-5)(-5)(-5)(-5)(-5) = (-5)^5$.

c. Sixteen cubed can be written as 16^3.

d. $8 \cdot 8 \cdot 15 \cdot 15 \cdot 15 \cdot 15 = 8^2 \cdot 15^4$

Self Check

Write each expression using exponents:

a. $(12)(12)(12)(12)(12)(12)$

b. $2 \cdot 9 \cdot 9 \cdot 9$

c. fifty squared

d. $(-30)(-30)(-30)$

Answers: **a.** 12^6,   **b.** $2 \cdot 9^3$,   **c.** 50^2,   **d.** $(-30)^3$ ■

In the next example, we use exponents to rewrite expressions involving repeated variable factors.

EXAMPLE 2   *Using exponents with variables.*   Write each product using exponents: **a.** $(a)(a)(a)(a)(a)(a)$ and   **b.** $4 \cdot \pi \cdot r \cdot r$.

Solution

a. $(a)(a)(a)(a)(a)(a) = a^6$ *a is repeated as a factor 6 times.*

b. $4 \cdot \pi \cdot r \cdot r = 4\pi r^2$ *r is repeated as a factor 2 times.*

Self Check

Write each product using exponents:

a. $y \cdot y \cdot y \cdot y$

b. $12 \cdot b \cdot b \cdot b \cdot c$

Answers: **a.** y^4,   **b.** $12b^3c$ ■

Powers of real numbers

EXAMPLE 3   *Evaluating exponential expressions.*   Find the value of each of the following: **a.** 5^3,   **b.** 10^1,   **c.** $(-3)^4$,   and   **d.** $(-3)^5$.

Solution

We write the base as a factor the number of times indicated by the exponent. Then we do the multiplication.

Self Check

Find each power:

a. 2^5

b. $(-6)^2$

c. $(-5)^3$

a. $5^3 = 5 \cdot 5 \cdot 5 = 125$ The base is 5, the exponent is 3.

b. $10^1 = 10$ The base is 10, the exponent is 1.

c. $(-3)^4 = (-3)(-3)(-3)(-3)$ Write -3 as a factor four times.

$\quad\quad = 9(-3)(-3)$ Work from left to right: $(-3)(-3) = 9$.

$\quad\quad = -27(-3)$ Work from left to right: $9(-3) = -27$.

$\quad\quad = 81$

d. $(-3)^5 = (-3)(-3)(-3)(-3)(-3)$ Write -3 as a factor five times.

$\quad\quad = 9(-3)(-3)(-3)$ Work from left to right: $(-3)(-3) = 9$.

$\quad\quad = -27(-3)(-3)$ Work from left to right: $9(-3) = -27$.

$\quad\quad = 81(-3)$ Work from left to right: $-27(-3) = 81$.

$\quad\quad = -243$

Answers: a. 32,   **b.** 36,   **c.** -125 ■

We can now make some observations about raising a negative number to an *even power* (2, 4, 6, 8, and so on) and raising a negative number to an *odd power* (1, 3, 5, 7, and so on). In part c of Example 3, we raised -3 to an even power, and the result was positive. In part d, we raised -3 to an odd power, and the result was negative. These results illustrate the following general rule.

Even and odd powers of a negative number

When a negative number is raised to an even power, the result is positive.

When a negative number is raised to an odd power, the result is negative.

 COMMENT   Although the expressions -4^2 and $(-4)^2$ look somewhat alike, they are not. In -4^2, the base is 4 and the exponent is 2. The $-$ sign in front of 4^2 means the opposite of 4^2. In $(-4)^2$, the base is -4 and the exponent is 2. When we find the value of each expression, it becomes clear that they are not equivalent.

$-4^2 = -(4 \cdot 4)$ Write 4 as a factor two times.

$\quad\quad = -16$ Multiply inside the parentheses.

$(-4)^2 = (-4)(-4)$ Write -4 as a factor two times.

$\quad\quad = 16$ The product of two negative numbers is positive.

Different results

Accent on Technology: **Finding a power**

On a scientific calculator, we can use the squaring key $\boxed{x^2}$ to find the square of a number, and we can use the exponential key $\boxed{y^x}$ (on some calculators labeled x^y) to raise a number to a power. For example, to evaluate 125^2 and 2^{10} using a scientific calculator, we enter these numbers and press these keys.

Keystrokes $125\ \boxed{x^2}$ $\boxed{15625}$

Keystrokes $2\ \boxed{y^x}\ 10\ \boxed{=}$ $\boxed{1024}$

Using a graphing calculator, we can evaluate 125^2 and 2^{10} by pressing these keys.

Keystrokes $125\ \boxed{x^2}\ \boxed{\text{ENTER}}$ $\boxed{\begin{array}{r}125^2\\15625\end{array}}$

Keystrokes $2\ \boxed{\wedge}\ 10\ \boxed{\text{ENTER}}$ $\boxed{\begin{array}{r}2\wedge10\\1024\end{array}}$

We have found that $125^2 = 15{,}625$ and $2^{10} = 1{,}024$.

EXAMPLE 4 *Powers of fractions and decimals.*   Find each power:
a. $\left(-\frac{2}{3}\right)^3$ and   **b.** $(0.6)^2$.

Solution

a. $\left(-\frac{2}{3}\right)^3 = \left(-\frac{2}{3}\right)\left(-\frac{2}{3}\right)\left(-\frac{2}{3}\right)$ Since $-\frac{2}{3}$ is the base and 3 is the exponent, we write $-\frac{2}{3}$ as a factor three times.

$$= \frac{4}{9}\left(-\frac{2}{3}\right)$$ Multiply: $\left(-\frac{2}{3}\right)\left(-\frac{2}{3}\right) = \frac{4}{9}$.

$$= -\frac{8}{27}$$ Do the multiplication.

b. $(0.6)^2 = (0.6)(0.6)$ Since 0.6 is the base and 2 is the exponent, we write 0.6 as a factor two times.

$$= 0.36$$ Do the multiplication.

Self Check

Find each power:

a. $\left(-\frac{3}{4}\right)^3$

b. $(-0.3)^2$

Answers: **a.** $-\frac{27}{64}$,   **b.** 0.09   ∎

Order of operations

Suppose you have been asked to contact a friend if you see a certain type of oriental rug for sale while you are traveling in Turkey. While in Turkey, you find the rug and send the following E-mail message:

> **E-Mail**
>
> FOUND RUG. $1500. SHOULD I BUY IT FOR YOU?

The next day, you get this response from your friend:

> **E-Mail**
>
> NO PRICE TOO HIGH! REPEAT...NO! PRICE TOO HIGH.

Something is wrong. One part of the response says to buy the rug at any price. The other part of the response says not to buy it, because it's too expensive. The placement of the exclamation point makes us read the two parts of the response differently, resulting in different interpretations. When reading a mathematical statement, the same kind of confusion is possible. For example, consider the expression

$$2 + 3 \cdot 6$$

This expression contains two operations: addition and multiplication. We can do the calculations in two ways. We can do the addition first and then do the multiplication. Or we can do the multiplication first and then do the addition. However, we get different results.

Method 1: Add first	**Method 2: Multiply first**
$2 + 3 \cdot 6 = 5 \cdot 6$ Add 2 and 3 first.	$2 + 3 \cdot 6 = 2 + 18$ Multiply 3 and 6 first.
$\qquad\qquad = 30$ Multiply 5 and 6.	$\qquad\qquad\quad = 20$ Add 2 and 18.

If we don't establish a uniform order of operations, the expression $2 + 3 \cdot 6$ has two different answers. To avoid this possibility, we always use the following set of priority rules.

Order of operations

1. Do all calculations within parentheses and other grouping symbols following the order listed in Steps 2–4 below, working from the innermost pair to the outermost pair.
2. Evaluate all exponential expressions.
3. Do all multiplications and divisions as they occur from left to right.
4. Do all additions and subtractions as they occur from left to right.

When grouping symbols have been removed, repeat Steps 2–4 to complete the calculation.

If a fraction is present, evaluate the expression above and the expression below the bar separately. Then do the division indicated by the fraction bar, if possible.

It may not be necessary to apply all of these steps in every problem. For example, the expression $2 + 3 \cdot 6$ does not contain any parentheses, and there are no exponential expressions. So next we look for multiplications and divisions to perform. To evaluate $2 + 3 \cdot 6$ correctly, we proceed as follows:

$$2 + 3 \cdot 6 = 2 + 18 \quad \text{Do the multiplication first: } 3 \cdot 6 = 18.$$
$$= 20 \quad \text{Do the addition.}$$

Therefore, the correct result when evaluating $2 + 3 \cdot 6$ is 20.

Evaluating expressions with no grouping symbols

EXAMPLE 5   *Order of operations.*   Evaluate $3 \cdot 2^3 - 4$.

Solution

To find the value of this expression, we must do the operations of multiplication, raising to a power, and subtraction. The rules for the order of operations tell us to begin by evaluating the exponential expression.

$$3 \cdot 2^3 - 4 = 3 \cdot 8 - 4 \quad \text{Evaluate the exponential expression: } 2^3 = 8.$$
$$= 24 - 4 \quad \text{Do the multiplication: } 3 \cdot 8 = 24.$$
$$= 20 \quad \text{Do the subtraction.}$$

Self Check

Evaluate $2 \cdot 3^2 + 17$.

Answer: 35

EXAMPLE 6   *Order of operations.*   Evaluate $-30 - 4 \cdot 5 + 9$.

Solution

To evaluate this expression, we must do the operations of subtraction, multiplication, and addition. The rules for the order of operations tell us to begin with the multiplication.

$$-30 - 4 \cdot 5 + 9 = -30 - 20 + 9 \quad \text{Do the multiplication: } 4 \cdot 5 = 20.$$
$$= -50 + 9 \quad \text{Working from left to right, do the subtraction:}$$
$$-30 - 20 = -30 + (-20) = -50.$$
$$= -41 \quad \text{Do the addition.}$$

Self Check

Evaluate $-40 - 9 \cdot 4 + 10$.

Answer: -66

    COMMENT   Some students think that additions are always done before subtractions. As you saw in Example 6, this is not true. Working from left to right, we do the additions or subtractions in the order in which they occur. The same is true for multiplications and divisions.

EXAMPLE 7 *Order of operations.* Evaluate $\dfrac{160}{-4} - 6(-2)3$.

Solution

Although this expression contains parentheses, there are no calculations to perform within them. Since there are no powers, we do multiplications and divisions as they are encountered from left to right.

$$\dfrac{160}{-4} - 6(-2)3 = \mathbf{-40} - 6(-2)3 \quad \text{Do the division: } \tfrac{160}{-4} = -40.$$

$$= -40 - (\mathbf{-12})3 \quad \text{Do the multiplication: } 6(-2) = -12.$$

$$= -40 - (\mathbf{-36}) \quad \text{Do the multiplication: } (-12)3 = -36.$$

$$= -40 + 36 \quad \text{Write the subtraction as addition of the opposite.}$$

$$= -4 \quad \text{Do the addition.}$$

Self Check

Evaluate $\dfrac{240}{-8} - 3(-2)4$.

Answer: -6 ■

Evaluating expressions containing grouping symbols

Grouping symbols serve as mathematical punctuation marks. They help determine the order in which an expression is to be evaluated. Examples of grouping symbols are parentheses ( ), brackets [ ], absolute value symbols | |, and the fraction bar —.

EXAMPLE 8 *Performing calculations within parentheses first.*
Evaluate $(6 - 3)^2$.

Solution

This expression contains parentheses. By the rules for the order of operations, we must do the operation within the parentheses first.

$$(6 - 3)^2 = 3^2 \quad \text{Do the subtraction within the parentheses: } 6 - 3 = 3.$$

$$= 9 \quad \text{Evaluate the exponential expression.}$$

Self Check

Evaluate $(12 - 6)^3$.

Answer: 216 ■

EXAMPLE 9 *Order of operations within grouping symbols.*
Evaluate $5^3 + 2(-8 - 3 \cdot 2)$.

Solution

First, we do the operations within the parentheses in the proper order.

$$5^3 + 2(-8 - \mathbf{3 \cdot 2}) = 5^3 + 2(-8 - \mathbf{6}) \quad \text{Do the multiplication within the parentheses: } 3 \cdot 2 = 6.$$

$$= 5^3 + 2(-14) \quad \text{Do the subtraction within the parentheses: } -8 - 6 = -8 + (-6) = -14.$$

$$= 125 + 2(-14) \quad \text{Evaluate the exponential expression: } 5^3 = 125.$$

$$= 125 + (-28) \quad \text{Do the multiplication: } 2(-14) = -28.$$

$$= 97 \quad \text{Do the addition.}$$

Self Check

Evaluate $-3[5 + 3(-2)] + 3^2$.

Answer: 12 ■

To evaluate the following expression, we begin by working within the innermost pair of grouping symbols. Then we work within the outermost pair.

Innermost pair

$$-4[-2 - 3(4 - 8^2)] - 2$$

Outermost pair

EXAMPLE 10 *An expression containing two pairs of grouping symbols.*   Evaluate $-4[-2 - 3(4 - 8^2)] - 2$.

Solution

We do the work within the innermost grouping symbols (the parentheses) first.

$-4[-2 - 3(4 - \mathbf{8^2})] - 2$

$\quad = -4[-2 - 3(4 - \mathbf{64})] - 2$ Evaluate the exponential expression within the parentheses: $8^2 = 64$.

$\quad = -4[-2 - 3(-60)] - 2$ Do the subtraction within the parentheses: $4 - 64 = 4 + (-64) = -60$.

$\quad = -4[-2 - (-180)] - 2$ Do the multiplication within the brackets: $3(-60) = -180$.

$\quad = -4(178) - 2$ Do the subtraction within the brackets: $-2 - (-180) = -2 + 180 = 178$.

$\quad = -712 - 2$ Do the multiplication: $-4(178) = -712$.

$\quad = -714$ Do the subtraction: $-712 - 2 = -712 + (-2) = -714$.

Self Check

Evaluate
$-5[2(5^2 - 15) + 4] - 10$

Answer: -130

EXAMPLE 11 *Simplifying a fractional expression.*   Evaluate $\dfrac{-3(3 + 2) + 5}{17 - 3(-4)}$.

Solution

We simplify the numerator and the denominator separately.

$\dfrac{-3(\mathbf{3 + 2}) + 5}{17 - 3(\mathbf{-4})} = \dfrac{-3(\mathbf{5}) + 5}{17 - (\mathbf{-12})}$ In the numerator, do the addition within the parentheses. In the denominator, do the multiplication.

$\qquad = \dfrac{-15 + 5}{17 + 12}$ In the numerator, do the multiplication. In the denominator, write the subtraction as addition of the opposite of -12, which is 12.

$\qquad = \dfrac{-10}{29}$ Do the additions.

$\qquad = -\dfrac{10}{29}$ Write the $-$ sign in front of the fraction: $\frac{-10}{29} = -\frac{10}{29}$.

Self Check

Evaluate
$\dfrac{-4(-2 + 8) + 6}{8 - 5(-2)}$

Answer: -1

Accent on Technology: **Order of operations and parentheses**

Calculators have the rules for the order of operations built in. A left parenthesis key $($ and a right parenthesis key $)$ should be used when grouping symbols are needed. To evaluate $\frac{320}{20 - 16}$ with a scientific calculator, we enter these numbers and press these keys.

Keystrokes   320 $\div$ $($ 20 $-$ 16 $)$ $=$ | 80 |

To evaluate $\frac{320}{20 - 16}$ with a graphing calculator, we enter these numbers and press these keys.

Keystrokes   320 $\div$ $($ 20 $-$ 16 $)$ ENTER | 320/(20-16) 80 |

The answer is 80. Note that if the parentheses are not entered, an incorrect answer of 0 is obtained because the calculator reads the entry as $\frac{320}{20} - 16$.

EXAMPLE 12 *Working with absolute value symbols.* Evaluate $10|9 - 15| - 2^5$.

Solution

The absolute value bars are grouping symbols. We do the calculation within them first.

$$10|9 - 15| - 2^5 = 10|-6| - 2^5 \quad \text{Subtract: } 9 - 15 = 9 + (-15) = -6.$$

$$= 10(6) - 2^5 \quad 10|-6| \text{ means 10 times } |-6|. \text{ Find the absolute value: } |-6| = 6.$$

$$= 10(6) - 32 \quad \text{Evaluate the exponential expression: } 2^5 = 32.$$

$$= 60 - 32 \quad \text{Do the multiplication: } 10(6) = 60.$$

$$= 28$$

Self Check

Evaluate

$$10^3 + 3|24 - 25|$$

Answer: 1,003 ■

The mean (average)

The **arithmetic mean** (or **average**) of a set of numbers is a value around which the values of the numbers are grouped. When finding the mean, we usually need to apply the rules for the order of operations.

Finding an arithmetic mean

> To find the **mean** of a set of values, divide the sum of the values by the number of values.

EXAMPLE 13 *Customer service.* To measure its effectiveness in serving customers, a store had the telephone company electronically record the number of times the telephone rang before an employee answered it. The results of the week-long survey are shown in Table 1-2. Find the average number of times the phone rang before an employee answered it that week.

Number of rings	Occurrences
1	11
2	46
3	45
4	28
5	20

TABLE 1-2

Solution To find the total number of rings, we multiply each *number of rings* (1, 2, 3, 4, and 5 rings) by the respective number of occurrences and add those subtotals.

Total number of rings $= 11(1) + 46(2) + 45(3) + 28(4) + 20(5)$

To find the total number of calls received, we add the number of occurrences in the right-hand column of the table.

Total number of calls received $= 11 + 46 + 45 + 28 + 20$

To find the average, we divide the total number of rings by the total number of calls and apply the rules for the order of operations to evaluate the expression.

$$\text{Average} = \frac{11(1) + 46(2) + 45(3) + 28(4) + 20(5)}{11 + 46 + 45 + 28 + 20}$$

$$\text{Average} = \frac{11 + 92 + 135 + 112 + 100}{150} \quad \begin{array}{l}\text{In the numerator, do the multiplications.}\\ \text{In the denominator, do the additions.}\end{array}$$

$$\text{Average} = \frac{450}{150} \quad \text{Do the addition.}$$

$$\text{Average} = 3 \quad \text{Do the division.}$$

The average number of times the phone rang before it was answered was 3. ■

STUDY SET Section 1.6 www

VOCABULARY *Fill in the blanks.*

1. In the exponential expression 3^2, 3 is the _____base_____, and 2 is the _____exponent_____.

2. 10^2 can be read as ten _____squared_____, and 10^3 can be read as ten _____cubed_____.

3. 7^5 is the fifth _____power_____ of seven.

4. An _____exponent_____ is used to represent repeated multiplication.

5. The rules for the _____order_____ of operations guarantee that an evaluation of a numerical expression will result in a single answer.

6. The arithmetic _____mean_____ or _____average_____ of a set of numbers is a value around which the values of the numbers are grouped.

CONCEPTS

7. Given: $4 + 5 \cdot 6$.
  a. What operations does this expression contain?
    addition and multiplication
  b. Evaluate the expression in two different ways, and state the two possible results.   54, 34
  c. Which result from part b is correct, and why?
    34; multiplication is to be done before addition.

8. a. What repeated multiplication does 5^3 represent?
    $5 \cdot 5 \cdot 5$
  b. Write a multiplication statement in which the factor x is repeated 4 times. Then write the expression in simpler form using an exponent. $x \cdot x \cdot x \cdot x = x^4$
  c. How can we represent the repeated addition $3 + 3 + 3 + 3 + 3$ in a simpler form?   5(3)

9. a. How is the mean (or average) of a set of scores found?
    Divide the sum of the scores by the number of scores.
  b. Find the average of 75, 81, 47, and 53.   64

10. In the expression $-8 + 2[15 - (-6 + 1)]$, which grouping symbols are innermost, and which are outermost?   innermost: parentheses; outermost: brackets

11. a. What operations does the expression $12 + 5^2(-3)$ contain?   addition, power, multiplication
  b. In what order should they be performed?
    power, multiplication, addition

12. a. What operations does the expression $20 - (-2)^2 + 3(-1)$ contain?
    subtraction, power, addition, multiplication
  b. In what order should they be performed?
    power, multiplication, subtraction, addition

13. Consider the expression $\frac{36 - 4(7)}{2(10 - 8)}$. In the numerator, what operation should be done first? In the denominator, what operation should be done first?
multiplication; subtraction

14. Explain the differences in evaluating $4 \cdot 2^2$ and $(4 \cdot 2)^2$. In $4 \cdot 2^2$, find the power, then multiply. In $(4 \cdot 2)^2$ multiply, then find the power.

15. To evaluate each expression, what operation should be performed first?
  a. $-80 - 3 + 5 - 2^2$ power
  b. $-80 - (3 + 5) - 2^2$ addition
  c. $-80 - 3 + (5 - 2)^2$ subtraction

16. To evaluate each expression, what operation should be performed first?
  a. $(65 - 3)^3$ subtraction
  b. $65 - 3^3$ power
  c. $6(5) - (3)^3$ power

NOTATION

17. Write an exponential expression with a base of 12 and an exponent of 6. 12^6

18. Tell the name of each grouping symbol: ( ), [ ], | |, and —.
parentheses, brackets, absolute value symbols, fraction bar

Complete each solution.

19. $50 + 6 \cdot 3^2 = 50 + 6 \cdot \boxed{9}$
          $= 50 + \boxed{54}$
          $= 104$

20. $-100 - (25 - 8 \cdot 2) = -100 - \left(25 - \boxed{16}\right)$
                    $= -100 - \boxed{9}$
                    $= -109$

21. $-19 - 2[(1 + 2) \cdot 3] = -19 - 2[\boxed{3} \cdot 3]$
                      $= -19 - 2(\boxed{9})$
                      $= -19 - \boxed{18}$
                      $= -37$

22. $\dfrac{46 - 2^3}{-3(5) - 4} = \dfrac{46 - \boxed{8}}{\boxed{-15} - 4}$
             $= \dfrac{\boxed{38}}{-19}$
             $= -2$

PRACTICE *Write each product using exponents.*

23. $3 \cdot 3 \cdot 3 \cdot 3$ 3^4
24. $m \cdot m \cdot m \cdot m \cdot m$ m^5
25. $10 \cdot 10 \cdot k \cdot k \cdot k$ $10^2 k^3$
26. $5(5)(5)(i)(i)$ $5^3 i^2$
27. $8 \cdot \pi \cdot r \cdot r \cdot r$ $8\pi r^3$
28. $4 \cdot \pi \cdot r \cdot r$ $4\pi r^2$
29. $6(x)(x)(y)(y)(y)$ $6x^2 y^3$
30. $76 \cdot s \cdot s \cdot s \cdot s \cdot t$ $76s^4 t$

Evaluate each expression.

31. $(-6)^2$ 36
32. -6^2 -36
33. -4^4 -256
34. $(-4)^4$ 256

35. $(-5)^3$ -125

36. -5^3 -125

37. $-(-6)^4$ $-1,296$

38. $-(-7)^2$ -49

39. $(-0.4)^2$ 0.16

40. $(-0.5)^2$ 0.25

41. $\left(-\frac{2}{5}\right)^3$ $-\frac{8}{125}$

42. $\left(-\frac{1}{4}\right)^3$ $-\frac{1}{64}$

43. $3 - 5 \cdot 4$ -17

44. $-4 \cdot 6 + 5$ -19

45. $3 \cdot 8^2$ 192

46. $(3 \cdot 4)^2$ 144

47. $8 \cdot 5 - 4 \div 2$ 38

48. $9 \cdot 5 - 6 \div 3$ 43

49. $100 - 8(10) + 60$ 80

50. $50 - 2(5) - 7$ 33

51. $-22 - (15 - 3)$ -34

52. $-(33 - 8) - 10$ -35

53. $-2(9) - 2(5)$ -28

54. $-75 - 7^2$ -124

55. $5^2 + 13^2$ 194

56. $3^3 - 2^3$ 19

57. $-4(6 + 5)$ -44

58. $-3(5 - 4)$ -3

59. $4^2 - (-2)^2$ 12

60. $3 + (-5)^2$ 28

61. $(-5 - 2)^2$ 49

62. $(-3 - 5)^2$ 64

63. $12 + 2\left(-\frac{9}{3}\right) - (-2)$ 8

64. $2 + 3\left(-\frac{25}{5}\right) - (-4)$ -9

65. $200 - (-6 + 5)^3$ 201

66. $19 - (-45 + 41)^3$ 83

67. $|5 \cdot 2^2 \cdot 4| - 30$ 50

68. $2 + |3 \cdot 2^2 \cdot 4|$ 50

69. $1(2)(3)(-4)$ -24

70. $3(4)(5)(-6)$ -360

71. $[6(5) - 5(5)]4$ 20

72. $5[9(2) - 2(8)]$ 10

73. $175 - 2 \cdot 3^4$ 13

74. $75 - 3 \cdot 1^2$ 72

75. $-6(130 - 4^3)$ -396

76. $-5(150 - 3^3)$ -615

77. $(17 - 5 \cdot 2)^3$ 343

78. $(4 + 2 \cdot 3)^4$ $10,000$

79. $-5(-2)^3(3)^2$ 360

80. $-3(-2)^5(2)^2$ 384

81. $-2\left(\frac{15}{-5}\right) - \frac{6}{2} + 9$ 12

82. $-6\left(\frac{25}{-5}\right) - \frac{36}{9} + 1$ 27

83. $\frac{5 \cdot 50 - 160}{-9}$ -10

84. $\frac{5(68 - 32)}{-9}$ -20

85. $5(10 + 2) - 1$ 59

86. $14 + 3(7 - 5)$ 20

87. $64 - 6[15 + (-3)3]$ 28

88. $4 + 2[26 + 5(-3)]$ 26

89. $(12 - 2)^3$ $1,000$

90. $(10 - 7)^2$ 49

91. $(-2)^3\left(\frac{-6}{2}\right)(-1)$ -24

92. $(-3)^3\left(\frac{-4}{2}\right)(-1)$ -54

93. $\frac{-7 - 3^2}{2 \cdot 4}$ -2

94. $\frac{-5 - 3^3}{2^3}$ -4

95. $\frac{1}{2}\left(\frac{1}{8}\right) + \left(-\frac{1}{4}\right)^2$ $\frac{1}{8}$

96. $-\frac{1}{9}\left(\frac{1}{4}\right) + \left(-\frac{1}{6}\right)^2$ 0

97. $-2|4 - 8|$ -8

98. $-5|1 - 8|$ -35

99. $|7 - 8(4 - 7)|$ 31

100. $|9 - 5(1 - 8)|$ 44

101. $3 + 2[-1 - 4(5)]$ -39

102. $4 + 2[-7 - 3(9)]$ -64

103. $-3[5^2 - (7 - 3)^2]$ -27

104. $3 - [3^3 + (3 - 1)^3]$ -32

105. $-(2 \cdot 3 - 4)^3$ -8

106. $-(3 \cdot 5 - 2 \cdot 6)^2$ -9

107. $\frac{(3 + 5)^2 + |-2|}{-2(5 - 8)}$ 11

108. $\frac{|-25| - 8(-5)}{2^4 - 29}$ -5

109. $\frac{2[-4 - 2(3 - 1)]}{3(-3)(-2)}$ $-\frac{8}{9}$

110. $\frac{3[-9 + 2(7 - 3)]}{(5 - 8)(7 - 9)}$ $-\frac{1}{2}$

111. $\frac{|6 - 4| + 2|-4|}{26 - 2^4}$ 1

112. $\frac{4|9 - 7| + |-7|}{3^2 - 2^2}$ 3

113. $\frac{(4^3 - 10) + (-4)}{5^2 - (-4)(-5)}$ 10

114. $\frac{(6 - 5)^4 - (-21)}{(-9)(-3) - 4^2}$ 2

115. $\frac{72 - (2 - 2 \cdot 1)}{10^2 - (90 + 2^2)}$ 12

116. $\frac{13^2 - 5^2}{-3(5 - 9)}$ 12

117. $-\left(\frac{40 - 1^3 - 2^4}{3(2 + 5) + 2}\right)$ -1

118. $-\left(\frac{8^2 - 10}{2(3)(4) - 5(3)}\right)$ -6

Evaluate each expression.

119. $\frac{3(3,246 - 1,111)}{561 - 546}$ 427

120. $54^3 - 16^4 + 19(3)$ $91,985$

121. $(23.1)^2 - (14.7)(-61)^3$ $3,337,154.31$

122. $12 - 7\left(-\frac{85.684}{34.55}\right)^3$ 118.770944

APPLICATIONS

123. LIGHT Illustration 1 shows that the light energy that passes through the first unit of area, 1 yard away from the bulb, spreads out as it travels away from the source. How much area does that light energy cover 2 yards, 3 yards, and 4 yards from the bulb? Express each answer using exponents.

2^2 square units, 3^2 square units, 4^2 square units

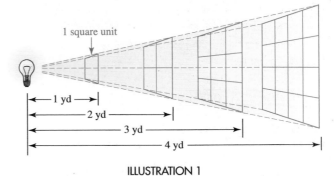

ILLUSTRATION 1

124. CHAIN LETTER A store owner sent two friends a letter advertising her store's low prices. The ad closed with the following request: "Please send a copy of this letter to two of your friends."

a. Assume that all those receiving letters respond and that everyone in the chain receives just one letter. Complete the table.

Level	Numbers of letters circulated
1st	$2 = 2^1$
2nd	$4 = 2^2$
3rd	$8 = 2^3$
4th	$16 = 2^4$

b. How many letters will be circulated in the 10th level of the mailing? $2^{10} = 1,024$

125. AUTO INSURANCE   See the premium comparison in Illustration 2. What is the average six-month insurance premium? $2,106

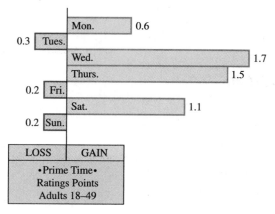

Allstate	$2,672	Mercury	$1,370
Auto Club	$1,680	State Farm	$2,737
Farmers	$2,485	20th Century	$1,692

Criteria: Six-month premium. Husband, 45, drives a 1995 Explorer, 12,000 annual miles. Wife, 43, drives a 1996 Dodge Caravan, 12,000 annual miles. Son, 17, is an occasional operator. All have clean driving records.

ILLUSTRATION 2

126. SWEEPS WEEK   During "sweeps week," television networks make a special effort to gain viewers by showing unusually flashy programming. Use the information in Illustration 3 to determine the average daily gain (or loss) of ratings points by a network for the 7-day "sweeps period."
a gain of 0.6 of a rating point

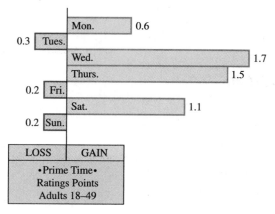

ILLUSTRATION 3

127. CASH AWARDS   A contest is to be part of a promotional kickoff for a new children's cereal. The prizes to be awarded are shown in Illustration 4.
a. How much money will be awarded in the promotion? $11,875

b. What is the average cash prize? $95

Coloring Contest
Grand prize: **Disney World vacation plus $2,500**
Four 1st place prizes of $500
Thirty-five 2nd place prizes of $150
Eighty-five 3rd place prizes of $25

ILLUSTRATION 4

128. ENERGY USAGE   See Illustration 5. Find the average number of therms of natural gas used per month. Then draw a dashed line across the graph showing the average.   31 therms

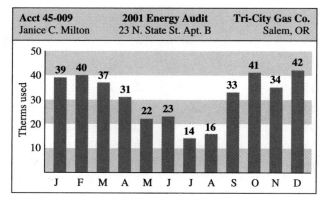

ILLUSTRATION 5

129. SCRABBLE   Illustration 6(a) shows a portion of the game board before and Illustration 6(b) shows it after the word *QUARTZY* is played. Determine the score. (The number on each tile gives the point value of the letter.) $3(10 + 1 + 1 + 1 + 1 + 2 \cdot 10 + 4) = 114$

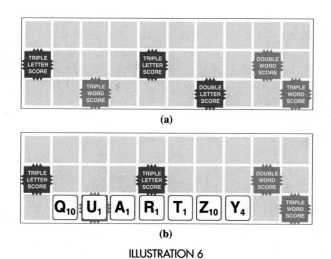

ILLUSTRATION 6

130. WRAPPING GIFTS   How much ribbon is needed to wrap the package shown in Illustration 7 if 15 inches of ribbon are needed to make the bow?   81 in.

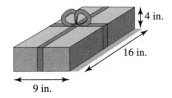

ILLUSTRATION 7

Judge	1	2	3	4	5	6	7	8
Terrier	14	11	11	10	12	12	13	13
Pekinese	10	9	8	11	11	12	9	10
Pomeranian	15	14	13	11	14	12	10	14

ILLUSTRATION 9

131. SPREADSHEETS The spreadsheet in Illustration 8 contains data collected by a chemist. For each row, the sum of the values in columns A and B is to be subtracted from the product of 6 and the value in column C. That result is then to be divided by 12 and entered in column D. Use this information to complete the spreadsheet.

	A	B	C	D
1	20	4	8	2
2	9	3	16	7
3	1	5	11	5

ILLUSTRATION 8

132. DOG SHOWS The final score for each dog competing in a "toy breeds" competition is computed by dividing the sum of the judges' marks, after the highest and lowest have been dropped, by 6. (See Illustration 9.)
a. What was their order of finish?
  Pomeranian, Terrier, Pekinese
b. Did any judge rate all the dogs the same?
  yes, judge 6

WRITING

133. Explain the difference between 2^3 and 3^2.

134. Explain why rules for the order of operations are necessary.

135. What does it mean when we say do all additions and subtractions *as they occur from left to right*?

136. In what settings do you encounter or use the concept of arithmetic mean (average) in your everyday life?

REVIEW

137. Match each term with the proper operation.
  a. sum ii   **i.** division
  b. difference iii   **ii.** addition
  c. product iv   **iii.** subtraction
  d. quotient i   **iv.** multiplication

138. What is the result when we add a number and its opposite? 0

139. What is the result when we divide a nonzero number by itself? 1

140. What is wrong with the following statement? Subtraction is the same as adding.
  Subtraction is the same as adding the opposite.

1.7 Algebraic Expressions

In this section, you will learn about

- Translating from words to mathematical symbols
- Writing algebraic expressions to represent unknown quantities
- Looking for hidden operations • Number and value
- Evaluating algebraic expressions • Making tables

INTRODUCTION. Since problems in algebra are often presented in words, the ability to interpret what you read is important. In this section, we will introduce several strategies that will help you translate English words into mathematical symbols. We will begin by discussing the most fundamental skill—spotting key words and phrases that represent four operations of arithmetic.

Translating from words to mathematical symbols

Recall that an **algebraic expression** is a collection of numbers and/or variables that are combined by using the operations of arithmetic. In the following tables, we list some words and phrases that are used to indicate addition, subtraction, multiplication, and division, and we show how they can be translated to form algebraic expressions.

ADDITION

The phrase	translates to
the sum of a and 8	$a + 8$
4 plus c	$4 + c$
16 added to m	$m + 16$
4 more than t	$t + 4$
20 greater than F	$F + 20$
T increased by r	$T + r$
Exceeds y by 35	$y + 35$

SUBTRACTION

The phrase	translates to
the difference of 23 and P	$23 - P$
550 minus h	$550 - h$
18 less than w	$w - 18$
7 decreased by j	$7 - j$
M reduced by x	$M - x$
12 subtracted from L	$L - 12$
5 less f	$5 - f$

MULTIPLICATION

The phrase	translates to
the product of 4 and x	$4x$
20 times B	$20B$
twice r	$2r$
triple the profit P	$3P$
$\frac{3}{4}$ of m	$\frac{3}{4}m$

DIVISION

The phrase	translates to
the quotient of R and 19	$\dfrac{R}{19}$
s divided by d	$\dfrac{s}{d}$
the ratio of c to d	$\dfrac{c}{d}$
k split into 4 equal parts	$\dfrac{k}{4}$

> **COMMENT** The phrase *greater than* is used to indicate addition. The phrase *is greater than* refers to the symbol $>$. Similarly, the phrase *less than* indicates subtraction, and the phrase *is less than* refers to the symbol $<$.

EXAMPLE 1   *Translating to symbols.*   Write each phrase as an algebraic expression.

a. The sum of the length l and the width 20

b. 5 less than the capacity c

c. The product of the weight w and 2,000, increased by 300

Solution

a. Key word: *sum*   **Translation:** add

The phrase translates to $l + 20$.

b. Key phrase: *less than*   **Translation:** subtract

The capacity c is to be made less, so we subtract 5 from it: $c - 5$.

Self Check

Write each phrase as an algebraic expression:

a. 80 cents less than t cents

b. $\frac{2}{3}$ of the time T

c. the difference of twice a and 15

c. Key word: *product*   **Translation:** multiply

   Key phrase: *increased by*   **Translation:** add

The weight *w* is to be multiplied by 2,000, and then 300 is to be added to the product: 2,000*w* + 300.

Answers: **a.** $t - 80$,   **b.** $\frac{2}{3}T$,
c. $2a - 15$

Writing algebraic expressions to represent unknown quantities

When solving problems, we often begin by letting a variable stand for an unknown quantity. Frequently, a problem will contain a second unknown but related quantity, which can be described using an algebraic expression involving the original variable.

EXAMPLE 2   *Writing an algebraic expression.*   A butcher trims 4 ounces of fat from a roast that originally weighed *x* ounces. Write an algebraic expression that represents the weight of the roast after it is trimmed.

Solution

We let *x* = the original weight of the roast (in ounces).

   Key word: *trimmed*   **Translation:** subtract

After 4 ounces of fat have been trimmed, the weight of the roast is $(x - 4)$ ounces.

Self Check

When a secretary rides the bus to work, it takes her *m* minutes. If she drives her own car, her travel time exceeds this by 15 minutes. How can we represent the time it takes her to get to work by car?

Answer: $(m + 15)$ minutes

EXAMPLE 3   *Writing an algebraic expression.*   The swimming pool in Figure 1-23 is *x* feet wide. If it is to be sectioned into 8 equally wide swimming lanes, write an algebraic expression that represents the width of each lane.

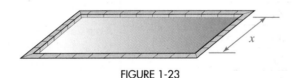

FIGURE 1-23

Solution

We let *x* = the width of the swimming pool (in feet).

   Key phrase: *sectioned into 8 equally wide lanes*   **Translation:** divide

The width of each lane is $\frac{x}{8}$ feet.

Self Check

A handyman estimates that it will take the same amount of time to sand as it will to paint some kitchen cabinets. If the entire job takes *x* hours, how can we express the time it will take him to do the painting?

Answer: $\frac{x}{2}$ hours

When we are solving problems, the variable to be used is rarely specified. We must decide what the unknown quantities are and how they will be represented using variables. The following examples illustrate how to approach these situations.

EXAMPLE 4   *Two unknown quantities.*   The value of a collectible doll is three times that of an antique toy truck. Express the value of each, using one variable.

Solution

There are two unknown quantities. Since the doll's value is related to the truck's value, we will let *x* = the value of the toy truck in dollars.

   Key phrase: 3 *times*   **Translation:** multiply by 3

The value of the doll is $3x.

Self Check

The McDonald's Chicken Deluxe sandwich has 5 fewer grams of fat than the Quarter Pounder hamburger. Express the number of grams of fat in each sandwich, using one variable.

Answers: *x* = the number of grams of fat in the hamburger; $x - 5$ = the number of grams of fat in the chicken sandwich

COMMENT   A variable is used to represent an unknown number. Therefore, in Example 4, it would be incorrect to write, "Let x = toy truck," because the truck is not a number. We need to write, "Let x = the *value* of the toy truck."

EXAMPLE 5   *Two unknown quantities.*
A 10-inch-long paintbrush has two parts: a handle and bristles. Choose a variable to represent the length of one of the parts. Then write an expression for the length of the other part.

Solution
A drawing is helpful in explaining this problem. If the entire paintbrush is 10 inches long, and if we let h represent the length of the handle, then the bristles are $(10 - h)$ inches long.

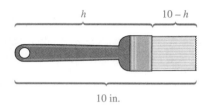

Self Check

Part of a $900 donation to a preschool was designated to go to the scholarship fund, the remainder to the building fund. Choose a variable to represent the amount donated to one of the funds. Write an expression for the amount donated to the other fund.

Answers: s = amount donated to scholarship fund in dollars; $900 - s$ = amount donated to building fund   ■

EXAMPLE 6   *An expression involving two operations.*
In the second semester, student enrollment in a retraining program at a college was 32 more than twice that of the first semester. Use a variable to express the student enrollment in the program each semester.

Solution
Since the second-semester enrollment is expressed in terms of the first-semester enrollment, we let x = the enrollment in the first semester.

>   **Key phrase:** *more than*   **Translation:** add
>   **Key word:** *twice*   **Translation:** multiply by 2

The enrollment for the second semester is $2x + 32$.

Self Check

The number of votes received by the incumbent in an election was 55 fewer than three times the number the challenger received. Use a variable to express the number of votes received by each candidate.

Answers: x = the number of votes received by the challenger; $3x - 55$ = the number of votes received by the incumbent   ■

Looking for hidden operations

When analyzing problems, we aren't always given key words or key phrases to help establish what mathematical operation to use. Sometimes a careful reading of the problem is needed to determine the hidden operations.

EXAMPLE 7   *Hidden operations.*
Disneyland, located in Anaheim, California, was in operation 16 years before the opening of Walt Disney World, in Orlando, Florida. Euro Disney, in Paris, France, was constructed 21 years after Disney World. Use algebraic expressions to express the ages (in years) of each of these Disney attractions.

Solution
The ages of Disneyland and Euro Disney are both related to the age of Walt Disney World. Therefore, we will let x = the age of Walt Disney World.

In carefully reading the problem, we find that Disneyland was built 16 years *before* Disney World, so its age is more than that of Disney World.

>   **Key phrase:** *more than*   **Translation:** add

In years, the age of Disneyland is $x + 16$. Euro Disney was built 21 years *after* Disney World, so its age is less than that of Disney World.

>   **Key phrase:** *less than*   **Translation:** subtract

In years, the age of Euro Disney is $x - 21$. The results are summarized in Table 1-3.

Attraction	Age
Disneyland	$x + 16$
Disney World	x
Euro Disney	$x - 21$

TABLE 1-3

■

EXAMPLE 8 *Looking for a pattern.* How many months are in *x* years?

Solution

Since there are no key words, we must carefully analyze the problem to write an expression that represents the number of months in *x* years. It is often helpful to consider some specific cases. For example, let's calculate the number of months in 1 year, 2 years, and 3 years. When we write the results in a table, a pattern is apparent.

Number of years	Number of months
1	12
2	24
3	36
x	12*x*

We multiply the number of years by 12 to find the number of months.

Therefore, if *x* = the number of years, the number of months is 12 · *x* or 12*x*.

Self Check

Complete the table. How many days is *h* hours?

Number of hours	Number of days
24	
48	
72	
h	

Answers: 1, 2, 3; $\dfrac{h}{24}$ ∎

Number and value

Some problems deal with quantities that have value. In these problems, we must distinguish between *the number of* and *the value of* the unknown quantity. For example, to find the value of 3 quarters, we multiply the number of quarters by the value (in cents) of one quarter. Therefore, the value of 3 quarters is 3 · 25¢ = 75¢.

The same distinction must be made if the number is unknown. For example, the value of *n* nickels is not *n*¢. The value of *n* nickels is *n* · 5¢ = (5*n*)¢. For problems of this type, we will use the relationship

Number · value = total value

EXAMPLE 9 *Number and value.* Suppose a roll of paper towels sells for 79¢. Find the cost of **a.** five rolls of paper towels, **b.** *x* rolls of paper towels, and **c.** *x* + 1 rolls of paper towels.

Solution

In each case, we will multiply the *number* of rolls of paper towels by the *value* of one roll (79¢) to find the total cost.

a. The cost of 5 rolls of paper towels is 5 · 79¢ = 395¢, or $3.95.

b. The cost of *x* rolls of paper towels is *x* · 79¢ = (79 · *x*)¢ = (79*x*)¢.

c. The cost of *x* + 1 rolls of paper towels is
(*x* + 1) · 79¢ = 79 · (*x* + 1)¢ = 79(*x* + 1)¢.

Self Check

Find the value of

a. six $50 savings bonds

b. *t* $100 savings bonds

c. (*x* − 4) $1,000 savings bonds

Answers: a. $300, **b.** $100*t*, **c.** $1,000(*x* − 4) ∎

Evaluating algebraic expressions

To **evaluate an algebraic expression,** we replace each variable with a given number value. (When we replace a variable with a number, we say we are **substituting** for the variable.) Then we do the necessary calculations following the rules for the order of operations. For example, to evaluate $x^2 - 2x + 1$ for *x* = 3, we begin by replacing each *x* with 3.

$$x^2 - 2x + 1 = 3^2 - 2(3) + 1 \quad \text{Replace } x \text{ with 3.}$$
$$= 9 - 2(3) + 1 \quad \text{Evaluate the exponential expression: } 3^2 = 9.$$
$$= 9 - 6 + 1 \quad \text{Do the multiplication: } 2(3) = 6.$$
$$= 4 \quad \text{Working left to right, do the subtraction and then the addition.}$$

We say that 4 is the **value** of this expression when $x = 3$.

> **COMMENT**   When replacing a variable with its numerical value, use parentheses around the replacement number to avoid possible misinterpretation. For example, when substituting 5 for x in $2x + 1$, we show the multiplication using parentheses: $2(5) + 1$. If we don't show the multiplication, we could misread the expression as $25 + 1$.

EXAMPLE 10   *Evaluating algebraic expressions.*   Evaluate
a. $-y$ and   **b.** $-3(y + x^2)$ when $x = 3$ and $y = -4$.

Solution

a. $-y = -(-4)$ Substitute -4 for y.

     $= 4$ The opposite of -4 is 4.

b. $-3(y + x^2) = -3(-4 + 3^2)$ Substitute 3 for x and -4 for y.

           $= -3(-4 + 9)$ Work within the parentheses first. Evaluate the exponential expression.

           $= -3(5)$ Do the addition within the parentheses.

           $= -15$

Self Check

Evaluate   **a.** $-x$
and   **b.** $5(x - y)$
when $x = -2$ and $y = 3$.

Answers: **a.** 2,   **b.** -25 ∎

EXAMPLE 11   *Surface area of a swim fin.*   Divers use swim fins because they provide a much larger surface area to push against the water than do bare feet. Consequently, the diver can swim faster wearing them. In Figure 1-24, we see that the fin is in the shape of a trapezoid. The algebraic expression $\frac{1}{2}h(b + d)$ gives the area of a trapezoid, where h is the height and b and d are the lengths of the lower and upper bases, respectively. To find the area of the fin shown here, we evaluate the algebraic expression for $h = 14$, $b = 3.5$, and $d = 8.5$.

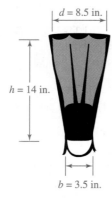

$d = 8.5$ in.

$h = 14$ in.

$b = 3.5$ in.

FIGURE 1-24

$$\frac{1}{2}h(b + d) = \frac{1}{2}(14)(3.5 + 8.5) \quad \text{Substitute 14 for } h, 3.5 \text{ for } b, \text{ and } 8.5 \text{ for } d.$$

$$= \frac{1}{2}(14)(12) \quad \text{Do the addition within the parentheses.}$$

$$= 7(12) \quad \text{Work from left to right: } \tfrac{1}{2}(14) = 7.$$

$$= 84$$

The fin has an area of 84 square inches.   ∎

EXAMPLE 12   *Temperature conversion.*   The expression $\frac{9C + 160}{5}$ converts a temperature in degrees Celsius (represented by C) to a temperature in degrees Fahrenheit. Convert $-170°$ C, the coldest temperature on the moon, to degrees Fahrenheit.

Self Check

On January 22, 1943, the temperature in Spearfish, South Dakota changed from $-20°$ C to $7.2°$ C in two minutes. Convert $-20°$ C to degrees Fahrenheit.

Solution

To convert $-170°$ C to degrees Fahrenheit, we evaluate the algebraic expression for $C = -170$.

$$\frac{9C + 160}{5} = \frac{9(-170) + 160}{5} \qquad \text{Substitute } -170 \text{ for } C.$$

$$= \frac{-1,530 + 160}{5} \qquad \text{Do the multiplication.}$$

$$= \frac{-1,370}{5} \qquad \text{Do the addition.}$$

$$= -274 \qquad \text{Do the division.}$$

In degrees Fahrenheit, the coldest temperature on the moon is $-274°$.

Answer: $-4°$ F   ■

Accent on Technology: **Evaluating algebraic expressions**

The rotating drum of a clothes dryer is a cylinder. (See Figure 1-25.) To find the capacity of the dryer, we can find its volume by evaluating the algebraic expression $\pi r^2 h$, where r represents the radius and h represents the height of the drum. (Here, the cylinder is lying on its side). If we substitute 13.5 for r and 20 for h, we obtain $\pi(13.5)^2(20)$. Using a scientific calculator, we can evaluate the expression by entering these numbers and pressing these keys.

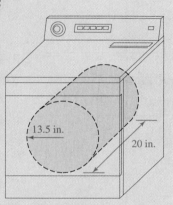

13.5 in.   20 in.

FIGURE 1-25

Keystrokes $\boxed{\pi}$ $\boxed{\times}$ 13.5 $\boxed{x^2}$ $\boxed{\times}$ 20 $\boxed{=}$ $\boxed{\texttt{11451.10522}}$

Using a graphing calculator, we can evaluate the expression by entering these numbers and pressing these keys.

Keystrokes $\boxed{\text{2nd}}$ $\boxed{\pi}$ $\boxed{\times}$ 13.5 $\boxed{x^2}$ $\boxed{\times}$ 20 $\boxed{\text{ENTER}}$

$\boxed{\begin{array}{l} \pi*13.5^2*20 \\ \hspace{2cm} \texttt{11451.10522} \end{array}}$

To the nearest cubic inch, the capacity of the dryer is 11,451 in.^{3}.

Making tables

EXAMPLE 13   *Ballistics.*   If a toy rocket is shot into the air with an initial velocity of 80 feet per second, its height (in feet) after t seconds in flight is given by the algebraic expression

$$80t - 16t^2$$

How many seconds after the launch will it hit the ground?

Solution

We can substitute positive values for t, the time in flight, until we find the one that gives a height of 0. At that time, the rocket will be on the ground. We will begin by finding the height after the rocket has been in flight for 1 second ($t = 1$) and record the result in a table.

Self Check

In Example 13, suppose the height of the rocket is given by $112t - 16t^2$. Complete the table to find out how many seconds after launch it would hit the ground.

t	$112t - 16t^2$
1	
3	
5	
7	

$$80t - 16t^2 = 80(1) - 16(1)^2 \quad \text{Substitute 1 for } t.$$
$$= 64$$

After 1 second in flight, the height of the rocket is 64 feet. We continue to pick more values of t until we find out when the height is 0.

As we evaluate $80t - 16t^2$ for various values of t, we can show the results in a **table of values.** In the column headed "t," we list each value of the variable to be used in the evaluations. In the column headed "$80t - 16t^2$," we write the result of each evaluation.

t	$80t - 16t^2$
1	64
2	96
3	96
4	64
5	0

Evaluate for $t = 2$:
$$80t - 16t^2 = 80(2) - 16(2)^2 = 96$$

Evaluate for $t = 3$:
$$80t - 16t^2 = 80(3) - 16(3)^2 = 96$$

Evaluate for $t = 4$:
$$80t - 16t^2 = 80(4) - 16(4)^2 = 64$$

Evaluate for $t = 5$:
$$80t - 16t^2 = 80(5) - 16(5)^2 = 0$$

Since the height of the rocket is 0 when $t = 5$, the rocket will hit the ground in 5 seconds.

Answer: 7 (the heights are 96, 192, 160, and 0)   ■

The two columns of a table of values are sometimes headed with the terms **input** and **output,** as shown in Table 1-4. The t-values are the inputs into the expression $80t - 16t^2$, and the resulting values are thought of as the outputs.

Input	Output
1	64
2	96
3	96
4	64
5	0

TABLE 1-4

STUDY SET Section 1.7

VOCABULARY   *Fill in the blanks.*

1. To _____evaluate_____ an algebraic expression, we substitute the values for the variables and then apply the rules for the order of operations.

2. Variables and/or numbers can be combined with the operation symbols of addition, subtraction, multiplication, and division to create algebraic _____expressions_____.

3. $2x + 5$ is an example of an algebraic _____expression_____, whereas $2x + 5 = 7$ is an example of an _____equation_____.

4. When we evaluate an algebraic expression, such as $5x - 8$, for several values of x, we can keep track of the results in an input/output _____table_____.

CONCEPTS

5. Write two algebraic expressions that contain the variable *x* and the numbers 6 and 20.

$6 + 20x; \frac{6 - x}{20}$ (answers may vary)

6. a. Complete the table to determine how many days are in *w* weeks.

Number of weeks	Number of days
1	7
2	14
3	21
w	7*w*

b. Complete the table to answer this question: *s* seconds is how many minutes?

Number of seconds	Number of minutes
60	1
120	2
180	3
s	$\frac{s}{60}$

7. When evaluating $3x - 6$ for $x = 4$, what misunderstanding can occur if we don't write parentheses around 4 when it is substituted for the variable?

We would obtain $34 - 6$; it looks like 34, not 3(4).

8. If the knife in Illustration 1 is 12 inches long, how long is the blade? $(12 - h)$ in.

ILLUSTRATION 1

9. a. In Illustration 2, the weight of the van is 500 pounds less than twice the weight of the car. Express the weight of the van and the car using the variable *x*.

x = weight of the car; $2x - 500$ = weight of the van

ILLUSTRATION 2

b. If the actual weight of the car is 2,000 pounds, what is the weight of the van?   3,500 lb

10. See Illustration 3.

a. If we let *b* represent the length of the beam, write an algebraic expression for the length of the pipe. $b - 15$

b. If we let *p* represent the length of the pipe, write an algebraic expression for the length of the beam. $p + 15$

ILLUSTRATION 3

11. Complete the table in Illustration 4.

Type of coin	Number	Value in cents	Total value in cents
Nickel	6	5	30
Dime	*d*	10	10*d*
Half dollar	*x* + 5	50	50(*x* + 5)

ILLUSTRATION 4

12. If $x = -9$, find the value of

a. $-x$ 9

b. $-(-x)$ -9

c. $-x^2$ -81

d. $(-x)^2$ 81

NOTATION   *Complete each solution.*

13. Evaluate the expression $9a - a^2$ for $a = 5$.

$$9a - a^2 = 9(\;5\;) - (\;5\;)^2$$
$$= 9(5) - \boxed{25}$$
$$= \boxed{45} - 25$$
$$= 20$$

14. Evaluate $\dfrac{4x^2 - 3y}{9(x - y)}$ when $x = 4$ and $y = -3$.

$$\frac{4x^2 - 3y}{9(x - y)} = \frac{4(4)^2 - 3(-3)}{9[4 - (-3)]}$$
$$= \frac{4(\;16\;) - 3(\;-3\;)}{9(\;7\;)}$$
$$= \frac{64 - (\;-9\;)}{63}$$
$$= \frac{73}{63}$$

PRACTICE   *Translate each phrase to an algebraic expression. If no variable is given, use x as the variable.*

15. The sum of the length *l* and 15 $l + 15$

16. The difference of a number and 10 $x - 10$

17. The product of a number and 50 $50x$

18. Three-fourths of the population p $\frac{3}{4}p$

19. The ratio of the amount won w and lost l $\frac{w}{l}$

20. The tax t added to c $c + t$

21. P increased by p $P + p$

22. 21 less than the total height h $h - 21$

23. The square of k minus 2,005 $k^2 - 2,005$

24. s subtracted from S $S - s$

25. J reduced by 500 $J - 500$

26. Twice the attendance a $2a$

27. 1,000 split n equal ways $\frac{1,000}{n}$

28. Exceeds the cost c by 25,000 $c + 25,000$

29. 90 more than the current price p $p + 90$

30. 64 divided by the cube of y $\frac{64}{y^3}$

31. The total of 35, h, and 300 $35 + h + 300$

32. x decreased by 17 $x - 17$

33. 680 fewer than the entire population p $p - 680$

34. Triple the number of expected participants $3x$

35. The product of d and 4, decreased by 15 $4d - 15$

36. Forty-five more than the quotient of y and 6 $\frac{y}{6} + 45$

37. Twice the sum of 200 and t $2(200 + t)$

38. The square of the quantity 14 less than x $(x - 14)^2$

39. The absolute value of the difference of a and 2 $|a - 2|$

40. The absolute value of a, decreased by 2 $|a| - 2$

In Exercises 41–44, if n represents a number, write a word description of each algebraic expression. (Answers may vary.)

41. $n - 7$ 7 less than a number

42. $n^2 + 7$ the square of a number, increased by 7

43. $7n + 4$ the product of 7 and a number, increased by 4

44. $3(n + 1)$ three times the sum of a number and 1

45. How many minutes there are in   **a.** 5 hours and **b.** h hours?   300; 60h

46. A woman watches television x hours a day. Express the number of hours she watches TV   **a.** in a week and   **b.** in a year.   7x; 365x

47. a. How many feet are in y yards?   3y
   b. How many yards are in f feet? $\frac{f}{3}$

48. A sales clerk earns \$$x$ an hour. How much does he earn in   **a.** an 8-hour day and   **b.** a 40-hour week?   \$8x; \$40x

49. If a car rental agency charges 29¢ a mile, express the rental fee if a car is driven x miles.   29x¢

50. A model's skirt is x inches long. The designer then lets the hem down 2 inches. How can we express the length (in inches) of the altered skirt?   x + 2

51. A soft drink manufacturer produced c cans of cola during the morning shift. Write an expression for how many six-packs of cola can be assembled from the morning shift's production. $\frac{c}{6}$

52. The tag on a new pair of 36-inch-long jeans warns that after washing, they will shrink x inches in length. Express the length (in inches) of the jeans after they are washed.   36 − x

53. A caravan of b cars, each carrying 5 people, traveled to the state capital for a political rally. Express how many people were in the car caravan.   5b

54. A caterer always prepares food for 10 more people than the order specifies. If p people are to attend a reception, write an expression for the number of people she should prepare for.   p + 10

55. Tickets to a circus cost \$5 each. Express how much tickets will cost for a family of x people if they also pay for two of their neighbors.   \$5(x + 2)

56. If each egg is worth e¢, express the value (in cents) of a dozen eggs.   12e¢

Complete each table of values.

57.

x	$x^3 - 1$
0	−1
−1	−2
−3	−28

58.

g	$g^2 - 7g + 1$
0	1
7	1
−10	171

59.

s	$\frac{5s + 36}{s}$
1	41
6	11
−12	2

60.

a	$2,500a + a^3$
2	5,008
4	10,064
−5	−12,625

61.

Input x	Output $2x - \frac{x}{2}$
100	150
−300	−450

62.

Input x	Output $\frac{x}{3} + \frac{x}{4}$
12	7
−36	−21

63.

x	$(x + 1)(x + 5)$
−1	0
−5	0
−6	5

64.

x	$\frac{1}{x + 8}$
−7	1
−9	−1
−8	undefined

Evaluate each expression, given that x = 3, y = −2, and z = −4.

65. $3y^2 - 6y - 4$ 20

66. $-z^2 - z - 12$ −24

67. $(3 + x)y$ −12

68. $(4 + z)y$ 0

69. $(x + y)^2 - |z + y|$ −5

70. $[(z - 1)(z + 1)]^2$ 225

71. $(4x)^2 + 3y^2$ 156

72. $4x^2 + (3y)^2$ 72

73. $-\dfrac{2x + y^3}{y + 2z}$ $-\frac{1}{5}$

74. $-\dfrac{2z^2 - y}{2x - y^2}$ −17

Evaluate each expression for the given values of the variables.

75. $b^2 - 4ac$ for $a = -1$, $b = 5$, and $c = -2$ 17

76. $(x - a)^2 + (y - b)^2$ for $x = -2$, $y = 1$, $a = 5$, and $b = -3$ 65

77. $a^2 + 2ab + b^2$ for $a = -5$ and $b = -1$ 36

78. $\dfrac{x - a}{y - b}$ for $x = -2$, $y = 1$, $a = 5$, and $b = 2$ 7

79. $\dfrac{n}{2}[2a + (n - 1)d]$ for $n = 10$, $a = -4$, and $d = 6$

230

80. $\dfrac{a(1 - r^n)}{1 - r}$ for $a = -5$, $r = 2$, and $n = 3$ −35

81. ▦ $\dfrac{a^2 + b^2}{2}$ for $a = 1.8$ and $b = -7.6$ 30.5

82. ▦ $(y^3 - 52y^2)^2$ for $y = 55$ 82,355,625

APPLICATIONS

83. ROCKETRY   The algebraic expression ▦ $64t - 16t^2$ gives the height of a toy rocket (in feet) t seconds after being launched. Find the height of the rocket for each of the times shown in Illustration 5. Present your results in an input/output table.

t	h
0	0
0.5	28
1	48
1.5	60
2	64
2.5	60
3	48
3.5	28
4	0

ILLUSTRATION 5

84. GROWING SOD   To determine the number of square feet of sod *remaining* in a field after filling an order (see Illustration 6), the manager of a sod farm uses the expression $20,000 - 3s$ (where s is the number of 1-foot-by-3-foot strips the customer has ordered). To sod a soccer field, a city orders 7,000 strips of sod. Evaluate the expression for this value of s and explain the result.
−1,000; the sod farm is short 1,000 ft² needed to fill the city's order.

1-ft-by-3-ft strips of sod, cut and ready to be loaded on a truck for delivery

ILLUSTRATION 6

85. The expression

$$\frac{5(F - 32)}{9}$$

converts a temperature in degrees Fahrenheit (given as F) to degrees Celsius. Convert the temperatures listed on the container of antifreeze shown in Illustration 7 to degrees Celsius. Round to the nearest degree.
−37° C, −64° C

FIGHTS FREEZE–UP

A 50/50 mix of
Advanced Formula
Antifreeze and water
provides maximum
freeze protection
to −34° F.
A 70/30 mix protects
to −84° F.

U.S. PAT #466481233
MADE IN USA AF–771

ILLUSTRATION 7

86. TEMPERATURE ON MARS   On Mars, maximum summer temperatures can reach 20° C. However, daily temperatures average −33° C. Convert each of these temperatures to degrees Fahrenheit. See Example 12 (page 68). Round to the nearest degree.   68° F, −27° F

87. The utility knife blade shown in Illustration 8 is in the shape of a trapezoid. Find the area of the front face of the blade. (See Example 11 on page 68 for the expression that gives the area of a trapezoid.) $1\frac{23}{64}$ in.²

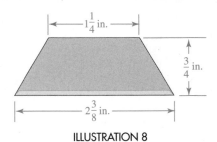

ILLUSTRATION 8

88. ▦ TRUMPET MUTE   The expression

$$\pi[b^2 + d^2 + (b + d)s]$$

can be used to find the total surface area of the trumpet mute shown in Illustration 9 on the next page. Evaluate the expression for the given dimensions to find the number of square inches of cardboard (to the nearest tenth) used to make the mute.   77.8 in.²

89. ▦ LANDSCAPING   A grass strip is to be planted around a tree, as shown in Illustration 10 on the next page. Find the number of square feet of sod to order by evaluating the expression $\pi(R^2 - r^2)$. Round to the nearest square foot.   235 ft²

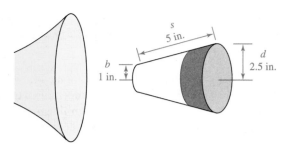

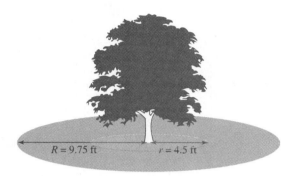

ILLUSTRATION 9

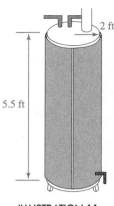

ILLUSTRATION 11

ILLUSTRATION 10

93. In this section, we substituted a number for a variable. List some other uses of the word *substitute* that you encounter in everyday life.

94. Explain why d dimes are not worth $d\cent$.

90. ⊞ ENERGY CONSERVATION   A fiberglass blanket wrapped around a water heater helps prevent heat loss. See Illustration 11. Find the number of square feet of heater surface the blanket covers by evaluating the algebraic expression $2\pi rh$, where r is the radius and h is the height. Round to the nearest square foot. 69 ft^2

REVIEW

95. Simplify -0. 0

96. Is the statement $-5 > -4$ true or false?   false

97. Evaluate $\left|-\frac{2}{3}\right|$. $\frac{2}{3}$

98. Evaluate $2^3 \cdot 3^2$. 72

99. Write $c \cdot c \cdot c \cdot c$ in exponential form. c^4

100. Evaluate $15 + 2[15 - (12 - 10)]$. 41

101. Find the mean (average) of the three test scores 84, 93, and 72. 83

102. Fill in the blanks: In the multiplication statement $5 \cdot x = 5x$, 5 and x are called ____factors____, and $5x$ is called the ____product____.

WRITING

91. What is an algebraic expression? Give some examples.

92. What is a variable? How are variables used in this section?

Variables

One of the major objectives of this course is for you to become comfortable working with **variables**. In Chapter 1, we have used the concept of variable in several ways.

Stating mathematical properties

Variables have been used to state properties of mathematics in a concise, "shorthand" notation.

Match each statement in words with its proper description expressed with a variable (or variables). Assume a, b, and c are real numbers and that there are no divisions by zero.

1. A nonzero number divided by itself is 1.   f

2. When we add opposites, the result is 0.   j

3. Two numbers can be multiplied in either order to get the same result.   h

4. It doesn't matter how we group numbers in multiplication.   a

5. When we multiply a number and its reciprocal, the result is 1.   b

6. When we multiply a number and 0, the result is 0.   e

7. It doesn't matter how we group numbers in addition.   c

8. Any number divided by 1 is the number itself.   i

9. Two numbers can be added in either order to get the same result.   d

10. When we add a number and 0, the number remains the same.   g

a. $(ab)c = a(bc)$

b. $a\left(\dfrac{1}{a}\right) = 1$

c. $(a + b) + c = a + (b + c)$

d. $a + b = b + a$

e. $a \cdot 0 = 0$

f. $\dfrac{a}{a} = 1$

g. $a + 0 = a$

h. $ab = ba$

i. $\dfrac{a}{1} = a$

j. $a + (-a) = 0$

Stating relationships between quantities

Variables are letters that stand for numbers. We have used variables to express known relationships between two or more quantities. These written relationships are called **formulas**.

11. Translate the word model to an equation (formula) that mathematically describes the situation.

The total cost is the sum of the purchase price of the item and the sales tax.

$C = p + t$ (Answers may vary depending on the variables that are chosen.)

12. Use the data in the table to state the relationship between the quantities using a formula.

$b = 2t$ (Answers may vary depending on the variables that are chosen.)

Picnic tables	Benches needed
2	4
3	6
4	8

Writing algebraic expressions

Variables and numbers can be combined with the operations of arithmetic to create **algebraic expressions**.

13. One year, a cruise company did x million dollars' worth of business. After a television celebrity was signed as a spokeswoman for the company, its business increased by $4 million the next year. Write an algebraic expression that represents the amount of business the cruise company had in the year the celebrity was the spokeswoman.

$x + 4 =$ amount of business ($ millions) in the year with the celebrity

14. Evaluate the algebraic expression for the given values of the variable, and enter the results in the table.

x	$3x^2 - 2x + 1$
0	1
4	41
6	97

ACCENT ON TEAMWORK

Section 1.1
PATTERNS   Examine the series of figures below.

a. Complete the table in Illustration 1, and then use the data to construct a line graph.

b. Suppose a figure has s stars in the bottom row. Write a formula for the total number of stars T in the figure.

Stars in the bottom row	1	2	3	4	5	6	7	8	9
Total stars in the figure									

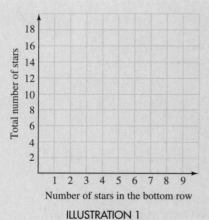

ILLUSTRATION 1

Section 1.2
GETTING TO KNOW YOU   Complete the questionnaire below. Express the results as fractions and decimals.

What fraction (decimal) of the students in your group . . .	Fraction	Decimal
have the letter a in their first names?		
have a birthday in January or February?		
work full-time or part-time?		
have ever been on television?		
live more than 10 miles from the campus?		
say that summer is their favorite season of the year?		

Section 1.3
REAL NUMBERS   Give some examples of situations in everyday life where you encounter whole numbers, zero, negative numbers, fractions, and decimals.

Section 1.4
GEOGRAPHY   Use the following data to determine the range (in feet) between the highest and lowest points on each of the seven continents of the world.

Continent	Highest point (ft)	Lowest point (ft)
Africa	19,340	−512
Antarctica	16,864	−8,327
Asia	29,028	−1,312
Australia	7,310	−52
Europe	18,510	−92
North America	20,320	−282
South America	22,834	−131

Based on data from the National Geographic Society

Section 1.5
OPERATIONS WITH INTEGERS   Prepare a presentation for the class in which you explain why the *sum* of −3 and −2 is negative and why the *product* of −3 and −2 is positive.

Section 1.6
ORDER OF OPERATIONS   To make a cake from a mix, you must follow the instructions carefully. Otherwise, the results can be disastrous. Think of two other multistep processes and explain why the steps must be performed in the proper order, or the outcome is adversely affected. Think of two processes where the order in which the steps are performed does not affect the outcome.

Section 1.7
EVALUATING ALGEBRAIC EXPRESSIONS   Find five examples of cylinders. Measure and record the diameter d of their bases and their heights h. Express the measurements as decimals. Find the radius r of each base by dividing the diameter by 2. Then find the volume of each cylinder by evaluating the expression $\pi r^2 h$. Round to the nearest tenth of a cubic unit. See the Accent on Technology on page 69 for an example. Present your results in a table of the form shown below.

Cylinder	d	r	h	Volume
Container of salt	$3\frac{1}{4}$ in. (3.25 in.)	$1\frac{5}{8}$ in. (1.625 in.)	$5\frac{3}{8}$ in. (5.375 in.)	44.6 in.^{3}

CHAPTER REVIEW

SECTION 1.1	*Describing Numerical Relationships*

CONCEPTS

Tables, bar graphs, and *line graphs* are used to describe numerical relationships.

REVIEW EXERCISES

1. Consider the line graph in Illustration 1 that shows the number of cars parked in a mall parking structure from 6 P.M. to 12 midnight on a Saturday.

   a. What units are used to scale the horizontal and vertical axes?
     1 hr; 100 cars

   b. How many cars were in the parking structure at 11 P.M.?   100

   c. At what time did the parking structure have 500 cars in it?   7 P.M.

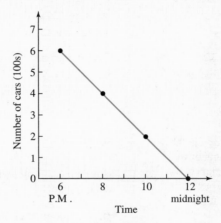

ILLUSTRATION 1

The result of an addition is called the *sum;* of a subtraction, the *difference;* of a multiplication, the *product;* and of a division, the *quotient.*

2. Express each statement in words.

   a. $15 - 3 = 12$
     The difference of 15 and 3 is 12.

   b. $15 + 3 = 18$
     The sum of 15 and 3 is 18.

   c. $15 \div 3 = 5$
     The quotient of 15 and 3 is 5.

   d. $15 \cdot 3 = 45$
     The product of 15 and 3 is 45.

3. a. Write the multiplication 4×9 in two ways: first with a raised dot $\cdot$, and then using parentheses. $4 \cdot 9$; $4(9)$

   b. Write the division $9 \div 3$ without using the symbols $\div$ or $\overline{)}$. $\frac{9}{3}$

Variables are letters used to stand for numbers.

4. Write each multiplication without a multiplication symbol.

   a. $8 \cdot b$ $8b$ **b.** $x \cdot y$ xy **c.** $2 \cdot l \cdot w$ $2lw$ **d.** $P \cdot r \cdot t$ Prt

An *equation* is a mathematical sentence that contains an $=$ sign. Variables and/or numbers can be combined with the operations of arithmetic to create *algebraic expressions.*

5. Classify each item as either an algebraic expression or an equation.

   a. $5 = 2x + 3$ equation   **b.** $2x + 3$ algebraic expression

   c. $\dfrac{t + 6}{12}$ algebraic expression   **d.** $P = 2l + 2w$ equation

Equations that express a known relationship between two or more variables are called *formulas.*

6. Use the formula $n = b + 5$ to complete the table in Illustration 2 (on the next page).

7. Use the data in Illustration 3 (on the next page) to write a formula that mathematically describes the relationship between the two quantities; then state the relationship in words. $f = 50c$; the total fees are the product of 50 and the number of children. (Answers may vary depending on the variables chosen.)

77

Number of brackets (*b*)	Number of nails (*n*)
5	10
10	15
20	25

ILLUSTRATION 2

Number of children	Total fees (dollars)
1	50
2	100
4	200

ILLUSTRATION 3

SECTION 1.2

Fractions and Decimals

Whole numbers can be written as the product of two or more whole-number *factors*.

A *prime number* is a whole number greater than 1 that has only 1 and itself as factors.

The fundamental property of fractions:
When we multiply or divide the numerator and denominator of a fraction by the same nonzero number, the resulting fraction is *equivalent* to the original fraction.

To multiply two fractions, multiply their numerators and multiply their denominators.

To divide two fractions, multiply the first fraction by the reciprocal of the second fraction.

To add (or subtract) fractions with the same denominator, add (or subtract) the numerators and keep the common denominator.

The *least common denominator (LCD)* for a set of fractions is the smallest number each denominator will divide exactly.

8. a. Write 24 as the product of two factors. $2 \cdot 12, 3 \cdot 8$ (answers may vary)
  b. Write 24 as the product of three factors. $2 \cdot 2 \cdot 6$ (answers may vary)
  c. List the factors of 24.   1, 2, 3, 4, 6, 8, 12, 24

9. Give the prime factorization of each number, if possible.
  a. 54 $3^3 \cdot 2$ **b.** 147 $7^2 \cdot 3$ **c.** 385 $11 \cdot 7 \cdot 5$ **d.** 41   prime

10. Simplify each fraction to lowest terms.
  a. $\dfrac{20}{35}$ $\frac{4}{7}$ **b.** $\dfrac{24}{18}$ $\frac{4}{3}$

11. Build up each fraction or whole number to an equivalent fraction with the indicated denominator.
  a. $\dfrac{5}{8}$, denominator 64 $\frac{40}{64}$ **b.** 12, denominator 3 $\frac{36}{3}$

12. Do each operation.
  a. $\dfrac{16}{35} \cdot \dfrac{25}{48}$ $\frac{5}{21}$ **b.** $5\dfrac{3}{5}\left(1\dfrac{11}{14}\right)$ 10
  c. $\dfrac{1}{3} \div \dfrac{15}{16}$ $\frac{16}{45}$ **d.** $16\dfrac{1}{4} \div 5$ $3\frac{1}{4}$

13. Do each operation.
  a. $\dfrac{17}{25} - \dfrac{7}{25}$ $\frac{2}{5}$ **b.** $\dfrac{17}{12} + \dfrac{7}{12}$ 2

14. MACHINE SHOP   See Illustration 4. How much must be milled off the $\frac{17}{24}$-inch-thick steel rod so that the collar will slip over the end of it? $\frac{17}{96}$ in.

Steel rod

ILLUSTRATION 4

15. Do each operation.
  a. $\dfrac{8}{11} - \dfrac{1}{2}$ $\frac{5}{22}$ **b.** $\dfrac{1}{4} + \dfrac{2}{3}$ $\frac{11}{12}$
  c. $61\dfrac{7}{8} + 19\dfrac{2}{3}$ $81\frac{13}{24}$ **d.** $34\dfrac{1}{9} - 13\dfrac{5}{6}$ $20\frac{5}{18}$

The *decimal numeration system* is an extension of the place value system used when working with whole numbers.

16. Do each operation.

  a. $2.3061 + 78 + 23.8$ 104.1061   **b.** $305.28 - 79.976$ 225.304

  c. $45.3 \cdot 5.6$ 253.68   **d.** $1,000(0.755)$ 755

  e. $35\overline{)250.95}$ 7.17   **f.** $\dfrac{0.0224}{0.08}$ 0.28

To write a fraction as a decimal, divide the numerator by the denominator.

17. Write each fraction as a decimal. Use an overbar if the result is a repeating decimal.

  a. $\dfrac{1}{250}$ 0.004   **b.** $\dfrac{17}{22}$ $0.7\overline{72}$

SECTION 1.3

The Real Numbers

The *natural numbers:*
  $\{1, 2, 3, 4, 5, 6, \ldots\}$
The *whole numbers:*
  $\{0, 1, 2, 3, 4, 5, 6, \ldots\}$
The *integers:*
  $\{\ldots, -3, -2, -1, 0, 1, 2, 3, \ldots\}$

18. Which number is a whole number but not a natural number?   0

19. Represent each of these situations with a signed number.

  a. A budget deficit of $65 billion
    $-$65 billion

  b. 206 feet below sea level
    -206 ft

Two *inequality symbols* are
  $>$ "is greater than"
  $<$ "is less than"

20. Use one of the symbols $>$ or $<$ to make each statement true.

  a. $0 < 5$ **b.** $-12 > -13$

A *rational number* is any number that can be written as a fraction with an integer numerator and a nonzero integer denominator.

21. Show that each of the following numbers is a rational number by expressing it as a fraction.

  a. 5 $\frac{5}{1}$ **b.** -12 $\frac{-12}{1}$ **c.** 0.7 $\frac{7}{10}$ **d.** $4\frac{2}{3}$ $\frac{14}{3}$

Rational numbers are either *terminating* or *repeating* decimals.

22. Graph each member of the set $\left\{\pi, 0.333\ldots, 3.75, -\frac{17}{4}, \frac{7}{8}, -2\right\}$ on the number line.

An *irrational number* is a nonterminating, nonrepeating decimal. Irrational numbers cannot be written as the ratio of two integers.

23. Use a calculator to approximate $\sqrt{2}$ to the nearest hundredth. $\sqrt{2} \approx 1.41$

A *real number* is any number that is either a rational or an irrational number.

24. Tell whether each statement is true or false.

  a. All integers are whole numbers.   false

  b. π is a rational number.   false

  c. The set of real numbers corresponds to all points on the number line.   true

  d. A real number is either rational or irrational.   true

The natural numbers are a *subset* of the whole numbers. The whole numbers are a subset of the integers. The integers are a subset of the rational numbers. The rational numbers are a subset of the real numbers.

25. Tell which numbers in the given set are natural numbers, whole numbers, integers, rational numbers, irrational numbers, and real numbers.

  $\left\{-\frac{4}{5}, 99.99, 0, \sqrt{2}, -12, 4\frac{1}{2}, 0.666\ldots, 8\right\}$

  natural: 8; whole: 0, 8; integers: 0, -12, 8; rational: $-\frac{4}{5}$, 99.99, 0, -12, $4\frac{1}{2}$, 0.666 . . . , 8; irrational: $\sqrt{2}$; real: all

Two numbers represented by points on a number line that are the same distance away from 0, but on opposite sides of it, are called *opposites*.

26. Write the expression in simpler form.
  a. The opposite of 10 -10
  b. The opposite of -3 3
  c. $-\left(-\dfrac{9}{16}\right)$ $\frac{9}{16}$
  d. -0 0

The *absolute value* of a number is the distance on the number line between the number and 0.

27. Insert one of the symbols $>$, $<$, or $=$ in the blank to make each statement true.
  a. $|-6| > |5|$
  b. $-9 > -|-10|$

| **SECTION 1.4** | *Adding and Subtracting Real Numbers* |

To add two real numbers with *like signs,* add their absolute values and attach their common sign to the sum.

28. Add the numbers.
  a. $12 + 33$ 45
  b. $-45 + (-37)$ -82
  c. $-15 + 37$ 22
  d. $25 + (-13)$ 12
  e. $12 + (-8) + (-15)$ -11
  f. $-25 + (-14) + 35$ -4
  g. $-9.9 + (-2.4)$ -12.3
  h. $\dfrac{5}{16} + \left(-\dfrac{1}{2}\right)$ $-\frac{3}{16}$
  i. $35 + (-13) + (-17) + 6$ 11
  j. $-21 + (-11) + 32 + (-45)$ -45
  k. $0 + (-7)$ -7
  l. $-7 + 7$ 0

To add two real numbers with *unlike signs,* subtract their absolute values, the smaller from the larger. To that result, attach the sign of the number with the larger absolute value.

The *commutative* and *associative* properties of addition:
  $a + b = b + a$
  $(a + b) + c = a + (b + c)$

29. Tell what property of addition guarantees that the quantities are equal.
  a. $-2 + 5 = 5 + (-2)$
    commutative property of addition
  b. $(-2 + 5) + 1 = -2 + (5 + 1)$
    associative property of addition

To *subtract* real numbers, add the opposite:
  $a - b = a + (-b)$

30. Subtract the numbers.
  a. $45 - 64$ -19
  b. $-17 - 32$ -49
  c. $-27 - (-12)$ -15
  d. $3.6 - (-2.1)$ 5.7

31. ASTRONOMY *Magnitude* is a term used in astronomy to designate the brightness of celestial objects as viewed from Earth. Smaller magnitudes are associated with brighter objects, and larger magnitudes refer to fainter objects. See Illustration 5. For each of the following pairs of objects, by how many magnitudes do their brightnesses differ?
  a. A full moon and the sun 14
  b. The star Beta Crucis and a full moon 13.78

Object	Magnitude
Sun	-26.5
Full moon	-12.5
Beta Crucis	1.28

Based on data from Abell, Morrison, and Wolf, *Exploration of the Universe* (Saunders College Publishing, 1987)

ILLUSTRATION 5

32. GEOGRAPHY   The tallest peak on earth is Mt. Everest, at 29,028 feet. The greatest ocean depth is the Mariana Trench, at −36,205 feet. Find the difference in the two elevations.   65,233 ft

---

| **SECTION 1.5** | *Multiplying and Dividing Real Numbers* |

To multiply two real numbers, multiply their absolute values.
1. The product of two real numbers with *like signs* is positive.
2. The product of two real numbers with *unlike signs* is negative.

33. Multiply the numbers.
  a. $-8 \cdot 7$ −56
  b. $(-9)(-6)$ 54
  c. $2(-3)(-2)$ 12
  d. $(-3)(4)(2)$ −24
  e. $(-3)(-4)(-2)$ −24
  f. $(-4)(-1)(-3)(-3)$ 36
  g. $-1.2(-5.3)$ 6.36
  h. $0.002(-1,000)$ −2
  i. $-\dfrac{2}{3}\left(\dfrac{1}{5}\right)$ $-\frac{2}{15}$
  j. $2\dfrac{1}{4}\left(-\dfrac{1}{3}\right)$ $-\frac{3}{4}$
  k. $-6 \cdot 0$ 0
  l. $(-3)(1)$ −3

The *commutative* and *associative* properties of multiplication:
  $ab = ba$
  $(ab)c = a(bc)$

34. Tell what property of multiplication guarantees that the quantities are equal.
  a. $(2 \cdot 3)5 = 2(3 \cdot 5)$
     associative property of multiplication
  b. $(-5)(-6) = (-6)(-5)$
     commutative property of multiplication

35. a. What is the additive inverse of −3?   3
    b. What is the multiplicative inverse of −3? $-\frac{1}{3}$

To divide two real numbers, divide their absolute values.
1. The quotient of two real numbers with *like signs* is positive.
2. The quotient of two real numbers with *unlike signs* is negative.

36. Do each division.
  a. $\dfrac{88}{44}$ 2
  b. $\dfrac{-100}{25}$ −4
  c. $\dfrac{-81}{-27}$ 3
  d. $\dfrac{0}{37}$ 0
  e. $-\dfrac{3}{5} \div \dfrac{1}{2}$ $-\frac{6}{5}$
  f. $\dfrac{-60}{0}$ undefined
  g. $\dfrac{-4.5}{1}$ −4.5
  h. $\dfrac{-5}{-5}$ 1

Division *of zero* by a nonzero number is 0. Division *by zero* is undefined.

37. MAGNIFICATION
  a. Find the high and low reading that is displayed on the screen of the emissions-testing device shown in Illustration 6.   high: 2, low: −3
  b. The picture on the screen can be magnified by switching a setting on the monitor. What would be the new high and low if every value were to be doubled?   high: 4, low: −6

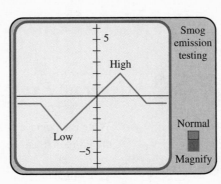

ILLUSTRATION 6

SECTION 1.6	*Exponents and Order of Operations*

An *exponent* is used to represent repeated multiplication. In the *exponential expression* a^n, a is the *base,* and n is the *exponent.*

38. Write each expression using exponents.

    a. $8 \cdot 8 \cdot 8 \cdot 8 \cdot 8$ 8^5 **b.** $5 \cdot 5 \cdot 5 \cdot 9 \cdot 9$ $5^3 \cdot 9^2$

    c. $a(a)(a)(a)$ a^4 **d.** $9 \cdot \pi \cdot r \cdot r$ $9\pi r^2$

    e. $x \cdot x \cdot x \cdot y \cdot y \cdot y \cdot y$ $x^3 y^4$ **f.** the sixth power of one 1^6

39. Evaluate each expression.

    a. 9^2 81   **b.** 2 cubed   8   **c.** 2^5 32   **d.** 50^1 50

Order of operations:

1. Do all calculations within grouping symbols, working from the innermost pair to the outermost pair, in the following order:

2. Evaluate all exponential expressions.

3. Do all multiplications and divisions, working from left to right.

4. Do all additions and subtractions, working from left to right.

40. How many operations does the expression $5 \cdot 4 - 3^2 + 1$ contain, and in what order should they be performed?   4; power, multiplication, subtraction, addition

41. Evaluate each expression.

    a. $24 - 3(6)(4)$ -48 **b.** $-(6 - 3)^2$ -9

    c. $4^3 + 2(-6 - 2 \cdot 2)$ 44   **d.** $10 - 5[-3 - 2(5 - 7^2)] - 5$ -420

    e. $\dfrac{-4(4 + 2) - 4}{|-18 - 4(5)|}$ $-\frac{14}{19}$ **f.** $(-3)^3 \left(\dfrac{-8}{2} \right) + 5$ 113

    g. $\dfrac{|-35| - 2(-7)}{2^4 - 23}$ -7 **h.** $-9^2 + (-9)^2$ 0

If the expression does not contain grouping symbols, begin with Step 2. In a fraction, simplify the numerator and denominator separately. Then simplify the fraction, if possible.

The *arithmetic mean* (or *average*) is a value around which number values are grouped.

$$\text{Mean} = \frac{\text{sum of values}}{\text{number of values}}$$

42. WALK-A-THON   Use the data in Illustration 7 to find the average (mean) donation to a charity walk-a-thon. $20

Donation	Number received
$5	20
$10	65
$20	25
$50	5
$100	10

ILLUSTRATION 7

SECTION 1.7	*Algebraic Expressions*

In order to describe numerical relationships, we need to translate the words of a problem into mathematical symbols.

43. Write each phrase as an algebraic expression.

    a. 25 more than the height h **b.** 15 less than the cutoff score s

       $h + 25$ $s - 15$

    c. $\frac{1}{2}$ of the time t $\frac{1}{2}t$ **d.** the product of 6 and x $6x$

44. See Illustration 8.

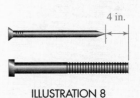

ILLUSTRATION 8

    a. If we let n represent the length of the nail, write an algebraic expression for the length of the bolt (in inches). $(n + 4)$ in.

    b. If we let b represent the length of the bolt, write an algebraic expression for the length of the nail (in inches). $(b - 4)$ in.

45. a. How many years are in d decades? $10d$

    b. If you have x donuts, how many dozen donuts do you have? $\frac{x}{12}$

    c. Five years after a house was constructed, a patio was added. How old, in years, is the patio if the house is x years old? $(x - 5)$ years

46. Complete the table in Illustration 9.

Type of coin	Number	Value (¢)	Total value (¢)
Nickel	6	5	30
Dime	d	10	$10d$

ILLUSTRATION 9

47. Complete the table of values.

x	$20x - x^3$
0	0
1	19
−4	−16

48. Evaluate each algebraic expression for the given value(s) of the variable(s).

    a. $7x^2 - \frac{x}{2}$ for $x = 4$ 110

    b. $b^2 - 4ac$ for $b = -10$, $a = 3$, and $c = 5$ 40

    c. $2(24 - 2c)^3$ for $c = 9$ 432

    d. $\dfrac{x + y}{-x - z}$ for $x = 19$, $y = 17$, and $z = -18$ −36

49. Use a calculator to find the volume, to the nearest tenth of a cubic inch, of the ice cream waffle cone in Illustration 10 by evaluating the algebraic expression

$$\frac{\pi r^2 h}{3}$$

17.7 in.^{3}

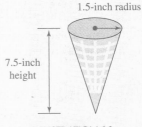

ILLUSTRATION 10

Sometimes we must rely on common sense and insight to find *hidden operations*.

Number $\cdot$ value = total value

When we replace the variable, or variables, in an algebraic expression with specific numbers and then apply the rules for the order of operations, we are *evaluating* the algebraic expression.

TAKING A MATH TEST

The best way to relieve anxiety about taking a mathematics test is to know that you are well-prepared for it and that you have a plan. Before any test, ask yourself three questions. When? What? How?

When will I study?

1. When is the test?

2. When will I begin to review for the test?

3. What are the dates and times that I will reserve for studying for the test?

What will I study?

1. What sections will the test cover?

2. Has the instructor indicated any types of problems that are guaranteed to be on the test?

How will I prepare for the test?

Put a check mark by each method you will use to prepare for the test.

☐ Review the class notes.

☐ Outline the chapter(s) to see how the topics relate to one another.

☐ Recite the important formulas, definitions, vocabulary, and rules into a tape recorder.

☐ Make flash cards for the important formulas, definitions, vocabulary, and rules.

☐ Rework problems from the homework assignments.

☐ Rework each of the Self Check problems in the text.

☐ Form a study group to discuss and practice the topics to be tested.

☐ Complete the appropriate Chapter Review(s) and the Chapter Test(s).

☐ Review the Comments given in the text.

☐ Work on improving my speed in answering questions.

☐ Review the methods that can be used to check my answers.

☐ Write a sample test, trying to think of the questions the instructor will ask.

☐ Complete the appropriate Cumulative Review Exercises.

☐ Get organized the night before the test. Have materials ready to go so that the trip to school will not be hurried.

☐ Take some time to relax immediately before the test. Don't study right up to the last minute.

Taking the test

Here are some tips that can help improve your performance on a mathematics test.

• Write down any formulas or rules as soon as you receive the test.

• When you receive the test, scan it, looking for the types of problems you had expected to see. Do them first.

• Read the instructions carefully.

• Don't spend too much time on any one problem until you have attempted all the problems.

• If your instructor gives partial credit, at least try to begin a solution.

• Don't be afraid to skip a problem and come back to it later.

• Save the most difficult problems for last.

• If you finish early, go back over your work and look for mistakes.

Chapter 1 Test

The graph in Illustration 1 shows the cost to hire a security guard. Use the graph to answer Problems 1 and 2.

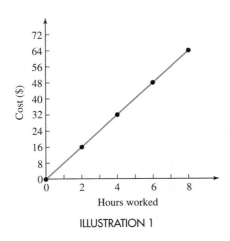

ILLUSTRATION 1

1. What will it cost to hire a security guard for 3 hours?
$24

2. If a school was billed $40 for hiring a security guard for a dance, for how long did the guard work?   5 hr

3. Use the formula $f = \frac{a}{5}$ to complete the table.

Area in square miles (a)	Number of fire stations (f)
15	3
100	20
350	70

4. Give the prime factorization of 180.
$5 \cdot 3 \cdot 3 \cdot 2 \cdot 2 = 2^2 \cdot 3^2 \cdot 5$

5. Simplify $\frac{42}{105}$ to lowest terms. $\frac{2}{5}$

6. SHOPPING   See Illustration 2. What is the cost of the amount of fruit on the scale? $3.57

7. Divide: $\frac{15}{16} \div \frac{5}{8}$. $\frac{3}{2} = 1\frac{1}{2}$

Oranges
84 cents a pound

ILLUSTRATION 2

8. Subtract: $\frac{11}{12} - \frac{2}{9}$. $\frac{25}{36}$

9. Add: $11\frac{2}{3} + 8\frac{2}{5}$. $20\frac{1}{15}$

10. Multiply: $0.49 \cdot 100$.   49

11. QUALITY CONTROL   An electronics company has strict specifications for silicon chips used in a computer. The company will install only chips that are within 0.05 centimeters of the specified thickness. Illustration 3 gives that specification for two types of chip. Fill in the blanks to complete the chart.

Chip type	Thickness specification	Acceptable range	
		Low	High
A	0.78 cm	0.73	0.83
B	0.643 cm	0.593	0.693

ILLUSTRATION 3

12. Write $\frac{5}{6}$ as a decimal. $0.8\overline{3}$

13. Graph each member of the set on the number line.
$\left\{ -1\frac{1}{4}, \sqrt{2}, -3.75, \frac{7}{2}, 0.5, -3 \right\}$

14. Tell whether each statement is true or false.
   a. Every integer is a rational number.   true
   b. Every rational number is an integer.   false
   c. π is an irrational number.   true
   d. 0 is a whole number.   true

15. Describe the set of real numbers.
The set of real numbers corresponds to all points on a number line. A real number is any number that is either a rational number or an irrational number.

16. Insert the proper symbol, $>$ or $<$, in the blank to make each statement true.
   a. $-2 > -3$ **b.** $-|-7| < 8$
   c. $|-4| < -(-5)$ **d.** $|-\frac{7}{8}| > 0.5$

17. COMMERCIAL REAL ESTATE   *Net absorption* is a term used to indicate how much office space in a city is being purchased. Use the information from the graph in Illustration 4 to determine the eight-quarter average net absorption figure for Long Beach, California.
0.0475 million ft^2

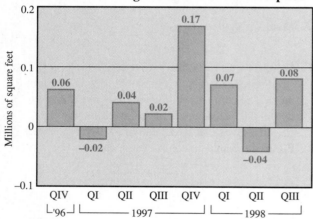

Downtown Long Beach Office Net Absorption

Based on information from *Los Angeles Times* (Oct. 13, 1998), Section C10

ILLUSTRATION 4

18. Add: $(-6) + 8 + (-4)$. -2

19. Add: $-\dfrac{1}{2} + \dfrac{7}{8}$. $\frac{3}{8}$

20. Subtract: $-10 - (-4)$. -6

21. Multiply: $(-2)(-3)(-5)$. -30

22. Divide: $\dfrac{-22}{-11}$.   2

23. Do each operation.
   a. $0(-3)$ 0   **b.** $\dfrac{0}{-3}$ 0
   c. $0 + (-3)$ -3 **d.** $3 + (-3)$ 0

24. What property of real numbers is illustrated below?
$(-12 + 97) + 3 = -12 + (97 + 3)$
associative property of addition

25. Rewrite each product using exponents:
   a. $9(9)(9)(9)(9)$ 9^5 **b.** $3 \cdot x \cdot x \cdot z \cdot z \cdot z$. $3x^2z^3$

26. Evaluate $8 + 2 \cdot 3^4$.   170

27. Evaluate $9^2 - 3[45 - 3(6 + 4)]$.   36

28. Evaluate $\dfrac{3(40 - 2^3)}{-2(6 - 4)^2}$. -12

29. Evaluate $3(x - y) - 5(x + y)$ for $x = 2$ and $y = -5$.   36

30. Complete the table in Illustration 5.

x	$2x - \frac{30}{x}$
5	4
10	17
-30	-59

ILLUSTRATION 5

31. A rock band recorded x songs for a CD. Technicians had to delete two songs from the album because of poor sound quality. Express the number of songs on the CD using an algebraic expression.
$x - 2 =$ number of songs on the CD

32. What is the value of q quarters in cents? $25q$

33. Explain the difference between an expression and an equation. Give an example of each.
An equation is a mathematical sentence that contains an $=$ sign. An expression does not contain an $=$ sign.

34. Explain this statement: $a - b = a + (-b)$.   Subtraction is the same as addition of the opposite.

Equations, Inequalities, and Problem Solving

2

IN MATHEMATICS AND ITS APPLICATIONS, EQUATIONS AND INEQUALITIES ARE USED TO DESCRIBE A WIDE VARIETY OF NUMERICAL RELATIONSHIPS.

2.1 Solving Equations

In this section, you will learn about

- Equations • Checking solutions • The subtraction property of equality
- The addition property of equality • The division property of equality
- The multiplication property of equality

INTRODUCTION. One of the most useful concepts in all of algebra is the equation. As you will see, writing and then solving an equation is a powerful problem-solving strategy that we will use throughout the course. In this section, we introduce some basic types of equations and discuss four fundamental properties that are used to solve them.

Equations

Recall that an **equation** is a statement indicating that two expressions are equal. In the equation $x + 5 = 15$, the expression $x + 5$ is called the **left-hand side,** and 15 is called the **right-hand side.**

An equation can be true or false. For example, $10 + 5 = 15$ is a true equation, whereas $11 + 5 = 15$ is a false equation. An equation containing a variable can be true or false, depending upon the value of the variable. If $x = 10$, the equation $x + 5 = 15$ is true, because

$$10 + 5 = 15 \quad \text{Substitute 10 for } x.$$

However, this equation is false for all other values of x.

Any number that makes an equation true when substituted for the variable is said to **satisfy** the equation. Such numbers are called **solutions** or **roots** of the equation. Because 10 is the only number that satisfies $x + 5 = 15$, it is the only solution of the equation.

Checking solutions

EXAMPLE 1   *Checking a solution.*   Is 9 a solution of $3y - 1 = 2y + 7$?

Solution

We begin by substituting 9 for each y in the equation. Then we use the rules for the order of operations to evaluate each side separately. If 9 is a solution, we will obtain a true statement.

$$3y - 1 = 2y + 7 \quad \text{The original equation.}$$
$$3(9) - 1 \stackrel{?}{=} 2(9) + 7 \quad \text{Substitute 9 for } y. \text{ Read } \stackrel{?}{=} \text{ as "is possibly equal to."}$$
$$27 - 1 \stackrel{?}{=} 18 + 7 \quad \text{Do the multiplications.}$$
$$26 = 25 \quad \text{Do the subtraction and the addition.}$$

Since the resulting equation is not true, 9 is *not* a solution of $3y - 1 = 2y + 7$.

Self Check

Is 25 a solution of $2(46 - x) = 41$?

Answer: no

EXAMPLE 2 *Checking a solution.* Verify that 6 is a solution of the equation $x^2 - 5x - 6 = 0$.

Solution

We substitute 6 for x in the equation and simplify.

$x^2 - 5x - 6 = 0$ The original equation.

$6^2 - 5(6) - 6 \overset{?}{=} 0$ Substitute 6 for x.

$36 - 30 - 6 \overset{?}{=} 0$ Evaluate the power: $6^2 = 36$. Do the multiplication: $5(6) = 30$.

$0 = 0$ Do the subtractions on the left-hand side.

Since the resulting equation is true, 6 is a solution.

Self Check

Is 8 a solution of the equation
$$\frac{m - 4}{4} = \frac{m + 4}{12}?$$

Answer: yes

The subtraction property of equality

In practice, we will not be told the solutions of an equation. We will have to find them ourselves. The process of finding the solutions of an equation is called *solving the equation*. To develop an understanding of the procedures used to solve an equation, we will first examine $x + 2 = 5$ and make some observations as we solve it in a practical way.

We can think of the scale shown in Figure 2-1(a) as representing the equation $x + 2 = 5$. The weight (in grams) on the left-hand side of the scale is $x + 2$, and the weight (in grams) on the right-hand side is 5. Because these weights are equal, the scale is in balance. To find x, we need to isolate it. That can be accomplished by removing 2 grams from the left-hand side of the scale. Common sense tells us that we must also remove 2 grams from the right-hand side if the scale is to remain in balance. In Figure 2-1(b), we can see that x grams will be balanced by 3 grams. Thus, $x = 3$. We say that we have *solved* the equation and that the *solution* is 3.

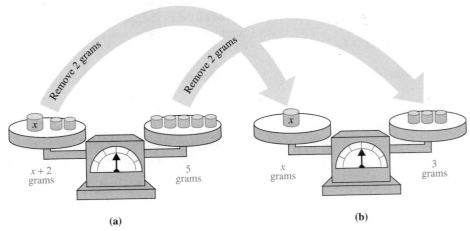

FIGURE 2-1

These observations illustrate a property of equality: *If the same quantity is subtracted from equal quantities, the results will be equal quantities.* We can express this property, called the **subtraction property of equality**, in symbols.

Subtraction property of equality

Let a, b, and c represent real numbers.

If $a = b$, then $a - c = b - c$.

When we use this property, the resulting equation will be equivalent to the original equation.

Equivalent equations	Two equations are **equivalent** when they have the same solutions.

In the previous example, we found that $x + 2 = 5$ is equivalent to $x = 3$. This is true because these equations have the same solution, $x = 3$.

We now show how to solve $x + 2 = 5$ using an algebraic approach.

EXAMPLE 3   *Solving an equation.*   Solve $x + 2 = 5$ and check the result.

Solution

To isolate x on the left-hand side of the equation, we use the subtraction property of equality. We can undo the addition of 2 by subtracting 2 from both sides.

$$x + 2 = 5$$
$$x + 2 - 2 = 5 - 2 \quad \text{Subtract 2 from both sides.}$$
$$x = 3 \quad \text{Do the subtractions: } 2 - 2 = 0 \text{ and } 5 - 2 = 3.$$

We check by substituting 3 for x in the original equation and simplifying. If 3 is the solution, we will obtain a true statement.

$$x + 2 = 5 \quad \text{The original equation.}$$
$$3 + 2 \stackrel{?}{=} 5 \quad \text{Substitute 3 for } x.$$
$$5 = 5 \quad \text{Do the addition: } 3 + 2 = 5.$$

Since the resulting equation is true, 3 is a solution.

Self Check

Solve $x + 24 = 50$ and check the result.

Answer: 26

The addition property of equality

A second property that we will use to solve equations is based on the following idea: *If the same quantity is added to equal quantities, the results will be equal quantities.* In symbols, we have the following property.

Addition property of equality	Let a, b, and c represent real numbers. If $a = b$, then $a + c = b + c$.

To illustrate the addition property of equality, we can think of the scale shown in Figure 2-2(a) as representing the equation $x - 2 = 3$. To find x, we add 2 grams of weight to each side. The scale will remain in balance. From the scale in Figure 2-2(b),

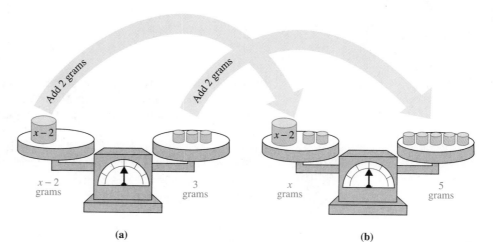

(a)   (b)

FIGURE 2-2

we can see that x grams will be balanced by 5 grams. Thus, $x = 5$ is a solution of $x - 2 = 3$.

To solve $x - 2 = 3$ algebraically, we apply the addition property of equality. We can isolate x on the left-hand side of the equation by adding 2 to both sides.

$$x - 2 = 3 \qquad \text{The equation to solve.}$$
$$x - 2 + 2 = 3 + 2 \quad \text{To undo the subtraction of 2, add 2 to both sides.}$$
$$x = 5 \qquad \text{On the left-hand side, adding 2 undoes the subtraction of 2 and leaves } x. \text{ On the right-hand side, } 3 + 2 = 5.$$

To check this result, we substitute 5 for x in the original equation and simplify.

$$x - 2 = 3$$
$$5 - 2 \stackrel{?}{=} 3 \quad \text{Substitute 5 for } x.$$
$$3 = 3 \quad \text{Do the subtraction.}$$

This is a true statement, so $x = 5$ is a solution.

EXAMPLE 4   *Isolating a variable.* Solve $19 = y - 7$ and check the result.

Solution

To isolate y on the right-hand side of the equation, we use the addition property of equality. We can undo the subtraction of 7 by adding 7 to both sides.

$$19 = y - 7$$
$$19 + 7 = y - 7 + 7 \quad \text{Add 7 to both sides.}$$
$$26 = y \qquad \text{On the left-hand side, } 19 + 7 = 26. \text{ On the right-hand side, adding 7 undoes the subtraction of 7 and leaves } y.$$
$$y = 26 \qquad \text{When stating a solution, it is common practice to write the variable first. If } 26 = y, \text{ then } y = 26.$$

We check by substituting 26 for y in the original equation and simplifying.

$$19 = y - 7 \quad \text{The original equation.}$$
$$19 \stackrel{?}{=} 26 - 7 \quad \text{Substitute 26 for } y.$$
$$19 = 19 \quad \text{Do the subtraction: } 26 - 7 = 19$$

This is a true statement, so 26 is a solution.

Self Check

Solve $75 = b - 38$ and check the result.

Answer: 113   ◼

The division property of equality

We can think of the scale in Figure 2-3(a) as representing the equation $2x = 8$. Since $2x$ means $2 \cdot x$, the equation can be written as $2 \cdot x = 8$. The weight (in grams) on the left-

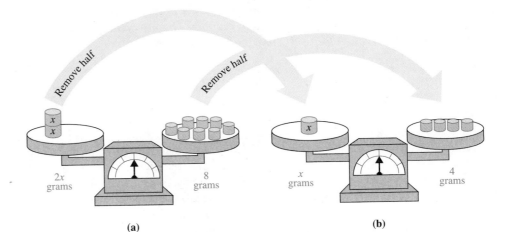

(a)   (b)

FIGURE 2-3

hand side of the scale is $2 \cdot x$, and the weight (in grams) on the right-hand side is 8. Because these weights are equal, the scale is in balance.

To find x, we need to isolate it on the left-hand side of the scale. That can be accomplished by removing half of the weight on the left-hand side. Common sense tells us that if the scale is to remain in balance, we need to remove half of the weight from the right-hand side. We can think of the process of removing half of each weight as dividing each weight by 2. In Figure 2-3(b), we can see that x grams will be balanced by 4 grams. Thus, $x = 4$.

These observations illustrate a property of equality: *If equal quantities are divided by the same nonzero quantity, the results will be equal quantities.* We can express this property, called the **division property of equality,** in symbols.

Division property of equality

> Let a, b, and c represent real numbers.
>
> If $a = b$, then $\dfrac{a}{c} = \dfrac{b}{c}$ $(c \neq 0)$

We will now show how to solve $2x = 8$ using an algebraic approach.

EXAMPLE 5 *Solving an equation.* Solve the equation $2x = 8$ and check the result.

Solution

Recall that $2x = 8$ means $2 \cdot x = 8$. To isolate x on the left-hand side of the equation, we use the division property of equality to undo the multiplication by 2 by dividing both sides of the equation by 2.

$$2x = 8$$

$$\frac{2x}{2} = \frac{8}{2} \quad \text{To undo the multiplication by 2, divide both sides by 2.}$$

$$x = 4 \quad \text{On the left-hand side: When } x \text{ is multiplied by 2, and that product is then divided by 2, the result is } x. \text{ On the right-hand side: } 8 \div 2 = 4.$$

The solution is 4. Check it as follows:

$$2x = 8 \quad \text{The original equation.}$$

$$2 \cdot 4 \overset{?}{=} 8 \quad \text{Substitute 4 for } x.$$

$$8 = 8 \quad \text{Do the multiplication: } 2 \cdot 4 = 8.$$

Self Check

Solve the equation $16x = 176$ and check the result.

Answer: 11

The multiplication property of equality

To solve some equations we will use the following idea: *If equal quantities are multiplied by the same nonzero quantity, the results will be equal quantities.* In symbols, we have the following property.

Multiplication property of equality

> Let a, b, and c represent real numbers.
>
> If $a = b$, then $ca = cb$ $(c \neq 0)$

To illustrate the multiplication property of equality, we can think of the scale shown in Figure 2-4(a) as representing the equation $\frac{x}{3} = 25$. The weight on the left-hand side of the scale is $\frac{x}{3}$ grams, and the weight on the right-hand side is 25 grams. Because these weights are equal, the scale is in balance. To find x, we triple (or multiply by 3) the weight on each side. The scale will remain in balance. From the scale shown in Figure 2-4(b), we can see that x grams will be balanced by 75 grams. Thus, $x = 75$.

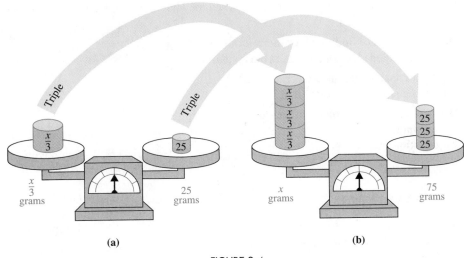

FIGURE 2-4

We now show how to solve a similar equation using an algebraic approach.

EXAMPLE 6   *Solving an equation.*   Solve the equation $\dfrac{s}{5} = 15$ and check the result.

Solution

To isolate s on the left-hand side, we use the multiplication property of equality. We can undo the division of the variable by 5 by multiplying both sides by 5.

$$\frac{s}{5} = 15$$

$$5 \cdot \frac{s}{5} = 5 \cdot 15 \quad \text{To undo the division by 5, multiply both sides by 5.}$$

$$s = 75 \quad \text{On the left-hand side: When } s \text{ is divided by 5 and that quotient is} $$
then multiplied by 5, the result is s. On the right-hand side: $5 \cdot 15 = 75$.

Check:

$$\frac{s}{5} = 15 \quad \text{The original equation.}$$

$$\frac{75}{5} \stackrel{?}{=} 15 \quad \text{Substitute 75 for } s.$$

$$15 = 15 \quad \text{Do the division: } \tfrac{75}{5} = 15.$$

Self Check

Solve the equation $\dfrac{t}{24} = 3$ and check the result.

Answer: 72

STUDY SET   Section 2.1   www

VOCABULARY   *Fill in the blanks.*

1. An ____equation____ is a statement indicating that two expressions are equal.

2. Any number that makes an equation true when substituted for its variable is said to ____satisfy____ the equation. Such numbers are called ____solutions____.

3. To ____check____ the solution of an equation, we substitute the value for the variable in the original equation and see whether the result is a true statement.

4. In $30 = t - 12$, the ____right-hand____ side of the equation is $t - 12$.

5. Two equations are ___equivalent___ when they have the same solutions.

6. The process of finding all of the solutions of an equation is called ___solving___ the equation.

7. To solve an equation, we ___isolate___ the variable on one side of the equals sign.

8. When solving an equation, the objective is to find all the values for the ___variable___ that will make the equation true.

CONCEPTS

9. For each equation, tell what operation is performed on the variable. Then tell how to undo that operation to isolate the variable.
   a. $x - 8 = 24$ subtraction of 8, addition of 8
   b. $x + 8 = 24$ addition of 8, subtraction of 8
   c. $\dfrac{x}{8} = 24$ division by 8, multiplication by 8
   d. $8x = 24$ multiplication by 8, division by 8

10.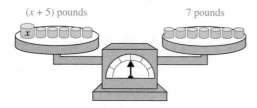

$(x + 5)$ pounds   7 pounds

ILLUSTRATION 1

   a. What equation is represented by the scale in Illustration 1? $x + 5 = 7$
   b. How will the scale react if 5 pounds is removed from the left side? It will be out of balance.
   c. How will the scale react if 5 pounds is then removed from the right side? It will be balanced.
   d. What algebraic property do the steps listed in parts b and c illustrate? subtraction property of equality
   e. After parts b and c, what equation will the scale represent, and what is its significance?
   $x = 2$; it is the solution of the original equation

11. Given $x + 6 = 12$,
   a. What forms the left-hand side of the equation?
   $x + 6$
   b. Is this equation true or false? neither
   c. Is $x = 5$ a solution? no
   d. Does $x = 6$ satisfy the equation? yes

12. Complete the following properties, and then give their names.
   a. If $x = y$ and c is any number, then $x + c = $ ___$y + c$___. addition property of equality
   b. If $x = y$ and c is any nonzero number, then $cx = $ ___cy___.
   multiplication property of equality

In Exercises 13–16, complete each flow chart.

13. Begin with the number 24.
↓
Add 6.
↓
Subtract 6.
↓
The result is 24 .

14. Begin with a number x.
↓
Multiply by 10.
↓
Divide by 10.
↓
The result is x .

15. Begin with a number n.
↓
Divide by 5.
↓
Multiply by 5.
↓
The result is n .

16. Begin with the number 45.
↓
Subtract 9.
↓
Add 9.
↓
The result is 45 .

17. To solve $2d = 14$, we divide both sides of the equation by 2. What is meant by the phrase *divide both sides*?
The left-hand side, $2d$, is divided by 2, and the right-hand side, 14, is divided by 2.

18. When solving $\dfrac{h}{10} = 20$, do we multiply both sides of the equation by 10 or 20? by 10

19. When solving $4k = 16$, do we subtract 4 from both sides of the equation or divide both sides by 4?
divide both sides by 4

20. After solving an equation, a student performed a check and obtained $15 = 16$. Assuming the student did not make a mistake in the checking process, what does that result indicate?
The student's "solution" is incorrect. A mistake was made while solving the equation.

21. In Illustration 2, the units are ounces. Find x. 2

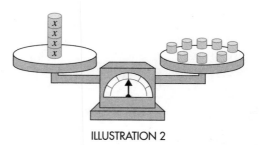

ILLUSTRATION 2

22. In Illustration 3, the units are ounces. Find x. 7

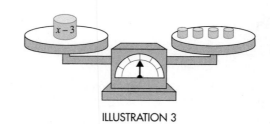

ILLUSTRATION 3

NOTATION *In Exercises 23–26, complete each solution.*

23. Solve: $x + 15 = 45$

$x + 15 - 15 = 45 - 15$

$x = 30$

Check: $x + 15 = 45$

$30 + 15 \overset{?}{=} 45$

$45 = 45$

30 is a solution.

24. Solve: $8x = 40$

$\dfrac{8x}{8} = \dfrac{40}{8}$

$x = 5$

Check: $8x = 40$

$8(5) \overset{?}{=} 40$

$40 = 40$

5 is a solution.

25. Solve: $\dfrac{c}{3} = 24$

$3 \cdot \dfrac{c}{3} = 3 \cdot 24$

$c = 72$

Check: $\dfrac{c}{3} = 24$

$\dfrac{72}{3} \overset{?}{=} 24$

$24 = 24$

72 is a solution.

26. Solve: $a - 6 = 200$

$a - 6 + 6 = 200 + 6$

$a = 206$

Check: $a - 6 = 200$

$206 - 6 \overset{?}{=} 200$

$200 = 200$

206 is a solution.

27. What does the symbol $\overset{?}{=}$ mean? is possibly equal to

28. Suppose you solve an equation and obtain $50 = x$. State the solution by writing the variable first. $x = 50$

PRACTICE *Tell whether the given number is a solution of the equation.*

29. $x + 12 = 18$; $x = 6$ yes

30. $x - 50 = 60$; $x = 110$ yes

31. $2b + 3 = 15$; $b = 5$ no

32. $5t - 4 = 16$; $t = 4$ yes

33. $0.5x = 2.9$; $x = 5$ no

34. $1.2 + x = 4.7$; $x = 3.5$ yes

35. $33 - \dfrac{x}{2} = 30$; $x = 6$ yes

36. $\dfrac{x}{4} + 98 = 100$; $x = 8$ yes

37. $|c - 8| = 10$; $c = 20$ no

38. $|30 - r| = 15$; $r = 20$ no

39. $3x - 2 = 4x - 5$; $x = 12$ no

40. $5y + 8 = 3y - 2$; $y = 5$ no

41. $x^2 - x - 6 = 0$; $x = 3$ yes

42. $y^2 + 5y - 3 = 0$; $y = 2$ no

43. $\dfrac{2}{a + 1} + 5 = \dfrac{12}{a + 1}$; $a = 1$ yes

44. $\dfrac{2t}{t - 2} - \dfrac{4}{t - 2} = 1$; $t = 4$ no

45. $\sqrt{x - 5} + 1 = 15$; $x = 201$ yes

46. $\sqrt{15 + y} - 3 = 20$; $y = 514$ yes

Use a property of equality to solve each equation. Check all solutions.

47. $x + 7 = 10$ 3

48. $15 + y = 24$ 9

49. $a - 5 = 66$ 71

50. $x - 34 = 19$ 53

51. $0 = n - 9$ 9

52. $3 = m - 20$ 23

53. $9 + p = 90$ 81

54. $16 + k = 71$ 55

55. $9 + p = 9$ 0

56. $88 + j = 88$ 0

57. $203 + f = 442$ 239

58. $y - 34 = 601$ 635

59. $4x = 16$ 4

60. $5y = 45$ 9

61. $369 = 9c$ 41

62. $840 = 105t$ 8

63. $4f = 0$ 0

64. $0 = 60k$ 0

65. $23b = 23$ 1

66. $16 = 16h$ 1

67. $\dfrac{x}{15} = 3$ 45

68. $\dfrac{y}{7} = 12$ 84

69. $\dfrac{l}{24} = 2$ 48

70. $\dfrac{k}{17} = 8$ 136

71. $35 = \dfrac{y}{4}$ 140

72. $550 = \dfrac{w}{3}$ 1,650

73. $0 = \dfrac{v}{11}$ 0

74. $\dfrac{d}{49} = 0$ 0

75. $a + 456{,}932 = 1{,}708{,}921$ 1,251,989

76. $229{,}989 = x - 84{,}863$ 314,852

77. $1{,}563x = 43{,}764$ 28

78. $999 = \dfrac{y}{5{,}565}$ 5,559,435

WRITING

79. What does it mean to solve an equation?

80. When solving an equation, we *isolate* the variable on one side of the equation. Write a sentence in which the word *isolate* is used in a different context.

81. Explain the error in the following work.

Solve x + 2 = 40.

$$x + 2 = 40$$
$$x + 2 - 2 = 40$$
$$x = 40$$

82. After solving an equation, how do we check the result?

REVIEW

83. What is the output of the expression $9 - 3x$ if 3 is the input?   0

84. Write a formula that would give the number of eggs in d dozen. $e = 12d$

85. Translate to symbols: the difference of 45 and *x*. $45 - x$

86. Evaluate $\dfrac{2^3 + 3(5 - 3)}{15 - 4 \cdot 2}$.   2

87. Approximate π to the nearest hundredth.   3.14

88. True or false? $-23 > -24$ true

2.2 *Problem Solving*

In this section, you will learn about

- Writing equations • A problem-solving strategy • Drawing diagrams
- Constructing tables • Solving percent problems
- Percent of increase or decrease

INTRODUCTION. One of the objectives of this course is for you to become a better problem solver. In this section, we introduce a five-step problem-solving strategy that we will use throughout the course. Quite often, the most challenging step of this strategy is the step in which we *form an equation*. This section offers some hints to improve your ability to form an equation by showing how we can translate key words to mathematical symbols, draw diagrams to visualize problems, and construct tables to organize facts.

Writing equations

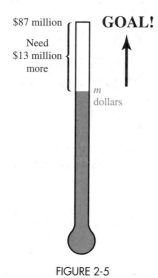

FIGURE 2-5

To solve a problem, it is often necessary to write an equation that describes the given situation. To write an equation, we must analyze the facts of the problem, looking for two different ways to describe the same quantity. As an introduction to this procedure, let's consider the following statement.

> If a charity fund-raising drive can raise $13 million more, the goal of $87 million will be reached.

Since we are not told the amount already raised, we will let the variable *m* represent this unknown amount. See Figure 2-5. The key word *more* tells us that if we add $13 million to the *m* dollars already raised, the goal will be reached. Therefore, the goal can be represented by the algebraic expression $m + 13$. We now have two ways to represent the fund-raising goal: $m + 13$ and 87. We can use an equation to state this.

$$m + 13 = 87$$

This describes the   This describes the
fund-raising goal   fund-raising goal
in one way.   in another way.

EXAMPLE 1   *Writing equations.*   Using the facts in the following statement, write an equation that describes the same quantity in two different ways.

If Nina had twice as much money in the bank as she has now, she would have enough to pay her tuition bill of $1,500.

Solution

Since we don't know how much money Nina has in the bank, we let $x =$ the amount currently in her account. The key word *twice* tells us to *multiply* the amount currently in her account by 2 to find an expression for the cost of tuition. Therefore, $2 \cdot x$, or $2x$, is the cost of tuition in dollars. We now have two ways to represent the tuition: $2x$ and 1,500. Thus,

$$2x = 1,500$$

Self Check

Using the facts in the following statement, write an equation that describes the same quantity in two different ways. "After having 5 feet trimmed off the top, the height of a pine tree is 46 feet." (*Hint:* Let $x =$ the original height of the tree.)

Answer: $x - 5 = 46$ ■

A problem-solving strategy

To become a good problem solver, you need a plan to follow, such as the following five-step problem-solving strategy.

Strategy for problem solving

1. **Analyze the problem** by reading it carefully to understand the given facts. What information is given? What are you asked to find? What vocabulary is given? Often, a diagram or table will help you visualize the facts of the problem.

2. **Form an equation** by picking a variable to represent the numerical value to be found. Then express all other unknown quantities as expressions involving that variable. Key words or phrases can be helpful. Finally, write an equation expressing a quantity in two different ways.

3. **Solve the equation.**

4. **State the conclusion.**

5. **Check the result** in the words of the problem.

EXAMPLE 2   *Systems analysis.*   A company's telephone use would have to increase by 350 calls per hour before the system would reach the maximum capacity of 1,500 calls per hour. Currently, how many calls are being made each hour on the system?

Analyze the problem   We are asked to find the number of calls currently being made each hour. We are given two facts:

- The maximum capacity of the system is 1,500 calls per hour.
- If the number of calls increases by 350, the system will reach capacity.

Form an equation   Let $n =$ the number of calls currently being made each hour. To form an equation involving n, we look for a key word or phrase in the problem.

Key phrase: *increase by 350*   **Translation:** addition

The key phrase tells us to add 350 to the current number of calls to obtain an expression for the maximum capacity of the system. Therefore, we can write the maximum capacity of the system in two ways.

The current number of calls per hour	increased by	350	equals	the maximum capacity of the system.
n	$+$	350	$=$	1,500

Solve the equation

$$n + 350 = 1,500$$

$$n + 350 - 350 = 1,500 - 350 \qquad \text{To undo the addition of 350, subtract 350 from both sides.}$$

$$n = 1,150 \qquad \text{Do the subtractions.}$$

State the conclusion   Currently, 1,150 calls per hour are being made.

> **Check the result**   If 1,150 calls are currently being made each hour and an increase of 350 calls per hour occurs, then $1,150 + 350 = 1,500$ calls will be made each hour. This is the capacity of the system. The answer (1,150) checks. ■

EXAMPLE 3   *Marine recruitment.*   The annual number of Marine recruits from a certain county tripled after an intense recruiting program was conducted at the area's high schools. If 384 students from the county decided to join the Marines, what was the previous year's county recruitment total?

Analyze the problem   We are asked to find the county recruitment total for last year. We are given two facts about the situation:

- 384 recruits were signed this year.
- The number of recruits this year is triple that of last year.

Form an equation   Let r = the number of recruits last year. To form an equation involving r, we look for a key word or phrase in the problem.

Key word: *tripled*   **Translation:** multiplication by 3

The key word tells us that we can multiply last year's number of recruits by 3 to obtain an expression for the number of recruits this year. Therefore, we can write this year's number of recruits in two ways.

3	times	the number of recruits last year	equals	384.
3	·	r	=	384

Solve the equation

$$3r = 384$$

$$\frac{3r}{3} = \frac{384}{3} \qquad \text{To undo the multiplication by 3, divide both sides by 3.}$$

$$r = 128 \qquad \text{Do the divisions.}$$

State the conclusion   The number of recruits last year was 128.

Check the result   If we multiply last year's number of recruits (128) by 3, we get $3 \cdot 128 = 384$. This is the number of recruits for this year. The answer checks. ■

Drawing diagrams

When solving problems, diagrams are often helpful; they allow us to visualize the facts of the problem.

EXAMPLE 4   *Airline travel.*   On a book tour that took her from New York City to Chicago to Los Angeles and back to New York City, an author flew a total of 4,910 miles. The flight from New York to Chicago was 714 miles, and the flight from Chicago to L.A. was 1,745 miles. How long was the direct flight back to New York City?

Analyze the problem We are asked to find the length of the flight from L.A. to New York City. We are given the following three facts.

- The total miles flown on the tour was 4,910.
- The flight from New York to Chicago was 714 miles.
- The flight from Chicago to L.A. was 1,745 miles.

In the diagram in Figure 2-6, we see that the three parts of the tour form a triangle. We know the lengths of two of the sides of the triangle (714 and 1,745) and the perimeter of the triangle (4,910).

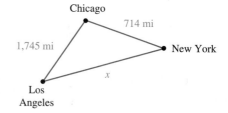

FIGURE 2-6

Form an equation We will let x = the length (in miles) of the flight from L.A. to New York and label the appropriate side of the triangle in Figure 2-6. There are two ways to describe the total number of miles traveled by the author on the book tour.

The miles from New York to Chicago	plus	the miles from Chicago to L.A.	plus	the miles from L.A. to New York	equals	4,910.
714	+	1,745	+	x	=	4,910

Solve the equation

$$714 + 1{,}745 + x = 4{,}910$$
$$2{,}459 + x = 4{,}910 \qquad \text{Simplify the left-hand side of the equation: } 714 + 1{,}745 = 2{,}459.$$
$$2{,}459 - \mathbf{2{,}459} + x = 4{,}910 - \mathbf{2{,}459} \qquad \text{Subtract 2,459 from both sides to isolate } x.$$
$$x = 2{,}451 \qquad \text{Do the subtractions: } 2{,}459 - 2{,}459 = 0 \text{ and } 4{,}910 - 2{,}459 = 2{,}451.$$

State the conclusion The flight from L.A. to New York was 2,451 miles.

Check the result If we add the three flight lengths, we get $714 + 1{,}745 + 2{,}451 = 4{,}910$. This was the total number of miles flown on the book tour. The answer (2,451) checks. ■

EXAMPLE 5 *Eye surgery.* A surgical technique called **radial keratotomy** is sometimes used to correct nearsightedness. This procedure involves equally spaced incisions in the cornea, as shown in Figure 2-7. Find the angle between each incision.

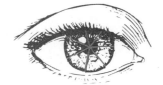

FIGURE 2-7

Solution

Analyze the problem From the diagram in Figure 2-8, we see that there are 7 angles of equal measure. We also know that 1 complete revolution is 360°.

Form an equation We will let x = the measure of one of the angles. We then have:

FIGURE 2-8

7	times	the measure of one of the angles	equals	360°.
7	·	x	=	360

Solve the equation	$7x = 360$
	$\dfrac{7x}{7} = \dfrac{360}{7}$ Divide both sides by 7.
	$x \approx 51.42857143$ Use a calculator to do the division.
	$x \approx 51.4°$ Round to the nearest tenth of a degree.

State the conclusion   The incisions are approximately 51.4° apart.

Check the result   If we multiply 51 by 7, we obtain 357. This is close to 360, so the result of 51.4° seems reasonable. ■

Constructing tables

Sometimes it is helpful to organize the given facts of the problem in a table.

EXAMPLE 6   *Labor statistics.*   The number of women (16 years and older) in the U.S. labor force has grown steadily over the past 100 years. From 1900 to 1940, the number grew by 8 million. By 1980, it had increased by an additional 32 million. By 1998, the number rose another 16 million; by the end of that year, 61 million women were in the labor force. How many women were in the labor force in 1900?

Analyze the problem   We are to find the number of women in the U.S. labor force in 1900. We know the following:

- The number grew by 8 million, increased by 32 million, and rose another 16 million.
- The number of women in the labor force in 1998 was 61 million.

Form an equation   We will let $x =$ the number of women (in millions) in the labor force in 1900. We can write algebraic expressions to represent the number of women in the work force in 1940, 1980, and 1998 by translating key words. See Table 2-1.

Year	Women in the labor force (millions)	
1900	x	
1940	$x + 8$	**Key word:** *grew* **Translation:** addition
1980	$x + 8 + 32$	**Key word:** *increased* **Translation:** addition
1998	$x + 8 + 32 + 16$	**Key word:** *rose* **Translation:** addition

TABLE 2-1

There are two ways to represent the number of women (in millions) in the 1998 labor force: $x + 8 + 32 + 16$ and 61. Therefore,

$$x + 8 + 32 + 16 = 61$$

Solve the equation	$x + 8 + 32 + 16 = 61$	
	$x + 56 = 61$	Simplify: $8 + 32 + 16 = 56$.
	$x + 56 - 56 = 61 - 56$	To undo the addition of 56, subtract 56 from both sides.
	$x = 5$	Do the subtractions.

State the conclusion   There were 5 million women in the U.S. labor force in 1900.

Check the result Adding the number of women (in millions) in the labor force in 1900 and the increases, we get $5 + 8 + 32 + 16 = 61$. In 1998, there were 61 million, so the answer (5) checks.

Solving percent problems

Percents are often used to present numeric information. Stores use them to advertise discounts; manufacturers use them to describe the contents of their products; and banks use them to list interest rates for loans and savings accounts.

Percent means parts per one hundred. For example, 93% means 93 out of 100 or $\frac{93}{100}$. There are three types of percent problems. Examples of these are shown below.

- What number is 8% of 215?
- 14 is what percent of 52?
- 80 is 20% of what number?

We can use the translating skills discussed in Chapter 1 and the equation-solving skills discussed in Section 2.1 to solve these problems.

EXAMPLE 7 *Solving percent problems.* What number is 8% of 215?

Solution

First, we translate the words into an equation. Here, the word *of* indicates multiplication, and the word *is* means equals.

What number	is	8%	of	215?	
↓	↓	↓	↓	↓	
x	$=$	8%	$\cdot$	215	Translate to mathematical symbols.

To do the multiplication on the right-hand side of the equation, we must change the percent to a decimal (or a fraction). To change 8% to a decimal, we proceed as follows.

$8\% = 8.0\%$ The number 8 has an understood decimal point to the right of the 8.

$\quad = .08.0$ Drop the % symbol and divide 8.0 by 100 by moving the decimal point 2 places to the left.

To complete the solution, we replace 8% with its decimal equivalent, 0.08, and do the multiplication.

$x = 8\% \cdot 215$ The original equation.

$x = 0.08 \cdot 215$ $8\% = 0.08$.

$x = 17.2$ Do the multiplication.

We have found that 17.2 is 8% of 215.

Self Check

What number is 5.6% of 40?

Answer: 2.24

In the statement "17.2 is 8% of 215," the number 17.2 is called the **amount,** 8% is called the **percent,** and 215 is called the **base.** The relationship among amount, percent, and base is given in the percent formula.

The percent formula	Amount = percent $\cdot$ base

EXAMPLE 8 *Best-selling song.* In 1993, Whitney Houston's "I Will Always Love You" was at the top of *Billboard*'s music charts for 14 weeks. What percent of the year did she have the #1 song? (Round to the nearest one percent.)

Solution

Analyze the problem
- For 14 out of 52 weeks in a year, she had the #1 song.
- We are asked to find what percent of the year she had the #1 song.

Form an equation   We let x = the unknown percent and translate the words of the problem into an equation.

14	equals	what percent	of	52?
14	=	x	$\cdot$	52

14 is the amount, x is the percent, and 52 is the base.

Solve the equation

$$14 = x \cdot 52$$

$$14 = 52x \qquad \text{Write } x \cdot 52 \text{ as } 52x.$$

$$\frac{14}{52} = \frac{52x}{52} \qquad \text{To isolate } x, \text{ undo the multiplication by 52 by dividing both sides by 52.}$$

(1) $0.2692307 \approx x \qquad$ Use a calculator to do the division.

We were asked to find what *percent* of the year she had the #1 song. To change the decimal 0.2692307 to a percent, we proceed as follows.

$0.2692307 = 0.26.92307\% \qquad$ Multiply 0.2692307 by 100 by moving the decimal point 2 places to the right, and then insert a % symbol.

$$= 26.92307\%$$

To complete the solution, we replace 0.2692307 with 26.92307% in Equation 1, and round to the nearest one percent.

$$0.2692307 \approx x$$

$26.92307\% \approx x \qquad$ $0.2692307 = 26.92307\%$.

$x \approx 27\% \qquad$ Round 26.92307% to the nearest one percent.

State the conclusion   To the nearest one percent, Whitney Houston had the #1 song for 27% of the year.

Check the result   We can check this result using estimation. Fourteen out of 52 weeks is approximately $\frac{14}{50}$ or $\frac{28}{100}$, which is 28%. The answer 27% seems reasonable.

EXAMPLE 9   *Aging population.*   By the year 2050, the U.S. Bureau of the Census estimates that about 20%, or 80 million, of the U.S. population will be more than 65 years of age. If this is true, what will the population of the country be at that time?

Solution

Analyze the problem
- 80 million people will be more than 65 years of age in the year 2050.
- 20% of the population will be more than 65 years of age in 2050.
- What will the population of the United States be in the year 2050?

Form an equation   We let x = the predicted population in the year 2050 and translate to form an equation.

80	is	20%	of	what number?
80	=	20%	$\cdot$	x

80 is the amount, 20 is the percent, and x is the base.

Solve the equation

$$80 = 20\% \cdot x$$

$80 = 0.20 \cdot x$ Change 20% to a decimal: 20% = 0.20.

$80 = 0.20x$ Write 0.20 · x as 0.20x.

$\dfrac{80}{0.20} = \dfrac{0.20x}{0.20}$ To undo the multiplication by 0.20, divide both sides by 0.20.

$400 = x$ Use a calculator to do the division.

State the conclusion   The census bureau is predicting a population of 400 million in the year 2050.

Check the result   80 million out of a population of 400 million is $\frac{80}{400} = \frac{40}{200} = \frac{20}{100}$, which is 20%. The answer checks.   ∎

Percent of increase or decrease

Percents are often used to describe how a quantity has changed. For example, a health care provider might increase the cost of medical insurance by 3%, or a police department might decrease the number of officers assigned to street patrols by 10%. To describe such changes, we use **percent of increase** or **percent of decrease.**

EXAMPLE 10   *Minimum wage.* In September of 2000, Congress considered a bill that would raise the federal hourly minimum wage to $6.15. See Table 2-2. Find the percent of increase in the minimum wage that this legislation would provide.

The federal hourly minimum wage	
Existing	**Proposed**
$5.15	$6.15

Source: U.S. Bureau of Labor Statistics

TABLE 2-2

Solution

Analyze the problem
- The minimum wage was to be increased. To find the *amount of increase,* we subtract the earlier minimum wage from the later minimum wage.

$$\$6.15 - \$5.15 = \$1.00$$ Subtract the existing minimum wage from the proposed minimum wage.

There was a $1.00 increase in the minimum wage.
- We are to find what percent of the original wage ($5.15) the $1.00 increase is.

Form an equation   We let x = the unknown percent and translate the words to an equation.

What percent	of	$5.15	is	$1.00?
↓	↓	↓	↓	↓
x	·	5.15	=	1.00

x is the percent, 5.15 is the base, and 1.00 is the amount.

$x \cdot 5.15 = 1.00$

$5.15x = 1.00$ Rewrite x · 5.15 as 5.15x.

$\dfrac{5.15x}{5.15} = \dfrac{1.00}{5.15}$ To undo the multiplication by 5.15, divide both sides by 5.15.

$x \approx 0.1941747573$ Use a calculator to do the division.

$x \approx 19.4\%$ To write the decimal as a percent, multiply by 100 by moving the decimal point two places to the right and insert a % symbol. Then round to the nearest tenth of a percent.

State the conclusion   The legislation provided a 19.4% increase of the federal hourly minimum wage.

Check the result   20% of the $5.15 minimum wage would be 20%($5.15)= 0.20($5.15) = $1.03. The actual increase was $1.00, so the answer of a 19.4% increase seems reasonable.   ■

COMMENT   When finding the percent of increase or decrease, we always find what percent the increase or decrease represents in relation to the *original* amount.

STUDY SET · Section 2.2

VOCABULARY   *Fill in the blanks.*

1. A letter that is used to represent a number is called a _____variable_____.

2. An _____equation_____ is a mathematical statement that two quantities are equal.

3. To _____solve_____ an equation means to find all the values of the variable that make the equation true.

4. _____Percent_____ means parts per one hundred.

5. In the statement "10 is 50% of 20," 10 is called the _____amount_____, 50% is the _____percent_____, and 20 is the _____base_____.

6. In mathematics, the word *of* often indicates _____multiplication_____, and _____is_____ means equals.

CONCEPTS

7. Fill in the blanks: When solving a real-world problem, we let a _____variable_____ represent the unknown quantity. Then we write an _____equation_____ that describes the same quantity in two different ways. Finally, we _____solve_____ the equation for the variable to find the unknown.

In Exercises 8–13, a diagram or a table gives various facts about a situation. Tell what the variable represents, and then write an equation that describes the same quantity in two ways.

8. A college choir's tour of three cities covers 1,240 miles.

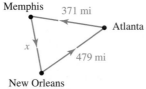

x = the distance from Memphis to New Orleans;
$x + 371 + 479 = 1,240$

9.

Triathlon–16 mi

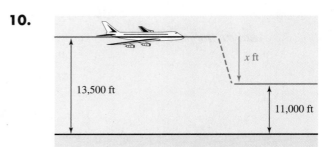

x = the length of the running portion of the triathlon;
$1 + 10 + x = 16$

10.

x = the number of feet the plane descended;
$x + 11,000 = 13,500$

11. The sections of a 430-page book are being assembled.

Section	Number of pages
Table of Contents	4
Preface	x
Text	400
Index	12

x = the number of pages in the preface;
$4 + x + 400 + 12 = 430$

12. A hamburger chain sold a total of 31 million hamburgers in its first 4 years of business.

Years in business	Running total of hamburgers sold (millions)
1	x
2	$x + 5$
3	$x + 5 + 8$
4	$x + 5 + 8 + 16$

x = millions of hamburgers sold the first year;
$x + 5 + 8 + 16 = 31$

13. A motorist traveled from Toledo to Columbus at 55 mph and from Columbus to Cincinnati at 50 mph. The entire trip covered 253 miles.

	Speed (mph)	Distance (mi)
Toledo to Columbus	55	145
Columbus to Cincinnati	50	x

x = the distance in miles from Columbus to Cincinnati;
$145 + x = 253$

14. What percent of the figure shown in Illustration 1 is shaded? 84%

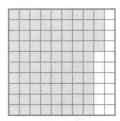

ILLUSTRATION 1

NOTATION In Exercises 15–16, translate each sentence into an equation.

15. 12 is 40% of what number? $12 = 0.40 \cdot x$

16. 99 is what percent of 200? $99 = x \cdot 200$

17. When computing with percents, the percent must be changed to a decimal or a fraction. Change each percent to a decimal.
  a. 35% 0.35　　**b.** 3.5% 0.035
  c. 350% 3.5　　**d.** $\frac{1}{2}$% 0.005

18. Change each decimal to a percent.
  a. 0.9 90%　　**b.** 0.09 9%
  c. 9 900%　　**d.** 0.999 99.9%

PRACTICE *An occupation is listed along with a statement that someone with that occupation might make. Identify the key word or phrase in the sentence and the operation it indicates.*

19. *Financial planner:* The profits from the sale were disbursed equally among the investors.
disbursed equally; division

20. *Auditor:* The cost of the project skyrocketed by a factor of 10. factor of 10; multiplication

21. *Park ranger:* Two feet of the snowpack had melted before February 1. melted; subtraction

22. *Ecologist:* After the flood, 6 acres of the marshy land were reclaimed. reclaimed; addition

23. *Race car driver:* The new tires helped shave off 2.5 seconds from each lap. shave off; subtraction

24. *Archaeologist:* The area to be excavated was sectioned off uniformly. sectioned off uniformly; division

25. *Producer:* Because of overflow crowds, the play's run was extended two weeks. extended; addition

26. *Optometrist:* The patient's pupils dilated to twice their size. twice their size; multiplication

Write an equation that describes the same quantity in two ways.

27. An existing 1,000-foot water line had to be extended to a length of 1,525 feet to reach a new restroom facility. Let x = the length of the extension. $1,000 + x = 1,525$

28. Because of overgrazing, state agriculture officials determined that the 4,500 head of cattle currently on the ranch had to be reduced to 2,750. Let x = the number of head of cattle to be removed. $4,500 - x = 2,750$

29. A length of gold chain, cut into 12-inch-long pieces, makes five bracelets. Let x = the length of the chain. $\frac{x}{12} = 5$

30. The 24 ounces of walnuts used to make a fruitcake were twice what was called for in the recipe. Let x = the number of ounces of walnuts called for in the recipe. $24 = 2x$

Translate each problem from words to an equation, and then solve the equation.

31. What number is 48% of 650? 312

32. What number is 60% of 200? 120

33. What percent of 300 is 78? 26%

34. What percent of 325 is 143? 44%

35. 75 is 25% of what number? 300

36. 78 is 6% of what number? 1,300

37. What number is 92.4% of 50? 46.2

38. What number is 2.8% of 220? 6.16

39. What percent of 16.8 is 0.42?   2.5%

40. What percent of 2,352 is 199.92?   8.5%

41. 128.1 is 8.75% of what number?   1,464

42. 1.12 is 140% of what number?   0.8

APPLICATIONS   *Complete each solution.*

43. MAJOR REQUIREMENTS   The business department of a college reduced by 6 the number of units of course work needed to obtain a degree. The department now requires the completion of 28 units. What was the old unit requirement?

Analyze the problem
- The unit requirement was reduced by 6 .
- The new unit requirement is 28 .
- We are asked to find the old unit requirement .

Form an equation   Let $x =$ the old unit requirement

   Key word: *reduced*   **Translation:** subtract

We can express the new requirement in two ways.

The old unit requirement	reduced by	6	is	the new unit requirement.
x	$-$	6	$=$	28

Solve the equation

$$x - 6 = 28$$
$$x + 6 - 6 = 28 + 6$$
$$x = 34$$

State the conclusion   The old unit requirement was 34 units.

Check the result   If we reduce the old unit requirement of 34 by 6, we have $34 - 6 = 28$. The answer checks.

44. BUSINESS LOSSES   After the membership fee to a health spa was raised, the number of new members joining each week was half of what it used to be. If, on average, 27 people per week are now joining, how many used to join each week?

Analyze the problem
- 27 people are now joining each week.
- The number of people now joining is half of what it used to be.
- We are asked to find how many used to join each week .

Form an equation
Let $x =$ the number that used to join each week

   Key phrase: *half of*   **Translation:** divide by 2

We can express the number now joining in two ways.

The number that used to join each week	divided by	2	is	the number that are now joining each week.
x	$\div$	2	$=$	27

Solve the equation

$$\frac{x}{2} = 27$$
$$2\left(\frac{x}{2}\right) = 2(27)$$
$$x = 54$$

State the conclusion   The number of people that used to join each week was 54 .

Check the result   If we divide the number of people that used to join each week by 2 , we have $\frac{54}{2} = 27$. The answer checks.

You can probably solve Exercises 45–50 without using algebra. Nevertheless, you should use the methods discussed in this section to solve the problems, so that you can gain experience in applying these concepts and procedures.

45. MONARCHY   George III reigned as king of Great Britain for 59 years. This is four years less than the longest-reigning British monarch, Queen Victoria. For how many years did Queen Victoria rule?   63

46. TENNIS   Billie Jean King won 40 Grand Slam tennis titles in her career. This is 14 less than the all-time leader, Martina Navratilova. How many Grand Slam titles did Navratilova win?   54

47. ATM RECEIPT   Use the information on the automatic-teller receipt in Illustration 2 to find the balance in the account before the withdrawal. $322.00

HOME SAVINGS OF AMERICA

Thank you for letting us
serve all your financial needs.

TRAN.	DATE	TIME	TERM
0286.	1/16/01	11:46 AM	HSOA822

CARD NO.	6125 8
WITHDRAWAL OF	$35.00
FROM CHECKING ACCT.	3325256-612
CHECKING BAL.	$287.00

ILLUSTRATION 2

48. ENTERTAINMENT   According to *Forbes* magazine, Oprah Winfrey made an estimated $125 million in 1999. This was $67 million more than Harrison Ford's estimated earnings for that year. How much did Harrison Ford make in 1999? $58 million

49. TV NEWS   An interview with a world leader was edited into equally long segments and broadcast in parts over a three-day period on a TV news program. If each daily segment of the interview lasted 9 minutes, how long was the original interview?   27 min

50. FLOODING   Torrential rains caused the width of a river to swell to 84 feet. If this was twice its normal size, how wide was the river before the flooding?   42 ft

In Exercises 51–56, use a table to help organize the facts of the problem; then find the solution.

51. STATEHOOD   From 1800 to 1850, 15 states joined the Union. From 1851 to 1900, an additional 14 states entered. Three states joined from 1901 to 1950. Since then, Alaska and Hawaii are the only others to enter the Union. How many states were part of the Union prior to 1800?   16

52. STUDIO TOUR   Over a four-year span, improvements in a Hollywood movie studio tour caused it to take longer. The first year, 10 minutes were added to the tour length. In the second, third, and fourth years, 5 minutes were added each year. If the tour now lasts 135 minutes, how long was it originally?   110 min

53. THEATER   The play *Romeo and Juliet,* by William Shakespeare, has 5 acts and a total of 24 scenes. The second act has the most scenes, 6. The third and fourth acts both have 5 scenes. The last act has the least number of scenes, 3. How many scenes are in the first act?   5

54. U.S. PRESIDENTS   As of December 31, 1999, there had been 42 presidents of the United States. George Washington and John Adams were the only presidents in the 18th century (1700–1799). During the 19th century (1800–1899), there were 23 presidents. How many presidents were there during the 20th century (1900–1999)?   17

55. ORCHESTRA   A 98-member orchestra is made up of a woodwind section with 19 musicians, a brass section with 23 players, a two-person percussion section, and a large string section. How many musicians make up the string section of the orchestra?   54

56. ANATOMY   A premed student has to know the names of all 206 bones that make up the human skeleton. So far, she has memorized the names of the 60 bones in the feet and legs, the 31 bones in the torso, and the 55 bones in the neck and head. How many more names does she have to memorize?   60

In Exercises 57–62, draw a diagram to help organize the facts of the problem, and then find the solution.

57. BERMUDA TRIANGLE   The Bermuda Triangle is a triangular region in the Atlantic Ocean where many ships and airplanes have disappeared. The perimeter of the triangle is about 3,075 miles. It is formed by three imaginary lines. The first, 1,100 miles long, is from Melbourne, Florida, to Puerto Rico. The second, 1,000 miles long, stretches from Puerto Rico to Bermuda. The third extends from Bermuda back to Florida. Find its length.   975 mi

58. FENCING   To cut down on vandalism, a lot on which a house was to be constructed was completely fenced. The north side of the lot was 205 feet in length. The west and east sides were 275 and 210 feet long, respectively. If 945 feet of fencing was used, how long is the south side of the lot?   255 ft

59. SPACE TRAVEL   The 364-foot-tall *Saturn V* rocket carried the first astronauts to the moon. Its first, second, and third stages were 138, 98, and 46 feet tall, respectively. Atop the third stage was the lunar module, and from it extended a 28-foot escape tower. How tall was the lunar module?   54 ft

60. PLANETS   Mercury, Venus, and Earth have approximately circular orbits around the sun. Earth is the farthest from the sun, at 93 million miles, and Mercury is the closest, at 36 million miles. The orbit of Venus is about 31 million miles from that of Mercury. How far is Earth's orbit from that of Venus?   26 million mi.

61. STOP SIGN   Find the measure of one angle of the octagonal stop sign shown in Illustration 3. (*Hint:* The sum of the measures of the angles of an octagon is 1,080°.)   135°

ILLUSTRATION 3

62. FERRIS WHEEL   What is the measure of the angle between each of the "spokes" of the Ferris wheel shown in Illustration 4?   30°

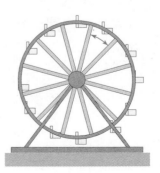

ILLUSTRATION 4

PERCENT PROBLEMS

63. CUSTOMER GUARANTEE   To assure its customers of low prices, the Home Club offers a "10% Plus" guarantee. If the customer finds the same item selling for less somewhere else, he or she receives the difference in price plus 10% of the difference. A woman bought miniblinds at the Home Club for $120 but later saw the same blinds on sale for $98 at another store. How much can she expect to be reimbursed? $24.20

64. TIPPING   When paying with a Visa card, the user must fill in the amount of the gratuity (tip) and then compute the total. Complete the sales draft in Illustration 5 if a 15% tip, rounded up to the nearest dollar, is to be left for the waiter.

STEAK STAMPEDE
Bloomington, MN
Server #12\ AT

VISA	67463777288
NAME	DALTON/ LIZ
AMOUNT	$75.18
GRATUITY $	12.00
TOTAL $	87.18

ILLUSTRATION 5

65. FEDERAL OUTLAYS   Illustration 6 shows the breakdown of the U.S. federal budget for fiscal year 1998. If total spending was approximately $1,653 billion, how much was paid for Social Security, Medicare, and other retirement (to the nearest billion dollars)? $612 billion

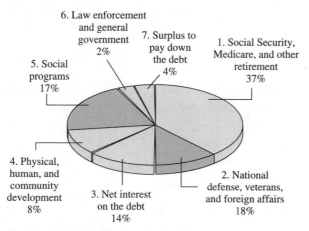

6. Law enforcement and general government 2%
7. Surplus to pay down the debt 4%
1. Social Security, Medicare, and other retirement 37%
5. Social programs 17%
4. Physical, human, and community development 8%
3. Net interest on the debt 14%
2. National defense, veterans, and foreign affairs 18%

Based on 1999 Federal Income Tax Form 1040

ILLUSTRATION 6

66. INCOME TAX   Use the Tax Table shown in Illustration 7 to compute the amount of federal income tax if the amount of taxable income entered on Form 1040, line 39, is $39,909. $8,301.52

Single Individual			
If the amount on Form 1040, line 39, is *Over—*	*But not over—*	Enter on Form 1040, line 40	*of the amount over—*
$0	$22,100	. . . . . . 15%	$0
22,100	53,500	$3,315 + 28%	22,100
53,500	115,000	12,107 + 31%	53,500
115,000	250,000	31,172 + 36%	115,000
250,000	. . . .	79,772 + 39.6%	250,000

ILLUSTRATION 7

67. COLLEGE ENTRANCE EXAMS   On the Scholastic Aptitude Test, or SAT, a high school senior scored 550 on the mathematics portion and 700 on the verbal portion. What percent of the maximum 1,600 points did this student receive?   78.125%

68. GENEALOGY   Through an extensive computer search, a genealogist determined that worldwide, 180 out of every 10 million people had his last name. What percent is this?   0.0018%

69. DENTAL RECORDS   The dental chart for an adult patient is shown in Illustration 8. The dentist marks each tooth that has had a filling. To the nearest percent, what percent of this patient's teeth have fillings?   19%

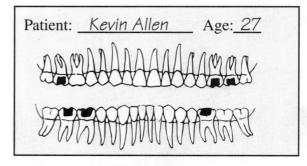

Patient: *Kevin Allen*   Age: *27*

ILLUSTRATION 8

70. AREA   The total area of the 50 states and the District of Columbia is 3,618,770 square miles. If Alaska covers 591,004 square miles, what percent is this of the U.S. total (to the nearest percent)?   16%

71. CHILD CARE   After the first day of registration, 84 children had been enrolled in a new day care center. That represented 70% of the available slots. What was the maximum number of children the center could enroll?   120

72. RACING PROGRAM   One month before a stock car race, the sale of ads for the official race program was slow. Only 12 pages, or just 60% of the available pages, had been sold. What was the total number of pages devoted to advertising in the program?   20

73. NUTRITION   The Nutrition Facts label from a can of New England clam chowder is shown in Illustration 9.
   a. Use the information on the label to determine the number of grams of fat and the number of grams of saturated fat that should be consumed daily. Round to the nearest gram.   fat: 65 g; saturated fat: 20 g
   b. To the nearest percent, what percent of the calories in a serving of clam chowder come from fat?   58%

Nutrition Facts

Serving Size 1 cup (240mL)
Servings Per Container about 2

Amount per serving	
Calories 240 Calories from Fat 140	
	% Daily Value*
Total Fat 15 g	**23%**
Saturated Fat 5 g	**25%**
Cholesterol 10 mg	**3%**
Sodium 980 mg	**41%**
Total Carbohydrate 21 g	**7%**
Dietary Fiber 2 g	**8%**
Sugars 1 g	
Protein 7 g	

ILLUSTRATION 9

74. CHARITABLE GIVING   Nonprofit organizations receive contributions from individuals, corporations, foundations, and bequests. In 1999, individuals contributed $144 billion to nonprofit organizations. If this was 76% of all charitable giving for that year, what was the total amount given to nonprofit organizations in 1999 (to the nearest billion dollars)? $190 billion

75. EXPORTS   The bar graph in Illustration 10 shows United States exports to Mexico for the years 1992 through 1999.
   a. Between what two years was there a decline in U.S. exports? Find the percent decrease, to the nearest percent.   1994–1995; 10%
   b. Between what two years was there the most dramatic increase in exports? Find the percent increase, to the nearest percent.   1996–1997; 25%

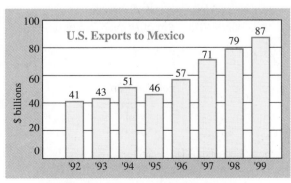

Based on data from www.census.gov/foreign-trade

ILLUSTRATION 10

76. AUCTION   A pearl necklace of former First Lady Jacqueline Kennedy Onassis, originally valued at $700, was sold at auction in 1996 for $211,500. What was the percent of increase in the value of the necklace? (Round to the nearest percent.)   30,114%

77. INSURANCE COST   A college student's good grades earned her a student discount on her car insurance premium. What was the percent of decrease, to the nearest percent, if her annual premium was lowered from $1,050 to $925?   12%

78. LIFE EXPECTANCY   Use the following life expectancy data for 1900 and 1998 to determine the percent of increase for males and for females. Round to the nearest percent.   males: 60%; females; 64%

Years of life expected at birth		
	Male	**Female**
1900	46.3 yr	48.3 yr
1998	73.9 yr	79.4 yr

WRITING

79. Explain the relationship in a percent problem between the amount, the percent, and the base.

80. Write a real-life situation that could be described by "9 is what percent of 20?"

81. Explain why 150% of a number is more than the number.

82. Explain why "Find 9% of 100" is an easy problem to solve.

REVIEW

83. Multiply: $9\frac{3}{5} \cdot 3\frac{3}{4}$.   36

84. What two numbers are a distance of 8 away from 4 on the number line?   12 and −4

85. Is $x = 34$ a solution of $x − 12 = 20$?   no

86. Evaluate $2 + 3[24 − 2(2 − 5)]$.   92

2.3 *Simplifying Algebraic Expressions*

In this section, you will learn about

- Simplifying algebraic expressions involving multiplication
- The distributive property • The vocabulary of algebraic expressions
- Like terms • Combining like terms

INTRODUCTION. In arithmetic, we often replace one numerical expression with another expression that is equivalent and simpler in form. For example, when we express $\frac{40}{80}$ as $\frac{1}{2}$, we say we have *simplified* $\frac{40}{80}$. In algebra, we must often simplify algebraic expressions. To **simplify an algebraic expression,** we use one or more properties of algebra to write the expression in an equivalent, less-complicated form.

Simplifying algebraic expressions involving multiplication

Two properties that are often used to simplify algebraic expressions are the associative and commutative properties of multiplication. Recall that the associative property of multiplication enables us to change the grouping of factors involved in a multiplication. The commutative property of multiplication enables us to change the order of the factors.

As an example, let's consider the expression $8(4x)$ and simplify it as follows:

$$8(4x) = 8 \cdot (4 \cdot x) \quad 4x = 4 \cdot x.$$

$$= (8 \cdot 4) \cdot x \quad \text{Apply the associative property of multiplication to group 4 with 8 instead of with } x.$$

$$= 32x \quad \text{Do the multiplication within the parentheses: } 8 \cdot 4 = 32.$$

Since $8(4x) = 32x$, we say that $8(4x)$ simplifies to $32x$. To verify that $8(4x)$ and $32x$ are **equivalent expressions** (represent the same number), we can evaluate each expression for several choices of x. For each value of x, the results should be the same.

If $x = 10$

$$8(4x) = 8[4(10)] \qquad 32x = 32(10)$$
$$= 8(40) \qquad\qquad = 320$$
$$= 320$$

If $x = -3$

$$8(4x) = 8[4(-3)] \qquad 32x = 32(-3)$$
$$= 8(-12) \qquad\qquad = -96$$
$$= -96$$

EXAMPLE 1 *Simplifying algebraic expressions involving multiplication.* Simplify each expression: **a.** $15a(-7)$, **b.** $5\left(\frac{4}{5}x\right)$, **c.** $-5r(-6s)$, and **d.** $3(7p)(-5p)$.

Solution

a. $15a(-7) = 15(-7)a$ Use the commutative property of multiplication to change the order of the factors.

$$= -105a \quad \text{Working left to right, do the multiplications.}$$

b. $5\left(\dfrac{4}{5}x\right) = \left(5 \cdot \dfrac{4}{5}\right)x$ Use the associative property of multiplication to group the numbers.

$$= 4x \quad \text{Multiply: } 5 \cdot \frac{4}{5} = \frac{5}{1} \cdot \frac{4}{5} = \frac{\overset{1}{\cancel{5}} \cdot 4}{1 \cdot \cancel{5}} = 4.$$

Self Check

Simplify each expression:

a. $9 \cdot 6s$
b. $8\left(\frac{7}{8}h\right)$
c. $21p(-3q)$
d. $-4(6m)(-2m)$

c. We note that the expression contains two variables.

$$-5r(-6s) = [-5(-6)][r \cdot s]$$ Use the commutative and associative properties of multiplication to group the numbers and group the variables.

$$= 30rs$$ Do the multiplications within the brackets: $-5(-6) = 30$ and $r \cdot s = rs$.

d. $3(7p)(-5p) = [3(7)(-5)](p \cdot p)$ Use the commutative and associative properties of multiplication to change the order and to regroup the factors.

$$= -105p^2$$ Do the multiplication within the grouping symbols: $3(7)(-5) = -105$ and $p \cdot p = p^2$.

Answers: **a.** $54s$,   **b.** $7h$,   **c.** $-63pq$,   **d.** $48m^2$ ■

The distributive property

To introduce the **distributive property,** we will examine the expression $4(5 + 3)$, which can be evaluated in two ways.

Method 1. Rules for the order of operations: In this method, we compute the sum within the parentheses first.

$$4(\mathbf{5 + 3}) = 4(\mathbf{8})$$ Do the addition within the parentheses first.

$$= 32$$ Do the multiplication.

Method 2. The distributive property: In this method, we multiply both 5 and 3 by 4, and then we add the results.

$$4(\mathbf{5 + 3}) = \mathbf{4}(5) + \mathbf{4}(3)$$ Distribute the multiplication by 4.

$$= 20 + 12$$ Do the multiplications.

$$= 32$$ Do the addition.

Notice that each method gives a result of 32.

We can interpret the distributive property geometrically. Figure 2-9 shows three rectangles that are divided into squares. Since the area of the rectangle on the left-hand side of the equals sign can be found by multiplying its width by its length, its area is $4(5 + 3)$ square units. We can evaluate this expression, or we can count squares; either way, we see that the area is 32 square units.

The area shown on the right-hand side is the sum of the areas of two rectangles: $4(5) + 4(3)$. Either by evaluating this expression or by counting squares, we see that this area is also 32 square units. Therefore,

$$4(5 + 3) = 4(5) + 4(3)$$

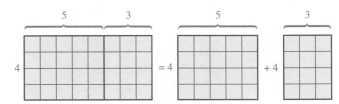

FIGURE 2-9

Figure 2-10 shows the general case where the width is a and the length is $b + c$.

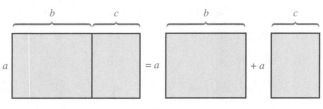

FIGURE 2-10

Using Figure 2-10 as a basis, we can now state the distributive property in symbols.

The distributive property   If a, b, and c represent real numbers, then
$$a(b + c) = ab + ac$$

Since subtraction is the same as adding the opposite, the distributive property also holds for subtraction.

The distributive property   If a, b, and c represent real numbers, then
$$a(b - c) = ab - ac$$

We can use the distributive property to remove the parentheses when an expression is multiplied by a quantity. For example, to remove the parentheses in the expression $5(x + 2)$, we distribute the factor of 5 that is outside the parentheses over x and 2, and add the products.

$5(x + 2) = 5(x) + 5(2)$ Distribute the multiplication by 5.

$\qquad\quad = 5x + 10$ Do the multiplications.

 COMMENT   Since the expression $5(x + 2)$ contains parentheses, some students are tempted to do the addition within the parentheses first. However, we cannot add x and 2, because we do not know the value of x. Instead, we should focus on the multiplication of $x + 2$ by 5, which requires the use of the distributive property.

EXAMPLE 2   *Applying the distributive property.*   Use the distributive property to remove parentheses:

a. $3(x - 8)$,   **b.** $-12(a + 1)$,   **c.** $-6(-3y - 8)$,   and   **d.** $x(x + 2)$.

Solution

a. $3(x - 8) = 3(x) - 3(8)$ Distribute the multiplication by 3.

$\qquad\qquad = 3x - 24$ Do the multiplications.

b. $-12(a + 1) = -12(a) + (-12)(1)$ Distribute the multiplication by -12.

$\qquad\qquad\quad = -12a + (-12)$ Do the multiplications.

$\qquad\qquad\quad = -12a - 12$ Write the addition of -12 as subtraction of 12.

c. $-6(-3y - 8) = -6(-3y) - (-6)(8)$ Distribute the multiplication by -6.

$\qquad\qquad\quad = 18y - (-48)$ Do the multiplications.

$\qquad\qquad\quad = 18y + 48$ Add the opposite of -48, which is 48.

d. $x(x + 2) = x(x) + x(2)$ Distribute the multiplication by x.

$\qquad\qquad = x^2 + 2x$ Do the multiplications: $x(x) = x^2$ and $x(2) = 2x$.

Self Check

Use the distributive property to remove parentheses:

a. $5(p + 2)$

b. $4(t - 1)$

c. $-8(2x - 4)$

d. $p(p - 5)$

Answers: **a.** $5p + 10$,
b. $4t - 4$ **c.** $-16x + 32$,
d. $p^2 - 5p$

COMMENT The fact that an expression contains parentheses does not necessarily mean that the distributive property can be applied. For example, the distributive property does not apply to the expressions

$$6(5x) \quad \text{or} \quad 6(-7 \cdot y)$$ Here a product is multiplied by 6. Simplifying, we have $6(5x) = 30x$ and $6(-7 \cdot y) = -42y$.

However, the distributive property does apply to the expressions

$$6(5 + x) \quad \text{or} \quad 6(-7 - y)$$ Here a sum or difference is multiplied by 6. Distributing the 6, we have $6(5 + x) = 30 + 6x$ and $6(-7 - y) = -42 - 6y$.

To use the distributive property to simplify $-(x + 10)$, we note that the negative sign in front of the parentheses represents -1.

The $-$ sign represents -1.

$$-(x + 10) = -1(x + 10)$$
$$= -1(x) + (-1)(10) \quad \text{Distribute the multiplication by } -1.$$
$$= -x + (-10) \quad \text{Multiply: } -1(x) = -x \text{ and } (-1)(10) = -10.$$
$$= -x - 10 \quad \text{Write the addition of } -10 \text{ as a subtraction.}$$

EXAMPLE 3 *Distributing a factor of -1.* Simplify $-(-12 - 3p)$.

Solution

$$-(-12 - 3p)$$
$$= -1(-12 - 3p) \quad \text{Change the } - \text{ sign in front of the parentheses to } -1.$$
$$= -1(-12) - (-1)(3p) \quad \text{Distribute the multiplication by } -1.$$
$$= 12 - (-3p) \quad \text{Multiply: } -1(-12) = 12 \text{ and } (-1)(3p) = -3p.$$
$$= 12 + 3p \quad \text{To subtract } -3p, \text{ add the opposite of } -3p, \text{ which is } 3p.$$

Self Check
Simplify $-(-5x + 18)$.

Answer: $5x - 18$ ■

Since multiplication is commutative, we can write the distributive property in the following forms.

$$(b + c)a = ba + ca \qquad (b - c)a = ba - ca$$

EXAMPLE 4 *Using the distributive property.* Multiply: $(6x + 4y)\dfrac{1}{2}$.

Solution

$$(6x + 4y)\frac{1}{2} = (6x)\frac{1}{2} + (4y)\frac{1}{2} \quad \text{Distribute the multiplication by } \tfrac{1}{2}.$$
$$= 3x + 2y \quad \text{Do the multiplications: } (6x)\tfrac{1}{2} = \left(6 \cdot \tfrac{1}{2}\right)x = 3x \text{ and } (4y)\tfrac{1}{2} = \left(4 \cdot \tfrac{1}{2}\right)y = 2y.$$

Self Check
Multiply:

$$(-6x - 24y)\frac{1}{3}$$

Answer: $-2x - 8y$ ■

The distributive property can be extended to situations in which there are more than two terms within parentheses.

The extended distributive property

If a, b, c, and d represent real numbers, then
$$a(b + c + d) = ab + ac + ad \quad \text{and} \quad a(b - c - d) = ab - ac - ad$$

EXAMPLE 5   *Applying the extended distributive property.*   Use the distributive property to remove parentheses: $-0.3(3a - 4b + 7)$.

Solution

$$-0.3(3a - 4b + 7)$$

$= -0.3(3a) - (-0.3)(4b) + (-0.3)(7)$	Distribute the multiplication by -0.3.
$= -0.9a - (-1.2b) + (-2.1)$	Do the three multiplications.
$= -0.9a + 1.2b + (-2.1)$	To subtract $-1.2b$, add its opposite, which is $1.2b$.
$= -0.9a + 1.2b - 2.1$	Write the addition of -2.1 as a subtraction.

Self Check

Use the distributive property to remove parentheses:
$-0.7(2r + 5s - 8)$

Answer: $-1.4r - 3.5s + 5.6$

The vocabulary of algebraic expressions

Addition signs separate algebraic expressions into parts called **terms.** The expression $5x + 8$ contains two terms, $5x$ and 8.

The $+$ sign separates the expression into two terms.

$$5x \quad + \quad 8$$

First term   Second term

A term may be

- a number. Examples are 8, 98.6, and -45.
- a variable, or a product of variables (which may be raised to powers). Examples are x, s^3, rt, and a^2bc^4.
- a product of a number and one or more variables (which may be raised to powers). Examples are $-35x$, $\frac{1}{2}bh$, and $\pi r^2 h$.

Since subtraction can be expressed as addition of the opposite, the expression $6x - 5$ can be written in the equivalent form $6x + (-5)$. We can then see that $6x - 5$ contains two terms, $6x$ and -5.

EXAMPLE 6   *Identifying terms.*   List the terms in each expression:
a. $-4p + 7 + 5p$,   **b.** $-12r^2st$,   and   **c.** $y^3 + 8y^2 - 3y - 24$.

Solution

a. $-4p + 7 + 5p$ has three terms: $-4p$, 7, and $5p$.

b. The expression $-12r^2st$ has one term: $-12r^2st$.

c. $y^3 + 8y^2 - 3y - 24$ can be written as $y^3 + 8y^2 + (-3y) + (-24)$. It contains four terms: y^3, $8y^2$, $-3y$, and -24.

Self Check

List the terms in each expression:

a. $\frac{1}{3}Bh$,   **b.** $3q + 5q - 1.2$,   and
c. $b^2 - 4ac$

Answers:
a. $\frac{1}{3}Bh$,   **b.** $3q, 5q, -1.2$,
c. $b^2, -4ac$

In a term that is the product of a number and one or more variables, the number factor is called the **numerical coefficient,** or simply the **coefficient.** In the expression $5x$, the coefficient is 5, and x is the variable part. Other examples are shown in Table 2-3.

Notice that when there is no number in front of a variable, the coefficient is 1. We say that such a term has an *implied coefficient* of 1. Similarly, when there is only a negative sign in front of the variable, the coefficient is an implied -1. For example, $-t = -1t$.

Term	Coefficient	Variable part
$8y^2$	8	y^2
$-0.9pq$	-0.9	pq
$\frac{3}{4}b$	$\frac{3}{4}$	b
$-\frac{x}{6}$	$-\frac{1}{6}$	x
x	1	x
$-t$	-1	t
15	15	none

TABLE 2-3

EXAMPLE 7 *Identifying coefficients of terms.* Identify the coefficient and the variable part of each term in the expression $-7x^2 + 3x - 6$.

Solution

Term	Coefficient	Variable part
$-7x^2$	-7	x^2
$3x$	3	x
-6	-6	none

Self Check

Identify the coefficient of each term in the expression $p^3 - 12p^2 + 3p - 4$.

Answers: $1, -12, 3, -4$ ■

 COMMENT It is important to be able to distinguish between a *term* of an expression and a *factor* of a term. Terms are separated by a + sign. Factors are numbers and/or variables that are multiplied together. For example, x is a term of the expression $18 + x$, because x and 18 are separated by a + sign. In the expression $18x + 9$, x is a factor of the term $18x$, because x and 18 are multiplied together.

Like terms

The expression $5p + 7q - 3p + 12$, which can be written $5p + 7q + (-3p) + 12$, contains four terms, $5p$, $7q$, $-3p$, and 12. Since the variable of $5p$ and $-3p$ are the same, we say that these terms are **like** or **similar terms.**

Like terms (similar terms)

> **Like terms** (or **similar terms**) are terms with exactly the same variables raised to exactly the same powers. Any numbers (called **constants**) in an expression are considered to be like terms.

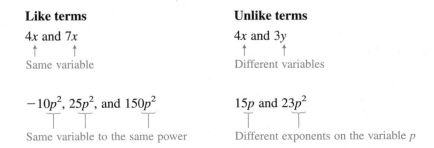

COMMENT   When looking for like terms, don't look at the coefficients of the terms. Consider only their variable parts.

EXAMPLE 8   *Identifying like terms.*   List like terms: **a.** $7r + 5 + 3r$, **b.** $x^4 - 6x^2 - 5$, and   **c.** $-7m + 7 - 2 + m$.

Solution

a. $7r + 5 + 3r$ contains the like terms $7r$ and $3r$.

b. $x^4 - 6x^2 - 5$ contains no like terms.

c. $-7m + 7 - 2 + m$ contains two pairs of like terms: $-7m$ and m are like terms, and the constants, 7 and -2, are like terms.

Self Check

List like terms:

a. $5x - 2y + 7y$

b. $-5pq + 17p - 12q - 2pq$

Answers: **a.** $-2y$ and $7y$,
b. $-5pq$ and $-2pq$ ■

Combining like terms

If we are to add (or subtract) objects, they must have the same units. For example, we can add dollars to dollars and inches to inches, but we cannot add dollars to inches. The same is true when we work with terms of an algebraic expression. They can be added or subtracted only when they are like terms.

This expression can be simplified, because it contains like terms.

$$3x + 4x$$

↑   ↑
Like terms
The variable parts are identical.

This expression cannot be simplified, because its terms are not like terms.

$$3x + 4y$$

↑   ↑
Unlike terms
The variable parts are not identical.

To simplify an expression containing like terms, we use the distributive property. For example, we can simplify $3x + 4x$ as follows:

$$3x + 4x = (3 + 4)x \quad \text{Apply the distributive property.}$$
$$= 7x \qquad \text{Do the addition within the parentheses: } 3 + 4 = 7.$$

We have simplified the expression $3x + 4x$ by **combining like terms.** The result is the equivalent expression $7x$. This example suggests the following general rule.

Combining like terms

To add or subtract like terms, combine their coefficients and keep the same variables with the same exponents.

EXAMPLE 9   *Simplifying algebraic expressions.*   Simplify by combining like terms: **a.** $-8p + (-12p)$ and   **b.** $0.5s^2 - 0.3s^2$.

Solution

a. $-8p + (-12p) = -20p$ Add the coefficients of the like terms: $-8 + (-12) = -20$. Keep the variable p.

b. $0.5s^2 - 0.3s^2 = 0.2s^2$ Subtract: $0.5 - 0.3 = 0.2$. Keep the variable part s^2.

Self Check

Simplify by combining like terms:

a. $5n + (-8n)$

b. $-1.2a^3 + (1.4a^3)$

Answers: **a.** $-3n$,   **b.** $0.2a^3$ ■

EXAMPLE 10   *Combining like terms.*   Simplify $7P - 8p - 12P + 25p$.

Solution

The uppercase P and the lowercase p are different variables. We can use the commutative property of addition to write like terms next to each other.

$$7P - 8p - 12P + 25p$$
$$= 7P + (-8p) + (-12P) + 25p \quad \text{Rewrite each subtraction as the addition of the opposite.}$$

Self Check

Simplify $8R + 7r - 14R - 21r$.

$$= 7P + (-12P) + (-8p) + 25p$$ Use the commutative property of addition to write the like terms together.

$$= -5P + 17p$$ Combine like terms: $7P + (-12P) = -5P$ and $-8p + 25p = 17p$.   **Answer:** $-6R - 14r$ ■

The expression in Example 10 contained two sets of like terms, and we rearranged the terms so that like terms were next to each other. With practice, you will be able to combine like terms without having to write them next to each other and without having to write each subtraction as addition of the opposite.

EXAMPLE 11   *Combining like terms without rearranging terms.*
Simplify $4(x + 5) - 3(2x - 4)$.

Solution
$$4(x + 5) - 3(2x - 4)$$
$$= 4x + 20 - 6x + 12$$ Use the distributive property twice.
$$= -2x + 32$$ Combine like terms: $4x - 6x = -2x$ and $20 + 12 = 32$.

Self Check
Simplify $-5(y - 4) + 2(4y + 6)$.

Answer: $3y + 32$ ■

STUDY SET Section 2.3

VOCABULARY *Fill in the blanks.*

1. To _____simplify_____ an algebraic expression, we use properties of algebra to write the expression in a less complicated form.

2. A _____term_____ is a number or a product of a number and one or more variables.

3. In the term $3x^2$, the number factor 3 is called the _____coefficient_____ and x^2 is called the _____variable_____ part.

4. Two terms with exactly the same variables and exponents are called _____like_____ terms.

5. We can use the distributive property to _____remove_____ the parentheses when an expression is multiplied by a quantity.

6. The _____commutative_____ property of multiplication enables us to change the order of the factors involved in a multiplication.

CONCEPTS

7. What property does the statement $a(b + c) = ab + ac$ illustrate?   the distributive property

8. Complete this statement:
$$a(b + c + d) = \underline{ab + ac + ad}$$

9. Illustration 1 shows an application of the distributive property. Fill in the blanks.

$$2(\;3 + 4\;) \quad = \quad 2(\;3\;) \quad + \quad 2(\;4\;)$$
ILLUSTRATION 1

10. Complete the table.

Term	Coefficient	Variable part
$6m$	6	m
$-75t$	-75	t
w	1	w
$\frac{1}{2}bh$	$\frac{1}{2}$	bh

11. Fill in the blanks.
  a. $2(x + 4) = 2x + 8$
  b. $2(x - 4) = 2x - 8$
  c. $-2(x + 4) = -2x - 8$
  d. $-2(x - 4) = -2x + 8$
  e. $-2(-x + 4) = 2x - 8$
  f. $-2(-x - 4) = 2x + 8$

12. Complete this statement: To add or subtract like terms, combine their _____coefficients_____ and keep the same variables and _____exponents_____.

13. A board was cut into two pieces, as shown in Illustration 2. Add the lengths of the two pieces. How long was the original board? $x + 20 - x = 20$; 20 ft

x ft $(20 - x)$ ft

ILLUSTRATION 2

14. Let x equal the number of miles driven on the first day of a 2-day driving trip. Translate the verbal model to mathematical symbols, and simplify by combining like terms. $x + x + 100 = 2x + 100$

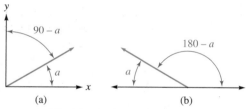

| the miles driven day 1 | plus | 100 miles more than the miles driven day 1 |

15. a. Two angles are called **complementary angles** if the sum of their measures is 90°. Add the measures of the angles in Illustration 3(a). Are they complementary angles? yes
b. Two angles are called **supplementary angles** if the sum of their measures is 180°. Add the measures of the angles in Illustration 3(b). Are they supplementary angles? yes

All angle measures are in degrees.

ILLUSTRATION 3

16. Simplify each expression, if possible.
a. $5(2x)$ and $5 + 2x$ $10x$; can't be simplified
b. $6(-7x)$ and $6 - 7x$ $-42x$; can't be simplified
c. $2(3x)(3)$ and $2 + 3x + 3$ $18x$; $3x + 5$
d. $x \cdot x$ and $x + x$ x^2; $2x$

NOTATION   *Complete each solution.*

17. $7(a + 2) = $ 7 $(a) + $ 7 (2)
$= 7a + $ 14

18. $6(b - 5) + 12b + 7 = 6($ b $) - 6($ 5 $) + 12b + 7$
$= 6b - $ 30 $ + 12b + 7$
$= 6b + $ 12 $b - $ 30 $ + 7$
$= 18b - 23$

19. a. Are $2K$ and $3k$ like terms?   no
b. Are $-d$ and d like terms?   yes

20. Fill in the blank to make the statement true.
$-(x + 10) = -$ 1 $(x + 10)$

21. Write each expression using fewer symbols.
a. $5x - (-1)$ $5x + 1$ **b.** $16t + (-6)$ $16t - 6$

22. In the following table, a student's answers to five homework problems are compared to the answers in the back of the book. Are the answers equivalent? (Write *yes* or *no*.)

Student's answer	Book's answer	Equivalent?
$10x$	$10 + x$	no
$3 + y$	$y + 3$	yes
$5 - 8a$	$8a - 5$	no
$3(x) + 4$	$3(x + 4)$	no
$2x$	x^2	no

PRACTICE   *Simplify each expression.*

23. $9(7m)$ $63m$
24. $12n(8)$ $96n$
25. $5(-7q)$ $-35q$
26. $-7(5t)$ $-35t$
27. $12\left(\dfrac{5}{12}x\right)$ $5x$
28. $15\left(\dfrac{4}{15}w\right)$ $4w$
29. $8\left(\dfrac{3}{4}y\right)$ $6y$
30. $27\left(\dfrac{2}{3}x\right)$ $18x$
31. $(-5p)(-4b)$ $20bp$
32. $(-7d)(-7c)$ $49cd$
33. $-5(4r)(-2r)$ $40r^2$
34. $7t(-4t)(-2)$ $56t^2$

Use the distributive property to remove parentheses.

35. $5(x + 3)$ $5x + 15$
36. $4(x + 2)$ $4x + 8$
37. $-2(b - 1)$ $-2b + 2$
38. $-7(p - 5)$ $-7p + 35$
39. $(3t - 2)8$ $24t - 16$
40. $(2q + 1)9$ $18q + 9$
41. $(2y - 1)6$ $12y - 6$
42. $(3w - 5)5$ $15w - 25$
43. $0.4(x - 4)$ $0.4x - 1.6$
44. $-2.2(2q + 1)$ $-4.4q - 2.2$
45. $-\dfrac{2}{3}(3w - 6)$ $-2w + 4$
46. $\dfrac{1}{2}(2y - 8)$ $y - 4$
47. $r(r - 10)$ $r^2 - 10r$
48. $h(h + 4)$ $h^2 + 4h$
49. $-(x - 7)$ $-x + 7$
50. $-(y + 1)$ $-y - 1$
51. $17(2x - y + 2)$ $34x - 17y + 34$
52. $-12(3a + 2b - 1)$ $-36a - 24b + 12$
53. $-(-14 + 3p - t)$ $14 - 3p + t$
54. $-(-x - y + 5)$ $x + y - 5$

55. Identify the coefficient of each term.
a. $-b$ -1
b. $-9.9x^3$ -9.9
c. $\dfrac{1}{4}x$ $\frac{1}{4}$
d. $-\dfrac{2x}{3}$ $-\frac{2}{3}$

56. Tell whether the variable x is used as a factor or as a term.
a. $24 - x$ term
b. $24x$ factor
c. $24 + 3x$ factor
d. $x - 12$ term

Identify the coefficient of each term.

57. $-5r + 4s$
$-5, 4$

58. $2m + n - 3m + 2n$
$2, 1, -3, 2$

59. $-15r^2s$
-15

60. $4b^2 - 5b + 6$
$4, -5, 6$

61. $50a + 2$
$50, 2$

62. $a^2 - ab + b^2$
$1, -1, 1$

63. $x^3 - 125$
$1, -125$

64. $-2.55x + 1.8$
$-2.55, 1.8$

Simplify each expression by combining like terms.

65. $3x + 17x$ $20x$

66. $12y - 15y$ $-3y$

67. $8x^2 - 5x^2$ $3x^2$

68. $17x^2 + 3x^2$ $20x^2$

69. $-4x + 4x$ 0

70. $-16y + 16y$ 0

71. $-7b^2 + 7b^2$ 0

72. $-2c^3 + 2c^3$ 0

73. $a + a + a$ $3a$

74. $t - t - t - t$ $-2t$

75. $0 - 3x$ $-3x$

76. $0 - 4a$ $-4a$

77. $0 - (-t)$ t

78. $0 - (-2y)$ $2y$

79. $3x + 5x - 7x$ x

80. $-y + 3y + 2y$ $4y$

81. $-13x^2 + 2x^2 - 5x^2$
$-16x^2$

82. $-8x^3 - x^3 + 2x^3$
$-7x^3$

83. $1.8h - 0.7h$ $1.1h$

84. $-5.7m + 4.3m$ $-1.4m$

85. $\dfrac{3}{5}t + \dfrac{1}{5}t$ $\frac{4}{5}t$

86. $\dfrac{3}{16}x - \dfrac{5}{16}x$ $-\frac{1}{8}x$

87. $-0.2r - (-0.6r)$
$0.4r$

88. $-1.1m - (-2.4m)$
$1.3m$

89. $2z + 5(z - 3)$
$7z - 15$

90. $12(m + 11) - 11$
$12m + 121$

91. $-(c + 7) - 2(c - 3)$
$-3c - 1$

92. $-(z + 2) + 5(3 - z)$
$-6z + 13$

93. $2x + 4(X - x) + 3X$
$7X - 2x$

94. $3p - 6(p + z) + p$
$-2p - 6z$

95. $(a + 2) - (a - b)$
$b + 2$

96. $3z + 2(Z - z) + Z$
$3Z + z$

97. $x(x + 3) - 3x^2$
$-2x^2 + 3x$

98. $2x + x(x - 3)$
$x^2 - x$

APPLICATIONS

99. THE AMERICAN RED CROSS
In 1891, Clara Barton founded the
Red Cross. Its symbol is a white
flag bearing a red cross. If each side
of the cross in Illustration 4 has
length x, write an algebraic expression for the perimeter (the total distance around the outside) of the
cross. $12x$

ILLUSTRATION 4

100. BILLIARDS   Billiard tables vary in size, but all
tables are twice as long as they are wide.

a. If the billiard table in Illustration 5 is x feet wide,
write an expression involving x that represents its
length. $2x$ ft

b. Write an expression for the perimeter of the table.
$6x$ ft

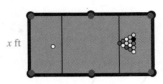

ILLUSTRATION 5

101. PING-PONG   Write an expression for the perimeter
of the ping-pong table shown in Illustration 6.
$(4x + 8)$ ft

ILLUSTRATION 6

102. SEWING   See Illustration 7. Write an expression for
the length of the yellow trim needed to outline a
pennant with the given side lengths. $(5x - 30)$ cm

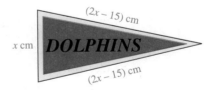

ILLUSTRATION 7

WRITING

103. Explain why the distributive property applies to
$2(3 + x)$ but not to $2(3x)$.

104. Explain why $3x^2y$ and $5x^2y$ are like terms, and explain
why $3x^2y$ and $5xy^2$ are not like terms.

105. Distinguish between a *factor* and a *term* of an algebraic expression. Give examples.

106. Tell how to combine like terms.

REVIEW   *Evaluate each expression for $x = -3$,*
$y = -5$, and $z = 0$.

107. $x^2z(y^3 - z)$ 0

108. $|y^3 - z|$ 125

109. $\dfrac{x - y^2}{2y - 1 + x}$ 2

110. $\dfrac{2y + 1}{x} - x$ 6

2.4 *More about Solving Equations*

In this section, you will learn about

- Solving equations by using more than one property of equality
- Simplifying expressions to solve equations
- Identities and impossible equations

INTRODUCTION. We have solved simple equations using the properties of equality. In this section, we will solve more-complicated equations. Our objective is to develop a general strategy that can be used to solve any kind of linear equation.

Solving equations by using more than one property of equality

Recall the following properties of equality:

- If the same quantity is added to (or subtracted from) equal quantities, the results will be equal quantities.

- If equal quantities are multiplied (or divided) by the same nonzero quantity, the results will be equal quantities.

We have already solved many simple equations using one of the properties listed above. For example, to solve $x + 6 = 10$, we isolate x by subtracting 6 from both sides.

$$x + 6 = 10$$
$$x + 6 - 6 = 10 - 6 \quad \text{To undo the addition of 6, subtract 6 from both sides.}$$
$$x = 4 \qquad \text{Do the subtractions.}$$

To solve $2x = 10$, we isolate x by dividing both sides by 2.

$$2x = 10$$
$$\frac{2x}{2} = \frac{10}{2} \quad \text{To undo the multiplication by 2, divide both sides by 2.}$$
$$x = 5 \quad \text{Do the divisions.}$$

Sometimes several properties of equality must be applied in succession to solve an equation. For example, on the left-hand side of $2x + 6 = 10$, the variable x is first multiplied by 2, and then 6 is added to that product. To isolate x, we use the rules for the order of operations in reverse. First, we undo the addition of 6, and then we undo the multiplication by 2.

$$2x + 6 = 10$$
$$2x + 6 - 6 = 10 - 6 \quad \text{To undo the addition of 6, subtract 6 from both sides.}$$
$$2x = 4 \qquad \text{Do the subtractions.}$$
$$\frac{2x}{2} = \frac{4}{2} \qquad \text{To undo the multiplication by 2, divide both sides by 2.}$$
$$x = 2 \qquad \text{Do the divisions.}$$

EXAMPLE 1 *Using two properties of equality.* Solve and check: $-12x + 5 = 17$.

Solution

On the left-hand side of the equation, x is multiplied by -12, and then 5 is added to that product. To isolate x, we undo these operations in the opposite order.

Self Check

Solve and check:

$8x - 13 = 43$

- To undo the addition of 5, we subtract 5 from both sides.
- To undo the multiplication by −12, we divide both sides by −12.

$$-12x + 5 = 17$$
$$-12x + 5 - 5 = 17 - 5 \quad \text{Subtract 5 from both sides.}$$
$$-12x = 12 \quad \text{Do the subtractions: } 5 - 5 = 0 \text{ and } 17 - 5 = 12.$$
$$\frac{-12x}{-12} = \frac{12}{-12} \quad \text{Divide both sides by } -12.$$
$$x = -1 \quad \text{Do the divisions.}$$

Check: $-12x + 5 = 17$ The original equation.
$$-12(-1) + 5 \stackrel{?}{=} 17 \quad \text{Substitute } -1 \text{ for } x.$$
$$12 + 5 \stackrel{?}{=} 17 \quad \text{Do the multiplication: } -12(-1) = 12.$$
$$17 = 17 \quad \text{Do the addition.}$$

Since the statement $17 = 17$ is true, -1 is a solution.

EXAMPLE 2   *Using two properties of equality.*   Solve and check: $\frac{2x}{3} = -6$.

Solution

On the left-hand side, x is multiplied by 2, and then that product is divided by 3. To solve this equation, we must undo these operations in the opposite order.

- To undo the division of 3, we multiply both sides by 3.
- To undo the multiplication by 2, we divide both sides by 2.

$$\frac{2x}{3} = -6$$
$$3\left(\frac{2x}{3}\right) = 3(-6) \quad \text{Multiply both sides by 3.}$$
$$2x = -18 \quad \text{On the left-hand side: } 3\left(\frac{2x}{3}\right) = \frac{\overset{1}{\cancel{3}}}{1}\left(\frac{2x}{\underset{1}{\cancel{3}}}\right) = 2x.$$
$$\frac{2x}{2} = \frac{-18}{2} \quad \text{Divide both sides by 2.}$$
$$x = -9 \quad \text{Do the divisions.}$$

Check: $\dfrac{2x}{3} = -6$ The original equation.
$$\frac{2(-9)}{3} \stackrel{?}{=} -6 \quad \text{Substitute } -9 \text{ for } x.$$
$$\frac{-18}{3} \stackrel{?}{=} -6 \quad \text{Do the multiplication: } 2(-9) = -18.$$
$$-6 = -6 \quad \text{Do the division.}$$

Since we obtain a true statement, -9 is a solution.

Self Check
Solve and check:
$$\frac{7h}{16} = -14$$

Answer: 7

Answer: -32

Another approach can be used to solve the equation from Example 2. To isolate the variable, we will use the fact that the product of a number and its **reciprocal,** or **multiplicative inverse,** is 1. Since $\frac{2x}{3} = \frac{2}{3}x$, the equation can be rewritten as

$$\frac{2}{3}x = -6$$

To isolate x, we multiply both sides by $\frac{3}{2}$, the reciprocal (multiplicative inverse) of $\frac{2}{3}$.

$$\frac{3}{2}\left(\frac{2}{3}x\right) = \frac{3}{2}(-6) \quad \text{The coefficient of } x \text{ is } \frac{2}{3}. \text{ Multiply both sides by the reciprocal of } \frac{2}{3}, \text{ which is } \frac{3}{2}.$$

$$\left(\frac{3}{2} \cdot \frac{2}{3}\right)x = \frac{3}{2}(-6) \quad \text{On the left-hand side, apply the associative property of multiplication to regroup factors.}$$

$$1x = -9 \quad \text{Do the multiplications: } \frac{3}{2} \cdot \frac{2}{3} = 1 \text{ and } \frac{3}{2}(-6) = -9.$$

$$x = -9 \quad \text{Simplify: } 1x = x.$$

EXAMPLE 3   *An implied coefficient of* -1.   Solve $-0.2 = -0.8 - y$.

Solution

To solve the equation, we begin by eliminating -0.8 from the right-hand side. We can do this by adding 0.8 to both sides.

$$-0.2 = -0.8 - y$$

$$-0.2 + \mathbf{0.8} = -0.8 - y + \mathbf{0.8} \quad \text{Add } 0.8 \text{ to both sides.}$$

$$0.6 = -y \qquad \text{Do the additions: } -0.2 + 0.8 = 0.6 \text{ and } -0.8 + 0.8 = 0.$$

Since the term $-y$ has an understood coefficient of -1, the equation can be rewritten as $0.6 = -1y$. To isolate y, either multiply both sides or divide both sides by -1.

$$0.6 = -1y \quad \text{Write } -y \text{ as } -1y.$$

$$\frac{0.6}{-1} = \frac{-1y}{-1} \quad \text{To undo the multiplication by } -1, \text{ divide both sides by } -1.$$

$$-0.6 = y \qquad \text{Do the divisions.}$$

$$y = -0.6$$

Verify that -0.6 satisfies the equation.

EXAMPLE 4   *Using three properties of equality.*   Solve $\frac{3}{4}x + 2 = -7$.

Solution

On the left-hand side, x is multiplied by 3, that product is divided by 4, and then 2 is added. To solve the equation, we must undo these operations in the opposite order.

- To undo the addition of 2, we subtract 2 from both sides.
- To undo the division by 4, we multiply both sides by 4.
- To undo the multiplication by 3, we divide both sides by 3.

$$\frac{3}{4}x + 2 = -7$$

$$\frac{3}{4}x + 2 - \mathbf{2} = -7 - \mathbf{2} \quad \text{Subtract 2 from both sides.}$$

$$\frac{3}{4}x = -9 \qquad \text{Do the subtractions: } 2 - 2 = 0 \text{ and } -7 - 2 = -9.$$

$$4\left(\frac{3}{4}x\right) = 4(-9) \qquad \text{Multiply both sides by 4.}$$

$$3x = -36 \qquad \text{On the left-hand side: } 4\left(\frac{3}{4}x\right) = \left(\frac{\overset{1}{\cancel{4}}}{1} \cdot \frac{3}{\underset{1}{\cancel{4}}}\right)x = 3x.$$

$$\frac{3x}{3} = \frac{-36}{3} \qquad \text{Divide both sides by 3.}$$

$$x = -12 \qquad \text{Do the divisions.}$$

Verify that -12 satisfies the equation.

Self Check

Solve $-6.6 - m = -2.7$.

Answer: -3.9

Self Check

Solve $\frac{2}{3}b - 3 = -15$.

Answer: -18

Simplifying expressions to solve equations

EXAMPLE 5 *Combining like terms.*   Solve and check: $3(k + 1) - 5k = 0$.

Solution

In this example, we must use the distributive property to remove parentheses.

$3(k + 1) - 5k = 0$

$3k + 3(1) - 5k = 0$ Distribute the multiplication by 3.

$3k + 3 - 5k = 0$ Do the multiplications.

$-2k + 3 = 0$ Combine like terms: $3k - 5k = -2k$.

$-2k + 3 - 3 = 0 - 3$ To undo the addition of 3, subtract 3 from both sides.

$-2k = -3$ Do the subtractions: $3 - 3 = 0$ and $0 - 3 = 3$.

$\dfrac{-2k}{-2} = \dfrac{-3}{-2}$ To undo the multiplication by -2, divide both sides by -2.

$k = \dfrac{3}{2}$ Simplify: $\frac{-3}{-2} = \frac{3}{2}$.

Check: $3(k + 1) - 5k = 0$ The original equation.

$3\left(\dfrac{3}{2} + 1\right) - 5\left(\dfrac{3}{2}\right) \stackrel{?}{=} 0$ Substitute $\frac{3}{2}$ for k.

$3\left(\dfrac{3}{2} + \dfrac{2}{2}\right) - 5\left(\dfrac{3}{2}\right) \stackrel{?}{=} 0$ To add $\frac{3}{2}$ and 1, write 1 as $\frac{2}{2}$.

$3\left(\dfrac{5}{2}\right) - 5\left(\dfrac{3}{2}\right) \stackrel{?}{=} 0$ Do the addition within the parentheses.

$\dfrac{15}{2} - \dfrac{15}{2} \stackrel{?}{=} 0$ Do the multiplications.

$0 = 0$ Do the subtraction.

Self Check

Solve and check:

$-5(x - 3) + 3x = 11$

Answer: 2

EXAMPLE 6 *Variable terms on both sides of the equation.*   Solve and check: $3x - 15 = 4x + 36$.

Solution

To solve for x, all the terms containing x must be on the same side of the equation. We can eliminate $3x$ from the left-hand side by subtracting $3x$ from both sides.

$3x - 15 = 4x + 36$

$3x - 15 - 3x = 4x + 36 - 3x$ Subtract $3x$ from both sides.

$-15 = x + 36$ Combine like terms: $3x - 3x = 0$ and $4x - 3x = x$.

$-15 - 36 = x + 36 - 36$ To undo the addition of 36, subtract 36 from both sides.

$-51 = x$ Do the subtractions.

$x = -51$

Check: $3x - 15 = 4x + 36$ The original equation.

$3(-51) - 15 \stackrel{?}{=} 4(-51) + 36$ Substitute -51 for x.

$-153 - 15 \stackrel{?}{=} -204 + 36$ Do the multiplications.

$-168 = -168$ Simplify each side.

Self Check

Solve and check:

$3n + 48 = -4n - 8$

Answer: -8

EXAMPLE 7 *Clearing an equation of fractions.* Solve $\dfrac{x}{6} - \dfrac{5}{2} = -\dfrac{1}{3}$.

Solution

Since integers are easier to work with, we will clear the equation of the fractions by multiplying both sides by the least common denominator (LCD), which is 6.

$$\frac{x}{6} - \frac{5}{2} = -\frac{1}{3}$$

$$6\left(\frac{x}{6} - \frac{5}{2}\right) = 6\left(-\frac{1}{3}\right)$$ 6 is the smallest number that each denominator will divide exactly. Multiply both sides by 6 to clear the equation of the fractions.

$$6\left(\frac{x}{6}\right) - 6\left(\frac{5}{2}\right) = 6\left(-\frac{1}{3}\right)$$ On the left-hand side, distribute the multiplication by 6.

$$x \quad - \quad 15 \quad = \quad -2$$ Do each multiplication by 6. Note that the resulting equation does not contain any fractions.

$$x - 15 + 15 = -2 + 15$$ To undo the subtraction of 15, add 15 to both sides.

$$x = 13$$ Do the additions: $-15 + 15 = 0$ and $-2 + 15 = 13$.

Verify that 13 satisfies the equation.

Self Check

Solve $\dfrac{x}{4} + \dfrac{1}{2} = -\dfrac{1}{8}$.

Answer: $-\dfrac{5}{2}$

The preceding examples suggest the following strategy for solving equations.

Strategy for solving equations

1. Clear the equation of fractions.
2. Use the distributive property to remove parentheses, if necessary.
3. Combine like terms, if necessary.
4. Undo the operations of addition and subtraction to get the variables on one side and the constants on the other.
5. Undo the operations of multiplication and division to isolate the variable.
6. Check the result.

EXAMPLE 8 *Applying the equation-solving strategy.* Solve and check: $\dfrac{3x + 11}{5} = x + 3$.

Solution

$$\frac{3x + 11}{5} = x + 3$$

$$5\left(\frac{3x + 11}{5}\right) = 5(x + 3)$$ Clear the equation of the fraction by multiplying both sides by 5.

$$3x + 11 = 5x + 15$$ On the left-hand side, simplify: $\dfrac{1}{\cancel{5}}{\cancel{1}}\left(\dfrac{3x + 11}{\cancel{5}}\right)$. On the right-hand side, distribute the multiplication by 5.

$$3x + 11 - 11 = 5x + 15 - 11$$ Subtract 11 from both sides.

$$3x = 5x + 4$$ Do the subtractions.

$$3x - 5x = 5x + 4 - 5x$$ To eliminate $5x$ from the right-hand side, subtract $5x$ from both sides.

$$-2x = 4$$ Combine like terms: $3x - 5x = -2x$ and $5x - 5x = 0$.

Self Check

Solve and check:

$$\frac{3x + 23}{7} = x + 5$$

$$\frac{-2x}{-2} = \frac{4}{-2}$$ To undo the multiplication by -2, divide both sides by -2.

$$x = -2$$ Do the divisions.

Verify that -2 satisfies the equation.

Answer: -3 ■

 COMMENT   Remember that when you multiply one side of an equation by a nonzero number, you must multiply the other side of the equation by the same number.

Identities and impossible equations

Equations in which some numbers satisfy the equation and others don't are called **conditional equations**. The equations in Examples 1–8 are conditional equations.

An equation that is true for all values of its variable is called an **identity**.

$x + x = 2x$ This is an identity, because it is true for all values of x.

An equation that is not true for any values of its variable is called an **impossible equation** or a **contradiction**. Such equations are said to have no solution.

$x = x + 1$ Because no number is 1 greater than itself, this is an impossible equation.

EXAMPLE 9   *Identities.*   Solve $3(x + 8) + 5x = 2(12 + 4x)$.

Solution

$$3(x + 8) + 5x = 2(12 + 4x)$$

$$3x + 24 + 5x = 24 + 8x$$ On each side of the equation, use the distributive property.

$$8x + 24 = 24 + 8x$$ Combine like terms.

$$8x + 24 - 8x = 24 + 8x - 8x$$ Subtract $8x$ from both sides.

$$24 = 24$$ Combine like terms: $8x - 8x = 0$.

In this case, the terms involving x drop out. Since the result $24 = 24$ is true for every number x, all values of x satisfy the original equation. This equation is an identity.

Self Check
Solve $3(x + 5) - 4(x + 4) = -x - 1$.

Answer: all values of x; this equation is an identity   ■

EXAMPLE 10   *Impossible equations.*   Solve $3(d + 7) - d = 2(d + 10)$.

Solution

$$3(d + 7) - d = 2(d + 10)$$

$$3d + 21 - d = 2d + 20$$ Use the distributive property.

$$2d + 21 = 2d + 20$$ Combine like terms.

$$2d + 21 - 2d = 2d + 20 - 2d$$ Subtract $2d$ from both sides.

$$21 = 20$$ Combine like terms.

In this case, the terms involving d drop out. Since the result $21 = 20$ is false, the original equation has no solution. It is an impossible equation.

Self Check
Solve $-4(c - 3) + 2c = 2(10 - c)$.

Answer: No solution. This equation is an impossible equation.   ■

STUDY SET Section 2.4   www

VOCABULARY   *Fill in the blanks.*

1. An ____equation____ is a statement that two quantities are equal.

2. To solve an equation, we must ____isolate____ the variable on one side of the equation.

3. If a number is a solution of an equation, the number is said to _____satisfy_____ the equation.

4. In $2(x - 7)$, "to remove parentheses" means to apply the _____distributive_____ property.

5. The product of a number and its _____reciprocal_____ is 1.

6. An equation that is true for all values of its variable is called an _____identity_____. An equation that has no solutions is called an _____impossible_____ equation or a contradiction.

CONCEPTS *In Exercises 7–10, fill in the blanks.*

7. To solve the equation $2x - 7 = 21$, we first undo the _____subtraction_____ of 7 by adding 7 to both sides. We then undo the _____multiplication_____ by 2 by dividing both sides by 2.

8. To solve the equation $\frac{x}{-2} + 3 = 5$, we first undo the _____addition_____ of 3 by subtracting 3 from both sides. We then undo the _____division_____ by -2 by multiplying both sides by -2.

9. To solve the equation $\frac{x}{2} + 3 = 5$, we first undo the _____addition_____ of 3 by subtracting 3 from both sides. We then undo the _____division_____ by 2 by multiplying both sides by 2.

10. To solve $\frac{s}{3} + \frac{1}{4} = -\frac{1}{2}$, we can clear the equation of the fractions by _____multiplying_____ both sides of the equation by 12.

11. One method of solving $-\frac{4}{5}x = 8$ is to multiply both sides of the equation by the reciprocal of $-\frac{4}{5}$. What is the reciprocal of $-\frac{4}{5}$? $-\frac{5}{4}$

12. a. Combine like terms on the left-hand side of $6x - 8 - 8x = -24$. $-2x - 8 = -24$
b. Combine like terms on the right-hand side of $5a + 1 = 9a + 16 + a$. $5a + 1 = 10a + 16$
c. Combine like terms on both sides of $12 - 3r + 5r = -8 - r - 2$. $12 + 2r = -10 - r$

13. What is the LCD for the fractions in the equation $\frac{x}{3} - \frac{4}{5} = \frac{1}{2}$? 30

14. Complete the three multiplications necessary to clear the given equation of fractions.

$$\frac{2}{3} - \frac{b}{2} = -\frac{4}{3}$$

$$6\left(\frac{2}{3} - \frac{b}{2}\right) = 6\left(-\frac{4}{3}\right)$$

$$6\left(\frac{2}{3}\right) - 6\left(\frac{b}{2}\right) = 6\left(-\frac{4}{3}\right)$$

$$\underbrace{4}_{} - \underbrace{3b}_{} = \underbrace{-8}_{}$$

15. a. Simplify $3x + 5 - x$. $2x + 5$
b. Solve $3x + 5 - x = 9$. 2
c. Evaluate $3x + 5 - x$ for $x = 9$. 23
d. Check: Is $x = -1$ a solution of $3x + 5 - x = 9$? no

16. a. Simplify $3(x - 4) - 4x$. $-x - 12$
b. Solve $3(x - 4) - 4x = 0$. -12
c. Evaluate $3(x - 4) - 4x$ for $x = 0$. -12
d. Check: Is $x = -1$ a solution of $3(x - 4) - 4x = 0$? no

NOTATION *In Exercises 17–18, complete the solution to solve each equation.*

17.
$$2x - 7 = 21$$
$$2x - 7 + 7 = 21 + 7$$
$$2x = 28$$
$$\frac{2x}{2} = \frac{28}{2}$$
$$x = 14$$

18.
$$\frac{x}{2} + 3 = 5$$
$$\frac{x}{2} + 3 - 3 = 5 - 3$$
$$\frac{x}{2} = 2$$
$$2\left(\frac{x}{2}\right) = 2\,(2)$$
$$x = 4$$

19. Fill in the blanks.
a. $-x = -1\ x$.
b. $\frac{3x}{5} = \frac{3}{5}\ x$.
c. If $-31 = x$, then $x = -31$

20. When checking a solution of an equation, the symbol $\stackrel{?}{=}$ is used. What does it mean?
is possibly equal to

PRACTICE *Solve each equation and check the result.*

21. $2x + 5 = 17$ 6   **22.** $3x - 5 = 13$ 6
23. $-5q - 2 = 1$ $-\frac{3}{5}$ **24.** $4p + 3 = 2$ $-\frac{1}{4}$
25. $0.6 = 4.1 - x$ 3.5   **26.** $1.2 - x = -1.7$ 2.9
27. $-g = -4$ 4   **28.** $-u = -20$ 20
29. $-8 - 3c = 0$ $-\frac{8}{3}$ **30.** $-5 - 2d = 0$ $-\frac{5}{2}$
31. $-\frac{5}{6}k = 10$ -12 **32.** $\frac{2c}{5} = 2$ 5
33. $-\frac{t}{3} + 2 = 6$ -12 **34.** $\frac{x}{5} - 5 = -12$ -35

35. $\dfrac{2x}{3} - 2 = 4$ 9
36. $\dfrac{2}{5}y + 3 = 9$ 15

37. $\dfrac{x + 5}{3} = 11$ 28
38. $\dfrac{x + 2}{13} = 3$ 37

39. $\dfrac{y - 2}{7} = -3$ −19
40. $\dfrac{x - 7}{3} = -1$ 4

41. $2(-3) + 4y = 14$ 5
42. $4(-1) + 3y = 8$ 4

43. $-2x - 4(1) = -6$ 1
44. $-5x - 3(5) = 0$ −3

45. $3(x + 2) - x = 12$ 3
46. $2(x - 4) + x = 7$ 5

47. $-3(2y - 2) - y = 5$ $\frac{1}{7}$
48. $-(3a + 1) + a = 2$ $-\frac{3}{2}$

49. $0 - 2y = 8$ −4
50. $0 - 7x = -21$ 3

51. $5x + 7.2 = 4x$ −7.2
52. $3x + 2.5 = 2x$ −2.5

53. $8y + 4 = 4y$ −1
54. $9y - 3 = 6y$ 1

55. $15x = x$ 0
56. $-7y = -8y$ 0

57. $4 + \dfrac{y}{2} = \dfrac{3}{5}$ $-\frac{34}{5}$
58. $5 + \dfrac{x}{3} = \dfrac{1}{2}$ $-\frac{27}{2}$

59. $\dfrac{1}{3} + \dfrac{c}{5} = -\dfrac{3}{2}$ $-\frac{55}{6}$
60. $\dfrac{1}{2} + \dfrac{x}{5} = \dfrac{3}{4}$ $\frac{5}{4}$

61. $\dfrac{y}{6} + \dfrac{y}{4} = -1$ $-\frac{12}{5}$
62. $\dfrac{x}{3} + \dfrac{x}{4} = -2$ $-\frac{24}{7}$

63. $-\dfrac{2}{9} = \dfrac{5x}{6} - \dfrac{1}{3}$ $\frac{2}{15}$
64. $\dfrac{2}{3} = -\dfrac{2x}{3} + \dfrac{3}{4}$ $\frac{1}{8}$

65. $\dfrac{1}{2}x - \dfrac{1}{9} = \dfrac{1}{3}$ $\frac{8}{9}$
66. $\dfrac{1}{4}y - \dfrac{2}{3} = \dfrac{1}{2}$ $\frac{14}{3}$

67. $\dfrac{2}{5}x + 1 = \dfrac{1}{3} + x$ $\frac{10}{9}$
68. $\dfrac{2}{3}y + 2 = \dfrac{1}{5} + y$ $\frac{27}{5}$

69. $3(a + 2) = 2(a - 7)$ −20
70. $9(t - 1) = 6(t + 2) - t$ $\frac{21}{4}$
71. $9(x + 11) + 5(13 - x) = 0$ −41
72. $3(x + 15) + 4(11 - x) = 0$ 89

73. $\dfrac{3t - 21}{2} = t - 6$ 9
74. $\dfrac{2t - 18}{3} = t - 8$ 6

75. $\dfrac{10 - 5s}{3} = s + 6$ −1
76. $\dfrac{40 - 8s}{5} = -2s$ −20

77. $2 - 3(x - 5) = 4(x - 1)$ 3
78. $2 - (4x + 7) = 3 + 2(x + 2)$ −2

Solve each equation. If it is an identity or an impossible equation, so indicate.

79. $8x + 3(2 - x) = 5(x + 2) - 4$ identity
80. $5(x + 2) = 5x - 2$ impossible equation
81. $-3(s + 2) = -2(s + 4) - s$ impossible equation
82. $21(b - 1) + 3 = 3(7b - 6)$ identity

83. $2(3z + 4) = 2(3z - 2) + 13$ impossible equation
84. $x + 7 = \dfrac{2x + 6}{2} + 4$ identity
85. $4(y - 3) - y = 3(y - 4)$ identity
86. $5(x + 3) - 3x = 2(x + 8)$ impossible equation

Solve each equation.

87. $1.73x = -4.952 - 2.27x$ −1.238
88. $\dfrac{h}{709} - 23,898 = -19,678$ 2,991,980
89. $20(x - 3.7) = 32,832$ 1,645.3
90. $9.35 - 1.4y = 7.32 + 1.5y$ 0.7

WRITING

91. Explain the difference between *simplifying* an expression and *solving* an equation. Give some examples.

92. To solve $3x - 4 = 5x + 1$, one student began by subtracting $3x$ from both sides. Another student solved the same equation by first subtracting $5x$ from both sides. Will the students get the same solution? Explain why or why not.

93. What does it mean to clear an equation such as $\frac{1}{4} + \frac{x}{2} = \frac{3}{8}$ of the fractions?

94. Explain the error in the following solution:

Solve $2x + 4 = 30$.

$$2x + 4 = 30$$
$$\dfrac{2x}{2} + 4 = \dfrac{30}{2}$$
$$x + 4 = 15$$
$$x + 4 - 4 = 15 - 4$$
$$x = 11$$

REVIEW

95. Simplify $-(-8)$.   8
96. Subtract: $-8 - (-8)$.   0
97. Multiply: $-8(-8)$.   64
98. Add: $\dfrac{1}{8} + \dfrac{1}{8}$. $\frac{1}{4}$
99. Multiply: $\dfrac{1}{8} \cdot \dfrac{1}{8}$. $\frac{1}{64}$
100. Divide: $\dfrac{0.8}{8}$.   0.1
101. Simplify $8x + 8 + 8x - 8$. $16x$
102. Evaluate -1^8.   −1

2.5 *Formulas*

In this section, you will learn about

- Formulas from business • Formulas from science • Formulas from geometry
- Solving formulas

INTRODUCTION. A **formula** is an equation that is used to state a known relationship between two or more variables. Formulas are used in many fields: economics, physical education, anthropology, biology, automotive repair, and nursing, to name a few. In this section, we will consider formulas from business, science, and geometry.

Formulas from business

A formula to find the retail price: To make a profit, a merchant must sell a product for more than he or she paid for it. The price at which the merchant sells the product, called the **retail price,** is the sum of what the item cost the merchant plus the **markup.**

Retail price	=	cost	+	markup

Using r to represent the retail price, c the wholesale cost, and m the markup, we can write this formula as

$$\boxed{r = c + m}$$

As an example, suppose a jeweler purchases a gold ring at a wholesale jewelry mart for $612.50. Then she sets the price of the ring at $837.95 for sale in her store. We can find the markup on the ring as follows:

$$r = c + m$$

$$837.95 = 612.50 + m \qquad \text{Substitute 837.95 for } r \text{ and 612.50 for } c.$$

$$837.95 - 612.50 = 612.50 + m - 612.50 \qquad \text{To undo the addition of 612.50, subtract 612.50 from both sides.}$$

$$225.45 = m \qquad \text{Do the subtractions.}$$

The markup on the ring is $225.45.

A formula for profit: The **profit** a business makes is the difference between the **revenue** (the money it takes in) and the costs.

Profit	=	revenue	−	costs

Using p to represent the profit, r the revenue, and c the costs, we can write this formula as

$$\boxed{p = r - c}$$

EXAMPLE 1   *Charitable giving.* In 1999, the Salvation Army collected $1.9 billion. Of that amount, $1.7 billion went directly to the support of its programs. What were the 1999 administrative costs of the organization?

Solution

The charity collected $1.9 billion in revenue. We can think of the $1.7 billion that was spent on programs as profit. We need to find the administrative costs, c.

Self Check

A PTA spaghetti dinner made a profit of $275.50. If the cost to host the dinner was $1,235, how much revenue did it generate?

$$p = r - c$$ The formula for profit.

$$1.7 = 1.9 - c$$ Substitute 1.7 for p and 1.9 for r.

$$1.7 - 1.9 = 1.9 - c - 1.9$$ To eliminate 1.9, subtract 1.9 from both sides.

$$-0.2 = -c$$ Subtract: $1.7 - 1.9 = -0.2$ and $1.9 - 1.9 = 0$.

$$\frac{-0.2}{-1} = \frac{-c}{-1}$$ Since $-c = -1c$, divide both sides by -1.

$$0.2 = c$$ Do the divisions.

In 1999, the Salvation Army had administrative costs of $0.2 billion.

Answer: $1,510.50 ■

A formula for simple interest: When money is borrowed, the lender expects to be paid back the amount of the loan plus an additional charge for the use of the money. The additional charge is called **interest.** When money is deposited in a bank, the depositor is paid for the use of the money. The money the deposit earns is also called interest. In general, interest is the money that is paid for the use of money.

Interest is calculated in two ways: either as **simple interest** or as **compound interest.** To find simple interest, we use the formula

$$\text{Interest} \quad = \quad \text{principal} \quad \cdot \quad \text{rate} \quad \cdot \quad \text{time}$$

Using I to represent the simple interest, P the principal (the amount of money that is invested, deposited, or borrowed), r the annual interest rate, and t the length of time in years, we can write the formula as

$$\boxed{I = Prt}$$

EXAMPLE 2 *Retirement income.* One year after investing $15,000 in a mini-mall development, a retired couple received a check for $1,125 in interest. What interest rate did their money earn that year?

Solution

The couple invested $15,000 (the principal) for 1 year (the time) and made $1,125 (the interest). We need to find the annual interest rate.

$$I = Prt$$ The formula for simple interest.

$$1,125 = 15,000r(1)$$ Substitute 1,125 for I, 15,000 for P, and 1 for t.

$$1,125 = 15,000r$$ Simplify the right-hand side.

$$\frac{1,125}{15,000} = \frac{15,000r}{15,000}$$ To solve for r, undo the multiplication by 15,000 by dividing both sides by 15,000.

$$0.075 = r$$ Do the divisions.

$$7.5\% = r$$ To write 0.075 as a percent, multiply 0.075 by 100 by moving the decimal point two places to the right and insert a % symbol.

The couple received an annual rate of 7.5% that year.

Self Check

A father lent his daughter and son-in-law $12,200 at a 2% annual simple interest rate for a down payment on a house. If the interest on the loan amounted to $610, for how long was the loan?

Answer: 2.5 years ■

Formulas from science

A formula for distance traveled: If we know the average rate (speed) at which we will be traveling and the time we will be traveling at that rate, we can find the distance traveled by using the formula

$$\text{Distance} \quad = \quad \text{rate} \quad \cdot \quad \text{time}$$

Using d to represent the distance, r the average rate (speed), and t the time, we can write this formula as

$$d = rt$$

 COMMENT   When using this formula, the units must be the same. For example, if the rate is given in miles per hour, the time must be expressed in hours.

EXAMPLE 3 *Finding the rate.*   As they migrate from the Bering Sea to Baja California, gray whales swim for about 20 hours each day, covering a distance of approximately 70 miles. Estimate their average swimming rate in miles per hour (mph).

Solution

Since the distance d is 70 miles and the time t is 20 hours, we substitute 70 for d and 20 for t in the formula $d = rt$, and then solve for r.

$$d = rt$$

$$70 = r(20) \quad \text{Substitute 70 for } d \text{ and 20 for } t.$$

$$\frac{70}{20} = \frac{20r}{20} \quad \text{To undo the multiplication by 20, divide both sides by 20.}$$

$$3.5 = r \quad \text{Do the divisions.}$$

The whales' average swimming rate is 3.5 mph.

Self Check

An elevator in a building travels at an average rate of 288 feet per minute. How long will it take the elevator to climb 30 stories, a distance of 360 feet?

Answer: 1.25 minutes ■

A formula for converting degrees Fahrenheit to degrees Celsius: Many marquees, like the one shown in Figure 2-11, flash two temperature readings, one in degrees Fahrenheit and one in degrees Celsius. The Fahrenheit scale is used in the American system of measurement. The Celsius scale is used in the metric system. The formula that relates a Fahrenheit temperature F to a Celsius temperature C is:

$$C = \frac{5(F - 32)}{9}$$

FIGURE 2-11

EXAMPLE 4 *Changing degrees Celsius to degrees Fahrenheit.*   Change the temperature reading on the sign in Figure 2-11 to degrees Fahrenheit.

Solution

Since the temperature C in degrees Celsius is 30°, we substitute 30 for C in the formula and solve for F.

$$C = \frac{5(F - 32)}{9}$$

$$30 = \frac{5(F - 32)}{9} \quad \text{Substitute 30 for } C.$$

$$9(30) = 9\left[\frac{5(F - 32)}{9}\right] \quad \text{To clear the equation of the fraction, multiply both sides by 9.}$$

$$270 = 5(F - 32) \quad \text{Simplify: } 9(30) = 270 \text{ and}$$
$$\frac{1}{\cancel{9}}\left[\frac{5(F - 32)}{\cancel{9}}\right] = 5(F - 32).$$

$$270 = 5F - 5(32) \quad \text{Distribute the multiplication by 5.}$$

Self Check

Change $-175°$C, the temperature on Saturn, to degrees Fahrenheit.

$$270 = 5F - 160$$ Do the multiplication: $5(32) = 160$.

$$270 + \mathbf{160} = 5F - 160 + \mathbf{160}$$ To undo the subtraction of 160, add 160 to both sides.

$$430 = 5F$$ Simplify: $270 + 160 = 430$ and $-160 + 160 = 0$.

$$\frac{430}{5} = \frac{5F}{5}$$ To undo the multiplication by 5, divide both sides by 5.

$$86 = F$$ Do the divisions.

Thus, 30°C is equivalent to 86°F.

Answer: -283°F ∎

Formulas from geometry

The **perimeter** of a geometric figure is the distance around it. Perimeter is measured in linear units, such as inches, feet, yards, and meters. The **area** of the figure is the amount of surface that it encloses. Area is measured in square units, such as square inches, square feet, square yards, and square meters (denoted as in.^2, ft^2, yd^2, and m^2, respectively). Table 2-4 shows the formulas for the perimeter P and area A of several geometric figures.

Square
$P = 4s$
$A = s^2$

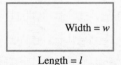

Rectangle
$P = 2l + 2w$
$A = lw$

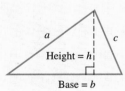

Triangle
$P = a + b + c$
$A = \frac{1}{2}bh$

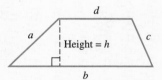

Trapezoid
$P = a + b + c + d$
$A = \frac{1}{2}h(b + d)$

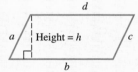

Parallelogram
$P = a + b + c + d$
$A = bh$

Circle
$C = 2\pi r$, where
$\pi \approx 3.1416$
C is the circumference of the circle and r is its radius.
$A = \pi r^2$

TABLE 2-4

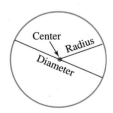

FIGURE 2-12

A **circle** (see Figure 2-12) is the set of all points in a plane that are a fixed distance from a point called its **center.** A segment drawn from the center of a circle to a point on the circle is called a **radius.** Since a **diameter** of a circle is a segment passing through the center that joins two points on the circle, the diameter D of a circle is twice as long as its radius r.

$$D = 2r$$

The perimeter of a circle is called its **circumference.** The formula for the circumference of a circle is

$$C = 2\pi r$$

EXAMPLE 5   *Finding perimeters and areas.*   Find   **a.** the perimeter of a square with sides 6 inches long   and   **b.** the area of a triangle with base 8 meters and height 13 meters.

Solution

a. The perimeter of a square is given by the formula $P = 4s$, where P is the perimeter and s is the length of one side. Since the sides of the square are 6 inches long, we substitute 6 for s and simplify.

$$P = 4s$$
$$P = 4(6) \quad \text{Substitute 6 for } s.$$
$$ = 24 \quad \text{Do the multiplication.}$$

The perimeter of the square is 24 inches.

b. The area of a triangle is given by the formula $A = \frac{1}{2}bh$. Since the base of the triangle is 8 meters and the height is 13 meters, we substitute 8 for b and 13 for h and simplify.

$$A = \frac{1}{2}bh$$
$$A = \frac{1}{2}(8)(13) \quad \text{Substitute 8 for } b \text{ and 13 for } h.$$
$$ = 4(13) \quad \tfrac{1}{2}(8) = \tfrac{8}{2} = 4.$$
$$ = 52 \quad \text{Do the multiplication.}$$

The area of the triangle is 52 square meters. This can be written as 52 m^2.

Self Check

a. The flag of Eritrea, a country in east Africa, is shown below. What is the perimeter of the flag?

b. Find the area of the red triangular region of the flag.

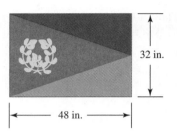

Answers: a. 160 in.,
b. 768 in.^{2} ∎

EXAMPLE 6   *Finding the area of a circle.*   To the nearest tenth, find the area of a circle with a diameter of 14 feet.

Solution

Since the radius of a circle is one-half its diameter, the radius of this circle is 7 feet. We can then substitute 7 for r in the formula for the area of a circle and simplify.

$$A = \pi r^2$$
$$A = \pi(7)^2$$
$$ = 49\pi \quad \text{First, evaluate the exponential expression: } 7^2 = 49.$$
$$ \approx 153.93804 \quad \text{Use a calculator to do the multiplication. Enter these numbers and}$$
$$ \text{press these keys on a scientific calculator: } 49 \times \pi = .$$

To the nearest tenth, the area is 153.9 ft^2.

Self Check

To the nearest hundredth, find the circumference of the circle of Example 6.

Answer: 43.98 ft   ∎

The **volume** of a three-dimensional geometric solid is the amount of space it encloses. Table 2-5 shows the formula for the volume V of several solids. Volume is measured in cubic units, such as cubic inches, cubic feet, and cubic meters (denoted as in.^{3}, ft^3, and m^3, respectively).

EXAMPLE 7   *Finding volumes.*   To the nearest tenth, find the volume of each figure.

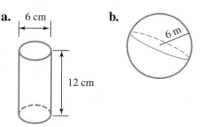

a. 6 cm

b. 6 m

12 cm

Self Check

Find the volume of each figure:
a. a rectangular solid with length 7 inches, width 12 inches, and height 15 inches   and   **b.** a cone whose base has radius 12 meters and whose height is 9 meters. Give the answer to the nearest tenth.

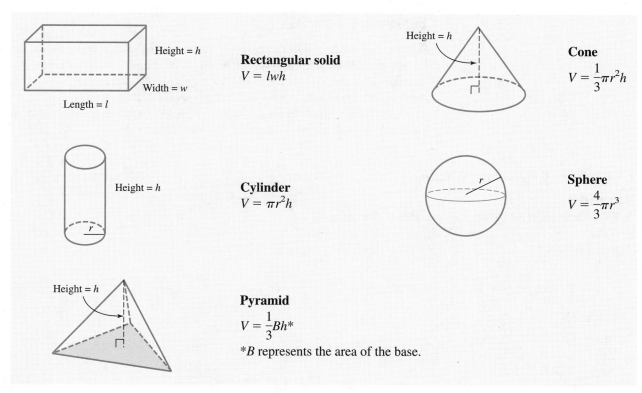

Rectangular solid
$V = lwh$

Cone
$V = \frac{1}{3}\pi r^2 h$

Cylinder
$V = \pi r^2 h$

Sphere
$V = \frac{4}{3}\pi r^3$

Pyramid
$V = \frac{1}{3}Bh*$

*B represents the area of the base.

TABLE 2-5

Solution

a. To find the volume of a cylinder, we use the formula $V = \pi r^2 h$, where r is the radius and h is the height. Since the radius of a circle is one-half its diameter, the radius of the cylinder is $\frac{1}{2}(6 \text{ cm}) = 3$ cm. The height of the cylinder is 12 cm. We substitute 3 for r and 12 for h in the formula for volume and proceed as follows.

$V = \pi r^2 h$ The formula for the volume of a cylinder.

$V = \pi(3)^2(12)$ Substitute 3 for r and 12 for h.

$ = \pi(9)(12)$ Evaluate the exponential expression: $(3)^2 = 9$.

$ = 108\pi$ Multiply: $9(12) = 108$.

$ \approx 339.2920066$ Use a calculator.

To the nearest tenth, the volume is 339.3 cubic centimeters. This can be written as 339.3 cm^3.

b. To find the volume of the sphere, we substitute 6 for r in the formula for the volume of a sphere and proceed as follows.

$V = \frac{4}{3}\pi r^3$ The formula for the volume of a sphere.

$V = \frac{4}{3}\pi(6)^3$ Since the radius of the sphere is 6 m, substitute 6 for r.

$ = \frac{4}{3}\pi(216)$ $(6)^3 = 6 \cdot 6 \cdot 6 = 216$.

$ = 288\pi$ Do the multiplication: $\frac{4}{3}(216) = \frac{4(216)}{3} = \frac{864}{3} = 288$.

$ \approx 904.7786842$ Use a calculator.

To the nearest tenth, the volume is 904.8 m^3.

Answers: **a.** 1,260 in.^{3},
b. 1,357.2 m^3

Solving formulas

Suppose we wish to find the bases of several triangles whose areas and heights are known. It could be tedious to substitute values for A and h into the formula and then repeatedly solve the formula for b. A better way is to solve the formula $A = \frac{1}{2}bh$ for b first, and then substitute values for A and h and compute b directly.

To **solve an equation for a variable** means to isolate that variable on one side of the equation, with all other quantities on the opposite side.

EXAMPLE 8 *Solving formulas.* Solve $A = \frac{1}{2}bh$ for b.

Solution

To solve for b, we must isolate b on one side of the equation.

$$A = \frac{1}{2}bh$$

$2A = 2 \cdot \frac{1}{2}bh$ To clear the equation of the fraction, multiply both sides by 2.

$2A = bh$ Simplify: $2 \cdot \frac{1}{2} = \frac{2}{2} = 1$.

$\dfrac{2A}{h} = \dfrac{bh}{h}$ To undo the multiplication by h, divide both sides by h.

$\dfrac{2A}{h} = b$ On the right-hand side, divide out the common factor of h: $\dfrac{b\overset{1}{\cancel{h}}}{\underset{1}{\cancel{h}}} = b$.

$b = \dfrac{2A}{h}$ Reverse the sides to write b on the left.

Self Check

Solve $V = lwh$ for w.

Answer: $w = \dfrac{V}{lh}$

EXAMPLE 9 *Solving formulas.* Solve $P = 2l + 2w$ for l.

Solution

To solve for l, we must isolate l on one side of the equation.

$$P = 2l + 2w$$

$P - 2w = 2l + 2w - 2w$ To undo the addition of $2w$, subtract $2w$ from both sides.

$P - 2w = 2l$ Combine like terms: $2w - 2w = 0$.

$\dfrac{P - 2w}{2} = \dfrac{2l}{2}$ To undo the multiplication by 2, divide both sides by 2.

$\dfrac{P - 2w}{2} = l$ Simplify the right-hand side.

We can write the result as $l = \dfrac{P - 2w}{2}$.

Self Check

Solve $P = 2l + 2w$ for w.

Answer: $w = \dfrac{P - 2l}{2}$

EXAMPLE 10 *Solving for y.* In Chapter 3, we will work with equations that involve the variables x and y, such as $2y - 4 = 3x$. Solve the equation for y.

Solution

$2y - 4 = 3x$ The given equation.

$2y - 4 + 4 = 3x + 4$ To undo the subtraction of 4, add 4 to both sides.

$2y = 3x + 4$ On the left-hand side, simplify: $-4 + 4 = 0$.

$\dfrac{2y}{2} = \dfrac{3x + 4}{2}$ To undo the multiplication by 2, divide both sides by 2.

Self Check

Solve $3y + 12 = x$.

$$y = \frac{3x}{2} + \frac{4}{2}$$ On the right-hand side, rewrite $\frac{3x+4}{2}$ as the sum of two fractions with like denominators, $\frac{3x}{2}$ and $\frac{4}{2}$.

$$y = \frac{3}{2}x + 2$$ Write $\frac{3x}{2}$ as $\frac{3}{2}x$. Simplify: $\frac{4}{2} = 2$.

Answer: $y = \frac{1}{3}x - 4$ ∎

EXAMPLE 11 *Solving for r^2.* Solve $V = \pi r^2 h$ for r^2.

Solution

We want to isolate r^2 on one side of the equation.

$$V = \pi r^2 h$$

$$\frac{V}{\pi h} = \frac{\pi r^2 h}{\pi h}$$ To undo the multiplication by π and h on the right-hand side, divide both sides by πh.

On the right-hand side, divide out the common factors of π and h:

$$\frac{V}{\pi h} = r^2 \qquad \frac{\overset{1}{\cancel{\pi}} r^2 \overset{1}{\cancel{h}}}{\underset{1}{\cancel{\pi}} \underset{1}{\cancel{h}}} = r^2.$$

$$r^2 = \frac{V}{\pi h}$$ Reverse the sides of the equation so that r^2 is on the left.

Self Check

Solve $a^2 + b^2 = c^2$ for b^2.

Answer: $b^2 = c^2 - a^2$ ∎

STUDY SET Section 2.5

VOCABULARY *Fill in the blanks.*

1. A ___formula___ is an equation that is used to state a known relationship between two or more variables.

2. The ___volume___ of a three-dimensional geometric solid is the amount of space it encloses.

3. The distance around a geometric figure is called its ___perimeter___.

4. A ___circle___ is the set of all points in a plane that are a fixed distance from a point called its center.

5. A segment drawn from the center of a circle to a point on the circle is called a ___radius___.

6. The amount of surface that is enclosed by a geometric figure is called its ___area___.

7. The perimeter of a circle is called its ___circumference___.

8. A segment passing through the center of a circle and connecting two points on the circle is called a ___diameter___.

CONCEPTS

9. Use variables to write the formula relating the following:
   a. Time, distance, rate $d = rt$
   b. Markup, retail price, cost $r = c + m$
   c. Costs, revenue, profit $p = r - c$
   d. Interest rate, time, interest, principal $I = Prt$
   e. Circumference, radius $C = 2\pi r$

10. Complete the table.

Principal ·	rate ·	time =	interest
$2,500	5%	2 yr	$250
$15,000	4.8%	1 yr	$720

11. Complete the table to find how far light and sound travel in 60 seconds. (*Hint*: mi/sec means miles per second.)

	Rate	· time =	distance
Light	186,282 mi/sec	60 sec	11,176,920 mi
Sound	1,088 ft/sec	60 sec	65,280 mi

12. Give the name of each figure.
   a. trapezoid
   b. cylinder

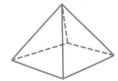

   c. pyramid
   d. sphere

e. cone

f. rectangular solid

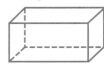

13. Tell which geometric concept—perimeter, circumference, area, or volume—should be used to find the following:

   a. The amount of storage in a freezer   volume

   b. How far a bicycle tire rolls in one revolution
   circumference

   c. The amount of land making up the Sahara Desert
   area

   d. The distance around a Monopoly game board
   perimeter

14. Tell which unit of measurement—ft, ft², or ft³—would be appropriate when finding the following:

   a. The amount of storage inside a safe   ft³

   b. The ground covered by a sleeping bag lying on the floor   ft²

   c. The distance the tip of an airplane propeller travels in one revolution   ft

   d. The size of the trunk of a car   ft³

15. Write an expression for the area of the figure shown in Illustration 1.
$(2x + 6)$ cm²

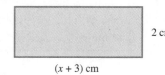

2 cm

$(x + 3)$ cm

ILLUSTRATION 1

16. Write an expression for the area of the figure shown in Illustration 2.
$(12x - 8)$ mm²

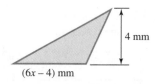

4 mm

$(6x - 4)$ mm

ILLUSTRATION 2

NOTATION   *In Exercises 17–18, complete each solution.*

17. Solve $V = \frac{1}{3}Bh$ for B.

$$V = \frac{1}{3}Bh$$

$$3\,(V) = 3\left(\frac{1}{3}\right)Bh$$

$$3V = Bh$$

$$\frac{3V}{h} = \frac{Bh}{h}$$

$$\frac{3V}{h} = B$$

$$B = \frac{3V}{h}$$

18. Solve $Ax + By = C$ for y.

$$Ax + By = C$$

$$Ax + By - Ax = C - Ax$$

$$By = C - Ax$$

$$\frac{By}{B} = \frac{C - Ax}{B}$$

$$y = \frac{C - Ax}{B}$$

19. a. Approximate π to the nearest hundredth.   3.14

   b. What does 98π mean? $98 \cdot \pi$

   c. In the formula for the volume of a cylinder, $V = \pi r^2 h$, what does r represent? What does h represent?
   the radius of the cylinder; the height of the cylinder

20. a. What does ft² mean?   square feet

   b. What does in.³ mean?   cubic inches

PRACTICE   *Use a formula discussed in this section to solve each problem.*

21. SWIMMING   In 1930, a man swam down the Mississippi River from Minneapolis to New Orleans, a total of 1,826 miles. He was in the water for 742 hours. To the nearest tenth, what was his average swimming rate?
2.5 mph

22. ROSE PARADE   Rose Parade floats travel down the 5.5-mile-long parade route at a rate of 2.5 mph. How long will it take a float to complete the parade if there are no delays?   2.2 hr

23. HOLLYWOOD   Figures for the summer of 1998 showed that the movie *Saving Private Ryan* had U.S. box-office receipts of $190 million. What were the production costs to make the movie if, at that time, the studio had made a $125 million profit? $65 million

24. SERVICE CLUB   After expenses of $55.15 were paid, a Rotary Club donated $875.85 in proceeds from a pancake breakfast to a local health clinic. How much did the pancake breakfast gross? $931

25. ENTREPRENEURS   To start a mobile dog-grooming service, a woman borrowed $2,500. If the loan was for 2 years and the amount of interest was $175, what simple interest rate was she charged?   3.5%

26. BANKING   Three years after opening an account that paid 6.45% annually, a depositor withdrew the $3,483 in interest earned. How much money was left in the account? $18,000

27. METALLURGY   Change 2,212°C, the temperature at which silver boils, to degrees Fahrenheit. Round to the nearest degree.   4,014°F

28. LOW TEMPERATURES   Cryobiologists freeze living matter to preserve it for future use. They can work with temperatures as low as −270°C. Change this to degrees Fahrenheit.   −454°F

29. VALENTINE'S DAY Find the markup on a dozen roses if a florist buys them wholesale for $12.95 and sells them for $37.50. $24.55

30. STICKER PRICE The factory invoice for a minivan shows that the dealer paid $16,264.55 for the vehicle. If the sticker price of the van is $18,202, how much over factor invoice is the sticker price? $1,937.45

31. YO-YO How far does a yo-yo travel during one revolution of the "around the world" trick if the length of the string is 21 inches? about 132 in.

32. HORSE TRAINING A horse trots in a perfect circle around its trainer at the end of a 28-foot-long rope. How far does the horse travel as it circles the trainer once? about 176 ft

Solve each formula for the given variable.

33. $E = IR$; for R $R = \frac{E}{I}$

34. $d = rt$; for t $t = \frac{d}{r}$

35. $V = lwh$; for w $w = \frac{V}{lh}$

36. $I = Prt$; for r $r = \frac{I}{Pt}$

37. $C = 2\pi r$; for r

$r = \frac{C}{2\pi}$

38. $V = \pi r^2 h$; for h

$h = \frac{V}{\pi r^2}$

39. $a + b + c = 180$; for a

$a = 180 - b - c$

40. $P = a + b + c$; for b

$b = P - a - c$

41. $y = mx + b$; for x

$x = \frac{y - b}{m}$

42. $P = 2l + 2w$; for l

$l = \frac{P - 2w}{2}$

43. $A = P + Prt$; for t

$t = \frac{A - P}{Pr}$

44. $S = 2\pi rh + 2\pi r^2$; for h

$h = \frac{S - 2\pi r^2}{2\pi r}$

45. $V = \frac{1}{3}\pi r^2 h$; for h

$h = \frac{3V}{\pi r^2}$

46. $K = \frac{1}{2}mv^2$; for m

$m = \frac{2k}{v^2}$

47. $x = \frac{a + b}{2}$; for b

$b = 2x - a$

48. $A = \frac{a + b + c}{3}$; for c

$c = 3A - a - b$

49. $D = \frac{C - s}{n}$; for s

$s = C - Dn$

50. $2E = \frac{T - t}{9}$; for t

$t = T - 18E$

51. $E = mc^2$; for c^2

$c^2 = \frac{E}{m}$

52. $s = 4\pi r^2$; for r^2

$r^2 = \frac{s}{4\pi}$

53. $c^2 = a^2 + b^2$; for a^2

$a^2 = c^2 - b^2$

54. $Kg = \frac{wv^2}{2}$; for v^2

$v^2 = \frac{2Kg}{w}$

55. $A = \frac{1}{2}h(b + d)$; for b

$b = \frac{2A}{h} - d$ or $b = \frac{2A - hd}{h}$

56. $h = vt + 16t^2$; for t^2

$t^2 = \frac{h - vt}{16}$

57. $3y - 9 = x$; for y

$y = \frac{1}{3}x + 3$

58. $5y - 25 = x$; for y

$y = \frac{1}{5}x + 5$

59. $4y + 16 = -3x$; for y

$y = -\frac{3}{4}x - 4$

60. $6y + 12 = -5x$; for y

$y = -\frac{5}{6}x - 2$

APPLICATIONS

61. PROPERTIES OF WATER The boiling point and the freezing point of water are to be given in both degrees

Celsius and degrees Fahrenheit on the thermometer in Illustration 3. Find the missing degree measures.
212°F, 0°C

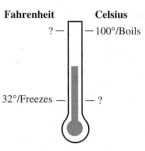

ILLUSTRATION 3

62. HIGHWAY SPEED LIMITS Several state speed limits for trucks are shown in Illustration 4. At each of these speeds, how far would a truck travel in $2\frac{1}{2}$ hours? Ohio: 137.5 mi; Indiana: 150 mi; Kentucky: 162.5 mi

ILLUSTRATION 4

63. AVON PRODUCTS, INC. Complete the financial statement shown in Illustration 5.

Quarterly financials Income statement (dollar amounts in millions except per share amounts)	Quarter ending Mar 00	Quarter ending Dec 99
Revenue	1,324.9	1,566.6
Cost of goods sold	497.3	606.6
Gross profit	827.6	960.0

Based on data from Hoover's Online

ILLUSTRATION 5

64. CREDIT CARDS The finance charge section of a person's credit card statement says, "annual percentage rate (APR) is 19.8%." Determine how much finance charges (interest) the card owner would have to pay if the account's average balance for the year was $2,500.
$495

65. CARPENTRY Find the perimeter and area of the truss shown in Illustration 6.
36 ft, 48 ft²

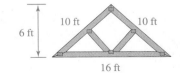

ILLUSTRATION 6

66. CAMPERS   Find the area of the window of the camper shell shown in Illustration 7.   784 in.²

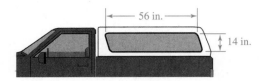

ILLUSTRATION 7

67. ARCHERY   To the nearest tenth, find the circumference and area of the target shown in Illustration 8.   50.3 in., 201.1 in.²

ILLUSTRATION 8

68. GEOGRAPHY   The circumference of the earth is about 25,000 miles. Find its diameter to the nearest mile.   7,958 mi

69. LANDSCAPING   Find the perimeter and the area of the redwood trellis in Illustration 9.   56 in., 144 in.²

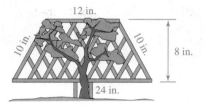

ILLUSTRATION 9

70. HAMSTER HABITAT   Find the amount of space in the plastic tube shown in Illustration 10.   about 85 in.³

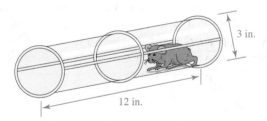

ILLUSTRATION 10

71. "THE WALL"   The Vietnam Veterans Memorial is a black granite wall recognizing the more than 58,000 Americans who lost their lives or remain missing. A diagram of the wall is shown in Illustration 11. Find the total area of the two triangular-shaped surfaces on which the names are inscribed.   2,450 ft²

ILLUSTRATION 11

72. SIGNAGE   Find the perimeter and area of the service station sign shown in Illustration 12.   11 ft, 7.5625 ft²

ILLUSTRATION 12

73. RUBBER MEETS THE ROAD   A sport truck tire has the road surface "footprint" shown in Illustration 13. Estimate the perimeter and area of the tire's footprint.   27.75 in., 47.8125 in.²

ILLUSTRATION 13

74. SOFTBALL   The strike zone in fast-pitch softball is between the batter's armpit and top of her knees, as shown in Illustration 14. Find the area of the strike zone.   442 in.²

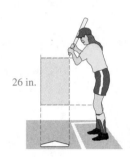

ILLUSTRATION 14

75. FIREWOOD   The dimensions of a cord of firewood are shown in Illustration 15. Find the area on which the wood is stacked and the volume the cord of firewood occupies.   32 ft², 128 ft³

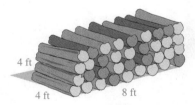

ILLUSTRATION 15

76. NATIVE AMERICAN DWELLING   The teepees constructed by the Blackfoot Indians were cone-shaped tents made of long poles and animal hide, about 10 feet high and about 15 feet across at the ground. (See Illustration 16.) Estimate the volume of a teepee with these dimensions, to the nearest cubic foot.   589 ft³

ILLUSTRATION 16

77. IGLOO During long journeys, some Canadian Inuit (Eskimos) built winter houses of snow blocks piled in the dome shape shown in Illustration 17. Estimate the volume of an igloo having an interior height of 5.5 feet to the nearest cubic foot. 348 ft^3

ILLUSTRATION 17

78. PYRAMID The Great Pyramid at Giza in northern Egypt is one of the most famous works of architecture in the world. Use the information in Illustration 18 to find the volume to the nearest cubic foot.
85,503,750 ft^3

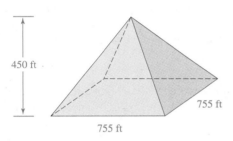

450 ft

755 ft

755 ft

ILLUSTRATION 18

79. BARBECUING See Illustration 19. Use the fact that the fish is 18 inches long to find the area of the barbecue grill to the nearest square inch. 254 in.^{2}

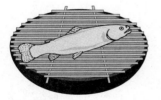

ILLUSTRATION 19

80. SKATEBOARDING A "half-pipe" ramp used for skateboarding is in the shape of a semicircle with a

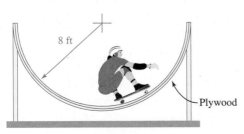

8 ft

Plywood

ILLUSTRATION 20

radius of 8 feet, as shown in Illustration 20. To the nearest tenth of a foot, what is the length of the arc that the skateboarder travels on the ramp? 25.1 ft

81. GEOMETRY The measure a of an interior angle of a regular polygon with n sides is given by the formula

$$a = 180° \left(1 - \frac{2}{n} \right)$$

See Illustration 21. Solve the formula for n. How many sides does a regular polygon have if an interior angle is 108°? (*Hint:* Distribute first.)

$n = \dfrac{360°}{180° - a}$; 5 sides

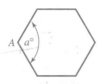

A $a°$

ILLUSTRATION 21

82. THERMODYNAMICS The Gibbs free-energy function is given by $G = U - TS + pV$. Solve this formula for the pressure p. $p = \dfrac{G - U + TS}{V}$

WRITING

83. The formula $P = 2l + 2w$ is also an equation, but an equation such as $2x + 3 = 5$ is not a formula. What equations do you think should be called formulas?

84. Explain what it means to solve the equation $P = 2l + 2w$ for w.

85. After solving $A = B + C + D$ for B, a student compared her answer with that of the back of the textbook.

Student's answer: $B = A - C - D$

Book's answer: $B = A - D - C$

Could this problem have two different-looking answers? Explain why or why not.

86. Suppose the volume of a cylinder is 28 cubic feet. Explain why it is incorrect to express the volume as 28^3 ft.

REVIEW

87. Find 82% of 168. 137.76

88. 29.05 is what percent of 415? 7%

89. What percent of 200 is 30? 15%

90. A woman bought a coat for $98.95 and some gloves for $7.95. If the sales tax was 6%, how much did the purchase cost her? $113.31

2.6 More about Problem Solving

In this section, you will learn about

- Finding more than one unknown
- Solving geometric problems
- Solving number–value problems
- Solving investment problems
- Solving uniform motion problems
- Solving mixture problems

INTRODUCTION. In this section, we will solve several different types of problems using the five-step problem-solving strategy.

Finding more than one unknown

EXAMPLE 1 *California coastline.* The first part of California's magnificent 17-Mile Drive scenic tour, shown in Figure 2-13, begins at the Pacific Grove entrance and continues to Seal Rock. It is 1 mile longer than the second part of the drive, which extends from Seal Rock to the Lone Cypress. The final part of the tour winds through the hills of the Monterey Peninsula, eventually returning to the entrance. This part of the drive is 1 mile longer than four times the length of the second part. How long is each of the three parts of 17-Mile Drive?

Analyze the problem In Figure 2-14, we "straighten out" the winding 17-Mile Drive so that it can be modeled with a line segment. The drive is composed of three parts. We need to find the length of each part.

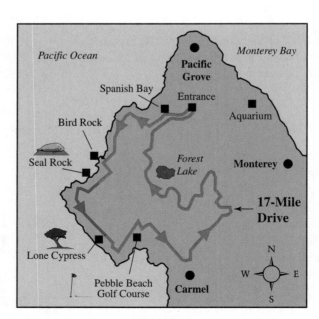

FIGURE 2-13

Form an equation Since the lengths of the first part and of the third part of the scenic drive are related to the length of the second part, we will let x represent the length of that part. We then express the other lengths in terms of that variable.

$x + 1$ represents the length of the first part of the drive.

$4x + 1$ represents the length of the third part of the drive.

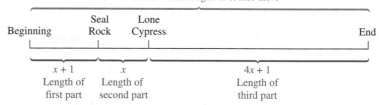

FIGURE 2-14

The sum of the lengths of the three parts of the drive must equal the total length of 17-Mile Drive.

The length of part 1	plus	the length of part 2	plus	the length of part 3	equals	the total length.
$x + 1$	$+$	x	$+$	$4x + 1$	$=$	17

Solve the equation

$$x + 1 + x + 4x + 1 = 17$$

$$6x + 2 = 17 \quad \text{Combine like terms: } x + x + 4x = 6x \text{ and } 1 + 1 = 2.$$

$$6x = 15 \quad \text{To undo the addition of 2, subtract 2 from both sides.}$$

$$\frac{6x}{6} = \frac{15}{6} \quad \text{To undo the multiplication by 6, divide both sides by 6.}$$

$$x = 2.5 \quad \text{Do the divisions.}$$

Recall that x represents the length of the *second* part of the drive. To find the lengths of the first and third parts, we evaluate the expressions $x + 1$ and $4x + 1$ for $x = 2.5$.

First part of drive　　**Third part of drive**

$$x + 1 = 2.5 + 1 \qquad 4x + 1 = 4(2.5) + 1 \quad \text{Substitute 2.5 for } x.$$

$$= 3.5 \qquad\qquad\qquad = 10 + 1$$

$$\qquad\qquad\qquad\qquad = 11$$

State the conclusion　The first part of the drive is 3.5 miles long, the second part is 2.5 miles long, and the third part is 11 miles long.

Check the result　Because the sum of 3.5 miles, 2.5 miles, and 11 miles is 17 miles, the answers check.　　　　　　　■

Solving geometric problems

EXAMPLE 2　*Dimensions of a garden.*　A gardener wants to use 62 feet of fencing bought at a garage sale to enclose a rectangular-shaped garden. Find the dimensions of the garden if its length is to be 4 feet longer than twice its width.

Analyze the problem　We can make a sketch of the garden, as shown in Figure 2-15. We know that its length is to be 4 feet longer than twice its width. We also know that its perimeter is to be 62 feet.

FIGURE 2-15

Form an equation　If we let w represent the width of the garden, then $2w + 4$ represents its length. Since the formula for the perimeter of a rectangle is $P = 2l + 2w$, the perimeter of the garden is $2(2w + 4) + 2w$, which is also 62. This fact enables us to form the equation.

	2	times	the length	plus	2	times	the width	is	the perimeter.
	2	$\cdot$	$(2w + 4)$	+	2	$\cdot$	w	=	62

Solve the equation

$2(2w + 4) + 2w = 62$

$4w + 8 + 2w = 62$ Use the distributive property to remove parentheses.

$6w + 8 = 62$ Combine like terms: $4w + 2w = 6w$.

$6w = 54$ To undo the addition of 8, subtract 8 from both sides.

$w = 9$ To undo the multiplication by 6, divide both sides by 6.

State the conclusion   The width of the garden is 9 feet. Since $2w + 4 = 2(9) + 4 = 22$, the length is 22 feet.

Check the result   If the garden has a width of 9 feet and a length of 22 feet, its length is 4 feet longer than twice the width $(2 \cdot 9 + 4 = 22)$. Since its perimeter is $(2 \cdot 22 + 2 \cdot 9)$ feet = 62 feet, the answers check.   ■

EXAMPLE 3   ***Isosceles triangles.***   If the vertex angle of an isosceles triangle is 56°, find the measure of each base angle.

Analyze the problem   An **isosceles triangle** has two sides of equal length, which meet to form the **vertex angle.** In this case, the measurement of the vertex angle is 56°. We can sketch the triangle as shown in Figure 2-16. The **base angles** opposite the equal sides are also equal. We need to find their measure.

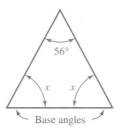

FIGURE 2-16

Form an equation   If we let x represent the measure of one base angle, the measure of the other base angle is also x. Since the sum of the angles of any triangle is 180°, the sum of the base angles and the vertex angle is 180°. We can use this fact to form the equation.

One base angle	plus	the other base angle	plus	the vertex angle	is	180°.
x	+	x	+	56	=	180

Solve the equation

$x + x + 56 = 180$

$2x + 56 = 180$ Combine like terms: $x + x = 2x$.

$2x = 124$ To undo the addition of 56, subtract 56 from both sides.

$x = 62$ To undo the multiplication by 2, divide both sides by 2.

State the conclusion   The measure of each base angle is 62°.

Check the result   The measure of each base angle is 62°, and the vertex angle measures 56°. Since $62° + 62° + 56° = 180°$, the answer checks.   ■

Solving number–value problems

Some problems deal with quantities that have a monetary value. In these problems, we must distinguish between the *number of* and the *value of* the unknown quantity. For problems of this type, we will use the relationship

Number · value = total value

EXAMPLE 4   *Dining area improvements.*   A restaurant owner needs to purchase some new tables, chairs, and dinner plates for the dining area of her establishment. She plans to buy four chairs and four plates for each new table. She also needs 20 additional plates to keep in case of breakage. If a table costs $100, a chair $50, and a plate $5, how many of each can she buy if she takes out a small business loan for $6,500 to pay for the new items?

Analyze the problem   We know the *value* of each item: Tables cost $100, chairs cost $50, and plates cost $5 each. We need to find the *number* of tables, chairs, and plates she can purchase for $6,500.

Form an equation   The number of chairs and plates she needs depends on the number of tables she buys. So we let t be the number of tables to be purchased. Since every table requires four chairs and four plates, she needs to order $4t$ chairs. Because an additional 20 plates are needed, she should order $4t + 20$ plates. The total value of each purchase is the *product* of the number of items bought and the price, or value, of each item.

Item	Number purchased ·	Price per item =	Total value
Tables	t	$100	$100t$
Chairs	$4t$	$50	$50(4t)$
Plates	$4t + 20$	$5	$5(4t + 20)$

The total purchase can be expressed in two ways.

The value of the tables	+	the value of the chairs	+	the value of the plates	is	the total value of the purchase.
$100t$	+	$50(4t)$	+	$5(4t + 20)$	=	6,500

Solve the equation

$$100t + 50(4t) + 5(4t + 20) = 6,500$$
$$100t + 200t + 20t + 100 = 6,500 \quad \text{Do the multiplications.}$$
$$320t + 100 = 6,500 \quad \text{Combine like terms.}$$
$$320t = 6,400 \quad \text{Subtract 100 from both sides.}$$
$$t = 20 \quad \text{Divide both sides by 320.}$$

State the conclusion   The purchases are summarized as follows:

Item	Number purchased	Price per item	Total value
Tables	$t = 20$	$100	$2,000
Chairs	$4t = 80$	$50	$4,000
Plates	$4t + 20 = 100$	$5	$500
Total			$6,500

Check the result   Because the total purchase is $6,500, the answer checks.   ■

Solving investment problems

To find the amount of simple interest I an investment earns, we use the formula

$$I = Prt$$

where P is the principal, r is the annual rate, and t is the time in years. When $t = 1$, the formula simplifies to $I = Pr$.

EXAMPLE 5   *Paying tuition.*   A college student invested the $12,000 inheritance he received and decided to use the annual interest earned to pay his yearly tuition costs of $945. The highest rate offered by a savings and loan at that time was 6% annual simple interest. At this rate, he could not earn the needed $945, so he invested some of the money in a riskier, but more lucrative, investment offering a 9% return. How much did he invest at each rate?

Analyze the problem   We know that $12,000 was invested for 1 year at two rates: 6% and 9%. We are asked to find the amount invested at each rate so that the total return would be $945.

Form an equation   Let x represent the amount invested at 6%. Then $12,000 - x$ represents the amount invested at 9%.

   If $\$x$ (the principal P) is invested at 6% (the rate r), the interest earned in 1 year would be Pr or $\$0.06x$. At 9%, the rest of the inheritance money, $\$(12,000 - x)$, would earn $\$0.09(12,000 - x)$ interest. These facts are summarized in the following table.

	P	$\cdot$ r $=$	I
Savings and loan	x	0.06	$0.06x$
Riskier investment	$12,000 - x$	0.09	$0.09(12,000 - x)$

The total interest earned can be expressed in two ways.

The interest earned at 6%	plus	the interest earned at 9%	is	the total interest.
$0.06x$	$+$	$0.09(12,000 - x)$	$=$	945

Solve the equation

$$0.06x + 0.09(12,000 - x) = 945$$

$$100[0.06x + 0.09(12,000 - x)] = 100(945) \qquad \text{Multiply both sides by 100 to clear the equation of decimals.}$$

$$100(0.06x) + 100(0.09)(12,000 - x) = 100(945) \qquad \text{Distribute the multiplication by 100.}$$

$$6x + 9(12,000 - x) = 94,500 \qquad \text{Do the multiplications by 100.}$$

$$6x + 108,000 - 9x = 94,500 \qquad \text{Use the distributive property.}$$

$$-3x + 108,000 = 94,500 \qquad \text{Combine like terms.}$$

$$-3x = -13,500 \qquad \text{Subtract 108,000 from both sides.}$$

$$x = 4,500 \qquad \text{Divide both sides by } -3.$$

State the conclusion   The student invested $4,500 at 6% and $12,000 - \$4,500 = \$7,500$ at 9%.

Check the result   The first investment earned 6% of $4,500, or $270. The second earned 9% of $7,500, or $675. The total return was $\$270 + \$675 = \$945$. The answers check.   ∎

Solving uniform motion problems

If we know the rate *r* at which we will be traveling and the time *t* we will be traveling at that rate, we can find the distance *d* traveled by using the formula

$$d = rt$$

EXAMPLE 6   *Coast Guard rescue.*   A cargo ship, heading into port, radios the Coast Guard that it is experiencing engine trouble and that its speed has dropped to 3 knots. Immediately, a Coast Guard cutter leaves the port and speeds at a rate of 25 knots directly toward the disabled craft, which is 21 nautical miles away. How long will it take the Coast Guard cutter to reach the cargo ship?

Analyze the problem   The diagram in Figure 2-17(a) shows the situation.

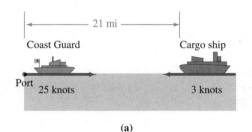

	r	$\cdot$ t	$=$ d
Coast Guard cutter	25	t	$25t$
Cargo ship	3	t	$3t$

(a)   (b)

FIGURE 2-17

We know the *rate* of each ship (25 knots and 3 knots), and we know that they must close a *distance* of 21 nautical miles between them. We don't know the *time* it will take them to do this.

Form an equation   Let *t* represent the time it takes for the ships to meet. Using $d = rt$, we find that $25t$ represents the distance traveled by the Coast Guard cutter and $3t$ represents the distance traveled by the cargo ship. This information is recorded in the table in Figure 2-17(b). We can use it to form the equation.

The distance the Coast Guard cutter travels	plus	the distance the cargo ship travels	is	the initial distance between the two ships.
$25t$	$+$	$3t$	$=$	21

Solve the equation

$$25t + 3t = 21$$
$$28t = 21 \qquad \text{Combine like terms.}$$
$$t = \frac{21}{28} \qquad \text{Divide both sides by 28.}$$
$$t = \frac{3}{4} \qquad \text{Simplify the fraction: } \frac{21}{28} = \frac{\overset{1}{\cancel{7}} \cdot 3}{\underset{1}{\cancel{7}} \cdot 4} = \frac{3}{4}.$$

State the conclusion   The ships will meet in three-quarters of an hour, or 45 minutes.

Check the result   In three-quarters of an hour, the Coast Guard cutter travels $25 \cdot \frac{3}{4} = \frac{75}{4}$ nautical miles, and the cargo ship travels $3 \cdot \frac{3}{4} = \frac{9}{4}$ nautical miles. Together, they travel $\frac{75}{4} + \frac{9}{4} = \frac{84}{4} = 21$ nautical miles. Since this is the initial distance between the ships, the answer checks.

Solving mixture problems

We now discuss how to solve two types of mixture problems. In the first type, a *liquid mixture* of a desired strength is made from two solutions with different concentrations.

EXAMPLE 7 *Mixing a solution.* A chemistry experiment calls for a 30% sulfuric acid solution. If the lab supply room has only 50% and 20% sulfuric acid solutions on hand, how much of each should be mixed to obtain 12 liters of a 30% acid solution?

Analyze the problem We must find how much of the 50% solution and how much of the 20% solution is needed to obtain 12 liters of a 30% acid solution.

Form an equation If x represents the numbers of liters (L) of the 50% solution used in the mixture, the remaining $(12 - x)$ liters must be the 20% solution. See Figure 2-18(a). Only 50% of the x liters, and only 20% of the $(12 - x)$ liters, is pure sulfuric acid. The total of these amounts is also the amount of acid in the final mixture, which is 30% of 12 liters. This information is shown in the chart in Figure 2-18(b).

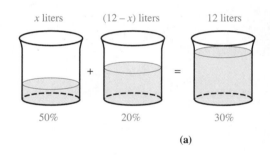

Solution	% acid ·	Liters =	Amount of acid
50% solution	0.50	x	$0.50x$
20% solution	0.20	$12 - x$	$0.20(12 - x)$
30% mixture	0.30	12	$0.30(12)$

(a)   (b)

FIGURE 2-18

We can form the equation.

The acid in the 50% solution	plus	the acid in the 20% solution	equals	the acid in the final mixture.
50% of x	+	20% of $(12 - x)$	=	30% of 12

Solve the equation

$$0.50x + 0.20(12 - x) = 0.30(12)$$ 50% = 0.50, 20% = 0.20, and 30% = 0.30.

$$5x + 2(12 - x) = 3(12)$$ Multiply both sides by 10 to clear the equation of decimals.

$$5x + 24 - 2x = 36$$ Distribute the multiplication by 2.

$$3x + 24 = 36$$ Combine like terms.

$$3x = 12$$ Subtract 24 from both sides.

$$x = 4$$ Divide both sides by 3.

State the conclusion The mixture will contain 4 liters of 50% solution and $12 - 4 = 8$ liters of 20% solution.

Check the result Verify that this answer checks. ■

In the next example, a *dry mixture* of a specified value is created from two differently priced components.

EXAMPLE 8   *Snack food.*   Because fancy cashews priced at $9 per pound were not selling, a market produce clerk decided to combine them with less expensive filberts and sell the mixture for $7 per pound. How many pounds of filberts, selling at $6 per pound, should be mixed with 50 pounds of cashews to obtain such a mixture?

Analyze the problem   We know the value of the cashews ($9 per pound) and the filberts ($6 per pound). We also know that 50 pounds of cashews are to be mixed with an unknown number of pounds of filberts to obtain a mixture worth $7 per pound.

Form an equation   To solve this problem, we use the formula $v = pn$, where v is value, p is the price per pound, and n is the number of pounds.

Suppose that x pounds of filberts are used in the mixture. At $6 per pound, they are worth $6x$. At $9 per pound, the 50 pounds of cashews are worth $9 \cdot 50 = \$450$. Their combined value will be $(6x + 450)$. We also know that the mixture weighs $(50 + x)$ pounds. At $7 per pound, that mixture will be worth $7(50 + x)$. This information is recorded in the table in Figure 2-19.

	p	$\cdot$ n	$=$ v
Filberts	6	x	$6x$
Cashews	9	50	450
Mixture	7	$50 + x$	$7(50 + x)$

FIGURE 2-19

We can use the information in the table to form the equation.

The value of the filberts	plus	the value of the cashews	equals	the value of the mixture.
$6x$	$+$	450	$=$	$7(50 + x)$

Solve the equation
$$6x + 450 = 7(50 + x)$$
$$6x + 450 = 350 + 7x \quad \text{Distribute the multiplication by 7.}$$
$$100 = x \quad \text{Subtract } 6x \text{ and } 350 \text{ from both sides.}$$

State the conclusion   Thus, 100 pounds of filberts should be used in the mixture.

Check the result
The value of 100 pounds of filberts at $6 per pound is $600
The value of 50 pounds of cashews at $9 per pound is $450
The value of the mixture is $1,050

The value of 150 pounds of the mixture at $7 per pound is also $1,050. The answer checks.

STUDY SET Section 2.6

VOCABULARY   *Fill in the blanks.*

1. The _____perimeter_____ of a triangle or a rectangle is the distance around it.

2. An _____isosceles_____ triangle is a triangle with two sides of the same length.

3. The equal sides of an isosceles triangle meet to form the _____vertex_____ angle.

4. The angles opposite the equal sides in an isosceles triangle are called _____base_____ angles, and they have equal measures.

CONCEPTS

5. PLUMBING   A plumber wants to cut a 17-foot pipe into three sections. The longest section is to be three times as long as the shortest, and the middle-sized section is to be 2 feet longer than the shortest.
 a. Complete the diagram in Illustration 1.

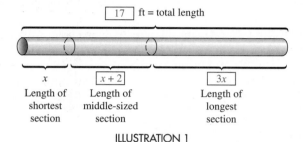

17   ft = total length

| x | $x + 2$ | $3x$ |
| Length of shortest section | Length of middle-sized section | Length of longest section |

ILLUSTRATION 1

 b. To solve this problem, an equation is formed, it is solved, and it is found that $x = 3$. How long is each section of pipe?   3 ft, 5 ft, 9 ft

6. What is the sum of the measures of the angles of any triangle?   180°

7. Use a ruler to draw an isosceles triangle with sides 3 inches long and a base that is 2 inches long. Label the vertex and the base angles.

8. a. Complete Illustration 2, which shows the inventory of nylon brushes that a paint store carries.

Paintbrush	Number	·	Value	=	Total value
1 inch	$\frac{x}{2}$		$4		$2x
2 inch	x		$5		$5x
3 inch	$x + 10$		$7		$7(x + 10)

ILLUSTRATION 2

 b. Which type of brush does the store have the largest number of?   3 in.
 c. What is the least expensive brush?   1 in.
 d. What is the total value of the inventory of nylon brushes? $(14x + 70)

9. In the advertisement in Illustration 3, what are the principal, the rate, and the time for the investment opportunity shown? $30,000, 14%, 1 yr

Invest in Mini Malls!
Builder seeks daring people who want to earn big $$$$$$. In just 1 year, you will earn a gigantic 14% on an investment of only $30,000! Call now.

ILLUSTRATION 3

10. a. Complete Illustration 4, which gives the details about two investments that were made by a retired couple.

	P	· r	= I
Certificate of deposit	x	0.04	$0.04x$
Brother-in-law's business	$2x$	0.06	$(0.06)2x$

ILLUSTRATION 4

 b. How much more money was invested in the brother-in-law's business than in the certificate of deposit?   twice as much
 c. What is the total amount of interest the couple will make from these investments?
   $0.04x + 0.12x = 0.16x$

11. COMMUTERS   When a husband and wife leave for work, they drive in opposite directions. Their average speeds are different; however, their drives last the same amount of time. Complete Illustration 5, which gives the details of each person's morning commute.

	r	· t	= d
Husband	35 mph	t hr	$35t$ mi
Wife	45 mph	t hr	$45t$ mi

ILLUSTRATION 5

12. Each bottle of dressing shown in Illustration 6 contains a mixture of oil and vinegar. After sitting overnight, the liquids separate completely, with the oil rising to the top. On each bottle, draw the line estimating where the separation would occur and shade the vinegar.

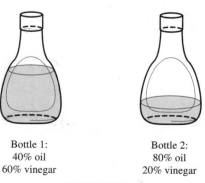

Bottle 1:
40% oil
60% vinegar

Bottle 2:
80% oil
20% vinegar

ILLUSTRATION 6

13. See Illustration 7.   **a.** How many gallons of acid are there in the second barrel?   16.8 gal

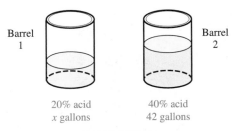

Barrel 1

Barrel 2

20% acid
x gallons

40% acid
42 gallons

ILLUSTRATION 7

b. Suppose the contents of the two barrels are poured into an empty third barrel. How many gallons of liquid will the third barrel contain? $(x + 42)$ gal

c. What would be a *reasonable* estimate of the concentration of the solution in the third barrel—19%, 32%, or 43% acid?   32%

14. Complete Illustration 8, which gives the details about the ingredients in a box of breakfast cereal.

	Price ($/oz)	Amount (oz)	Value
Blueberries	$0.38	x	$0.38x$
Bran Flakes	$0.08	14	$1.12
Blueberries & Bran Flakes Cereal	$0.21	$14 + x$	$0.21(14 + x)$

ILLUSTRATION 8

PRACTICE *In Exercises 15–16, solve the equation by first clearing it of decimals.*

15. $0.08x + 0.07(15,000 - x) = 1,110$ 6,000

16. $0.108x + 0.07(16,000 - x) = 1,500$ 10,000

17. Two angles are called **complementary angles** when the sum of their measures is 90°. Find the measures of the complementary angles shown in Illustration 9.   22°, 68°

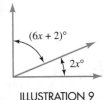

$(6x + 2)°$

$2x°$

ILLUSTRATION 9

18. Two angles are called **supplementary angles** when the sum of their measures is 180°. Find the measures of the supplementary angles shown in Illustration 10.
40°, 140°

$(4x + 40)°$

$(x + 15)°$

ILLUSTRATION 10

19. In Illustration 11, two lines intersect to form **vertical angles.** Use the fact that vertical angles have the same measure to find *x*.   15

$(2x + 5)°$ $(3x - 10)°$

ILLUSTRATION 11

20. Find the measures of the vertical angles shown in Illustration 12. (See Exercise 19.)   150°

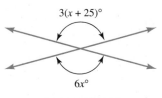

$3(x + 25)°$

$6x°$

ILLUSTRATION 12

APPLICATIONS

21. CARPENTRY   The 12-foot board in Illustration 13 has been cut into two sections, one twice as long as the other. How long is each section?   4 ft, 8 ft

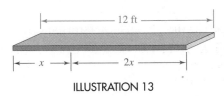

12 ft

x $2x$

ILLUSTRATION 13

22. ROBOTICS   The robotic arm shown in Illustration 14 will extend a total distance of 18 feet. Find the length of each section.   5 ft, 9 ft, 4 ft

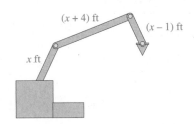

$(x + 4)$ ft

$(x - 1)$ ft

x ft

ILLUSTRATION 14

23. SOLAR HEATING   One solar panel in Illustration 15 is 3.4 feet wider than the other. Find the width of each panel.   7.3 ft, 10.7 ft

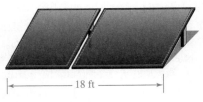

18 ft

ILLUSTRATION 15

24. PLUMBING   A 20-foot pipe has been cut into two sections, one 3 times as long as the other. How long is each section?   15 ft, 5 ft

25. TOURING An American rock group plans to travel for a total of 38 weeks, making three major concert tours. They will be in Japan for 4 more weeks than they will be in Australia. Their stay in Sweden will be 2 weeks less than that in Australia. How many weeks will they be in each country?
Australia: 12 wk; Japan: 16 wk; Sweden: 10 wk

26. PUBLISHER'S INVENTORY A novel can be purchased in a hardcover edition for $15.95 or in paperback for $4.95. The publisher printed 11 times as many paperbacks as hardcover books. A total of 114,000 books were printed. How many of each type were printed? 9,500 hardcovers, 104,500 paperbacks

27. COUNTING CALORIES A slice of pie with a scoop of ice cream has 850 calories. The calories in the pie alone are 100 more than twice the calories in the ice cream alone. How many calories are in each food? 250 calories in ice cream, 600 calories in pie

28. WASTE DISPOSAL Two tanks hold a total of 45 gallons of a toxic solvent. One tank holds 6 gallons more than twice the amount in the other. How many gallons does each tank hold? 13 gal, 32 gal

29. NET INCOME From the information given in Illustration 16, determine the net income of Sears, Roebuck and Co. for each quarter of 1999.
in millions: $148, $330, $235, $740

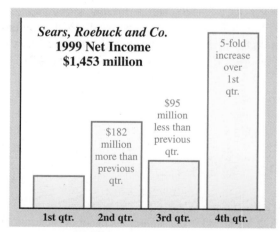

Sears, Roebuck and Co.
1999 Net Income
$1,453 million

5-fold increase over 1st qtr.

$95 million less than previous qtr.

$182 million more than previous qtr.

1st qtr.   2nd qtr.   3rd qtr.   4th qtr.

Based on data from Hoover's Online

ILLUSTRATION 16

30. LOCKS The three numbers of the combination for the lock shown in Illustration 17 are **consecutive integers,** and their sum is 81. (Consecutive integers follow each other, like 7, 8, 9.) Complete the instructions below that will open the lock. (*Hint:* If x represents the smallest integer, $x + 1$ represents the next integer, and $x + 2$ represents the largest integer.)

    Spin dial to the right one complete revolution to __26__. Turn to the left to __27__. Turn to the right to __28__, and lift the handle.

ILLUSTRATION 17

31. TRUSS The truss in Illustration 18 is in the form of an isosceles triangle. Each of the two equal sides is 4 feet less than the third side. If the perimeter is 25 feet, find the lengths of the sides. 7 ft, 7 ft, 11 ft

ILLUSTRATION 18

32. FIRST AID The sling shown in Illustration 19 is in the shape of an isosceles triangle with a perimeter of 144 inches. The longest side of the sling is 18 inches longer than either of the other two sides. Find the lengths of each side. 60 in., 42 in., 42 in.

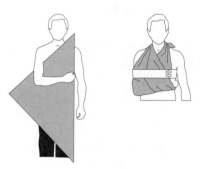

ILLUSTRATION 19

33. SWIMMING POOL The seawater Orthlieb Pool in Casablanca, Morocco is the largest swimming pool in the world. With a perimeter of 1,110 meters, this rectangular-shaped pool has a length that is 30 meters more than 6 times its width. Find its dimensions.
75 m by 480 m

34. ART The *Mona Lisa,* shown in Illustration 20, was completed by Leonardo da Vinci in 1506. The length of the picture is 11.75 inches less than twice the width. If the perimeter of the picture is 102.5 inches, find its dimensions. 21 in. by 30.25 in.

ILLUSTRATION 20

35. GUY WIRES   The two guy wires shown in Illustration 21 form an isosceles triangle. Each of the base angles of the triangle is 4 times the third angle (the vertex angle). Find the measure of the vertex angle.   20°

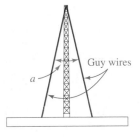

ILLUSTRATION 21

36. MOUNTAIN BICYCLE   For the bicycle frame in Illustration 22, the angle that the horizontal crossbar makes with the seat support is 15° less than twice the angle at the steering column. The angle at the pedal gear is 25° more than the angle at the steering column. Find these three angle measures.   42.5°, 70°, 67.5°

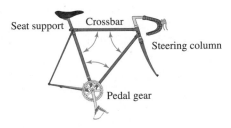

ILLUSTRATION 22

37. WAREHOUSING COSTS   A store warehouses 40 more portables than big-screen TV sets, and 25 fewer consoles than portables. Storage costs for the different TV sets are shown in Illustration 23. If storage costs $276 per month, how many big-screen sets are in stock?   12

Type of TV	Monthly cost
Portable	$1.50
Console	$4.00
Big-screen	$7.50

ILLUSTRATION 23

38. APARTMENT RENTAL   The owners of an apartment building rent 1-, 2-, and 3-bedroom units. They rent equal numbers of each, with the monthly rents given in Illustration 24. If the total monthly income is $36,550, how many of each type of unit are there?   17

Unit	Rent
One-bedroom	$550
Two-bedroom	$700
Three-bedroom	$900

ILLUSTRATION 24

39. SOFTWARE SALES   Three software applications are priced as shown in Illustration 25. Spreadsheet and database programs sold in equal numbers, but 15 more word processing applications were sold than the other two combined. If the three applications generated sales of $72,000, how many spreadsheets were sold?   90

Software	Price
Spreadsheet	$150
Database	$195
Word processing	$210

ILLUSTRATION 25

40. INVENTORY   With summer approaching, the number of air conditioners sold is expected to be double that of stoves and refrigerators combined. Stoves sell for $350, refrigerators for $450, and air conditioners for $500, and sales of $56,000 are expected. If stoves and refrigerators sell in equal numbers, how many of each appliance should be stocked?   20 stoves, 20 refrigerators, 80 air conditioners

41. INTEREST INCOME   On December 31, 2000, Terrell Washington opened two savings accounts. At the end of 2001, his bank mailed him the form shown in Illustration 26, for income tax purposes. If a total of $12,000 was initially deposited and if no further deposits or withdrawals were made, how much money was originally deposited in account number 721-94? $5,500

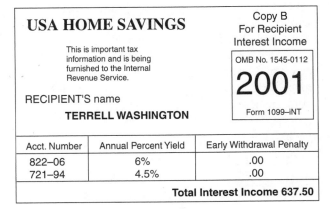

ILLUSTRATION 26

42. MAKING A PRESENTATION   A financial planner recommends a plan for a client who has $65,000 to invest. (See Illustration 27 on the next page.) At the end of the presentation, the client asks, "How much will be invested at each rate?" Answer this question using the given information. $42,200 at 12%, $22,800 at 6.2%

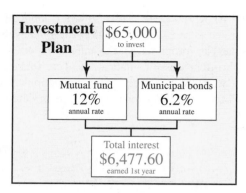

ILLUSTRATION 27

43. INVESTMENTS   Equal amounts are invested in each of three accounts paying 7%, 8%, and 10.5% annually. If one year's combined interest income is $1,249.50, how much is invested in each account? $4,900

44. RETIREMENT   A professor wants to supplement her retirement income with investment interest. If she invests $15,000 at 6% interest, how much more would she have to invest at 7% to achieve a goal of $1,250 per year in supplemental income? $5,000

45. FINANCIAL PLANNING   A plumber has a choice of two investment plans:

• An insured fund that pays 11% interest

• A risky investment that pays a 13% return

If the same amount invested at the higher rate would generate an extra $150 per year, how much does the plumber have to invest? $7,500

46. INVESTMENTS   The amount of annual interest earned by $8,000 invested at a certain rate is $200 less than $12,000 would earn at a rate 1% lower. At what rate is the $8,000 invested?   8%

47. TORNADO   During a storm, two teams of scientists leave a university at the same time in specially designed vans to search for tornadoes. The first team travels east at 20 mph and the second travels west at 25 mph, as shown in Illustration 28. If their radios have a range of up to 90 miles, how long will it be before they lose radio contact?   2 hr

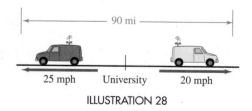

ILLUSTRATION 28

48. SEARCH AND RESCUE   Two search-and rescue teams leave base at the same time looking for a lost boy. The first team, on foot, heads north at 2 mph and the other, on horseback, south at 4 mph. How long will it take them to search a distance of 21 miles between them?   3.5 hr

49. SPEED OF TRAINS   Two trains are 330 miles apart, and their speeds differ by 20 mph. Find the speed of each train if they are traveling toward each other and will meet in 3 hours.   65 mph, 45 mph

50. AVERAGE SPEED   A car averaged 40 mph for part of a trip and 50 mph for the remainder. If the 5-hour trip covered 210 miles, for how long did the car average 40 mph?   4 hr

51. AIR TRAFFIC CONTROL   An airliner leaves Berlin, Germany, headed for Montreal, Canada, flying at an average speed of 450 mph. At the same time, an airliner leaves Montreal headed for Berlin, averaging 500 mph. If the airports are 3,800 miles apart, when will the air traffic controllers have to make the pilots aware that the planes are passing each other?   4 hr into the flights

52. ROAD TRIP   A bus, carrying the members of a marching band, and a truck, carrying their instruments, leave a high school at the same time. The bus travels at 65 mph and the truck at 55 mph. In how many hours will they be 75 miles apart?   7.5 hr

53. SALT SOLUTION   How many gallons of a 3% salt solution must be mixed with 50 gallons of a 7% solution to obtain a 5% solution?   50

54. MAKING CHEESE   To make low-fat cottage cheese, milk containing 4% butterfat is mixed with 10 gallons of milk containing 1% butterfat to obtain a mixture containing 2% butterfat. How many gallons of the richer milk must be used?   5

55. ANTISEPTIC SOLUTION   A nurse wants to add water to 30 ounces of a 10% solution of benzalkonium chloride to dilute it to an 8% solution. How much water must she add?   7.5 oz

56. PHOTOGRAPHIC CHEMICALS   A photographer wishes to mix 2 liters of a 5% acetic acid solution with a 10% solution to get a 7% solution. How many liters of 10% solution must be added? $1\frac{1}{3}$

57. MIXING FUELS   How many gallons of fuel costing $1.15 per gallon must be mixed with 20 gallons of a fuel costing $0.85 per gallon to obtain a mixture costing $1 per gallon? See Illustration 29.   20

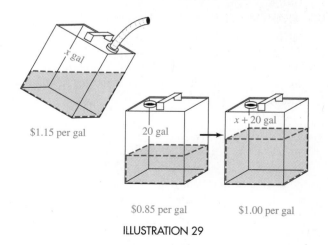

ILLUSTRATION 29

58. MIXING PAINT   Paint costing $19 per gallon is to be mixed with 5 gallons of a $3-per-gallon thinner to make a paint that can be sold for $14 per gallon. How much paint will be produced?   16 gal

59. MIXING CANDY   Lemon drops worth $1.90 per pound are to be mixed with jelly beans that cost $1.20 per pound to make 100 pounds of a mixture worth $1.48 per pound. How many pounds of each candy should be used?   40 lb lemon drops, 60 lb jelly beans

60. MIXING CANDY   See Illustration 30. Twenty pounds of lemon drops are to be mixed with cherry chews to make a mixture that will sell for $1.80 per pound. How much of the more expensive candy should be used?
10 lb

Candy	Price per pound
Peppermint patties	$1.35
Lemon drops	$1.70
Licorice lumps	$1.95
Cherry chews	$2.00

ILLUSTRATION 30

61. BLENDING COFFEE   A store sells regular coffee for $4 a pound and gourmet coffee for $7 a pound. To get rid of 40 pounds of the gourmet coffee, a shopkeeper makes a blend to put on sale for $5 a pound. How many pounds of regular coffee should he use?   80

62. BLENDING LAWN SEED   A store sells bluegrass seed for $6 per pound and ryegrass seed for $3 per pound. How much ryegrass must be mixed with 100 pounds of bluegrass to obtain a blend that will sell for $5 per pound?   50 lb

WRITING

63. Create a mixture problem of your own, and solve it.

64. Use an example to explain the difference between the quantity and the value of the materials being combined in a mixture problem.

65. A car travels at 60 mph for 15 minutes. Why can't we multiply the rate, 60, and the time, 15, to find the distance traveled by the car?

66. Create a geometry problem that could be answered by solving the equation $2w + 2(w + 5) = 26$.

REVIEW   *Use the distributive property to remove parentheses.*

67. $-25(2x - 5)$
$-50x + 125$

68. $-12(3a + 4b - 32)$
$-36a - 48b + 384$

69. $-(-3x - 3)$ $3x + 3$

70. $\frac{1}{2}(4b - 8)$ $2b - 4$

Combine like terms.

71. $8p - 9q + 11p + 20q$ $19p + 11q$

72. $-5(t - 120) - 7(t + 5)$ $-12t + 565$

2.7 *Inequalities*

In this section, you will learn about

- Inequality symbols • Graphing inequalities • Interval notation
- Solving inequalities • Graphing compound inequalities
- Solving compound inequalities • An application

INTRODUCTION. Inequalities are expressions indicating that two quantities are not necessarily equal. They appear in many situations:

- An airplane is rated to fly at altitudes that are less than 36,000 feet.
- To melt ice, the temperature must be greater than 32°F.
- To earn a B, I need a final exam score of at least 80%.

Inequality symbols

We can use **inequality symbols** to show that two expressions are not equal.

Inequality symbols	$\ne$	means	"is not equal to"
	$<$	means	"is less than"
	$>$	means	"is greater than"
	$\le$	means	"is less than or equal to"
	$\ge$	means	"is greater than or equal to"

EXAMPLE 1   *Reading inequalities.*

a. $6 \ne 9$ is read as "6 is not equal to 9."

b. $8 > 4$ is read as "8 is greater than 4."

c. $12 \ge 0$ is read as "12 is greater than or equal to 0." This is true, because $12 > 0$.

d. $5 \le 5$ is read as "5 is less than or equal to 5." This is true, because $5 = 5$.

Self Check

Write each inequality in words:
a. $15 < 20$,   **b.** $y \ge 9$,
c. $10 \ge 1$,   and   **d.** $30 \le 30$.

Answers: **a.** 15 is less than 20.
b. y is greater than or equal to 9.
c. 10 is greater than or equal to 1.
d. 30 is less than or equal to 30.

If two numbers are graphed on a number line, the one to the right is the greater. For example, from Figure 2-20, we see that $-1 > -4$, because -1 lies to the right of -4.

FIGURE 2-20

Inequalities can be written so that the inequality symbol points in the opposite direction. For example, the following statements both indicate that 27 is a smaller number than 32.

$27 < 32$ (27 is less than 32)   and $32 > 27$ (32 is greater than 27)

The following statements both indicate that 9 is greater than or equal to 6.

$9 \ge 6$ (9 is greater than or equal to 6)   and $6 \le 9$ (6 is less than or equal to 9)

Variables can be used with inequality symbols to show mathematical relationships. For example, consider the statement, "You must be taller than 54 inches to ride the roller coaster." If we let h represent a person's height in inches, then to ride the roller coaster, $h > 54$ inches.

EXAMPLE 2   *Writing inequalities.*   Express the following situation using an inequality symbol: "The occupancy of the dining room cannot exceed 200 people."

Solution

If p represents the number of people that can occupy the room, then p cannot be greater than (exceed) 200. Another way to state this is that p must be *less than or equal to 200*.

$p \le 200$

Self Check

Express the following statement using an inequality symbol: "The thermostat on the pool heater is set so that the water temperature t is at least 72°."

Answer: $t \ge 72$

Graphing inequalities

Graphs of inequalities involving real numbers are **intervals** on the number line. For example, two versions of the graph of all real numbers x such that $x > -3$ are shown in Figure 2-21.

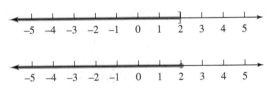

All real numbers greater than –3

FIGURE 2-21

The red arrow pointing to the right shows that all numbers to the right of -3 are in the graph. The **parenthesis** (or open circle) at -3 indicates that -3 is not in the graph.

Interval notation

The interval shown in Figure 2-21 can be expressed in **interval notation** as $(-3, \infty)$. Again, the first parenthesis indicates that -3 is not included in the interval. The infinity symbol ∞ does not represent a number. It indicates that the interval continues on forever to the right.

Figure 2-22 shows two versions of the graph of $x \le 2$. The thick red arrow pointing to the left shows that all numbers to the left of 2 are in the graph. The **bracket** (or closed circle) at 2 indicates that 2 is included in the graph. We can express this interval as $(-\infty, 2]$. Here the bracket indicates that 2 is included in the interval.

From now on, we will use parentheses or brackets when graphing intervals, because they are consistent with interval notation.

All real numbers less than or equal to 2

FIGURE 2-22

EXAMPLE 3   *Writing an inequality from its graph.*   What inequality is represented by each graph?

a.

b.

Solution

a. This is the interval $(-\infty, 3]$, which consists of all real numbers less than or equal to 3. The inequality is $x \le 3$.

b. This is the interval $(-1, \infty)$, consisting of all real numbers greater than -1. The inequality is $x > -1$.

Self Check

What inequality is represented by each graph?

a.

b.

Answers:

a. $x \le -1, (-\infty, -1]$

b. $x > -4, (-4, \infty)$

Solving inequalities

A **solution of an inequality** is any number that makes the inequality true. For example, 2 is a solution of $x \le 3$, because $2 \le 3$.

To solve more complicated inequalities, we will use the addition, subtraction, multiplication, and division properties of inequality. When we use one of these properties, the resulting inequality will always be equivalent to the original one.

Addition and subtraction properties of inequality

> For real numbers a, b, and c,
>
> If $a < b$,   then $a + c < b + c$.
>
> If $a < b$,   then $a - c < b - c$.
>
> Similar statements can be made for the symbols $>$, $\leq$, and $\geq$.

The **addition property of inequality** can be stated this way: *If a quantity is added to both sides of an inequality, the resulting inequality will have the same direction as the original one.*

The **subtraction property of inequality** can be stated this way: *If a quantity is subtracted from both sides of an inequality, the resulting inequality will have the same direction as the original one.*

EXAMPLE 4   *Solving inequalities.*   Solve $x + 3 > 2$ and graph its solution.

Solution

To isolate the x on the left-hand side of the $>$ sign, we proceed as we would when solving equations.

$$x + 3 > 2$$
$$x + 3 - 3 > 2 - 3 \quad \text{To undo the addition of 3, subtract 3 from both sides.}$$
$$x > -1 \quad \text{Do the subtractions: } 3 - 3 = 0 \text{ and } 2 - 3 = 2 + (-3) = -1.$$

All real numbers greater than -1 are solutions of $x + 3 > 2$. This means the inequality has *infinitely many* solutions. The graph of the solutions (see Figure 2-23) includes all points to the right of -1 but does not include -1. Expressed as an interval, this is $(-1, \infty)$.

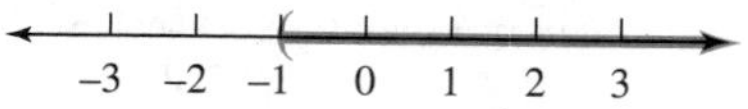

FIGURE 2-23

Since the solution contains infinitely many numbers, we cannot check to see if each of them satisfies the original inequality. As an informal check, we pick several numbers in the graph, such as 1 and 30, substitute each number for x in the inequality, and see whether it satisfies the inequality.

$$x + 3 > 2$$
$$1 + 3 \overset{?}{>} 2 \quad \text{Substitute 1 for } x.$$
$$4 > 2 \quad \text{Do the addition.}$$

$$x + 3 > 2$$
$$30 + 3 \overset{?}{>} 2 \quad \text{Substitute 30 for } x.$$
$$33 > 2 \quad \text{Do the addition.}$$

Since $4 > 2$, we know that 1 satisfies the inequality. Since $33 > 2$, we know that 30 satisfies the inequality. The result ($x > -1$) appears to be correct.

Self Check

Solve $x - 3 \leq -2$ and graph its solution. Then use interval notation to describe the solution.

Answer: $x \leq 1$, $(-\infty, 1]$

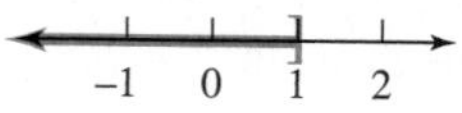

If both sides of the inequality $2 < 5$ are multiplied by a *positive* number, such as 3, another true inequality results.

$$2 < 5$$
$$3 \cdot 2 < 3 \cdot 5 \quad \text{Multiply both sides by 3.}$$
$$6 < 15 \quad \text{Do the multiplications: } 3 \cdot 2 = 6 \text{ and } 3 \cdot 5 = 15.$$

However, if we multiply both sides of $2 < 5$ by a *negative* number, such as -3, the direction of the inequality symbol must be reversed to produce another true inequality.

$$2 < 5$$

$$-3 \cdot 2 > -3 \cdot 5 \quad \text{Multiply both sides by the negative number } -3 \text{ and reverse the direction of the inequality.}$$

$$-6 > -15 \quad \text{Do the multiplications: } -3 \cdot 2 = -6 \text{ and } -3 \cdot 5 = -15.$$

The inequality $-6 > -15$ is true because -6 is to the right of -15 on the number line.

Multiplication and division properties of inequalities

For real numbers a, b, and c,

If $a < b$ and $c > 0$, then $ac < bc$.

If $a < b$ and $c < 0$, then $ac > bc$.

If $a < b$ and $c > 0$, then $\frac{a}{c} < \frac{b}{c}$.

If $a < b$ and $c < 0$, then $\frac{a}{c} > \frac{b}{c}$.

Similar statements can be made for the symbols $>$, $\leq$, and $\geq$.

The **multiplication property of inequality** can be stated this way:

If both sides of an inequality are multiplied by the same positive number, the resulting inequality will have the same direction as the original one.

If both sides of an inequality are multiplied by the same negative number, the resulting inequality will have the opposite direction from the original one.

The **division property of inequality** can be stated this way:

If both sides of an inequality are divided by the same positive number, the resulting inequality will have the same direction as the original one.

If both sides of an inequality are divided by the same negative number, the resulting inequality will have the opposite direction from the original one.

EXAMPLE 5 *Solving inequalities.* Solve $-5 \geq 3x + 7$ and graph the solution.

Self Check

Solve $2x - 7 > -13$ and graph the solution. Then use interval notation to describe the solution.

Solution

$$-5 \geq 3x + 7$$

$$-5 - 7 \geq 3x + 7 - 7 \quad \text{To undo the addition of 7, subtract 7 from both sides.}$$

$$-12 \geq 3x \quad \text{Subtract: } -5 - 7 = -5 + (-7) = -12 \text{ and } 7 - 7 = 0.$$

$$\frac{-12}{3} \geq \frac{3x}{3} \quad \text{To undo the multiplication by 3, divide both sides by 3.}$$

$$-4 \geq x \quad \text{Do the divisions.}$$

It is common practice to present a solution such as $-4 \geq x$ in an equivalent form with the variable on the left-hand side. If -4 is greater than or equal to x, then x must be less than or equal to -4, and we can write the solution as

$$x \leq -4$$

The graph (shown in Figure 2-24) consists of all real numbers less than or equal to -4. Using interval notation, we have $(-\infty, -4]$.

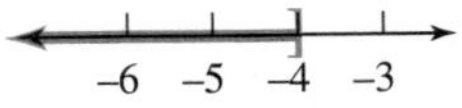

FIGURE 2-24

To check, we can pick several numbers in the graph, such as -6 and -20, and see whether each one satisfies the inequality.

For $x = -6$

$-5 \geq 3x + 7$

$-5 \overset{?}{\geq} 3(-6) + 7$ Substitute -6 for x.

$-5 \overset{?}{\geq} -18 + 7$ Do the multiplication.

$-5 \geq -11$ Do the addition.

For $x = -20$

$-5 \geq 3x + 7$

$-5 \overset{?}{\geq} 3(-20) + 7$

$-5 \overset{?}{\geq} -60 + 7$

$-5 \geq -53$

Answer: $x > -3, (-3, \infty)$

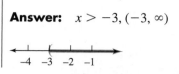

Since $-5 \geq -11$, we know that -6 satisfies the inequality. Since $-5 \geq -53$, we know that -20 satisfies the inequality. The result ($x \leq -4$) appears to be correct.

EXAMPLE 6   *Reversing the inequality symbol.*   Solve $5 - 3x < 14$ and graph the solution.

Self Check

Solve $-2x - 5 \geq -11$ and graph the solution. Then use interval notation to describe the solution.

Solution

$$5 - 3x < 14$$

$5 - 3x - 5 < 14 - 5$ To isolate $-3x$ on the left-hand side, subtract 5 from both sides.

$-3x < 9$ Do the subtractions: $5 - 5 = 0$ and $14 - 5 = 9$.

$\dfrac{-3x}{-3} > \dfrac{9}{-3}$ To undo the multiplication by -3, divide both sides by -3. Since we are dividing by a negative number, we reverse the direction of the $<$ symbol.

$x > -3$

The graph is shown in Figure 2-25. This is the interval $(-3, \infty)$, which consists of all real numbers greater than -3.

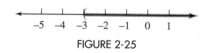

FIGURE 2-25

Answer: $x \leq 3, (-\infty, 3]$

Check the result.

EXAMPLE 7   *Reversing the inequality symbol.*   Solve $\dfrac{x}{-15} \geq -6$ and graph the solution.

Self Check

Solve $\dfrac{h}{-20} < 10$ and graph the solution.

Solution

$$\frac{x}{-15} \geq -6$$

$-15\left(\dfrac{x}{-15}\right) \leq -15(-6)$ To undo the division by -15, multiply both sides by -15. Since we are multiplying by a negative number, we reverse the direction of the $\geq$ symbol.

$x \leq 90$ Do the multiplications.

The graph is shown in Figure 2-26. This is the interval $(-\infty, 90]$, which consists of all real numbers less than or equal to 90.

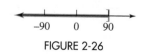

FIGURE 2-26

Answer: $h > -200, (-200, \infty)$

COMMENT   Remember that if both sides of an inequality are multiplied or divided by a negative number, the direction of the inequality symbol must be reversed.

EXAMPLE 8 *Solving inequalities.* Solve $5(x + 1) \leq 2(x - 3)$ and graph the solution.

Solution

$$5(x + 1) \leq 2(x - 3)$$

$5x + 5 \leq 2x - 6$	Use the distributive property on both sides of the inequality.
$5x + 5 - 2x \leq 2x - 6 - 2x$	To eliminate $2x$ from the right side, subtract $2x$ from both sides.
$3x + 5 \leq -6$	Combine like terms on both sides.
$3x + 5 - 5 \leq -6 - 5$	To undo the addition of 5, subtract 5 from both sides.
$3x \leq -11$	Do the subtractions.
$\dfrac{3x}{3} \leq \dfrac{-11}{3}$	To undo the multiplication by 3, divide both sides by 3.
$x \leq -\dfrac{11}{3}$	

The graph is shown in Figure 2-27. This is the interval $\left(-\infty, -\frac{11}{3}\right]$, which consists of all real numbers less than or equal to $-\frac{11}{3}$. We note that $-\frac{11}{3} = -3\frac{2}{3}$.

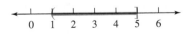

FIGURE 2-27

Check the result.

Self Check

Solve $3(x - 2) > -(x + 1)$ and graph the solution. Then use interval notation to describe the solution.

Answer: $x > \dfrac{5}{4}, \left(\dfrac{5}{4}, \infty\right)$

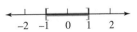

Graphing compound inequalities

Two inequalities can be combined into a **compound inequality** to indicate that numbers lie *between* two fixed values. For example, $-2 < x < 3$ is a combination of

$$-2 < x \quad \text{and} \quad x < 3$$

It indicates that x is greater than -2 and that x is also less than 3. The solution of $-2 < x < 3$ consists of all numbers that lie *between* -2 and 3. The graph of this interval appears in Figure 2-28. We can express this interval as $(-2, 3)$.

FIGURE 2-28

EXAMPLE 9 *Writing an inequality from its graph.* What inequality is represented by the graph below?

Solution

$1 < x \leq 5$. This is the interval $(1, 5]$.

Self Check

What inequality is represented by the graph below?

Answer: $-1 \leq x \leq 1$. This is the interval $[-1, 1]$.

EXAMPLE 10 *Graphing compound inequalities.*   Graph the interval $-4 < x \leq 0$.

Solution

The interval $-4 < x \leq 0$ consists of all real numbers between -4 and 0, including 0. The graph appears in Figure 2-29. This is the interval $(-4, 0]$.

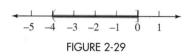

FIGURE 2-29

To check, we pick a number, such as -2, in the graph and see whether it satisfies the inequality. Since $-4 < -2 \leq 0$, the answer appears to be correct.

Self Check

Graph the interval $-2 \leq x < 1$. Then use interval notation to describe the solution.

Answer: $[-2, 1)$

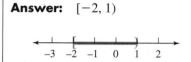

Solving compound inequalities

To solve compound inequalities, we use the same methods we used for solving equations. However, instead of applying the properties of equality to both sides of an equation, we will apply the properties of inequality to all three parts of the inequality.

EXAMPLE 11 *Solving compound inequalities.*   Solve $-4 < 2(x - 1) \leq 4$ and graph the solution.

Solution

$$-4 < 2(x - 1) \leq 4$$

$$-4 < 2x - 2 \leq 4 \qquad \text{Distribute the multiplication by 2.}$$

$$-4 + 2 < 2x - 2 + 2 \leq 4 + 2 \qquad \text{To undo the subtraction of 2, add 2 to all three parts.}$$

$$-2 < 2x \leq 6 \qquad \text{Do the additions.}$$

$$-1 < x \leq 3 \qquad \text{To undo the multiplication by 2, divide all three parts by 2.}$$

The graph of the solution appears in Figure 2-30. This is the interval $(-1, 3]$.

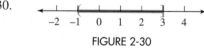

FIGURE 2-30

Check the solution.

Self Check

Solve $-6 \leq 3(x + 2) \leq 6$ and graph the solution. Then use interval notation to describe the solution.

Answer: $-4 \leq x \leq 0, [-4, 0]$

An application

When solving problems, phrases such as "not more than," "at least," or "should exceed" suggest that an *inequality* should be written instead of an *equation*.

EXAMPLE 12   *Grades.*   A student has scores of 72%, 74%, and 78% on three exams. What percent score does he need on the last exam to earn no less than a grade of B (80%)?

Analyze the problem   We know three of the student's scores. We are to find what he must score on the last exam to earn at least a B grade.

Form an inequality   We can let x represent the score on the fourth (and last) exam. To find the average grade, we add the four scores and divide by 4. To earn no less than a grade of B, the student's average must be greater than or equal to 80%.

The average of the four grades	must be greater than or equal to	80.
$\dfrac{72 + 74 + 78 + x}{4}$	$\geq$	80

Solve the inequality   We can solve this inequality for *x*.

$$\frac{224 + x}{4} \geq 80 \quad \text{Simplify the numerator: } 72 + 74 + 78 = 224.$$

$$224 + x \geq 320 \quad \text{To clear the inequality of the fraction, multiply both sides by 4.}$$

$$x \geq 96 \quad \text{To undo the addition of 224, subtract 224 from both sides.}$$

State the conclusion   To earn a B, the student must score 96% or better on the last exam. Of course, the student cannot score higher than 100%. The graph appears in Figure 2-31. This is the interval [96, 100].

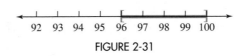

FIGURE 2-31

Check the result   Pick some numbers in the interval, and verify that the average of the four scores will be 80% or greater.   ∎

STUDY SET Section 2.7

VOCABULARY   *Fill in the blanks.*

1. An expression containing one of the symbols $>, <, \geq, \leq,$ or $\neq$ is called an ___inequality___.

2. Graphs of inequalities involving real numbers are called ___intervals___ on the number line.

3. A ___solution___ of an inequality is any real number that makes the inequality true.

4. The inequality $-4 < x \leq 12$ is an example of a ___compound___ inequality.

CONCEPTS

5. Tell whether each statement is true or false.
   a. $35 \geq 34$ true   **b.** $5.61 \geq 5.61$ true
   c. $-16 \leq -17$ false   **d.** $0 \leq -2\frac{1}{8}$ false
   e. $\frac{3}{4} \leq 0.75$ true   **f.** $-0.6 \geq -0.5$ false

6. Tell whether each number is a solution of $3x + 7 < 4x - 2$.
   a. $x = 12$ yes   **b.** $x = -6$ no
   c. $x = 0$ no   **d.** $x = 9$ no

In Exercises 7–10, fill in the blanks.

7. If a quantity is added to or subtracted from both sides of an inequality, the resulting inequality will have the ___same___ direction as the original one.

8. If both sides of an inequality are multiplied or divided by a positive number, the resulting inequality will have the ___same___ direction as the original one.

9. If both sides of an inequality are multiplied or divided by a negative number, the resulting inequality will have the ___opposite___ direction from the original one.

10. To solve compound inequalities, the properties of inequalities are applied to all ___three___ parts of the inequality.

11. The solution of an inequality is graphed below.

   a. If 3 is substituted for the variable in the inequality, will a true or a false statement result?
   a true statement
   b. If -3 is substituted for the variable in the inequality, will a true or a false statement result?
   a false statement

12. The solution of a compound inequality is graphed below.

   a. If 3 is substituted for the variable in the inequality, will a true or a false statement result?
   a false statement
   b. If -3 is substituted for the variable in the inequality, will a true or a false statement result?
   a true statement

13. Solve the inequality $2x - 4 > 12$, and give the solution:
   a. in words   all real numbers greater than 8
   b. using a graph
   c. using interval notation $(8, \infty)$

14. Solve the compound inequality $-4 < 2x < 12$, and give the solution:

   a. in words   all real numbers between -2 and 6

   b. using a graph

   c. using interval notation $(-2, 6)$

NOTATION *In Exercises 15–18, fill in the blanks.*

15. The symbol $<$ means "___is less than___," and the symbol $>$ means "___is greater than___."

16. The symbol $\geq$ means "___is greater than___ or equal to," and the symbol $\leq$ means "is less than ___or equal to___."

17. The symbol $\neq$ means "___is not equal to___."

18. In the interval $[4, 8)$, the endpoint 4 is ___included___, but the endpoint 8 is not included.

19. Suppose you solve an inequality and obtain $-2 < x$. Rewrite this inequality so that x is on the left-hand side. $x > -2$

20. Explain what is wrong with the compound inequality $8 < x < -1$.   8 is not less than -1.

Write each inequality so that the inequality symbol points in the opposite direction.

21. $17 \geq -2$ $-2 \leq 17$

22. $-32 < -10$ $-10 > -32$

Complete the solution to solve each inequality.

23.
$$4x - 5 \geq 7$$
$$4x - 5 + \;5\; \geq 7 + \;5\;$$
$$4x \geq \;12\;$$
$$\frac{4x}{4} \geq \frac{12}{4}$$
$$x \geq 3$$

24.
$$\frac{-x}{2} + 4 < 5$$
$$\frac{-x}{2} + 4 - \;4\; < 5 - \;4\;$$
$$\frac{-x}{2} < \;1\;$$
$$2\left(\frac{-x}{2}\right) < \;2\; (1)$$
$$-x < 2$$
$$\frac{-x}{-1} > \frac{2}{-1}$$
$$x > -2$$

PRACTICE *Graph each inequality. Then describe the graph using interval notation.*

25. $x < 5$ $(-\infty, 5)$

26. $x \geq -2$ $[-2, \infty)$

27. $-3 < x \leq 1$ $(-3, 1]$

28. $-1 \leq x \leq 3$ $[-1, 3]$

Write the inequality that is represented by each graph. Then describe the graph using interval notation.

29. $x < -1, (-\infty, -1)$

30. $x \geq 2, [2, \infty)$

31. $-7 < x \leq 2, (-7, 2]$

32. $-3 \leq x \leq 1, [-3, 1]$

Solve each inequality, graph the solution, and use interval notation to describe the solution.

33. $x + 2 > 5$
$x > 3, (3, \infty)$

34. $x + 5 \geq 2$
$x \geq -3, [-3, \infty)$

35. $-x - 3 \leq 7$
$x \geq -10, [-10, \infty)$

36. $-x - 9 > 3$
$x < -12, (-\infty, -12)$

37. $3 + x < 2$
$x < -1, (-\infty, -1)$

38. $5 + x \geq 3$
$x \geq -2, [-2, \infty)$

39. $2x - 0.3 \leq 0.5$
$x \leq 0.4, (-\infty, 0.4]$

40. $-3x - 0.5 < 0.4$
$x > -0.3, (-0.3, \infty)$

41. $-3x - 7 > -1$
$x < -2, (-\infty, -2)$

42. $-5x + 7 \leq 12$
$x \geq -1, [-1, \infty)$

43. $-4x + 6 > 17$
$x < -\frac{11}{4}, \left(-\infty, -\frac{11}{4}\right)$

44. $7x - 1 > 5$
$x > \frac{6}{7}, \left(\frac{6}{7}, \infty\right)$

45. $\frac{y}{4} + 1 \leq -9$
$y \leq -40, (-\infty, -40]$

46. $\frac{r}{8} - 7 \geq -8$
$r \geq -8, [-8, \infty)$

47. $-\dfrac{1}{2}n \geq -1$

$n \leq 2, (-\infty, 2]$

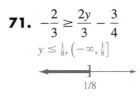

48. $-\dfrac{1}{3}t \leq -3$

$t \geq 9, [9, \infty)$

49. $\dfrac{x}{-42} - 1 > -1$

$x < 0, (-\infty, 0)$

50. $\dfrac{a}{-25} + 3 < 3$

$a > 0, (0, \infty)$

51. $\dfrac{2}{3}x \geq 2$ $\quad x \geq 3, [3, \infty)$

52. $\dfrac{3}{4}x < 3$ $\quad x < 4, (-\infty, 4)$

53. $-\dfrac{7}{8}x \leq 21$

$x \geq -24, [-24, \infty)$

54. $-\dfrac{3}{16}x \geq -9$

$x \leq 48, (-\infty, 48]$

55. $2x + 9 \leq x + 8$

$x \leq -1, (-\infty, -1]$

56. $3x + 7 \leq 4x - 2$

$x \geq 9, [9, \infty)$

57. $9x + 13 \geq 8x$

$x \geq -13, [-13, \infty)$

58. $7x - 16 < 6x$

$x < 16, (-\infty, 16)$

59. $8x + 4 > 3x + 4$

$x > 0, (0, \infty)$

60. $7x + 6 \geq 4x + 6$

$x \geq 0, [0, \infty)$

61. $5x + 7 < 2x + 1$

$x < -2, (-\infty, -2)$

62. $7x + 2 \geq 4x - 1$

$x \geq -1, [-1, \infty)$

63. $7 - x \leq 3x - 2$

$x \geq \dfrac{9}{4}, \left[\dfrac{9}{4}, \infty\right)$

64. $9 - 3x \geq 6 + x$

$x \leq \dfrac{3}{4}, \left(-\infty, \dfrac{3}{4}\right]$

65. $3(x - 8) < 5x + 6$

$x > -15, (-15, \infty)$

66. $9(x - 11) > 13 + 7x$

$x > 56, (56, \infty)$

67. $8(5 - x) \leq 10(8 - x)$

$x \leq 20, (-\infty, 20]$

68. $17(3 - x) \geq 3 - 13x$

$x \leq 12, (-\infty, 12]$

69. $\dfrac{1}{2} + \dfrac{x}{5} > \dfrac{3}{4}$

$x > \dfrac{5}{4}, \left(\dfrac{5}{4}, \infty\right)$

70. $\dfrac{1}{3} + \dfrac{c}{5} > -\dfrac{3}{2}$

$c > -\dfrac{55}{6}, \left(-\dfrac{55}{6}, \infty\right)$

71. $-\dfrac{2}{3} \geq \dfrac{2y}{3} - \dfrac{3}{4}$

$y \leq \dfrac{1}{8}, \left(-\infty, \dfrac{1}{8}\right]$

72. $-\dfrac{2}{9} \geq \dfrac{5x}{6} - \dfrac{1}{3}$

$x \leq \dfrac{2}{15}, \left(-\infty, \dfrac{2}{15}\right]$

Solve each inequality, graph the solution, and use interval notation to describe the solution.

73. $2 < x - 5 < 5$

$7 < x < 10, (7, 10)$

74. $3 < x - 2 < 7$

$5 < x < 9, (5, 9)$

75. $-5 < x + 4 \leq 7$

$-9 < x \leq 3, (-9, 3]$

76. $-9 \leq x + 8 < 1$

$-17 \leq x < -7, [-17, -7)$

77. $0 \leq x + 10 \leq 10$

$-10 \leq x \leq 0, [-10, 0]$

78. $-8 < x - 8 < 8$

$0 < x < 16, (0, 16)$

79. $4 < -2x < 10$

$-5 < x < -2, (-5, -2)$

80. $-4 \leq -4x < 12$

$-3 < x \leq 1, (-3, 1]$

81. $-3 \leq \dfrac{x}{2} \leq 5$

$-6 \leq x \leq 10, [-6, 10]$

82. $-12 < \dfrac{x}{3} < 0$

$-36 < x < 0, (-36, 0)$

83. $3 \leq 2x - 1 < 5$

$2 \leq x < 3, [2, 3)$

84. $4 < 3x - 5 \leq 7$

$3 < x \leq 4, (3, 4]$

85. $0 < 10 - 5x \leq 15$

$-1 \leq x < 2, [-1, 2)$

86. $1 \leq -7x + 8 \leq 15$

$-1 \leq x \leq 1, [-1, 1]$

Solve each inequality.

87. $0.6(0.5x - 2.94) < -1.353$

$x < 1.37, (-\infty, 1.37)$

88. $-0.7688 \leq \dfrac{m}{3.5} - 0.1988$

$m \geq -1.995, [-1.995, \infty)$

89. $9(0.05 - 0.3x) + 0.162 \leq 0.081 + 15x$

$x \geq 0.03, [0.03, \infty)$

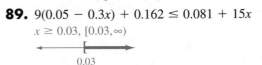

90. $-1,630 \leq \dfrac{b + 312,451}{47} < 42,616$

$-389,061 \leq b < 1,690,501, \ [-389,061, 1,690,501)$

$-389,061 \qquad 1,690,501$

APPLICATIONS

91. CALCULATING GRADES   A student has test scores of 68%, 75%, and 79% in a government class. What must she score on the last exam to earn a B (80% or better) in the course?   98% or better

92. OCCUPATIONAL TESTING   Before taking on a client, an employment agency requires the applicant to average at least 70% on a battery of four job skills tests. If an applicant scored 70%, 74%, and 84% on the first three exams, what must he score on the fourth test to maintain a 70% or better average?   52% or better

93. FLEET AVERAGES   A car manufacturer produces three models in equal quantities. One model has an economy rating of 17 miles per gallon, and the second model is rated for 19 mpg. If governmental regulations require the manufacturer to have a fleet average of at least 21 mpg, what economy rating is required for the third model?   27 mpg or better

94. SERVICE CHARGES   When the average daily balance of a customer's checking account falls below $500 in any week, the bank assesses a $5 service charge. Illustration 1 shows the daily balances of one customer. What must Friday's balance be to avoid the service charge? $869.20 or more

Day	Balance
Monday	$540.00
Tuesday	$435.50
Wednesday	$345.30
Thursday	$310.00

ILLUSTRATION 1

95. DOING HOMEWORK   A Spanish teacher requires that students devote no less than 1 hour a day to their homework assignments. Write an inequality that describes the number of minutes m a student should spend each week on Spanish homework. $t \geq 420$ min

96. CHILD LABOR   A child labor law reads, "The number of hours a full-time student under 16 years of age can work on a weekday shall not exceed 4 hours." Write an inequality that describes the number of hours h such a student can work Monday through Friday. $h \leq 20$ hr

97. SAFETY CODE   Illustration 2 shows the acceptable and preferred angles of "pitch" or slope for ladders, stairs, and ramps. Use a compound inequality to describe each safe-angle range.
  a. Ramps or inclines $0° < a \leq 18°$
  b. Stairs $18° \leq a \leq 50°$
  c. Preferred range for stairs $30° \leq a \leq 37°$
  d. Ladders with cleats $75° \leq a < 90°$

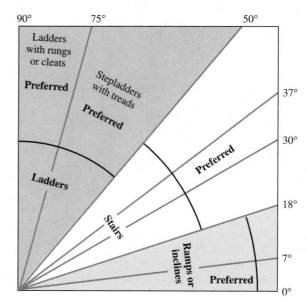

ILLUSTRATION 2

98. WEIGHT CHART   Illustration 3 (next page) is used to classify the weight of a baby boy from birth to 1 year. Estimate the weight range w for boys in the following classifications, using a compound inequality:
  a. 10 months old, "heavy" 26 lb $\leq w \leq 31$ lb
  b. 5 months old, "light" 12 lb $\leq w \leq 14$ lb
  c. 8 months old, "average" 18.5 lb $\leq w \leq 20.5$ lb
  d. 3 months old, "moderately light"
     11 lb $\leq w \leq 13$ lb

99. LAND ELEVATIONS   The land elevations in Nevada range from the 13,143-foot height of Boundary Peak to the Colorado River at 470 feet. Use a compound inequality to express the range of these elevations.
  a. in feet 470 ft $\leq x \leq 13,143$ ft
  b. in miles (round to the nearest tenth)
     (*Hint:* 1 mile is 5,280 feet.) 0.1 mi $\leq x \leq 2.5$ mi

100. COMPARING TEMPERATURES   To hold the temperature of a room between 19°C and 22°C, what Fahrenheit temperatures must be maintained? $\left(\textit{Hint:} \text{ Fahrenheit temperature } F \text{ and Celsius temperature } C \text{ are related by the formula } F = \frac{9C + 160}{5}.\right)$
  $66.2° < F < 71.6°$

101. DRAFTING   In Illustration 4, the $\pm$ (read "plus or minus") symbol means that the width of a plug a manufacturer produces can range from $1.497 - 0.001$ inches to $1.497 + 0.001$ inches. Write the range of acceptable widths w for the plug and the opening it fits into using compound inequalities.
  1.496 in. $\leq w \leq 1.498$ in.; 1.5000 in. $\leq w \leq 1.5010$ in.

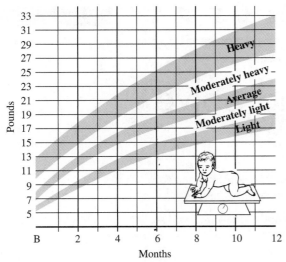

Based on data from *Better Homes and Gardens Baby Book* (Meredith Corp., 1969)

ILLUSTRATION 3

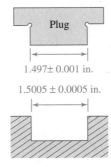

Plug

1.497± 0.001 in.

1.5005 ± 0.0005 in.

ILLUSTRATION 4

102. COUNTER SPACE   In a large discount store, a rectangular counter is being built for the customer

service department. If designers have determined that the outside perimeter of the counter (shown in red) needs to be at least 150 feet, use the plan in Illustration 5 to determine the acceptable values for x.

$x \geq 35$ ft

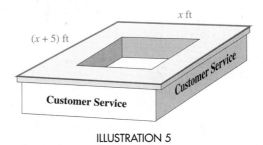

ILLUSTRATION 5

WRITING

103. Explain why multiplying both sides of an inequality by a negative number reverses the direction of the inequality.

104. Explain the use of parentheses and brackets for graphing intervals.

REVIEW   *Find each power.*

105. -5^3 -125 **106.** $(-3)^4$ 81

Complete each input/output table.

107.

x	$x^2 - 3$
-2	1
0	-3
3	6

108.

x	$\frac{x}{3} + 2$
-6	0
0	2
12	6

Simplify and Solve

Two of the most often used instructions in this book are **simplify** and **solve.** In algebra, we *simplify expressions* and we *solve equations and inequalities.*

To simplify an expression, we write it in a less complicated form. To do so, we apply the rules of arithmetic as well as algebraic concepts such as combining like terms, the distributive property, and the properties of 0 and 1.

To solve an equation or an inequality means to find the numbers that make the equation or inequality true, when substituted for its variable. We use the addition, subtraction, multiplication, and division properties of equality or inequality to solve equations and inequalities. Quite often, we must simplify expressions on the left- or right-hand sides of an equation or inequality when solving it.

In Exercises 1–4, use the procedures and the properties that we have studied to simplify the expression in part a and to solve the equation or inequality in part b.

Simplify

1. a. $-3x + 2 + 5x - 10$ $2x - 8$

2. a. $4(y + 2) - 3(y + 1)$ $y + 5$

3. a. $\dfrac{1}{3}a + \dfrac{1}{3}a$ $\frac{2}{3}a$

4. a. $-(2x + 10)$ $-2x - 10$

Solve

b. $-3x + 2 + 5x - 10 = 4$ $x = 6$

b. $4(y + 2) = 3(y + 1)$ $y = -5$

b. $\dfrac{1}{3}a + \dfrac{1}{3} = \dfrac{1}{2}$ $a = \frac{1}{2}$

b. $-2x \geq -10$ $x \leq 5$

5. In the student's work on the right, where was the mistake made? Explain what the student did wrong.

The mistake is on the third line. The student made an equation out of the answer, which is $x - 6$, by writing "0 =" on the left. Then the student solved that equation.

Simplify $2(x + 3) - x - 12$.

$$2(x + 3) - x - 12 = 2x + 6 - x - 12$$
$$= x - 6$$
$$0 = x - 6$$
$$0 + 6 = x - 6 + 6$$
$$\boxed{6 = x}$$

Section 2.1

SUBTRACTION PROPERTY OF EQUALITY   Check out a scale and some weights from your school's science department. Use them as part of a class presentation to explain how the subtraction property of equality is used to solve the equation $x + 2 = 5$. See the discussion and Figure 2-1 on page 89 for some suggestions on how to do this.

Section 2.2

TRANSLATION   Determine whether addition, subtraction, multiplication, or division is suggested by each of the following words or phrases. If you are unsure of a word, a dictionary may be helpful.

annexed	*remission*	*partition*
abate	*bisect*	*shrink*
magnify	*eroded*	*evaporate*
boost	*dwindling*	*wane*
quadrupled	*to contract*	*upsurge*
corrode	*hike*	*to taper off*
trisect	*elongate*	*wax*
amplify	*to protract*	*leavening*
diminish	*broaden*	*receding*

Section 2.3

THE DISTRIBUTIVE PROPERTY Draw a geometric model on the graph paper below that illustrates why

$$5(4 + 2) = 5(4) + 5(2)$$

A similar example can be found in Figure 2-9 on page 111.

Section 2.4

SOLVING EQUATIONS   Make a presentation to the class explaining how we "undo" operations to isolate the variable when solving an equation. As a visual aid, bring in a box, tied shut with string, that contains a toy wrapped in tissue paper. Compare the three-step process a person would use to get to the toy inside the box to the three-step process we could use to solve the equation $\frac{2x}{3} - 4 = 2$.

SOLVING EQUATIONS   In Section 2.1, a scale was used to illustrate the steps used to solve an equation.

a. What equation is being solved in Illustration 1? What is the solution?

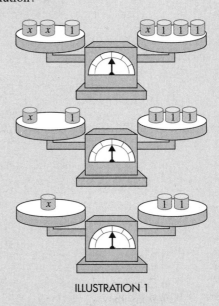

ILLUSTRATION 1

b. Draw a similar series of pictures showing the solution of each of the following equations.

   (1) $3x + 1 = 2x + 4$ **(2)** $2x + 6 = 4x + 2$

Section 2.5

GEOMETRY GOURMET   Find snack foods that have the shapes of the geometric figures in Table 2-4 and Table 2-5 on pages 131 and 133. For example, tortilla chips can be triangular in shape, and malted milk balls are spheres. If you are unable to find a particular shape already available, decide on a way to make a snack in that shape. Make up a tray of snacks to bring to class. Discuss the various shapes of the snacks as you enjoy the food in your groups.

Section 2.6

MIXTURES   Get several cans of orange juice concentrate and make four pitchers that are 10%, 30%, 50%, and 70% solutions. For example, a 30% solution would consist of three paper cups of concentrate and seven paper cups of water. Pour amounts of each mixture into cups. Have students taste each solution and see whether they can put the mixtures in order from least concentrated to most concentrated.

Section 2.7

INEQUALITIES   In most states, a person must be at least 16 years old to have a driver's license. We can describe this situation with the inequality $a \geq 16$, where a represents a person's age in years. Think of other situations that can be described using an inequality or a compound inequality.

CHAPTER REVIEW

Solving Equations

CONCEPTS

An *equation* is a statement indicating that two expressions are equal. Any number that makes an equation true when substituted for its variable is said to *satisfy* the equation. Such numbers are called *solutions* or *roots*.

To *solve an equation,* isolate the variable on one side of the equation by undoing the operations performed on it.

Two equations are *equivalent* when they have the same solutions.

If the same number is added to, or subtracted from, both sides of an equation, an equivalent equation results.

If both sides of an equation are multiplied, or divided, by the same nonzero number, an equivalent equation results.

REVIEW EXERCISES

1. Tell whether the given number is a solution of the equation.

   a. $x - 34 = 50; x = 84$ yes
   b. $5y + 2 = 12; y = 3$ no

   c. $\dfrac{x}{5} = 6; x = 30$ yes
   d. $a^2 - a - 1 = 0; a = 2$ no

   e. $5b - 2 = 3b + 3; b = 3$ no
   f. $\dfrac{2}{y + 1} = \dfrac{12}{y + 1} - 5; y = 1$ yes

2. Fill in the blanks: When solving the equation $x + 8 = 10$, we are to find all the values of the _____variable_____ that make the equation a _____true_____ statement.

3. Solve each equation. Check each result.

   a. $x - 9 = 12$ 21
   b. $y + 15 = 32$ 17

   c. $4 = v - 1$ 5
   d. $100 = 7 + x$ 93

   e. $2x = 40$ 20
   f. $120 = 15c$ 8

   g. $x - 11 = 0$ 11
   h. $p + 3 = 3$ 0

   i. $\dfrac{t}{8} = 12$ 96
   j. $3 = \dfrac{q}{26}$ 78

   k. $6b = 0$ 0
   l. $\dfrac{x}{14} = 0$ 0

Problem Solving

To solve a problem, follow these steps:
1. Analyze the problem.
2. Form an equation.
3. Solve the equation.
4. State the conclusion.
5. Check the result.

Drawing a diagram or creating a table is often helpful in problem solving.

4. Write an equation that describes the same quantity in two ways: At the end of the holiday season, a bakery had sold 165 cherry cheesecakes. This was 28 cheesecakes less than the projected sales total. Let $x =$ the number of cheesecakes the bakery had hoped to sell. $x - 28 = 165$

5. SOCIAL WORK A human services program assigns each of its social workers a caseload of 75 clients. How many clients are served by this program if it employs 20 social workers? 1,500

6. HISTORIC TOUR A driving tour of three historic cities is an 858-mile round trip. Beginning in Boston, the drive to Philadelphia is 296 miles. From Philadelphia to Washington, DC is another 133 miles. How long will the return trip to Boston be? 429 mi

7. CARDS A standard deck of 54 playing cards contains 2 jokers, 4 aces, and 12 face cards; the remainder are numbered cards. How many numbered cards are there in a standard deck? 36

8. CHROME WHEELS   Find the measure of the angle between each of the spokes on the wheel shown in Illustration 1.   60°

ILLUSTRATION 1

We can translate a percent problem from words into an equation. A variable is used to stand for the unknown number; *is* can be translated to an = sign; and *of* means multiply.

The percent formula:
   Amount = percent · base

9. Translate "16 is 5% of an unknown number" into an equation. $16 = 0.05x$

10. COST OF LIVING   A retired trucker receives a monthly Social Security check of $764. If she is to receive a 3.5% cost-of-living increase soon, how much larger will her check be? $26.74

11. 4.81 is 2.5% of what number?   192.4

12. FAMILY BUDGET   It is recommended that a family pay no more than 30% of its monthly income (after taxes) on housing. If a family has an after-tax income of $1,890 per month and pays $625 in housing costs each month, are they within the recommended range?   no

13. ADVERTISING   In 1999, $215 billion was spent on advertising in the United States. The circle graph in Illustration 2 shows the individual expenditures in percents. Find the amount of money spent on television advertising. $51.6 billion

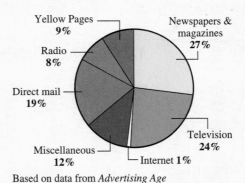

Yellow Pages
9%

Newspapers & magazines
27%

Radio
8%

Direct mail
19%

Miscellaneous
12%

Internet 1%

Television
24%

Based on data from *Advertising Age*

ILLUSTRATION 2

To find *percent of increase or decrease,* find what percent the increase or decrease is of the original amount.

14. COLLECTIBLES   A collector of football trading cards paid $6 for a 1984 Dan Marino rookie card several years ago. If the card is now worth $100, what is the percent of increase in the card's value? (Round to the nearest one percent.)   1,567%

SECTION 2.3   *Simplifying Algebraic Expressions*

To *simplify* an algebraic expression means to write it in less complicated form.

The *distributive property:*
   $a(b + c) = ab + ac$

   $a(b - c) = ab - ac$

15. Simplify each expression.
   a. $-4(7w)$ $-28w$
   b. $-3r(-5r)$ $15r^2$
   c. $3(-2x)(-4y)$ $24xy$
   d. $0.4(5.2f)$ $2.08f$

16. Write each expression without parentheses.
   a. $5(x + 3)$ $5x + 15$
   b. $-2(2x + 3 - y)$ $-4x - 6 + 2y$
   c. $-(a - 4)$ $-a + 4$
   d. $\frac{3}{4}(4c - 8)$ $3c - 6$

A *term* is a number or a product of a number and one or more variables. Addition signs separate algebraic expressions into terms.

17. How many terms are in each expression?

   a. $3x^2 + 2x - 5$ 3
   b. $-12xyz$ 1

In a term, the numerical factor is called the *coefficient*.

18. Identify the coefficient of each term.

   a. $2x - 5$ $2, -5$
   b. $16x^2 - 5x + 25$ $16, -5, 25$

   c. $\frac{1}{2}x + y$ $\frac{1}{2}, 1$
   d. $9.6t^2 - t$ $9.6, -1$

Like terms are terms with exactly the same variables raised to exactly the same powers.

19. Simplify each expression by combining like terms.

   a. $8p + 5p - 4p$ $9p$
   b. $-5m + 2n - 2m - 2n$ $-7m$
   c. $6a + 2b - 8a - 12b$
      $-2a - 10b$
   d. $5(p - 2) - 2(3p + 4)$
      $-p - 18$
   e. $x^2 - x(x - 1)$ x
   f. $8a^3 + 4a^3 - 20a^3$ $-8a^3$

20. Write an algebraic expression in simplified form for the perimeter of the triangle in Illustration 3.
$(4x + 4)$ ft

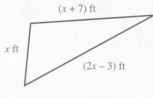

$(x + 7)$ ft

x ft

$(2x - 3)$ ft

ILLUSTRATION 3

SECTION 2.4

More about Solving Equations

To solve an equation means to find all the values of the variable that, when substituted for the variable, make a true statement.

An equation that is true for all values of its variable is called an *identity*.

An equation that is not true for any values of its variable is called an *impossible equation*.

21. Solve each equation.

   a. $5x + 4 = 14$ 2
   b. $-1.2y + 0.8 = 2.0$ -1

   c. $\frac{n}{5} - 2 = 4$ 30
   d. $\frac{b - 5}{4} = -6$ -19

   e. $5(2x - 4) - 5x = 0$ 4
   f. $-2(x - 5) = 5(-3x + 4) + 3$ 1

   g. $\frac{3}{4} = \frac{1}{2} + \frac{d}{5}$ $\frac{5}{4}$
   h. $-\frac{2}{3}f = 4$ -6

   i. $3(a + 8) = 6(a + 4) - 3a$
      identity, all values of a
   j. $2(y + 10) + y = 3(y + 8)$
      impossible equation, no solution

SECTION 2.5

Formulas

A *formula* is an equation that is used to state a known relationship between two or more variables.

Retail price: $r = c + m$

Profit: $p = r - c$

Distance: $d = rt$

22. Find the markup on a CD player whose wholesale cost is $219 and whose retail price is $395. $176

23. One month, a restaurant had sales of $13,500 and made a profit of $1,700. Find the expenses for the month. $11,800

24. INDY 500 In 1996, the winner of the Indianapolis 500-mile automobile race averaged 147.956 mph. To the nearest hundredth of an hour, how long did it take him to complete the race? 3.38 hr

Temperature: $C = \dfrac{5(F - 32)}{9}$

Formulas from geometry:

Square: $P = 4s, A = s^2$

Rectangle: $P = 2l + 2w,$
$A = lw$

Triangle: $P = a + b + c$
$A = \frac{1}{2}bh$

Trapezoid:
$P = a + b + c + d$
$A = \frac{1}{2}h(b + d)$

Circle: $D = 2r$
$C = 2\pi r$
$A = \pi r^2$

Rectangular solid: $V = lwh$

Cylinder: $V = \pi r^2 h$

Pyramid: $V = \frac{1}{3}Bh$
Cone: $V = \frac{1}{3}\pi r^2 h$
Sphere: $V = \frac{4}{3}\pi r^3$

25. JEWELRY MAKING   Gold melts at about 1,065°C. Change this to degrees Fahrenheit.   1,949°F

26. CAMPING   Find the perimeter of the air mattress in Illustration 4.   168 in.

27. CAMPING   Find the amount of sleeping area on the top surface of the air mattress in Illustration 4.   1,440 in.^{2}

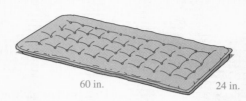

60 in.   24 in.

ILLUSTRATION 4

28. Find the area of a triangle with a base 17 meters long and a height of 9 meters.   76.5 m^2

29. Find the area of a trapezoid with bases 11 inches and 13 inches long and a height of 12 inches.   144 in.^{2}

30. To the nearest hundredth, find the circumference of a circle with a radius of 8 centimeters.   50.27 cm

31. To the nearest hundredth, find the area of the circle in Exercise 30.   201.06 cm^2

32. CAMPING   Find the approximate volume of the air mattress in Illustration 4 if it is 3 inches thick.   4,320 in.^{3}

33. Find the volume of a 12-foot cylinder whose circular base has a radius of 0.5 feet. Give the result to the nearest tenth.   9.4 ft^3

34. Find the volume of a pyramid that has a square base, measuring 6 feet on a side, and a height of 10 feet.   120 ft^3

35. HALLOWEEN   After being cleaned out, a spherical-shaped pumpkin has an inside diameter of 9 inches. To the nearest hundredth, what is its volume?   381.70 in.^{3}

36. Solve each formula for the required variable.
   a. $A = 2\pi rh$ for h $h = \frac{A}{2\pi r}$ **b.** $P = 2l + 2w$ for l $l = \frac{P - 2w}{2}$

SECTION 2.6	*More about Problem Solving*

To solve problems, use the five-step problem-solving strategy.
1. Analyze the problem.
2. Form an equation.
3. Solve the equation.
4. State the conclusion.
5. Check the result.

37. SOUND SYSTEM   A 45-foot-long speaker wire is to be cut into three pieces. One piece is to be 15 feet long. Of the remaining pieces, one must be 2 feet less than 3 times the length of the other. Find the length of the shorter piece of wire.   8 ft

38. UTILITY BILLS   The electric company charges $17.50 per month plus 18 cents for every kilowatt hour of energy used. One resident's bill was $43.96. How many kilowatt hours were used that month?   147

39. ART HISTORY   *American Gothic,* shown in Illustration 5, was painted in 1930 by American artist Grant Wood. The length of the rectangular painting is 5 inches more than the width. Find the dimensions of the painting if it has a perimeter of $109\frac{1}{2}$ inches.   24.875 in. × 29.875 in. ($24\frac{7}{8}$ in. × $29\frac{7}{8}$ in.)

ILLUSTRATION 5

The sum of the measures of the angles of a triangle is 180°.

40. Find the missing angle measures of the triangle in Illustration 6.   76.5°, 76.5°

ILLUSTRATION 6

Total value = number · value

41. What is the value of x video games each costing $45? $45x$

Interest = principal · rate · time
$I = Prt$

42. INVESTMENT INCOME   A woman has $27,000. Part is invested for one year in a certificate of deposit paying 7% interest, and the remaining amount in a cash management fund paying 9%. After 1 year, the total interest on the two investments is $2,110. How much is invested at each rate? $16,000 at 7%, $11,000 at 9%

Distance = rate · time
$d = rt$

43. WALKING AND BICYCLING   A bicycle path is 5 miles long. A man walks from one end at the rate of 3 mph. At the same time, a friend bicycles from the other end, traveling at 12 mph. In how many minutes will they meet?   20

The value v of a commodity is its price per pound p times the number of pounds n:
$v = pn$

44. MIXTURE   A store manager mixes candy worth 90¢ per pound with gumdrops worth $1.50 per pound to make 20 pounds of a mixture worth $1.20 per pound. How many pounds of each kind of candy does he use?   10 lb of each

45. SOLUTION   How much acetic acid is in x gallons of a solution that is 12% acetic acid? $0.12x$ gal

---

SECTION 2.7   *Inequalities*

An *inequality* is a mathematical expression that contains a >, <, ≥, ≤, or ≠ symbol.

A *solution of an inequality* is any number that makes the inequality true.

A *parenthesis* indicates that a number is not on the graph. A *bracket* indicates that a number is included in the graph.

Interval notation can be used to describe a set of real numbers.

46. Solve each inequality, graph the solution, and use interval notation to describe the solution.

a. $3x + 2 < 5$
   $x < 1, (-\infty, 1)$

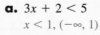

b. $-5x - 8 > 7$
   $x < -3, (-\infty, -3)$

c. $5x - 3 \geq 2x + 9$
   $x \geq 4, [4, \infty)$

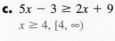

d. $7x + 1 \leq 8x - 5$
   $x \geq 6, [6, \infty)$

e. $5(3 - x) \leq 3(x - 3)$
$x \geq 3, [3, \infty)$

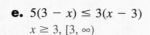

f. $-\dfrac{3}{4}x \geq -9$
$x \leq 12, (-\infty, 12]$

g. $8 < x + 2 < 13$
$6 < x < 11, (6, 11)$

h. $0 \leq 2 - 2x < 6$
$-2 < x \leq 1, (-2, 1]$

47. Graph the interval represented by $[-13, \infty)$.

48. SPORTS EQUIPMENT   The acceptable weight of ping-pong balls used in competition can range from 2.40 to 2.53 grams. Express this range using a compound inequality. $2.40 \text{ g} < w < 2.53 \text{ g}$

49. SIGNS   A large office complex has a strict policy about signs. Any sign to be posted in the building must meet three requirements:

- It must be rectangular in shape.
- Its width must be 18 inches.
- Its perimeter is not to exceed 132 inches.

What possible sign lengths meet these specifications?
The sign length must be 48 inches or less.

Chapter 2 Test

1. Is $x = 3$ a solution of the equation $2x + 3 = 4x - 6$?
no

2. Solve $5 = x - 25$.   30

3. MULTIPLE BIRTHS IN THE UNITED STATES   In 1998, about 7,620 women gave birth to three or more babies at one time. This is about six times the number of such births in 1978, 20 years earlier. How many multiple births occurred in 1978?   1,270

4. DOWN PAYMENT   To buy a house, a woman was required to make a down payment of $11,400. What did the house sell for if this was 15% of the purchase price? $76,000

5. SPORTS STATISTICS   In sports, percentages are most often expressed as three-place decimals instead of percents. For example, if a basketball player makes 75.8% of his free throws, the sports page will list this as .758. Use this format to complete Illustration 1.

All-Time Best Regular-Season Winning Percentages		
Team	**Won–lost record**	**Winning percentage**
1996 Chicago Bulls Basketball	72–10	.878
1972 Miami Dolphins Football	14–0	1.000

ILLUSTRATION 1

6. BODY TEMPERATURE   Suppose a person's body temperature rises from 98.6°F to 101.6°F. What is the percent increase? Round to the nearest one percent.   3%

7. How many terms are in the expression $4x^2 + 5x - 7$? What is the coefficient of the second term?   3; 5

8. What property is illustrated below?

$2(x + 7) = 2x + 2(7)$ the distributive property

Simplify each expression.

9. $5(-4x)$ $-20x$

10. $-8(-7t)(4t)$ $224t^2$

11. $3(x + 2) + 3(4 - x)$
18

12. $-1.1d^2 - 3.8d^2$
$-4.9d^2$

Solve each equation.

13. $12x = -144$ -12

14. $\frac{4}{5}t = -4$ -5

15. $\frac{c}{7} = -1$ -7

16. $0.3x = 0.5 - 0.2x$ 1

17. $\frac{m}{2} - \frac{1}{3} = \frac{1}{4}$
$\frac{7}{6}$

18. $23 - 5(x + 10) = -12$
-3

19. Solve the equation for the variable indicated.

$A = P + Prt$; for r $r = \frac{A - P}{Pt}$

20. On its first night of business, a pizza parlor brought in $445. The owner estimated his costs that night to be $295. What was the profit? $150

21. Find the Celsius temperature reading if the Fahrenheit reading is 14°. $-10°$ C

22. PETS   The spherical fishbowl shown in Illustration 2 is three-quarters full of water. To the nearest cubic inch, what is the volume of water in the bowl?   393 in.^{3}

10 in.

ILLUSTRATION 2

23. TRAVEL TIMES   A car leaves Rockford, Illinois at the rate of 65 mph, bound for Madison, Wisconsin. At the same time, a truck leaves Madison at the rate of 55 mph, bound for Rockford. If the cities are 72 miles apart, how long will it take for the car and the truck to meet? $\frac{3}{5}$ hr

24. SALT SOLUTION   How many liters of a 2% brine solution must be added to 30 liters of a 10% brine solution to dilute it to an 8% solution?   10

25. GEOMETRY   If the vertex angle of an isosceles triangle is 44°, find the measure of each base angle.   68°

26. INVESTMENT PROBLEM   Part of $13,750 is invested at 9% annual interest, and the rest is invested at 8%. After one year, the accounts paid $1,185 in interest. How much was invested at the lower rate? $5,250

In Problems 27–28, solve each inequality, graph the solution, and use interval notation to describe the solution.

27. $-8x - 20 \le 4$

$x \ge -3$, $[-3, \infty)$

28. $-4 \le 2(x + 1) < 10$

$-3 \le x < 4$, $[-3, 4)$

29. After we have solved an equation, how can we check the answer to be sure that it is a solution?

Substitute the answer for the variable. If it is a solution, a true statement will result.

30. What are like terms? Give an example.

Like terms are terms with exactly the same variables, raised to exactly the same powers. $10p^2$ and $6p^2$ are like terms.

Chapters 1-2   Cumulative Review Exercises

1. Classify each of the following as an equation or an expression.

a. $4m - 3 + 2m$
expression

b. $4m = 3 + 2m$
equation

2. Use the formula $t = \dfrac{w}{5}$ to complete the table.

Weight (lb)	Cooking time (hr)
15	3
20	4
25	5

3. Give the prime factorization of 200.
$5 \cdot 5 \cdot 2 \cdot 2 = 2^2 \cdot 5^2$

4. Simplify $\dfrac{24}{36}$. $\frac{2}{3}$

5. Multiply: $\dfrac{11}{21}\left(-\dfrac{14}{33}\right)$. $-\frac{2}{9}$

6. COOKING   A recipe calls for $\frac{3}{4}$ cup of flour, and the only measuring container you have holds $\frac{1}{8}$ of a cup. How many $\frac{1}{8}$ cups of flour would you need to add to follow the recipe?   6

7. Add: $\dfrac{4}{5} + \dfrac{2}{3}$. $\frac{22}{15} = 1\frac{7}{15}$

8. Subtract: $42\dfrac{1}{8} - 29\dfrac{2}{3}$. $12\frac{11}{24}$

9. Write $\dfrac{15}{16}$ as a decimal.   0.9375

10. Multiply: $0.45(100)$.   45

11. Evaluate each expression.

a. $|-65|$ 65
b. $-|-12|$ -12

12. What property of real numbers is illustrated below?

$x \cdot 5 = 5x$ the commutative property of multiplication

In Exercises 13–16, classify each number as a natural number, a whole number, an integer, a rational number, an irrational number, and a real number. Each number may have several classifications.

13. 3   natural number, whole number, integer, rational number, real number

14. -1.95 rational number, real number

15. $\dfrac{17}{20}$ rational number, real number

16. π irrational number, real number

17. Write each product using exponents.

a. $4 \cdot 4 \cdot 4$ 4^3
b. $\pi \cdot r \cdot r \cdot h$ $\pi r^2 h$

18. Do each operation.

a. $-6 + (-12) + 8$ -10
b. $-15 - (-1)$ -14
c. $2(-32)$ -64
d. $\dfrac{0}{35}$ 0

19. Write each phrase as an algebraic expression.

a. The sum of the width w and 12. $w + 12$
b. Four less than a number n. $n - 4$

20. SICK DAYS   Use the data in Illustration 1 to find the average (mean) number of sick days used by this group of employees this year.   4

Name	Sick days	Name	Sick days
Chung	4	Ryba	0
Cruz	8	Nguyen	5
Damron	3	Tomaka	4
Hammond	2	Young	6

ILLUSTRATION 1

21. Complete the table of values.

x	$x^2 - 3$
-2	1
0	-3
3	6

22. Translate to mathematical symbols.

The loudness of a stereo speaker	is	2,000	divided by	the square of the distance of the listener from the speaker.

$l = \dfrac{2,000}{d^2}$ (Answers may vary depending on the variables chosen.)

23. LAND OF THE RISING SUN   The flag of Japan is a red disc (representing sincerity and passion) on a white background (representing honesty and purity).

a. What is the area of the rectangular-shaped flag in Illustration 2 (on the next page)? $6\ \text{ft}^2$
b. To the nearest tenth of a square foot, what is the area of the red disc? $1.2\ \text{ft}^2$

c. Use the results from parts a and b to find what percent of the area of the Japanese flag is occupied by the red disc.   20%

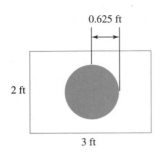

0.625 ft

2 ft

3 ft

ILLUSTRATION 2

24. 45 is 15% of what number?   300

Let x = −5, y = 3, and z = 0. Evaluate each expression.

25. $(3x − 2y)z$ 0

26. $\dfrac{x − 3y + |z|}{2 − x}$ −2

27. $x^2 − y^2 + z^2$ 16

28. $\dfrac{x}{y} + \dfrac{y + 2}{3 − z}$ 0

Simplify each expression.

29. $−8(4d)$
$−32d$

30. $5(2x − 3y + 1)$
$10x − 15y + 5$

31. $2x + 3x$ $5x$

32. $3a + 6a − 17a$ $−8a$

33. $q(q − 5) + 7q^2$
$8q^2 − 5q$

34. $5(t − 4) + 3t$
$8t − 20$

35. What is the length of the longest side of the triangle in Illustration 3? $(x + 3)$ ft

36. Write an algebraic expression in simplest form for the perimeter of the triangle in Illustration 3. $3x$ ft

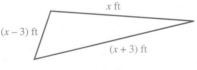

x ft

$(x − 3)$ ft

$(x + 3)$ ft

ILLUSTRATION 3

In Exercises 37–44, solve each equation.

37. $3x − 4 = 23$ 9

38. $\dfrac{x}{5} + 3 = 7$ 20

39. $−5p + 0.7 = 3.7$
$−0.6$

40. $\dfrac{y − 4}{5} = 3$
19

41. $−\dfrac{4}{5}x = 16$ $−20$

42. $−9(n + 2) − 2(n − 3) = 10$ $−2$

43. $9y − 3 = 6y$ 1

44. $\dfrac{1}{2} + \dfrac{x}{5} = \dfrac{3}{4}$ $\frac{5}{4}$

45. Find the area of a rectangle with sides of 5 meters and 13 meters.   65 m²

46. Find the volume of a cone that is 10 centimeters tall and has a circular base whose diameter is 12 centimeters. Round to the nearest hundredth.   376.99 cm³

47. Solve $A = P + Prt$ for t. $t = \dfrac{A − P}{Pr}$

48. WORK   Physicists say that *work* is done when an object is moved a distance d by a force F. To find the work done, we can use the formula $W = Fd$. Find the work done in lifting the bundle of newspapers shown in Illustration 4 onto the workbench. (*Hint:* The force that must be applied to lift the newspapers is equal to the weight of the newspapers.)   37.5 ft-lb

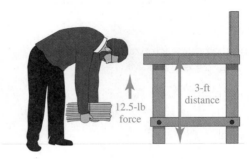

12.5-lb force

3-ft distance

ILLUSTRATION 4

49. WORK   See Exercise 48. Find the weight of a 1-gallon can of paint if the amount of work done to lift it onto the workbench is 28.35 foot-pounds.   9.45 lb

50. Find the unknown angle measure represented by x.   55°, 55°

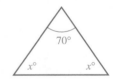

70°

$x°$ $x°$

51. INVESTING   An investment club invested part of $10,000 at 9% annual interest and the rest at 8%. If the annual income from these investments was $860, how much was invested at 8%? $4,000

52. GOLDSMITH   How many ounces of a 40% gold alloy must be mixed with 10 ounces of a 10% gold alloy to obtain an alloy that is 25% gold?   10 oz

Solve each inequality, graph the solution, and use interval notation to describe the solution.

53. $x − 4 > −6$
$x > −2, (−2, ∞)$ −2

54. $−6x ≥ −12$
$x ≤ 2, (−∞, 2]$ 2

55. $8x + 4 ≥ 5x + 1$
$x ≥ −1, [−1, ∞)$ −1

56. $−1 ≤ 2x + 1 < 5$
$−1 ≤ x < 2, [−1, 2)$ −1   2

Graphs, Linear Equations, and Functions

3

R<small>ELATIONSHIPS BETWEEN TWO QUANTITIES CAN BE</small>

D<small>ESCRIBED BY A TABLE, A GRAPH, OR AN EQUATION.</small>

3.1 Graphing Using the Rectangular Coordinate System

In this section, you will learn about

- The rectangular coordinate system • Graphing mathematical relationships
- Reading graphs • Step graphs

INTRODUCTION. It is often said, "A picture is worth a thousand words." In this section, we will show how numerical relationships can be described using mathematical pictures called **graphs.** We will also show how graphs are constructed and how we can obtain important information by reading graphs.

The rectangular coordinate system

When designing the Gateway Arch in St. Louis, shown in Figure 3-1(a), architects created a mathematical model called a **rectangular coordinate graph.** This graph, shown in Figure 3-1(b), is drawn on a grid called a **rectangular coordinate system.** This coordinate system is sometimes called a **Cartesian coordinate system,** after the 17th-century French mathematician René Descartes.

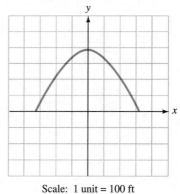

Scale: 1 unit = 100 ft

(a)   (b)

FIGURE 3-1

A rectangular coordinate system (see Figure 3-2) is formed by two perpendicular number lines. The horizontal number line is called the **x-axis,** and the vertical number line is called the **y-axis.** The positive direction on the *x*-axis is to the right, and the positive direction on the *y*-axis is upward. The scale on each axis should fit the data. For example, the axes of the graph of the arch shown in Figure 3-1(b) are scaled in units of 100 feet.

 COMMENT If no scale is indicated on the axes, we assume that the axes are scaled in units of 1.

The point where the axes cross is called the **origin.** This is the zero point on each axis. The axes form a **coordinate plane** and divide it into four regions called **quadrants,** which are numbered using Roman numerals as shown in Figure 3-2. The axes are not considered to be in any quadrant.

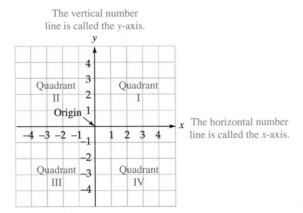

FIGURE 3-2

Each point in a coordinate plane can be identified by a pair of real numbers x and y written in the form (x, y). The first number x in the pair is called the **x-coordinate,** and the second number y is called the **y-coordinate.** The numbers in the pair are called the **coordinates** of the point. Some examples of such pairs are $(3, -4), \left(-1, -\frac{3}{2}\right)$, and $(0, 2.5)$.

$$(3, -4)$$

The x-coordinate is listed first. The y-coordinate is listed second.

 COMMENT Don't be confused by this new use of parentheses. The notation $(3, -4)$ represents a point on the coordinate plane, whereas $3(-4)$ indicates multiplication.

The process of locating a point in the coordinate plane is called **graphing** or **plotting** the point. In Figure 3-3(a), we use two blue arrows to show how to graph the point with coordinates of $(3, -4)$. Since the **x-coordinate,** 3, is positive, we start at the origin and move 3 units to the *right* along the x-axis. Since the **y-coordinate,** -4, is negative, we then move *down* 4 units to locate point A. Point A is the **graph** of $(3, -4)$ and lies in quadrant IV.

In Figure 3-3(a), two red arrows are used to show how to plot the point $(-4, 3)$. We start at the origin, move 4 units to the left along the x-axis, and then move up 3 units to locate point B. Point B lies in quadrant II.

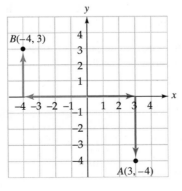

(a)

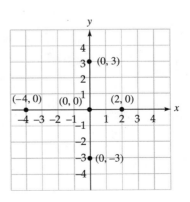

(b)

FIGURE 3-3

> **COMMENT**   Note that point *A* with coordinates (3, −4) is not the same as point *B* with coordinates (−4, 3). Since the order of the coordinates of a point is important, we call the pairs **ordered pairs.**

In Figure 3-3(b) on the previous page, we see that the points (−4, 0), (0, 0), and (2, 0) lie on the *x*-axis. In fact, all points with a *y*-coordinate of zero will lie on the *x*-axis. We also see that the points (0, −3), (0, 0), and (0, 3) lie on the *y*-axis. All points with an *x*-coordinate of zero lie on the *y*-axis. We can also see that the coordinates of the origin are (0, 0).

EXAMPLE 1   *Graphing points.*   Plot the points: **a.** $A(-2, 3)$, **b.** $B\left(-1, -\frac{3}{2}\right)$,   **c.** $C(0, 2.5)$,   and   **d.** $D(4, 2)$.

Solution

See Figure 3-4. (Note: If no scale is indicated on the axes, we assume that the axes are scaled in units of 1.)

a. To plot point *A* with coordinates (−2, 3), we start at the origin, move 2 units to the *left* on the *x*-axis, and move 3 units *up*. Point *A* lies in quadrant II.

b. To plot point *B* with coordinates $\left(-1, -\frac{3}{2}\right)$, we start at the origin and move 1 unit to the *left* and $\frac{3}{2}$ (or $1\frac{1}{2}$) units *down*. Point *B* lies in quadrant III.

c. To graph point *C* with coordinates (0, 2.5), we start at the origin and move 0 units on the *x*-axis and 2.5 units *up*. Point *C* lies on the *y*-axis.

d. To graph point *D* with coordinates (4, 2), we start at the origin and move 4 units to the *right* and 2 units *up*. Point *D* lies in quadrant I.

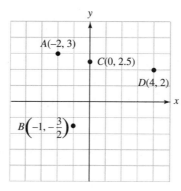

FIGURE 3-4

Self Check

Plot the points:

a. $E(2, -2)$
b. $F(-4, 0)$
c. $G\left(1.5, \frac{5}{2}\right)$
d. $H(0, 5)$

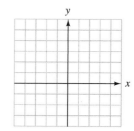

Answers:

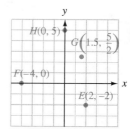

EXAMPLE 2   *Orbit of Earth.*   The circle shown in Figure 3-5 is an approximate **graph** of the orbit of Earth. The graph is made up of infinitely many points, each with its own *x*- and *y*-coordinates. Use the graph to find the coordinates of Earth's position during the months of February, May, August, and December.

Solution

To find the coordinates of each position, we start at the origin and move left or right along the *x*-axis to find the *x*-coordinate and then up or down to find the *y*-coordinate.

Month	Position of Earth on graph	Coordinates
February	3 units to the *right*, then 4 units *up*	(3, 4)
May	4 units to the *left*, then 3 units *up*	(−4, 3)
August	3.5 units to the *left*, then 3.5 units *down*	(−3.5, −3.5)
December	5 units to the *right*, no units *up* or *down*	(5, 0)

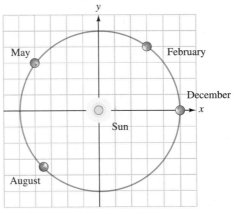

Scale: 1 unit = 18,600,000 mi

FIGURE 3-5

Graphing mathematical relationships

Every day, we deal with quantities that are related:

- The distance that we travel depends on how fast we are going.
- Our weight depends on how much we eat.
- The amount of water in a tub depends on how long the water has been running.

We often use graphs to visualize relationships between two quantities. For example, suppose we know the number of gallons of water that are in a tub at several time intervals after the water has been turned on. We can list that information in a **table.** (See Figure 3-6.)

The information in the table can be used to construct a graph that shows the relationship between the amount of water in the tub and the time the water has been running. Since the amount of water in the tub depends on the time, we will associate *time* with the *x*-axis and *amount of water* with the *y*-axis.

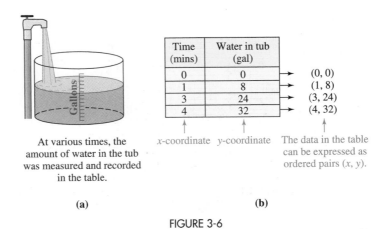

Time (mins)	Water in tub (gal)	
0	0	(0, 0)
1	8	(1, 8)
3	24	(3, 24)
4	32	(4, 32)

At various times, the amount of water in the tub was measured and recorded in the table.

x-coordinate *y*-coordinate   The data in the table can be expressed as ordered pairs (*x*, *y*).

(a)   (b)

FIGURE 3-6

To construct the graph in Figure 3-7 (next page), we plot the four ordered pairs and draw a straight line through the resulting data points. The *y*-axis is scaled in larger units (4 gallons) because the data range from 0 to 32 gallons.

From the graph, we can see that the amount of water in the tub steadily increases as the water is allowed to run. We can also use the graph to make observations about the amount of water in the tub at other times. For example, the dashed line on the graph shows that in 5 minutes, the tub will contain 40 gallons of water.

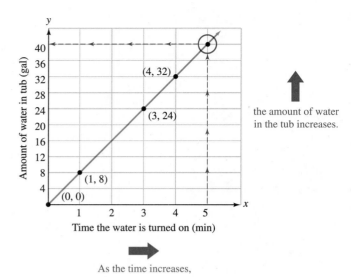

x	y	(x, y)
0	0	(0, 0)
1	8	(1, 8)
3	24	(3, 24)
4	32	(4, 32)

The data can be
listed in a table with
headings x, y, and
(x, y).

the amount of water
in the tub increases.

As the time increases,

FIGURE 3-7

Reading graphs

Valuable information can be obtained from a graph, as can be seen in the next example.

EXAMPLE 3   *Reading a graph.*   The graph in Figure 3-8 shows the number of people in an audience before, during, and after the taping of a television show. On the x-axis, zero represents the time when taping began. Use the graph to answer the following questions, and record each result in a table.

a. How many people were in the audience when taping began?

b. What was the size of the audience 10 minutes before taping began?

c. At what times were there exactly 100 people in the audience?

Self Check

Use the graph in Figure 3-8 to answer the following questions.

a. At what times were there exactly 50 people in the audience?

b. What was the size of the audience that watched the taping?

c. How long did it take for the audience to leave the studio after the taping ended?

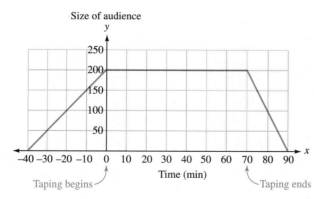

FIGURE 3-8

Solution

a. The time when taping began is represented by 0 on the x-axis. Since the point on the graph directly above 0 has a y-coordinate of 200, the point (0, 200) is on the graph. The y-coordinate of this point indicates that 200 people were in the audience when the taping began. We enter this result in the table at the right.

Time (min) x	Size of audience y
0	200
−10	150
−20	100
80	100

b. Ten minutes before taping began is represented by -10 on the x-axis. Since the point on the graph directly above -10 has a y-coordinate of 150, the point $(-10, 150)$ is on the graph. The y-coordinate of this point indicates that 150 people were in the audience 10 minutes before the taping began. We enter this result in the table.

c. We can draw a horizontal line passing through 100 on the y-axis. This line intersects the graph twice, at $(-20, 100)$ and at $(80, 100)$. So there are two times when 100 people were in the audience. The first time was 20 minutes before taping began (-20), and the second time was 80 minutes after taping began (80). The y-coordinates of these points indicate that there were 100 people in the audience 20 minutes before and 80 minutes after taping began. We enter these results in the table.

Answers: **a.** 30 min before and 85 min after taping began, **b.** 200, **c.** 20 min ■

Step graphs

The graph in Figure 3-9 shows the cost of renting a trailer for different periods of time. For example, the cost of renting the trailer for 4 days is $60, which is the y-coordinate of the point $(4, 60)$. The cost of renting the trailer for a period lasting over 4 and up to 5 days jumps to $70. Since the jumps in cost form steps in the graph, we call this graph a **step graph.**

EXAMPLE 4 Use the information in Figure 3-9 to answer the following questions. Write the results in a table.

a. Find the cost of renting the trailer for 2 days.

b. Find the cost of renting the trailer for $5\frac{1}{2}$ days.

c. How long can you rent the trailer if you have $50?

d. Is the rental cost per day the same?

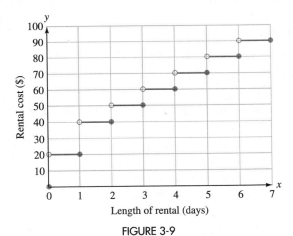

FIGURE 3-9

Solution

a. The solid dot at the end of each step indicates the rental cost for 1, 2, 3, 4, 5, 6, or 7 days. An open circle indicates that that point is not on the graph. We locate 2 days on the x-axis and move up to locate the point on the graph directly above the 2. Since the point has coordinates $(2, 40)$, a 2-day rental would cost $40. We enter this ordered pair in the table at the left.

b. We locate $5\frac{1}{2}$ days on the x-axis and move straight up to locate the point with coordinates $\left(5\frac{1}{2}, 80\right)$, which indicates that a $5\frac{1}{2}$-day rental would cost $80. We then enter this ordered pair in the table.

c. We draw a horizontal line through the point labeled 50 on the y-axis. Since this line intersects one step in the graph, we can look down to the x-axis to find the x-values that correspond to a y-value of 50. From the graph, we see that the trailer can be rented for more than 2 and up to 3 days for $50. We write $(3, 50)$ in the table.

d. No. If we look at the y-coordinates, we see that for the first day, the rental fee is $20. The second day, the cost jumps another $20. The third day, and all subsequent days, the cost jumps only $10. ■

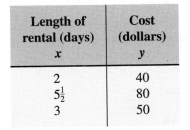

Length of rental (days)	Cost (dollars)
x	y
2	40
$5\frac{1}{2}$	80
3	50

STUDY SET   Section 3.1

VOCABULARY   *Fill in the blanks.*

1. The pair of numbers $(-1, -5)$ is called an
   _____ordered_____ pair.

2. In the ordered pair $\left(-\frac{3}{2}, -5\right)$, the -5 is called the
   _____y-coordinate_____.

3. The point with coordinates $(0, 0)$ is called the
   _____origin_____.

4. The x- and y-axes divide the coordinate plane into four
   regions called _____quadrants_____.

5. The point with coordinates $(4, 2)$ can be graphed on a
   _____rectangular_____ coordinate system.

6. The process of locating the position of a point on a coordinate plane is called _graphing or plotting_ the point.

CONCEPTS   *In Exercises 7–8, fill in the blanks.*

7. To plot the point with coordinates $(-5, 4.5)$, we start at
   the _____origin_____ and move 5 units to the
   _____left_____ and then move 4.5 units
   _____up_____.

8. To plot the point with coordinates $\left(6, -\frac{3}{2}\right)$, we start at
   the _____origin_____ and move 6
   units to the _____right_____ and then move $\frac{3}{2}$ units
   _____down_____.

9. Do $(3, 2)$ and $(2, 3)$ represent the same point?   no

10. In the ordered pair $(4, 5)$, is the number 4 associated
   with the horizontal or the vertical axis?   horizontal

11. In which quadrant do points with a negative x-coordi-
   nate and a positive y-coordinate lie?   quadrant II

12. In which quadrant do points with a positive x-coordi-
   nate and a negative y-coordinate lie?   quadrant IV

13. In Illustration 1, fill in the missing coordinate of each
   highlighted point on the graph of the circle.

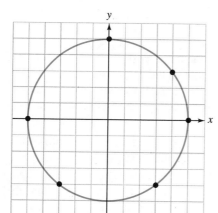

a. $(4, \ 3\ )$
b. $(3, \ -4\ )$
c. $(5, \ 0\ )$
d. $(-3, \ -4\ )$
e. $(-5, \ 0\ )$
f. $(0, \ 5\ )$

ILLUSTRATION 1

14. In Illustration 2, fill in the missing coordinate of each
   point on the graph of the line.

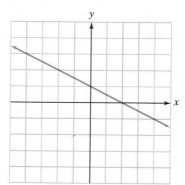

a. $(-4, \ 3\ )$
b. $(\ 2\ , 0)$
c. $(\ -2\ , 2)$
d. $(\ 4\ , -1)$
e. $(-4, \ 3\ )$
f. $(\ 0\ , 1)$

ILLUSTRATION 2

*The graph in Illustration 3 gives the heart rate of a woman
before, during, and after an aerobic workout. In Exercises
15–22, use the graph to answer the questions.*

15. What information does the point $(-10, 60)$ give us?
   10 min before the workout, her heart rate was 60 beats/min.

16. After beginning her workout, how long did it take
   the woman to reach her training-zone heart rate?
   10 min

17. What was the woman's heart rate half an hour after beginning the workout?   150 beats/min

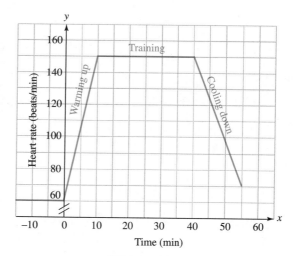

ILLUSTRATION 3

18. For how long did the woman work out at her training
   zone?   30 min

19. At what time was her heart rate 100 beats per
   minute?   approximately 5 min and 50 min after starting

20. How long was her cool-down period?   15 min

21. What was the difference in the woman's heart rate
   before the workout and after the cool-down period?
   10 beats/min faster after cool-down

22. What was her approximate heart rate 8 minutes after
   beginning?   about 135 beats/min

NOTATION

23. Explain the difference between (3, 5), 3(5), and 5(3 + 5).

(3, 5) is an ordered pair, 3(5) indicates multiplication, and 5(3 + 5) is an expression containing grouping symbols.

24. In the table, which column contains values associated with the vertical axis of a graph?   the 2nd column

x	y
2	0
5	−2
−1	−$\frac{1}{2}$

25. Do these ordered pairs name the same point?

$\left(2.5, -\frac{7}{2}\right), \left(2\frac{1}{2}, -3.5\right), \left(2.5, -3\frac{1}{2}\right)$ yes

26. Do these ordered pairs name the same point?

$(-1.25, 4), \left(-1\frac{1}{4}, 4.0\right), \left(-\frac{5}{4}, 4\right)$ yes

PRACTICE   *Graph each point on the coordinate grid provided.*

27. $A(-3, 4)$
$B(4, 3.5)$
$C\left(-2, -\frac{5}{2}\right)$
$D(0, -4)$
$E\left(\frac{3}{2}, 0\right)$
$F(3, -4)$

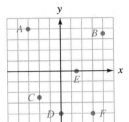

28. $G(4, 4)$
$H(0.5, -3)$
$I(-4, -4)$
$J(0, -1)$
$K(0, 0)$
$L(0, 3)$
$M(-2, 0)$

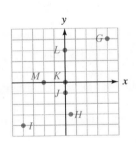

APPLICATIONS

29. CONSTRUCTION   The graph in Illustration 4 shows a side view of a bridge design. Make a table with three columns; label them *rivets, welds,* and *anchors.* List the coordinates of the points at which each category is located.

rivets: (−6, 0), (−2, 0), (2, 0), (6, 0); welds: (−4, 3), (0, 3), (4, 3); anchors: (−6, −3), (6, −3)

30. WATER PRESSURE   The graph in Illustration 5 shows how the path of a stream of water changes when the hose is held at two different angles.
   a. At which angle does the stream of water shoot up higher? How much higher?   60°; 4 ft
   b. At which angle does the stream of water shoot out farther? How much farther?   30°; 4 ft

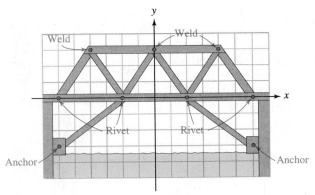

Scale: 1 unit = 8 ft

ILLUSTRATION 4

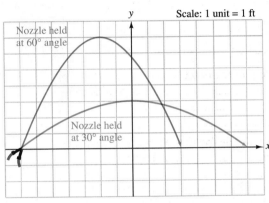

ILLUSTRATION 5

31. GOLF SWING   To correct her swing, a golfer is videotaped and then has her image displayed on a computer monitor so that it can be analyzed by a golf pro. (See Illustration 6.) Give the coordinates of the points that are highlighted on the arc of her swing.

(−3, 10), (−2, 7), (−1, 4.8), (0, 3), (1, 1.8), (2.5, 0.5), (4, 0)

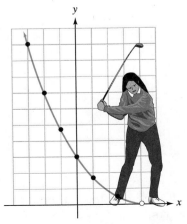

Scale: 1 unit = 6 in.

ILLUSTRATION 6

32. MEDICINE   Scoliosis is a lateral curvature of the spine that can be more easily detected when a grid is superimposed over an X ray. In Illustration 7, find the coordinates of the "center points" of the indicated vertebrae. Note that T3 means the third thoracic vertebra, L4 means the fourth lumbar vertebra, and so on.

T3(2, 21), T6(3, 16), T9(3, 10), T11(2.5, 6.5), L1(1, 2.5), L2(0, 0), L4(−1, −5), L5(0, −8)

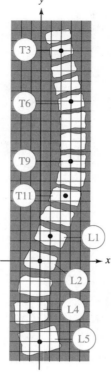

Scale: 1 unit = 0.5 in.

ILLUSTRATION 7

33. VIDEO RENTAL   The charges for renting a video are shown in the graph in Illustration 8.
  a. Find the charge for a 1-day rental. $2
  b. Find the charge for a 2-day rental. $4
  c. What is the charge if a tape is kept for 5 days? $7
  d. What is the charge if a tape is kept for a week? $9

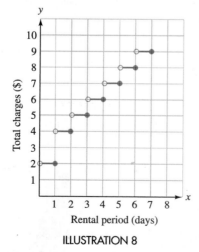

ILLUSTRATION 8

34. POSTAGE RATES   The graph shown in Illustration 9 gives the first-class postage rates in 2001 for mailing items weighing up to 5 ounces.
  a. Find the postage costs for mailing each of the following letters first class: a 1-ounce letter, a 4-ounce letter, and a $2\frac{1}{2}$-ounce letter.   34¢, 97¢, 76¢

  b. Find the difference in postage for a 3.75-ounce letter and a 4.75-ounce letter.   24¢
  c. What is the heaviest letter that could be mailed for 55¢ first class?   2 oz

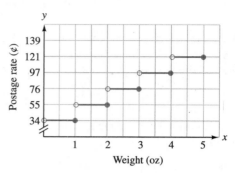

ILLUSTRATION 9

35. GAS MILEAGE   The table in Illustration 10 gives the number of miles (*y*) that a truck can be driven on *x* gallons of gasoline. Plot the ordered pairs and draw a line connecting the points.

x	*y*
2	10
3	15
5	25

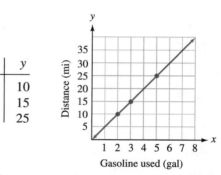

ILLUSTRATION 10

  a. Estimate how far the truck can go on 7 gallons of gasoline.   35 mi
  b. How many gallons of gas are needed to travel a distance of 20 miles?   4
  c. How far can the truck go on 6.5 gallons of gasoline?   32.5 mi

36. VALUE OF A CAR   The table in Illustration 11 shows the value *y* (in thousands of dollars) of a car that is *x* years old. Plot the ordered pairs and draw a line connecting the points.

x	*y*
3	7
4	5.5
5	4

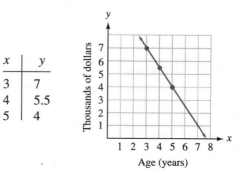

ILLUSTRATION 11

a. What does the point (3, 7) on the graph tell you?
A 3-year-old car is worth $7,000.

b. Estimate the value of the car when it is 7 years old. $1,000

c. After how many years will the car be worth $2,500? 6

37. ROAD MAPS Road maps usually have a coordinate system to help locate cities. Use the map in Illustration 12 to locate Rockford, Mount Carroll, Harvard, and the intersection of state Highway 251 and U.S. Highway 30. Express each answer in the form (number, letter).
Rockford (5, B), Mount Carroll (1, C), Harvard (7, A), intersection (5, E)

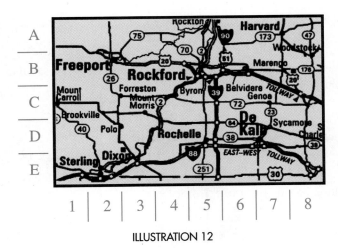

ILLUSTRATION 12

38. BATTLESHIP In the game Battleship, the player uses coordinates to drop depth charges from a battleship to hit a hidden submarine. What coordinates should be used to make three hits on the exposed submarine shown in Illustration 13? Express each answer in the form (letter, number). (E, 4), (F, 3), (G, 2)

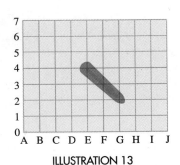

ILLUSTRATION 13

WRITING

39. Explain why the point $(-3, 3)$ is not the same as the point $(3, -3)$.

40. Explain what is meant when we say that the rectangular coordinate graph of the St. Louis Gateway Arch is made up of *infinitely many* points.

41. Explain how to plot the point $(-2, 5)$.

42. Explain why the coordinates of the origin are (0, 0).

REVIEW

43. Evaluate $-3 - 3(-5)$. 12

44. Evaluate $(-5)^2 + (-5)$. 20

45. What is the opposite of -8? 8

46. Simplify $|-1 - 9|$. 10

47. Solve $-4x + 7 = -21$. 7

48. Solve $P = 2l + 2w$ for w. $w = \dfrac{P - 2l}{2}$

49. Evaluate $(x + 1)(x + y)^2$ for $x = -2$ and $y = -5$.
-49

50. Simplify $-6(x - 3) - 2(1 - x)$. $-4x + 16$

3.2 *Equations Containing Two Variables*

In this section, you will learn about

- Solving equations in two variables • Constructing tables of solutions
- Graphing equations • Using different variables

INTRODUCTION. In this section, we will discuss equations that contain two variables. Such equations are often used to describe relationships between two quantities. To see a mathematical picture of these relationships, we will construct graphs of their equations.

Solving equations in two variables

We have previously solved equations containing one variable. For example, we can show that the solution of each of the following equations is $x = 3$.

$$2x + 3 = 9, \qquad -5x + 1 = 4 - 6x, \qquad \text{and} \qquad -3(x + 1) = 2x - 18$$

If we graph the solution $x = 3$ on a number line, we get the graph shown in Figure 3-10.

FIGURE 3-10

To describe relationships between two quantities mathematically, we use equations with two variables. Some examples of equations in two variables are

$$y = x - 1, \qquad y = x^2, \qquad y = |x|, \quad \text{and} \quad y = x^3$$

Solutions of equations in two variables are ordered pairs. For example, one solution of $y = x - 1$ is the ordered pair $(5, 4)$, because the equation is true when $x = 5$ and $y = 4$.

$y = x - 1$ The original equation.

$4 \stackrel{?}{=} 5 - 1$ Substitute 5 for x and 4 for y.

$4 = 4$ Do the subtraction on the right-hand side: $5 - 1 = 4$.

Since $4 = 4$ is a true statement, the ordered pair $(5, 4)$ is a solution, and we say that $(5, 4)$ **satisfies** the equation.

EXAMPLE 1 *Verifying a solution.* Is the ordered pair $(-1, -3)$ a solution of $y = x - 1$?

Self Check

Is $(9, 8)$ a solution of $y = x - 1$?

Solution

We substitute -1 for x and -3 for y and see whether the resulting equation is a true statement.

$y = x - 1$ The original equation.

$-3 \stackrel{?}{=} -1 - 1$ Substitute -1 for x and -3 for y.

$-3 = -2$ Do the subtraction: $-1 - 1 = -2$.

Since $-3 = -2$ is a false statement, $(-1, -3)$ is not a solution.

Answer: yes

EXAMPLE 2 *Verifying a solution.* Is the ordered pair $(-6, 36)$ a solution of $y = x^2$?

Self Check

Is $(-2, 5)$ a solution of $y = x^2$?

Solution

We substitute -6 for x and 36 for y and see whether the resulting equation is a true statement.

$y = x^2$ The original equation.

$36 \stackrel{?}{=} (-6)^2$ Substitute -6 for x and 36 for y.

$36 = 36$ Find the power: $(-6)^2 = 36$.

Since the equation $36 = 36$ is true, $(-6, 36)$ is a solution.

Answer: no

Constructing tables of solutions

To find solutions of equations in x and y, we can pick numbers at random, substitute them for x, and find the corresponding values of y. For example, to find some ordered pairs that satisfy the equation $y = x - 1$, we can let $x = -4$ (called the **input value**), substitute -4 for x, and solve for y (called the **output value**).

$y = x - 1$

x	y	(x, y)
-4	-5	$(-4, -5)$

$y = x - 1$ The original equation.

$y = -4 - 1$ Substitute the input -4 for x.

$y = -5$ The output is -5.

$y = x - 1$

x	y	(x, y)
-4	-5	$(-4, -5)$
-2	-3	$(-2, -3)$

$y = x - 1$

x	y	(x, y)
-4	-5	$(-4, -5)$
-2	-3	$(-2, -3)$
0	-1	$(0, -1)$

$y = x - 1$

x	y	(x, y)
-4	-5	$(-4, -5)$
-2	-3	$(-2, -3)$
0	-1	$(0, -1)$
2	1	$(2, 1)$

$y = x - 1$

x	y	(x, y)
-4	-5	$(-4, -5)$
-2	-3	$(-2, -3)$
0	-1	$(0, -1)$
2	1	$(2, 1)$
4	3	$(4, 3)$

The ordered pair $(-4, -5)$ is a solution. We list this ordered pair in red in the **table of solutions** (or **table of values**) on the previous page.

To find another ordered pair that satisfies $y = x - 1$, we let $x = -2$.

$y = x - 1$ The original equation.

$y = -2 - 1$ Substitute the input -2 for x.

$y = -3$ The output is -3.

A second solution is $(-2, -3)$, and we list it in the table of solutions.

If we let $x = 0$, we can find a third ordered pair that satisfies $y = x - 1$.

$y = x - 1$ The original equation.

$y = 0 - 1$ Substitute the input 0 for x.

$y = -1$ The output is -1.

A third solution is $(0, -1)$, which we also add to the table of solutions.

If we let $x = 2$, we can find a fourth solution.

$y = x - 1$ The original equation.

$y = 2 - 1$ Substitute the input 2 for x.

$y = 1$ The output is 1.

A fourth solution is $(2, 1)$, and we add it to the table of solutions.

If we let $x = 4$, we have

$y = x - 1$ The original equation.

$y = 4 - 1$ Substitute the input 4 for x.

$y = 3$ The output is 3.

A fifth solution is $(4, 3)$.

Since we can choose any real number for x, and since any choice of x will give a corresponding value of y, it is apparent that the equation $y = x - 1$ has *infinitely many solutions*. We have found five of them: $(-4, -5)$, $(-2, -3)$, $(0, -1)$, $(2, 1)$, and $(4, 3)$.

Graphing equations

To graph the equation $y = x - 1$, we plot the ordered pairs listed in the table of solutions on a rectangular coordinate system, as shown in Figure 3-11(a). From the figure, we can see that the five points lie on a line.

In Figure 3-11(b), we draw a straight line through the points, because the graph of any solution of $y = x - 1$ will lie on this line. The arrowheads show that the line continues forever in both directions. The line is a picture of all the solutions of the equation $y = x - 1$. This line is called the **graph** of the equation.

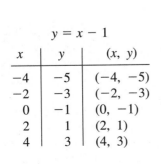

$y = x - 1$

x	y	(x, y)
-4	-5	$(-4, -5)$
-2	-3	$(-2, -3)$
0	-1	$(0, -1)$
2	1	$(2, 1)$
4	3	$(4, 3)$

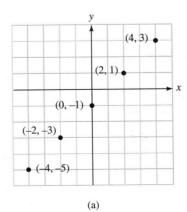

(a)

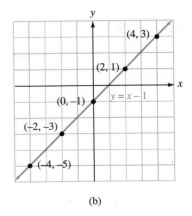

(b)

FIGURE 3-11

To graph an equation in x and y, we follow these steps.

Graphing an equation **in *x* and *y***	**1.** Make a table of solutions containing several ordered pairs of numbers (*x*, *y*) that satisfy the equation. Do this by picking values for *x* and finding the corresponding values for *y*. **2.** Plot each ordered pair on a rectangular coordinate system. **3.** Carefully draw a line or smooth curve through the points.

Since we will usually choose a number for *x* and then find the corresponding value of *y*, the value of *y* depends on *x*. For this reason, we call *y* the **dependent variable** and *x* the **independent variable.** The value of the independent variable is the input value, and the value of the dependent variable is the output value.

EXAMPLE 3 *Graphing equations.* Graph $y = -2x - 2$.

Solution

To make a table of solutions, we choose numbers for *x* and find the corresponding values of *y*. If $x = -3$, we have

$y = -2x - 2$ The original equation.

$y = -2(-3) - 2$ Substitute -3 for *x*.

$y = 6 - 2$ Do the multiplication: $-2(-3) = 6$.

$y = 4$ Do the subtraction.

Thus, $x = -3$ and $y = 4$ is a solution. In a similar manner, we find the corresponding *y*-values for *x*-values of $-2, -1, 0$, and 1 and record the results in the table of solutions in Figure 3-12(a). After plotting the ordered pairs, we draw a line through the points to get the graph shown in the Figure 3-12(b).

$$y = -2x - 2$$

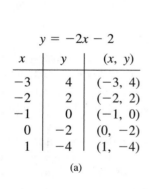

x	*y*	(*x*, *y*)
−3	4	(−3, 4)
−2	2	(−2, 2)
−1	0	(−1, 0)
0	−2	(0, −2)
1	−4	(1, −4)

(a)

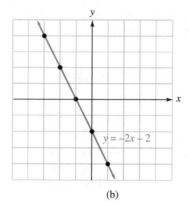

(b)

FIGURE 3-12

Self Check

Graph $y = -3x + 1$.

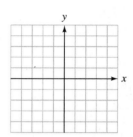

Answer:

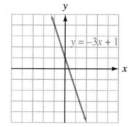

EXAMPLE 4 *Graphing equations.* Graph $y = x^2$.

Solution

To make a table of solutions, we will choose numbers for *x* and find the corresponding values of *y*. If $x = -3$, we have

$y = x^2$ The original equation.

$y = (-3)^2$ Substitute the input -3 for *x*.

$y = 9$ The output is 9.

Thus, $x = -3$ and $y = 9$ is a solution. In a similar manner, we find the corresponding *y*-values for *x*-values of $-2, -1, 0, 1, 2$, and 3. If we plot the ordered pairs listed in the table in Figure 3-13 and join the points with a smooth curve, we get the graph shown in the figure, which is called a **parabola.**

Self Check

Graph $y = x^2 - 2$ and compare the result to the graph of $y = x^2$. What do you notice?

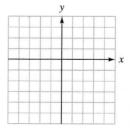

$y = x^2$

x	y	(x, y)
-3	9	$(-3, 9)$
-2	4	$(-2, 4)$
-1	1	$(-1, 1)$
0	0	$(0, 0)$
1	1	$(1, 1)$
2	4	$(2, 4)$
3	9	$(3, 9)$

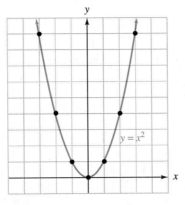

FIGURE 3-13

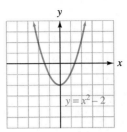

Answer: The graph has the same shape, but is 2 units lower.

EXAMPLE 5 *Graphing equations.* Graph $y = |x|$.

Solution

To make a table of solutions, we will choose numbers for x and find the corresponding values of y. If $x = -5$, we have

$y = |x|$ The original equation.

$y = |-5|$ Substitute the input -5 for x.

$y = 5$ The output is 5.

The ordered pair $(-5, 5)$ satisfies the equation. This pair and several others that satisfy the equation are listed in the table of solutions in Figure 3-14. If we plot the ordered pairs in the table, we see that they lie in a "V" shape. We join the points to complete the graph shown in the figure.

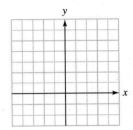

$y = |x|$

x	y	(x, y)
-5	5	$(-5, 5)$
-4	4	$(-4, 4)$
-3	3	$(-3, 3)$
-2	2	$(-2, 2)$
-1	1	$(-1, 1)$
0	0	$(0, 0)$
1	1	$(1, 1)$
2	2	$(2, 2)$
3	3	$(3, 3)$

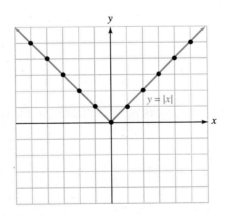

FIGURE 3-14

Answer: The graph has the same shape, but is 2 units higher.

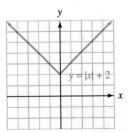

EXAMPLE 6 *Graphing equations.* Graph $y = x^3$.

Solution

If we let $x = -2$, we have

$y = x^3$ The original equation.

$y = (-2)^3$ Substitute the input -2 for x.

$y = -8$ The output is -8.

The ordered pair $(-2, -8)$ satisfies the equation. This ordered pair and several others that satisfy the equation are listed in the table of solutions in Figure 3-15. Plotting the ordered pairs and joining them with a smooth curve gives us the graph shown in the figure.

$$y = x^3$$

x	y	(x, y)
-2	-8	$(-2, -8)$
-1	-1	$(-1, -1)$
0	0	$(0, 0)$
1	1	$(1, 1)$
2	8	$(2, 8)$

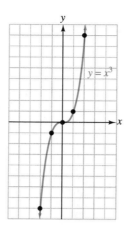

FIGURE 3-15

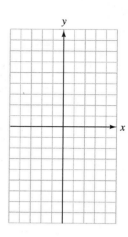

Answer: The graph has the same shape but is 2 units to the right.

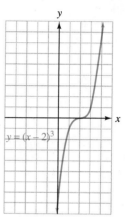

Accent on Technology: *Using a graphing calculator to graph an equation*

FIGURE 3-16

So far, we have graphed equations by making tables of solutions and plotting points. The task of graphing is made much easier when we use a graphing calculator. The instructions in this discussion will be general in nature. For specific details about your calculator, please consult your owner's manual.

The viewing window: All graphing calculators have a viewing **window,** used to display graphs. The **standard window** has settings of

$$\text{Xmin} = -10, \qquad \text{Xmax} = 10, \qquad \text{Ymin} = -10, \qquad \text{and} \qquad \text{Ymax} = 10$$

which indicate that the minimum x- and y-coordinates used in the graph will be -10, and that the maximum x- and y-coordinates will be 10.

Graphing an equation: To graph the equation $y = x - 1$ using a graphing calculator, we press the $\boxed{Y =}$ key and enter the right-hand side of the equation after the symbol Y_1. The display will show the equation

$$Y_1 = x - 1$$

Then we press the $\boxed{\text{GRAPH}}$ key to produce the graph shown in Figure 3-17.

Next, we will graph the equation $y = |x - 4|$. Since absolute values are always nonnegative, the minimum y-value is zero. To obtain a reasonable viewing window, we set the Ymin value slightly lower, at Ymin $= -3$. We set Ymax to be 10 units greater than Ymin, at Ymax = 7. The minimum value of y occurs when $x = 4$. To center the graph in the viewing window, we set the Xmin and Xmax values 5 units to the left and right of 4. Therefore, Xmin = −1 and Xmax = 9.

After entering the right-hand side of the equation, we obtain the graph shown in Figure 3-18. Consult your owner's manual to learn how to enter an absolute value.

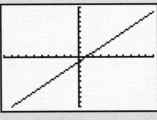
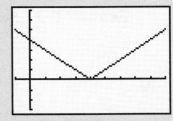

FIGURE 3-17   FIGURE 3-18

Changing the viewing window: The choice of viewing windows is extremely important when graphing equations. To show this, let's graph $y = x^2 - 25$ with x-values from −1 to 6 and y-values from −5 to 5.

To graph this equation, we set the x and y window values and enter the right-hand side of the equation. The display will show

$$Y_1 = x^2 - 25$$

Then we press the ⬚ GRAPH ⬚ key to produce the graph shown in Figure 3-19(a). Although the graph appears to be a straight line, it is not. Actually, we are seeing only part of a parabola. If we pick a viewing window with x-values of −6 to 6 and y-values of −30 to 2, as in Figure 3-19(b), we can see that the graph is a parabola.

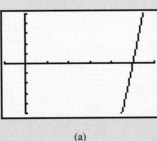
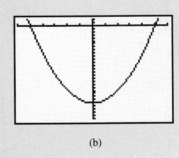

(a)   (b)

FIGURE 3-19

STUDY SET   *Use a graphing calculator to graph each equation. Use a viewing window of $x = -5$ to 5 and $y = -5$ to 5.*

Graph each equation in a viewing window of $x = -4$ to 4 and $y = -4$ to 4. Each graph is not what it first appears to be. Pick a better viewing window and find a better representation of the true graph.

1. $y = 2.1x - 1.1$

2. $y = 1.12x^2 - 1$

5. $y = -x^3 - 8.2$

6. $y = -|x - 4.01|$

3. $y = |x + 0.7|$

4. $y = 0.1x^3 + 1$

7. $y = x^2 + 5.9$

8. $y = -x + 7.95$

Using different variables

We will often encounter equations with variables other than *x* and *y*. When we make tables of solutions and graph these equations, we must know which is the independent variable (the input values) and which is the dependent variable (the output values). The independent variable is usually associated with the horizontal axis of the coordinate system, and the dependent variable is usually associated with the vertical axis.

EXAMPLE 7   *Speed limit.*   In some states, the maximum speed limit on a U.S. interstate highway is 75 mph. The distance covered by a vehicle traveling at 75 mph depends on the time the vehicle travels at that speed. This relationship is described by the equation $d = 75t$, where *d* represents the distance (in miles) and *t* represents the time (in hours). Graph the equation.

FIGURE 3-20

Solution   Since *d* depends on *t* in the equation $d = 50t$, *t* is the independent variable (the input) and *d* is the dependent variable (the output). Therefore, we choose values for *t* and find the corresponding values of *d*. Since *t* represents the time spent traveling at 75 mph, we choose no negative values for *t*.

If $t = 0$, we have

$d = 75t$ The original equation.

$d = 75(\mathbf{0})$ Substitute the input 0 for *t*.

$d = 0$ Do the multiplication.

The pair $t = 0$ and $d = 0$, or (0, 0), is a solution. This ordered pair and others that satisfy the equation are listed in the table of solutions shown in Figure 3-21(a). If we plot the ordered pairs and draw a line through them, we obtain the graph shown in Figure 3-21(b). From the graph, we see (as expected) that the distance covered steadily increases as the traveling time increases.

$d = 75t$

d	*t*	(*d*, *t*)
0	0	(0, 0)
1	75	(1, 75)
2	150	(2, 150)
3	225	(3, 225)
4	300	(4, 300)
5	375	(5, 375)

Adjust the scale on the vertical axis to fit the data.

(a)

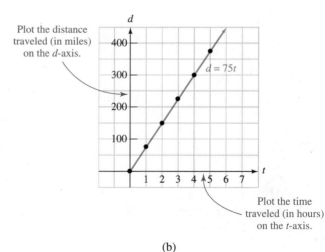

(b)

FIGURE 3-21

STUDY SET Section 3.2

VOCABULARY   *Fill in the blanks.*

1. The equation $y = x + 1$ is an equation in ____two____ variables.

2. An ordered pair is a ____solution____ of an equation if the numbers in the ordered pair satisfy the equation.

3. In equations containing the variables x and y, x is called the ___independent___ variable and y is called the ___dependent___ variable.

4. When constructing a ___table___ of solutions, the values of x are the ___input___ values and the values of y are the ___output___ values.

CONCEPTS

5. Consider the equation $y = -2x + 6$.
   a. How many variables does the equation contain?   2
   b. Does the ordered pair $(4, -2)$ satisfy the equation?   yes
   c. Is $x = -3$ and $y = 12$ a solution?   yes
   d. How many solutions does this equation have?
      infinitely many

6. How many variables does the equation $x + 2 = 6$ have? How many solutions does it have? Graph the solution(s).

   one, one
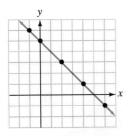

7. To graph an equation, five solutions were found, they were plotted (in black), and a straight line was drawn through them, as shown in Illustration 1. From the graph, determine three other solutions of the equation.

   $(1, 4), (3, 2), (5, 0)$ (answers may vary)

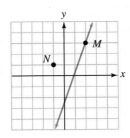

ILLUSTRATION 1

8. Consider the graph of an equation shown in Illustration 2.

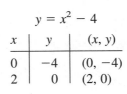

ILLUSTRATION 2

   a. If the coordinates of point M are substituted into the equation, is the result a true or false statement?   true
   b. If the coordinates of point N are substituted into the equation, is the result a true or false statement?   false

9. Complete the table of solutions.

$$y = x^3$$

x (inputs)	y (outputs)
0	0
-1	-1
-2	-8
1	1
2	8

10. What is wrong with the graph of $y = x - 3$ shown in Illustration 3?

The line is too short, and arrowheads are not drawn on both ends of the line.

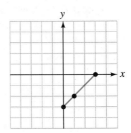

ILLUSTRATION 3

11. To graph $y = -x + 1$, a student constructed a table of solutions and plotted the ordered pairs as shown in Illustration 4. Instead of drawing a crooked line through the points, what should he have done?

He should have checked his computations. At least one of his "solutions" is wrong. The graph should be a straight line.

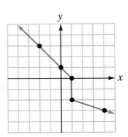

ILLUSTRATION 4

12. To graph $y = x^2 - 4$, a table of solutions is constructed and a graph is drawn, as shown in Illustration 5. Explain the error made here.

Not enough ordered pairs were found—the correct graph is a parabola.

$$y = x^2 - 4$$

x	y	(x, y)
0	-4	$(0, -4)$
2	0	$(2, 0)$

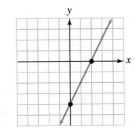

ILLUSTRATION 5

13. Explain the error with the graph of $y = x^2$ shown in Illustration 6.

A smooth curve should be drawn through the points.

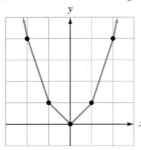

ILLUSTRATION 6

14. Several solutions of an equation are listed in the table of solutions. When graphing them, with what variable should the horizontal and vertical axes of the graph be labeled?   horizontal: *t*; vertical: *s*

t	s	(t, s)
0	4	(0, 4)
1	5	(1, 5)
2	10	(2, 10)

NOTATION   *Complete each solution.*

15. Verify that $(-2, 6)$ satisfies $y = -x + 4$.

$$y = -x + 4$$
$$6 \stackrel{?}{=} -(-2) + 4$$
$$6 \stackrel{?}{=} 2 + 4$$
$$6 = 6$$

16. For the equation $y = |x - 2|$, if $x = -3$, find y.

$$y = |x - 2|$$
$$y = |-3 - 2|$$
$$y = |-5|$$
$$y = 5$$

PRACTICE   *Tell whether the ordered pair satisfies the equation.*

17. $y = 2x - 4; (4, 4)$ yes

18. $y = x^2; (8, 48)$ no

19. $y = |x - 2|; (4, -3)$ no

20. $y = x^3 + 1; (-2, -7)$ yes

Complete each table of solutions.

21. $y = x - 3$

x	y
0	-3
1	-2
-2	-5

22. $y = |x - 3|$

x	$|x - 3|$
0	3
-1	4
3	0

23. $y = x^2 - 3$

Input	Output
0	-3
2	1
-2	1

24. $y = x + 1$

Input	Output
0	1
2	3
-1	0

Construct a table of solutions and then graph each equation.

25. $y = 2x - 3$

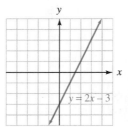

26. $y = 3x + 1$

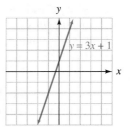

27. $y = -2x + 1$

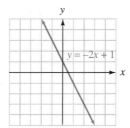

28. $y = -3x + 2$

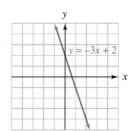

Construct a table of solutions and then graph each equation. Compare it to the graph of $y = x^2$.

29. $y = x^2 + 1$

1 unit higher

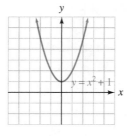

30. $y = -x^2$

It is turned upside down.

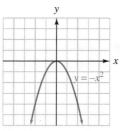

31. $y = (x - 2)^2$

2 units to the right

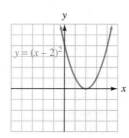

32. $y = (x + 2)^2$

2 units to the left

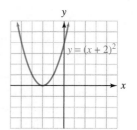

Construct a table of solutions and then graph each equation. Compare it to the graph of y = |x|.

33. $y = -|x|$
It is turned upside down.

34. $y = |x| - 2$
2 units lower

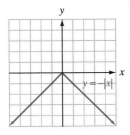

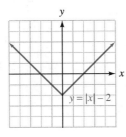

35. $y = |x + 2|$
2 units to the left

36. $y = |x - 2|$
2 units to the right

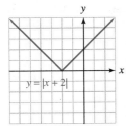

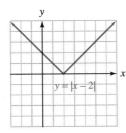

Construct a table of solutions and then graph each equation. Compare it to the graph of y = x³.

37. $y = -x^3$
It is turned upside down.

38. $y = x^3 + 2$
2 units higher

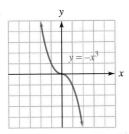

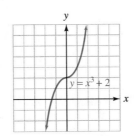

39. $y = x^3 - 2$
2 units lower

40. $y = (x + 2)^3$
2 units to the left

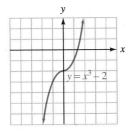

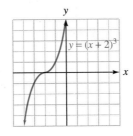

APPLICATIONS

41. 8 BALL   Illustration 7 shows the path traveled by the 8 ball as it is banked off of a cushion into the right corner pocket. Use the information in the illustration to complete the table.

x	-1	2	5	8
y	0	4	0	-4

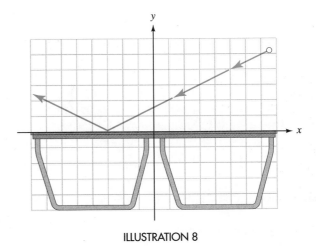

ILLUSTRATION 7

42. TABLE TENNIS   Illustration 8 shows the path traveled by a Ping-Pong ball as it bounces off the table. Use the information in the illustration to complete the table below.

x	-7	-3	1	3	5
y	2	0	2	3	4

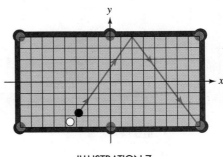

ILLUSTRATION 8

43. SUSPENSION BRIDGE   The suspension cables of a bridge hang in the shape of a parabola, as shown in Illustration 9. Use the information in the illustration to complete the table.

x	0	2	4	−2	−4
y	0	1	4	1	4

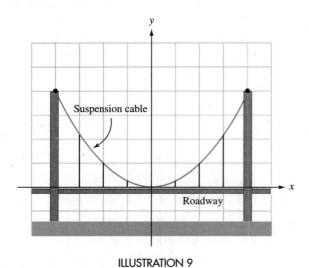

ILLUSTRATION 9

44. FIRE BOAT   A stream of water from a high-pressure hose on a fire boat travels in the shape of a parabola, as shown in Illustration 10. Use the information in the graph to complete the table.

x	1	2	3	4
y	3	4	3	0

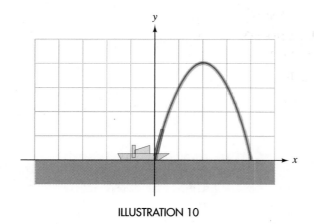

ILLUSTRATION 10

45. MANUFACTURING   The graph in Illustration 11 shows the relationship between the length *l* (in inches) of a machine bolt and the cost *C* (in cents) to manufacture it.
   a. What information does the point (2, 8) on the graph give us?   It costs 8¢ to make a 2-in. bolt.
   b. How much does it cost to make a 7-inch bolt?   12¢
   c. What length bolt is the least expensive to make?   a 4-in. bolt

d. Describe how the cost changes as the length of the bolt increases.
   It decreases as the length approaches 4 in., then increases as the length increases to 7 in.

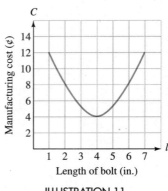

ILLUSTRATION 11

46. SOFTBALL   The graph in Illustration 12 shows the relationship between the distance *d* (in feet) traveled by a batted softball and the height *h* (in feet) it attains.
   a. What information does the point (40, 40) on the graph give us?
   After the ball has traveled 40 ft, its height is 40 ft.
   b. At what distance from home plate does the ball reach its maximum height?   100 ft
   c. Where will the ball land?   200 ft from home plate

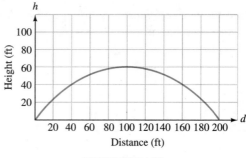

ILLUSTRATION 12

47. MARKET VALUE OF A HOUSE   The graph in Illustration 13 shows the relationship between the market value *v* of a house and the time *t* since it was purchased.

ILLUSTRATION 13

a. What was the purchase price of the house? $90,000

b. When did the value of the house reach its lowest point? the 3rd yr after being bought

c. When did the value of the house begin to surpass the purchase price? after the 6th yr

d. Describe how the market value of the house changed over the 8-year period.

It decreased in value for 3 yr, then increased in value for 5 yr.

48. POLITICAL SURVEY The graph in Illustration 14 shows the relationship between the percent P of those surveyed who rated their senator's job performance as satisfactory or better and the time t she had been in office.

a. When did her job performance rating reach a maximum? the 8th month after being elected

b. When was her job performance rating at or above the 60% mark? between the 4th and 12th months

c. Describe how her job performance rating changed over the 12-month period.

After the election, it increased for 8 mo to a high of 70%. Then it decreased for 4 mo.

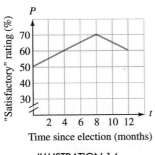

ILLUSTRATION 14

WRITING

49. What is a table of solutions?

50. To graph an equation in two variables, how many solutions of the equation must be found?

51. Give an example of an equation in one variable and an equation in two variables. How do their solutions differ?

52. When we say that $(-2, -6)$ is a solution of $y = x - 4$, what do we mean?

53. On a quiz, students were asked to graph $y = 3x - 1$. One student made the table of solutions on the left. Another student made the one on the right. Which table is incorrect? Or could they both be correct? Explain.

x	y	(x, y)	x	y	(x, y)
0	-1	$(0, -1)$	-2	-7	$(-2, -7)$
2	5	$(2, 5)$	-1	-4	$(-1, -4)$
3	8	$(3, 8)$	1	2	$(1, 2)$
4	11	$(4, 11)$	-3	-10	$(-3, -10)$
5	14	$(5, 14)$	2	5	$(2, 5)$

54. What does it mean when we say that an equation in two variables has infinitely many solutions?

REVIEW

55. Solve $\dfrac{x}{8} = -12$. -96

56. Combine like terms: $3t - 4T + 5T - 6t$. $-3t + T$

57. Is $\dfrac{x + 5}{6}$ an expression or an equation? an expression

58. What formula is used to find the perimeter of a rectangle? $P = 2l + 2w$

59. What number is 0.5% of 250? 1.25

60. Solve $-3x + 5 > -7$. $x < 4$

61. Find $-2.5 - (-2.6)$. 0.1

62. Evaluate $(-5)^3$. -125

3.3 *Graphing Linear Equations*

In this section, you will learn about

- Linear equations • Solutions of linear equations • Graphing linear equations
- The intercept method • Graphing horizontal and vertical lines
- An application of linear equations

INTRODUCTION. In Section 3.2, we graphed the equations shown in Figure 3-22. Because the graph of the equation $y = x - 1$ is a line, we call it a *linear equation*. Since the graphs of $y = x^2$, $y = |x|$, and $y = x^3$ are *not* lines, they are *nonlinear equations*.

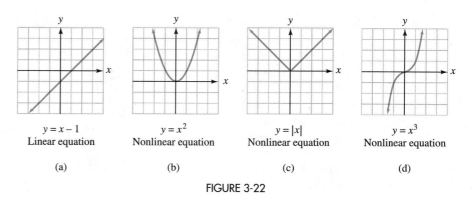

$y = x - 1$
Linear equation

(a)

$y = x^2$
Nonlinear equation

(b)

$y = |x|$
Nonlinear equation

(c)

$y = x^3$
Nonlinear equation

(d)

FIGURE 3-22

In this section, we will discuss how to graph linear equations and show how to use their graphs to solve problems.

Linear equations

Any equation, such as $y = x - 1$, whose graph is a straight line is called a **linear equation in x and y.** Some other examples of linear equations are

$$y = \frac{1}{2}x + 2, \qquad 3x - 2y = 8, \qquad 5y - x + 2 = 0, \qquad y = 4, \quad \text{and} \quad x = -3$$

A linear equation in x and y is any equation that can be written in a special form, called **general** (or **standard**) form.

General form of a linear equation

> If A, B, and C represent real numbers, the equation
> $$Ax + By = C \quad (A \text{ and } B \text{ are not both zero})$$
> is called the **general form** (or **standard form**) of the equation of a line.

Whenever possible, we will write the general form $Ax + By = C$ so that A, B, and C are integers and $A \geq 0$. Note that in a linear equation in x and y, the exponents on x and y are 1.

EXAMPLE 1   *Identifying linear equations.* Which of the following equations are linear equations?   **a.** $3x = 1 - 2y$ **b.** $y = x^3 + 1$ **c.** $y = -\frac{1}{2}x$

Solution

a. Since the equation $3x = 1 - 2y$ can be written in $Ax + By = C$ form, it is a linear equation.

$$3x = 1 - 2y \qquad \text{The original equation.}$$
$$3x + 2y = 1 - 2y + 2y \quad \text{Add } 2y \text{ to both sides.}$$
$$3x + 2y = 1 \qquad \text{Simplify the right-hand side: } -2y + 2y = 0.$$

Here $A = 3$, $B = 2$, and $C = 1$.

b. Since the exponent on x in $y = x^3 + 1$ is 3, the equation is a nonlinear equation.

c. Since the equation $y = -\frac{1}{2}x$ can be written in $Ax + By = C$ form, it is a linear equation.

$$y = -\frac{1}{2}x \qquad \text{The original equation.}$$

$$-2(y) = -2\left(-\frac{1}{2}x\right) \quad \text{Multiply both sides by } -2 \text{ so that the coefficient of } x \text{ will be } 1.$$

Self Check

Which of the following are linear equations and which are nonlinear?

a. $y = |x|$

b. $-x = 6 - y$

c. $y = x$

$-2y = x$ Simplify the right-hand side: $-2\left(-\frac{1}{2}\right) = 1$.

$0 = x + 2y$ Add $2y$ to both sides.

$x + 2y = 0$ Write the equation in general form.

Here $A = 1$, $B = 2$, and $C = 0$.

Answers
a. nonlinear, **b.** linear,
c. linear

Solutions of linear equations

To find solutions of linear equations, we substitute arbitrary values for one variable and solve for the other.

EXAMPLE 2 *Finding solutions of linear equations.* Complete the table of solutions for $3x + 2y = 5$.

x	y	(x, y)
7		$(7, \quad)$
	4	$(\quad, 4)$

Self Check

Complete the table of solutions for $3x + 2y = 5$.

x	y	(x, y)
	-2	$(\quad, -2)$
5		$(5, \quad)$

Solution

In the first row, we are given an x-value of 7. To find the corresponding y-value, we substitute 7 for x and solve for y.

$3x + 2y = 5$ The original equation.

$3(7) + 2y = 5$ Substitute 7 for x.

$21 + 2y = 5$ Do the multiplication: $3(7) = 21$.

$2y = -16$ Subtract 21 from both sides: $5 - 21 = -16$.

$y = -8$ Divide both sides by 2.

A solution of $3x + 2y = 5$ is $(7, -8)$.

In the second row, we are given a y-value of 4. To find the corresponding x-value, we substitute 4 for y and solve for x.

$3x + 2y = 5$ The original equation.

$3x + 2(4) = 5$ Substitute 4 for y.

$3x + 8 = 5$ Do the multiplication: $2(4) = 8$.

$3x = -3$ Subtract 8 from both sides: $5 - 8 = -3$.

$x = -1$ Divide both sides by 3.

Another solution is $(-1, 4)$. The completed table is as follows:

x	y	(x, y)
7	-8	$(7, -8)$
-1	4	$(-1, 4)$

Answer:

x	y	(x, y)
3	-2	$(3, -2)$
5	-5	$(5, -5)$

Graphing linear equations

Since two points determine a line, only two points are needed to graph a linear equation. However, we will often plot a third point as a check. If the three points do not lie on a straight line, then at least one of them is in error.

Graphing linear equations

> **1.** Find three pairs (x, y) that satisfy the equation by picking arbitrary numbers for x and finding the corresponding values of y.
>
> **2.** Plot each resulting pair (x, y) on a rectangular coordinate system. If the three points do not lie on a straight line, check your computations.
>
> **3.** Draw the straight line passing through the points.

EXAMPLE 3   *Graphing linear equations.*   Graph $y = -3x$.

Solution

To find three ordered pairs that satisfy the equation, we begin by choosing three x-values: $-2, 0,$ and 2.

If $x = -2$	If $x = 0$	If $x = 2$
$y = -3x$	$y = -3x$	$y = -3x$
$y = -3(-2)$	$y = -3(0)$	$y = -3(2)$
$y = 6$	$y = 0$	$y = -6$

We enter the results in a table of solutions, plot the points, and draw a straight line through the points. The graph appears in Figure 3-23. Check this work with a graphing calculator.

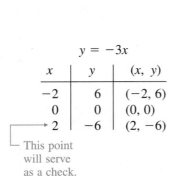

$y = -3x$

x	y	$(x, \ y)$
-2	6	$(-2, 6)$
0	0	$(0, 0)$
2	-6	$(2, -6)$

This point will serve as a check.

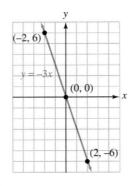

FIGURE 3-23

Self Check
Graph $y = -3x + 2$ and compare the result to the graph of $y = -3x$. What do you notice?

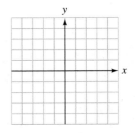

Answer: It is a line 2 units above the graph of $y = -3x$.

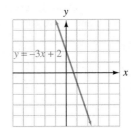

When graphing linear equations, it is often easier to find solutions of the equation if it is first solved for y.

EXAMPLE 4   *Solving for y.*   Graph $2y = 4 - x$.

Solution

To solve for y, we undo the multiplication of 2 by dividing both sides by 2.

$2y = 4 - x$

$\dfrac{2y}{2} = \dfrac{4}{2} - \dfrac{x}{2}$ On the right-hand side, dividing each term by 2 is equivalent to dividing the entire side by 2: $\frac{4-x}{2} = \frac{4}{2} - \frac{x}{2}$.

$y = 2 - \dfrac{x}{2}$ Simplify: $\frac{4}{2} = 2$.

Since each value of x will be divided by 2, we will choose values of x that are divisible by 2. Three such choices are $-4, 0,$ and 4. If $x = -4$, we have

$y = 2 - \dfrac{x}{2}$

$y = 2 - \dfrac{-4}{2}$ Substitute -4 for x.

$y = 2 - (-2)$ Divide: $\frac{-4}{2} = -2$.

$y = 4$ Do the subtraction.

A solution is $(-4, 4)$. This pair and two others satisfying the equation are shown in the table in Figure 3-24. If we plot the points and draw a straight line through them, we will obtain the graph shown in the figure. Check this work with a graphing calculator.

Self Check
Solve $3y = 3 + x$ for y. Then graph the equation.

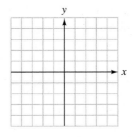

$$y = 2 - \frac{x}{2}$$

x	y	(x, y)
-4	4	$(-4, 4)$
0	2	$(0, 2)$
4	0	$(4, 0)$

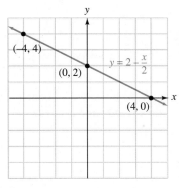

FIGURE 3-24

Answer: $y = 1 + \dfrac{x}{3}$

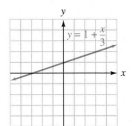

The intercept method

In Figure 3-25, the graph of $3x + 4y = 12$ intersects the y-axis at the point $(0, 3)$; we call this point the **y-intercept** of the graph. Since the graph intersects the x-axis at $(4, 0)$, the point $(4, 0)$ is the **x-intercept.**

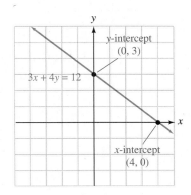

FIGURE 3-25

In general, we have the following definitions.

y- and x-intercepts

> The **y-intercept** of a line is the point $(0, b)$ where the line intersects the y-axis. To find b, substitute 0 for x in the equation of the line and solve for y.
>
> The **x-intercept** of a line is the point $(a, 0)$ where the line intersects the x-axis. To find a, substitute 0 for y in the equation of the line and solve for x.

Plotting the x- and y-intercepts of a graph and drawing a straight line through them is called the **intercept method of graphing a line.** This method is useful when graphing equations written in general form.

EXAMPLE 5   *The intercept method.*   Graph $3x - 2y = 8$.

Solution

To find the x-intercept, we let $y = 0$ and solve for x.

$$3x - 2y = 8$$

$3x - 2(0) = 8$ Substitute 0 for y.

$\quad\quad 3x = 8$ Simplify the left-hand side: $2(0) = 0$.

$\quad\quad x = \dfrac{8}{3}$ Divide both sides by 3.

$\quad\quad x = 2\dfrac{2}{3}$ Write $\frac{8}{3}$ as a mixed number.

The x-intercept is $\left(2\frac{2}{3}, 0\right)$. This ordered pair is entered in the table in Figure 3-26. To find the y-intercept, we let $x = 0$ and solve for y.

Self Check

Graph $4x + 3y = 6$ using the intercept method.

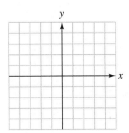

$$3x - 2y = 8$$
$$3(\mathbf{0}) - 2y = 8 \quad \text{Substitute 0 for } x.$$
$$-2y = 8 \quad \text{Simplify the left-hand side: } 3(0) = 0.$$
$$y = -4 \quad \text{Divide both sides by } -2.$$

The y-intercept is $(0, -4)$. It is entered in the table below. As a check, we find one more point on the line. If $x = 4$, then $y = 2$. We plot these three points and draw a straight line through them. The graph of $3x - 2y = 8$ is shown in Figure 3-26.

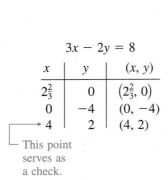

$3x - 2y = 8$

x	y	(x, y)
$2\frac{2}{3}$	0	$(2\frac{2}{3}, 0)$
0	-4	$(0, -4)$
4	2	$(4, 2)$

This point serves as a check.

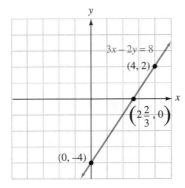

FIGURE 3-26

Answer:

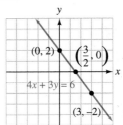

Graphing horizontal and vertical lines

Equations such as $y = 4$ and $x = -3$ are linear equations, because they can be written in the general form $Ax + By = C$.

$$y = 4 \qquad \text{is equivalent to} \qquad 0x + 1y = 4$$
$$x = -3 \qquad \text{is equivalent to} \qquad 1x + 0y = -3$$

We now discuss how to graph these types of linear equations.

EXAMPLE 6 *Graphing horizontal lines.* Graph $y = 4$.

Solution
We can write the equation in general form as $0x + y = 4$. Since the coefficient of x is 0, the numbers chosen for x have no effect on y. The value of y is always 4. For example, if $x = 2$, we have

$$0x + y = 4 \quad \text{The original equation written in general form.}$$
$$0(\mathbf{2}) + y = 4 \quad \text{Substitute 2 for } x.$$
$$y = 4 \quad \text{Simplify the left-hand side: } 0(2) = 0.$$

The table of solutions shown in Figure 3-27 contains three ordered pairs that satisfy the equation $y = 4$. If we plot the points and draw a straight line through them, the result is a horizontal line. The y-intercept is $(0, 4)$, and there is no x-intercept.

Self Check
Graph $y = -2$.

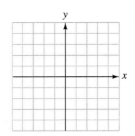

Answer:

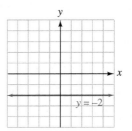

$y = 4$

x	y	(x, y)
2	4	$(2, 4)$
-1	4	$(-1, 4)$
-3	4	$(-3, 4)$

Note that each y-coordinate is 4.

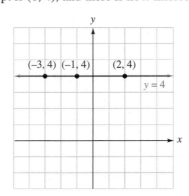

FIGURE 3-27

EXAMPLE 7 *Graphing vertical lines.* Graph $x = -3$.

Solution

We can write the equation in general form as $x + 0y = -3$. Since the coefficient of y is 0, the numbers chosen for y have no effect on x. The value of x is always -3. For example, if $y = -2$, we have

$$x + 0y = -3 \quad \text{The original equation written in general form.}$$
$$x + 0(-2) = -3 \quad \text{Substitute } -2 \text{ for } y.$$
$$x = -3 \quad \text{Simplify the left-hand side: } 0(-2) = 0.$$

The table of solutions shown in Figure 3-28 contains three ordered pairs that satisfy the equation $x = -3$. If we plot the points and draw a line through them, the result is a vertical line. The x-intercept is $(-3, 0)$, and there is no y-intercept.

$x = -3$

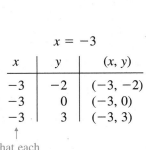

x	y	(x, y)
-3	-2	$(-3, -2)$
-3	0	$(-3, 0)$
-3	3	$(-3, 3)$

↑
Note that each x-coordinate is -3.

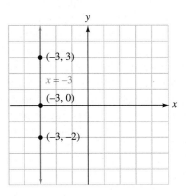

FIGURE 3-28

Self Check
Graph $x = 4$.

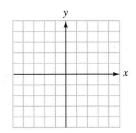

Answer:

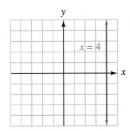

From the results of Examples 6 and 7, we have the following facts.

Equations of horizontal and vertical lines

The equation $y = b$ represents the horizontal line that intersects the y-axis at $(0, b)$. If $b = 0$, the line is the x-axis.

The equation $x = a$ represents the vertical line that intersects the x-axis at $(a, 0)$. If $a = 0$, the line is the y-axis.

An application of linear equations

EXAMPLE 8 *Birthday parties.* A restaurant offers a party package that includes food, drinks, cake, and party favors for a cost of $25 plus $3 per child. Write a linear equation that will give the cost for a party of any size, and then graph the equation.

Solution We can let c represent the cost of the party. The cost c is the sum of the basic charge of $25 and the cost per child times the number of children attending. If the number of children attending is n, at $3 per child, the total cost for the children is $3n$.

The cost	is	the basic $25 charge	plus	$3	times	the number of children.
c	$=$	25	$+$	3	$\cdot$	n

For the equation $c = 25 + 3n$, the independent variable (input) is n, the number of children. The dependent variable (output) is c, the cost of the party. We will find three points on the graph of the equation by choosing n-values of 0, 5, and 10 and finding the corresponding c-values. The results are recorded in the table.

If $n = 0$	If $n = 5$	If $n = 10$	$c = 25 + 3n$

$$c = 25 + 3(0)$$ $$c = 25 + 3(5)$$ $$c = 25 + 3(10)$$

$$c = 25$$ $$c = 25 + 15$$ $$c = 25 + 30$$

$$c = 40$$ $$c = 55$$

n	c
0	25
5	40
10	55

Next, we graph the points and draw a line through them (Figure 3-29). We don't draw an arrowhead on the left, because it doesn't make sense to have a negative number of children attend a party. Note that the c-axis is scaled in units of $5 to accommodate costs ranging from $0 to $65. We can use the graph to determine the cost of a party of any size. For example, to find the cost of a party with 8 children, we locate 8 on the horizontal axis and then move up to find a point on the graph directly above the 8. Since the coordinates of that point are (8, 49), the cost for 8 children would be $49.

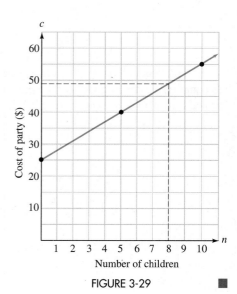

FIGURE 3-29

STUDY SET Section 3.3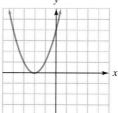

VOCABULARY   *Fill in the blanks.*

1. An equation whose graph is a line and whose variables are to the first power is called a ____linear____ equation.

2. The equation $Ax + By = C$ is the __standard or general__ form of the equation of a line.

3. The ____y-intercept____ of a line is the point $(0, b)$ where the line intersects the y-axis.

4. The ____x-intercept____ of a line is the point $(a, 0)$ where the line intersects the x-axis.

5. Lines parallel to the y-axis are ____vertical____ lines.

6. Lines parallel to the x-axis are ____horizontal____ lines.

CONCEPTS

7. Classify each equation as linear or nonlinear.
  a. $y = x^3$ nonlinear
  b. $2x + 3y = 6$ linear
  c. $y = |x + 2|$ nonlinear
  d. $x = -2$ linear
  e. $y = -x^2$ nonlinear

8. Classify each of the following as the graph of a linear equation or of a nonlinear equation.
  a. nonlinear   **b.** linear

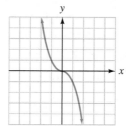

  c. nonlinear   **d.** nonlinear

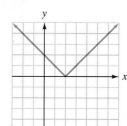

9. Find the power of each variable in the following equations.
  a. $y = 2x - 6$ y: 1st power; x: 1st power
  b. $y = x^2 - 6$ y: 1st power; x: 2nd power
  c. $y = x^3 + 2$ y: 1st power; x: 3rd power

10. In a linear equation in x and y, what are the exponents on x and y?   1

Complete each table of solutions.

11. $5y = 2x + 10$

x	y
10	6
-5	0
5	4

12. $2x + 4y = 24$

x	y
4	4
-2	7
-4	8

13. $x - 2y = 4$

x	y
0	-2
4	0
1	$-\frac{3}{2}$

14. $5x - y = 3$

x	y
0	-3
$\frac{3}{5}$	0
1	2

Consider the graph of a linear equation shown in Illustration 1.

15. Why will the coordinates of point A, when substituted into the equation, yield a true statement?

because A is on the line

16. Why will the coordinates of point B, when substituted into the equation, yield a false statement?

because B is not on the line

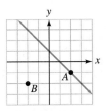

ILLUSTRATION 1

17. A student found three solutions of a linear equation and plotted them as shown in Illustration 2. What conclusion can be made?

The student made a mistake; the points should lie on a straight line.

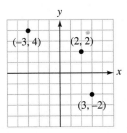

ILLUSTRATION 2

18. How many solutions are there for a linear equation in two variables?

infinitely many

19. Give the x- and y-intercepts of the graph in Illustration 3.

x-intercept: $(-3, 0)$; y-intercept: $(0, -1)$

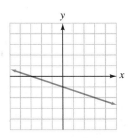

ILLUSTRATION 3

20. On the same coordinate system:
   a. Draw the graph of a line with no x-intercept.
   b. Draw the graph of a line with no y-intercept.
   c. Draw a line with an x-intercept of $(2, 0)$.
   d. Draw a line with a y-intercept of $\left(0, -\frac{5}{2}\right)$.

Answers may vary.

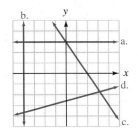

21. Fill in the blanks.
   a. To find the y-intercept of the graph of a linear equation, we let $x = 0$ and solve for y.
   b. To find the x-intercept of the graph of a linear equation, we let $y = 0$ and solve for x.

22. a. What is another name for the line $x = 0$?   the y-axis
   b. What is another name for the line $y = 0$?   the x-axis

NOTATION

23. Write each equation in general form.
   a. $-4x = -y - 6$ $4x - y = 6$
   b. $y = \frac{1}{2}x$ $x - 2y = 0$
   c. $3 = \frac{x}{3} + y$ $x + 3y = 9$
   d. $x = 12$ $x + 0y = 12$

24. Solve each equation for y.
   a. $x + y = 8$ $y = 8 - x$
   b. $2x - y = 8$ $y = 2x - 8$
   c. $3x + \frac{y}{2} = 4$ $y = -6x + 8$
   d. $y - 2 = 0$ $y = 2$

PRACTICE   *Find three solutions of the equation, and then graph it.*

25. $y = -x + 2$

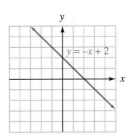

26. $y = -x - 1$

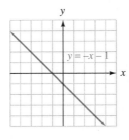

27. $y = 2x + 1$

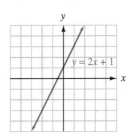

28. $y = 3x - 2$

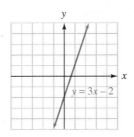

29. $y = x$

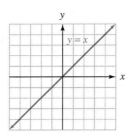

30. $y = 3x$

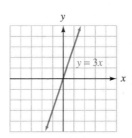

31. $y = -3x$

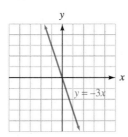

32. $y = -2x$

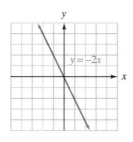

33. $y = \dfrac{x}{3}$

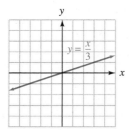

34. $y = -\dfrac{x}{3} - 1$

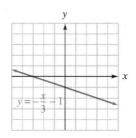

35. $y = -\dfrac{3}{2}x + 2$

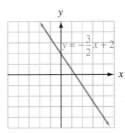

36. $y = \dfrac{2}{3}x - 2$

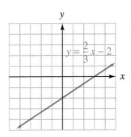

Solve each equation for y, find three solutions of the equation, and then graph it.

37. $2y = 4x - 6$

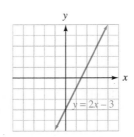

38. $3y = 6x - 3$

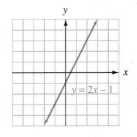

39. $2y = x - 4$

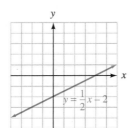

40. $4y = x + 16$

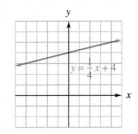

41. $2y + x = -2$

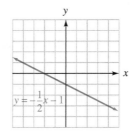

42. $4y + 2x = -8$

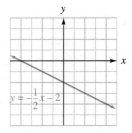

Graph each equation.

43. $y = 4$

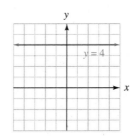

44. $y = -3$

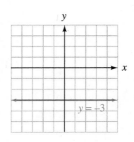

45. $x = -2$

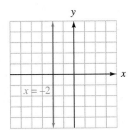

46. $x = 5$

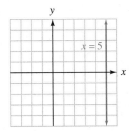

47. $y = -\dfrac{1}{2}$

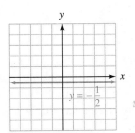

48. $y = \dfrac{5}{2}$

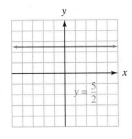

49. $x = \dfrac{4}{3}$

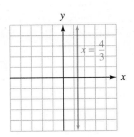

50. $x = -\dfrac{5}{3}$

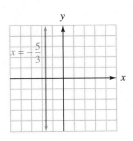

Graph each equation using the intercept method.

51. $2y - 2x = 6$

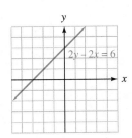

52. $3x - 3y = 9$

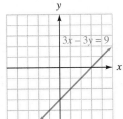

53. $-4y + 9x = -9$

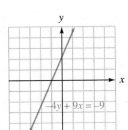

54. $-4y + 5x = -15$

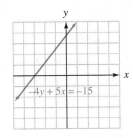

55. $4x + 5y = 20$

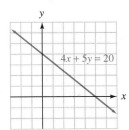

56. $3x + y = -3$

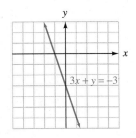

57. $3x + 4y = 12$

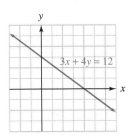

58. $4x - 3y = 12$

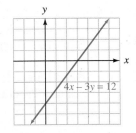

59. $15y + 5x = -15$

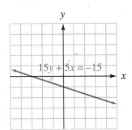

60. $8x + 4y = -24$

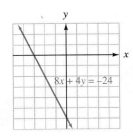

61. $3x + 4y = 8$

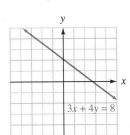

62. $2x + 3y = 9$

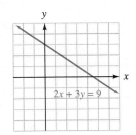

APPLICATIONS

63. EDUCATION COSTS   Each semester, a college charges a services fee of $50 plus $25 for each unit taken by a student.
   a. Write a linear equation that gives the total enrollment cost c for a student taking u units.
   $c = 50 + 25u$
   b. Complete the table of solutions and graph the equation. (See Illustration 4 on the next page.)
   c. Use the graph to find the total cost for a student taking 18 units the first semester and 12 units the second semester. $850
   d. What does the y-intercept of the line tell you?
   The service fee is $50.

u	c
4	150
8	250
14	400

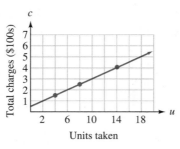

ILLUSTRATION 4

r	h
7	56.2
8.5	62.1
9	64.0

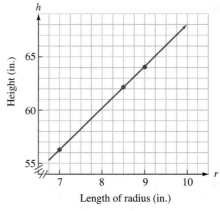

ILLUSTRATION 6

64. GROUP RATES   To promote the sale of tickets for a cruise to Alaska, a travel agency reduces the regular ticket price of $3,000 by $5 for each individual traveling in the group.

   a. Write a linear equation that would find the ticket price t for the cruise if a group of p people travel together. $t = 3,000 - 5p$

   b. Complete the table of solutions and graph the equation. (See Illustration 5.)

   c. As the size of the group increases, what happens to the ticket price?   It decreases.

   d. Use the graph to determine the cost of an individual ticket if a group of 25 will be traveling together. $2,875

66. RESEARCH EXPERIMENT   A psychology major found that the time t (in seconds) that it took a white rat to complete a maze was related to the number of trials n the rat had been given. The resulting equation was $t = 25 - 0.25n$.

   a. Complete the table of solutions in Illustration 7 and then graph the equation.

   b. Complete this sentence: From the graph, we see that the more trials the rat had, the . . . .
   less time it took it to complete the maze.

   c. From the graph, estimate the time it will take the rat to complete the maze on its 32nd trial.   17 sec

p	t
10	2,950
30	2,850
60	2,700

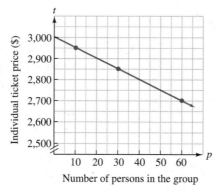

ILLUSTRATION 5

n	t
4	24
12	22
16	21

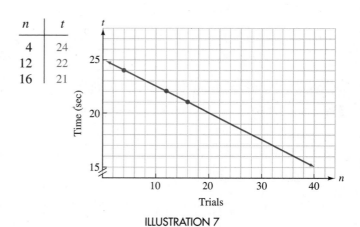

ILLUSTRATION 7

65. PHYSIOLOGY   Physiologists have found that a woman's height h in inches can be approximated using the linear equation $h = 3.9r + 28.9$, where r represents the length of her radius bone in inches.

   a. Complete the table of solutions in Illustration 6. Round to the nearest tenth and then graph the equation.

   b. Complete this sentence: From the graph, we see that the longer the radius bone, the . . . .
   taller the woman is.

   c. From the graph, estimate the height of a woman whose radius bone is 7.5 inches long.   58 in.

WRITING

67. A linear equation and a graph are two ways of mathematically describing a relationship between two quantities. Which do you think is more informative and why?

68. From geometry, we know that two points determine a line. Explain why it is a good practice when graphing linear equations to find and plot three points instead of just two.

69. How can we tell by looking at an equation if its graph will be a straight line?

70. Can the *x*-intercept and the *y*-intercept of a line be the same point? Explain.

REVIEW

71. Simplify $-(-5 -4c)$. $5 + 4c$

72. List the integers. $\{\ldots, -3, -2, -1, 0, 1, 2, 3, \ldots\}$

73. Solve $\dfrac{x + 6}{2} = 1$. -4

74. Evaluate $-2^2 + 2^2$. 0

75. Write a formula that relates profit, revenue, and costs.   profit = revenue − costs

76. Find the volume, to the nearest tenth, of a sphere with radius 6 feet. 904.8 ft^3

77. Evaluate $1 + 2[-3 - 4(2 - 8^2)]$. 491

78. Evaluate $\dfrac{x + y}{x - y}$ for $x = -2$ and $y = -4$. -3

3.4 *Rate of Change and the Slope of a Line*

In this section, you will learn about

- Rates of change • Slope of a line • The slope formula
- Positive and negative slope • Slopes of horizontal and vertical lines
- Using slope to graph a line

INTRODUCTION. Since our world is one of constant change, we must be able to describe change so that we can plan effectively for the future. In this section, we will show how to describe the amount of change of one quantity in relation to the amount of change of another quantity by finding a *rate of change*.

Rates of change

The line graph in Figure 3-30(a) shows the number of business permits issued each month by a city over a 12-month period. From the shape of the graph, we can see that the number of permits issued *increased* each month.

For situations such as the one graphed in Figure 3-30(a), it is often useful to calculate a rate of increase (called a **rate of change**). We do so by finding the **ratio** of the change in the number of business permits issued each month to the number of months over which that change took place.

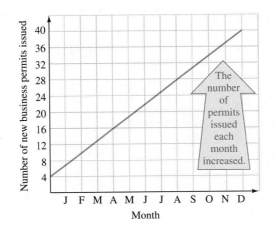

(a)

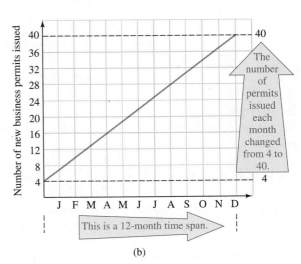

(b)

FIGURE 3-30

Ratios and rates

> A **ratio** is the quotient of two numbers or the quotient of two quantities with the same units. In symbols, if a and b represent two numbers, the ratio of a to b is $\frac{a}{b}$. Ratios that are used to compare quantities with different units are called **rates.**

In Figure 3-30(b) on the previous page, we see that the number of permits issued prior to the month of January was 4. By the end of the year, the number of permits issued during the month of December was 40. This is a change of $40 - 4$, or 36, over a 12-month period. So we have

$$\text{Rate of change} = \frac{\text{change in number of permits issued each month}}{\text{change in time}} \qquad \text{The rate of change is a ratio.}$$

$$= \frac{36 \text{ permits}}{12 \text{ months}}$$

$$= \frac{\overset{1}{\cancel{12}} \cdot 3 \text{ permits}}{\underset{1}{\cancel{12}} \text{ months}} \qquad \begin{array}{l}\text{Factor 36 as } 12 \cdot 3 \text{ and} \\ \text{divide out the common} \\ \text{factor of 12.}\end{array}$$

$$= \frac{3 \text{ permits}}{1 \text{ month}}$$

The number of business permits being issued increased at a rate of 3 per month, denoted as 3 permits/month.

EXAMPLE 1 *Finding rate of change.* The graph in Figure 3-31 shows the number of subscribers to a newspaper. Find the rate of change in the number of subscribers over the first 5-year period. Write the rate in simplest form.

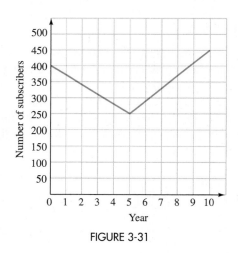

FIGURE 3-31

Self Check

Find the rate of change in the number of subscribers over the second 5-year period. Write the rate in simplest form.

Solution

We need to write the ratio of the change in the number of subscribers over the change in time.

$$\text{Rate of change} = \frac{\text{change in number of subscribers}}{\text{change in time}} \qquad \text{Set up the ratio.}$$

$$= \frac{(250 - 400) \text{ subscribers}}{5 \text{ years}} \qquad \begin{array}{l}\text{Subtract the earlier number of} \\ \text{subscribers from the later} \\ \text{number of subscribers.}\end{array}$$

$$= \frac{-150 \text{ subscribers}}{5 \text{ years}} \qquad 250 - 400 = -150$$

$$= \frac{-30 \cdot \overset{1}{\cancel{5}} \text{ subscribers}}{\underset{1}{\cancel{5}} \text{ years}}$$

Factor -150 as $-30 \cdot 5$ and divide out the common factor of 5.

$$= \frac{-30 \text{ subscribers}}{1 \text{ year}}$$

The number of subscribers for the first 5 years *decreased* by 30 per year, as indicated by the negative sign in the result. We can write this as -30 subscribers/year.

Answer: 40 subscribers/year

Slope of a line

The **slope** of a nonvertical line is a number that measures the line's steepness. We can calculate the slope by picking two points on the line and writing the ratio of the vertical change (called the **rise**) to the corresponding horizontal change (called the **run**) as we move from one point to the other. As an example, we will find the slope of the line that was used to describe the number of building permits issued and show that it gives the rate of change.

In Figure 3-32 (a modified version of Figure 3-30(a)), the line passes through points $P(0, 4)$ and $Q(12, 40)$. Moving along the line from point P to point Q causes the value of y to change from $y = 4$ to $y = 40$, an increase of $40 - 4 = 36$ units. We say that the *rise* is 36.

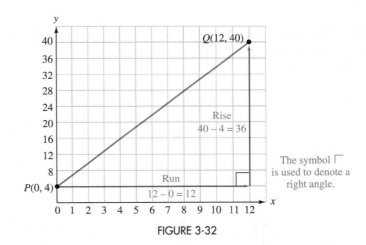

FIGURE 3-32

Moving from point P to point Q, the value of x increases from $x = 0$ to $x = 12$, an increase of $12 - 0 = 12$ units. We say that the *run* is 12. The slope of a line, usually denoted with the letter m, is defined to be the ratio of the change in y to the change in x.

$$m = \frac{\text{change in } y\text{-values}}{\text{change in } x\text{-values}}$$

Slope is a ratio.

$$= \frac{40 - 4}{12 - 0}$$

To find the change in y (the rise), subtract the y-values.
To find the change in x (the run), subtract the x-values.

$$= \frac{36}{12}$$

Do the subtractions.

$$= 3$$

Do the division.

This is the same value we obtained when we found the rate of change of the number of business permits issued over the 12-month period. Therefore, by finding the slope of the line, we found a rate of change.

EXAMPLE 2   *Finding the slope of a line from a graph.*   Find the slope of the line shown in Figure 3-33(a)

Self Check

Find the slope of the line shown in Figure 3-33(a) using two points different from those used in the solution of Example 2.

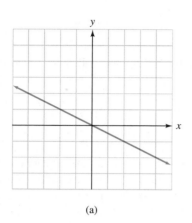

(a)

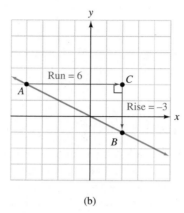

(b)

FIGURE 3-33

Solution

In Figure 3-33(b), we begin by choosing two points on the line—call them A and B. Then we draw right triangle ABC, having a horizontal leg and a vertical leg. The longest side $\overline{AB}$ of the right triangle is called the **hypotenuse.** As we move from A to B (shown using blue arrows), we move to the right, a run of 6, and then down, a rise of -3. To find the slope of the line, we write a ratio.

$m = \dfrac{\text{rise}}{\text{run}}$ The slope of a line is the ratio of the rise to the run.

$m = \dfrac{-3}{6}$ From Figure 3-33(b), the rise is -3 and the run is 6.

$m = -\dfrac{1}{2}$ Simplify the fraction.

The slope of the line is $-\frac{1}{2}$

Answer: $-\dfrac{1}{2}$

    COMMENT   The identical answers from Example 2 and the Self Check illustrate an important fact about slope: The same value for the slope of a line will result no matter which two points on the line are used to determine the rise and the run.

The slope formula

The slope of a line can be described in several ways.

$$\text{Slope} = m = \frac{\text{vertical change}}{\text{horizontal change}} = \frac{\text{rise}}{\text{run}} = \frac{\text{change in } y}{\text{change in } x}$$

To distinguish between the coordinates of two points, say points P and Q (see Figure 3-34), we often use **subscript notation.**

- Point P is denoted as $P(x_1, y_1)$.   Read as "point P with coordinates of x sub 1 and y sub 1."

- Point Q is denoted as $Q(x_2, y_2)$.   Read as "point Q with coordinates of x sub 2 and y sub 2."

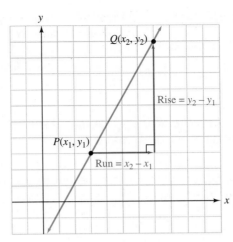

FIGURE 3-34

As a point on the line in Figure 3-34 moves from P to Q, its y-coordinate changes by the amount $y_2 - y_1$ (the rise), while its x-coordinate changes by $x_2 - x_1$ (the run). Since the slope is the ratio $\frac{\text{rise}}{\text{run}}$, we have the following formula for calculating slope.

Slope of a nonvertical line

The **slope** of a nonvertical line passing through points (x_1, y_1) and (x_2, y_2) is

$$m = \frac{y_2 - y_1}{x_2 - x_1}$$

EXAMPLE 3   *Using the slope formula.*
Find the slope of line l_1 shown in Figure 3-35.

Solution
To find the slope of l_1, we will use two points on the line whose coordinates are given: (1, 2) and (5, 5). If (x_1, y_1) is (1, 2) and (x_2, y_2) is (5, 5), then

$$\begin{aligned} x_1 &= 1 \\ y_1 &= 2 \end{aligned} \quad \text{and} \quad \begin{aligned} x_2 &= 5 \\ y_2 &= 5 \end{aligned}$$

To find the slope of line l_1, we substitute these values into the formula for slope and simplify.

$$m = \frac{y_2 - y_1}{x_2 - x_1} \quad \text{The slope formula.}$$

$$= \frac{5 - 2}{5 - 1} \quad \text{Substitute 5 for } y_2, \text{ 2 for } y_1, \text{ 5 for } x_2, \text{ and 1 for } x_1.$$

$$= \frac{3}{4} \quad \text{Do the subtractions.}$$

The slope of l_1 is $\frac{3}{4}$. We would have obtained the same result if we had let $(x_1, y_1) = (5, 5)$ and $(x_2, y_2) = (1, 2)$.

$$m = \frac{y_2 - y_1}{x_2 - x_1} = \frac{2 - 5}{1 - 5} = \frac{-3}{-4} = \frac{3}{4}$$

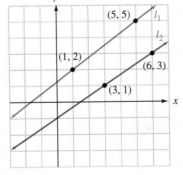

FIGURE 3-35

Self Check
Find the slope of line l_2 shown in Figure 3-35.

Answer: $\dfrac{2}{3}$

COMMENT When finding the slope of a line, always subtract the y-values and the x-values in the same order. Otherwise your answer will have the wrong sign:

$$m \neq \frac{y_2 - y_1}{x_1 - x_2} \quad \text{and} \quad m \neq \frac{y_1 - y_2}{x_2 - x_1}$$

EXAMPLE 4 *Using the slope formula.* Find the slope of the line that passes through $(-2, 4)$ and $(5, -6)$ and draw its graph.

Solution
Since we know the coordinates of two points on the line, we can find its slope. If (x_1, y_1) is $(-2, 4)$ and (x_2, y_2) is $(5, -6)$, then

$$\begin{aligned} x_1 &= -2 \\ y_1 &= 4 \end{aligned} \quad \text{and} \quad \begin{aligned} x_2 &= 5 \\ y_2 &= -6 \end{aligned}$$

$m = \dfrac{y_2 - y_1}{x_2 - x_1}$ The slope formula.

$m = \dfrac{-6 - 4}{5 - (-2)}$ Substitute -6 for y_2, 4 for y_1, 5 for x_2, and -2 for x_1.

$m = -\dfrac{10}{7}$ Simplify the numerator: $-6 - 4 = -10$.
Simplify the denominator: $5 - (-2) = 7$.

The slope of the line is $-\frac{10}{7}$. Figure 3-36 shows the graph of the line. Note that the line "falls" from left to right—a fact that is indicated by its negative slope.

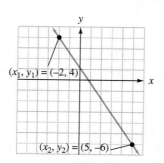

FIGURE 3-36

Self Check
Find the slope of the line that passes through $(-1, -2)$ and $(1, -7)$.

Answer: $-\dfrac{5}{2}$

Positive and negative slope

In Example 3, the slope of line l_1 was positive $\left(\frac{3}{4}\right)$. In Example 4, the slope of the line was negative $\left(-\frac{10}{7}\right)$. In general, lines that rise from left to right have a positive slope, and lines that fall from left to right have a negative slope, as shown in Figure 3-37.

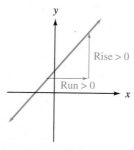

Positive slope

(a)

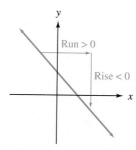

Negative slope

(b)

FIGURE 3-37

Slopes of horizontal and vertical lines

In the next two examples, we will calculate the slope of a horizontal line and show that a vertical line has no defined slope.

EXAMPLE 5 **Slope of a horizontal line.** Find the slope of the line $y = 3$.

Solution To find the slope of the line $y = 3$, we need to know two points on the line. In Figure 3-38, we graph the horizontal line $y = 3$ and label two points on the line: $(-2, 3)$ and $(3, 3)$.

If (x_1, y_1) is $(-2, 3)$ and (x_2, y_2) is $(3, 3)$, we have

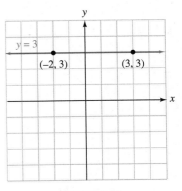

FIGURE 3-38

$$m = \frac{y_2 - y_1}{x_2 - x_1} \qquad \text{The slope formula.}$$

$$m = \frac{3 - 3}{3 - (-2)} \qquad \text{Substitute 3 for } y_2, \text{ 3 for } y_1, \text{ 3 for } x_2, \text{ and } -2 \text{ for } x_1.$$

$$m = \frac{0}{5} \qquad \text{Simplify the numerator and the denominator.}$$

$$m = 0$$

The slope of the line $y = 3$ is 0.

    The y-values of any two points on any horizontal line will be the same, and the x-values will be different. Thus, the numerator of

$$\frac{y_2 - y_1}{x_2 - x_1}$$

will always be zero, and the denominator will always be nonzero. Therefore, the slope of a horizontal line is zero.

EXAMPLE 6 **Slope of a vertical line.** If possible, find the slope of the line $x = -2$.

Solution To find the slope of the line $x = -2$, we need to know two points on the line. In Figure 3-39, we graph the vertical line $x = -2$ and label two points on the line: $(-2, -1)$ and $(-2, 3)$.

If (x_1, y_1) is $(-2, -1)$ and (x_2, y_2) is $(-2, 3)$, we have

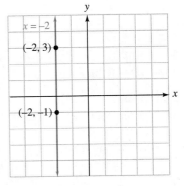

$$m = \frac{y_2 - y_1}{x_2 - x_1} \qquad \text{The slope formula.}$$

$$m = \frac{3 - (-1)}{-2 - (-2)} \qquad \text{Substitute 3 for } y_2, \text{ } -1 \text{ for } y_1, \text{ } -2 \text{ for } x_2, \text{ and } -2 \text{ for } x_1.$$

FIGURE 3-39

$$m = \frac{4}{0} \qquad \text{Simplify the numerator and the denominator.}$$

Since division by zero is undefined, $\frac{4}{0}$ has no meaning. The slope of the line $x = -2$ is undefined.

    The y-values of any two points on a vertical line will be different, and the x-values will be the same. Thus, the numerator of

$$\frac{y_2 - y_1}{x_2 - x_1}$$

will always be nonzero, and the denominator will always be zero. Therefore, the slope of a vertical line is undefined.

We now summarize the results from Examples 5 and 6.

Slopes of horizontal and vertical lines	Horizontal lines (lines with equations of the form $y = b$) have a slope of 0. (See Figure 3-40a.)
	Vertical lines (lines with equations of the form $x = a$) have undefined slope. (See Figure 3-40b.)

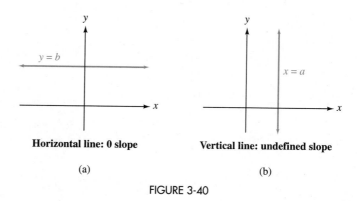

Horizontal line: 0 slope

(a)

Vertical line: undefined slope

(b)

FIGURE 3-40

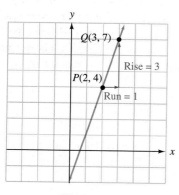

FIGURE 3-41

Using slope to graph a line

We can graph a line whenever we know the coordinates of one point on the line and the slope of the line. For example, to graph the line that passes through $P(2, 4)$ and has a slope of 3, we first plot $P(2, 4)$, as in Figure 3-41. We can express the slope of 3 as a fraction: $3 = \frac{3}{1}$. Therefore, the line *rises* 3 units for every 1 unit it *runs* to the right. We can find a second point on the line by starting at $P(2, 4)$ and moving 1 unit to the right (run) and then 3 units up (rise). This brings us to a point that we will call Q with coordinates $(2 + 1, 4 + 3)$ or $(3, 7)$. The required line must pass through points P and Q.

EXAMPLE 7   *Using slope to graph a line.*   Graph the line that passes through the point $(-3, 4)$ with slope $-\frac{2}{5}$.

Solution

We plot the point $(-3, 4)$ as shown in Figure 3-42. Then, after writing the slope $-\frac{2}{5}$ as $\frac{-2}{5}$, we see that the *rise* is -2 and the *run* is 5. From the point $(-3, 4)$, we can find a second point on the line by moving 5 units to the right (run) and then 2 units down (a rise of -2 means to move down 2 units). This brings us to the point with coordinates of $(-3 + 5, 4 - 2) = (2, 2)$. We then draw a line that passes through the two points.

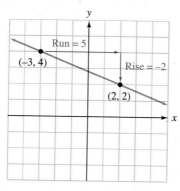

FIGURE 3-42

Self Check

Graph the line that passes through the point $(-4, 2)$ with slope -4.

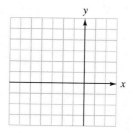

Answer:

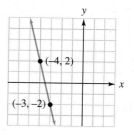

STUDY SET   Section 3.4

VOCABULARY   *Fill in the blanks.*

1. A _____ratio_____ is the quotient of two numbers.

2. Ratios used to compare quantities with different units are called _____rates_____.

3. The _____slope_____ of a line is defined to be the ratio of the change in *y* to the change in *x*.

4. $m = \dfrac{\text{vertical change}}{\text{horizontal change}} = \dfrac{\text{rise}}{\text{run}} = \dfrac{\text{change in } y}{\text{change in } x}$

5. The rate of _____change_____ of a linear relationship can be found by finding the slope of the graph of the line.

6. _____Horizontal_____ lines have a slope of 0. Vertical lines have _____undefined_____ slope.

CONCEPTS

7. Which line graphed in Illustration 1 has
  a. a positive slope? l_2
  b. a negative slope? l_1
  c. zero slope? l_4
  d. undefined slope? l_3

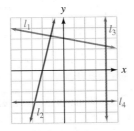

ILLUSTRATION 1

8. For the line graphed in Illustration 2:
  a. Find its slope using points *A* and *B*. $\frac{1}{2}$
  b. Find its slope using points *B* and *C*. $\frac{1}{2}$
  c. Find its slope using points *A* and *C*. $\frac{1}{2}$
  d. What observation is suggested by your answers to parts a, b, and c?
  When finding the slope of a line, any two points on the line give the same result.

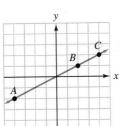

ILLUSTRATION 2

9. Use the information in the table of solutions for a linear equation to determine what the slope of the line would be if it were graphed. -1

x	*y*
-4	2
5	-7

10. Fill in the blanks.
  a. A line with positive slope _____rises_____ from left to right.
  b. A line with negative slope _____falls_____ from left to right.

11. GROWTH RATE   Use the graph in Illustration 3 to find the rate of change of a boy's height during the time shown. 3 in./yr

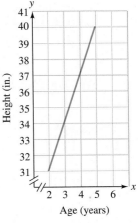

ILLUSTRATION 3

12. IRRIGATION   The graph in Illustration 4 shows the number of gallons of water remaining in a reservoir as water is discharged from it to irrigate a field. Find the rate of change in the number of gallons of water for the time the field was being irrigated. -875 gal/hr

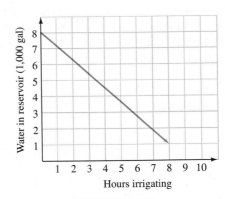

ILLUSTRATION 4

13. DEPRECIATION   The graph in Illustration 5 shows how the value of some sound equipment decreased over the years. Find the rate of change of its value during this time. $-\$2,500$/year

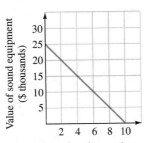

ILLUSTRATION 5

14. WAL-MART   On the graph in Illustration 6, draw a straight line through the points (1991, 34) and (1999, 138). This line approximates Wal-Mart's annual net sales for the years 1991–1999. Give the rate of increase in sales by finding the slope of the line. $13 billion/yr

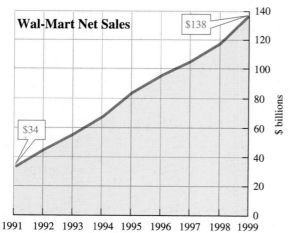

Based on data from Wal-Mart, *USA TODAY* (November 6, 1998), and Hoover's online

ILLUSTRATION 6

15. THE UNCOLA

    a. From the graph in Illustration 7, estimate the rate of change in the sales of 7-Up for the years 1995–1999. Interpret this result.

      0; sales of 7-Up were not changing—each year about the same number of cases were sold

    b. From 1998–1999, which noncola had the greatest rate of change in sales?   Mountain Dew

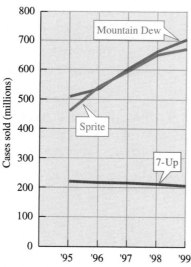

Based on data from *Beverage Digest*

ILLUSTRATION 7

16. COMMERCIAL JETS   Examine the graph in Illustration 8, and consider trips of more than 7,000 miles by a

Boeing 777. Use a rate of change to estimate how the maximum payload decreases as the distance traveled increases. Explain your result in words.

    −15 lb/mi; for every mile over 7,000 miles that the plane travels, the maximum payload is reduced by about 15 pounds

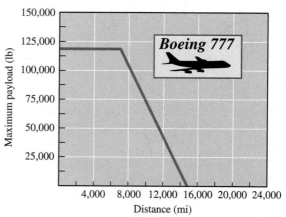

Based on data from Lawrence Livermore National Laboratory and *Los Angeles Times* (October 22, 1998)

ILLUSTRATION 8

NOTATION

17. What is the formula used to find the slope of the line passing through (x_1, y_1) and (x_2, y_2)?

$$m = \frac{y_2 - y_1}{x_2 - x_1}$$

18. Explain the difference between y^2 and y_2.

    y^2 means $y \cdot y$ and y_2 means y sub 2.

PRACTICE   *Find the slope of the line passing through the given points, when possible.*

19. (2, 4) and (1, 3)   1

20. (1, 3) and (2, 5)   2

21. (3, 4) and (2, 7)   −3

22. (3, 6) and (5, 2)   −2

23. (0, 0) and (4, 5) $\frac{5}{4}$

24. (4, 3) and (7, 8) $\frac{5}{3}$

25. (−3, 5) and (−5, 6) $-\frac{1}{2}$

26. (6, −2) and (−3, 2) $-\frac{4}{9}$

27. (−2, −2) and (−12, −8) $\frac{3}{5}$

28. (−1, −2) and (−10, −5) $\frac{1}{3}$

29. (5, 7) and (−4, 7)   0

30. (−1, −12) and (6, −12)   0

31. (8, −4) and (8, −3)   undefined

32. (−2, 8) and (−2, 15)   undefined

33. (−6, 0) and (0, −4) $-\frac{2}{3}$

34. $(0, -9)$ and $(-6, 0)$ $-\frac{3}{2}$

35. 🖩 $(-2.5, 1.75)$ and $(-0.5, -7.75)$ -4.75

36. 🖩 $(6.4, -7.2)$ and $(-8.8, 4.2)$ -0.75

Find the slope of each line.

37. $m = \frac{2}{3}$

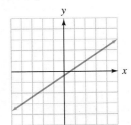

38. $m = -1$

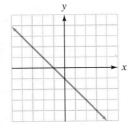

39. $m = \frac{4}{3}$

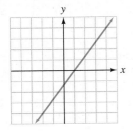

40. $m = 4$

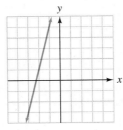

41. $m = -\frac{7}{8}$

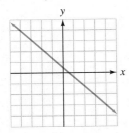

42. $m = -2$

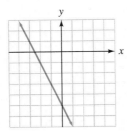

43. $m = -\frac{1}{5}$

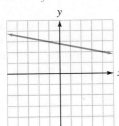

44. $m = 0$

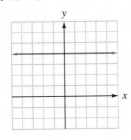

Graph the line that passes through the given point and has the given slope.

45. $(0, 1), m = 2$

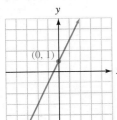

46. $(-4, 1), m = -3$

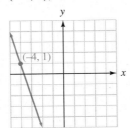

47. $(-3, -3), m = -\frac{3}{2}$

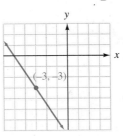

48. $(-2, -1), m = \frac{4}{3}$

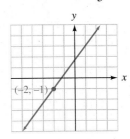

49. $(5, -3), m = \frac{3}{4}$

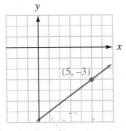

50. $(2, -4), m = \frac{2}{3}$

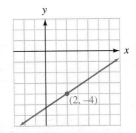

51. $(0, 0), m = -4$

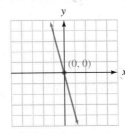

52. $(0, 0), m = 5$

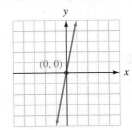

53. $(-5, 1), m = 0$

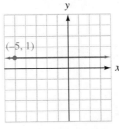

54. $(0, 3)$, undefined slope

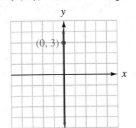

55. $(-1, -4)$, undefined slope

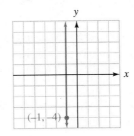

56. $(-3, -2), m = 0$

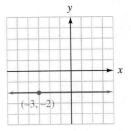

APPLICATIONS

57. POOL DESIGN   Find the slope of the bottom of the swimming pool as it drops off from the shallow end to the deep end, as shown in Illustration 9. $\frac{2}{5}$

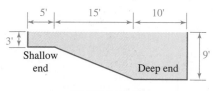

ILLUSTRATION 9

58. DRAINAGE To measure the amount of fall (slope) of a concrete patio slab in Illustration 10, a 10-foot-long 2-by-4, a 1-foot ruler, and a level were used. Find the amount of fall in the slab. Explain what it means.
$\frac{1}{40}$; 1-in. fall for every 40 in. of horizontal run

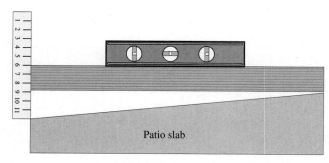

ILLUSTRATION 10

59. GRADE OF A ROAD The vertical fall of the road shown in Illustration 11 is 264 feet for a horizontal run of 1 mile. Find the slope of the decline and use that fact to complete the roadside warning sign for truckers. (*Hint:* 1 mile = 5,280 feet.) $\frac{1}{20}$; 5%

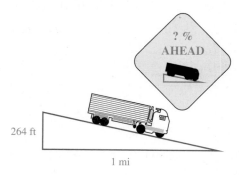

? %
AHEAD

264 ft

1 mi

ILLUSTRATION 11

60. TREADMILL For each height setting listed in the table, find the resulting slope of the jogging surface of the treadmill shown in Illustration 12. Express each incline as a percent.

61. ACCESSIBILITY Illustration 13 shows two designs to make the upper level of a stadium wheelchair-accessible.
a. Find the slope of the ramp in design 1. $\frac{1}{8}$
b. Find the slopes of the ramps in design 2. $\frac{1}{12}$
c. Give one advantage and one drawback of each design.

1: less expensive, steeper; 2: not as steep, more expensive

Height setting	% incline
2 inches	4%
4 inches	8%
6 inches	12%

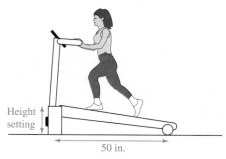

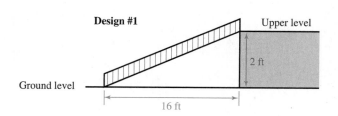

Height setting

50 in.

ILLUSTRATION 12

Design #1   Upper level

Ground level

2 ft

16 ft

Design #2   Upper level

Ground level

1 ft

1 ft

4 ft

ILLUSTRATION 13

62. ARCHITECTURE Since the slope of the roof of the house shown in Illustration 14 is to be $\frac{2}{5}$, there will be a 2-foot rise for every 5-foot run. Draw the roof line if it is to pass through the given black points. Find the coordinates of the peak of the roof. (10, 10)

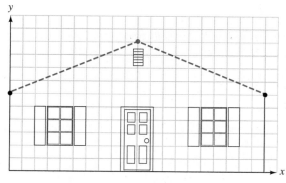

ILLUSTRATION 14

63. ENGINE OUTPUT   Use the graph in Illustration 15 to find the rate of change in the horsepower (hp) produced by an automobile engine for engine speeds in the range of 2,400–4,800 revolutions per minute (rpm).
3 hp/40 rpm

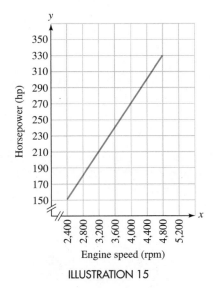

ILLUSTRATION 15

64. UNEMPLOYMENT   See Illustration 16.
   a. Between what two years did the unemployment rate increase the most? Find the rate of change for that period of time.   1989–1991; 0.75%/yr
   b. Between what two years did the unemployment rate decrease the most? Find the rate of change for that period of time.   1993–1995; −0.65%/yr

WRITING

65. Explain why the slope of a vertical line is undefined.

66. How do we distinguish between a line with positive slope and a line with negative slope?

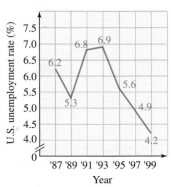

Based on data from the Bureau of Labor Statistics

ILLUSTRATION 16

67. Give an example of a rate of change that government officials might be interested in knowing so they can plan for the future needs of our country.

68. Explain the difference between a rate of change that is positive and one that is negative. Given an example of each.

REVIEW

69. In what quadrant does the point $(-3, 6)$ lie?
quadrant II

70. What is the name given the point $(0, 0)$?   origin

71. Is $(-1, -2)$ a solution of $y = x^2 + 1$?   no

72. What basic shape does the graph of the equation $y = |x - 2|$ have?   V-shape

73. Is the equation $y = 2x + 2$ linear or nonlinear?   linear

74. Solve $-3x \leq 15$. $x \geq -5$

3.5 *Describing Linear Relationships*

In this section, you will learn about

- Slope–intercept form of the equation of a line • Parallel lines
- Perpendicular lines

INTRODUCTION. Numerical relationships are often described by using tables or graphs. For example, various lengths of pipe and their corresponding weights are listed in the table in Figure 3-43. When this information is plotted as ordered pairs, we see that the points lie in a straight line. We say that the relationship between length and weight in this example is *linear*.

Length of pipe (ft)	Weight of pipe (lb)
x	*y*
6	120
10	200
14	280
20	400

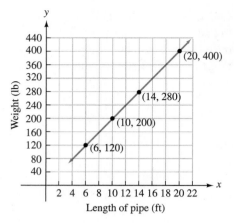

FIGURE 3-43

Figure 3-44 shows a graph of the time a cup of coffee has been sitting on a kitchen counter and its temperature. Since the graph is not a straight line, the relationship between time and temperature in this example is not linear.

Time on counter (min)	Temperature of coffee (°F)
x	*y*
1	180
5	140
10	110
20	80
30	72
45	70

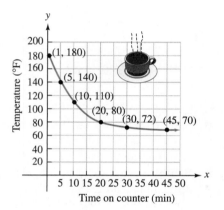

FIGURE 3-44

In this section, we will begin discussing a special type of relationship between two quantities whose graph is a straight line. Our objective is to learn how to write equations in two variables that describe these *linear relationships*.

Slope–intercept form of the equation of a line

The graph of $2x + 3y = 12$ shown in Figure 3-45 enables us to see that the slope of the line is $-\frac{2}{3}$ and that the *y*-intercept is (0, 4).

$$2x + 3y = 12$$

x	*y*	(*x*, *y*)
6	0	(6, 0)
0	4	(0, 4)

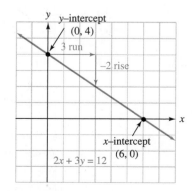

FIGURE 3-45

If we solve the equation for y, we will observe some interesting results.

$$2x + 3y = 12$$

$$3y = -2x + 12 \quad \text{Subtract } 2x \text{ from both sides.}$$

$$\frac{3y}{3} = \frac{-2x}{3} + \frac{12}{3} \quad \begin{array}{l}\text{To undo the multiplication by 3, divide both sides by 3. On} \\ \text{the right-hand side, dividing each term by 3 is equivalent to} \\ \text{dividing the entire side by 3: } \frac{-2x + 12}{3} = \frac{-2x}{3} + \frac{12}{3}. \end{array}$$

$$y = -\frac{2}{3}x + 4 \quad \text{Do the divisions. Rewrite } \frac{-2x}{3} \text{ as } -\frac{2}{3}x.$$

In the equation $y = -\frac{2}{3}x + 4$, the *slope* of the graph $\left(-\frac{2}{3}\right)$ is the coefficient of x, and the constant (4) is the y-coordinate of the y-*intercept* of the graph.

$$y = -\frac{2}{3}x + 4$$

The slope of the line.   The y-intercept is $(0, 4)$.

These observations suggest the following form of an equation of a line.

Slope–intercept form of the equation of a line	If a linear equation is written in the form $$y = mx + b$$ where m and b represent constants, the graph of the equation is a line with slope m and y-intercept $(0, b)$.

EXAMPLE 1   *Slope–intercept form.*

Find the slope and the y-intercept of the graph of each equation: **a.** $y = 6x - 2$,   **b.** $y = -\frac{5}{4}x$,   and   **c.** $y = \frac{x}{2} + 6$.

Solution

a. If we write the subtraction as the addition of the opposite, the equation will be in $y = mx + b$ form:

$$y = 6x + (-2)$$

Since $m = 6$ and $b = -2$, the slope of the line is 6 and the y-intercept is $(0, -2)$.

b. Writing $y = -\frac{5}{4}x$ in slope-intercept form, we have

$$y = -\frac{5}{4}x + 0$$

Since $m = -\frac{5}{4}$ and $b = 0$, the slope of the line is $-\frac{5}{4}$ and the y-intercept is $(0, 0)$.

c. Since $\frac{x}{2}$ means $\frac{1}{2}x$, we can rewrite $y = \frac{x}{2} + 6$ as

$$y = \frac{1}{2}x + 6$$

We see that $m = \frac{1}{2}$ and $b = 6$, so the slope of the line is $\frac{1}{2}$ and the y-intercept is $(0, 6)$.

Self Check

Find the slope and the y-intercept:

a. $y = -5x - 1$

b. $y = \frac{7}{8}x$

c. $y = 5 - \frac{x}{3}$

Answers: **a.** $m = -5, (0, -1)$;
b. $m = \frac{7}{8}, (0, 0)$;   **c.** $m = -\frac{1}{3}, (0, 5)$ ■

COMMENT   If a linear equation is written in the form $y = mx + b$, the slope of the graph is the *coefficient* of x, not the term involving x. For example, it would be incorrect to say that the graph of $y = 5x + 1$ has a slope of $m = 5x$. Its graph has slope $m = 5$.

EXAMPLE 2   *Slope–intercept form.*   Find the slope and the *y*-intercept of the line determined by $6x - 3y = 9$. Then graph it.

Solution

To find the slope and the *y*-intercept of the line, we need to write the equation in slope-intercept form. We do this by solving for *y*.

$$6x - 3y = 9$$

$$-3y = -6x + 9 \qquad \text{Subtract } 6x \text{ from both sides.}$$

$$\frac{-3y}{-3} = \frac{-6x}{-3} + \frac{9}{-3} \qquad \begin{array}{l}\text{To undo the multiplication by } -3\text{, divide both sides by } -3. \\ \text{On the right-hand side, dividing each term by } -3 \text{ is} \\ \text{equivalent to dividing the entire side by } -3: \\ \frac{-6x+9}{-3} = \frac{-6x}{-3} + \frac{9}{-3}.\end{array}$$

$$y = 2x - 3 \qquad \text{Do the divisions. Here, } m = 2 \text{ and } b = -3.$$

From the equation, we see that the slope is 2 and the *y*-intercept is $(0, -3)$.

To graph $y = 2x - 3$, we plot the *y*-intercept $(0, -3)$, as shown in Figure 3-46. Since the slope is $\frac{\text{rise}}{\text{run}} = 2 = \frac{2}{1}$, the line rises 2 units for every unit it moves to the right. If we begin at $(0, -3)$ and move 1 unit to the right (run) and then 2 units up (rise), we locate the point $(1, -1)$, which is a second point on the line. We then draw a line through $(0, -3)$ and $(1, -1)$.

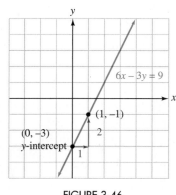

FIGURE 3-46

Self Check

Find the slope and the *y*-intercept of the line determined by $8x - 2y = -2$. Then graph it.

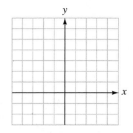

Answer: $m = 4, (0, 1)$

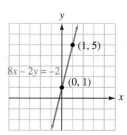

If we are given the slope and *y*-intercept of a line, we can write its equation, as in the next example.

EXAMPLE 3   *Limo service.*   On weekends, a limousine service charges a fee of $100, plus 50¢ per mile, for the rental of a stretch limo. Write a linear equation that describes the relationship between the rental cost and the number of miles driven. Graph the result.

Solution   To write an equation describing this relationship, we will let *x* represent the number of miles driven and *y* represent the cost (in dollars). We can make two observations:

- The cost increases by $0.50 or 50¢ for each mile driven. This is the *rate of change* of the rental cost to miles driven, and it will be the *slope* of the graph of the equation. Thus, $m = 0.50$.

- The basic fee is $100. Before driving any miles (that is, when $x = 0$), the cost *y* is 100. The ordered pair $(0, 100)$ will be the *y*-intercept of the graph of the equation. So we know that $b = 100$.

We substitute 0.50 for *m* and 100 for *b* in the slope–intercept form to get

$$y = 0.50x + 100 \qquad \begin{array}{l}\text{Here the cost } y \text{ depends on } x, \\ \text{the number of miles driven.}\end{array}$$
$$\uparrow\uparrow$$
$$m = 0.50 \qquad b = 100$$

To graph $y = 0.50x + 100$, we plot its *y*-intercept, $(0, 100)$, as shown in Figure 3-47. Since the slope is $0.50 = \frac{50}{100} = \frac{5}{10}$, we can start at $(0, 100)$ and locate a second point on the line by moving 10 units to the right (run) and then 5 units up (rise). This point will have coordinates $(0 + 10, 100 + 5)$ or $(10, 105)$. We draw a straight line through these two points to get a graph that illustrates the relationship between the rental cost and the number of miles driven. We draw the graph only in quadrant I, because the number of miles driven is always positive.

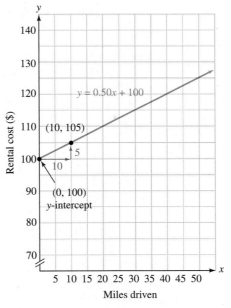

FIGURE 3-47

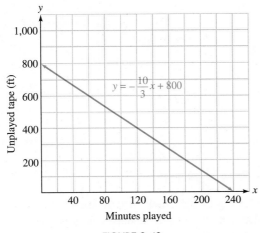

EXAMPLE 4   *Videotapes.*   A VHS videocassette contains 800 feet of tape. In the long play (LP) mode, it plays 10 feet of tape every 3 minutes. Write a linear equation that relates the number of feet of tape yet to be played and the number of minutes the tape has been playing. Graph the equation.

Solution

The number of feet yet to be played depends on the time the tape has been playing. To write an equation describing this relationship, we let x represent the number of minutes the tape has been playing and y represent the number of feet of tape yet to be played. We can make two observations:

- Since the VCR plays 10 feet of tape every 3 minutes, the number of feet remaining is constantly *decreasing*. This rate of change $\left(-\frac{10}{3} \text{ feet per minute}\right)$ will be the slope of the graph of the equation. Thus, $m = -\frac{10}{3}$.

- The cassette tape is 800 feet long. Before any of the tape is played (that is, when $x = 0$), the amount of tape yet to be played is $y = 800$. Written as an ordered pair, we have $(0, 800)$. Thus, $b = 800$.

Writing the equation in slope–intercept form, we have $y = -\frac{10}{3}x + 800$. Its graph is shown in Figure 3-48.

FIGURE 3-48

Self Check

In Example 4, let's say that the VCR is in super long play (SLP) mode, which plays 11 feet every 5 minutes. Use Figure 3-48 to graph the equation and then make an observation.

Answer: $y = -\frac{11}{5}x + 800$; the graphs have the same y-intercept but different slopes.

Parallel lines

Suppose it costs $75, plus 50¢ per mile, to rent the limo discussed in Example 3 on a weekday. If we substitute 0.50 for m and 75 for b in the slope–intercept form of a line, we have

$$y = 0.50x + 75$$

The graph of this equation and the graph of the equation

$$y = 0.50x + 100$$

appear in Figure 3-49.

From the figure, we see that the lines, each with slope 0.50, are parallel (do not intersect). This observation suggests the following fact.

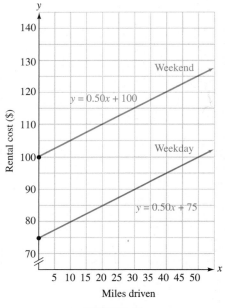

FIGURE 3-49

Slopes of parallel lines	Two different lines with the same slope are parallel.

EXAMPLE 5   *Parallel lines.*   Graph $y = -\frac{2}{3}x$ and $y = -\frac{2}{3}x + 3$ on the same set of axes.

Solution

The graph of first equation has a slope of $-\frac{2}{3}$ and a y-intercept of $(0, 0)$. The graph of second equation has a slope of $-\frac{2}{3}$ and a y-intercept of $(0, 3)$. We graph each equation as in Figure 3-50. Since the lines have the same slope of $-\frac{2}{3}$, they are parallel.

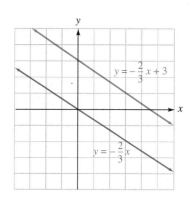

FIGURE 3-50

Self Check

Graph $y = \frac{5}{2}x - 2$ and $y = \frac{5}{2}x$ on the same set of axes.

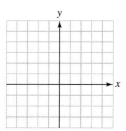

Answer:

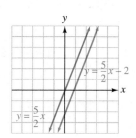

Perpendicular lines

The two lines shown in Figure 3-51 meet at right angles and are called **perpendicular lines.** In the figure, the symbol ⌐ is used to denote a right angle. Each of the four angles that are formed has a measure of 90°.

The product of the slopes of two (nonvertical) perpendicular lines is -1. For example, the perpendicular lines shown in Figure 3-51 have slopes of $\frac{3}{2}$ and $-\frac{2}{3}$. If we find the product of their slopes, we have

$$\frac{3}{2}\left(-\frac{2}{3}\right) = -\frac{6}{6} = -1$$

Two numbers whose product is -1 are called **negative reciprocals.** The numbers $\frac{3}{2}$ and $-\frac{2}{3}$, for example, are negative reciprocals, because their product is -1. The term *negative reciprocal* can be used to relate perpendicular lines and their slopes.

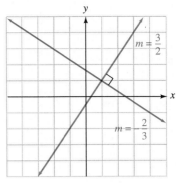

FIGURE 3-51

Slopes of perpendicular lines

> If two nonvertical lines are perpendicular, their slopes are negative reciprocals.
>
> If the slopes of two lines are negative reciprocals, the lines are perpendicular.

We can also state the fact given above symbolically: If the slopes of two nonvertical lines are m_1 and m_2, then the lines are perpendicular if

$$m_1 \cdot m_2 = -1 \qquad \text{or} \qquad m_2 = \frac{1}{m_1}$$

Because a horizontal line is perpendicular to a vertical line, a line with a slope of 0 is perpendicular to a line with no defined slope.

EXAMPLE 6 *Parallel and perpendicular lines.* Determine whether the graphs of $y = -5x + 6$ and $y = \frac{x}{5} - 2$ are parallel, perpendicular, or neither.

Solution
The slope of the line $y = -5x + 6$ is -5. The slope of the line $y = \frac{x}{5} - 2$ is $\frac{1}{5}$. $\left(\text{Recall that } \frac{x}{5} = \frac{1}{5}x.\right)$ Since the slopes are not equal, the lines are not parallel. If we find the product of their slopes, we have

$$-5\left(\frac{1}{5}\right) = -\frac{5}{5} = -1$$

Since the product of their slopes is -1, the lines are perpendicular.

Self Check
Determine whether the graphs of $y = 4x + 4$ and $y = \frac{1}{4}x$ are parallel, perpendicular, or neither.

Answer: neither ∎

STUDY SET Section 3.5

VOCABULARY *Fill in the blanks.*

1. The equation $y = mx + b$ is called the __slope–intercept__ form for the equation of a line.

2. The graph of the linear equation $y = mx + b$ has a __y-intercept__ of $(0, b)$ and a __slope__ of m.

3. __Parallel__ lines do not intersect.

4. The slope of a line is a __rate__ of change.

5. The numbers $\frac{5}{6}$ and $-\frac{6}{5}$ are called negative __reciprocals__. Their product is -1.

6. The product of the slopes of __perpendicular__ lines is -1.

CONCEPTS

7. TREE GROWTH Graph the values shown in Illustration 1 and connect the points with a smooth curve. Does the graph indicate a linear relationship between the age of the tree and its height? Explain your answer.

No, because the graph is not a straight line.

Age	Height
0	0
5	8
10	15
15	28
20	45
25	62
30	85
35	100
40	112
45	118

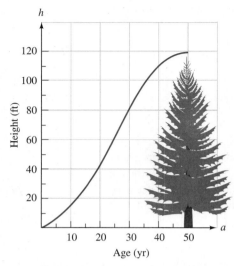

ILLUSTRATION 1

10. In Illustration 4, the slope of line l_1 is 2.
 a. What is the slope of line l_2? $-\frac{1}{2}$
 b. What is the slope of line l_3? 2
 c. What is the slope of line l_4? $-\frac{1}{2}$
 d. Which lines have the same y-intercept? l_1 and l_2

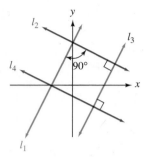

ILLUSTRATION 4

8. See Illustration 2.
 a. What is the slope of the line? $-\frac{1}{2}$
 b. What is the y-intercept of the line? $(0, -4)$
 c. Write the equation of the line. $y = -\frac{1}{2}x - 4$

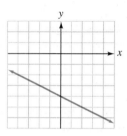

ILLUSTRATION 2

11. a. What is the y-intercept of line l_1 (graphed in Illustration 5)? $(0, 0)$
 b. What do lines l_1 and l_2 have in common? How are they different?
 same slope, different y-intercepts

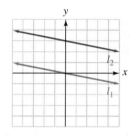

ILLUSTRATION 5

9. NAVIGATION   The graph in Illustration 3 shows the recommended speed at which a ship should proceed into head waves of various heights.
 a. What information does the y-intercept of the graph give?
 When there are no head waves, the ship could travel at 18 knots.
 b. What is the rate of change in the recommended speed of the ship as the wave height increases?
 $-\frac{1}{2}$ knot/ft
 c. Write the equation of the graph. $y = -\frac{1}{2}x + 18$

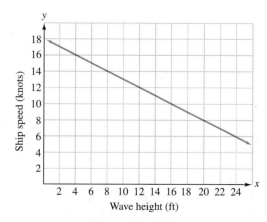

ILLUSTRATION 3

12. Use the graph in Illustration 6 to determine m and b; then write the equation of the line in slope–intercept form.
 $m = \frac{5}{4}, b = 0; y = \frac{5}{4}x$

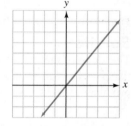

ILLUSTRATION 6

13. What is the slope of the line defined by each equation?
 a. $y = \dfrac{-2x}{3} - 2$ $-\frac{2}{3}$ **b.** $y = \dfrac{x}{4} + 1$ $\frac{1}{4}$
 c. $y = 2 - 8x$ -8 **d.** $y = 3x$ 3
 e. $y = x$ 1 **f.** $y = -x$ -1

14. Without graphing, tell whether the graphs of each pair of lines are parallel, perpendicular, or neither.
 a. $y = 0.5x - 3; y = \frac{1}{2}x + 3$ parallel
 b. $y = 0.75x; y = -\frac{4}{3}x + 2$ perpendicular
 c. $y = -x; y = x$ perpendicular

15. To solve $-2y = 6x - 12$ for y, both sides of the equation were divided by -2. Complete each of the three divisions shown below.

$$\frac{-2y}{-2} = \frac{6x}{-2} - \frac{12}{-2}$$
$$y = -3x + 6$$

16. A graphing calculator was used to graph
$y = -2.5x - 1.25$, as shown below. What important
feature of the graph is typed at the bottom of the
screen?   It shows that the *y*-intercept is $(0, -1.25)$.

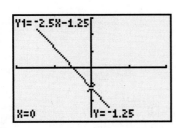

NOTATION   *Complete each solution by solving the
equation for y. Then find the slope and the y-intercept of
its graph.*

17.
$$6x - 2y = 10$$
$$6x - \boxed{6x} - 2y = -6x + 10$$
$$-2y = \boxed{-6x} + 10$$
$$\frac{-2y}{-2} = \frac{-6x}{-2} + \frac{10}{-2}$$
$$y = \boxed{3x} - 5$$

The slope is $\boxed{3}$ and the *y*-intercept is $\boxed{(0, -5)}$.

18.
$$2x + 5y = 15$$
$$2x + 5y - \boxed{2x} = \boxed{-2x} + 15$$
$$5y = -2x + 15$$
$$\frac{5y}{5} = \frac{-2x}{5} + \frac{15}{5}$$
$$y = -\frac{2}{5}x + 3$$

The slope is $\boxed{-\frac{2}{5}}$ and the *y*-intercept is $\boxed{(0, 3)}$.

PRACTICE   *Find the slope and the y-intercept of the
graph of each equation.*

19. $y = 4x + 2$
4, (0, 2)

20. $y = -4x - 2$
-4, $(0, -2)$

21. $y = \dfrac{x}{4} - \dfrac{1}{2}$ $\frac{1}{4}, \left(0, -\frac{1}{2}\right)$

22. $4x - 2 = y$ 4, (0, −2)

23. $y = \frac{1}{2}x + 6$ $\frac{1}{2}, (0, 6)$

24. $y = 6 - x$ -1, (0, 6)

25. $6y = x - 6$ $\frac{1}{6}, (0, -1)$

26. $6x - 1 = y$ 6, (0, −1)

27. $x + y = 8$
-1, (0, 8)

28. $x - y = -30$
1, (0, 30)

29. $2x + 3y = 6$
$-\frac{2}{3}$, (0, 2)

30. $3x - 5y = 15$
$\frac{3}{5}$, (0, −3)

31. $3y - 13 = 0$
$0, \left(0, \frac{13}{3}\right)$

32. $-5y - 2 = 0$
$0, \left(0, -\frac{2}{5}\right)$

33. $y = -5x$ -5, (0, 0)

34. $y = 14x$ 14, (0, 0)

*Write the equation of the line with the given slope and
y-intercept. Then graph it.*

35. $m = 5$, $(0, -3)$
$y = 5x - 3$

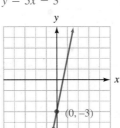

36. $m = -2$, $(0, 1)$
$y = -2x + 1$

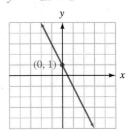

37. $m = \frac{1}{4}$, $(0, -2)$
$y = \frac{1}{4}x - 2$

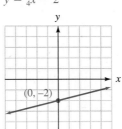

38. $m = \frac{1}{3}$, $(0, -5)$
$y = \frac{1}{3}x - 5$

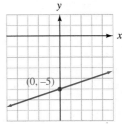

39. $m = -3$, $(0, 6)$
$y = -3x + 6$

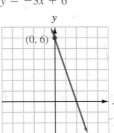

40. $m = -2$, $(0, 1)$
$y = -2x + 1$

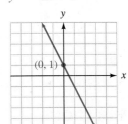

41. $m = -\frac{8}{3}$, $(0, 5)$
$y = -\frac{8}{3}x + 5$

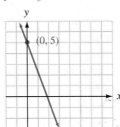

42. $m = -\frac{7}{6}$, $(0, 2)$
$y = -\frac{7}{6}x + 2$

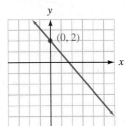

*Find the slope and the y-intercept of the graph of each
equation. Then graph it.*

43. $y = 3x + 3$

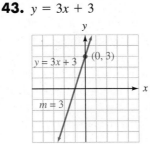

44. $y = -3x + 5$

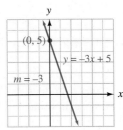

45. $y = -\dfrac{x}{2} + 2$ **46.** $y = \dfrac{x}{3}$

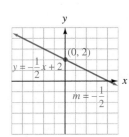

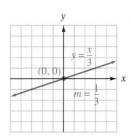

47. $3x + 4y = 16$ **48.** $2x + 3y = 9$

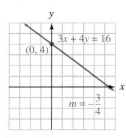

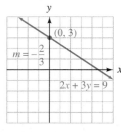

49. $10x - 5y = 5$ **50.** $4x - 2y = 6$

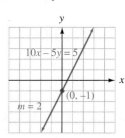

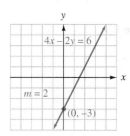

APPLICATIONS

51. PRODUCTION COSTS   A television production company charges a basic fee of $5,000 and then $2,000 an hour when filming a commercial.

   a. Write a linear equation that describes the relationship between the total production costs y and the hours of filming x. $y = 2{,}000x + 5{,}000$

   b. Use your answer to part a to find the production costs if a commercial required 8 hours of filming. $21,000

52. COLLEGE FEES   Each semester, students enrolling at a community college must pay tuition costs of $20 per unit as well as a $40 student services fee.

   a. Write a linear equation that gives the total fees y to be paid by a student enrolling at the college and taking x units. $y = 20x + 40$

   b. Use your answer to part a to find the enrollment cost for a student taking 12 units. $280

53. CHEMISTRY EXPERIMENT   Illustration 7 shows a portion of a student's chemistry lab manual. Use the information to write a linear equation relating the temperature y (in degrees Fahrenheit) of the compound to the time x (in minutes) elapsed during the lab procedure.
$y = 5x - 10$

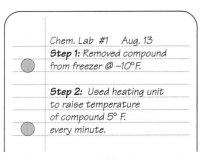

ILLUSTRATION 7

54. INCOME PROPERTY   See Illustration 8. Use the information in the newspaper advertisement to write a linear equation that gives the amount of income y (in dollars) the apartment owner will receive when the unit is rented for x months. $y = 500x + 250$

> **APARTMENT FOR RENT**
> 1 bedroom/1 bath, with garage
> $500 per month +
> $250 nonrefundable security fee.

ILLUSTRATION 8

55. SALAD BAR   For lunch, a delicatessen offers a "Salad and Soda" special where customers serve themselves at a well-stocked salad bar. The cost is $1.00 for the drink and 20¢ an ounce for the salad.

   a. Write a linear equation that will find the cost y of a "Salad and Soda" lunch when a salad weighing x ounces is purchased. $y = 0.20x + 1.00$

   b. Graph the equation (see Illustration 9).

   c. How would the graph from part b change if the delicatessen began charging $2.00 for the drink?
   same slope, different y-intercept

   d. How would the graph from part b change if the cost of the salad changed to 30¢ an ounce?
   same y-intercept, steeper slope

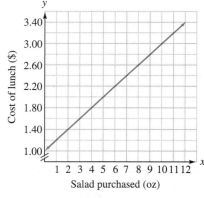

ILLUSTRATION 9

56. SEWING COSTS   A tailor charges a basic fee of $20 plus $2.50 per letter to sew an athlete's name on the back of a jacket.

   a. Write a linear equation that will find the cost y to have a name containing x letters sewn on the back of a jacket. $y = 2.50x + 20$

b. Graph the equation (see Illustration 10).

c. Suppose the tailor raises the basic fee to $30. On your graph from part b, draw the new graph showing the increased cost.

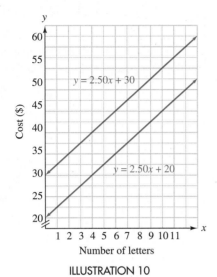

ILLUSTRATION 10

57. EMPLOYMENT SERVICE A policy statement of LIZCO, Inc., is shown in Illustration 11. Suppose a secretary had to pay an employment service $500 to get placed in a new job at LIZCO. Write a linear equation that tells the secretary the actual cost y of the employment service to her x months after being hired.

$y = -20x + 500$

> **Policy no. 23452**– A new hire will be reimbursed by LIZCO for any employment service fees paid by the employee at the rate of $20 per month.

ILLUSTRATION 11

58. COMPUTER DRAFTING Illustration 12 shows a computer-generated drawing of an automobile engine mount. When the designer clicks the mouse on a line of the drawing, the computer finds the equation of the line. Determine whether the two lines selected in the drawing are perpendicular.

not quite: $(0.128)(-7.615) = -0.97472 \neq -1$

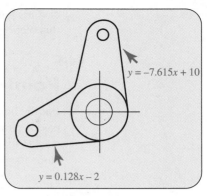

ILLUSTRATION 12

WRITING

59. Explain the advantages of writing the equation of a line in slope–intercept form ($y = mx + b$) as opposed to general form ($Ax + By = C$).

60. Why is $y = mx + b$ called the slope–intercept form of the equation of a line?

61. What is the minimum number of points needed to draw the graph of a line? Explain why.

62. List some examples of parallel and perpendicular lines that you see in your daily life.

REVIEW

63. Find the slope of the line passing through the points $(6, -2)$ and $(-6, 1)$. $-\frac{1}{4}$

64. Is $(3, -7)$ a solution of $y = 3x - 2$? no

65. Evaluate $-4 - (-4)$. 0

66. Solve $2(x - 3) = 3x$. -6

67. To evaluate $[-2(4 - 8) + 4^2]$, which operation should be performed first? subtraction

68. Translate to mathematical symbols: four less than twice the price p. $2p - 4$

69. What percent of 6 is 1.5? 25%

70. Does $x = -6.75$ make $x + 1 > -9$ true? yes

3.6 *Writing Linear Equations*

In this section, you will learn about

- Point–slope form of the equation of a line
- Writing the equation of a line through two points • Horizontal and vertical lines

INTRODUCTION. If we know the slope of a line and its y-intercept, we can use the slope–intercept form to write the equation of the line. The question that now arises is, can *any* point on the line be used in combination with its slope to write its equation? In this section, we will answer this question.

Point–slope form of the equation of a line

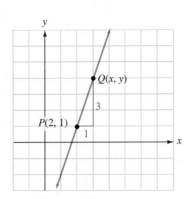

FIGURE 3-52

For the line shown in Figure 3-52, suppose we know that it has a slope of 3 and that it passes through the point $P(2, 1)$. If we pick another point on the line and call it $Q(x, y)$, we can find the slope of the line by using the coordinates of points P and Q. Using the slope formula, we have

$$\frac{y_2 - y_1}{x_2 - x_1} = m \quad \text{The slope formula.}$$

$$\frac{y - 1}{x - 2} = m \quad \text{Substitute } y \text{ for } y_2, 1 \text{ for } y_1, x \text{ for } x_2, \text{ and } 2 \text{ for } x_1.$$

Since the slope of the line is given to be 3, we can substitute 3 for m in the previous equation.

$$\frac{y - 1}{x - 2} = m$$

$$\frac{y - 1}{x - 2} = 3$$

We then multiply both sides by $x - 2$ to get

$$\frac{y - 1}{x - 2}(x - 2) = 3(x - 2) \quad \text{Clear the equation of the fraction.}$$

$$y - 1 = 3(x - 2) \quad \text{Simplify the left-hand side.}$$

The resulting equation displays the slope of the line and the coordinates of one point on the line:

$$\underset{\substack{\uparrow \\ \text{y-coordinate} \\ \text{of the point}}}{y - 1} = 3(\underset{\substack{\uparrow \\ \text{x-coordinate} \\ \text{of the point}}}{x} - 2)$$

Slope of the line

In general, suppose we know that the slope of a line is m and that the line passes through the point (x_1, y_1). Then if (x, y) is any other point on the line, we can use the definition of slope to write

$$\frac{y - y_1}{x - x_1} = m$$

If we multiply both sides by $x - x_1$, we have

$$y - y_1 = m(x - x_1)$$

This form of a linear equation is called the **point–slope form.** It can be used to write the equation of a line when the slope and one point on the line are known.

Point–slope form of the equation of a line

If a line with slope m passes through the point (x_1, y_1), the equation of the line is

$$y - y_1 = m(x - x_1)$$

EXAMPLE 1 *Point–slope form.*
Write the equation of a line that has a slope of -3 and passes through $(-1, 5)$. Express the result in slope–intercept form.

Solution
Since we are given the slope and a point on the line, we will use the point–slope form.

$y - y_1 = m(x - x_1)$ The point–slope form.

$y - 5 = -3[x - (-1)]$ Substitute -3 for m, -1 for x_1, and 5 for y_1.

$y - 5 = -3(x + 1)$ Simplify within the brackets.

We can write this result in slope–intercept form, as follows:

$y - 5 = -3x - 3$ Distribute the multiplication by -3.

$y = -3x + 2$ To undo the subtraction of 5, add 5 to both sides: $-3 + 5 = 2$.

In slope–intercept form, the equation is $y = -3x + 2$.

Answer: $y = -2x + 5$ ∎

EXAMPLE 2 *Temperature drop.*
A refrigeration unit can lower the temperature in a railroad car by 6°F every 5 minutes. One day, the temperature in a car was 76°F after the cooler had run for 10 minutes. Find a linear equation that describes the relationship between the time the cooler has been running and the temperature in the car.

Graph the equation and use it to find the temperature in the car before the cooler was turned on and the temperature in the car after the cooler had run for 25 minutes.

Solution
We will let x represent the time, in minutes, that the cooler was running, and y will represent the air temperature in the car. We can make two observations:

• With the cooler on, the temperature in the railroad car drops 6° every 5 minutes. The rate of change of $-\frac{6}{5}$ degrees per minute is the slope of the graph of the linear equation that we want to find. Thus, $m = -\frac{6}{5}$.

• We know that after the cooler had been running for 10 minutes ($x = 10$), the temperature in the car was 76° ($y = 76$). We can express these facts with the ordered pair $(10, 76)$. This is a point on the graph of the linear equation.

To write the linear equation, we substitute $-\frac{6}{5}$ for m, 10 for x_1, and 76 for y_1, into the point–slope form of the equation of a line.

$y - y_1 = m(x - x_1)$ Point–slope form.

$y - 76 = -\dfrac{6}{5}(x - 10)$ Substitute: $m = -\frac{6}{5}$, $x_1 = 10$, and $y_1 = 76$.

$y - 76 = -\dfrac{6}{5}x - \left(-\dfrac{6}{5}\right)10$ Distribute the multiplication by $-\frac{6}{5}$.

$y - 76 = -\dfrac{6}{5}x - (-12)$ Do the multiplication: $\left(-\frac{6}{5}\right)10 = \left(-\frac{6}{5}\right)\frac{10}{1} = -12$.

$y - 76 = -\dfrac{6}{5}x + 12$ On the right-hand side, change the subtraction to the addition of the opposite.

$y - 76 + 76 = -\dfrac{6}{5}x + 12 + 76$ To undo the subtraction of 76, add 76 to both sides.

$y = -\dfrac{6}{5}x + 88$ Do the additions.

The graph of $y = -\frac{6}{5}x + 88$ is shown in Figure 3-53. From the graph, we see that the temperature in the railroad car before the cooler was turned on was 88°F. This is given by the y-intercept of the graph, $(0, 88)$. If we locate 25 on the x-axis and move straight up to intersect the graph, we will see that the temperature in the car was 58°F. This shows that after the cooler ran for 25 minutes, the temperature was about 58°F.

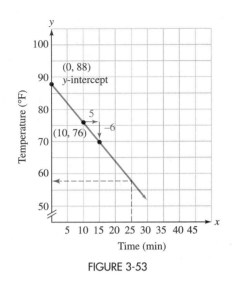

FIGURE 3-53

Writing the equation of a line through two points

In the next example, we will show that it is possible to write the equation of a line when we know the coordinates of two points on the line.

EXAMPLE 3   *Given two points on a line.*   Write the equation of the line passing through $(4, 0)$ and $(6, -8)$.

Solution
First we find the slope of the line that passes through $(4, 0)$ and $(6, -8)$.

$$m = \frac{y_2 - y_1}{x_2 - x_1} \quad \text{The slope formula.}$$

$$= \frac{-8 - 0}{6 - 4} \quad \text{Substitute } -8 \text{ for } y_2, \ 0 \text{ for } y_1, \ 6 \text{ for } x_2, \text{ and } 4 \text{ for } x_1.$$

$$= \frac{-8}{2} \quad \text{Simplify.}$$

$$= -4$$

Since the line passes through both $(4, 0)$ and $(6, -8)$, we can choose either point and substitute its coordinates into the point–slope form. If we choose $(4, 0)$, we substitute 4 for x_1, 0 for y_1, and -4 for m and proceed as follows.

$$y - y_1 = m(x - x_1) \quad \text{Point–slope form.}$$

$$y - 0 = -4(x - 4) \quad \text{Substitute } -4 \text{ for } m, \ 4 \text{ for } x_1, \text{ and } 0 \text{ for } y_1.$$

$$y = -4x + 16 \quad \text{Distribute the multiplication by } -4.$$

The equation of the line is $y = -4x + 16$.

Self Check
Write the equation of the line passing through $(0, -3)$ and $(2, 1)$.

Answer: $y = 2x - 3$

EXAMPLE 4   *Market research.*   A company that makes a breakfast cereal has found that the number of discount coupons redeemed for its product is linearly related to the coupon's value. In one advertising campaign, 10,000 of the "10¢ off" coupons were redeemed. In another campaign, 45,000 of the "50¢ off" coupons were redeemed. How many coupons can the company expect to be redeemed if it issues a "35¢ off" coupon?

Solution   If we let x represent the value of a coupon and y represent the number of coupons that will be redeemed, ordered pairs will have the form

(coupon value, number redeemed)

Two points on the graph of the equation are (10, 10,000) and (50, 45,000). These points are plotted on the graph shown in Figure 3-54. To write the equation of the line passing through the points, we first find the slope of the line.

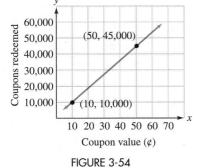

FIGURE 3-54

$$m = \frac{y_2 - y_1}{x_2 - x_1} \qquad \text{The slope formula.}$$

$$= \frac{45,000 - 10,000}{50 - 10} \qquad \text{Substitute 45,000 for } y_2, \text{ 10,000 for } y_1, \text{ 50 for } x_2, \text{ and 10 for } x_1.$$

$$= \frac{35,000}{40}$$

$$= 875$$

We then substitute 875 for m and the coordinates of one known point—say, (10, 10,000)—into the point–slope form of the equation of a line and proceed as follows.

$$y - y_1 = m(x - x_1) \qquad \text{Point–slope form.}$$
$$y - 10,000 = 875(x - 10) \qquad \text{Substitute for } m, x_1, \text{ and } y_1.$$
$$y - 10,000 = 875x - 8,750 \qquad \text{Distribute the multiplication by 875.}$$
$$y = 875x + 1,250 \qquad \text{Add 10,000 to both sides.}$$

To find the expected number of coupons that will be redeemed, we substitute the value of the coupon, 35¢, into the equation $y = 875x + 1,250$ and find y.

$$y = 875x + 1,250$$
$$y = 875(35) + 1,250 \qquad \text{Substitute 35 for } x.$$
$$y = 30,625 + 1,250 \qquad \text{Do the multiplication.}$$
$$y = 31,875$$

The company can expect 31,875 of the 35¢ coupons to be redeemed.   ■

Horizontal and vertical lines

We have graphed horizontal and vertical lines. We will now discuss how to write their equations.

EXAMPLE 5   *Equations of horizontal and vertical lines.*   Write the equation of each line and then graph it: **a.** A horizontal line passing through $(-2, -4)$ and   **b.** A vertical line passing through (1, 3).

Solution

a. The equation of a horizontal line can be written in the form $y = b$. Since the y-coordinate of $(-2, -4)$ is -4, the equation of the line is $y = -4$. The graph is shown in Figure 3-55.

b. The equation of a vertical line can be written in the form $x = a$. Since the x-coordinate of (1, 3) is 1, the equation of the line is $x = 1$. The graph is shown in Figure 3-55.

Self Check

Write the equation of each line and then graph it:

a. a horizontal line passing through (3, 2)

b. a vertical line passing through $(-1, -3)$

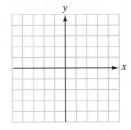

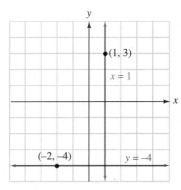

FIGURE 3-55

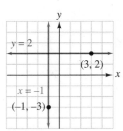

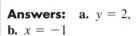

STUDY SET Section 3.6

VOCABULARY *Fill in the blanks.*

1. $y - y_1 = m(x - x_1)$ is called the ___point–slope___ form of the equation of a line.

2. The line in Illustration 1 ___passes___ through point P.

3. In Illustration 1, point P has an ___x-coordinate___ of 2 and a ___y-coordinate___ of -1.

4. The ___slope___ of a line gives a rate of change.

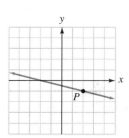

ILLUSTRATION 1

CONCEPTS

5. **a.** The linear equation $y = 2x - 3$ is written in *slope–intercept* form. What are the slope and the y-intercept of the graph of this line?
The slope is 2; the y-intercept is $(0, -3)$.

b. The linear equation $y - 4 = 6(x - 5)$ is written in *point–slope* form. What point does the graph of this equation pass through, and what is the line's slope?
The graph passes through $(5, 4)$; the slope is 6.

6. Is the following statement true or false? The equations

$$y - 1 = 2(x - 2)$$
$$y = 2x - 3$$
$$2x - y = 3$$

all describe the same line.   true

7. **a.** Find two points on the line shown in Illustration 2 whose coordinates are integers. $(-4, -2), (3, 2)$

b. What is the slope of the line? $\frac{4}{7}$

c. Use your answers to parts a and b to write the equation of the line. Answer in point–slope form.
$y + 2 = \frac{4}{7}(x + 4)$ or $y - 2 = \frac{4}{7}(x - 3)$

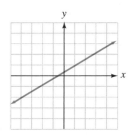

ILLUSTRATION 2

8. In each of the following cases, a linear relationship between two quantities is described. If the relationship were graphed, what would be the slope of the line?

a. The sales of new cars increased by 15 every 2 months. $\frac{15}{2}$

b. There were 35 fewer robberies for each dozen police officers added to the force. $-\frac{35}{12}$

c. Withdrawals were occurring at the rate of $700 every 45 minutes. $-\frac{700}{45} = -\frac{140}{9}$

d. One acre of forest is being destroyed every 30 seconds. $-\frac{1}{30}$

9. In each of the following cases, is the given information sufficient to write the equation of the line?

a. It passes through $(2, -7)$.   no

b. Its slope is $-\frac{3}{4}$.   no

c. It has the following table of values: yes

x	y
2	3
-3	-6

10. In each of the following cases, is the given information sufficient to write the equation of the line?

   a. It is horizontal. no

   b. It is vertical and passes through $(-1, 1)$. yes

   c. It has the following table of values:

x	y
4	5

no

NOTATION

11. Fill in the blank. In $y - y_1 = m(x - x_1)$, we read x_1 as "x ____sub____ one."

12. Write the equation of a horizontal line passing through $(0, b)$. $y = b$

Write the equation in slope–intercept form.

13.
$$y - 2 = -3(x - 4)$$
$$y - 2 = \;-3x\; + \;12$$
$$y - 2 + \;2\; = -3x + 12 + \;2$$
$$y = -3x + 14$$

14.
$$y + 2 = \frac{1}{2}(x + 2)$$
$$y + 2 = \;\frac{1}{2}x\; + \;1$$
$$y + 2 - \;2\; = \frac{1}{2}x + 1 - \;2$$
$$y = \frac{1}{2}x - 1$$

Complete each solution.

15. Write the equation of the line with slope -2 that passes through the point $(-1, 5)$.
$$y - y_1 = m(x - x_1)$$
$$y - \;5\; = -2\big[x - \big(\;-1\;\big)\big]$$
$$y - 5 = \;-2x\; - 2$$
$$y = -2x + 3$$

16. Write the equation of the line with slope 4 that passes through the point $(0, 3)$.
$$y - y_1 = m(x - x_1)$$
$$y - \;3\; = 4\big(x - \;0\;\big)$$
$$y - 3 = \;4x$$
$$y = 4x + 3$$

PRACTICE *Use the point–slope form to write the equation of the line with the given slope and point.*

17. $m = 3$, passes through $(2, 1)$ $y - 1 = 3(x - 2)$

18. $m = 2$, passes through $(4, 3)$ $y - 3 = 2(x - 4)$

19. $m = -\dfrac{4}{5}$, passes through $(-5, -1)$ $y + 1 = -\frac{4}{5}(x + 5)$

20. $m = -\dfrac{7}{8}$, passes through $(-2, -9)$ $y + 9 = -\frac{7}{8}(x + 2)$

Use the point–slope form to first write the equation of the line with the given slope and point. Then write your result in slope–intercept form.

21. $m = \dfrac{1}{5}$, passes through $(10, 1)$ $y = \frac{1}{5}x - 1$

22. $m = \dfrac{1}{4}$, passes through $(8, 1)$ $y = \frac{1}{4}x - 1$

23. $m = -5$, passes through $(-9, 8)$ $y = -5x - 37$

24. $m = -4$, passes through $(-2, 10)$ $y = -4x + 2$

25. $m = -\dfrac{4}{3}$,

x	y
6	-4

$y = -\frac{4}{3}x + 4$

26. $m = -\dfrac{3}{2}$,

x	y
-2	1

$y = -\frac{3}{2}x - 2$

27. $m = -\dfrac{2}{3}$, passes through $(3, 0)$ $y = -\frac{2}{3}x + 2$

28. $m = -\dfrac{2}{5}$, passes through $(15, 0)$ $y = -\frac{2}{5}x + 6$

29. $m = 8$, passes through $(0, 4)$ $y = 8x + 4$

30. $m = 6$, passes through $(0, -4)$ $y = 6x - 4$

31. $m = -3$, passes through the origin $y = -3x$

32. $m = -1$, passes through the origin $y = -x$

Write the equation of the line that passes through the two given points. Write your result in slope–intercept form.

33. Passes through $(1, 7)$ and $(-2, 1)$ $y = 2x + 5$

34. Passes through $(-2, 2)$ and $(2, -8)$ $y = -\frac{5}{2}x - 3$

35.

x	y
-4	3
2	0

$y = -\frac{1}{2}x + 1$

36.

x	y
-1	-4
1	-2

$y = x - 3$

37. Passes through $(5, 5)$ and $(7, 5)$ $y = 5$

38. Passes through $(-2, 1)$ and $(-2, 15)$ $x = -2$

39. Passes through $(5, 1)$ and $(-5, 0)$ $y = \frac{1}{10}x + \frac{1}{2}$

40. Passes through $(-3, 0)$ and $(3, 1)$ $y = \frac{1}{6}x + \frac{1}{2}$

41. Passes through $(-8, 2)$ and $(-8, 17)$ $x = -8$

42. Passes through $\left(\frac{2}{3}, 2\right)$ and $(0, 2)$ $y = 2$

Write the equation of the line with the given characteristics.

43. Vertical, passes through $(4, 5)$ $x = 4$

44. Vertical, passes through $(-2, -5)$ $x = -2$

45. Horizontal, passes through (4, 5) $y = 5$

46. Horizontal, passes through (−2, −5) $y = -5$

APPLICATIONS

47. POLE VAULT   See Illustration 3.
  a. For each of the four positions of the vault shown, give two points that the pole passes through.
    position 1: (0, 0), (−5, 2); position 2: (0, 0), (−3, 6); position 3: (0, 0), (−1, 7); position 4: (0, 0), (0, 10)
  b. Write the equations of the lines that describe the position of the pole for parts 1, 3, and 4 of the jump. $y = -\frac{2}{5}x, y = -7x, x = 0$
  c. Why can't we write a linear equation describing the position of the pole for part 2?
    The pole is not in the shape of a straight line.

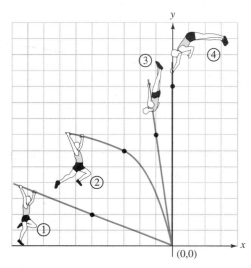

ILLUSTRATION 3

48. FREEWAY DESIGN   The graph in Illustration 4 shows the route of a proposed freeway.
  a. Give the coordinates of the points where the proposed freeway will join Interstate 25 and Highway 40.   (−3, −4), (6, 2)

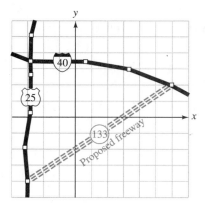

ILLUSTRATION 4

  b. Write the equation of the line that mathematically describes the route of the proposed freeway. Answer in slope–intercept form. $y = \frac{2}{3}x - 2$

49. TOXIC CLEANUP   Three months after cleanup began at a dump site, 800 cubic yards of toxic waste had yet to be removed. Two months later, that number had been lowered to 720 cubic yards.
  a. Write an equation that mathematically describes the linear relationship between the length of time x (in months) the cleanup crew has been working and the number of cubic yards y of toxic waste remaining.
    $y = -40x + 920$
  b. Use your answer to part a to predict the number of cubic yards of waste that will still be on the site one year after the cleanup project began.   440 yd^3

50. DEPRECIATION   To lower its corporate income tax, accountants of a large company depreciated a word processing system over several years using a linear model, as shown in the worksheet in Illustration 5.
  a. Use the information in Illustration 5 to write a linear equation relating the years since the system was purchased x and its value y, in dollars.
    $y = -15,000x + 90,000$
  b. Find the purchase price of the system by substituting $x = 0$ into your answer from part a. $90,000

Tax Worksheet		
Method of depreciation: *Linear*		
Property	Value	Years after purchase
Word processing system	$60,000	2
"	$30,000	4

ILLUSTRATION 5

51. COUNSELING   In the first year of her practice, a family counselor saw 75 clients. In her second year, the number of clients grew to 105. If a linear trend continues, write an equation that gives the number of clients c the counselor will have t years after beginning her practice. $c = 30t + 45$

52. U.S. HEALTH CARE   See Illustration 6. When the per person health care expenditures for the years 1990–1998 are graphed, the data nearly lie on a straight line. The expenditures can be approximated by the straight line drawn through two of the data points.
  a. Use the two highlighted points on the graph to write the equation of the line. Let $x = 0$ represent 1990, $x = 1$ represent 1991, and so on. Answer in slope–intercept form. $y = 212.50x + 2,495$
  b. Use your answer to part a to predict the per person health care expenditure in the year 2020. $6,745

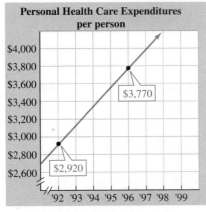

Personal Health Care Expenditures per person

$3,770

$2,920

'92 '93 '94 '95 '96 '97 '98 '99

Based on data from the Health Care Financing Administration

ILLUSTRATION 6

Radius (ft)	Approximate length of padding (ft)
3	19
7	44

Protective pad

radius

ILLUSTRATION 8

53. CONVERTING TEMPERATURES   The relationship between Fahrenheit temperature, F, and Celsius temperature, C, is linear.
   a. Use the data in Illustration 7 to write two ordered pairs of the form (C, F).   (0, 32); (100, 212)
   b. Use your answer to part a to write a linear equation relating the Fahrenheit and Celsius scales.
   $F = \frac{9}{5}C + 32$

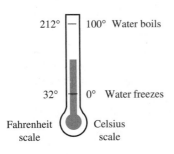

212° | 100° Water boils

32° | 0° Water freezes

Fahrenheit scale   Celsius scale

ILLUSTRATION 7

54. TRAMPOLINE   The relationship between the circumference of a circle and its radius is linear. For instance, the length l of the protective pad that wraps around a trampoline is related to the radius r of the trampoline. Use the data in Illustration 8 to write a linear equation that approximates the length of pad needed for any trampoline radius. $l = 6.25r + 0.25$

55. AIR-CONDITIONING   An air-conditioning unit can lower the air temperature in a classroom 4° every 15 minutes. After the air conditioner had been running for half an hour, the air temperature in the room was 75°F. Write a linear equation relating the time in minutes x the unit had been on and the temperature y of the classroom. (*Hint:* How many minutes are there in half an hour?)
$y = -\frac{4}{15}x + 83$

56. AUTOMATION   An automated production line uses distilled water at a rate of 300 gallons every 2 hours to make shampoo. After the line had run for 7 hours, planners noted that 2,500 gallons of distilled water remained in the storage tank. Write a linear equation relating the time in hours x since the production line began and the number of gallons y of distilled water in the storage tank. $y = -150x + 3,550$

WRITING

57. Why is $y - y_1 = m(x - x_1)$ called the point–slope form of the equation of a line?

58. If we know two points that a line passes through, we can write its equation. Explain how this is done.

59. If we know the slope of a line and a point it passes through, we can write its equation. Explain how this is done.

60. Think of several points on the graph of the horizontal line $y = 4$. What do the points have in common? How do they differ?

REVIEW

61. Find the slope of the line passing through the points $(2, 4)$ and $(-6, 8)$. $-\frac{1}{2}$

62. Is the graph of $y = x^2$ a straight line?   no

63. Find the area of a circle with a diameter of 12 feet. Round to the nearest tenth. 113.1 ft^2

64. If a 15-foot board is cut into two pieces and we let x represent the length of one piece (in feet), how long is the other piece? $(15 - x)$ ft

65. Evaluate $(-1)^5$. -1

66. Solve $\dfrac{x - 3}{4} = -4$. -13

67. What is the coefficient of the second term of $-4x^2 + 6x - 13$?   6

68. Simplify $(-2p)(-5)(4x)$. $40px$

3.7 *Functions*

In this section, you will learn about

- Functions • Domain and range of a function • Function notation
- Graphs of functions • The vertical line test

INTRODUCTION. In everyday life, we see a wide variety of situations where one quantity depends on another:

- The distance traveled by a car depends on its speed.
- The cost of renting a video depends on the number of days it is rented.
- A state's number of representatives in Congress depends on the state's population.

In this section, we will discuss many situations where one quantity depends on another according to a specific rule, called a *function*. For example, the equation $y = 2x - 3$ sets up a rule where each value of y depends on the choice of some number x. The rule is: *To find y, double the value of x and subtract* 3. In this case, y (the *dependent variable*) depends on x (the *independent variable*).

Functions

We have previously described relationships between two quantities in different ways:

Using words

| The number of tires to order | is | two | times | the number of bicycles to be manufactured. |

Here words are used to state that the number of bicycle tires to order depends on the number of bicycles to be manufactured.

Using equations

$$t = 1,500 - d$$

This equation describes how the amount of take-home pay t depends on the amount of deductions d.

Using graphs

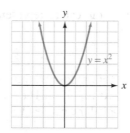

This rectangular coordinate graph shows many ordered pairs (x, y) that satisfy the equation $y = x^2$, where the value of the y-coordinate depends on the value of the x-coordinate.

Using tables

Acres	Schools
400	4
800	8
1,000	10
2,000	20

This table shows that the number of schools needed depends on the size of the housing development.

Two observations can be made about these examples:

- Each one establishes a relationship between two sets of values. For example, the number of bicycle tires that must be ordered *depends* on the number of bicycles to be manufactured.

• In these relationships, each value in one set is assigned a *single* value of a second set. For example, for each number of bicycles to be manufactured, there is exactly one number of tires to order.

Relationships between two quantities that exhibit both of these characteristics are called **functions.**

Functions

> A **function** is a rule that assigns to each value of one variable (the **independent variable**) a single value of another variable (the **dependent variable**).

Using the variables x and y, we can restate the previous definition as follows: For y to be a function of x, each value of x must determine exactly one value of y.

EXAMPLE 1 *Identifying functions.* **a.** Does $y = 4x + 1$ define a function? **b.** Does the table define y as a function of x?

x	y
0	6
5	3
9	1
5	7
10	8

Solution

a. For each value of the independent variable x, we apply the rule: *Multiply x by 4 and add 1*. Since this arithmetic gives a single value of the dependent variable y, the equation defines a function.

b. Since the table assigns two different values of y, 3 and 7, to the x-value of 5, it does not define y as a function of x.

Self Check

a. Does $y = 2 - x^2$ define a function?

b. Does the table below define a function?

x	y
2	4
1	1
0	0
−1	1
−2	4

Answers: **a.** yes **b.** yes

 COMMENT The table in the above Self Check illustrates an important fact about functions. In a function, different values of x can determine the *same* value of y. In the table, x-values of 2 and −2 determine a y-value of 4, and x-values of 1 and −1 determine a y-value of 1. Nevertheless, each value of x determines exactly one value of y, so the table does define a function.

Domain and range of a function

We have seen that functions can be represented by equations in two variables. Some examples of functions are

$$y = 2x - 10, \qquad y = x^2 + 2x - 3, \qquad \text{and} \qquad s = 5 - 16t$$

For a function, the set of all possible values of the independent variable (the inputs) is called the **domain of the function.** The set of all possible values of the dependent variable (the outputs) is called the **range of the function.**

EXAMPLE 2 *Finding the domain and range of a function.* Find the domain and range of $y = |x|$.

Solution

To find the domain of $y = |x|$, we determine which real numbers are allowable inputs for x. Since we can find the absolute value of any real number, the domain is the set of all real numbers. Since the absolute value of any real number x is greater than or equal to zero, the range of $y = |x|$ is the set of all real numbers greater than or equal to zero.

Self Check

Find the domain and range of the function $y = -x$.

Answer: domain: all real numbers; range: all real numbers

Function notation

When the variable y is a function of x, there is a special notation that we can use to denote the function.

Function notation	The notation $y = f(x)$ denotes that y is a function of x.

The notation $y = f(x)$ is read as "y equals f of x." Note that y and $f(x)$ are two different notations for the same quantity. Thus, the equations $y = 4x + 1$ and $f(x) = 4x + 1$ represent the same relationship.

 COMMENT   The symbol $f(x)$ denotes a function. It does not mean "f times x."

The notation $y = f(x)$ provides a way of denoting the value of y that corresponds to some number x. For example, if $f(x) = 4x + 1$, the value of y that is determined when $x = 2$ is denoted by $f(2)$.

$$f(x) = 4x + 1 \qquad \text{The function.}$$
$$f(2) = 4(2) + 1 \qquad \text{Replace } x \text{ with 2.}$$
$$= 8 + 1$$
$$= 9$$

Thus, $f(2) = 9$.

The letter f used in the notation $y = f(x)$ represents the word *function*. However, other letters can be used to represent functions. For example, $y = g(x)$ and $y = h(x)$ also denote functions involving the variable x.

EXAMPLE 3   *Evaluating functions.*   For $g(x) = 3 - 2x$ and $h(x) = x^3 - 1$, find   **a.** $g(3)$ and   **b.** $h(-2)$.

Solution

a. To find $g(3)$, we use the function rule $g(x) = 3 - 2x$ and replace x with 3.

$$g(x) = 3 - 2x$$
$$g(3) = 3 - 2(3) \qquad \text{Substitute 3 for } x.$$
$$= 3 - 6 \qquad \text{Do the multiplication.}$$
$$= -3$$

So $g(3) = -3$.

b. To find $h(-2)$, we use the function rule $h(x) = x^3 - 1$ and replace x with -2.

$$h(x) = x^3 - 1$$
$$h(-2) = (-2)^3 - 1 \qquad \text{Substitute } -2 \text{ for } x.$$
$$= -8 - 1 \qquad \text{Evaluate the power.}$$
$$= -9$$

So $h(-2) = -9$.

Self Check

Find $g(0)$ and $h(4)$ using the functions in Example 3.

Answers: a. 3,   **b.** 63   ■

We can think of a function as a machine that takes some input x and turns it into some output $f(x)$, as shown in Figure 3-56(a). The machine in Figure 3-56(b) turns the input value of -2 into the output value of -9, and we can write $f(-2) = -9$.

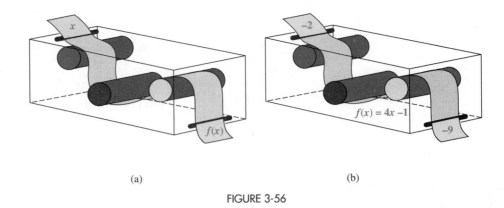

(a)   (b)

FIGURE 3-56

Accent on Technology: **Business profits**

Accountants have found that the function $f(x) = -0.000065x^2 + 12x - 278,000$ estimates the profit a bowling alley will make when x games are bowled per year. Suppose that management predicts that 90,000 games will be bowled in the upcoming year. The expected profit for that year can be found by evaluating $f(90,000)$ on a scientific calculator.

$$f(\mathbf{90,000}) = -0.000065(\mathbf{90,000})^2 + 12(\mathbf{90,000}) - 278,000$$

Keystrokes   .000065 $\boxed{+/-}$ $\boxed{\times}$ 90000 $\boxed{x^2}$ $\boxed{+}$ 12 $\boxed{\times}$ 90000 $\boxed{-}$ 278000 $\boxed{=}$

$$\boxed{275500}$$

To evaluate $f(90,000)$ with a graphing calculator, we enter these numbers and press these keys.

Keystrokes $\boxed{(-)}$ .000065 $\boxed{\times}$ 90000 $\boxed{x^2}$ $\boxed{+}$ 12 $\boxed{\times}$ 90000 $\boxed{-}$ 278000 $\boxed{\text{ENTER}}$

```
-.000065*90000² +
12*90000 - 278000
                275500
```

Graphs of functions

We have seen that a function, such as $f(x) = 4x + 1$, assigns to each value of x a single value of y. The ordered pairs (x, y) that a function determines can be shown on a graph. Since $y = f(x)$, the graph of the function $f(x) = 4x + 1$ is the same as the graph of the equation $y = 4x + 1$. We can graph the function by making a **table of values,** plotting the points, and drawing the graph.

To make a table of values for $f(x) = 4x + 1$, we will choose numbers for x and find the corresponding values of $f(x)$. If $x = -1$, we have

$$f(x) = 4x + 1$$
$$f(\mathbf{-1}) = 4(\mathbf{-1}) + 1 \quad \text{Substitute } -1 \text{ for } x.$$
$$= -4 + 1 \quad\quad \text{Do the multiplication.}$$
$$= -3$$

We have found that $f(-1) = -3$. In a similar manner, we find the corresponding values for $f(x)$ for x-values of 0 and 2 and record them in the table of values in Figure 3-57 (next page). If we plot the ordered pairs in the table and draw a straight line through them, we get the graph of the function $f(x) = 4x + 1$ shown in the figure.

$$f(x) = 4x + 1$$

x	$f(x)$	$(x, f(x))$
-1	-3	$(-1, -3)$
0	1	$(0, 1)$
2	9	$(2, 9)$

Pick input values from the domain.

Find each corresponding output value: $f(-1)$, $f(0)$, and $f(2)$.

Form ordered pairs.

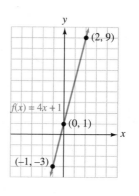

FIGURE 3-57

Any linear equation, except those of the form $x = a$, can be written using function notation by writing it in slope–intercept form ($y = mx + b$) and then replacing y with $f(x)$. We call this type of function a **linear function.**

Figure 3-58 shows the graphs of four basic functions.

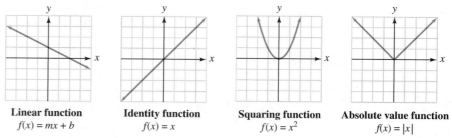

Linear function	**Identity function**	**Squaring function**	**Absolute value function**
$f(x) = mx + b$	$f(x) = x$	$f(x) = x^2$	$f(x) = \lvert x \rvert$

FIGURE 3-58

The vertical line test

We can use the **vertical line test** to determine whether a given graph is the graph of a function. If any vertical line intersects a graph more than once, the graph cannot represent a function, because to one value of x, there corresponds more than one value of y. The graph in Figure 3-59(a), shown in red, is not the graph of a function, because the x-value -1 determines three different y-values: 3, -1, and -4.

The graph shown in Figure 3-59(b) does represent a function, because every vertical line intersects the graph exactly once.

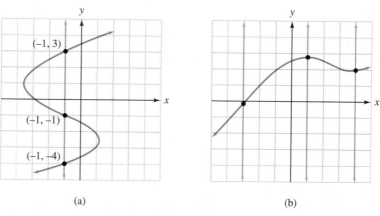

(a)   (b)

FIGURE 3-59

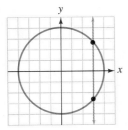

EXAMPLE 4 *The vertical line test.* Which of the following graphs in red are graphs of functions?

a.

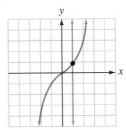

b.

Solution

a. This graph is not the graph of a function, because the vertical line intersects the graph at more than one point.

b. This graph is the graph of a function, because no vertical line will intersect the graph at more than one point.

Self Check

Which of the following graphs are graphs of functions?

a.

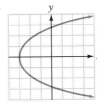

b.

Answers:
a. function,   **b.** not a function

STUDY SET Section 3.7

VOCABULARY *Fill in the blanks.*

1. A _____function_____ is a rule that assigns to each value of the independent variable a single value of another variable.

2. The set of all possible input values for a function is called the _____domain_____, and the set of all possible output values is called the _____range_____.

3. For $y = 2x + 8$, x is called the _____independent_____ variable, and y is called the _____dependent_____ variable.

4. $f(x) = 6 - 5x$ is an example of _____function_____ notation.

CONCEPTS

5. Consider the function $f(x) = x^2$.
  a. If positive real numbers are substituted for x, what type of numbers result?   positive numbers
  b. If negative real numbers are substituted for x, what type of numbers result?   positive numbers
  c. If zero is substituted for x, what number results?   0
  d. What are the domain and range of the function?
    D: all reals; R: real numbers greater than or equal to 0

6. Consider the function $g(x) = x^4$.
  a. What type of numbers can be inputs in this function? What is the special name for this set?
    all real numbers; domain

b. What type of numbers will be outputs in this function? What is the special name for this set?
    real numbers greater than or equal to 0; range

7. Consider the following problems. Fill in the blank so that they ask for the same thing.
  1. In the equation $y = -5x + 1$, find the value of y when $x = -1$.
  2. In the equation $f(x) = -5x + 1$, find $f(-1)$.

8. A function can be thought of as a machine that converts inputs into outputs. Use the terms *domain, range, input,* and *output* to label the diagram of a function machine in Illustration 1. Then find $f(2)$. $f(2) = 4$

domain   input   output   range

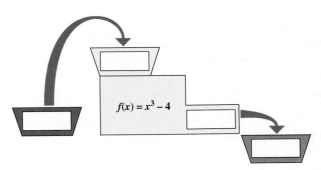

ILLUSTRATION 1

9. See Illustration 2.

a. Give the coordinates of the points where the given vertical line intersects the graph. $(-2, 4), (-2, -4)$

b. Is this the graph of a function? Explain your answer.

No; the x-value -2 is assigned to more than one y-value $(4$ and $-4)$.

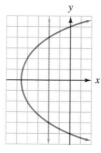

ILLUSTRATION 2

10. A student was asked to determine whether the graph in Illustration 3 is the graph of a function. What is wrong with the following reasoning?

When I draw a vertical line through the graph, it intersects the graph only once. By the vertical line test, this is the graph of a function.

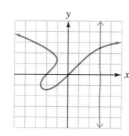

ILLUSTRATION 3

Drawing a single vertical line that does not cross the graph more than once, and then concluding that it is the graph of a function, is not a proper application of the vertical line test. We must determine whether *any* vertical line would cross the graph more than once. This is not a graph of a function.

NOTATION

11. Fill in the blanks to make the statements true. The function notation $f(4) = -5$ states that when 4 is substituted for x in function f, the result is -5. This fact can be illustrated graphically by plotting the point $(4, -5)$.

12. Fill in the blank: $f(x) = 6 - 5x$ is read as "f _____of_____ x is $6 - 5x$."

13. Fill in the blanks: If $f(x) = 6 - 5x$, then $f(0) = 6$ is read as "f _____of_____ zero _____is_____ 6."

14. Tell whether this statement is true or false: The equations $y = 3x + 5$ and $f(x) = 3x + 5$ are the same.
true

PRACTICE *Tell whether a function is defined. If it is not, indicate an input for which there is more than one output.*

15. $y = 2x + 10$ yes

16. $y = x - 15$ yes

17. $y = x^2$ yes

18. $y = |x|$ yes

19. $y^2 = x$
no; $(4, 2), (4, -2)$

20. $|y| = x$
no; $(1, 1), (1, -1)$

21. $y = x^3$ yes

22. $y = -x$ yes

23. $x = 3$ no; $(3, 1), (3, 2)$

24. $y = 3$ yes

25.

x	y
1	7
2	15
3	23
4	16
5	8

yes

26.

x	y
-1	1
-3	1
-5	1
-7	1
-9	1

yes

27.

x	y
-4	6
-1	0
0	-3
2	4
-1	2

no; $(-1, 0), (-1, 2)$

28.

x	y
30	2
30	4
30	6
30	8
30	10

no; $(30, 2), (30, 4)$
(answers may vary)

29.

t	d
3	4
3	-4
4	3
4	-3

no; $(3, 4), (3, -4)$
or $(4, 3), (4, -3)$

30.

x	y
1	1
2	2
3	3
4	4

yes

31.

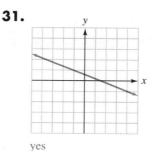

yes

32.

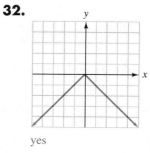

yes

33.

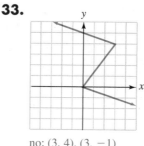

no; $(3, 4), (3, -1)$
(answers may vary)

34.

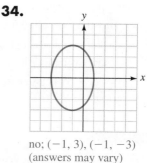

no; $(-1, 3), (-1, -3)$
(answers may vary)

35.

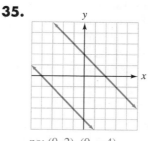

no; $(0, 2), (0, -4)$
(answers may vary)

36.

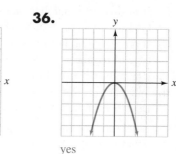

yes

Find the domain and range of the function.

37. $f(x) = x + 1$
D: all reals; R: all reals

38. $f(x) = 3x - 2$
D: all reals; R: all reals

39. $y = x^2$
D: all reals; R: real numbers greater than or equal to 0

40. $y = -|x|$
D: all reals; R: real numbers less than or equal to 0

41. $f(x) = x^3$
D: all reals; R: all reals

42. $f(x) = x$
D: all reals; R: all reals

Find each value.

43. $f(x) = 4x - 1$
  a. $f(1)$ 3
  b. $f(-2)$ -9
  c. $f\left(\dfrac{1}{4}\right)$ 0
  d. $f(50)$ 199

44. $g(x) = 1 - 5x$
  a. $g(0)$ 1
  b. $g(-75)$ 376
  c. $g(0.2)$ 0
  d. $g\left(-\dfrac{4}{5}\right)$ 5

45. $h(t) = 2t^2$
  a. $h(0.4)$ 0.32
  b. $h(-3)$ 18
  c. $h(1,000)$ 2,000,000
  d. $h\left(\dfrac{1}{8}\right)$ $\frac{1}{32}$

46. $v(t) = 6 - t^2$
  a. $v(30)$ -894
  b. $v(6)$ -30
  c. $v(-1)$ 5
  d. $v(0.5)$ 5.75

47. $s(x) = |x - 7|$
  a. $s(0)$ 7
  b. $s(-7)$ 14
  c. $s(7)$ 0
  d. $s(8)$ 1

48. $f(x) = |2 + x|$
  a. $f(0)$ 2
  b. $f(2)$ 4
  c. $f(-2)$ 0
  d. $f(-99)$ 97

49. $f(x) = x^3 - x$
  a. $f(1)$ 0
  b. $f(10)$ 990
  c. $f(-3)$ -24
  d. $f(6)$ 210

50. $g(x) = x^4 + x$
  a. $g(1)$ 2
  b. $g(-2)$ 14
  c. $g(0)$ 0
  d. $g(10)$ 10,010

51. ▦ If $f(x) = 3.4x^2 - 1.2x + 0.5$, find $f(-0.3)$.
  1.166

52. ▦ If $g(x) = x^4 - x^3 + x^2 - x$, find $g(-12)$.
  22,620

Complete each table of values and graph each function.

53. $f(x) = -2 - 3x$

x	$f(x)$
0	-2
1	-5
-1	1
-2	4

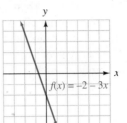

54. $h(x) = |1 - x|$

x	$h(x)$
0	1
1	0
2	1
3	2
-1	2
-2	3

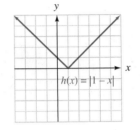

55. $f(x) = \frac{1}{2}x - 2$

x	y
-2	-3
0	-2
2	-1

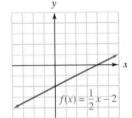

56. $f(x) = -\frac{2}{3}x + 3$

x	y
0	3
3	1
6	-1

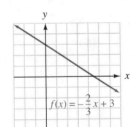

57. $s(x) = 2 - x^2$

x	$s(x)$
0	2
1	1
2	-2
-1	1
-2	-2

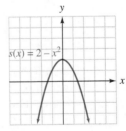

58. $g(x) = 1 + x^3$

x	$g(x)$
0	1
1	2
2	9
-1	0
-2	-7

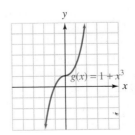

APPLICATIONS

59. REFLECTIONS   When a beam of light hits a mirror, it is reflected off the mirror at the same angle that the incoming beam struck the mirror, as shown in Illustration 4. What type of function could serve as a mathematical model for the path of the light beam shown here? $f(x) = |x|$

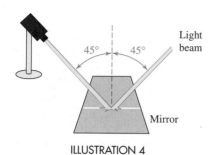

45°   45°

Light beam

Mirror

ILLUSTRATION 4

60. MATHEMATICAL MODELS   Illustration 5 shows the path of a basketball shot taken by a player. What type of function could be used to mathematically model the path of the basketball? $f(x) = -x^2$

ILLUSTRATION 5

61. TIDES   Illustration 6 shows the graph of a function f, which gives the height of the tide for a 24-hour period in Seattle, Washington. (Note that military time is used on the x-axis: 3 A.M. = 3, noon = 12, 3 P.M. = 15, 9 P.M. = 21, and so on.)

  a. Find the domain of the function.   all real numbers from 0 through 24
  b. Find $f(3)$.   0.5
  c. Find $f(6)$.   1.5
  d. Estimate $f(15)$. -1.4
  e. What information does $f(12)$ give?
    The low tide mark was -2.5 m.
  f. Estimate $f(21)$.   1.6

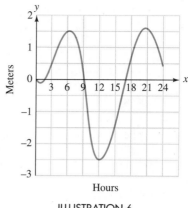

Meters

Hours

ILLUSTRATION 6

62. SOCCER   Illustration 7 shows the graphs of three functions on the same coordinate system: $g(x)$ represents the number of girls, $f(x)$ represents the number of boys, and $t(x)$ represents the total number playing high school soccer in year x.

  a. What is the domain of each of these functions?
    77 to 95
  b. Find $g(87)$, $f(86)$, and $t(93)$.
    100,000, 200,000, and 400,000
  c. Estimate $g(95)$, $f(95)$, and $t(95)$.
    190,000, 290,000, 470,000
  d. For what year x was $g(x) = 75,000$?   1984
  e. For what year x was $f(x) = 225,000$?   1990
  f. For what year x was $t(x)$ first greater than 350,000?
    1991

U.S. High School Soccer Participation 1977-1995

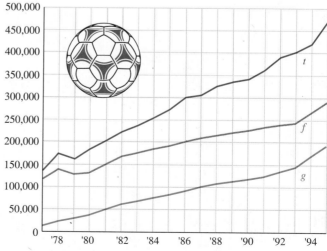

Based on data from *Los Angeles Times* (Dec. 12, 1996), p. A5

ILLUSTRATION 7

63. LAWN SPRINKLERS   The function $A(r) = \pi r^2$ can be used to determine the area that will be watered by a rotating sprinkler that sprays out a stream of water r feet. See Illustration 8. Find $A(5)$, $A(10)$, and $A(20)$. Round to the nearest tenth.
78.5 ft^2, 314.2 ft^2, 1,256.6 ft^2

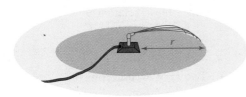

ILLUSTRATION 8

64. PARTS LIST   The function

$$f(r) = 2.30 + 3.25(r + 0.40)$$

approximates the length (in feet) of the belt that joins the two pulleys shown in Illustration 9. r is the radius (in feet) of the smaller pulley. Find the belt length needed for each pulley in the parts list.

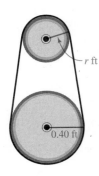

Parts list		
Pulley	r	**Belt length**
P-45M	0.32	4.64
P-08D	0.24	4.38
P-00A	0.18	4.185
P-57X	0.38	4.835

ILLUSTRATION 9

WRITING

65. In the function $y = -5x + 2$, why do you think x is called the *independent* variable and y the *dependent* variable?

66. Explain what a politician meant when she said, "The speed at which the downtown area will be redeveloped is a function of the number of low-interest loans made available to the property owners."

REVIEW

67. Give the equation of the horizontal line passing through $(-3, 6)$. $y = 6$

68. Is $t = -3$ a solution of $t^2 - t + 1 = 13$?   yes

69. Write the formula that relates profit, revenue, and costs.
profit = revenue − costs

70. What is the word used to represent the perimeter of a circle?   circumference

71. Use the distributive property to remove the parentheses in $-3(2x - 4)$. $-6x + 12$

72. Evaluate $r^2 - r$ for $r = -0.5$.   0.75

73. Write an expression for how many eggs there are in d dozen.   12d

74. On a rectangular coordinate graph, what variable is associated with the horizontal axis? x

Describing Linear Relationships

In Chapter 3, we discussed ways to mathematically describe linear relationships between two quantities.

Equations in Two Variables

The general form of the equation of a line is $Ax + By = C$. Two very useful forms of the equation of a line are the slope–intercept form and the point–slope form.

1. Write the equation of a line with a slope of -3 and a y-intercept of $(0, -4)$. $y = -3x - 4$

2. Write the equation of the line that passes through $(5, 2)$ and $(-5, 0)$. Answer in slope–intercept form. $y = \frac{1}{5}x + 1$

Rectangular Coordinate Graphs

The graph of an equation is a "picture" of all of its solutions (x, y). Important information can be obtained from a graph.

3. Complete the table of solutions for $2x - 4y = 8$. Then graph the equation.

$2x - 4y = 8$

x	y
0	-2
4	0
-2	-3

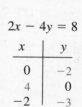
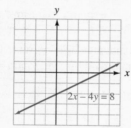

4. See Illustration 1.

a. What information does the y-intercept of the graph give us? When new, the press cost $40,000.

b. What is the slope of the line and what does it tell us? $-5,000$; the value of the press decreased $5,000/yr

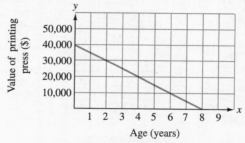

ILLUSTRATION 1

5. Consider the line graphed in Illustration 2.

a. Find a point on the line. $(-2, -2)$ (answers may vary)

b. Determine the slope of the line. -2

c. Write the equation of the line. Express your answer in slope–intercept form. $y = -2x - 6$

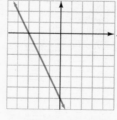

ILLUSTRATION 2

6. Write the equation of the line that passes through $(1, -1)$ and is parallel to the line graphed in Illustration 3. $x = 1$

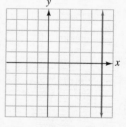

ILLUSTRATION 3

Linear Functions

We can use the notation $f(x) = mx + b$ to describe linear functions.

7. The function $f(x) = 35x + 25$ gives the cost (in dollars) to rent a cement mixer for x days. Find $f(3)$. What does it represent? 130; the cost to rent the mixer for 3 days

8. The function $T(x) = \frac{1}{4}x + 40$ predicts the outdoor temperature T in degrees Fahrenheit using the number of cricket chirps x per minute. Find $T(160)$. $80°F$

ACCENT ON TEAMWORK

Section 3.1

DAILY HIGH TEMPERATURE   For a 2-week period, plot the daily high temperature for your city on a rectangular coordinate system. You can normally find this information in a local newspaper. Label the x-axis "observation day" and the y-axis "daily high temperature in degrees Fahrenheit." For example, the ordered pair $(3, 72)$ indicates that on day 3 of the observation period, the high temperature was $72°F$. At the end of the 2-week period, see whether any temperature trend is apparent from the graph.

Section 3.2

TRANSLATIONS   On a piece of graph paper, sketch the graph of $y = |x|$ with a black marker. Using a different color, sketch the graphs of $y = |x| + 2$ and $y = |x| - 2$ on the same coordinate system. On another piece of graph paper, do the same for $y = |x|$ and $y = |x + 2|$ and $y = |x - 2|$. Make some observations about how the graph of $y = |x|$ is "moved" or "translated" by the addition or subtraction of 2. Use what you have learned to discuss the graphs of $y = x^2$, $y = x^2 + 2$, $y = x^2 - 2$, $y = (x + 2)^2$, and $y = (x - 2)^2$.

Section 3.3

COMPUTER GRAPHING PROGRAMS   If your school has a mathematics computer lab, ask the lab supervisor whether there is a graphing program on the system. If so, familiarize yourself with the operation of the program and then graph each of the equations from Figure 3-22 and from Examples 3–6 in Section 3.3. Print out each graph and compare with those in the textbook.

Section 3.4

MEASURING SLOPE   Use a tape measure (and a level if necessary) to find the slopes of five objects by finding $\frac{\text{rise}}{\text{run}}$. See the applications in Study Set 3.4 for some ideas about what you can measure. Record your results in a chart like the one shown in Illustration 1. List the examples in increasing order of magnitude, starting with the smallest slope.

Section 3.5

SHOPPING   Visit a local grocery store and find the price per pound of bananas. Make a rectangular coordinate graph that could be posted next to the scale in the produce area so that shoppers could determine from the graph the cost of a banana

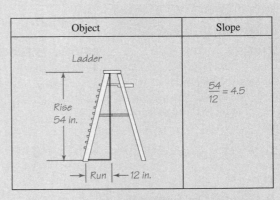

Object	Slope
Ladder Rise 54 in. Run 12 in.	$\frac{54}{12} = 4.5$

ILLUSTRATION 1

purchase up to 8 pounds in weight. Label the x-axis in quarters of a pound and label the y-axis in cents.

Section 3.6

MATCHING GAME   Have a student in your group write 10 linear equations on 3×5 note cards, one equation per card. Then have him or her graph each equation on a separate set of 10 cards. Shuffle each set of cards. Then put all the equation cards on one side of a table and all the cards with graphs on the other side. Work together to match each equation with its proper graph.

Section 3.7

FUNCTIONS   We have seen that a function can be thought of as a machine that takes some input x and turns it into some output $f(x)$. (See Illustration 2.) Write a function that takes an input of 6 and turns it into an output of 19, where

a. only 1 operation is performed to get the output.
b. 2 operations are performed to get the output.
c. 3 operations are performed to get the output.
d. 4 operations are performed to get the output.

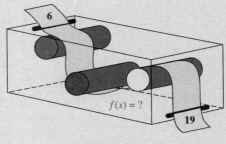

ILLUSTRATION 2

Graphing Using the Rectangular Coordinate System

CONCEPTS

A *rectangular coordinate system* is composed of a horizontal number line called the *x*-axis and a vertical number line called the *y*-axis.

The coordinates of the *origin* are (0, 0).

To *graph* ordered pairs means to locate their position on a coordinate system.

The two axes divide the coordinate plane into four distinct regions called *quadrants*.

REVIEW EXERCISES

1. a. Graph the points with coordinates (−1, 3), (0, 1.5), (−4, −4), $\left(2, \frac{7}{2}\right)$, and (4, 0).

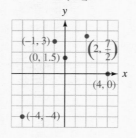

b. Use the graph in Illustration 1 to complete the table.

x	y
3	−1
0	0
−3	1

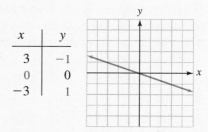

ILLUSTRATION 1

2. In what quadrant does the point (−3, −4) lie?   quadrant III

3. SNOWFALL   The amount of snow on the ground at a mountain resort was measured once each day over a 7-day period. (See Illustration 2.)

  a. On the first day, how much snow was on the ground?   2 ft

  b. What was the difference in the amount of snow on the ground when the measurements were taken the second and third day?   2 ft

  c. How much snow was on the ground on the sixth day?   6 ft

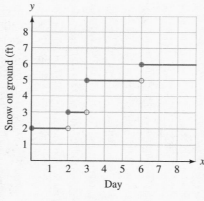

ILLUSTRATION 2

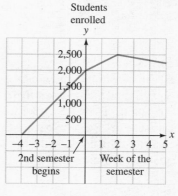

ILLUSTRATION 3

4. COLLEGE ENROLLMENT   The graph in Illustration 3 gives the number of students enrolled at a college for the period from 4 weeks before to 5 weeks after the semester began.

  a. What was the maximum enrollment and when did it occur?   2,500; week 2

  b. How many students had enrolled 2 weeks before the semester began?   1,000

  c. When was enrollment 2,250?   1st week and 5th week

| **SECTION 3.2** | *Equations Containing Two Variables* |

An ordered pair is a *solution* if, after substituting the values of the ordered pair for the variables in the equation, the result is a true statement.

Solutions of an equation can be shown in a *table of solutions.*

In an equation in x and y, x is called the *independent variable,* or *input,* and y is called the *dependent variable,* or *output.*

To graph an equation in two variables:
1. Make a table of solutions that contains several solutions written as ordered pairs.
2. Plot each ordered pair.
3. Draw a line or smooth curve through the points.

In many application problems, we encounter equations that contain variables other than x and y.

5. Check to see whether $(-3, 5)$ is a solution of $y = |2 + x|$.   not a solution

6. a. Complete the table of solutions and graph the equation $y = -x^3$.

$$y = -x^3$$

x	y	(x, y)
-2	8	$(-2, 8)$
-1	1	$(-1, 1)$
0	0	$(0, 0)$
1	-1	$(1, -1)$
2	-8	$(2, -8)$

b. How would the graph of $y = -x^3 + 2$ compare to the graph of the equation given in part a?

It would be 2 units higher.

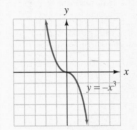

7. The graph in Illustration 4 shows the relationship between the number of oranges O an acre of land will yield if t orange trees are planted on it.

a. If $t = 70$, what is O?   9,000

b. What importance does the point $(40, 18)$ on the graph have?

It tells us that 40 trees on an acre give the highest yield, 18,000 oranges.

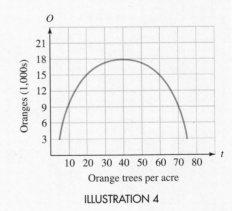

ILLUSTRATION 4

| **SECTION 3.3** | *Graphing Linear Equations* |

An equation whose graph is a straight line and whose variables are raised to the first power is called a *linear equation.*

The *general* or *standard form* of a linear equation is $Ax + By = C$, where A, B, and C are real numbers and A and B are not both zero.

8. Classify each equation as either linear or nonlinear.

a. $y = |x + 2|$ nonlinear

b. $3x + 4y = 12$ linear

c. $y = 2x - 3$ linear

d. $y = x^2 - x$ nonlinear

9. The equation $5x + 2y = 10$ is in general form; what are A, B, and C?

$A = 5, B = 2, C = 10$

10. Complete the table of solutions for the equation $3x + 2y = -18$.

x	y	(x, y)
-2	-6	$(-2, -6)$
-8	3	$(-8, 3)$

To graph a linear equation:
1. Find three (x, y) pairs that satisfy the equation by picking three arbitrary x-values and finding their corresponding y-values.

2. Plot each ordered pair.

3. Draw a straight line through the points.

11. Solve the equation $x + 2y = 6$ for y, find three solutions, and then graph it.

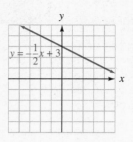

To find the y-*intercept* of a linear equation, substitute 0 for x in the equation of the line and solve for y. To find the x-*intercept* of a linear equation, substitute 0 for y in the equation of the line and solve for x.

12. Graph $-4x + 2y = 8$ by finding its x- and y-intercepts.

x-intercept: $(-2, 0)$; y-intercept: $(0, 4)$

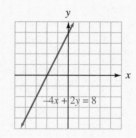

The equation $y = b$ represents the horizontal line that intersects the y-axis at $(0, b)$. The equation $x = a$ represents the vertical line that intersects the x-axis at $(a, 0)$.

13. Graph each equation.

a. $y = 4$

b. $x = -1$

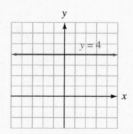

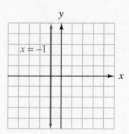

14. Since two points determine a line, only two points are needed to graph a linear equation. Why is it is a good idea to plot a third point?

It serves as a check. If the three points do not lie on a line, then at least one of them is in error.

SECTION 3.4 | *Rate of Change and the Slope of a Line*

The *slope m* of a nonvertical line is a number that measures "steepness" by finding the ratio $\frac{\text{rise}}{\text{run}}$.

$$m = \frac{\text{change in the } y\text{-values}}{\text{change in the } x\text{-values}}$$

15. In each case, find the slope of the line.

a. $\frac{1}{4}$

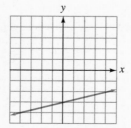

b. The line with the table of solutions shown here. -7

x	y	(x, y)
2	-3	$(2, -3)$
4	-17	$(4, -17)$

If $P(x_1, y_1)$ and $Q(x_2, y_2)$ are two points on a nonvertical line, the slope m of line PQ is

$$m = \frac{y_2 - y_1}{x_2 - x_1}$$

Lines that rise from left to right have a *positive slope,* and lines that fall from left to right have a *negative slope.*

Horizontal lines have a slope of zero. Vertical lines have *undefined* slope.

The slope of a line gives a rate of change.

c. The line passing through the points $(2, -5)$ and $(5, -5)$.　0

d. The line passing through the points $(1, -4)$ and $(3, -7)$.　$-\frac{3}{2}$

16. Graph the line that passes through $(-2, 4)$ and has slope $m = -\frac{4}{5}$.

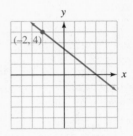

17. TOURISM　The graph in Illustration 5 shows the number of international travelers to the United States from 1986–1998, in two-year increments.

a. Between what two years did the largest decline in the number of visitors occur? What was the rate of change?　1992–1994; -1.25 million people/year

b. Between what two years did the largest increase in the number of visitors occur? What was the rate of change?　1986–1988; 4.05 million people/year

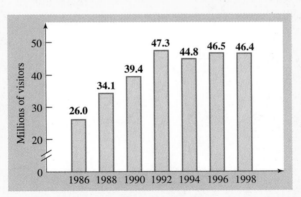

Based on data from *World Almanac 2000*

ILLUSTRATION 5

SECTION 3.5 | *Describing Linear Relationships*

If a linear equation is written in *slope–intercept* form,

$$y = mx + b$$

the graph of the equation is a line with slope m and y-intercept $(0, b)$.

18. Find the slope and the y-intercept of each line.

a. $y = \dfrac{3}{4}x - 2$

$m = \frac{3}{4}$; y-intercept: $(0, -2)$

b. $y = -4x$

$m = -4$; y-intercept: $(0, 0)$

19. Find the slope and the y-intercept of the line determined by $9x - 3y = 15$. Then graph it.

$m = 3$; y-intercept: $(0, -5)$

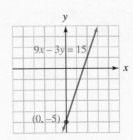

The *rate of change* is the slope of the graph of a linear equation.

20. COPIER USAGE   A business buys a used copy machine that, when purchased, has already produced 75,000 copies.

    a. If the business plans to run 300 copies a week, write a linear equation that would find the number of copies c the machine has made in its lifetime after the business has used it for w weeks. $c = 300w + 75,000$

    b. Use your result to part a to predict the total number of copies that will have been made on the machine 1 year, or 52 weeks, after being purchased by the business. 90,600

Two lines with the same slope are *parallel*.

The product of the slopes of *perpendicular* lines is -1.

21. Without graphing, tell whether graphs of the given pairs of lines would be parallel, perpendicular, or neither.

    a. $y = -\dfrac{2}{3}x + 6$

        $y = -\dfrac{2}{3}x - 6$ parallel

    b. $x + 5y = -10$

        $y = 5x$ perpendicular

SECTION 3.6

Writing Linear Equations

If a line with slope m passes through the point (x_1, y_1), the equation of the line in *point–slope* form is

$$y - y_1 = m(x - x_1)$$

22. Write the equation of a line with the given slope that passes through the given point. Express the result in slope–intercept form and graph the equation.

    a. $m = 3, (1, 5)$ $y = 3x + 2$

    b. $m = -\dfrac{1}{2}, (-4, -1)$ $y = -\frac{1}{2}x - 3$

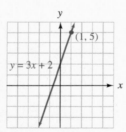
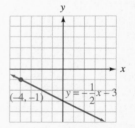

23. Write the equation of the line with the following characteristics. Express the result in slope–intercept form.

    a. passing through $(3, 7)$ and $(-6, 1)$ $y = \frac{2}{3}x + 5$

    b. horizontal, passing through $(6, -8)$ $y = -8$

24. CAR REGISTRATION   When it was 2 years old, the annual registration fee for a Dodge Caravan was \$380. When it was 4 years old, the registration fee dropped to \$310. If the relationship is linear, write an equation that gives the registration fee f in dollars for the van when it is x years old. $f = -35x + 450$

SECTION 3.7

Functions

A *function* is a rule that assigns to each input value a single output value.

25. In each case, tell whether a function is defined.

    a. $y = 3x - 2$ yes

    b. $y^2 = x$ no

    c.

x	2	2	3	4	5	6	no
y	-2	2	3	-4	5	-6	

For a function, the set of all possible values of the independent variable *x* (the inputs) is called the *domain,* and the set of all possible values of the dependent variable *y* (the outputs) is called the *range.*

The notation $y = f(x)$ denotes that *y* is a function of *x*.

26. Find the domain and range of each function.

a. $f(x) = x + 10$

D: all reals; R: all reals

b. $y = x^2$

D: all reals; R: real numbers greater than or equal to 0

27. For the function $g(x) = 1 - 6x$, find each value.

a. $g(1)$ -5

b. $g(-6)$ 37

c. $g(0.5)$ -2

d. $g\left(\dfrac{3}{2}\right)$ -8

Four basic functions are

Linear: $f(x) = mx + b$
Identity: $f(x) = x$
Squaring: $f(x) = x^2$
Absolute value: $f(x) = |x|$

28. Complete the table of values and graph the function.

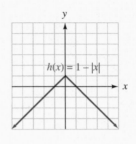

$h(x) = 1 - |x|$

x	$h(x)$
0	1
1	0
2	-1
-1	0
-2	-1
-3	-2

We can use the *vertical line test* to determine whether a graph is the graph of a function.

29. Tell whether each graph is the graph of a function.

a. no

b. yes

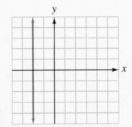

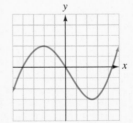

30. The function $f(r) = 15.7r^2$ estimates the volume in cubic inches of a can 5 inches tall with a radius of *r* inches. Find the volume of the can in Illustration 6. Round to the nearest tenth. $1{,}004.8$ in.^{3}

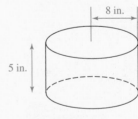

ILLUSTRATION 6

Chapter 3 Test

The graph in Illustration 1 shows the number of dogs being boarded in a kennel over a 3-day holiday weekend. Use the graph to answer Problems 1–4.

1. How many dogs were in the kennel 2 days before the holiday?   10

2. What is the maximum number of dogs that were boarded on the holiday weekend?   60

3. When were there 30 dogs in the kennel?
1 day before and the 3rd day of the holiday

4. What information does the y-intercept of the graph give?   50 dogs were in the kennel when the holiday began.

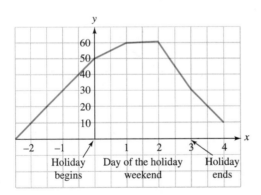

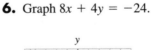

ILLUSTRATION 1

5. Graph $y = x^2 - 4$.

6. Graph $8x + 4y = -24$.

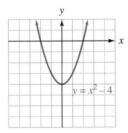

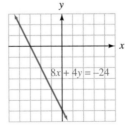

7. Is $(-3, -4)$ a solution of $3x - 4y = 7$?   yes

8. Is $y = x^3$ a linear equation?   no

9. What are the x- and y-intercepts of the graph of $2x - 3y = 6$? x-intercept: $(3, 0)$; y-intercept: $(0, -2)$

10. Find the slope and the y-intercept of $x + 2y = 8$.
$m = -\frac{1}{2}$; $(0, 4)$

11. Graph $x = -4$.

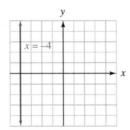

12. Graph the line passing through $(-2, -4)$ having a slope of $\frac{2}{3}$.

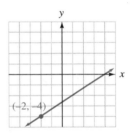

13. What is the slope of the line passing through $(-1, 3)$ and $(3, -1)$? -1

14. What is the slope of a vertical line?   undefined

15. What is the slope of a line that is perpendicular to a line with slope $-\frac{7}{8}$? $\frac{8}{7}$

16. When graphed, are the lines $y = 2x + 6$ and $6x - 3y = 0$ parallel, perpendicular, or neither?
parallel

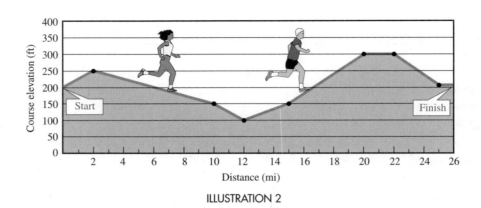

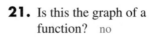

ILLUSTRATION 2

In Problems 17–18, refer to the graph in Illustration 2, which shows the elevation changes in a 26-mile marathon course. Give the rate of change of the part of the course that has . . .

17. the steepest incline

the 15–20 mi segment: 30 ft/mi

18. the steepest decline

the 22–25 mi segment: $-\frac{100}{3}$ ft/mi $= -33\frac{1}{3}$ ft/mi

19. DEPRECIATION   After it is purchased, a $15,000 computer loses $1,500 in resale value every year. Write a linear equation that gives the resale value v of the computer x years after being purchased.
$v = 15,000 - 1,500x$

20. Write the equation of the line passing through $(-2, 5)$ and $(-3, -2)$. Answer in slope–intercept form.
$y = 7x + 19$

21. Is this the graph of a function?   no

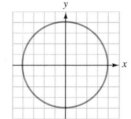

22. Find the domain and range of the function $f(x) = -|x|$.
D: all reals; R: real numbers less than or equal to 0

23. Does the equation $y = 2x - 8$ define a function?   yes

24. If $f(x) = 2x - 7$, find $f(-3)$. -13

25. If $g(x) = 3.5x^3$ find $g(6)$.   756

26. Explain what is meant by the statement slope $= \frac{\text{rise}}{\text{run}}$.

Chapters 1-3 Cumulative Review Exercises

1. TWA The graph in Illustration 1 shows the 1999 and 2000 quarterly net losses for Trans World Airlines.
  a. In which quarter was the loss the least? Estimate it.
  QII, 2000: $-\$5$ million
  b. In which quarter was the loss the greatest? Estimate it.
  QIV, 1999; $-\$270$ million

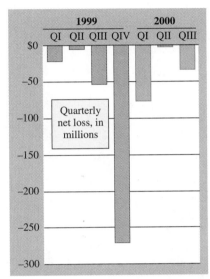

1999   2000

Based on data from Trans World Airlines and *Bloomberg News*.

ILLUSTRATION 1

2. Give the prime factorization of 108. $2^2 \cdot 3^3$

3. Write $\frac{1}{250}$ as a decimal. 0.004

4. Tell whether each statement is true or false.
  a. Every whole number is an integer. true
  b. Every integer is a real number. true
  c. 0 is a whole number, an integer, and a rational number. true

5. ▦ AUTO SALES Illustration 2 shows the top 5 best-selling vehicles in the United States in the year 2000, as reported by the automakers. Complete the table. Round to the nearest tenth of one percent.

6. Evaluate each expression.
  a. $12 - 2 \cdot 3$ 6
  b. $\dfrac{(6-5)^4 - (-21)}{-27 + 4^2}$ -2
  c. $19 - 2[(-3.1 + 6.1) \cdot 3]$ 1
  d. $64 - 6[15 - (3)3]$ 28

7. Evaluate $b^2 - 4ac$ for $a = 2$, $b = -8$, and $c = 4$. 32

8. Suppose x sheets from a 500-sheet ream of paper have been used. How many sheets are left? $500 - x$

9. How many terms does the algebraic expression $3x^2 - 2x + 1$ have? What is the coefficient of the second term? 3, -2

10. Use the distributive property to remove parentheses.
  a. $2(x + 4)$ $2x + 8$ **b.** $2(x - 4)$ $2x - 8$
  c. $-2(x + 4)$ $-2x - 8$ **d.** $-2(x - 4)$ $-2x + 8$

Simplify each expression.

11. $5a + 10 - a$ $4a + 10$

12. $-2b^2 + 6b^2$ $4b^2$

13. $(a + 2) - (a - 2)$ 4

14. $-y - y - y$ $-3y$

Solve each equation.

15. $3x - 5 = 13$ 6

16. $1.2 - x = -1.7$ 2.9

17. $\dfrac{2x}{3} - 2 = 4$ 9

18. $\dfrac{y - 2}{7} = -3$ -19

19. $-3(2y - 2) - y = 5$ $\frac{1}{7}$

20. $9y - 3 = 6y$ 1

21. $\dfrac{1}{3} + \dfrac{c}{5} = -\dfrac{3}{2}$ $-\frac{55}{6}$

22. $5(x + 2) = 5x - 2$ no solution

| Rank | Vehicle | Units sold | | '99 ranks | % change |
		2000	1999		
1	Ford F-Series pickup	876,716	869,001	1	+0.9
2	Chevrolet Silverado pickup	642,119	636,150	2	+0.9
3	Ford Explorer	445,157	428,772	5	+3.8
4	Toyota Camry	422,961	448,162	3	-5.6
5	Honda Accord	404,515	404,192	6	+0.1

Based on information from Reuters

ILLUSTRATION 2

23. Solve the equation for the indicated variable.
$y = mx + b$; for x $x = \frac{y - b}{m}$

24. Find the perimeter and the area of the gauze pad of the bandage shown in Illustration 3. $3\frac{1}{8}$ in., $\frac{39}{64}$ in.^{2}

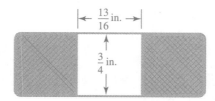

ILLUSTRATION 3

25. If the vertex of an isosceles triangle is 22°, find the measure of each base angle.   79°

26. Complete the table.

Solution	% acid	Liters	Amount of acid
50% solution	0.50	x	$0.50x$
25% solution	0.25	$13 - x$	$0.25(13 - x)$
30% mixture	0.30	13	$0.30(13)$

27. ROAD TRIP   A bus, carrying the members of a marching band, and a truck, carrying their instruments, leave a high school at the same time. The bus travels at 60 mph and the truck at 50 mph. In how many hours will they be 75 miles apart?   7.5 hr

28. MIXING CANDY   Candy corn worth $1.90 per pound is to be mixed with black gumdrops that cost $1.20 per pound to make 200 pounds of a mixture worth $1.48 per pound. How many pounds of each candy should be used?

80 lb candy corn, 120 lb gumdrops

Solve each inequality, graph the solution set, and use interval notation to describe the solution.

29. $-\dfrac{3}{16}x \geq -9$ $x \leq 48$, ⟨———┤———⟩ , $(-\infty, 48]$
                                                                48

30. $8x + 4 > 3x + 4$

$x > 0$, ⟨———(———⟩ , $(0, \infty)$
                    0

31. MEDICATION   Dosages for a certain medication are shown in Illustration 4. What is the dosage for
a. a 5-year-old child?   1 tsp
b. a 9-year-old child?   3 tsp

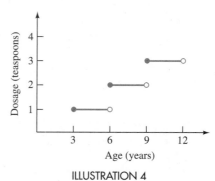

ILLUSTRATION 4

32. Is $(-2, 4)$ a solution of $y = 2x - 8$?   no

Graph each equation.

33. $y = |x - 2|$

34. $4y + 2x = -8$

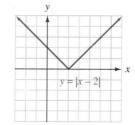

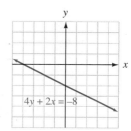

35. What is the slope of the graph of the line $y = 5$?   0

36. What is the slope of the line passing through $(-2, 4)$ and $(5, -6)$? $-\frac{10}{7}$

37. Find the slope and the y-intercept of the graph of the line described by $4x - 6y = -12$. $\frac{2}{3}, (0, 2)$

38. Write the equation of the line that has slope -2 and y-intercept of $(0, 1)$. $y = -2x + 1$

39. Write the equation of the line that has slope $-\frac{7}{8}$ and passes through $(2, -9)$. Express the answer in point–slope form. $y + 9 = -\frac{7}{8}(x - 2)$

40. If $f(x) = x^2 - 3x$, find $f(-2)$.   10

Exponents and Polynomials

4

IN THIS CHAPTER, WE INTRODUCE THE RULES FOR EXPONENTS AND USE THEM WHEN PERFORMING OPERATIONS ON POLYNOMIALS.

4.1 *Natural-Number Exponents*

In this section, you will learn about

- The product rule for exponents • The quotient rule for exponents
- The power rule for exponents • Power rules for products and quotients

INTRODUCTION. We have used natural-number exponents to indicate repeated multiplication. For example,

$9^2 = 9 \cdot 9 = 81$ Write 9 as a factor 2 times.

$7^3 = 7 \cdot 7 \cdot 7 = 343$ Write 7 as a factor 3 times.

$(-2)^4 = (-2)(-2)(-2)(-2) = 16$ Write -2 as a factor 4 times.

$-2^4 = -(2 \cdot 2 \cdot 2 \cdot 2) = -16$ The $-$ sign in front of 2^4 means the opposite of 2^4.

These examples illustrate a definition for x^n, where n is a natural number.

Natural-Number Exponents

> If n is a natural number, then
>
> $$x^n = \overbrace{x \cdot x \cdot x \cdot \ \cdot \ \cdot \ \cdot \ x}^{n \text{ factors of } x}$$

In the **exponential expression** x^n, x is called the **base** and n is called the **exponent.** The entire expression is called a **power of x.**

base $\longrightarrow x^n \longleftarrow$ exponent

If an exponent is a natural number, it tells how many times its base is to be used as a factor. An exponent of 1 indicates that its base is to be used one time as a factor, an exponent of 2 indicates that its base is to be used two times as a factor, and so on. The base of an exponential expression can be a number, a variable, or a combination of numbers and variables.

$$x^1 = x \qquad (y + 1)^2 = (y + 1)(y + 1) \qquad (-5s)^3 = (-5s)(-5s)(-5s)$$

In this section, we will continue our study of exponents as we discuss how to simplify exponential expressions that are multiplied, divided, and raised to powers. To perform these simplifications, we will use several rules for exponents.

The product rule for exponents

To develop a rule for multiplying exponential expressions with the same base, we consider the product $x^2 \cdot x^3$. Since the expression x^2 means that x is to be used as a factor two times, and the expression x^3 means that x is to be used as a factor three times, we have

$$x^2 \cdot x^3 = \overbrace{x \cdot x}^{\text{2 factors of } x} \cdot \overbrace{x \cdot x \cdot x}^{\text{3 factors of } x}$$

$$= \overbrace{x \cdot x \cdot x \cdot x \cdot x}^{\text{5 factors of } x}$$

$$= x^5$$

In general,

$$x^m \cdot x^n = \overbrace{x \cdot x \cdot x \cdot \cdots \cdot x}^{m \text{ factors of } x} \overbrace{x \cdot x \cdot x \cdot \cdots \cdot x}^{n \text{ factors of } x}$$

$$= \overbrace{x \cdot x \cdot x \cdot x \cdot x \cdot x \cdot \cdots \cdot x \cdot x \cdot x}^{m + n \text{ factors of } x}$$

$$= x^{m+n}$$

This discussion suggests the following rule: *To multiply two exponential expressions with the same base, keep the common base and add the exponents.*

Product rule for exponents

> If m and n represent natural numbers, then
> $$x^m x^n = x^{m+n}$$

EXAMPLE 1   *Multiplying powers with like bases.*   Simplify each expression: **a.** $9^5(9^6)$,   **b.** $x^3 \cdot x^4$,   **c.** $y^2 y^4 y$,   and   **d.** $(c^2 d^3)(c^4 d^5)$.

Solution

a. To simplify $9^5(9^6)$ means to write it in an equivalent form using one base and one exponent.

$9^5(9^6) = 9^{5+6}$ Use the product rule for exponents: Keep the common base, which is 9, and add the exponents.

$\quad\quad = 9^{11}$ Do the addition.

b. $x^3 \cdot x^4 = x^{3+4}$ Keep the common base x and add the exponents.

$\quad\quad = x^7$ Do the addition.

c. $y^2 y^4 y = y^{2+4} y$ Working from left to right, keep the common base y and add the exponents.

$\quad\quad = y^6 y$ Do the addition.

$\quad\quad = y^{6+1}$ Keep the common base and add the exponents.

$\quad\quad = y^7$ Do the addition.

d. $(c^2 d^3)(c^4 d^5) = c^2 d^3 c^4 d^5$ Use the associative property of multiplication.

$\quad\quad = c^2 c^4 d^3 d^5$ Change the order of the factors.

$\quad\quad = c^{2+4} d^{3+5}$ Keep the common base c and add the exponents. Keep the common base d and add the exponents.

$\quad\quad = c^6 d^8$ Do the additions.

Self Check

Simplify:

a. $7^8(7^7)$

b. $z \cdot z^3$

c. $x^2 x^3 x^6$

d. $(s^4 t^3)(s^4 t^4)$

Answers: **a.** 7^{15},   **b.** z^4,   **c.** x^{11},   **d.** $s^8 t^7$ ■

COMMENT   When simplifying expressions, note the operations that are involved. For example, we cannot simplify $x^3 + x^4$ or $x^3 - x^4$, because x^3 and x^4 are not like terms. However, we can simplify $x^3 \cdot x^4$, because x^3 and x^4 have the same base: $x^3 \cdot x^4 = x^{12}$.

Furthermore, the expressions $x^2 + y^3$ and $x^2 - y^3$ cannot be simplified, because they do not contain like terms; neither can the expression $x^2 y^3$, because x^2 and y^3 have different bases.

The quotient rule for exponents

We now consider the fraction

$$\frac{4^5}{4^2}$$

where the exponent in the numerator is greater than the exponent in the denominator. We can simplify this fraction as follows:

$$\frac{4^5}{4^2} = \frac{4 \cdot 4 \cdot 4 \cdot 4 \cdot 4}{4 \cdot 4}$$

$$= \frac{\overset{1}{\cancel{4}} \cdot \overset{1}{\cancel{4}} \cdot 4 \cdot 4 \cdot 4}{\underset{1}{\cancel{4}} \cdot \underset{1}{\cancel{4}}} \qquad \text{Divide out the common factors of 4.}$$

$$= 4^3$$

The result of 4^3 has a base of 4 and an exponent $5 - 2$ (or 3). This suggests that *to divide exponential expressions with the same base, we keep the common base and subtract the exponents.*

Quotient rule for exponents

If m and n represent natural numbers, $m > n$, and $x \neq 0$, then

$$\frac{x^m}{x^n} = x^{m-n}$$

EXAMPLE 2 *Dividing powers with like bases.* Simplify each expression. Assume that there are no divisions by 0.

a. $\dfrac{20^{16}}{20^9}$, **b.** $\dfrac{x^4}{x^3}$, **c.** $\dfrac{a^3 b^8}{ab^5}$

Solution

a. To simplify $\dfrac{20^{16}}{20^9}$ means to write it in an equivalent form using one base and one exponent.

$$\frac{20^{16}}{20^9} = 20^{16-9} \qquad \text{Use the quotient rule for exponents: Keep the common base, which is 20, and subtract the exponents.}$$

$$= 20^7 \qquad \text{Do the subtraction: } 16 - 9 = 7.$$

b. $\dfrac{x^4}{x^3} = x^{4-3}$ Keep the common base x and subtract the exponents.

$$= x^1 \qquad \text{Do the subtraction.}$$

$$= x$$

c. $\dfrac{a^3 b^8}{ab^5} = \dfrac{a^3}{a} \cdot \dfrac{b^8}{b^5}$

$$= a^{3-1} b^{8-5} \qquad \begin{array}{l} \text{Keep the common base } a \text{ and subtract the exponents.} \\ \text{Keep the common base } b \text{ and subtract the exponents.} \end{array}$$

$$= a^2 b^3 \qquad \text{Do the subtractions.}$$

Self Check
Simplify:

a. $\dfrac{55^{30}}{55^5}$

b. $\dfrac{a^5}{a^3}$

c. $\dfrac{b^{15} c^4}{b^4 c}$

Answers: **a.** 55^{25}, **b.** a^2, **c.** $b^{11} c^3$

EXAMPLE 3 *Using two rules for exponents.* Simplify $\dfrac{a^3 a^5 a^7}{a^4 a}$.

Solution

We use the product rule for exponents to simplify the numerator and denominator separately and proceed as follows.

$\dfrac{a^3 a^5 a^7}{a^4 a} = \dfrac{a^{15}}{a^5}$ In the numerator, keep the common base a and add the exponents. In the denominator, keep the common base a and add the exponents.

$= a^{15-5}$ Use the quotient rule for exponents: Keep the common base a and subtract the exponents.

$= a^{10}$ Do the subtraction.

Self Check

Simplify:

$$\dfrac{b^2 b^6 b}{b^4 b^4}$$

Answer: b

The power rule for exponents

To find another rule for exponents, we consider the expression $(x^3)^4$, which can be written as $x^3 \cdot x^3 \cdot x^3 \cdot x^3$. Because each of the four factors of x^3 contains three factors of x, there are $4 \cdot 3$ (or 12) factors of x. This product can be written as x^{12}.

$$(x^3)^4 = x^3 \cdot x^3 \cdot x^3 \cdot x^3$$

$$\overbrace{= x \cdot x \cdot x \cdot x \cdot x \cdot x \cdot x \cdot x \cdot x \cdot x \cdot x \cdot x}^{12 \text{ factors of } x}$$
$$\underbrace{}_{x^3} \underbrace{}_{x^3} \underbrace{}_{x^3} \underbrace{}_{x^3}$$

$$= x^{12}$$

In general,

$$(x^m)^n = \overbrace{x^m \cdot x^m \cdot x^m \cdots \cdots x^m}^{n \text{ factors of } x^m}$$
$$= \overbrace{x \cdot x \cdot x \cdot x \cdot x \cdot x \cdot x \cdots \cdots x}^{m \cdot n \text{ factors of } x}$$
$$= x^{m \cdot n}$$

This discussion illustrates the following rule: *To raise an exponential expression to a power, keep the base and multiply the exponents.*

Power rule for exponents

If m and n represent natural numbers, then

$$(x^m)^n = x^{m \cdot n} \qquad \text{or, more simply,} \qquad (x^m)^n = x^{mn}$$

EXAMPLE 4 *The power rule for exponents.* Simplify each expression:
a. $(2^3)^7$ and **b.** $(z^8)^8$.

Solution

a. To simplify $(2^3)^7$ means to write it in an equivalent form using one base and one exponent.

$(2^3)^7 = 2^{3 \cdot 7}$ Keep the base of 2 and multiply the exponents.

$= 2^{21}$ Do the multiplication.

b. $(z^8)^8 = z^{8 \cdot 8}$ Keep the base and multiply the exponents.

$= z^{64}$ Do the multiplication.

Self Check

Simplify each expression:

a. $(5^3)^4$

b. $(y^5)^2$

Answer: **a.** 5^{12}, **b.** y^{10}

EXAMPLE 5 *Using two rules for exponents.* Simplify each expression:
a. $(x^2x^5)^2$ and **b.** $(z^2)^4(z^3)^3$.

Solution

a. We begin by using the product rule for exponents. Then we use the power rule.

$(x^2x^5)^2 = (x^7)^2$ Within the parentheses, keep the base x and add the exponents.

$\quad\quad\quad = x^{14}$ Keep the base x and multiply the exponents.

b. We begin by using the power rule for exponents twice. Then we use the product rule.

$(z^2)^4(z^3)^3 = z^8z^9$ For each power of z raised to a power, keep the base z and multiply the exponents.

$\quad\quad\quad = z^{17}$ Keep the base z and add the exponents.

Power rules for products and quotients

To develop two more rules for exponents, we consider the expression $(2x)^3$, which is a *power of the product* of 2 and x, and the expression $\left(\frac{2}{x}\right)^3$, which is a *power of the quotient* of 2 and x.

$$(2x)^3 = (2x)(2x)(2x) \qquad\qquad \left(\frac{2}{x}\right)^3 = \left(\frac{2}{x}\right)\left(\frac{2}{x}\right)\left(\frac{2}{x}\right) \quad (x \neq 0)$$

$$= (2 \cdot 2 \cdot 2)(x \cdot x \cdot x) \qquad = \frac{2 \cdot 2 \cdot 2}{x \cdot x \cdot x} \quad \begin{array}{l}\text{Multiply the numerators.}\\\text{Multiply the denominators.}\end{array}$$

$$= 2^3x^3 \qquad\qquad\qquad = \frac{2^3}{x^3}$$

$$= 8x^3 \qquad\qquad\qquad = \frac{8}{x^3}$$

These examples illustrate the following rules: *To raise a product to a power, we raise each factor of the product to that power,* and *to raise a fraction to a power, we raise both the numerator and the denominator to that power.*

Powers of a product and a quotient

If n represents a natural number, then

$$(xy)^n = x^ny^n \qquad \text{and if } y \neq 0, \text{ then} \qquad \left(\frac{x}{y}\right)^n = \frac{x^n}{y^n}$$

EXAMPLE 6 *Powers of products.* Simplify **a.** $(3c)^3$, **b.** $(x^2y^3)^5$, and **c.** $(-2a^3b)^2$.

Solution

a. Since $3c$ is the product of 3 and c, the expression $(3c)^3$ is a power of a product.

$(3c)^3 = 3^3c^3$ Use the power rule for products: Raise each factor of the product $3c$ to the 3rd power.

$\quad\quad = 27c^3$ Evaluate 3^3.

b. $(x^2y^3)^5 = (x^2)^5(y^3)^5$ Raise each factor of the product x^2y^3 to the 5th power.

$\quad\quad\quad = x^{10}y^{15}$ For each power of a power, keep the base and multiply the exponents.

c. $(-2a^3b)^2 = (-2)^2(a^3)^2b^2$ Raise each of the three factors of the product $-2a^3b$ to the 2nd power.

$\quad\quad\quad = 4a^6b^2$ Evaluate $(-2)^2$. Keep the base a and multiply the exponents.

EXAMPLE 7 *Using three rules for exponents.* Simplify $\dfrac{(a^3b^4)^2}{ab^5}$.

Solution

$\dfrac{(a^3b^4)^2}{ab^5} = \dfrac{(a^3)^2(b^4)^2}{ab^5}$ In the numerator, raise each factor within the parentheses to the 2nd power.

$= \dfrac{a^6b^8}{ab^5}$ In the numerator, for each power of a power, keep the base and multiply the exponents.

$= a^{6-1}b^{8-5}$ Keep each of the bases, a and b, and subtract the exponents.

$= a^5b^3$ Do the subtractions.

Self Check

Simplify $\dfrac{(c^4d^5)^3}{c^2d^3}$

Answer: $c^{10}d^{12}$ ∎

EXAMPLE 8 *Powers of quotients.* Simplify **a.** $\left(\dfrac{4}{k}\right)^3$ and **b.** $\left(\dfrac{3x^2}{2y^3}\right)^5$.

Solution

a. Since $\frac{4}{k}$ is the quotient of 4 and k, the expression $\left(\frac{4}{k}\right)^3$ is a power of a quotient.

$\left(\dfrac{4}{k}\right)^3 = \dfrac{4^3}{k^3}$ Use the power rule for quotients: Raise the numerator and denominator to the 3rd power.

$= \dfrac{64}{k^3}$ Evaluate 4^3.

b. $\left(\dfrac{3x^2}{2y^3}\right)^5 = \dfrac{(3x^2)^5}{(2y^3)^5}$ Raise the numerator and the denominator to the 5th power.

$= \dfrac{3^5(x^2)^5}{2^5(y^3)^5}$ In the numerator and denominator, raise each factor within the parentheses to the 5th power.

$= \dfrac{243x^{10}}{32y^{15}}$ Evaluate 3^5 and 2^5. For each power of a power, keep the base and multiply the exponents.

Self Check

Simplify:

a. $\left(\dfrac{x}{7}\right)^3$

b. $\left(\dfrac{2x^3}{3y^2}\right)^4$

Answers: **a.** $\dfrac{x^3}{343}$, **b.** $\dfrac{16x^{12}}{81y^8}$ ∎

EXAMPLE 9 *Using two rules for exponents.* Simplify $\dfrac{(5b)^9}{(5b)^6}$.

Solution

$\dfrac{(5b)^9}{(5b)^6} = (5b)^{9-6}$ Keep the common base $5b$, and subtract the exponents.

$= (5b)^3$ Do the subtraction.

$= 5^3b^3$ Raise each factor within the parentheses to the 3rd power.

$= 125b^3$ Evaluate 5^3.

Self Check

Simplify $\dfrac{(-2h)^{20}}{(-2h)^{14}}$.

Answer: $64h^6$ ∎

The rules for natural-number exponents are summarized below.

Rules for exponents

If n represents a natural number, then

$$x^n = \overbrace{x \cdot x \cdot x \cdot \ \cdots \ \cdot x}^{n \text{ factors of } x}$$

If m and n represent natural numbers and there are no divisions by zero, then

1. $x^m x^n = x^{m+n}$ **2.** $\dfrac{x^m}{x^n} = x^{m-n}$ **3.** $(x^m)^n = x^{m \cdot n}$

4. $(xy)^n = x^n y^n$ **5.** $\left(\dfrac{x}{y}\right)^n = \dfrac{x^n}{y^n}$

STUDY SET Section 4.1

VOCABULARY *Fill in the blanks.*

1. The ___base___ of the exponential expression $(-5)^3$ is -5. The ___exponent___ is 3.

2. The ___exponential___ expression x^4 represents a repeated multiplication where x is to be written as a ___factor___ four times.

3. x^n is called a ___power___ of x.

4. The expression $(2x^2b)^5$ is a power of a ___product___, and $\left(\dfrac{2x^2}{b}\right)^5$ is a power of a ___quotient___.

CONCEPTS *Fill in the blanks.*

5. $(3x)^4$ means $3x \cdot 3x \cdot 3x \cdot 3x$

6. Using an exponent, $(-5y)(-5y)(-5y)$ can be written as $(-5y)^3$.

7. $x^m x^n = x^{m+n}$ **8.** $(xy)^n = x^n y^n$

9. $\left(\dfrac{a}{b}\right)^n = \dfrac{a^n}{b^n}$ **10.** $(a^b)^c = a^{bc}$

11. $\dfrac{x^m}{x^n} = x^{m-n}$ **12.** $x = x^1$

13. $(xy) = (xy)^1$ **14.** $(t^3)^2 = t^3 \cdot t^3$

15. a. Write a power of a product that has two factors.
$(3x^2)^6$ (answers may vary)

    b. Write a power of a quotient.
$\left(\dfrac{3a^3}{b}\right)^2$ (answers may vary)

16. a. To simplify $(2y^3z^2)^4$, how many factors within the parentheses must be raised to the fourth power? 3

    b. To simplify $\left(\dfrac{y^3}{z^2}\right)^4$ what two expressions must be raised to the fourth power? y^3 and z^2

Simplify each expression, if possible.

17. a. $x^2 + x^2$ $2x^2$ **b.** $x^2 - x^2$ 0

    c. $x^2 \cdot x^2$ x^4 **d.** $\dfrac{x^2}{1}$ x^2

18. a. $x^2 + x$ **b.** $x^2 - x$
doesn't simplify   doesn't simplify

    c. $x^2 \cdot x$ x^3 **d.** $\dfrac{x^2}{x}$ x

19. a. $x^3 + x^2$ **b.** $x^3 - x^2$
doesn't simplify   doesn't simplify

    c. $x^3 \cdot x^2$ x^5 **d.** $\dfrac{x^3}{x^2}$ x

20. Simplify each expression, if possible.

    a. $x^3 + y^3$ **b.** $x^3 - y^3$
doesn't simplify   doesn't simplify

    c. $x^3 y^3$ **d.** $\dfrac{x^3}{y^3}$
doesn't simplify   doesn't simplify

Find the area or volume of each figure, whichever is appropriate. You may leave π in your answer.

21. a^{10} mi^2 **22.** $16y^6\pi$ yd^2

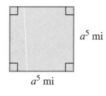

23. x^9 m^3 **24.** x^{21} cm^3

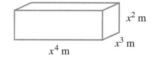
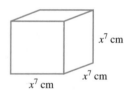

NOTATION *Complete each solution.*

25. $(x^4 x^2)^3 = \left(x^6 \right)^3$
      $= x^{18}$

26. $\dfrac{a^3 a^4}{a^2} = \dfrac{a^7}{a^2}$
      $= a^{7-2}$
      $= a^5$

Identify the base and the exponent in each expression.

27. 4^3
base 4, exponent 3

28. $(-8)^2$
base -8, exponent 2

29. x^5 base x, exponent 5

30. $\left(\dfrac{5}{x}\right)^3$ base $\frac{5}{x}$, exponent 3

31. $(-3x)^2$
base $-3x$, exponent 2

32. $-x^4$
base x, exponent 4

33. $-\dfrac{1}{3}y^6$
base y, exponent 6

34. $3.14r^4$
base r, exponent 4

Evaluate each expression.

35. $(-4)^2$ 16   **36.** $(-5)^2$ 25

37. -4^2 -16 **38.** -5^2 -25

Write the repeated multiplication that is indicated.

39. x^5
$x \cdot x \cdot x \cdot x \cdot x$

40. $(-7y)^4$
$(-7y)(-7y)(-7y)(-7y)$

41. $\left(\dfrac{t^2}{2}\right)^3$ $\left(\dfrac{t^2}{2}\right)\left(\dfrac{t^2}{2}\right)\left(\dfrac{t^2}{2}\right)$

42. $c^3 d^2$ $c \cdot c \cdot c \cdot d \cdot d$

Write each expression using an exponent.

43. $4t(4t)(4t)(4t)$ $(4t)^4$

44. $-5u(-5u)$ $(-5u)^2$

45. $-4 \cdot t \cdot t \cdot t$ $-4t^3$

46. $-5 \cdot u \cdot u$ $-5u^2$

PRACTICE   Write each expression as an expression involving one base and one exponent.

47. $12^3 \cdot 12^4$ 12^7

48. $3^4 \cdot 3^6$ 3^{10}

49. $2(2^3)(2^2)$ 2^6

50. $5(5^5)(5^3)$ 5^9

51. $a^3 \cdot a^3$ a^6

52. $m^7 \cdot m^7$ m^{14}

53. $x^4 x^3$ x^7

54. $y^5 y^2$ y^7

55. $a^3 a a^5$ a^9

56. $b^2 b^3 b$ b^6

57. $y^3(y^2 y^4)$ y^9

58. $(y^4 y)y^6$ y^{11}

59. $\dfrac{8^{12}}{8^4}$ 8^8

60. $\dfrac{10^4}{10^2}$ 10^2

61. $\dfrac{x^{15}}{x^3}$ x^{12}

62. $\dfrac{y^6}{y^3}$ y^3

63. $\dfrac{c^{10}}{c^9}$ c

64. $\dfrac{h^{20}}{h^{10}}$ h^{10}

65. $(3^2)^4$ 3^8

66. $(4^3)^3$ 4^9

67. $(y^5)^3$ y^{15}

68. $(b^3)^6$ b^{18}

69. $(m^{50})^{10}$ m^{500}

70. $(n^{25})^4$ n^{100}

Simplify. Assume there are no divisions by 0.

71. $(a^2 b^3)(a^3 b^3)$ $a^5 b^6$

72. $(u^3 v^5)(u^4 v^5)$ $u^7 v^{10}$

73. $(cd^4)(cd)$ $c^2 d^5$

74. $ab^3 c^4 \cdot ab^4 c^2$ $a^2 b^7 c^6$

75. $xy^2 \cdot x^2 y$ $x^3 y^3$

76. $s^8 t^2 s^2 t^7$ $s^{10} t^9$

77. $\dfrac{y^3 y^4}{yy^2}$ y^4

78. $\dfrac{b^4 b^5}{b^2 b^3}$ b^4

79. $\dfrac{c^3 d^7}{cd}$ $c^2 d^6$

80. $\dfrac{r^8 s^9}{rs}$ $r^7 s^8$

81. $(x^2 x^3)^5$ x^{25}

82. $(y^3 y^4)^4$ y^{28}

83. $(3zz^2 z^3)^5$ $243z^{30}$

84. $(4t^3 t^6 t^2)^2$ $16t^{22}$

85. $(x^5)^2(x^7)^3$ x^{31}

86. $(y^3 y)^2(y^2)^2$ y^{12}

87. $(uv)^4$ $u^4 v^4$

88. $(xy)^3$ $x^3 y^3$

89. $(a^3 b^2)^3$ $a^9 b^6$

90. $(r^3 s^2)^2$ $r^6 s^4$

91. $(-2r^2 s^3)^3$ $-8r^6 s^9$

92. $(-3x^2 y^4)^2$ $9x^4 y^8$

93. $\left(\dfrac{a}{b}\right)^3$ $\dfrac{a^3}{b^3}$

94. $\left(\dfrac{r}{s}\right)^4$ $\dfrac{r^4}{s^4}$

95. $\left(\dfrac{x^2}{y^3}\right)^5$ $\dfrac{x^{10}}{y^{15}}$

96. $\left(\dfrac{u^4}{v^2}\right)^6$ $\dfrac{u^{24}}{v^{12}}$

97. $\left(\dfrac{-2a}{b}\right)^5$ $\dfrac{-32a^5}{b^5}$

98.

99. $\dfrac{(6k)^7}{(6k)^4}$ $216k^3$

100

101. $\dfrac{(a^2 b)^{15}}{(a^2 b)^9}$ $a^{12} b^6$

10?

103. $\dfrac{a^2 a^3 a^4}{(a^4)^2}$ a

104. $\dfrac{(aa^2)^3}{a^2 a^3}$ a^4

105. $\dfrac{(ab^2)^3}{(ab)^2}$ ab^4

106. $\dfrac{(m^3 n^4)^3}{(mn^2)^3}$ $m^6 n^6$

107. $\dfrac{(r^4 s^3)^4}{(rs^3)^3}$ $r^{13} s^3$

108. $\dfrac{(x^2 y^5)^5}{(x^3 y)^2}$ $x^4 y^{23}$

109. $\left(\dfrac{y^3 y}{2yy^2}\right)^3$ $\dfrac{y^3}{8}$

110. $\left(\dfrac{2y^3 y}{yy^2}\right)^3$ $8y^3$

111. $\left(\dfrac{3t^3 t^4 t^5}{4t^2 t^6}\right)^3$ $\dfrac{27t^{12}}{64}$

112. $\left(\dfrac{4t^3 t^4 t^5}{3t^2 t^6}\right)^3$ $\dfrac{64t^{12}}{27}$

APPLICATIONS

113. ART HISTORY   Leonardo da Vinci's drawing relating a human figure to a square and a circle is shown in Illustration 1.

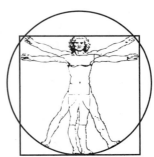

ILLUSTRATION 1

a. Find the area of the square if the man's height is $5x$ feet. $25x^2$ ft^2

b. Find the area of the circle if the distance from his waist to his feet is $3x$ feet. You may leave π in your answer. $9\pi x^2$ ft^2

114. PACKAGING   Use Illustration 2 to find the volume of the bowling ball and the cardboard box it is packaged in. You may leave π in your answer. $36\pi x^3$ in.^{3}, $216x^3$ in.^{3}

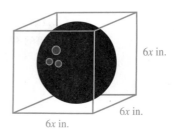

6x in.

6x in.

6x in.

ILLUSTRATION 2

BOUNCING BALL A ball is dropped from a height of 32 feet. Each rebound is one-half of its previous height.

a. Draw a diagram of the path of the ball, showing four bounces.

b. Explain why the expressions $32\left(\frac{1}{2}\right)$, $32\left(\frac{1}{2}\right)^2$, $32\left(\frac{1}{2}\right)^3$, and $32\left(\frac{1}{2}\right)^4$ represent the height of the ball on the first, second, third, and fourth bounces, respectively. Find the heights of the first four bounces.   16 ft, 8 ft, 4 ft, 2 ft

116. HAVING BABIES The probability that a couple will have n baby boys in a row is given by the formula $\left(\dfrac{1}{2}\right)^n$. Find the probability that a couple will have four baby boys in a row. $\frac{1}{16}$

117. COMPUTERS Text is stored by computers using a sequence of eight 0's and 1's. Such a sequence is called a **byte.** An example of a byte is 10101110.

a. Write four other bytes, all ending in 1.
11000001, 11010001, 11001101, 11000011 (answers may vary)

b. Each of the eight digits of a byte can be chosen in *two* ways (either 0 or 1). The total number of different bytes can be represented by an exponential expression with base 2. What is it? 2^8

118. ☷ INVESTING Guess the answer to the following problem. Then use a calculator to find the correct answer. Were you close?
If the value of 1¢ is to double every day, what will the penny be worth after 31 days? $21,474,836.48

WRITING

119. Explain the mistake in the following work.
$$2^3 \cdot 2^2 = 4^5$$
$$= 1{,}024$$

120. Are the expressions $2x^3$ and $(2x)^3$ equivalent? Explain.

121. Is the operation of raising to a power commutative? That is, is $a^b = b^a$? Explain.

122. When a number is raised to a power, is the result always larger than the original number? Support your answer with some examples.

REVIEW *Match each equation with its graph below.*

123. $y = 2x - 1$ c

124. $y = 3x - 1$ a

125. $y = 3$ d

126. $x = 3$ b

a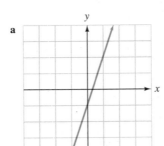

b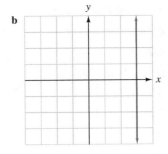

c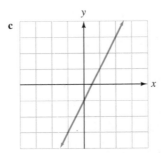

d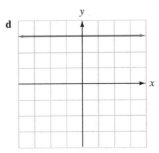

4.2 *Zero and Negative Integer Exponents*

In this section, you will learn about

• Zero exponents • Negative integer exponents • Variable exponents

INTRODUCTION. In the previous section, we discussed natural-number exponents. We now extend the discussion to include exponents that are zero and exponents that are negative integers.

Zero exponents

When we discussed the quotient rule for exponents in the previous section, the exponent in the numerator was always greater than the exponent in the denominator. We now consider what happens when the exponents are equal. To develop the definition of a zero exponent, we will simplify the expression

$$\frac{5^3}{5^3}$$

in two ways. If we use the quotient rule for exponents, where the exponents in the numerator and denominator are equal, we obtain 5^0. However, by dividing out common factors of 5, we obtain 1.

$$\frac{5^3}{5^3} = 5^{3-3} = 5^0 \qquad \frac{5^3}{5^3} = \frac{\overset{1}{5} \cdot \overset{1}{5} \cdot \overset{1}{5}}{\underset{1}{5} \cdot \underset{1}{5} \cdot \underset{1}{5}} = 1$$

These must be equal.

For this reason, we will define 5^0 to be equal to 1. This example suggests the following rule.

Zero exponents

> If x represents any nonzero real number, then
> $$x^0 = 1$$

EXAMPLE 1 *Zero exponents.* Write each expression without using exponents.

a. $\left(\frac{1}{13}\right)^0 = 1$

b. $\dfrac{x^5}{x^5} = x^{5-5} \quad (x \neq 0)$

$ = x^0$

$ = 1$

c. $3x^0 = 3(1)$ The base is x;
$ = 3$ the exponent is 0.

d. $(3x)^0 = 1$ The base is $3x$;
             the exponent is 0.

Parts c and d point out that $3x^0 \neq (3x)^0$.

Self Check

Write each expression without using exponents:

a. $(-0.115)^0$

b. $-5a^0b$

Answers: a. 1, **b.** $-5b$ ■

Negative integer exponents

To develop the definition of a negative exponent, we will simplify the expression

$$\frac{6^2}{6^5}$$

in two ways. If we use the quotient rule for exponents, where the exponent in the numerator is less than the exponent in the denominator, we obtain 6^{-3}. However, by dividing out two factors of 6, we obtain $\frac{1}{6^3}$.

$$\frac{6^2}{6^5} = 6^{2-5} = 6^{-3} \qquad \frac{6^2}{6^5} = \frac{\overset{1}{6} \cdot \overset{1}{6}}{\underset{1}{6} \cdot \underset{1}{6} \cdot 6 \cdot 6 \cdot 6} = \frac{1}{6^3}$$

These must be equal.

For this reason, we define 6^{-3} to be equal to $\frac{1}{6^3}$. In general, we have the following rule.

Negative exponents   If x represents any nonzero number and n represents a natural number, then

$$x^{-n} = \frac{1}{x^n}$$

The definition of a negative exponent states that another way to write x^{-n} is to write its reciprocal, changing the sign of the exponent. We can use this definition to write expressions that contain negative exponents as expressions without negative exponents.

EXAMPLE 2   *Negative exponents.* Simplify by using the definition of negative exponents: **a.** 3^{-5} and   **b.** $(-2)^{-3}$.

Solution

a. $3^{-5} = \dfrac{1}{3^5}$ Write the reciprocal of 3^{-5} and change the exponent from -5 to 5.

$= \dfrac{1}{243}$ Evaluate 3^5.

b. $(-2)^{-3} = \dfrac{1}{(-2)^3}$ Write the reciprocal of $(-2)^{-3}$ and change the exponent from -3 to 3.

$= -\dfrac{1}{8}$ Evaluate $(-2)^3$.

Self Check

Simplify by using the definition of negative exponents:

a. 4^{-4}

b. $(-5)^{-3}$

Answers: **a.** $\dfrac{1}{256}$,   **b.** $-\dfrac{1}{125}$

 COMMENT   A negative exponent does not indicate a negative number. It indicates a reciprocal.

$$4^{-2} = \frac{1}{4^2} \qquad 4^{-2} \neq -16 \qquad 4^{-2} \neq -\frac{1}{4^2}$$

EXAMPLE 3   *Negative exponents.* Simplify by using the definition of negative exponents:

a. $\dfrac{1}{5^{-2}}$ and   **b.** $\dfrac{2^{-3}}{3^{-4}}$.

Solution

a. $\dfrac{1}{5^{-2}} = \dfrac{1}{\dfrac{1}{5^2}}$ In the denominator, write the reciprocal of 5^{-2} and change the exponent from -2 to 2.

$= 1 \div \dfrac{1}{5^2}$ The fraction bar indicates division of 1 by $\dfrac{1}{5^2}$.

$= 1 \cdot \dfrac{5^2}{1}$ To divide by $\dfrac{1}{5^2}$, we multiply by its reciprocal.

$= 5^2$ Simplify.

$= 25$ Evaluate 5^2.

b. $\dfrac{2^{-3}}{3^{-4}} = \dfrac{\dfrac{1}{2^3}}{\dfrac{1}{3^4}}$ In the numerator, write the reciprocal of 2^{-3} and change the exponent from -3 to 3.
In the denominator, write the reciprocal of 3^{-4} and change the exponent from -4 to 4.

Self Check

Simplify by using the definition of negative exponents:

a. $\dfrac{1}{9^{-1}}$

b. $\dfrac{8^{-2}}{7^{-1}}$

$$= \frac{1}{2^3} \cdot \frac{3^4}{1} \qquad \text{To divide by } \frac{1}{3^4}, \text{ we multiply by its reciprocal.}$$

$$= \frac{3^4}{2^3} \qquad \text{Multiply the fractions.}$$

$$= \frac{81}{8} \qquad \text{Evaluate } 3^4 \text{ and } 2^3.$$

Answers: a. 9,   **b.** $\dfrac{7}{64}$ ∎

The results from Example 3 suggest that we can move factors that have negative exponents between the numerator and denominator of a fraction if we change the sign of their exponents. For example,

$$\frac{3^{-3}}{b^{-1}} = \frac{b^1}{3^3} = \frac{b}{27}$$

EXAMPLE 4   *Negative exponents.* Simplify by using the definition of negative exponents. Assume that no denominators are zero.

a. $x^{-4} = \dfrac{1}{x^4}$

b. $\dfrac{x^{-3}}{y^{-7}} = \dfrac{y^7}{x^3}$

c. $(-2x)^{-2} = \dfrac{1}{(-2x)^2}$

$\qquad\quad = \dfrac{1}{4x^2}$

d. $-2x^{-2} = -2\left(\dfrac{1}{x^2}\right)$

$\qquad\quad = -\dfrac{2}{x^2}$

Self Check

Simplify by using the definition of negative exponents:

a. a^{-5}

b. $\dfrac{r^{-4}}{s^{-5}}$

c. $3y^{-3}$

Answers: a. $\dfrac{1}{a^5}$,   **b.** $\dfrac{s^5}{r^4}$,

c. $\dfrac{3}{y^3}$ ∎

The rules for exponents discussed in Section 4.1 (the product, power, and quotient rules) are also true for zero and negative exponents.

Rules for exponents

If *m* and *n* represent integers and there are no divisions by zero, then

$$x^m x^n = x^{m+n} \qquad (x^m)^n = x^{m \cdot n} \qquad (xy)^n = x^n y^n \qquad \left(\frac{x}{y}\right)^n = \frac{x^n}{y^n}$$

$$x^0 = 1 \quad (x \neq 0) \qquad x^{-n} = \frac{1}{x^n} \qquad \frac{x^m}{x^n} = x^{m-n}$$

EXAMPLE 5   *Using two rules for exponents.* Write $\left(\dfrac{5}{16}\right)^{-1}$ without using exponents.

Solution

$$\left(\frac{5}{16}\right)^{-1} = \frac{5^{-1}}{16^{-1}} \qquad \text{Use the quotient rule for exponents: Raise the numerator and denominator to the } -1 \text{ power.}$$

$$= \frac{16^1}{5^1} \qquad \text{Move the factors that have negative exponents between the numerator and denominator.}$$

$$= \frac{16}{5}$$

Self Check

Write $\left(\dfrac{3}{7}\right)^{-2}$ without using exponents.

Answer: $\dfrac{49}{9}$ ∎

EXAMPLE 6   *Using rules for exponents.*   Simplify and write the result without using negative exponents. Assume that no denominators are zero.

a. $(x^{-3})^2 = x^{-6}$

$$= \frac{1}{x^6}$$

b. $\dfrac{x^3}{x^7} = x^{3-7}$

$$= x^{-4}$$

$$= \frac{1}{x^4}$$

c. $(x^3x^2)^{-3} = (x^5)^{-3}$

$$= \frac{1}{(x^5)^3}$$

$$= \frac{1}{x^{15}}$$

d. $\dfrac{y^{-4}y^{-3}}{y^{-20}} = \dfrac{y^{-7}}{y^{-20}}$

$$= y^{-7-(-20)}$$

$$= y^{-7+20}$$

$$= y^{13}$$

e. $\dfrac{12a^3b^4}{4a^5b^2} = 3a^{3-5}b^{4-2}$

$$= 3a^{-2}b^2$$

$$= \frac{3b^2}{a^2}$$

f. $\left(-\dfrac{x^3y^2}{xy^{-3}}\right)^{-2} = \left(-x^{3-1}y^{2-(-3)}\right)^{-2}$

$$= (-x^2y^5)^{-2}$$

$$= \frac{1}{(-x^2y^5)^2}$$

$$= \frac{1}{x^4y^{10}}$$

Self Check

Simplify and write the result without using negative exponents:

a. $(x^4)^{-3}$

b. $\dfrac{a^4}{a^8}$

c. $\dfrac{a^{-4}a^{-5}}{a^{-3}}$

d. $\dfrac{20x^5y^3}{5x^3y^6}$

Answers: a. $\dfrac{1}{x^{12}}$,   **b.** $\dfrac{1}{a^4}$,

c. $\dfrac{1}{a^6}$,   **d.** $\dfrac{4x^2}{y^3}$

Variable exponents

We can apply the rules for exponents to simplify expressions involving variable exponents.

EXAMPLE 7   *Variable exponents.*   Simplify each expression. Assume that there are no divisions by 0.

a. $\dfrac{6^n}{6^n} = 6^{n-n}$ Keep the common base and subtract the exponents.

$$= 6^0$$ Combine like terms: $n - n = 0$.

$$= 1$$

b. $x^{2m}x^{3m} = x^{2m+3m}$ Keep the common base and add the exponents.

$$= x^{5m}$$ Combine like terms: $2m + 3m = 5m$.

c. $\dfrac{y^{2m}}{y^{4m}} = y^{2m-4m}$ Keep the base and subtract the exponents.

$$= y^{-2m}$$ Combine like terms: $2m - 4m = -2m$.

$$= \frac{1}{y^{2m}}$$ Write the reciprocal of y^{-2m} and change the exponent to $2m$.

Self Check

Simplify each expression:

a. $\dfrac{x^m}{x^m}$

b. $z^{3n}z^{2n}$

c. $\dfrac{z^{3n}}{z^{5n}}$

Answers: a. 1,   **b.** z^{5n},

c. $\dfrac{1}{z^{2n}}$

Accent on Technology: **Finding present value**

As a gift for their newborn grandson, the grandparents want to deposit enough money in the bank now so that when he turns 18, the young man will have a college fund of $20,000 waiting for him. How much should they deposit now if the money will earn 6% annually?

To find how much money P must be invested at an annual rate i (expressed as a decimal) to have $$A$ in n years, we use the formula $P = A(1 + i)^{-n}$. If we substitute 20,000 for A, 0.06 (6%) for i, and 18 for n, we have

$$P = A(1 + i)^{-n}$$ P is called the **present value.**

$$P = 20{,}000(1 + 0.06)^{-18}$$

To find P with a scientific calculator, we enter these numbers and press these keys.

Keystrokes   (1 + .06) y^x 18 +/− × 20000 =   7006.875823

To evaluate the expression with a graphing calculator, we use the following keystrokes.

Keystrokes   20000 × (1 + .06) ∧ (−) 18 ENTER

```
20000*(1+.06)^-1
8
        7006.875823
```

They must invest approximately $7,006.88 to have $20,000 in 18 years.

STUDY SET Section 4.2

VOCABULARY *Fill in the blanks.*

1. In the exponential expression 8^{-3}, 8 is the _____base_____ and -3 is the _____exponent_____.

2. In the exponential expression 5^{-1}, the exponent is a _____negative_____ integer.

3. Another way to write 2^{-3} is to write its _____reciprocal_____ and to change the sign of the exponent:

$$2^{-3} = \frac{1}{2^3}$$

4. In the exponential expression z^m, the exponent is a _____variable_____.

CONCEPTS

5. In parts a and b, fill in the blanks as you simplify the fraction in two different ways. Then complete the sentence in part c.

a. $\dfrac{6^4}{6^4} = 6^{4-4}$ **b.** $\dfrac{6^4}{6^4} = \dfrac{6 \cdot 6 \cdot 6 \cdot 6}{6 \cdot 6 \cdot 6 \cdot 6}$

$= 6^{\,0}$ $= 1$

c. So we define 6^0 to be 1 , and in general, if x is any nonzero real number, then $x^0 = $ 1 .

6. In parts a and b, fill in the blanks as you simplify the fraction in two different ways. Then complete the sentence in part c.

a. $\dfrac{8^3}{8^5} = 8^{3-5}$ **b.** $\dfrac{8^3}{8^5} = \dfrac{8 \cdot 8 \cdot 8}{8 \cdot 8 \cdot 8 \cdot 8 \cdot 8}$

$= 8^{-2}$ $= \dfrac{1}{8^{\,2}}$

c. So we define 8^{-2} to be $\frac{1}{8^2}$, and in general, if x is any nonzero real number, then $x^{-n} = \frac{1}{x^n}$.

Complete each table.

7.

x	3^x
2	9
1	3
0	1
-1	$\frac{1}{3}$
-2	$\frac{1}{9}$

8.

x	4^x
2	16
1	4
0	1
-1	$\frac{1}{4}$
-2	$\frac{1}{16}$

9.

x	$(-9)^x$
2	81
1	-9
0	1
-1	$-\frac{1}{9}$
-2	$\frac{1}{81}$

10.

x	$(-5)^x$
2	25
1	-5
0	1
-1	$-\frac{1}{5}$
-2	$\frac{1}{25}$

...etermine the missing y-coordinates
...ss each y-coordinate as a power

18. First tell the base and the exponent, and then evaluate
each expression.
  a. $(-7)^2$ $-7; 2; 49$
  b. -7^{-2} $7; -2; -\frac{1}{49}$
  c. $(-7)^{-2}$ $-7; -2; \frac{1}{49}$

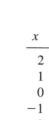

x	y	y as a power of 2
2	4	2^2
1	2	2^1
0	1	2^0
-1	$\frac{1}{2}$	2^{-1}
-2	$\frac{1}{4}$	2^{-2}

PRACTICE *Simplify each expression. Write each
answer without using parentheses or negative exponents.*

19. 7^0 1 **20.** 9^0 1

21. $\left(\frac{1}{4}\right)^0$ 1 **22.** $\left(\frac{3}{8}\right)^0$ 1

23. $2x^0$ 2 **24.** $(2x)^0$ 1

25. $(-x)^0$ 1 **26.** $-x^0$ -1

27. $\left(\frac{a^2b^3}{ab^4}\right)^0$ 1 **28.** $\frac{2}{3}\left(\frac{xyz}{x^2y}\right)^0$ $\frac{2}{3}$

29. $\frac{5}{2x^0}$ $\frac{5}{2}$ **30.** $\frac{4}{3a^0}$ $\frac{4}{3}$

31. 12^{-2} $\frac{1}{144}$ **32.** 11^{-2} $\frac{1}{121}$

33. $(-4)^{-1}$ $-\frac{1}{4}$ **34.** $(-8)^{-1}$ $-\frac{1}{8}$

35. $\frac{1}{5^{-3}}$ 125 **36.** $\frac{1}{3^{-3}}$ 27

37. $\frac{2^{-4}}{3^{-1}}$ $\frac{3}{16}$ **38.** $\frac{7^{-2}}{2^{-3}}$ $\frac{8}{49}$

39. -4^{-3} $-\frac{1}{64}$ **40.** -6^{-3} $-\frac{1}{216}$

41. $-(-4)^{-3}$ $\frac{1}{64}$ **42.** $-(-4)^{-2}$ $-\frac{1}{16}$

43. x^{-2} $\frac{1}{x^2}$ **44.** y^{-3} $\frac{1}{y^3}$

45. $-b^{-5}$ $-\frac{1}{b^5}$ **46.** $-c^{-4}$ $-\frac{1}{c^4}$

47. $(2y)^{-4}$ $\frac{1}{16y^4}$ **48.** $(-3x)^{-1}$ $-\frac{1}{3x}$

49. $(ab^2)^{-3}$ $\frac{1}{a^3b^6}$ **50.** $(m^2n^3)^{-2}$ $\frac{1}{m^4n^6}$

51. $2^5 \cdot 2^{-2}$ 8 **52.** $10^2 \cdot 10^{-4}$ $\frac{1}{100}$

53. $4^{-3} \cdot 4^{-2} \cdot 4^5$ 1 **54.** $3^{-4} \cdot 3^5 \cdot 3^{-3}$ $\frac{1}{9}$

12.

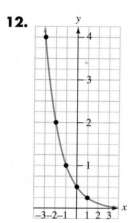

x	y	y as a power of 2
1	$\frac{1}{4}$	2^{-2}
0	$\frac{1}{2}$	2^{-1}
-1	1	2^0
-2	2	2^1
-3	4	2^2

NOTATION *Complete each solution.*

13. $(y^5y^3)^{-5} = \left(y^8\right)^{-5}$
  $= y^{-40}$
  $= \frac{1}{y^{40}}$

14. $\left(\frac{a^2b^3}{a^{-3}b}\right)^{-3} = \left(a^{2-(-3)}b^{3\ -1}\right)^{-3}$
  $= (a^{\,5}\,b^{\,2})^{-3}$
  $= \frac{1}{(a^5b^2)^{\,3}}$
  $= \frac{1}{a^{15}b^6}$

15. In the expression $3x^{-2}$, what is the base and what is the
exponent? base x, exponent -2

16. In the expression $-3x^{-2}$, what is the base and what is
the exponent? base x, exponent -2

17. First tell the base and the exponent, and then evaluate
each expression.
  a. -4^2 $4; 2; -16$
  b. 4^{-2} $4; -2; \frac{1}{16}$
  c. -4^{-2} $4; -2; -\frac{1}{16}$

55. $\left(\frac{7}{8}\right)^{-1}$ $\frac{8}{7}$ **56.** $\left(\frac{16}{5}\right)^{-1}$ $\frac{5}{16}$

57. $\frac{3^5 \cdot 3^{-2}}{3^3}$ 1 **58.** $\frac{6^2 \cdot 6^{-3}}{6^{-2}}$ 6

59. $\frac{y^4}{y^5}$ $\frac{1}{y}$ **60.** $\frac{t^7}{t^{10}}$ $\frac{1}{t^3}$

61. $\frac{(r^2)^3}{(r^3)^4}$ $\frac{1}{r^6}$ **62.** $\frac{(b^3)^4}{(b^5)^4}$ $\frac{1}{b^8}$

63. $\dfrac{y^4 y^3}{y^4 y^{-2}}$ y^5

64. $\dfrac{x^{12} x^{-7}}{x^3 x^4}$ $\dfrac{1}{x^2}$

65. $\dfrac{10a^4 a^{-2}}{5a^2 a^0}$ 2

66. $\dfrac{9b^0 b^3}{3b^{-3} b^4}$ $3b^2$

67. $(ab^2)^{-2}$ $\dfrac{1}{a^2 b^4}$

68. $(c^2 d^3)^{-2}$ $\dfrac{1}{c^4 d^6}$

69. $(x^2 y)^{-3}$ $\dfrac{1}{x^6 y^3}$

70. $(-xy^2)^{-4}$ $\dfrac{1}{x^4 y^8}$

71. $(x^{-4} x^3)^3$ $\dfrac{1}{x^3}$

72. $(y^{-2} y)^3$ $\dfrac{1}{y^3}$

73. $(a^{-2} b^3)^{-4}$ $\dfrac{a^8}{b^{12}}$

74. $(y^{-3} z^5)^{-6}$ $\dfrac{y^{18}}{z^{30}}$

75. $(-2x^3 y^{-2})^{-5}$ $-\dfrac{y^{10}}{32x^{15}}$

76. $(-3u^{-2} v^3)^{-3}$ $-\dfrac{u^6}{27v^9}$

77. $\left(\dfrac{a^3}{a^{-4}}\right)^2$ a^{14}

78. $\left(\dfrac{a^4}{a^{-3}}\right)^3$ a^{21}

79. $\left(\dfrac{b^5}{b^{-2}}\right)^{-2}$ $\dfrac{1}{b^{14}}$

80. $\left(\dfrac{b^{-2}}{b^3}\right)^3$ $\dfrac{1}{b^{15}}$

81. $\left(\dfrac{4x^2}{3x^{-5}}\right)^4$ $\dfrac{256x^{28}}{81}$

82. $\left(\dfrac{-3r^4 r^{-3}}{r^{-3} r^7}\right)^3$ $-\dfrac{27}{r^9}$

83. $\left(\dfrac{12y^3 z^{-2}}{3y^{-4} z^3}\right)^2$ $\dfrac{16y^{14}}{z^{10}}$

84. $\left(\dfrac{6xy^3}{3x^{-1} y}\right)^3$ $8x^6 y^6$

Simplify each expression. Assume that there are no divisions by 0.

85. $x^{2m} x^m$ x^{3m}

86. $y^{3m} y^{2m}$ y^{5m}

87. $u^{2m} u^{-3m}$ $\dfrac{1}{u^m}$

88. $r^{5m} r^{-6m}$ $\dfrac{1}{r^m}$

89. $\dfrac{y^{3m}}{y^{2m}}$ y^m

90. $\dfrac{z^{4m}}{z^{2m}}$ z^{2m}

91. $\dfrac{x^{3n}}{x^{6n}}$ $\dfrac{1}{x^{3n}}$

92. $\dfrac{x^m}{x^{5m}}$ $\dfrac{1}{x^{4m}}$

APPLICATIONS

93. THE DECIMAL NUMERATION SYSTEM   Decimal numbers are written by putting digits into place-value columns that are separated by a decimal point. Express the value of each of the columns shown in Illustration 1 using a power of 10. $10^2, 10^1, 10^0, 10^{-1}, 10^{-2}, 10^{-3}, 10^{-4}$

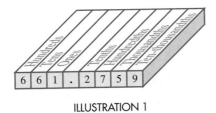

ILLUSTRATION 1

94. UNIT COMPARISON   Consider the relative sizes of the items listed in the table in Illustration 2. In the

column titled "measurement," write the most appropriate number from the following list. Each number is used only once.

10^0 meter

10^{-1} meter

10^{-2} meter

10^{-3} meter

10^{-4} meter

10^{-5} meter

Item	Measurement (m)
Thickness of a dime	10^{-3}
Height of a bathroom sink	10^0
Length of a pencil eraser	10^{-2}
Thickness of soap bubble film	10^{-5}
Width of a video cassette	10^{-1}
Thickness of a piece of paper	10^{-4}

ILLUSTRATION 2

95. RETIREMENT YEARS   How much money should a young married couple invest now at an 8% annual rate if they want to have $100,000 in the bank when they reach retirement age in 40 years? (See the Accent on Technology in this section for the formula.)
approximately $4,603.09

96. BIOLOGY   During bacterial reproduction, the time required for a population to double is called the **generation time**. If b bacteria are introduced into a medium, then after the generation time has elapsed, there will be $2b$ bacteria. After n generations, there will be $b \cdot 2^n$ bacteria. Explain what this expression represents when $n = 0$.   It gives the initial number of bacteria b.

WRITING

97. Explain how you would help a friend understand that 2^{-3} is not equal to -8.

98. Describe how you would verify on a calculator that

$$2^{-3} = \dfrac{1}{2^3}$$

REVIEW

99. IQ TEST   An IQ (intelligence quotient) is a score derived from the formula

$$\text{IQ} = \dfrac{\text{mental age}}{\text{chronological age}} \cdot 100$$

Find the mental age of a 10-year-old girl if she has an IQ of 135.   13.5 yr

100. DIVING   When you are under water, the pressure in your ears is given by the formula

Pressure = depth · density of water

Find the density of water (in lb/ft^3) if, at a depth of 9 feet, the pressure on your eardrum is 561.6 lb/ft^2.
62.4 lb/ft^3

101. Write the equation of the line having slope $\frac{3}{4}$ and y-intercept -5. $y = \frac{3}{4}x - 5$

102. Find $f(-6)$ if $f(x) = x^2 - 3x + 1$.   55

4.3 *Scientific Notation*

In this section, you will learn about

- Scientific notation • Writing numbers in scientific notation
- Changing from scientific notation to standard notation
- Using scientific notation to simplify computations

INTRODUCTION. Scientists often deal with extremely large and extremely small numbers. Two examples are shown in Figure 4-1.

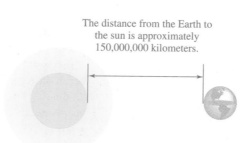
The distance from the Earth to the sun is approximately 150,000,000 kilometers.

The influenza virus, which causes "flu" symptoms of cough, sore throat, headache, and congestion, has a diameter of 0.00000256 inch.

FIGURE 4-1

The large number of zeros in 150,000,000 and 0.00000256 makes them difficult to read and hard to remember. In this section, we will discuss a notation that will make such numbers easier to use.

Scientific notation

Scientific notation provides a compact way of writing large and small numbers.

Scientific notation

> A number is written in **scientific notation** when it is written as the product of a number between 1 (including 1) and 10 and an integer power of 10.

These numbers are written in scientific notation:

3.67×10^6, 2.24×10^{-4},   and 9.875×10^{22}

Every number written in scientific notation has the following form:

An integer exponent

$\underbrace{} \cdot \times 10$

A decimal between 1 and 10

Writing numbers in scientific notation

EXAMPLE 1   *Writing numbers in scientific notation.*   Change 150,000,000 to scientific notation.

Solution

We note that 1.5 lies between 1 and 10. To obtain 150,000,000, the decimal point in 1.5 must be moved eight places to the right.

$$1 . 5\,0\,0\,0\,0\,0\,0\,0$$
8 places to the right

Because multiplying a number by 10 moves the decimal point one place to the right, we can accomplish this by multiplying 1.5 by 10 eight times. We can show the multiplication of 1.5 by 10 eight times using the notation 10^8. Thus, 150,000,000 written in scientific notation is 1.5×10^8.

> **Self Check**
> The distance from Earth to the sun is approximately 93,000,000 miles. Write this number in scientific notation.
>
> **Answer:** 9.3×10^7 ■

EXAMPLE 2   *Writing numbers in scientific notation.*   Change 0.00000256 to scientific notation.

Solution

We note that 2.56 is between 1 and 10. To obtain 0.00000256, the decimal point in 2.56 must be moved six places to the left.

$$0\,0\,0\,0\,0\,2 . 56$$
6 places to the left

We can accomplish this by dividing 2.56 by 10^6, which is equivalent to multiplying 2.56 by $\frac{1}{10^6}$ (or by 10^{-6}). Thus, 0.00000256 written in scientific notation is 2.56×10^{-6}.

> **Self Check**
> The *Salmonella* bacterium, which causes food poisoning, is 0.00009055 inch long. Write this number in scientific notation.
>
> **Answer:** 9.055×10^{-5} ■

EXAMPLE 3   *Writing numbers in scientific notation.*   Write
a. 235,000   and   **b.** 0.0000073 in scientific notation.

Solution

a. $235,000 = 2.35 \times 10^5$ Because $2.35 \times 10^5 = 235,000$ and 2.35 is between 1 and 10.

b. $0.0000073 = 7.3 \times 10^{-6}$ Because $7.3 \times 10^{-6} = 0.0000073$ and 7.3 is between 1 and 10.

> **Self Check**
> Write in scientific notation:
>
> **a.** 17,500
> **b.** 0.657
>
> **Answers:** **a.** 1.75×10^4,
> **b.** 6.57×10^{-1} ■

From Examples 1, 2, and 3, we see that in scientific notation, a positive exponent is used when writing a number that is greater than 1. A negative exponent is used when writing a number that is between 0 and 1.

EXAMPLE 4   *Writing numbers in scientific notation.*   Write 432.0×10^5 in scientific notation.

Solution

The number 432.0×10^5 is not written in scientific notation, because 432.0 is not a number between 1 and 10. To write this number in scientific notation, we proceed as follows:

$$432.0 \times 10^5 = 4.32 \times 10^2 \times 10^5 \quad \text{Write 432.0 in scientific notation.}$$
$$= 4.32 \times 10^7 \qquad\qquad 10^2 \times 10^5 = 10^{2+5} = 10^7.$$

> **Self Check**
> Write 85×10^{-3} in scientific notation.
>
> **Answer:** 8.5×10^{-2} ■

$Accent\ on\ Technology$: **Calculators and scientific notation**

When displaying a very large or a very small number as an answer, most scientific calculators express it in scientific notation. To show this, we will find the values of $(453.46)^5$ and $(0.0005)^{12}$. We enter these numbers and press these keys.

Keystrokes   453.46 $\boxed{y^x}$ 5 $\boxed{=}$
$$\boxed{1.917321395 \quad 13}$$

.0005 $\boxed{y^x}$ 12 $\boxed{=}$
$$\boxed{2.44140625 \quad ^{-40}}$$

Since the answers in standard notation require more space than the calculator display has, the calculator gives each result in scientific notation. The first display represents $1.917321395 \times 10^{13}$, and the second represents $2.44140625 \times 10^{-40}$.

If we evaluate the same two expressions using a graphing calculator, we see that the letter E is used when displaying a number in scientific notation.

Keystrokes   453.46 $\boxed{\wedge}$ 5 $\boxed{\text{ENTER}}$
```
453.46^5
       1.917321395E13
```

.0005 $\boxed{\wedge}$ 12 $\boxed{\text{ENTER}}$
```
.0005^12
       2.44140625E-40
```

Changing from scientific notation to standard notation

We can change a number written in scientific notation to **standard notation.** For example, to write 9.3×10^7 in standard notation, we multiply 9.3 by 10^7.

$$9.3 \times 10^7 = 9.3 \times 10,000,000 \quad \text{10^7 is equal to 1 followed by 7 zeros.}$$
$$= 93,000,000$$

EXAMPLE 5 *Writing numbers in standard notation.*   Write
a. 3.4×10^5 and   **b.** 2.1×10^{-4} in standard notation.

Solution

a. $3.4 \times 10^5 = 3.4 \times 100,000$
$$= 340,000$$

b. $2.1 \times 10^{-4} = 2.1 \times \dfrac{1}{10^4}$
$$= 2.1 \times \dfrac{1}{10,000}$$
$$= 2.1 \times 0.0001$$
$$= 0.00021$$

Self Check

Write in standard notation:

a. 4.76×10^5

b. 9.8×10^{-3}

Answers: **a.** 476,000,
b. 0.0098

The following numbers are written in both scientific and standard notation. In each case, the exponent gives the number of places that the decimal point moves, and the sign of the exponent indicates the direction that it moves.

$$5.32 \times 10^5 = 5\,3\,2\,0\,0\,0. \qquad \text{5 places to the right.}$$
$$8.95 \times 10^{-4} = 0.0\,0\,0\,8\,9\,5 \qquad \text{4 places to the left.}$$
$$9.77 \times 10^0 = 9.77 \qquad \text{No movement of the decimal point.}$$

Using scientific notation to simplify computations

Another advantage of scientific notation becomes apparent when we evaluate products or quotients that contain very large or very small numbers.

EXAMPLE 6   *Stars.*   Except for the sun, the nearest star visible to the naked eye from most parts of the United States is Sirius. Light from Sirius reaches Earth in about 70,000 hours. If light travels at approximately 670,000,000 mph, how far from Earth is Sirius?

Solution

We are given the rate at which light travels (670,000,000 mph) and the time it takes the light to travel from Sirius to Earth (70,000 hr). We can find the distance the light travels using the formula $d = rt$.

$$d = rt$$

$d = 670{,}000{,}000(70{,}000)$ Substitute 670,000,000 for r and 70,000 for t.

$\quad = (6.7 \times 10^8)(7.0 \times 10^4)$ Write each number in scientific notation.

$\quad = (6.7 \cdot 7.0) \times (10^8 \cdot 10^4)$ Group the numbers together and the powers of 10 together.

$\quad = (6.7 \cdot 7.0) \times 10^{8+4}$ Keep the base and add the exponents.

$\quad = 46.9 \times 10^{12}$ Do the multiplication. Do the addition.

We note that 46.9 is not between 0 and 1, so 46.9×10^{12} is not written in scientific notation. To answer in scientific notation, we proceed as follows.

$\quad = 4.69 \times 10^1 \times 10^{12}$ Write 46.9 in scientific notation as 4.69×10^1.

$\quad = 4.69 \times 10^{13}$ Keep the base of 10 and add the exponents.

Sirius is approximately 4.69×10^{13} or 46,900,000,000,000 miles from Earth.   ■

EXAMPLE 7   *Atoms.*   Scientific notation is used in chemistry. As an example, we can approximate the weight (in grams) of one atom of the heaviest naturally occurring element, uranium, by evaluating the following expression.

$$\frac{2.4 \times 10^2}{6.0 \times 10^{23}}$$

Solution

$\dfrac{2.4 \times 10^2}{6.0 \times 10^{23}} = \dfrac{2.4}{6.0} \times \dfrac{10^2}{10^{23}}$ Divide the numbers and the powers of 10 separately.

$\quad = \dfrac{2.4}{6.0} \times 10^{2-23}$ For the powers of 10, keep the base and subtract the exponents.

$\quad = 0.4 \times 10^{-21}$ Do the division. Then subtract the exponents:

$\quad = 4.0 \times 10^{-1} \times 10^{-21}$ Write 0.4 in scientific notation as 4.0×10^{-1}.

$\quad = 4.0 \times 10^{-22}$ Keep the base and add the exponents.

One atom of uranium weighs 4.0×10^{-22} gram. Written in standard notation, this is 0.00000000000000000000004 g.

Self Check

Find the approximate weight (in grams) of one atom of gold by evaluating

$$\frac{1.98 \times 10^2}{6.0 \times 10^{23}}$$

Answer: 3.3×10^{-22} g   ■

Accent on Technology: **Entering numbers in scientific notation**

We can evaluate the expression from Example 7 by entering the numbers written in scientific notation, using | EE | the key on a scientific calculator.

Keystrokes   2.4 | EE | 2 | ÷ | 6 | EE | 23 | = |

$$\boxed{\qquad\qquad\qquad\qquad 4. ^{-22}}$$

The result shown in the display means 4.0×10^{-23}.
If we use a graphing calculator, the keystrokes are similar.

Keystrokes   2.4 | 2nd | | EE | 2 | ÷ | 6 | 2nd | | EE | 23 | ENTER |

$$\boxed{\begin{array}{l} \mathtt{2.4\ E2/6\ E23} \\ \qquad\qquad \mathtt{4\ E-22} \end{array}}$$

STUDY SET Section 4.3

VOCABULARY *Fill in the blanks.*

1. A number is written in ___scientific___ notation when it is written as the product of a number between 1 (including 1) and 10 and an integer power of 10.

2. The number 125,000 is written in ___standard___ notation.

CONCEPTS *Fill in the blanks.*

3. $2.5 \times 10^2 =$ ___250___

4. $2.5 \times 10^{-2} =$ ___0.025___

5. $2.5 \times 10^{-5} =$ ___0.000025___

6. $2.5 \times 10^5 =$ ___250,000___

7. $387,000 = 3.87 \times 10^5$

8. $38.7 = 3.87 \times 10^1$

9. $0.00387 = 3.87 \times 10^{-3}$

10. $0.000387 = 3.87 \times 10^{-4}$

11. When we multiply a decimal by 10^5, the decimal point moves 5 places to the ___right___.

12. When we multiply a decimal by 10^{-7}, the decimal point moves 7 places to the ___left___.

13. Dividing a decimal by 10^4 is equivalent to multiplying it by 10^{-4}.

14. Multiplying a decimal by 10^0 does not move the decimal point, because $10^0 = 1$.

15. When a real number greater than 1 is written in scientific notation, the exponent on 10 is a ___positive___ number.

16. When a real number between 0 and 1 is written in scientific notation, the exponent on 10 is a ___negative___ number.

NOTATION *Complete each solution.*

17. Write 63.7×10^5 in scientific notation.
$$63.7 \times 10^5 = 6.37 \times 10^1 \times 10^5$$
$$= 6.37 \times 10^{1+5}$$
$$= 6.37 \times 10^6$$

18. Simplify $\dfrac{64,000}{0.00004}$.
$$\frac{64,000}{0.00004} = \frac{6.4 \times 10^4}{4 \times 10^{-5}}$$
$$= \frac{6.4}{4} \times \frac{10^4}{10^{-5}}$$
$$= 1.6 \times 10^{4-(-5)}$$
$$= 1.6 \times 10^9$$

PRACTICE *Write each number in scientific notation.*

19. 23,000 2.3×10^4

20. 4,750 4.75×10^3

21. 1,700,000 1.7×10^6

22. 290,000 2.9×10^5

23. 0.062 6.2×10^{-2}

24. 0.00073 7.3×10^{-4}

25. 0.0000051 5.1×10^{-6}

26. 0.04 4×10^{-2}

27. 42.5×10^2 4.25×10^3

28. 0.3×10^3 3×10^2

29. 0.25×10^{-2}
2.5×10^{-3}

30. 25.2×10^{-3}
2.52×10^{-2}

Write each number in standard notation.

31. 2.3×10^2 230

32. 3.75×10^4 37,500

33. 8.12×10^5 812,000

34. 1.2×10^3 1,200

35. 1.15×10^{-3} 0.00115

36. 4.9×10^{-2} 0.049

37. 9.76×10^{-4}
0.000976

38. 7.63×10^{-5}
0.0000763

39. 25×10^6 25,000,000

40. 0.07×10^3 70

41. 0.51×10^{-3} 0.00051

42. 617×10^{-2} 6.17

43. ASTRONOMY   The distance from Earth to Alpha Centauri (the nearest star outside our solar system) is about 25,700,000,000,000 miles. Express this number in scientific notation. 2.57×10^{13} mi

44. SPEED OF SOUND   The speed of sound in air is 33,100 centimeters per second. Express this number in scientific notation. 3.31×10^4 cm/sec

45. GEOGRAPHY   The largest ocean in the world is the Pacific Ocean, which covers 6.38×10^7 square miles. Express this number in standard notation.
63,800,000 mi²

46. ATOMS   The number of atoms in 1 gram of iron is approximately 1.08×10^{22}. Express this number in standard notation.   10,800,000,000,000,000,000,000

47. LENGTH OF A METER   One meter is approximately 0.00622 mile. Use scientific notation to express this number. 6.22×10^{-3} mi

48. ANGSTROM   One angstrom is 1.0×10^{-7} millimeter. Express this number in standard notation.
0.0000001 mm

Use scientific notation and the rules for exponents to simplify each expression. Give all answers in standard notation.

49. $(3.4 \times 10^2)(2.1 \times 10^3)$ 714,000

50. $(4.1 \times 10^{-3})(3.4 \times 10^4)$ 139.4

51. $\dfrac{9.3 \times 10^2}{3.1 \times 10^{-2}}$ 30,000

52. $\dfrac{7.2 \times 10^6}{1.2 \times 10^8}$ 0.06

53. $\dfrac{96,000}{(12,000)(0.00004)}$ 200,000

54. $\dfrac{(0.48)(14,400,000)}{96,000,000}$ 0.072

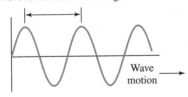 *Evaluate each expression.*

55. $(456.4)^6$ $9.038030748 \times 10^{15}$

56. $(0.053)^8$ $6.225969041 \times 10^{-11}$

57. $(0.009)^{-6}$ $1.881676423 \times 10^{12}$

58. 225^{-5} $1.734152992 \times 10^{-12}$

59. $\left(\dfrac{1}{3}\right)^{-55}$ $1.74449211 \times 10^{26}$

60. $\left(\dfrac{8}{5}\right)^{50}$ $1.606938044 \times 10^{10}$

APPLICATIONS

61. WAVELENGTH Transmitters, vacuum tubes, and lights emit energy that can be modeled as a wave, as shown in Illustration 1. Examples of the most common types of electromagnetic waves are given in the table. List the wavelengths in order from shortest to longest.
g, x, u, v, i, m, r

This distance between the two crests of the wave is called the wavelength.

Wave motion →

ILLUSTRATION 1

Type	Use	Wavelength (m)
visible light	lighting	9.3×10^{-6}
infrared	photography	3.7×10^{-5}
x-ray	medical	2.3×10^{-11}
radio wave	communication	3.0×10^2
gamma ray	treating cancer	8.9×10^{-14}
microwave	cooking	1.1×10^{-2}
ultraviolet	sun lamp	6.1×10^{-8}

62. EXPLORATION On July 4, 1997, the Pathfinder, carrying the rover vehicle called Sojourner, landed on Mars to perform a scientific investigation of the planet. The distance from Mars to Earth is approximately

3.5×10^7 miles. Use scientific notation to express this distance in feet. (*Hint:* 5,280 feet = 1 mile.)
1.848×10^{11} ft

63. PROTON The mass of one proton is approximately 1.7×10^{-24} gram. Use scientific notation to express the mass of 1 million protons. 1.7×10^{-18} g

64. SPEED OF SOUND The speed of sound in air is approximately 3.3×10^4 centimeters per second. Use scientific notation to express this speed in kilometers per second. (*Hint:* 100 centimeters = 1 meter and 1,000 meters = 1 kilometer.) 3.3×10^{-1} km/sec

65. LIGHT YEAR One light year is about 5.87×10^{12} miles. Use scientific notation to express this distance in feet. (*Hint:* 5,280 feet = 1 mile.) 3.099363×10^{16} ft

66. OIL RESERVES As of January 1, 1999, Saudi Arabia was believed to have crude oil reserves of about 2.615×10^{11} barrels. A barrel contains 42 gallons of oil. Use scientific notation to express its oil reserves in gallons. 1.0983×10^{13} gal

67. INTEREST EARNED As of December 31, 1998, the Federal Deposit Insurance Corporation (FDIC) reported that the total insured deposits in U.S. banks and savings and loans was approximately 5.09×10^{12} dollars. If this money was invested at a rate of 4% simple annual interest, how much would it earn in one year? (Use scientific notation to express the answer.)
2.036×10^{11} dollars

68. CURRENCY As of March 31, 1999, the U.S. Treasury reported that the number of $20 bills in circulation was approximately 4.35×10^9. What was the total value of the currency? (Use scientific notation to express the answer.) 8.7×10^{10} dollars

69. SIZE OF THE MILITARY The graph in Illustration 2 shows the number of U.S. troops for 1979–1998. Estimate each of the following and express your answers in scientific and standard notation.
a. The number of troops in 1993 1.7×10^6; 1,700,000
b. The smallest and largest numbers of troops during these years
1999: 1.4×10^6, 1,400,000; 1986: 2.05×10^6, 2,050,000

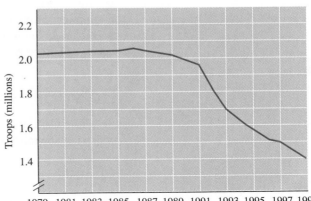

Based on data from the U.S. Department of Defense

ILLUSTRATION 2

70. 🖩   THE NATIONAL DEBT   The graph in Illustration 3 shows the growth of the national debt for the fiscal years 1992–1999.

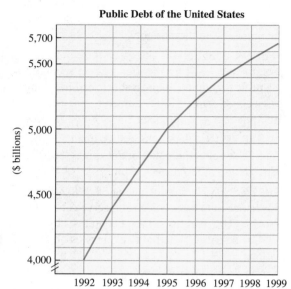

Public Debt of the United States

Based on data from the U.S. Department of the Treasury

ILLUSTRATION 3

a. Use scientific notation to express the debt as of 1994, 1995, and 1997.
   4.7×10^{12} dollars, 5.0×10^{12} dollars, 5.4×10^{12} dollars

b. In 1999, the population of the United States was about 2.75×10^8. Estimate the share of the debt for each man, woman, and child in the United States. Answer in standard notation.   about $20,500

WRITING

71. In what situations would scientific notation be more convenient than standard notation?

72. To multiply a number by a power of 10, we move the decimal point. Which way, and how far? Explain.

73. 2.3×10^{-3} contains a negative sign but represents a positive number. Explain.

74. Is this a true statement? $2.0 \times 10^3 = 2 \times 10^3$. Explain.

REVIEW

75. If $y = -1$, find the value of $-5y^{55}$.   5

76. What is the y-intercept of the graph of $y = -3x - 5$?
   $(0, -5)$

Tell which property of real numbers justifies each statement.

77. $5 + z = z + 5$ commutative property of addition

78. $7(u + 3) = 7u + 7 \cdot 3$ distributive property

Solve each equation.

79. $3(x - 4) - 6 = 0$ 6

80. $8(3x - 5) - 4(2x + 3) = 12$ 4

4.4 *Polynomials*

In this section, you will learn about

- Polynomials • Monomials, binomials, and trinomials
- Degree of a polynomial • Evaluating polynomial functions

INTRODUCTION. In arithmetic, we learned how to add, subtract, multiply, divide, and find powers of numbers. In algebra, we will learn how to perform these operations on *polynomials*. In this section, we will introduce polynomials, classify them into groups, define their degrees, and show how to evaluate them at specific values of their variables.

Polynomials

Recall that a **term** is a number or a product of a number and one or more variables, which may be raised to powers. Examples of terms are

$$3x, \qquad -4y^2, \qquad \frac{1}{2}a^2b^3, \qquad t, \qquad \text{and} \qquad 25$$

The **numerical coefficients,** or simply **coefficients,** of the first four of these terms are 3, -4, $\frac{1}{2}$, and 1, respectively. Because $25 = 25x^0$, 25 is considered to be the numerical coefficient of the term 25.

Polynomials

> A **polynomial** is a term or a sum of terms in which all variables have whole-number exponents.

Here are some examples of polynomials:

$$3x + 2, \qquad 4y^2 - 2y - 3, \qquad -8xy^2, \qquad \text{and} \qquad a^3 + 3a^2b + 3ab^2 + b^3$$

The polynomial $3x + 2$ has two terms, $3x$ and 2, and we say it is a **polynomial in x.** A single number is called a **constant,** and so its last term, 2, is called the **constant term.**

Since $4y^2 - 2y - 3$ can be written as $4y^2 + (-2y) + (-3)$, it is the sum of three terms, $4y^2$, $-2y$, and -3. It is written in **decreasing** or **descending powers** of y, because the powers on y decrease from left to right.

$-8xy^2$ is a polynomial with just one term. We say that it is a **polynomial in x and y.**

The four-term polynomial $a^3 + 3a^2b + 3ab^2 + b^3$ is written in descending powers of a and **ascending powers** of b.

 COMMENT The expression $2x^3 - 3x^{-2} + 5$ is not a polynomial, because the second term contains a variable with an exponent that is not a whole number. Similarly, $y^2 - \frac{7}{y}$ is not a polynomial, because $\frac{7}{y}$ can be written $7y^{-1}$.

EXAMPLE 1 *Identifying polynomials.* Tell whether each expression is a polynomial.

a. $x^2 + 2x + 1$ Yes.

b. $3a^{-1} - 2a - 3$ No. In the first term, the exponent on the variable is not a whole number.

c. $\frac{1}{2}x^3 - 2.3x$ Yes, since it can be written as the sum $\frac{1}{2}x^3 + (-2.3x)$.

d. $\frac{p + 3}{p - 1}$ No. Variables cannot be in the denominator of a fraction.

Self Check

Tell whether each expression is a polynomial:

a. $3x^{-4} + 2x^2 - 3$

b. $7.5p^3 - 4p^2 - 3p + 4$

Answers: **a.** no   **b.** yes

Monomials, binomials, and trinomials

A polynomial with one term is called a **monomial.** A polynomial with two terms is called a **binomial.** A polynomial with three terms is called a **trinomial.** Here are some examples.

Monomials	Binomials	Trinomials
$-6x$	$3u^3 - 4u^2$	$-5t^2 + 4t + 3$
$5x^2y$	$18a^2b + 4ab$	$27x^3 - 6x - 2$
29	$-29z^{17} - 1$	$a^2 + 2ab + b^2$

EXAMPLE 2 *Classifying polynomials.* Classify each polynomial as a monomial, a binomial, or a trinomial.

a. $5.2x^4 + 3.1x$ Since the polynomial has two terms, $5.2x^4$ and $3.1x$, it is a binomial.

b. $7g^4 - 5g^3 - 2$ Since the polynomial has three terms, $7g^4$, $-5g^3$, and -2, it is a trinomial.

c. $-5x^2y^3$ Since the polynomial has one term, it is a monomial.

Self Check

Classify each polynomial as a monomial, a binomial, or a trinomial:

a. $5x$

b. $-5x^2 + 2x - 0.5$

c. $16x^2 - 9y^2$

Answers: **a.** monomial, **b.** trinomial, **c.** binomial

Degree of a polynomial

The monomial $7x^6$ is called a **monomial of sixth degree** or a **monomial of degree 6,** because the variable x occurs as a factor six times. The monomial $3x^3y^4$ is a monomial of seventh degree, because the variables x and y occur as factors a total of seven times. Here are some more examples:

     $2.7a$ is a monomial of degree 1.

     $-2x^3$ is a monomial of degree 3.

     $47x^2y^3$ is a monomial of degree 5.

     8 is a monomial of degree 0, because $8 = 8x^0$.

These examples illustrate the following definition.

Degree of a monomial

> If a represents a nonzero constant, the **degree of the monomial** ax^n is n.
>
> The **degree of a monomial** in several variables is the sum of the exponents on those variables.

COMMENT   Note that the degree of ax^n is not defined when $a = 0$. Since $ax^n = 0$ when $a = 0$, the constant 0 has no defined degree.

Because each term of a polynomial is a monomial, we define the degree of a polynomial by considering the degrees of each of its terms.

Degree of a polynomial

> The **degree of a polynomial** is determined by the term with the largest degree.

Here are some examples:

     $x^2 + 2x$ is a binomial of degree 2, because the degree of its first term is 2 and the degree of its second term is less than 2.

     $d^3 - 3d^2 + 1$ is a trinomial of degree 3, because the degree of its first term is 3 and the degree of each of its other terms is less than 3.

     $25y^{13} - 15y^8z^{10} - 32y^{10}z^8 + 4$ is a polynomial of degree 18, because its second and third terms are of degree 18. Its other terms have degree less than 18.

EXAMPLE 3   *Degree of a polynomial.*   Find the degree of each polynomial:

a. $-4x^3 - 5x^2 + 3x,$ **b.** $1.6w - 1.6,$ and   **c.** $-17a^2b^3 + 12ab^6.$

Solution

a. The trinomial $-4x^3 - 5x^2 + 3x$ has terms of degree 3, 2, and 1. Therefore, its degree is 3.

b. The first term of $1.6w - 1.6$ has degree 1 and the second term has degree 0, so the binomial has degree 1.

c. The degree of the first term of $-17a^2b^3 + 12ab^6$ is 5 and the degree of the second term is 7, so the binomial has degree 7.

Self Check

Find the degree of each polynomial:

a. $15p^3 - 15p^2 - 3p + 4$

b. $-14st^4 + 12s^3t$

Answers: **a.** 3,   **b.** 5   ■

If written in descending powers of the variable, the **leading term** of a polynomial is the term of highest degree. For example, the leading term of $-4x^3 - 5x^2 + 3x$ is $-4x^3$. The coefficient of the leading term (in this case, -4) is called the **leading coefficient.**

Evaluating polynomial functions

Each of the equations below defines a function, because each input x-value determines exactly one output value. Since the right-hand side of each equation is a polynomial, these functions are called **polynomial functions.**

$$f(x) = 6x + 4 \qquad\qquad g(x) = 3x^2 + 4x - 5 \qquad\qquad h(x) = -x^3 + x^2 - 2x + 3$$

This polynomial has two terms. Its degree is 1.

This polynomial has three terms. Its degree is 2.

This polynomial has four terms. Its degree is 3.

To evaluate a polynomial function for a specific value, we replace the variable in the defining equation with the input value. Then we simplify the resulting expression to find the output. For example, suppose we wish to evaluate the polynomial function $f(x) = 6x + 4$ for $x = 1$. Then $f(1)$ (read as "f of 1") represents the value of $f(x) = 6x + 4$ when $x = 1$. We find $f(1)$ as follows.

$$f(x) = 6x + 4 \qquad \text{The given function.}$$
$$f(1) = 6(1) + 4 \qquad \text{Substitute 1 for } x. \text{ The number 1 is the input.}$$
$$= 6 + 4 \qquad \text{Do the multiplication.}$$
$$= 10 \qquad \text{Do the addition. 10 is the output.}$$

Thus, $f(1) = 10$.

EXAMPLE 4 *Evaluating polynomial functions.* Consider the function $g(x) = 3x^2 + 4x - 5$. Find   **a.** $g(0)$ and   **b.** $g(-2)$.

Solution

a. $g(x) = 3x^2 + 4x - 5$ The given function.

$g(0) = 3(0)^2 + 4(0) - 5$ To find $g(0)$, substitute 0 for x.

$= 3(0) + 4(0) - 5$ Evaluate the power.

$= 0 + 0 - 5$ Do the multiplications.

$g(0) = -5$

b. $g(x) = 3x^2 + 4x - 5$ The given function.

$g(-2) = 3(-2)^2 + 4(-2) - 5$ To find $g(-2)$, substitute -2 for x.

$= 3(4) + 4(-2) - 5$ Evaluate the power.

$= 12 + (-8) - 5$ Do the multiplications.

$g(-2) = -1$

Self Check

Consider the function

$$h(x) = -x^3 + x - 2x + 3$$

Find

a. $h(0)$

b. $h(-3)$

Answers: **a.** 3,   **b.** 33

EXAMPLE 5 *Supermarket display.* The polynomial function

$$f(c) = \frac{1}{3}c^3 + \frac{1}{2}c^2 + \frac{1}{6}c$$

gives the number of cans used in a display shaped like a square pyramid, having a square base formed by c cans per side. Find the number of cans of soup used in the display shown in Figure 4-2.

Solution

Since each side of the square base of the display is formed by 4 cans, $c = 4$. We can find the number of cans used in the display by finding $f(4)$.

FIGURE 4-2

$$f(c) = \frac{1}{3}c^3 + \frac{1}{2}c^2 + \frac{1}{6}c \qquad \text{The given function.}$$

$$f(4) = \frac{1}{3}(4)^3 + \frac{1}{2}(4)^2 + \frac{1}{6}(4) \qquad \text{Substitute 4 for } c.$$

$$= \frac{1}{3}(64) + \frac{1}{2}(16) + \frac{1}{6}(4) \qquad \text{Find the powers.}$$

$$= \frac{64}{3} + 8 + \frac{2}{3} \qquad \text{Do the multiplication, and then simplify: } \frac{4}{6} = \frac{2}{3}.$$

$$= \frac{66}{3} + 8 \qquad \text{Add the fractions.}$$

$$= 22 + 8$$

$$= 30$$

30 cans of soup were used in the display. ■

STUDY SET Section 4.4 🌐www

VOCABULARY *Fill in the blanks.*

1. A ___polynomial___ is a term or a sum of terms in which all variables have whole-number exponents.

2. The numerical ___coefficient___ of the term $-25x^2y^3$ is -25.

3. The degree of a polynomial is the same as the degree of its ___term___ with the largest degree.

4. A ___monomial___ is a polynomial with one term. A ___binomial___ is a polynomial with two terms.

5. The ___degree___ of the monomial $3x^7$ is 7.

6. For the polynomial $6x^2 + 3x - 1$, the ___leading___ term is $6x^2$, and the leading ___coefficient___ is 6. The ___constant___ term is -1.

7. $-x^3 - 6x^2 + 9x - 2$ is a polynomial ___in___ x and is written in ___decreasing or descending___ powers of x.

8. A ___trinomial___ is a polynomial with three terms.

9. The notation $f(x)$ is read as f ___of___ x.

10. $f(2)$ represents the ___value___ of a function when $x = 2$.

CONCEPTS *Tell whether each expression is a polynomial.*

11. $x^3 - 5x^2 - 2$ yes

12. $x^{-4} - 5x$ no

13. $\dfrac{1}{2x} + 3$ no

14. $x^3 - 1$ yes

15. $x^2 - y^2$ yes

16. $a^4 + a^3 + a^2 + a$ yes

Classify each polynomial as a monomial, a binomial, a trinomial, or none of these.

17. $3x + 7$ binomial

18. $3y - 5$ binomial

19. $y^2 + 4y + 3$ trinomial

20. $3xy$ monomial

21. $3z^2$ monomial

22. $3x^4 - 2x^3 + 3x - 1$ none of these

23. $t - 32$ binomial

24. $9x^2y^3z^4$ monomial

25. $s^2 - 23s + 31$ trinomial

26. $2x^3 - 5x^2 + 6x - 3$ none of these

27. $3x^5 - x^4 - 3x^3 + 7$ none of these

28. x^3 monomial

29. $2a^2 - 3ab + b^2$ trinomial

30. $a^3 - b^3$ binomial

Find the degree of each polynomial.

31. $3x^4$ 4th

32. $3x^5$ 5th

33. $-2x^2 + 3x + 1$ 2nd

34. $-5x^4 + 3x^2 - 3x$ 4th

35. $3x - 5$ 1st

36. $y^3 + 4y^2$ 3rd

37. $-5r^2s^2 - r^3s + 3$ 4th

38. $4r^2s^3 - 5r^2s^8$ 10th

39. $x^{12} + 3x^2y^3$ 12th

40. $17ab^5 - 12a^3b$ 6th

41. 38 0th

42. -24 0th

NOTATION *Complete each solution.*

43. If $f(x) = -2x^2 + 3x - 1$, find $f(2)$.

$$f(2) = -2(\ 2\ )^2 + 3(\ 2\ ) - 1$$
$$= -2(\ 4\ ) + 6 - 1$$
$$= -8 + 6 - 1$$
$$= -2 - 1$$
$$= -3$$

44. If $f(x) = -2x^2 + 3x - 1$, find $f(-2)$.

$$f(-2) = -2(\,-2\,)^2 + 3(\,-2\,) - 1$$
$$= -2(\,4\,) + (\,-2\,) - 1$$
$$= -8 + (-6) - 1$$
$$= -14 - 1$$
$$= -15$$

45. Explain why $f(x) = x^3 + 2x^2 - 3$ is called a polynomial function.   because $x^3 + 2x^2 - 3$ is a polynomial

46. a. Write $x - 9 + 3x^2$ in descending powers of x.
$3x^2 + x - 9$

   b. Write $-2xy + y^2 + x^2$ in descending powers of x.
$x^2 - 2xy + y^2$

PRACTICE   *Let $f(x) = 5x - 3$. Find each value.*

47. $f(2)$ 7

48. $f(0)$ -3

49. $f(-1)$ -8

50. $f(-2)$ -13

51. $f\left(\dfrac{1}{5}\right)$ -2

52. $f\left(\dfrac{4}{5}\right)$ 1

53. $f(-0.9)$ -7.5

54. $f(-1.2)$ -9

Let $g(x) = -x^2 - 4$. Find each value.

55. $g(0)$ -4

56. $g(1)$ -5

57. $g(-1)$ -5

58. $g(-2)$ -8

Let $h(x) = x^2 - 4$. Find each value.

59. $g(1.3)$ -5.69

60. $g(2.4)$ -9.76

61. $g(-13.6)$ -188.96

62. $g(-25.3)$ -644.09

Let $h(x) = x^3 - 2x + 3$. Find each value.

63. $h(0)$ 3

64. $h(3)$ 24

65. $h(-2)$ -1

66. $h(-1)$ 4

Let $h(x) = x^3 - 2x + 3$. Find each value.

67. $h(0.9)$ 1.929

68. $h(0.4)$ 2.264

69. $h(-8.1)$ -512.241

70. $h(-7.7)$ -438.133

Let $f(x) = -x^4 - x^3 + x^2 + x - 1$. Find each value.

71. $f(1)$ -1

72. $f(-1)$ -1

73. $f(-2)$ -7

74. $f(2)$ -19

APPLICATIONS   *In Exercises 75–82, use a calculator to help solve each problem.*

75. PACKAGING   To make boxes, a manufacturer cuts equal-sized squares from each corner of a 10 in. × 12 in. piece of cardboard, and then folds up the sides.

(See Illustration 1.) The polynomial function $f(x) = 4x^3 - 44x^2 + 120x$ gives the volume (in cubic inches) of the resulting box when a square with sides x inches long is cut from each corner. Find the volume of a box if 3-inch squares are cut out.   72 in.^{3}

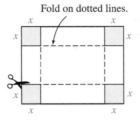

Fold on dotted lines.

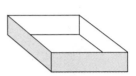

ILLUSTRATION 1

76. MAXIMIZING REVENUE   The revenue (in dollars) that a manufacturer of office desks receives is given by the polynomial function

$$f(d) = -0.08d^2 + 100d$$

where d is the number of desks manufactured.

   a. Find the total revenue if 625 desks are manufactured.   \$31,250

   b. Does increasing the number of desks being manufactured to 650 increase the revenue?   no

77. WATER BALLOONS   Some college students launched water balloons from the balcony of their dormitory on unsuspecting sunbathers on the college quad. The height in feet of the balloons at a time t seconds after being launched is given by the polynomial function

$$f(t) = -16t^2 + 12t + 20$$

What was the height of the balloons 0.5 second and 1.5 seconds after being launched?   22 ft, 2 ft

78. STOPPING DISTANCE   The number of feet that a car travels before stopping depends on the driver's reaction time and the braking distance, as shown in Illustration 2. For one driver, the stopping distance is given by the polynomial function

$$f(v) = 0.04v^2 + 0.9v$$

where v is the velocity of the car. Find the stopping distance when the driver is traveling at 30 mph.   63 ft

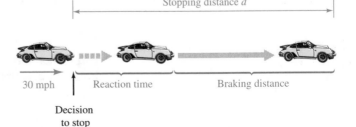

ILLUSTRATION 2

79. SUSPENSION BRIDGE   See Illustration 3. The function

$$f(s) = 400 + 0.0066667s^2 - 0.0000001s^4$$

approximates the length of the cable between the two vertical towers of a suspension bridge, where s is the sag in the cable. Estimate the length of the cable if the sag is 24.6 feet.   about 404 ft

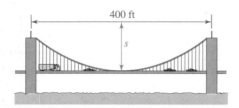

ILLUSTRATION 3

80. PRODUCE DEPARTMENT   Suppose a grocer is going to set up a pyramid-shaped display of cantaloupes like that shown in Figure 4-2 in Example 5. If each side of the square base of the display is made of six cantaloupes, how many will be used in the display?   91

81. DOLPHINS   At a marine park, three trained dolphins jump in unison over an arching stream of water whose path can be described by the polynomial function

$$f(x) = -0.05x^2 + 2x$$

See Illustration 4. Given the takeoff points for each dolphin, how high must each dolphin jump to clear the stream of water?   18.75 ft, 20 ft, 15 ft

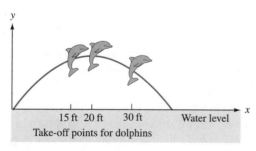

ILLUSTRATION 4

82. TUNNEL   The arch at the entrance to a tunnel is described by the polynomial function

$$f(x) = -0.25x^2 + 23$$

See Illustration 5. What is the height of the arch at the edge of the pavement?   14 ft

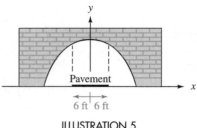

ILLUSTRATION 5

WRITING

83. Describe how to determine the degree of a polynomial.

84. List some words that contain the prefixes *mono, bi,* or *tri.*

REVIEW   *Solve each inequality and graph the solution set.*

85. $-4(3y + 2) \le 28$
$y \ge -3$

86. $-5 < 3t + 4 \le 13$
$-3 < t \le 3$

Write each expression without using parentheses or negative exponents.

87. $(x^2x^4)^3$ x^{18} **88.** $(a^2)^3(a^3)^2$ a^{12}

89. $\left(\dfrac{y^2y^5}{y^4}\right)^3$ y^9 **90.** $\left(\dfrac{2t^3}{t}\right)^{-4}$ $\dfrac{1}{16t^8}$

4.5   *Adding and Subtracting Polynomials*

In this section, you will learn about

- Adding monomials • Subtracting monomials • Adding polynomials
- Subtracting polynomials • Adding and subtracting multiples of polynomials
- An application of adding polynomials

INTRODUCTION. In Figure 4-3(a), the heights of the Seattle Space Needle and the Eiffel Tower in Paris are given. Using rules from arithmetic, we can find the difference in the heights of the towers by subtracting two numbers.

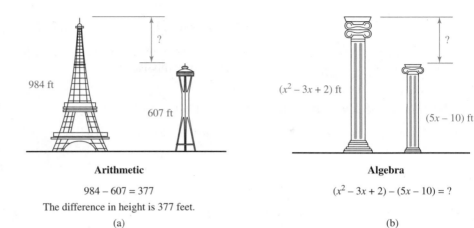

Arithmetic	Algebra
$984 - 607 = 377$	$(x^2 - 3x + 2) - (5x - 10) = ?$
The difference in height is 377 feet.	
(a)	(b)

FIGURE 4-3

In Figure 4-3(b), the heights of two types of classical Greek columns are expressed using *polynomials*. To find the difference in their heights, we must subtract the polynomials. In this section, we will discuss the algebraic rules that are used to do this. Since any subtraction can be written in terms of addition, we will consider the procedures used to add polynomials first. We begin with monomials, which are polynomials having just one term.

Adding monomials

Recall that like terms have the same variables with the same exponents:

Like terms	Unlike terms
$-7x$ and $15x$	$-7x$ and $15a$
$4y^3$ and $16y^3$	$4y^3$ and $16y^2$
$\frac{1}{2}xy^2$ and $-\frac{1}{3}xy^2$	$\frac{1}{2}xy^2$ and $-\frac{1}{3}x^2y$

Also recall that to combine like terms, we combine their coefficients and keep the same variables with the same exponents. For example,

$$4y + 5y = (4 + 5)y \qquad \text{and} \qquad 8x^2 - x^2 = (8 - 1)x^2$$
$$= 9y \qquad\qquad\qquad = 7x^2$$

Likewise,

$$3a + 4b - 6a + 3b = -3a + 7b \qquad \text{and} \qquad -4cd^3 + 9cd^3 = 5cd^3$$

These examples suggest that to add like monomials, we simply combine like terms.

EXAMPLE 1 *Adding monomials.* Do the following additions.

a. $4x^4 + 81x^4 = 85x^4$

b. $-8x^2y^2 + 6x^2y^2 + x^2y^2 = -2x^2y^2 + x^2y^2$ Work from left to right. Combine like terms.

$$= -x^2y^2 \qquad\qquad \text{Combine like terms.}$$

c. $32c^2 + 10c + 4c^2 = 32c^2 + 4c^2 + 10c$ Write the like terms together.

$$= 36c^2 + 10c \qquad\qquad \text{Combine like terms.}$$

Self Check

Do the following additions:

a. $27x^6 + 8x^6$

b. $-12pq^2 + 5pq^2 + 8pq^2$

c. $6a^3 + 15a + a^3$

Answers: **a.** $35x^6$,   **b.** pq^2,   **c.** $7a^3 + 15a$

 COMMENT When performing operations on polynomials, it is standard practice to write the terms of the solution in decreasing (or descending) powers of one variable. For instance, in Example 1, part c, the solution was written as $36c^2 + 10c$ instead of as $10c + 36c^2$.

Subtracting monomials

To subtract one monomial from another, we add the opposite of the monomial that is to be subtracted. In symbols, $x - y = x + (-y)$.

EXAMPLE 2   *Subtracting monomials.*   Find each difference.

a. $8x^2 - 3x^2 = 8x^2 + (-3x^2)$ Add the opposite of $3x^2$, which is $-3x^2$.

$\qquad\qquad = 5x^2$ Combine like terms.

b. $6xy - 9xy = 6xy + (-9xy)$

$\qquad\qquad = -3xy$

c. $-3r - 5 - 4r = -3r + (-5) + (-4r)$ Add the opposite of 5 and $4r$.

$\qquad\qquad = -3r + (-4r) + (-5)$ Group like terms together.

$\qquad\qquad = -7r - 5$ Combine like terms. Write the addition of -5 as a subtraction of 5.

Self Check

Find each difference:

a. $12m^3 - 7m^3$

b. $-4pq - 27p - 8pq$

Answers: **a.** $5m^3$,
b. $-12pq - 27p$ ■

Adding polynomials

Because of the distributive property, we can remove parentheses enclosing several terms when the sign preceding the parentheses is a + sign. We simply drop the parentheses.

$+(3x^2 + 3x - 2) = +1(3x^2 + 3x - 2)$

$\qquad\qquad = 1(3x^2) + 1(3x) + 1(-2)$ Distribute the multiplication by 1.

$\qquad\qquad = 3x^2 + 3x + (-2)$

$\qquad\qquad = 3x^2 + 3x - 2$

We can add polynomials by removing parentheses, if necessary, and then combining any like terms that are contained within the polynomials.

EXAMPLE 3   *Adding polynomials.*
Add $(3x^2 - 3x + 2) + (2x^2 + 7x - 4)$.

Solution

$(3x^2 - 3x + 2) + (2x^2 + 7x - 4)$

$\qquad = 3x^2 - 3x + 2 + 2x^2 + 7x - 4$ Drop the parentheses.

$\qquad = 3x^2 + 2x^2 - 3x + 7x + 2 - 4$ Write like terms together.

$\qquad = 5x^2 + 4x - 2$ Combine like terms.

Self Check

Add
$(2a^2 - a + 4) + (5a^2 + 6a - 5)$.

Answer: $7a^2 + 5a - 1$ ■

Problems such as Example 3 are often written with like terms aligned vertically. We can then add column by column.

$$+\begin{array}{r} 3x^2 - 3x + 2 \\ 2x^2 + 7x - 4 \\ \hline 5x^2 + 4x - 2 \end{array}$$

EXAMPLE 4   *Adding polynomials vertically.*   Add $4x^2 - 3$ and $3x^2 - 8x + 8$.

Solution

Since the first polynomial does not have an x-term, we leave a space so that the constant terms can be aligned.

$$+\begin{array}{r} 4x^2 \qquad - 3 \\ 3x^2 - 8x + 8 \\ \hline 7x^2 - 8x + 5 \end{array}$$

Self Check

Add $4q^2 - 7$ and $2q^2 - 8q + 9$ vertically.

Answer: $6q^2 - 8q + 2$ ■

Subtracting polynomials

Because of the distributive property, we can remove parentheses enclosing several terms when the sign preceding the parentheses is a − sign. We simply drop the minus sign and the parentheses, and *change the sign of every term within the parentheses.*

$$-(3x^2 + 3x - 2) = -1(3x^2 + 3x - 2)$$
$$= -1(3x^2) + (-1)(3x) + (-1)(-2)$$
$$= -3x^2 + (-3x) + 2$$
$$= -3x^2 - 3x + 2$$

This suggests that the way to subtract polynomials is to remove parentheses, change the sign of each term of the second polynomial, and combine like terms.

EXAMPLE 5 *Subtracting polynomials.* Find each difference.

a. $(3x - 4) - (5x + 7) = 3x - 4 - 5x - 7$ Change the sign of each term inside $(5x + 7)$.

$$= -2x - 11$$ Combine like terms.

b. $(3x^2 - 4x - 6) - (2x^2 - 6x) = 3x^2 - 4x - 6 - 2x^2 + 6x$

$$= x^2 + 2x - 6$$

c. $(-t^3 - 2t^2 - 1) - (-t^3 - 2t^2 + 1) = -t^3 - 2t^2 - 1 + t^3 + 2t^2 - 1$

$$= -2$$

Self Check
Find the difference:

$$(-2a^2 + 5) - (-5a^2 - 7)$$

Answer: $3a^2 + 12$ ■

To subtract polynomials in vertical form, we add the opposite of the **subtrahend** (the bottom polynomial) to the **minuend** (the top polynomial).

EXAMPLE 6 *Subtracting polynomials vertically.* Subtract $3x^2 - 2x$ from $2x^2 + 4x$.

Solution
Since $3x^2 - 2x$ is to be subtracted from $2x^2 + 4x$, we write $3x^2 - 2x$ below $2x^2 + 4x$ in vertical form. Then we change the signs of the terms of $3x^2 - 2x$ and add:

$$\begin{array}{r} 2x^2 + 4x \\ - \underline{3x^2 - 2x} \end{array} \longrightarrow \begin{array}{r} 2x^2 + 4x \\ + \underline{-3x^2 + 2x} \\ -x^2 + 6x \end{array}$$

Self Check
Subtract $2p^2 + 2p - 8$ from $5p^2 - 6p + 7$.

Answer: $3p^2 - 8p + 15$ ■

EXAMPLE 7 *Combining polynomials.* Subtract $12a - 7$ from the sum of $6a + 5$ and $4a - 10$.

Solution
We will use brackets to show that $(12a - 7)$ is to be subtracted from the *sum* of $(6a + 5)$ and $(4a - 10)$.

$$[(6a + 5) + (4a - 10)] - (12a - 7)$$

Next, we remove the grouping symbols to obtain

$$= 6a + 5 + 4a - 10 - 12a + 7$$ Change the sign of each term in $(12a - 7)$.

$$= -2a + 2$$ Combine like terms.

Self Check
Subtract $-2q^2 - 2q$ from the sum of $q^2 - 6q$ and $3q^2 + q$.

Answer: $6q^2 - 3q$ ■

Adding and subtracting multiples of polynomials

Because of the distributive property, we can remove parentheses enclosing several terms when a monomial precedes the parentheses. We simply multiply every term within the parentheses by that monomial. For example, to add $3(2x + 5)$ and $2(4x - 3)$, we proceed as follows:

$$3(2x + 5) + 2(4x - 3) = 6x + 15 + 8x - 6 \qquad \text{Distribute the multiplication by 3 and by 2.}$$

$$= 6x + 8x + 15 - 6 \qquad 15 + 8x = 8x + 15.$$

$$= 14x + 9 \qquad \text{Combine like terms.}$$

EXAMPLE 8 *Adding and subtracting multiples of polynomials.*
Use the distributive property to remove parentheses and simplify.

a. $3(x^2 + 4x) + 2(x^2 - 4) = 3x^2 + 12x + 2x^2 - 8$

$$= 5x^2 + 12x - 8$$

b. $-8(y^2 - 2y + 3) - 4(2y^2 + y - 6) = -8y^2 + 16y - 24 - 8y^2 - 4y + 24$

$$= -16y^2 + 12y$$

Self Check

Remove parentheses and simplify:

$$2(a^2 - 3a) + 5(a^2 + 2a)$$

Answer: $7a^2 + 4a$ ■

An application of adding polynomials

EXAMPLE 9 **Property values.**   A house purchased for $95,000 is expected to appreciate according to the polynomial function $f(x) = 2{,}500x + 95{,}000$, where y is the value of the house after x years. A second house purchased for $125,000 is expected to appreciate according to the equation $f(x) = 4{,}500x + 125{,}000$. Find one polynomial function that will give the total value of both properties after x years.

Solution

The value of the first house after x years is given by the polynomial $2{,}500x + 95{,}000$. The value of the second house after x years is given by the polynomial $4{,}500x + 125{,}000$. The value of both houses will be the sum of these two polynomials.

$$(2{,}500x + 95{,}000) + (4{,}500x + 125{,}000) = 7{,}000x + 220{,}000$$

The total value y of the properties is given by the polynomial function $f(x) = 7{,}000x + 220{,}000$. ■

STUDY SET Section 4.5

VOCABULARY *Fill in the blanks.*

1. The expression $(x^2 - 3x + 2) + (x^2 - 4x)$ is the sum of two ___polynomials___.

2. ___Like___ terms have the same variables and the same exponents.

3. "To add or subtract like terms" means to combine their ___coefficients___ and keep the same variables with the same exponents.

4. When we write $3x^2 + 4x - 1$ with the constant term first, the x-term second, and the x^2-term last, we say we have written the polynomial in ___increasing or ascending___ powers of x.

CONCEPTS *Fill in the blanks.*

5. To add like monomials, combine like ___terms___.

6. $a - b = a + \underline{\;(-b)\;}$

7. To add two polynomials, combine any ___like___ terms contained in the polynomials.

8. To subtract two polynomials, change the ___sign___ of each term in the second polynomial, and combine like terms.

9. When the sign preceding parentheses is a $-$ sign, we can remove the parentheses by dropping the sign and the parentheses, and ___changing___ the sign of every term within the parentheses.

10. When a monomial precedes parentheses, we can remove the parentheses by ___multiplying___ every term within the parentheses by that monomial.

11. $-(-2x^2 - 3x + 4) = $ $2x^2 + 3x - 4$

12. $-3(-2x^2 - 3x + 4) = $ $6x^2 + 9x - 12$

13. JETS Find the polynomial representing the length of the passenger jet in Illustration 1. $(11x - 12)$ ft

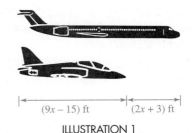

$(9x - 15)$ ft $(2x + 3)$ ft

ILLUSTRATION 1

14. WATER SKIING Find the polynomial representing the distance of the water skier from the boat in Illustration 2. $(9y - 4)$ m

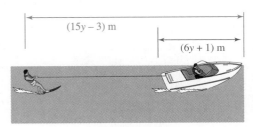

$(15y - 3)$ m

$(6y + 1)$ m

ILLUSTRATION 2

NOTATION *Complete each solution.*

15. $(5x^2 + 3x) - (7x^2 - 2x)$
$= 5x^2 + 3x - 7x^2 + 2x$
$= 5x^2 - 7x^2 + 3x + 2x$
$= -2x^2 + 5x$

16. $4(3x^2 - 2x) - (2x + 4)$
$= 12x^2 - 8x - 2x - 4$
$= 12x^2 - 10x^2 - 4$

PRACTICE *Simplify each expression, if possible.*

17. $4y + 5y$ $9y$

18. $-2x + 3x$ x

19. $8t^2 + 4t^2$ $12t^2$

20. $15x^2 + 10x^2$ $25x^2$

21. $-32u^3 - 16u^3$ $-48u^3$

22. $-25x^3 - 7x^3$ $-32x^3$

23. $1.8x - 1.9x$ $-0.1x$

24. $1.7y - 2.2y$ $-0.5y$

25. $\frac{1}{2}st + \frac{3}{2}st$ $2st$

26. $\frac{2}{5}at + \frac{1}{5}at$ $\frac{3}{5}at$

27. $3r - 4r + 7r$ $6r$

28. $-2b + 7b - 3b$ $2b$

29. $-4ab + 4ab - ab$
$-ab$

30. $xy - 4xy - 2xy$
$-5xy$

31. $(3x)^2 - 4x^2 + 10x^2$
$15x^2$

32. $(2x)^4 - (3x^2)^2$
$7x^4$

Do the operations.

33. $(3x + 7) + (4x - 3)$ $7x + 4$

34. $(2y - 3) + (4y + 7)$ $6y + 4$

35. $(4a + 3) - (2a - 4)$ $2a + 7$

36. $(5b - 7) - (3b - 5)$ $2b - 2$

37. $(2x + 3y) + (5x - 10y)$ $7x - 7y$

38. $(5x - 8y) - (-2x + 5y)$ $7x - 13y$

39. $(-8x - 3y) - (-11x + y)$ $3x - 4y$

40. $(-4a + b) + (5a - b)$ a

41. $(3x^2 - 3x - 2) + (3x^2 + 4x - 3)$ $6x^2 + x - 5$

42. $(3a^2 - 2a + 4) - (a^2 - 3a + 7)$ $2a^2 + a - 3$

43. $(2b^2 + 3b - 5) - (2b^2 - 4b - 9)$ $7b + 4$

44. $(4c^2 + 3c - 2) + (3c^2 + 4c + 2)$ $7c^2 + 7c$

45. $(2x^2 - 3x + 1) - (4x^2 - 3x + 2) + (2x^2 + 3x + 2)$
$3x + 1$

46. $(-3z^2 - 4z + 7) + (2z^2 + 2z - 1) - (2z^2 - 3z + 7)$
$-3z^2 + z - 1$

47. 🖩 $(4.52x^2 + 1.13x - 0.89) + (9.02x^2 - 7.68x + 7.04)$
$13.54x^2 - 6.55x + 6.15$

48. 🖩 $(0.891a^4 - 0.442a^2 + 0.121a) - (-0.160a^4 + 0.249a^2 + 0.789a)$
$1.051a^4 - 0.691a^2 - 0.668a$

Add the polynomials.

49. $\begin{aligned}&3x^2 + 4x + 5\\+&\underline{2x^2 - 3x + 6}\\&5x^2 + x + 11\end{aligned}$

50. $\begin{aligned}&2x^3 + 2x^2 - 3x + 5\\+&\underline{3x^3 - 4x^2 - x - 7}\\&5x^3 - 2x^2 - 4x - 2\end{aligned}$

51. $\begin{aligned}&2x^3 - 3x^2 + 4x - 7\\+&\underline{-9x^3 - 4x^2 - 5x + 6}\\&-7x^3 - 7x^2 - x - 1\end{aligned}$

52. $\begin{aligned}&-3x^3 + 4x^2 - 4x + 9\\+&\underline{2x^3 \qquad\quad + 9x - 3}\\&-x^3 + 4x^2 + 5x + 6\end{aligned}$

53. $\begin{aligned}&-3x^2 + 4x + 25\\+&\underline{5x^2 \qquad\; - 12}\\&2x^2 + 4x + 13\end{aligned}$

54. $\begin{aligned}&-6x^3 - 4x^2 + 7\\+&\underline{-7x^3 + 9x^2}\\&-13x^3 + 5x^2 + 7\end{aligned}$

Find each difference.

55. $\begin{aligned}&\;\;3x^2 + 4x - 5\\-&\underline{-2x^2 - 2x + 3}\\&\;\;5x^2 + 6x - 8\end{aligned}$

56. $\begin{array}{r} 3y^2 - 4y + 7 \\ -\underline{6y^2 - 6y - 13} \\ -3y^2 + 2y + 20 \end{array}$

57. $\begin{array}{r} 4x^3 + 4x^2 - 3x + 10 \\ -\underline{5x^3 - 2x^2 - 4x - 4} \\ -x^3 + 6x^2 + x + 14 \end{array}$

58. $\begin{array}{r} 3x^3 + 4x^2 + 7x + 12 \\ -\underline{-4x^3 + 6x^2 + 9x - 3} \\ 7x^3 - 2x^2 - 2x + 15 \end{array}$

59. $\begin{array}{r} -2x^2y^2 \quad\quad + 12y^2 \\ -\underline{10x^2y^2 + 9xy - 24y^2} \\ -12x^2y^2 - 9xy + 36y^2 \end{array}$

60. $\begin{array}{r} 25x^3 \quad\quad + 31xz^2 \\ -\underline{12x^3 + 27x^2z - 17xz^2} \\ 13x^3 - 27x^2z + 48xz^2 \end{array}$

61. Find the difference when $t^3 - 2t^2 + 2$ is subtracted from the sum of $3t^3 + t^2$ and $-t^3 + 6t - 3$.
$t^3 + 3t^2 + 6t - 5$

62. Find the difference when $-3z^3 - 4z + 7$ is subtracted from the sum of $2z^2 + 3z - 7$ and $-4z^3 - 2z - 3$.
$-z^3 + 2z^2 + 5z - 17$

63. Find the sum when $3x^2 + 4x - 7$ is added to the sum of $-2x^2 - 7x + 1$ and $-4x^2 + 8x - 1$.
$-3x^2 + 5x - 7$

64. Find the difference when $32x^2 - 17x + 45$ is subtracted from the sum of $23x^2 - 12x - 7$ and $-11x^2 + 12x + 7$. $-20x^2 + 17x - 45$

Simplify each expression.

65. $2(x + 3) + 4(x - 2)$ $6x - 2$

66. $3(y - 4) - 5(y + 3)$ $-2y - 27$

67. $-2(x^2 + 7x - 1) - 3(x^2 - 2x + 2)$ $-5x^2 - 8x - 4$

68. $-5(y^2 - 2y - 6) + 6(2y^2 + 2y - 5)$ $7y^2 + 22y$

69. $2(2y^2 - 2y + 2) - 4(3y^2 - 4y - 1) + 4(y^2 - y - 1)$
$-4y^2 + 8y + 4$

70. $-4(z^2 - 5z) - 5(4z^2 - 1) + 6(2z - 3)$
$-24z^2 + 32z - 13$

71. $2(ab^2 - b) - 3(a + 2ab) + (b - a + a^2b)$
$a^2b + 2ab^2 - 6ab - 4a - b$

72. $3(xy + y) - 2(x - 4 + y) + 2(y^3 + y^2)$
$2y^3 + 2y^2 + 3xy - 2x + y + 8$

Find the polynomial that represents the perimeter of each figure.

73. $(3x^2 + 6x - 2)$ yd

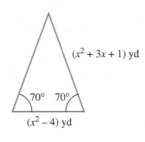

$(x^2 + 3x + 1)$ yd

$70°$ $70°$

$(x^2 - 4)$ yd

74.

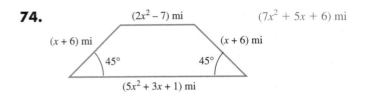

$(2x^2 - 7)$ mi $(7x^2 + 5x + 6)$ mi

$(x + 6)$ mi $(x + 6)$ mi

$45°$ $45°$

$(5x^2 + 3x + 1)$ mi

APPLICATIONS

75. GREEK ARCHITECTURE   Find the difference in the heights of the columns shown in Figure 4-3 at the beginning of this section. $(x^2 - 8x + 12)$ ft

76. CLASSICAL GREEK COLUMNS   If the columns shown in Figure 4-3(b) at the beginning of this section were stacked one atop the other, to what height would they reach? $(x^2 + 2x - 8)$ ft

77. AUTO MECHANICS   Find the polynomial representing the length of the fan belt shown in Illustration 3. The dimensions are in inches. Your answer will involve π. $(3x^2 + 11x + 4.5\pi)$ in.

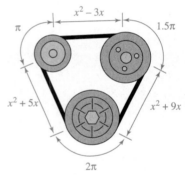

$x^2 - 3x$

π 1.5π

$x^2 + 5x$ $x^2 + 9x$

2π

ILLUSTRATION 3

78. READING BLUEPRINTS
  a. What is the difference in the length and width of the one-bedroom apartment shown in Illustration 4?
  $(6x + 5)$ ft
  b. Find the perimeter of the apartment. $(4x^2 + 26)$ ft

In Exercises 79–82, consider the following information: If a house is purchased for $105,000 and is expected to appreciate $900 per year, its value y after x years is given by the polynomial function $f(x) = 900x + 105,000$.

79. VALUE OF A HOUSE   Find the expected value of the house in 10 years. $114,000

80. VALUE OF A HOUSE   A second house is purchased for $120,000 and is expected to appreciate $1,000 per year.
  a. Find a polynomial function that will give the value y of the house in x years. $f(x) = 1,000x + 120,000$
  b. Find the value of this second house after 12 years.
  $132,000

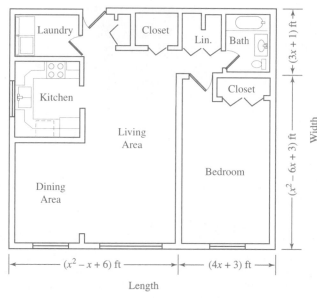

$\leftarrow (x^2 - x + 6)\ \text{ft} \rightarrow$ $\leftarrow (4x + 3)\ \text{ft} \rightarrow$

Length

ILLUSTRATION 4

81. VALUE OF TWO HOUSES   Find one polynomial function that will give the combined value y of both houses after x years. $f(x) = 1,900x + 225,000$

82. VALUE OF TWO HOUSES   Find the value of the two houses after 20 years by
 a. substituting 20 into the polynomial functions $f(x) = 900x + 105,000$ and $f(x) = 1,000x + 120,000$ and adding. $\$263,000$
 b. substituting into the result of Exercise 81. $\$263,000$

Consider the following information: A business purchases two computers, one for \$6,600 and the other for \$9,200. The first computer is expected to depreciate \$1,100 per year and the second \$1,700 per year.

83. VALUE OF A COMPUTER   Write a polynomial function that gives the value of the first computer after x years. $f(x) = -1,100x + 6,600$

84. VALUE OF A COMPUTER   Write a polynomial function that gives the value of the second computer after x years. $f(x) = -1,700x + 9,200$

85. VALUE OF TWO COMPUTERS   Find one polynomial function that gives the combined value of both computers after x years. $f(x) = -2,800x + 15,800$

86. VALUE OF TWO COMPUTERS   In two ways, find the combined value of the two computers after 3 years. $\$7,400$

WRITING

87. How do you recognize like terms?

88. How do you add like terms?

89. Explain the concept that is illustrated by the statement
$$-(x^2 + 3x - 1) = -1(x^2 + 3x - 1)$$

90. Explain the mistake made in the solution.
Simplify $(12x - 4) - (3x - 1)$.
$$(12x - 4) - (3x - 1) = 12x - 4 - 3x - 1$$
$$= 9x - 5$$

REVIEW

91. What is the sum of the measures of the angles of a triangle? $180°$

92. What is the sum of the measures of two complementary angles? $90°$

93. Solve the inequality $-4(3x - 3) \ge -12$ and graph the solution. $x \le 2$

94. CURLING IRON   A curling iron is plugged into a 110-volt electrical outlet and used for $\frac{1}{4}$ hour. If its resistance is 10 ohms, find the electrical power (in kilowatt hours, kwh) used by the curling iron by applying the formula
$$\text{kwh} = \frac{(\text{volts})^2}{1,000 \cdot \text{ohms}} \cdot \text{hours}   \quad 0.3025 \text{ kwh}$$

4.6 *Multiplying Polynomials*

In this section, you will learn about

- Multiplying monomials • Multiplying a polynomial by a monomial
- Multiplying a binomial by a binomial • The FOIL method
- Special products • Multiplying a polynomial by a binomial
- Multiplying three polynomials • Multiplying binomials to solve equations

INTRODUCTION. In Figure 4-4(a) on the next page, the length and width of a dollar bill are given. We can find the area of the bill by multiplying its length and width.

Arithmetic	Algebra
$15.6(6.5) = 101.4$	$(2x + 1)(3x - 1) = ?$
The area is 101.4 cm².	
(a)	(b)

FIGURE 4-4

In Figure 4-4(b), the length and the width of a postage stamp are represented by binomials. To find the area of the stamp, we must multiply the binomials. In this section, we will discuss the algebraic rules that are used to do this. We begin the discussion of multiplication of polynomials with the simplest case, the product of two monomials.

Multiplying monomials

To multiply two monomials, such as $8x^2$ and $-3x^4$, we use the commutative and associative properties of multiplication to group the numerical factors and the variable factors. Then we multiply the numerical factors and multiply the variable factors.

$$8x^2(-3x^4) = 8(-3)x^2x^4$$
$$= -24x^6$$

This example suggests the following rule.

Multiplying monomials | To multiply two monomials, multiply the numerical factors and then multiply the variable factors.

EXAMPLE 1 *Multiplying monomials.* Multiply **a.** $3x^4(2x^5)$, **b.** $-2a^2b^3(5ab^2)$, and **c.** $-4y^5z^2(2y^3z^3)(3yz)$.

Solution

a. $3x^4(2x^5) = 3(2) x^4x^5$

$= 6x^9$ Multiply the numerical factors, 3 and 2. Multiply the variable factors: $x^4x^5 = x^{4+5} = x^9$.

b. $-2a^2b^3(5ab^2) = -2(5)a^2ab^3b^2$

$= -10a^3b^5$

c. $-4y^5z^2(2y^3z^3)(3yz) = -4(2)(3)y^5y^3yz^2z^3z$

$= -24y^9z^6$

Self Check

Multiply:

a. $(5a^2b^3)(6a^3b^4)$

b. $(-15p^3q^2)(5p^3q^2)$

Answers: **a.** $30a^5b^7$,
b. $-75p^6q^4$

Multiplying a polynomial by a monomial

To find the product of a polynomial (with more than one term) and a monomial, we use the distributive property. To multiply $2x + 4$ by $5x$, for example, we proceed as follows:

$$5x(2x + 4) = 5x(2x) + 5x(4)$$ Distribute the multiplication by $5x$.

$$= 10x^2 + 20x$$ Multiply the monomials: $5x(2x) = 10x^2$ and $5x(4) = 20x$.

This example suggests the following rule.

Multiplying polynomials by monomials	To multiply a polynomial with more than one term by a monomial, use the distributive property to remove parentheses and simplify.

EXAMPLE 2   *Multiplying a polynomial by a monomial.*   Multiply:
a. $3a^2(3a^2 - 5a)$ and   **b.** $-2xz^2(2x - 3z + 2z^2)$.

Solution

a. $3a^2(3a^2 - 5a) = 3a^2(3a^2) - 3a^2(5a)$ Distribute the multiplication by $3a^2$.

$$= 9a^4 - 15a^3$$ Multiply the monomials.

b. $-2xz^2(2x - 3z + 2z^2)$

$$= -2xz^2(2x) - (-2xz^2)(3z) + (-2xz^2)(2z^2)$$ Use the distributive property.

$$= -4x^2z^2 - (-6xz^3) + (-4xz^4)$$ Multiply the monomials.

$$= -4x^2z^2 + 6xz^3 - 4xz^4$$

Self Check

Multiply:

a. $2p^3(3p^2 - 5p)$

b. $-5a^2b(3a + 2b - 4ab)$

Answers: **a.** $6p^5 - 10p^4$,
b. $-15a^3b - 10a^2b^2 + 20a^3b^2$ ∎

Multiplying a binomial by a binomial

To multiply two binomials, we must use the distributive property more than once. For example, to multiply $2a - 4$ by $3a + 5$, we proceed as follows.

$$(2a - 4)(3a + 5) = (2a - 4)(3a) + (2a - 4)(5)$$ Distribute the multiplication by $(2a - 4)$.

$$= 3a(2a - 4) + 5(2a - 4)$$ Use the commutative property of multiplication.

$$= 3a(2a) - 3a(4) + 5(2a) - 5(4)$$ Distribute the multiplication by $3a$ and by 5.

$$= 6a^2 - 12a + 10a - 20$$ Do the multiplications.

$$= 6a^2 - 2a - 20$$ Combine like terms.

This example suggests the following rule.

Multiplying two binomials	To multiply two binomials, multiply each term of one binomial by each term of the other binomial and combine like terms.

The FOIL method

We can use a shortcut method, called the **FOIL** method, to multiply binomials. FOIL is an acronym for **F**irst terms, **O**uter terms, **I**nner terms, and **L**ast terms. To use the FOIL method to multiply $2a - 4$ by $3a + 5$, we

1. multiply the **F**irst terms $2a$ and $3a$ to obtain $6a^2$,

2. multiply the **O**uter terms $2a$ and 5 to obtain $10a$,

3. multiply the **I**nner terms -4 and $3a$ to obtain $-12a$, and

4. multiply the **L**ast terms -4 and 5 to obtain -20.

Then we simplify the resulting polynomial, if possible.

$$(2a - 4)(3a + 5) = 2a(3a) + 2a(5) + (-4)(3a) + (-4)(5)$$

$$= 6a^2 + 10a - 12a - 20 \quad \text{Do the multiplications.}$$

$$= 6a^2 - 2a - 20 \quad \text{Combine like terms:}$$
$$10a - 12a = -2a.$$

EXAMPLE 3   *Using the FOIL method.*   Find each product.

a. $(x + 5)(x + 7) = x(x) + x(7) + 5(x) + 5(7)$

$$= x^2 + 7x + 5x + 35$$

$$= x^2 + 12x + 35$$

b. $(3x + 4)(2x - 3) = 3x(2x) + 3x(-3) + 4(2x) + 4(-3)$

$$= 6x^2 - 9x + 8x - 12$$

$$= 6x^2 - x - 12$$

c. $(a - 7b)(a - 4b) = a(a) + a(-4b) + (-7b)(a) + (-7b)(-4b)$

$$= a^2 - 4ab - 7ab + 28b^2$$

$$= a^2 - 11ab + 28b^2$$

d. $(2r - 3s)(2r + t) = 2r(2r) + 2r(t) - 3s(2r) - 3s(t)$

$$= 4r^2 + 2rt - 6rs - 3st \quad \text{There are no like terms.}$$

Self Check

Find each product:

a. $(y + 3)(y + 1)$

b. $(2a - 1)(3a + 2)$

c. $(5y - 2z)(2y + 3z)$

Answers: a. $y^2 + 4y + 3$,
b. $6a^2 + a - 2$,
c. $10y^2 + 11yz - 6z^2$ ■

EXAMPLE 4   *Simplifying expressions.*   Simplify each expression.

a. $3(2x - 3)(x + 1) = 3(2x^2 + 2x - 3x - 3)$ Multiply the binomials.

$$= 3(2x^2 - x - 3) \quad \text{Combine like terms.}$$

$$= 6x^2 - 3x - 9 \quad \text{Distribute the multiplication by 3.}$$

b. $(x + 1)(x - 2) - 3x(x + 3) = x^2 - 2x + x - 2 - 3x^2 - 9x$

$$= -2x^2 - 10x - 2 \quad \text{Combine like terms.}$$

Self Check

Simplify
$(x + 3)(2x - 1) + 2x(x - 1)$.

Answer: $4x^2 + 3x - 3$ ■

Special products

Certain products of binomials occur so frequently in algebra that it is worthwhile to learn formulas for computing them. To develop a rule to find the *square of a sum,* we consider $(x + y)^2$.

$$(x + y)^2 = (x + y)(x + y) \qquad \text{In } (x + y)^2, \text{ the base is } (x + y) \text{ and the exponent is 2.}$$
$$= x^2 + xy + xy + y^2 \quad \text{Multiply the binomials.}$$
$$= x^2 + 2xy + y^2 \qquad \text{Combine like terms: } xy + xy = 2xy.$$

We note that the terms of this result are related to the terms of the original expression. That is, $(x + y)^2$ is equal to the square of its first term (x^2), plus twice the product of both its terms $(2xy)$, plus the square of its last term (y^2).

To develop a rule to find the *square of a difference,* we consider $(x - y)^2$.

$$(x - y)^2 = (x - y)(x - y)$$
$$= x^2 - xy - xy + y^2 \quad \text{Multiply the binomials.}$$
$$= x^2 - 2xy + y^2 \qquad \text{Combine like terms: } -xy - xy = -2xy.$$

Again, the terms of the result are related to the terms of the original expression. When we find $(x - y)^2$, the product is composed of the square of its first term (x^2), twice the product of both its terms $(-2xy)$, and the square of its last term (y^2).

The final special product is the product of two binomials that differ only in the signs of the last terms. To develop a rule to find the product of a *sum and a difference,* we consider $(x + y)(x - y)$.

$$(x + y)(x - y) = x^2 - xy + xy - y^2 \quad \text{Multiply the binomials.}$$
$$= x^2 - y^2 \qquad \text{Combine like terms: } -xy + xy = 0.$$

The product is the square of the first term (x^2) minus the square of the second term (y^2). The expression $x^2 - y^2$ is called a **difference of two squares.**

Because these special products occur so often, it is wise to memorize their forms.

Special products	
$(x + y)^2 = x^2 + 2xy + y^2$	The square of a sum
$(x - y)^2 = x^2 - 2xy + y^2$	The square of a difference
$(x + y)(x - y) = x^2 - y^2$	The product of a sum and difference

EXAMPLE 5   *Finding special products.*   Find   **a.** $(t + 9)^2$,
b. $(8a - 5)^2$,   and   **c.** $(3y + 4z)(3y - 4z)$.

Solution

a. This is the square of a sum. The terms of the binomial being squared are t and 9.

$$(t + 9)^2 = \underbrace{t^2}_{\substack{\text{The square} \\ \text{of the first} \\ \text{term, } t.}} + \underbrace{2(t)(9)}_{\substack{\text{Twice the} \\ \text{product of} \\ \text{both terms.}}} + \underbrace{9^2}_{\substack{\text{The square} \\ \text{of the last} \\ \text{term, 9.}}}$$

$$= t^2 + 18t + 81$$

b. This is the square of a difference. The terms of the binomial being squared are $8a$ and -5.

$$(8a - 5)^2 = \underbrace{(8a)^2}_{\substack{\text{The square} \\ \text{of the first} \\ \text{term, } 8a.}} - \underbrace{2(8a)(5)}_{\substack{\text{Twice the} \\ \text{product of} \\ \text{both terms.}}} + \underbrace{5^2}_{\substack{\text{The square} \\ \text{of the last} \\ \text{term, 5.}}}$$

$$= 64a^2 - 80a + 25 \quad \text{Use the power rule for products:}$$
$$(8a)^2 = 8^2 a^2 = 64a^2.$$

c. The binomials differ only in the signs of the last terms. This is the product of a sum and a difference.

$$(3y + 4z)(3y - 4z) = (3y)^2 - (4z)^2 \quad \text{The square of the first term minus the}$$
$$\text{square of the second term.}$$

$$= 9y^2 - 16z^2 \quad \text{Use the power rule for products twice.}$$

Self Check

Find:

a. $(r + 6)^2$

b. $(7g - 2)^2$

c. $(5m - 9n)(5m + 9n)$

Answers: **a.** $r^2 + 12r + 36$,
b. $49g^2 - 28g + 4$,
c. $25m^2 - 81n^2$ ∎

COMMENT   A common error when squaring a binomial is to forget the middle term of the product. For example, $(x + 2)^2 \neq x^2 + 4$ and $(x - 2)^2 \neq x^2 - 4$. Applying the special product formulas, we have $(x + 2)^2 = x^2 + 4x + 4$ and $(x - 2)^2 = x^2 - 4x + 4$.

Multiplying a polynomial by a binomial

We must use the distributive property more than once to multiply a polynomial by a binomial. For example, to multiply $3x^2 + 3x - 5$ by $2x + 3$, we proceed as follows:

$$(2x + 3)(3x^2 + 3x - 5) = (2x + 3)3x^2 + (2x + 3)3x - (2x + 3)5$$
$$= 3x^2(2x + 3) + 3x(2x + 3) - 5(2x + 3)$$
$$= 6x^3 + 9x^2 + 6x^2 + 9x - 10x - 15$$
$$= 6x^3 + 15x^2 - x - 15$$

This example suggests the following rule.

Multiplying polynomials

> To multiply one polynomial by another, multiply each term of one polynomial by each term of the other polynomial and combine like terms.

It is often convenient to organize the work vertically.

EXAMPLE 6   *Multiplying polynomials using vertical form.*

a. Multiply:

$$
\begin{array}{r}
3a^2 - 4a + 7 \\
2a + 5 \\
\hline
15a^2 - 20a + 35 \\
6a^3 - 8a^2 + 14a \\
\hline
6a^3 + 7a^2 - 6a + 35
\end{array}
$$

    Multiply $3a^2 - 4a + 7$ by 5.
    Multiply $3a^2 - 4a + 7$ by $2a$.
    In each column, combine like terms.

b. Multiply:

$$
\begin{array}{r}
3y^2 - 5y + 4 \\
-4y^2 - 3 \\
\hline
-9y^2 + 15y - 12 \\
-12y^4 + 20y^3 - 16y^2 \\
\hline
-12y^4 + 20y^3 - 25y^2 + 15y - 12
\end{array}
$$

    Multiply $3y^2 - 5y + 4$ by -3.
    Multiply $3y^2 - 5y + 4$ by $-4y^2$.

Self Check

Multiply:

a. $(3x + 2)(2x^2 - 4x + 5)$

b. $(-2x^2 + 3)(2x^2 - 4x - 1)$

Answers:
a. $6x^3 - 8x^2 + 7x + 10$,
b. $-4x^4 + 8x^3 + 8x^2 - 12x - 3$

Multiplying three polynomials

When finding the product of three polynomials, we begin by multiplying any two of them, and then we multiply that result by the third polynomial.

EXAMPLE 7   *Multiplying three polynomials.*   Find the product: $-3a(4a + 1)(a - 7)$.

Solution

First, we find the product of $4a + 1$ and $a - 7$. Then we multiply that result by $-3a$.

$$-3a(4a + 1)(a - 7) = -3a(4a^2 - 28a + a - 7) \quad \text{Multiply the two binomials.}$$
$$= -3a(4a^2 - 27a - 7) \quad \text{Combine like terms.}$$
$$= -12a^3 + 81a^2 + 21a \quad \text{Distribute the multiplication by } -3a.$$

Self Check

Find the product:
$-2y(y + 3)(3y - 2)$

Answer: $-6y^3 - 14y^2 + 12y$

Multiplying binomials to solve equations

To solve an equation such as $(x + 2)(x + 3) = x(x + 7)$, we can do the multiplication on each side and proceed as follows:

$$(x + 2)(x + 3) = x(x + 7)$$

$$x^2 + 3x + 2x + 6 = x^2 + 7x$$

$$x^2 + 3x + 2x + 6 - x^2 = x^2 + 7x - x^2 \quad \text{Subtract } x^2 \text{ from both sides.}$$

$$5x + 6 = 7x \qquad \text{Combine like terms: } x^2 - x^2 = 0 \text{ and } 3x + 2x = 5x.$$

$$6 = 2x \qquad \text{Subtract } 5x \text{ from both sides.}$$

$$3 = x \qquad \text{Divide both sides by 2.}$$

Check: $(x + 2)(x + 3) = x(x + 7)$

$$(3 + 2)(3 + 3) \overset{?}{=} 3(3 + 7) \quad \text{Replace } x \text{ with 3.}$$

$$5(6) \overset{?}{=} 3(10) \qquad \text{Do the additions within parentheses.}$$

$$30 = 30$$

EXAMPLE 8 A square painting is surrounded by a border 2 inches wide. If the area of the border is 96 square inches, find the dimensions of the painting.

Analyze the problem Refer to Figure 4-5, which shows a square painting surrounded by a border 2 inches wide. We know that the area of this border is 96 square inches, and we are to find the dimensions of the painting.

Form an equation Let x represent the length of each side of the square painting. Since the border is 2 inches wide, the length and the width of the outer rectangle are both $(x + 2 + 2)$ inches. Then the outer rectangle is also a square, and its dimensions are $(x + 4)$ by $(x + 4)$ inches. Since the area of a square is the product of its length and width, the area of the larger square is $(x + 4)(x + 4)$, and the area of the painting is $x \cdot x$. If we subtract the area of the painting from the area of the larger square, the difference is 96.

FIGURE 4-5

The area of the large square	minus	the area of the square painting	is	the area of the border.
$(x + 4)(x + 4)$	$-$	$x \cdot x$	$=$	96

Solve the equation

$$(x + 4)(x + 4) - x^2 = 96 \quad x \cdot x = x^2.$$

$$x^2 + 8x + 16 - x^2 = 96 \quad (x + 4)(x + 4) = (x + 4)^2 = x^2 + 8x + 16.$$

$$8x + 16 = 96 \quad \text{Combine like terms: } x^2 - x^2 = 0.$$

$$8x = 80 \quad \text{Subtract 16 from both sides.}$$

$$x = 10 \quad \text{Divide both sides by 8.}$$

State the conclusion The dimensions of the painting are 10 inches by 10 inches.

Check the result Verify that the 2-inch-wide border of a 10-inch-square painting would have an area of 96 square inches. ∎

STUDY SET Section 4.6

VOCABULARY *Fill in the blanks.*

1. The expression $(2a - 4)(3a + 5)$ is the product of two ___binomials___.

2. The expression $(2a - 4)(3a^2 + 5a - 1)$ is the product of a ___binomial___ and a ___trinomial___.

3. In the acronym FOIL, F stands for ___first___ terms, O for ___outer___ terms, I for ___inner___ terms, and L for ___last___ terms.

4. $(x + 5)^2$ is the square of a ___sum___, and $(x - 5)^2$ is the square of a ___difference___. The expression $x^2 - y^2$ is called a difference of ___squares___.

CONCEPTS *Consider the product* $(2x + 5)(3x - 4)$.

5. The product of the first terms is $6x^2$.

6. The product of the outer terms is $-8x$.

7. The product of the inner terms is $15x$.

8. The product of the last terms is -20.

9. STAMPS Find the area of the stamp shown in Figure 4-4(b) at the beginning of this section. $(6x^2 + x - 1)\,\text{cm}^2$

10. LUGGAGE Find the volume of the garment bag shown in Illustration 1. $(2x^3 - 4x^2 - 6x)\,\text{in.}^3$

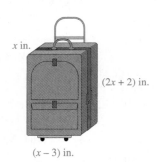

x in.

$(2x + 2)$ in.

$(x - 3)$ in.

ILLUSTRATION 1

NOTATION *Complete each solution.*

11. $7x(3x^2 - 2x + 5) = 7x\ (3x^2) - 7x\ (2x) + 7x\ (5)$
$= 21x^3 - 14x^2 + 35x$

12. $(2x + 5)(3x - 2) = 2x(3x) - 2x\ (2) + 5\ (3x) - 5\ (2)$
$= 6x^2 - 4x + 15x - 10$
$= 6x^2 + 11x - 10$

PRACTICE *Find each product.*

13. $(3x^2)(4x^3)$ $12x^5$

14. $(-2a^3)(3a^2)$ $-6a^5$

15. $(3b^2)(-2b)(4b^3)$ $-24b^6$

16. $(3y)(2y^2)(-y^4)$ $-6y^7$

17. $(2x^2y^3)(3x^3y^2)$ $6x^5y^5$

18. $(-5x^3y^6)(x^2y^2)$ $-5x^5y^8$

19. $(x^2y^5)(x^2z^5)(-3z^3)$
$-3x^4y^5z^8$

20. $(-r^4st^2)(2r^2st)(rst)$
$-2r^7s^3t^4$

21. $3(x + 4)$ $3x + 12$

22. $-3(a - 2)$ $-3a + 6$

23. $-4(t + 7)$ $-4t - 28$

24. $6(s^2 - 3)$ $6s^2 - 18$

25. $3x(x - 2)$ $3x^2 - 6x$

26. $4y(y + 5)$ $4y^2 + 20y$

27. $-2x^2(3x^2 - x)$
$-6x^4 + 2x^3$

28. $4b^3(2b^2 - 2b)$
$8b^5 - 8b^4$

29. $3xy(x + y)$
$3x^2y + 3xy^2$

30. $-4x^2z(3x^2 - z)$
$-12x^4z + 4x^2z^2$

31. $2x^2(3x^2 + 4x - 7)$
$6x^4 + 8x^3 - 14x^2$

32. $3y^3(2y^2 - 7y - 8)$
$6y^5 - 21y^4 - 24y^3$

33. $(3x)(-2x^2)(x + 4)$
$-6x^4 - 24x^3$

34. $(-2a^2)(-3a^3)(3a - 2)$
$18a^6 - 12a^5$

35. $(a + 4)(a + 5)$
$a^2 + 9a + 20$

36. $(y - 3)(y + 5)$
$y^2 + 2y - 15$

37. $(3x - 2)(x + 4)$
$3x^2 + 10x - 8$

38. $(t + 4)(2t - 3)$
$2t^2 + 5t - 12$

39. $(2a + 4)(3a - 5)$
$6a^2 + 2a - 20$

40. $(2b - 1)(3b + 4)$
$6b^2 + 5b - 4$

41. $(3x - 5)(2x + 1)$
$6x^2 - 7x - 5$

42. $(2y - 5)(3y + 7)$
$6y^2 - y - 35$

43. $(x + 3)(2x - 3)$
$2x^2 + 3x - 9$

44. $(2x + 3)(2x - 5)$
$4x^2 - 4x - 15$

45. $(2t + 3s)(3t - s)$
$6t^2 + 7st - 3s^2$

46. $(3a - 2b)(4a + b)$
$12a^2 - 5ab - 2b^2$

47. $(x + y)(x + z)$
$x^2 + xz + xy + yz$

48. $(a - b)(x + y)$
$ax + ay - bx - by$

49. $(4t - u)(-3t + u)$
$-12t^2 + 7tu - u^2$

50. $(-3t + 2s)(2t - 3s)$
$-6t^2 + 13st - 6s^2$

Simplify each expression.

51. $4(2x + 1)(x - 2)$ $8x^2 - 12x - 8$

52. $-5(3a - 2)(2a + 3)$ $-30a^2 - 25a + 30$

53. $3a(a + b)(a - b)$ $3a^3 - 3ab^2$

54. $-2r(r + s)(r + s)$ $-2r^3 - 4r^2s - 2rs^2$

55. $2t(t + 2) + 3t(t - 5)$ $5t^2 - 11t$

56. $3y(y + 2) + (y + 1)(y - 1)$ $4y^2 + 6y - 1$

57. $(x + y)(x - y) + x(x + y)$ $2x^2 + xy - y^2$

58. $(3x + 4)(2x - 2) - (2x + 1)(x + 3)$ $4x^2 - 5x - 11$

Find each special product.

59. $(x + 4)(x + 4)$
$x^2 + 8x + 16$

60. $(a + 3)(a + 3)$
$a^2 + 6a + 9$

61. $(t - 3)(t - 3)$
$t^2 - 6t + 9$

62. $(z - 5)(z - 5)$
$z^2 - 10z + 25$

63. $(r + 4)(r - 4)$
$r^2 - 16$

64. $(b + 2)(b - 2)$
$b^2 - 4$

65. $(4x + 5)(4x - 5)$
$16x^2 - 25$

66. $(5z + 1)(5z - 1)$
$25z^2 - 1$

67. $(2s + 1)(2s + 1)$
$4s^2 + 4s + 1$

68. $(3t - 2)(3t - 2)$
$9t^2 - 12t + 4$

69. $(x + 5)^2$
$x^2 + 10x + 25$

70. $(y - 6)^2$
$y^2 - 12y + 36$

71. $(x - 2y)^2$
$x^2 - 4xy + 4y^2$

72. $(3a + 2b)^2$
$9a^2 + 12ab + 4b^2$

73. $(2a - 3b)^2$
$4a^2 - 12ab + 9b^2$

74. $(2x + 5y)^2$
$4x^2 + 20xy + 25y^2$

75. $(4x + 5y)^2$
$16x^2 + 40xy + 25y^2$

76. $(6p - 5q)^2$
$36p^2 - 60pq + 25q^2$

Find the area of each figure. You may leave π in your answer.

77.

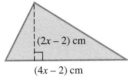

$(2x - 2)$ cm

$(4x - 2)$ cm

$(4x^2 - 6x + 2)$ cm^2

78.

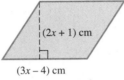

$(2x + 1)$ cm

$(3x - 4)$ cm

$(6x^2 - 5x - 4)$ m^2

79.

$(x + 3)$ in.

$(x^2 + 6x + 9)\pi$ in.^{2}

80.

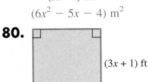

$(3x + 1)$ ft

$(3x + 1)$ ft

$(9x^2 + 6x + 1)$ ft^2

Find each product.

81. $(x + 2)(x^2 - 2x + 3)$ $x^3 - x + 6$

82. $(x - 5)(x^2 + 2x - 3)$ $x^3 - 3x^2 - 13x + 15$

83. $(4t + 3)(t^2 + 2t + 3)$ $4t^3 + 11t^2 + 18t + 9$

84. $(3x + 1)(2x^2 - 3x + 1)$ $6x^3 - 7x^2 + 1$

85. $(-3x + y)(x^2 - 8xy + 16y^2)$
$-3x^3 + 25x^2y - 56xy^2 + 16y^3$

86. $(3x - y)(x^2 + 3xy - y^2)$ $3x^3 + 8x^2y - 6xy^2 + y^3$

87. $x^2 - 2x + 1$
$\underline{\qquad x + 2}$
$x^3 - 3x + 2$

88. $5r^2 + r + 6$
$\underline{\qquad 2r - 1}$
$10r^3 - 3r^2 + 11r - 6$

89. $4x^2 + 3x - 4$
$\underline{\qquad 3x + 2}$
$12x^3 + 17x^2 - 6x - 8$

90. $x^2 - x + 1$
$\underline{\qquad x + 1}$
$x^3 + 1$

Solve each equation.

91. $(s - 4)(s + 1) = s^2 + 5$ -3

92. $(y - 5)(y - 2) = y^2 - 4$ 2

93. $z(z + 2) = (z + 4)(z - 4)$ -8

94. $(z + 3)(z - 3) = z(z - 3)$ 3

95. $(x + 4)(x - 4) = (x - 2)(x + 6)$ -1

96. $(y - 1)(y + 6) = (y - 3)(y - 2) + 8$ 2

97. $(a - 3)^2 = (a + 3)^2$ 0

98. $(b + 2)^2 = (b - 1)^2$ $-\frac{1}{2}$

APPLICATIONS

99. TOYS   Find the perimeter and the area of the screen of the Etch A Sketch® shown in Illustration 2.
$(24x + 14)$ cm, $(35x^2 + 43x + 12)$ cm^2

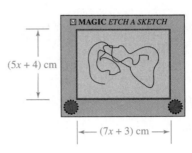

$(5x + 4)$ cm

$(7x + 3)$ cm

ILLUSTRATION 2

100. SUNGLASSES   An ellipse is an oval-shaped closed curve. The area of an ellipse is approximately $3.14ab$, where a is its length and b is its width. Find the polynomial that approximates the total area of the elliptical-shaped lenses of the sunglasses shown in Illustration 3. $(6.28x^2 - 6.28)$ in.^{2}

$(x - 1)$ in.

$(x + 1)$ in.

ILLUSTRATION 3

101. GARDENING   See Illustration 4.
  a. What is the area of the region planted with corn? tomatoes? beans? carrots? Use your answers to find the total area of the garden.
  x^2 ft^2, $6x$ ft^2, $5x$ ft^2, 30 ft^2; $(x^2 + 11x + 30)$ ft^2
  b. What is the length of the garden? What is its width? Use your answers to find its area.
  $(x + 6)$ ft, $(x + 5)$ ft; $(x^2 + 11x + 30)$ ft^2
  c. How do the answers from parts a and b for the area of the garden compare?   They are the same.

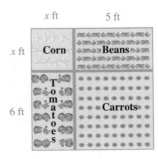

x ft 5 ft

x ft   Corn   Beans

6 ft   Tomatoes   Carrots

ILLUSTRATION 4

102. PAINTING   See Illustration 5. To purchase the correct amount of enamel to paint these two garage doors, a painter must find their areas. Find a polynomial that gives the number of square feet to be painted. All dimensions are in feet, and the windows are squares with sides of x feet. $(36x^2 + 36x + 6)$ ft^2

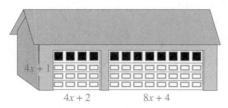

$4x + 1$

$4x + 2$ $8x + 4$

ILLUSTRATION 5

103. INTEGER PROBLEM   The difference between the squares of two consecutive positive integers is 11. Find the integers. (Hint: Let x and x + 1 represent the consecutive integers.)   5 and 6

104. INTEGER PROBLEM   If 3 less than a certain integer is multiplied by 4 more than the integer, the product is 6 less than the square of the integer. Find the integer.   6

105. STONE-GROUND FLOUR   The radius of one mill-stone in Illustration 6 is 3 meters greater than the radius of another, and their areas differ by 15π square meters. Find the radius of the larger millstone.   4 m

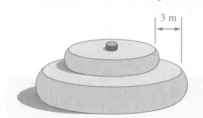

3 m

ILLUSTRATION 6

106. BOOKBINDING   Two square sheets of cardboard used for making book covers differ in area by 44 square inches. An edge of the larger square is 2 inches greater than an edge of the smaller square. Find the length of an edge of the smaller square.   10 in.

107. BASEBALL   In major league baseball, the distance between bases is 30 feet greater than it is in softball. The bases in major league baseball mark the corners of a square that has an area 4,500 square feet greater than for softball. Find the distance between the bases in baseball.   90 ft

108. PULLEY DESIGN   The radius of one pulley in Illustration 7 is 1 inch greater than the radius of the second pulley, and their areas differ by 4π square inches. Find the radius of the smaller pulley. $\frac{3}{2}$ in.

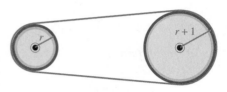

r $r + 1$

ILLUSTRATION 7

WRITING

109. Describe the steps involved in finding the product of $x + 2$ and $x - 2$.

110. Writing $(x + y)^2$ as $x^2 + y^2$ illustrates a common error. Explain.

REVIEW

Refer to Illustration 8.

111. What is the slope of line AB?   1

112. What is the slope of line BC?   undefined

113. What is the slope of line CD? $-\frac{2}{3}$

114. What is the slope of the x-axis?   0

115. What is the y-intercept of line AB? $(0, 2)$

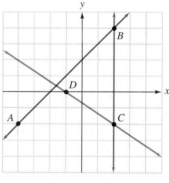

ILLUSTRATION 8

116. What is the x-intercept of line AB? $(-2, 0)$

4.7 *Dividing Polynomials by Monomials*

In this section, you will learn about

- Dividing a monomial by a monomial • Dividing a polynomial by a monomial
- An application of dividing a polynomial by a monomial

INTRODUCTION. In this section, we will discuss how to divide polynomials by monomials. We will first divide monomials by monomials and then divide polynomials with more than one term by monomials.

Dividing a monomial by a monomial

Recall that to simplify a fraction, we write both its numerator and denominator as the product of several factors and then divide out all common factors:

$$\frac{4}{6} = \frac{2 \cdot 2}{2 \cdot 3} \quad \text{Factor: } 4 = 2 \cdot 2 \text{ and } 6 = 2 \cdot 3.$$

$$\frac{20}{25} = \frac{4 \cdot 5}{5 \cdot 5} \quad \text{Factor: } 20 = 4 \cdot 5 \text{ and } 25 = 5 \cdot 5.$$

$$= \frac{2 \cdot \overset{1}{2}}{2 \cdot 3} \quad \text{Divide out the common factor of 2.}$$

$$= \frac{4 \cdot \overset{1}{5}}{\overset{}{5} \cdot 5} \quad \text{Divide out the common factor of 5.}$$

$$= \frac{2}{3}$$

$$= \frac{4}{5}$$

We can use the same method to simplify algebraic fractions that contain variables.

$$\frac{3p^2}{6p} = \frac{3 \cdot p \cdot p}{2 \cdot 3 \cdot p} \quad \text{Factor: } p^2 = p \cdot p \text{ and } 6 = 2 \cdot 3.$$

$$= \frac{\overset{1}{3} \cdot \overset{1}{p} \cdot p}{2 \cdot \overset{}{3} \cdot \overset{}{p}} \quad \text{Divide out the common factors of 3 and } p.$$

$$= \frac{p}{2}$$

To divide monomials, we can use either the preceding method for simplifying arithmetic fractions or the rules for exponents.

EXAMPLE 1 *Dividing monomials.* Simplify: **a.** $\dfrac{x^2 y}{xy^2}$ and **b.** $\dfrac{-8a^3 b^2}{4ab^3}$.

Solution

By simplifying fractions

a. $\dfrac{x^2 y}{xy^2} = \dfrac{x \cdot x \cdot y}{x \cdot y \cdot y}$

$$= \frac{\overset{1}{x} \cdot x \cdot \overset{1}{y}}{\overset{}{x} \cdot y \cdot \overset{}{y}}$$

$$= \frac{x}{y}$$

b. $\dfrac{-8a^3 b^2}{4ab^3} = \dfrac{-2 \cdot 4 \cdot a \cdot a \cdot a \cdot b \cdot b}{4 \cdot a \cdot b \cdot b \cdot b}$

$$= \frac{-2 \cdot \overset{1}{4} \cdot \overset{1}{a} \cdot a \cdot a \cdot \overset{1}{b} \cdot \overset{1}{b}}{\overset{}{4} \cdot \overset{}{a} \cdot \overset{}{b} \cdot \overset{}{b} \cdot b}$$

$$= -\frac{2a^2}{b}$$

Using the rules for exponents

$$\frac{x^2 y}{xy^2} = x^{2-1} y^{1-2}$$

$$= x^1 y^{-1}$$

$$= \frac{x}{y}$$

$$\frac{-8a^3 b^2}{4ab^3} = \frac{-2^3 a^3 b^2}{2^2 ab^3}$$

$$= -2^{3-2} a^{3-1} b^{2-3}$$

$$= -2^1 a^2 b^{-1}$$

$$= -\frac{2a^2}{b}$$

Self Check

Simplify $\dfrac{-5p^2 q^3}{10pq^4}$.

Answer: $-\dfrac{p}{2q}$ ∎

EXAMPLE 2 *Dividing monomials.*   Simplify $\dfrac{25(s^2t^3)^2}{15(st^3)^3}$. Write the result using positive exponents only.

Solution

To divide these monomials, we will use the method for simplifying fractions and several rules for exponents.

$$\frac{25(s^2t^3)^2}{15(st^3)^3} = \frac{25s^4t^6}{15s^3t^9}$$

Use the power rules for exponents:
$(xy)^n = x^ny^n$ and $(x^m)^n = x^{m \cdot n}$.

$$= \frac{5 \cdot 5 \cdot s^{4-3}t^{6-9}}{5 \cdot 3}$$

Factor 25 and 15. Use the quotient rule for exponents: $\dfrac{x^m}{x^n} = x^{m-n}$.

$$= \frac{5 \cdot \overset{1}{\cancel{5}} \cdot s^1t^{-3}}{\underset{1}{\cancel{5}} \cdot 3}$$

Divide out the common factors of 5. Do the subtractions.

$$= \frac{5s}{3t^3}$$

Use the negative integer exponent rule: $t^{-3} = \dfrac{1}{t^3}$.

Self Check

Simplify $\dfrac{-24(h^3p)^5}{20(h^2p^2)^3}$.

Answer: $-\dfrac{6h^9}{5p}$ ■

Dividing a polynomial by a monomial

In Section 1.2, we used the following rule to add and subtract fractions with like denominators.

Adding and subtracting fractions with like denominators

To add (or subtract) fractions with like denominators, we add (or subtract) their numerators and keep the common denominator. In symbols, if a, b, and d represent numbers,

$$\frac{a}{d} + \frac{b}{d} = \frac{a+b}{d} \qquad \text{and} \qquad \frac{a}{d} - \frac{b}{d} = \frac{a-b}{d} \qquad \text{(provided } d \neq 0\text{)}$$

We can use this rule "in reverse" to divide polynomials by monomials.

EXAMPLE 3 *Dividing a binomial by a monomial.*   Divide $9x + 6$ by 3.

Solution

$$\frac{9x + 6}{3} = \frac{9x}{3} + \frac{6}{3}$$ Divide each term of the numerator by the denominator.

$$= 3x + 2$$ Simplify each fraction.

Self Check

Simplify $\dfrac{4 - 8b}{4}$.

Answer: $1 - 2b$ ■

EXAMPLE 4 *Dividing a trinomial by a monomial.*

Divide $\dfrac{6x^2y^2 + 4x^2y - 2xy}{2xy}$.

Solution

$$\frac{6x^2y^2 + 4x^2y - 2xy}{2xy}$$

$$= \frac{6x^2y^2}{2xy} + \frac{4x^2y}{2xy} - \frac{2xy}{2xy}$$ Divide each term of the numerator by the denominator.

$$= 3xy + 2x - 1$$ Simplify each fraction.

Self Check

Simplify $\dfrac{9a^2b - 6ab^2 + 3ab}{3ab}$.

Answer: $3a - 2b + 1$ ■

EXAMPLE 5   *Dividing a trinomial by a monomial.*

Divide $\dfrac{12a^3b^2 - 4a^2b + a}{6a^2b^2}$.

Self Check

Simplify $\dfrac{14p^3q + pq^2 - p}{7p^2q}$.

Solution

$\dfrac{12a^3b^2 - 4a^2b + a}{6a^2b^2}$

$= \dfrac{12a^3b^2}{6a^2b^2} - \dfrac{4a^2b}{6a^2b^2} + \dfrac{a}{6a^2b^2}$ Divide each term of the numerator by the denominator.

$= 2a - \dfrac{2}{3b} + \dfrac{1}{6ab^2}$ Simplify each fraction.

Answer: $2p + \dfrac{q}{7p} - \dfrac{1}{7pq}$ ∎

EXAMPLE 6   *Dividing by a monomial.*   Simplify $\dfrac{(x - y)^2 - (x + y)^2}{xy}$.

Self Check

Simplify $\dfrac{(x + y)^2 - (x - y)^2}{xy}$.

Solution

$\dfrac{(x - y)^2 - (x + y)^2}{xy}$

$= \dfrac{x^2 - 2xy + y^2 - (x^2 + 2xy + y^2)}{xy}$ Use the special product rules to square the binomials in the numerator.

$= \dfrac{x^2 - 2xy + y^2 - x^2 - 2xy - y^2}{xy}$ Change the sign of each term within $(x^2 + 2xy + y^2)$.

$= \dfrac{-4xy}{xy}$ Combine like terms.

$= -4$ Divide out the common factors of x and y.

Answer: 4 ∎

An application of dividing a polynomial by a monomial

The area of the trapezoid shown in Figure 4-6 is given by the formula $A = \frac{1}{2}h(B + b)$, where B and b are its bases and h is its height. To solve the formula for b, we proceed as follows.

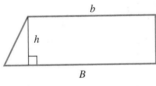

FIGURE 4-6

$$A = \frac{1}{2}h(B + b)$$

$2 \cdot A = 2 \cdot \dfrac{1}{2}h(B + b)$ Multiply both sides by 2 to clear the equation of the fraction.

$2A = h(B + b)$ Simplify: $2 \cdot \frac{1}{2} = \frac{2}{2} = 1$.

$2A = hB + hb$ Distribute the multiplication by h.

$2A - hB = hB + hb - hB$ Subtract hB from both sides.

$2A - hB = hb$ Combine like terms: $hB - hB = 0$.

$\dfrac{2A - hB}{h} = \dfrac{hb}{h}$ To undo the multiplication by h, divide both sides by h.

$\dfrac{2A - hB}{h} = b$

EXAMPLE 7   *Confirming answers.*   Another student worked the previous problem in a different way and got a result of $b = \frac{2A}{h} - B$. Is this result correct?

Self Check

Suppose another student got $b = 2A - \frac{hB}{h}$. Is this result correct?

Solution

To determine whether this result is correct, we must show that

$$\frac{2A - hB}{h} = \frac{2A}{h} - B$$

We can do this by dividing $2A - hB$ by h.

$$\frac{2A - hB}{h} = \frac{2A}{h} - \frac{hB}{h} \qquad \text{Divide each term of } 2A - hB \text{ by the denominator, which is } h.$$

$$= \frac{2A}{h} - B \qquad \text{Simplify the second fraction: } \frac{\overset{1}{\cancel{h}}B}{\underset{1}{\cancel{h}}} = B.$$

The results are the same.

Answer: no

STUDY SET Section 4.7 www

VOCABULARY *Fill in the blanks.*

1. A __polynomial__ is an algebraic expression that is the sum of one or more terms containing whole-number exponents.

2. A __monomial__ is a polynomial with one term.

3. A binomial is a polynomial with __two__ terms.

4. A trinomial is a polynomial with __three__ terms.

5. $\dfrac{x^m}{x^n} = x^{m-n}$ is a rule for __exponents__.

6. To __simplify__ a fraction, we divide out common factors of the numerator and denominator.

CONCEPTS *In Exercises 7–8, fill in the blanks.*

7. $\dfrac{18x + 9}{9} = \dfrac{18x}{9} + \dfrac{9x}{9}$

8. $\dfrac{30x^2 + 12x - 24}{6} = \dfrac{30x^2}{6} + \dfrac{12x}{6} - \dfrac{24}{6}$

9. What do the slashes and the small 1's mean?

$$\frac{4}{6} = \frac{\overset{1}{\cancel{2}} \cdot 2}{\underset{1}{\cancel{2}} \cdot 3} \qquad \begin{array}{l}\text{In the numerator and denominator, a} \\ \text{common factor of 2 was divided out.}\end{array}$$

10. Complete each rule of exponents.

  a. $\dfrac{x^m}{x^n} = x^{m-n}$

  b. $x^{-n} = \dfrac{1}{x^n}$

11. a. Solve the formula $d = rt$ for t. $t = \dfrac{d}{r}$

   b. Use your answer from part a to complete the table.

	r	$\cdot$	t	$=$	d
Motorcycle	$2x$		$3x^2$		$6x^3$

12. a. Solve the formula $I = Prt$ for r. $r = \dfrac{I}{Pt}$

   b. Use your answer from part a to complete the table.

	P	$\cdot$	r	$\cdot$	t	$=$	I
Savings account	$8x^3$		$\frac{3}{2}x^2$		$2x$		$24x^6$

13. How many nickels would have a value of $(10x + 35)$ cents? $2x + 7$

14. How many twenty-dollar bills would have a value of $\$(60x - 100)$? $3x - 5$

NOTATION *Complete each solution.*

15. $\dfrac{a^2 b^3}{a^3 b^2} = \dfrac{a \cdot a \cdot b \cdot b \cdot b}{a \cdot a \cdot a \cdot b \cdot b}$

$$= \frac{\overset{1}{\cancel{a}} \cdot \overset{1}{\cancel{a}} \cdot \overset{1}{\cancel{b}} \cdot \overset{1}{\cancel{b}} \cdot b}{\underset{1}{\cancel{a}} \cdot \underset{1}{\cancel{a}} \cdot a \cdot \underset{1}{\cancel{b}} \cdot \underset{1}{\cancel{b}}}$$

$$= \frac{b}{a}$$

16. $\dfrac{6pq^2 - 9p^2q^2 + pq}{3p^2q}$

$$= \frac{6pq^2}{3p^2q} - \frac{9p^2q^2}{3p^2q} + \frac{pq}{3p^2q}$$

$$= \frac{6 \cdot p \cdot q \cdot q}{3 \cdot p \cdot p \cdot q} - \frac{9 \cdot p \cdot p \cdot q \cdot q}{3 \cdot p \cdot p \cdot q} + \frac{p \cdot q}{3 \cdot p \cdot p \cdot q}$$

$$= \frac{2q}{p} - 3q + \frac{1}{3p}$$

PRACTICE *Simplify each fraction.*

17. $\dfrac{5}{15}$ $\frac{1}{3}$

18. $\dfrac{64}{128}$ $\frac{1}{2}$

19. $\dfrac{-125}{75}$ $-\frac{5}{3}$

20. $\dfrac{-98}{21}$ $-\frac{14}{3}$

21. $\dfrac{120}{160}$ $\frac{3}{4}$

22. $\dfrac{70}{420}$ $\frac{1}{6}$

23. $\dfrac{-3,612}{-3,612}$ 1

24. $\dfrac{-288}{-112}$ $\frac{18}{7}$

Do each division by simplifying the fraction.

25. $\dfrac{x^5}{x^2}$ x^3

26. $\dfrac{a^{12}}{a^8}$ a^4

27. $\dfrac{r^3 s^2}{rs^3}$ $\frac{r^2}{s}$

28. $\dfrac{y^4 z^3}{y^2 z^2}$ $y^2 z$

29. $\dfrac{8x^3 y^2}{4xy^3}$ $\frac{2x^2}{y}$

30. $\dfrac{-3y^3 z}{6yz^2}$ $-\frac{y^2}{2z}$

31. $\dfrac{12u^5 v}{-4u^2 v^3}$ $-\frac{3u^3}{v^2}$

32. $\dfrac{16rst^2}{-8rst^3}$ $-\frac{2}{t}$

33. $\dfrac{-16r^3 y^2}{-4r^2 y^4}$ $\frac{4r}{y^2}$

34. $\dfrac{35xyz^2}{-7x^2 yz}$ $-\frac{5z}{x}$

35. $\dfrac{-65rs^2 t}{15r^2 s^3 t}$ $-\frac{13}{3rs}$

36. $\dfrac{112u^3 z^6}{-42u^3 z^6}$ $-\frac{8}{3}$

37. $\dfrac{x^2 x^3}{xy^6}$ $\frac{x^4}{y^6}$

38. $\dfrac{x^2 y^2}{x^2 y^3}$ $\frac{1}{y}$

39. $\dfrac{(a^3 b^4)^3}{ab^4}$ $a^8 b^8$

40. $\dfrac{(a^2 b^3)^3}{a^6 b^6}$ b^3

41. $\dfrac{15(r^2 s^3)^2}{-5(rs^5)^3}$ $-\frac{3r}{s^9}$

42. $\dfrac{-5(a^2 b)^3}{10(ab^2)^3}$ $-\frac{a^3}{2b^3}$

43. $\dfrac{-32(x^3 y)^3}{128(x^2 y^2)^3}$ $-\frac{x^3}{4y^3}$

44. $\dfrac{68(a^6 b^7)^2}{-96(abc^2)^3}$ $-\frac{17a^9 b^{11}}{24c^6}$

45. $\dfrac{-(4x^3 y^3)^2}{(x^2 y^4)^3}$ $-\frac{16}{y^6}$

46. $\dfrac{(2r^3 s^2)^2}{-(4r^2 s^2)^2}$ $-\frac{r^2}{4}$

47. $\dfrac{(a^2 a^3)^4}{(a^4)^3}$ a^8

48. $\dfrac{(b^3 b^4)^5}{(bb^2)^2}$ b^{29}

Do each division.

49. $\dfrac{6x + 9}{3}$ $2x + 3$

50. $\dfrac{8x + 12y}{4}$ $2x + 3y$

51. $\dfrac{5x - 10y}{25xy}$ $\frac{1}{5y} - \frac{2}{5x}$

52. $\dfrac{2x - 32}{16x}$ $\frac{1}{8} - \frac{2}{x}$

53. $\dfrac{3x^2 + 6y^3}{3x^2 y^2}$ $\frac{1}{y^2} + \frac{2y}{x^2}$

54. $\dfrac{4a^2 - 9b^2}{12ab}$ $\frac{a}{3b} - \frac{3b}{4a}$

55. $\dfrac{15a^3 b^2 - 10a^2 b^3}{5a^2 b^2}$

$3a - 2b$

56. $\dfrac{9a^4 b^3 - 16a^3 b^4}{12a^2 b}$

$\frac{3a^2 b^2}{4} - \frac{4ab^3}{3}$

57. $\dfrac{4x - 2y + 8z}{4xy}$

$\dfrac{1}{y} - \dfrac{1}{2x} + \dfrac{2z}{xy}$

58. $\dfrac{5a^2 + 10b^2 - 15ab}{5ab}$

$\dfrac{a}{b} + \dfrac{2b}{a} - 3$

59. $\dfrac{12x^3 y^2 - 8x^2 y - 4x}{4xy}$

$3x^2 y - 2x - \dfrac{1}{y}$

60. $\dfrac{12a^2 b^2 - 8a^2 b - 4ab}{4ab}$

$3ab - 2a - 1$

61. $\dfrac{-25x^2 y + 30xy^2 - 5xy}{-5xy}$ $5x - 6y + 1$

62. $\dfrac{-30a^2 b^2 - 15a^2 b - 10ab^2}{-10ab}$ $3ab + \dfrac{3a}{2} + b$

Simplify each numerator and then do the division.

63. $\dfrac{5x(4x - 2y)}{2y}$ $\dfrac{10x^2}{y} - 5x$

64. $\dfrac{9y^2(x^2 - 3xy)}{3x^2}$ $3y^2 - \dfrac{9y^3}{x}$

65. $\dfrac{(-2x)^3 + (3x^2)^2}{6x^2}$ $-\dfrac{4x}{3} + \dfrac{3x^2}{2}$

66. $\dfrac{(-3x^2 y)^3 + (3xy^2)^3}{27x^3 y^4}$ $-\dfrac{x^3}{y} + y^2$

67. $\dfrac{4x^2 y^2 - 2(x^2 y^2 + xy)}{2xy}$ $xy - 1$

68. $\dfrac{-5a^3 b - 5a(ab^2 - a^2 b)}{10a^2 b^2}$ $-\dfrac{1}{2}$

69. $\dfrac{(3x - y)(2x - 3y)}{6xy}$ $\dfrac{x}{y} - \dfrac{11}{6} + \dfrac{y}{2x}$

70. $\dfrac{(2m - n)(3m - 2n)}{-3m^2 n^2}$ $-\dfrac{2}{n^2} + \dfrac{7}{3mn} - \dfrac{2}{3m^2}$

71. $\dfrac{(a + b)^2 - (a - b)^2}{2ab}$ 2

72. $\dfrac{(x - y)^2 + (x + y)^2}{2x^2 y^2}$ $\dfrac{1}{y^2} + \dfrac{1}{x^2}$

APPLICATIONS

73. POOL   The rack shown in Illustration 1 is used to set up the balls when beginning a game of pool. If the perimeter of the rack, in inches, is given by the polynomial $6x^2 - 3x + 9$, what is the length of one side? $(2x^2 - x + 3)$ in.

ILLUSTRATION 1

74. CHECKERBOARD   If the perimeter (in inches) of the checkerboard, shown in Illustration 2, is $12x^2 - 8x + 32$, what is the length of one side?
$(3x^2 - 2x + 8)$ in.

ILLUSTRATION 2

75. AIR CONDITIONING   If the volume occupied by the air conditioning unit shown in Illustration 3 is $(36x^3 - 24x^2)$ cubic feet, find its height. $(3x - 2)$ ft

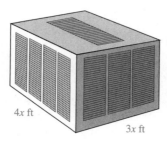

$4x$ ft

$3x$ ft

ILLUSTRATION 3

76. MINI-BLINDS   The area covered by the mini-blinds shown in Illustration 4 is $(3x^3 - 6x)$ square feet. How long are the blinds? $(x^2 - 2)$ ft

$3x$ ft

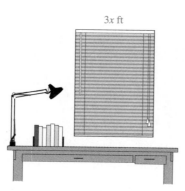

ILLUSTRATION 4

77. CONFIRMING FORMULAS   Are these formulas the same?

$$l = \frac{P - 2w}{2} \quad \text{and} \quad l = \frac{P}{2} - w \quad \text{yes}$$

78. CONFIRMING FORMULAS   Are these formulas the same?

$$r = \frac{G + 2b}{2b} \quad \text{and} \quad r = \frac{G}{2b} + b \quad \text{no}$$

79. ELECTRIC BILLS   On an electric bill, the following two formulas are used to compute the average cost of x kwh of electricity. Are the formulas equivalent?   no

$$\frac{0.08x + 5}{x} \quad \text{and} \quad 0.08x + \frac{5}{x}$$

80. PHONE BILLS   On a phone bill, the following two formulas are used to compute the average cost per minute of x minutes of phone usage. Are the formulas equivalent?   yes

$$\frac{0.15x + 12}{x} \quad \text{and} \quad 0.15 + \frac{12}{x}$$

WRITING

81. Explain the error in the following work.

$$\frac{3x + 5}{5} = \frac{3x + \overset{1}{\cancel{5}}}{\underset{1}{\cancel{5}}}$$

$$= 3x$$

82. Explain how to do this division.

$$\frac{4x^2y + 8xy^2}{4xy}$$

REVIEW   In Exercises 83–86, identify each polynomial as a monomial, a binomial, a trinomial, or none of these.

83. $5a^2b + 2ab^2$ binomial

84. $-3x^3y$ monomial

85. $-2x^3 + 3x^2 - 4x + 12$ none of the above

86. $17t^2 - 15t + 27$ trinomial

87. What is the degree of the trinomial $3x^2 - 2x + 4$?   2

88. What is the numerical coefficient of the second term of the trinomial $-7t^2 + 5t + 17$?   5

4.8 *Dividing Polynomials by Polynomials*

In this section, you will learn about

- Dividing polynomials by polynomials • Writing powers in descending order
- Missing terms

INTRODUCTION. In this section, we will conclude our discussion on operations with polynomials by discussing how to divide one polynomial by another.

Dividing polynomials by polynomials

To divide one polynomial by another, we use a method similar to long division in arithmetic. We illustrate the method with several examples.

EXAMPLE 1   *Dividing polynomials.*   Divide $x^2 + 5x + 6$ by $x + 2$.

Solution

Here the divisor is $x + 2$, and the dividend is $x^2 + 5x + 6$.

Step 1:
$$\begin{array}{r} x \\ x + 2 \overline{)\, x^2 + 5x + 6} \end{array}$$
How many times does x divide x^2? $x^2 \div x = x$. Place the x above the division symbol.

Step 2:
$$\begin{array}{r} x \\ x + 2 \overline{)\, x^2 + 5x + 6} \\ x^2 + 2x \end{array}$$
Multiply each term in the divisor by x. Place the product under $x^2 + 5x$ and draw a line.

Step 3:
$$\begin{array}{r} x \\ x + 2 \overline{)\, x^2 + 5x + 6} \\ \underline{x^2 + 2x} \\ 3x + 6 \end{array}$$
Subtract $x^2 + 2x$ from $x^2 + 5x$. Work vertically, column by column: $x^2 - x^2 = 0$ and $5x - 2x = 3x$.

Bring down the 6.

Step 4:
$$\begin{array}{r} x\ \ + 3 \\ x + 2 \overline{)\, x^2 + 5x + 6} \\ \underline{x^2 + 2x} \\ 3x + 6 \end{array}$$
How many times does x divide $3x$? $3x \div x = +3$. Place the $+3$ above the division symbol.

Step 5:
$$\begin{array}{r} x\ \ + 3 \\ x + 2 \overline{)\, x^2 + 5x + 6} \\ \underline{x^2 + 2x} \\ 3x + 6 \\ 3x + 6 \end{array}$$
Multiply each term in the divisor by 3. Place the product under $3x + 6$ and draw a line.

Step 6:
$$\begin{array}{r} x\ \ + 3 \\ x + 2 \overline{)\, x^2 + 5x + 6} \\ \underline{x^2 + 2x} \\ 3x + 6 \\ \underline{3x + 6} \\ 0 \end{array}$$
Subtract $3x + 6$ from $3x + 6$. Work vertically: $3x - 3x = 0$ and $6 - 6 = 0$.

The quotient is $x + 3$ and the remainder is 0.

Step 7:   Check the work by verifying that $(x + 2)(x + 3)$ is $x^2 + 5x + 6$.

$$(x + 2)(x + 3) = x^2 + 3x + 2x + 6$$
$$= x^2 + 5x + 6$$

The answer checks.

EXAMPLE 2   *Dividing polynomials.*   Divide $\dfrac{6x^2 - 7x - 2}{2x - 1}$.

Solution

Here the divisor is $2x - 1$ and the dividend is $6x^2 - 7x - 2$.

Step 1:
$$\begin{array}{r} 3x \\ 2x - 1 \overline{)\, 6x^2 - 7x - 2} \end{array}$$
How many times does $2x$ divide $6x^2$? $6x^2 \div 2x = 3x$. Place the $3x$ above the division symbol.

Self Check

Divide $x^2 + 7x + 12$ by $x + 3$.

Answer: $x + 4$ ∎

Self Check

Divide $\dfrac{8x^2 + 6x - 3}{2x + 3}$.

Step 2: $2x - 1\overline{)6x^2 - 7x - 2}$ $\overset{\overset{3x}{\frown}}{}$
$\underline{6x^2 - 3x}$

Multiply each term in the divisor by $3x$. Place the product under $6x^2 - 7x$ and draw a line.

Step 3: $2x - 1\overline{)6x^2 - 7x - 2}$ $\overset{3x}{}$
$\underline{6x^2 - 3x}$
$-4x - 2$

Subtract $6x^2 - 3x$ from $6x^2 - 7x$. Work vertically:
$6x^2 - 6x^2 = 0$ and $-7x - (-3x) = -7x + 3x = -4x$.

Bring down the -2.

Step 4: $2x - 1\overline{)6x^2 - 7x - 2}$ $\overset{3x \ - \ 2}{}$
$\underline{6x^2 - 3x}$
$-4x - 2$

How many times does $2x$ divide $-4x$? $-4x \div 2x = -2$. Place the -2 above the division symbol.

Step 5: $2x - 1\overline{)6x^2 - 7x - 2}$ $\overset{\overset{3x \ - \ 2}{\frown}}{}$
$\underline{6x^2 - 3x}$
$-4x - 2$
$\underline{-4x + 2}$

Multiply each term in the divisor by -2. Place the product under $-4x - 2$ and draw a line.

Step 6: $2x - 1\overline{)6x^2 - 7x - 2}$ $\overset{3x \ - \ 2}{}$
$\underline{6x^2 - 3x}$
$-4x - 2$
$\underline{-4x + 2}$
-4

Subtract $-4x + 2$ from $-4x - 2$. Work vertically:
$-4x - (-4x) = -4x + 4x = 0$ and $-2 - 2 = -4$.

Here the quotient is $3x - 2$ and the remainder is -4. It is common to write the answer as either

$$3x - 2 + \frac{-4}{2x - 1} \quad \text{or} \quad 3x - 2 - \frac{4}{2x - 1} \qquad \text{Quotient} + \frac{\text{remainder}}{\text{divisor}}.$$

Step 7: To check the answer, we multiply

$$3x - 2 + \frac{-4}{2x - 1} \qquad \text{by} \qquad 2x - 1$$

The product should be the dividend.

$$(2x - 1)\left(3x - 2 + \frac{-4}{2x - 1}\right) = (2x - 1)(3x - 2) + (2x - 1)\left(\frac{-4}{2x - 1}\right)$$

$$= (2x - 1)(3x - 2) - 4$$

$$= 6x^2 - 4x - 3x + 2 - 4$$

$$= 6x^2 - 7x - 2$$

Because the result is the dividend, the answer checks.

Answer: $4x - 3 + \dfrac{6}{2x + 3}$ ■

Writing powers in descending order

The division method works best when the terms of the divisor and the dividend are written in descending powers of the variable. This means that the term involving the highest power of x appears first, the term involving the second-highest power of x appears second, and so on. For example, the terms in

$$3x^3 + 2x^2 - 7x + 5$$

have their exponents written in descending order.

If the powers in the dividend or divisor are not in descending order, we use the commutative property of addition to write them that way.

EXAMPLE 3 *Dividing polynomials.* Divide $4x^2 + 2x^3 + 12 - 2x$ by $x + 3$.

Solution

We write the dividend so that the exponents are in descending order.

$$
\begin{array}{r}
2x^2 - 2x + 4 \\
x + 3\overline{)2x^3 + 4x^2 - 2x + 12} \\
\underline{2x^3 + 6x^2} \\
-2x^2 - 2x \\
\underline{-2x^2 - 6x} \\
4x + 12 \\
\underline{4x + 12} \\
0
\end{array}
$$

Check: $(x + 3)(2x^2 - 2x + 4) = 2x^3 - 2x^2 + 4x + 6x^2 - 6x + 12$
$$= 2x^3 + 4x^2 - 2x + 12$$

Self Check

Divide $x^2 - 10x + 6x^3 + 4$ by $2x - 1$.

Answer: $3x^2 + 2x - 4$ ∎

Missing terms

When we write the terms of a dividend in descending powers of x, we must determine whether some powers of the variable are missing. When this happens, we should write such terms with a coefficient of 0 or leave a blank space for them.

EXAMPLE 4 *Dividing polynomials.* Divide $\dfrac{x^2 - 4}{x + 2}$.

Solution

Since $x^2 - 4$ does not have a term involving x, we must either include the term $0x$ or leave a space for it.

$$
\begin{array}{r}
x - 2 \\
x + 2\overline{)x^2 + 0x - 4} \\
\underline{x^2 + 2x} \\
-2x - 4 \\
\underline{-2x - 4} \\
0
\end{array}
$$

Check: $(x + 2)(x - 2) = x^2 - 2x + 2x - 4$
$$= x^2 - 4$$

Self Check

Divide $\dfrac{x^2 - 9}{x - 3}$.

Answer: $x + 3$ ∎

STUDY SET Section 4.8

VOCABULARY *Fill in the blanks.*

1. In the division $x + 1\overline{)x^2 + 2x + 1}$, the expression $x + 1$ is called the ___divisor___ and $x^2 + 2x + 1$ is called the ___dividend___.

2. The answer to a division problem is called the ___quotient___.

3. If a division does not come out even, the leftover part is called a ___remainder___.

4. The exponents in $2x^4 + 3x^3 + 4x^2 - 7x - 2$ are said to be written in ___descending___ order.

CONCEPTS *Write each polynomial with the powers in descending order.*

5. $4x^3 + 7x - 2x^2 + 6$ $4x^3 - 2x^2 + 7x + 6$

6. $5x^2 + 7x^3 - 3x - 9$ $7x^3 + 5x^2 - 3x - 9$

7. $9x + 2x^2 - x^3 + 6x^4$ $6x^4 - x^3 + 2x^2 + 9x$

8. $7x^5 + x^3 - x^2 + 2x^4$ $7x^5 + 2x^4 + x^3 - x^2$

Identify the missing terms in each polynomial.

9. $5x^4 + 2x^2 - 1$ $0x^3$ and $0x$

10. $-3x^5 - 2x^3 + 4x - 6$ $0x^4$ and $0x^2$

In Exercises 11–12, without doing the division, determine which of the three possible quotients seems reasonable.

11. $\dfrac{x^4 - 81}{x - 3}$ $x^2 + 3x + 9$
$x^3 + 3x^2 + 9x + 27 \leftarrow$ quotient
$x^4 + 3x^3 + 9x^2 + 27x + 1$

12. $\dfrac{8x^3 - 27}{2x - 3}$ $4x^2 + 6x + 9 \leftarrow$ quotient
$4x^3 - 6x^2 - 9$
$4x^4 - 6x^3 - 9x^2 + 1$

13. a. Solve $d = rt$ for r. $r = \frac{d}{t}$
  b. Use your answer to part a and the long division method to complete the table.

	r	$\cdot$	t	$=$	d
Subway	$x - 3$		$x + 4$		$x^2 + x - 12$

14. a. Solve $I = Prt$ for P. $P = \frac{I}{rt}$
  b. Use your answer to part a and the long division method to complete the table.

	P	$\cdot$	r	$\cdot$	t	$=$	I
Bonds	$x + 3$		$x + 4$		1		$x^2 + 7x + 12$

15. Using long division, a student found that
$$\frac{3x^2 + 8x + 4}{3x + 2} = x + 2$$
Use multiplication to see whether the result is correct.
It is correct.

16. Using long division, a student found that
$$\frac{x^2 + 4x - 21}{x - 3} = x - 7$$
Use multiplication to see whether the result is correct.
It is incorrect.

NOTATION *Complete each division.*

17.
$$
\begin{array}{r}
x + 2 \\
x + 2 \overline{) x^2 + 4x + 4} \\
\underline{x^2 + 2x} \\
2x + 4 \\
\underline{2x + 4} \\
0
\end{array}
$$

18.
$$
\begin{array}{r}
x^2 + x - 2 + \frac{7}{2x+1} \\
2x + 1 \overline{) 2x^3 + 3x^2 - 3x + 5} \\
\underline{2x^3 + x^2} \\
2x^2 - 3x \\
\underline{2x^2 + x} \\
-4x + 5 \\
\underline{-4x - 2} \\
7
\end{array}
$$

PRACTICE *Do each division.*

19. Divide $x^2 + 4x - 12$ by $x - 2$. $x + 6$

20. Divide $x^2 - 5x + 6$ by $x - 2$. $x - 3$

21. Divide $y^2 + 13y + 12$ by $y + 1$. $y + 12$

22. Divide $z^2 - 7z + 12$ by $z - 3$. $z - 4$

23. $\dfrac{6a^2 + 5a - 6}{2a + 3}$ $3a - 2$

24. $\dfrac{8a^2 + 2a - 3}{2a - 1}$ $4a + 3$

25. $\dfrac{3b^2 + 11b + 6}{3b + 2}$ $b + 3$

26. $\dfrac{3b^2 - 5b + 2}{3b - 2}$ $b - 1$

Write the terms so that the powers of x are in descending order. Then do each division.

27. $5x + 3 \overline{) 11x + 10x^2 + 3}$ $2x + 1$

28. $2x - 7 \overline{) -x - 21 + 2x^2}$ $x + 3$

29. $4 + 2x \overline{) -10x - 28 + 2x^2}$ $x - 7$

30. $1 + 3x \overline{) 9x^2 + 1 + 6x}$ $3x + 1$

31. $2x - 1 \overline{) x - 2 + 6x^2}$ $3x + 2$

32. $2 + x \overline{) 3x + 2x^2 - 2}$ $2x - 1$

33. $3 + x \overline{) 2x^2 - 3 + 5x}$ $2x - 1$

34. $x - 3 \overline{) 2x^2 - 3 - 5x}$ $2x + 1$

Do each division.

35. $2x + 3 \overline{) 2x^3 + 7x^2 + 4x - 3}$ $x^2 + 2x - 1$

36. $2x - 1 \overline{) 2x^3 - 3x^2 + 5x - 2}$ $x^2 - x + 2$

37. $3x + 2 \overline{) 6x^3 + 10x^2 + 7x + 2}$ $2x^2 + 2x + 1$

38. $4x + 3 \overline{) 4x^3 - 5x^2 - 2x + 3}$ $x^2 - 2x + 1$

39. $2x + 1 \overline{) 2x^3 + 3x^2 + 3x + 1}$ $x^2 + x + 1$

40. $3x - 2 \overline{) 6x^3 - x^2 + 4x - 4}$ $2x^2 + x + 2$

Do each division. If there is a remainder, write the answer in quotient $+ \dfrac{remainder}{divisor}$ form.

41. $\dfrac{2x^2 + 5x + 2}{2x + 3}$
$x + 1 + \dfrac{-1}{2x + 3}$

42. $\dfrac{3x^2 - 8x + 3}{3x - 2}$
$x - 2 + \dfrac{-1}{3x - 2}$

43. $\dfrac{4x^2 + 6x - 1}{2x + 1}$
$2x + 2 + \dfrac{-3}{2x + 1}$

44. $\dfrac{6x^2 - 11x + 2}{3x - 1}$
$2x - 3 + \dfrac{-1}{3x - 1}$

45. $\dfrac{x^3 + 3x^2 + 3x + 1}{x + 1}$

$x^2 + 2x + 1$

46. $\dfrac{x^3 + 6x^2 + 12x + 8}{x + 2}$

$x^2 + 4x + 4$

47. $\dfrac{2x^3 + 7x^2 + 4x + 3}{2x + 3}$

$x^2 + 2x - 1 + \dfrac{6}{2x + 3}$

48. $\dfrac{6x^3 + x^2 + 2x + 1}{3x - 1}$

$2x^2 + x + 1 + \dfrac{2}{3x - 1}$

49. $\dfrac{2x^3 + 4x^2 - 2x + 3}{x - 2}$

$2x^2 + 8x + 14 + \dfrac{31}{x - 2}$

50. $\dfrac{3y^3 - 4y^2 + 2y + 3}{y + 3}$

$3y^2 - 13y + 41 + \dfrac{-120}{y + 3}$

Do each division.

51. $\dfrac{x^2 - 1}{x - 1}$ $x + 1$

52. $\dfrac{x^2 - 9}{x + 3}$ $x - 3$

53. $\dfrac{4x^2 - 9}{2x + 3}$ $2x - 3$

54. $\dfrac{25x^2 - 16}{5x - 4}$ $5x + 4$

55. $\dfrac{x^3 + 1}{x + 1}$ $x^2 - x + 1$

56. $\dfrac{x^3 - 8}{x - 2}$ $x^2 + 2x + 4$

57. $\dfrac{a^3 + a}{a + 3}$

$a^2 - 3a + 10 + \dfrac{-30}{a + 3}$

58. $\dfrac{y^3 - 50}{y - 5}$

$y^2 + 5y + 25 + \dfrac{75}{y - 5}$

59. $3x - 4 \overline{)15x^3 - 23x^2 + 16x}$ $5x^2 - x + 4 + \dfrac{16}{3x - 4}$

60. $2y + 3 \overline{)21y^2 + 6y^3 - 20}$ $3y^2 + 6y - 9 + \dfrac{7}{2y + 3}$

APPLICATIONS

61. FURNACE FILTER   The area of the furnace filter shown in Illustration 1 is $(x^2 - 2x - 24)$ square inches.
   a. Find its length. $(x - 6)$ in.
   b. Find its perimeter.
      $(4x - 4)$ in.

$(x + 4)$ in.

ILLUSTRATION 1

62. SHELF SPACE   The formula $V = Bh$ gives the volume of a cylinder where B is the area of the base and h is the height. Find the amount of shelf space that the container of potato chips shown in Illustration 2 occupies if its volume is $(2x^3 - 4x - 2)$ cubic inches.
$(x^2 - x - 1)$ in.

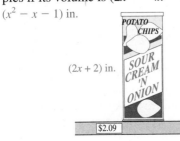

$(2x + 2)$ in.

$2.09

ILLUSTRATION 2

63. COMMUNICATION   See Illustration 3. Telephone poles were installed every $(2x - 3)$ feet along a stretch of railroad track $(8x^3 - 6x^2 + 5x - 21)$ feet long. How many poles were used? $4x^2 + 3x + 7$

$(2x - 3)$ ft

ILLUSTRATION 3

64. CONSTRUCTION COSTS   Find the price per square foot to remodel each of the three rooms listed in the chart.

Room	Remodeling cost	Area (ft²)	Cost (per ft²)
Bathroom	$(2x^2 + x - 6)$	$2x - 3$	$(x + 2)$
Bedroom	$(x^2 + 9x + 20)$	$x + 4$	$(x + 5)$
Kitchen	$(3x^3 - 9x - 6)$	$3x + 3$	$(x^2 - x - 2)$

WRITING

65. Explain how the following are related: *dividend, divisor, quotient,* and *remainder.*

66. How would you check the results of a division?

REVIEW

67. Simplify $(x^5 x^6)^2$. x^{22}

68. Simplify $(a^2)^3 (a^3)^4$. a^{18}

In Exercises 69–70, simplify each expression.

69. $3(2x^2 - 4x + 5) + 2(x^2 + 3x - 7)$ $8x^2 - 6x + 1$

70. $-2(y^3 + 2y^2 - y) - 3(3y^3 + y)$ $-11y^3 - 4y^2 - y$

71. What can be said about the slopes of two parallel lines?
   They are the same.

72. What is the slope of a line perpendicular to a line with a slope of $\frac{3}{4}$? $-\frac{4}{3}$

Polynomials

A **polynomial** is a term or a sum of terms in which all variables have whole-number exponents. Some examples are

$$-16a^4b, \qquad y + 8, \qquad x^2 + 2xy + y^2, \quad \text{and} \quad x^3 - 2x^2 + 6x - 8$$

The Vocabulary of Polynomials

1. Consider $x^3 - 2x^2 + 6x - 8$.
   a. Fill in: This is a polynomial in x. It is written in _____descending_____ powers of x.
   b. How many terms does the polynomial have?   4
   c. Give the degree of each term.   3, 2, 1, 0
   d. What is the degree of the polynomial?   3
   e. Give the coefficient of each term. $1, -2, 6, -8$

2. Consider $x^2 + 2xy + y^2$.
   a. Fill in: This is a polynomial in x and y. It is written in _____descending_____ powers of x and _____ascending_____ powers of y.
   b. How many terms does the polynomial have?   3
   c. Give the degree of each term.   2, 2, 2
   d. What is the degree of the polynomial?   2
   e. Give the coefficient of each term.   1, 2, 1

3. Classify each polynomial as a monomial, binomial, trinomial, or none of these.
   a. $x^2 - y^2$ binomial
   b. $s^2t + st^2 - st + 1$ none of these
   c. $4y^2 - 10y + 16$ trinomial
   d. $15h$ monomial

4. a. Explain why ab is a monomial while $a + b$ is a binomial.
   ab is one term. Because of the $+$ sign, $a + b$ is two terms.
   b. Is every term of a polynomial a monomial?   yes
   c. The degree of x^2 is 2. What is the degree of 3^2? Explain your answer.   0; Since $3^2 = 9$, and the degree of a constant is 0, the degree of 3^2 is 0.
   d. For $3x^2 - 4x + 9$, what is the leading term, the leading coefficient, and the constant term? $3x^2$, 3, 9

Operations with Polynomials

Just like numbers in arithmetic, polynomials can be added, subtracted, multiplied, divided, and raised to powers. We have discussed some rules for performing operations with polynomials that have more than one terms.

Fill in the blanks.

5. To add two polynomials, remove the parentheses and _____combine_____ any like terms.

6. To subtract two polynomials, drop the minus sign and the parentheses, and _____change_____ the sign of every term within the parentheses of the second polynomial. Then combine like terms.

7. To multiply two polynomials, multiply _____each_____ term of one polynomial by _____each_____ term of the other polynomial and combine like terms.

8. To divide two polynomials, use the _____long_____ division method.

Do the operations.

9. $(2x + 3) + (x - 8)$ $3x - 5$

10. $(2x + 3) - (x - 8)$ $x + 11$

11. $(2x + 3)(x - 8)$ $2x^2 - 13x - 24$

12. $(2x^2 + 3)^2$ $4x^4 + 12x^2 + 9$

13. $(y^2 + y - 6) + (y + 3)$ $y^2 + 2y - 3$

14. $(y^2 + y - 6) - (y + 3)$ $y^2 - 9$

15. $(y^2 + y - 6)(y + 3)$ $y^3 + 4y^2 - 3y - 18$

16. $(y^2 + y - 6) \div (y + 3)$ $y - 2$

Polynomial Functions

Polynomial functions can be used to describe such situations as the stopping distance of a car, the appreciation of a house, and the area of a geometric figure.

17. If $f(x) = x^3 - 2x + 5$, find $f(-2)$.   1

18. STOPPING DISTANCE   A vehicle's stopping distance in feet is given by the polynomial function $f(v) = 0.04v^2 + 0.9v$, where v is the velocity. Find the stopping distance when the vehicle is traveling at 40 mph.   100 ft

Section 4.1

RULES FOR EXPONENTS   Have a student in your group write each of the five rules for exponents listed on page 273 on separate 3×5 cards. On a second set of cards, write an explanation of each rule using words. On a third set of cards, write a separate example of the use of each rule for exponents. Shuffle the cards and work together to match the symbolic description, the word description, and the example for each of the five rules for exponents.

Section 4.2

GRAPHING   Complete Table 1, plot the ordered pairs on a rectangular coordinate system, and then draw a smooth curve through the points. Do the same for Table 2, using the same coordinate system. Compare the graphs. How are they similar, and how do they differ?

x	2^x	x	2^{-x}
-2		-2	
-1		-1	
0		0	
1		1	
2		2	
3		3	

TABLE 1   TABLE 2

Section 4.3

SCIENTIFIC NOTATION   Go to the library and find five examples of extremely large and five examples of extremely small positive numbers. Encyclopedias, government statistics books, and science books are good places to look. Write each number in scientific notation on a separate piece of paper. Include a brief explanation of what the number represents. Present the ten examples in numerical order, beginning with the smallest number first.

Section 4.4

POLYNOMIAL FUNCTIONS   The height (in feet) of a rock from the floor of the Grand Canyon t seconds after being thrown downward from the rim with an initial velocity of 6 feet per second is given by the polynomial

$$f(t) = -16t^2 - 6t + 5,292$$

a. Find $f(0)$ and $f(18)$ and explain their significance.
b. Find $f(3)$, $f(6)$, $f(9)$, $f(12)$, and $f(15)$. Use this information to show the position of the rock for these times on the scale shown in Illustration 1.

c. Are the distances the rock fell during each 3-second time interval the same?

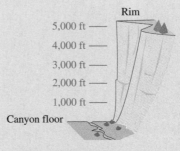

ILLUSTRATION 1

Section 4.5

ADDING POLYNOMIALS   An old adage is that "You can't add apples and oranges." Give an example of how this concept applies when adding two polynomials.

Section 4.6

MULTIPLYING BINOMIALS   Recall that the formula for the area of a rectangle is $A = lw$ and the formula for the area of a square is $A = s^2$.

a. Express the area of each of the large figures in Illustration 2 as a product of two binomials.
b. Find the area of each large figure by finding the sum of the areas of each of its parts.
c. In each case, show the relationship between your answers to part a and part b.

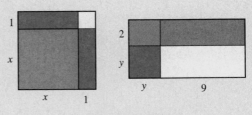

ILLUSTRATION 2

Section 4.7

WORKING WITH MONOMIALS   For the monomials $15a^3$ and $5a^2$, show, if possible, how they are added, subtracted, multiplied, and divided. If an operation cannot be done, explain why this is so.

Section 4.8

WORKING WITH POLYNOMIALS   Add, subtract, multiply, and divide the polynomials $6a^2 - 7a + 2$ and $2a - 1$.

325

CHAPTER REVIEW

SECTION 4.1	*Natural-Number Exponents*

CONCEPTS

If n represents a natural number, then

$$x^n = \overbrace{x \cdot x \cdot x \cdot \,\cdots\, \cdot x}^{n \text{ factors of } x}$$

where x is called the *base* and n is called the *exponent*.

Rules for exponents:
If m and n represent integers, then

$$x^m x^n = x^{m+n}$$
$$(x^m)^n = x^{m \cdot n}$$
$$(xy)^n = x^n y^n$$
$$\left(\frac{x}{y}\right)^n = \frac{x^n}{y^n} \quad (y \neq 0)$$
$$\frac{x^m}{x^n} = x^{m-n} \quad (x \neq 0)$$

REVIEW EXERCISES

1. Write each expression without using exponents.

   a. $-3x^4$ $-3 \cdot x \cdot x \cdot x \cdot x$
   b. $\left(\frac{1}{2}pq\right)^3$ $\left(\frac{1}{2}pq\right)\left(\frac{1}{2}pq\right)\left(\frac{1}{2}pq\right)$

2. Evaluate each expression.

   a. 5^3 125
   b. $(-8)^2$ 64
   c. -8^2 -64
   d. $(5-3)^2$ 4

3. Simplify each expression.

   a. $x^3 x^2$ x^5
   b. $-3y(y^5)$ $-3y^6$
   c. $(y^7)^3$ y^{21}
   d. $(3x)^4$ $81x^4$
   e. $b^3 b^4 b^5$ b^{12}
   f. $-z^2(z^3 y^2)$ $-y^2 z^5$
   g. $(-16s)^2 s$ $256s^3$
   h. $(2x^2 y)^2$ $4x^4 y^2$
   i. $(x^2 x^3)^3$ x^{15}
   j. $\left(\frac{x^2 y}{xy^2}\right)^2$ $\frac{x^2}{y^2}$
   k. $\frac{x^7}{x^3}$ x^4
   l. $\frac{(5y^2 z^3)^3}{(yz)^5}$ $125yz^4$

4. Find the area or the volume of each figure, whichever is appropriate.

   a. $64x^{12}$ in.^{3}
   b. y^4 m^2

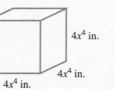

$4x^4$ in.
$4x^4$ in.
$4x^4$ in.

y^2 m
y^2 m

SECTION 4.2	*Zero and Negative Integer Exponents*

Zero exponents:
$$x^0 = 1 \quad (x \neq 0)$$

Negative integer exponents:
$$x^{-n} = \frac{1}{x^n} \quad (x \neq 0)$$

5. Write each expression without using negative exponents or parentheses.

   a. x^0 1
   b. $(3x^2 y^2)^0$ 1
   c. $(3x^0)^2$ 9
   d. 10^{-3} $\frac{1}{1,000}$
   e. $\left(\frac{3}{4}\right)^{-1}$ $\frac{4}{3}$
   f. -5^{-2} $-\frac{1}{25}$
   g. x^{-5} $\frac{1}{x^5}$
   h. $-6y^4 y^{-5}$ $-\frac{6}{y}$
   i. $\frac{x^{-3}}{x^7}$ $\frac{1}{x^{10}}$
   j. $(x^{-3} x^{-4})^{-2}$ x^{14}
   k. $\left(\frac{x^2}{x}\right)^{-5}$ $\frac{1}{x^5}$
   l. $\left(\frac{3z^4}{z^3}\right)^{-2}$ $\frac{1}{9z^2}$

6. Write each expression with a single exponent.

   a. $y^{3n}y^{4n}$ y^{7n}

   b. $\dfrac{z^{8c}}{z^{10c}}$ $\dfrac{1}{z^{2c}}$

SECTION 4.3   *Scientific Notation*

A number is written in *scientific notation* if it is written as the product of a number between 1 (including 1) and 10 and an integer power of 10.

7. Write each number in scientific notation.

   a. 728 7.28×10^2 **b.** 9,370,000 9.37×10^6

   c. 0.0136 1.36×10^{-2} **d.** 0.00942 9.42×10^{-3}

   e. 0.018×10^{-2} 1.8×10^{-4} **f.** 753×10^3 7.53×10^5

8. Write each number in standard notation.

   a. 7.26×10^5 726,000   **b.** 3.91×10^{-4} 0.000391

   c. 2.68×10^0 2.68   **d.** 5.76×10^1 57.6

Scientific notation provides an easier way to do some computations.

9. Simplify each fraction by first writing each number in scientific notation, then do the arithmetic. Express the result in standard notation.

   a. $\dfrac{(0.00012)(0.00004)}{0.00000016}$ 0.03   **b.** $\dfrac{(4,800)(20,000)}{600,000}$ 160

10. WORLD POPULATION   As of 2000, the world's population was estimated to be 6.08 billion. Write this number in standard notation and in scientific notation. $6,080,000,000; 6.08 \times 10^9$

11. ATOMS   Illustration 1 shows a cross section of an atom. How many nuclei, placed end-to-end, would it take to stretch across the atom?
$1.0 \times 10^5 = 100,000$

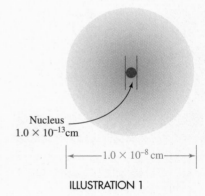

Nucleus
1.0×10^{-13}cm

$\longleftarrow 1.0 \times 10^{-8} \text{ cm} \longrightarrow$

ILLUSTRATION 1

SECTION 4.4   *Polynomials*

A *polynomial* is a term or a sum of terms in which all variables have whole-number exponents.

12. Tell whether each expression is a polynomial.

   a. $x^3 - x^2 - x - 1$ yes   **b.** $x^{-2} - x^{-1} - 1$ no

   c. $\dfrac{11}{y} + 4y$ no   **d.** $-16x^2y + 5xy^2$ yes

13. Consider the polynomial $3x^3 - x^2 + x + 10$.

   a. How many terms does the polynomial have?   4

   b. What is the leading term? $3x^3$

   c. What is the coefficient of the second term? -1

   d. What is the constant term?   10

The *degree of a monomial ax^n* is n. The *degree of a monomial* in several variables is the sum of the exponents on those variables. The *degree of a polynomial* is the same as the degree of its term with the largest degree.

14. Find the degree of each polynomial and classify it as a monomial, binomial, trinomial, or none of these.

   a. $13x^7$ 7th, monomial   **b.** $-16a^2b$ 3rd, monomial

   c. $5^3x + x^2$ 2nd, binomial   **d.** $-3x^5 + x - 1$ 5th, trinomial

   e. $9xy^2 + 21x^3y^3$ **f.** $4s^4 - 3s^2 + 5s + 4$

      6th, binomial   4th, none of these

If $f(x)$ is a polynomial function in x, then $f(3)$ is the value of the function when $x = 3$.

15. Let $f(x) = 3x^2 + 2x + 1$. Find each value.

   a. $f(3)$ 34   **b.** $f(0)$ 1

   c. $f(-2)$ 9   **d.** $f(-0.2)$ 0.72

16. ▦ DIVING   See Illustration 2. The number of inches that the woman deflects the diving board is given by the function

$$f(x) = 0.1875x^2 - 0.0078125x^3$$

where x is the number of feet that she stands from the front anchor point of the board. Find the amount of deflection if she stands on the end of the diving board, 8 feet from the anchor point.   8 in.

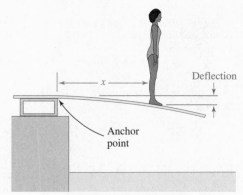

ILLUSTRATION 2

SECTION 4.5   *Adding and Subtracting Polynomials*

When *adding* or *subtracting polynomials,* add or subtract like terms by combining the numerical coefficients and using the same variables and the same exponents.

17. Simplify each expression.

   a. $3x^6 + 5x^5 - x^6$ $2x^6 + 5x^5$ **b.** $x^2y^2 - 3x^2y^2$ $-2x^2y^2$

   c. $(3x^2 + 2x) + (5x^2 - 8x)$ $8x^2 - 6x$

   d. $3(9x^2 + 3x + 7) - 2(11x^2 - 5x + 9)$ $5x^2 + 19x + 3$

Polynomials can be added or subtracted *vertically.*

18. Do the operations.

   a. $\begin{array}{r} 3x^2 + 5x + 2 \\ +\ \ \ x^2 - 3x + 6 \\ \hline 4x^2 + 2x + 8 \end{array}$ **b.** $\begin{array}{r} 20x^3 \quad\quad\ \ + 12x \\ -\ \ 12x^3 + 7x^2 - 7x \\ \hline 8x^3 - 7x^2 + 19x \end{array}$

SECTION 4.6   *Multiplying Polynomials*

To multiply two monomials, first multiply the numerical factors and then multiply the variable factors.

19. Find each product.

   a. $(2x^2)(5x)$ $10x^3$ **b.** $(-6x^4z^3)(x^6z^2)$ $-6x^{10}z^5$

   c. $(2rst)(-3r^2s^3t^4)$ $-6r^3s^4t^5$ **d.** $5b^3 \cdot 6b^2 \cdot 4b^6$ $120b^{11}$

To multiply a polynomial with more than one term by a monomial, multiply each term of the polynomial by the monomial and simplify.

20. Find each product.

a. $5(x + 3)$ $5x + 15$

b. $x^2(3x^2 - 5)$ $3x^4 - 5x^2$

c. $x^2y(y^2 - xy)$ $x^2y^3 - x^3y^2$

d. $-2y^2(y^2 - 5y)$ $-2y^4 + 10y^3$

e. $2x(3x^4)(x + 2)$
$6x^6 + 12x^5$

f. $-3x(x^2 - x + 2)$
$-3x^3 + 3x^2 - 6x$

To multiply two binomials, use the *FOIL method:*
   F: First
   O: Outer
   I: Inner
   L: Last

21. Find each product.

a. $(x + 3)(x + 2)$ $x^2 + 5x + 6$

b. $(2x + 1)(x - 1)$ $2x^2 - x - 1$

c. $(3a - 3)(2a + 2)$ $6a^2 - 6$

d. $6(a - 1)(a + 1)$ $6a^2 - 6$

e. $(a - b)(2a + b)$
$2a^2 - ab - b^2$

f. $(-3x - y)(2x + y)$
$-6x^2 - 5xy - y^2$

Special products:

$(x + y)^2 = x^2 + 2xy + y^2$

$(x - y)^2 = x^2 - 2xy + y^2$

$(x + y)(x - y) = x^2 - y^2$

22. Find each product.

a. $(x + 3)(x + 3)$ $x^2 + 6x + 9$

b. $(x + 5)(x - 5)$ $x^2 - 25$

c. $(a - 3)^2$ $a^2 - 6a + 9$

d. $(x + 4)^2$ $x^2 + 8x + 16$

e. $(-2y + 1)^2$ $4y^2 - 4y + 1$

f. $(y^2 + 1)(y^2 - 1)$ $y^4 - 1$

To multiply one polynomial by another, multiply each term of one polynomial by each term of the other polynomial, and simplify.

23. Find each product.

a. $(3x + 1)(x^2 + 2x + 1)$
$3x^3 + 7x^2 + 5x + 1$

b. $(2a - 3)(4a^2 + 6a + 9)$
$8a^3 - 27$

24. Solve each equation.

a. $x^2 + 3 = x(x + 3)$ 1

b. $x^2 + x = (x + 1)(x + 2)$ -1

c. $(x + 2)(x - 5) = (x - 4)(x - 1)$ 7

d. $(x + 5)(3x + 1) = x^2 + (2x - 1)(x - 5)$ 0

25. APPLIANCE   Find the perimeter of the base, the area of the base, and the volume occupied by the dishwasher shown in Illustration 3.
$(6x + 10)$ in.; $(2x^2 + 11x - 6)$ in.²;
$(6x^3 + 33x^2 - 18x)$ in.³

$3x$ in.

$(x + 6)$ in.

$(2x - 1)$ in.

ILLUSTRATION 3

| **SECTION 4.7** | *Dividing Polynomials by Monomials* |

To divide monomials, use the method for simplifying fractions or use the rules for exponents.

26. Simplify each expression ($x > 0$, $y > 0$).

a. $\dfrac{-14x^2y}{21xy^3}$ $-\dfrac{2x}{3y^2}$

b. $\dfrac{(x^2)^2}{xx^4}$ $\dfrac{1}{x}$

To divide a polynomial by a monomial, divide each term of the numerator by the denominator.

27. Do each division. All the variables represent positive numbers.

a. $\dfrac{8x + 6}{2}$ $4x + 3$

b. $\dfrac{14xy - 21x}{7xy}$ $2 - \dfrac{3}{y}$

c. $\dfrac{15a^2b + 20ab^2 - 25ab}{5ab}$

$3a + 4b - 5$

d. $\dfrac{(x + y)^2 + (x - y)^2}{-2xy}$

$-\dfrac{x}{y} - \dfrac{y}{x}$

28. SAVINGS BONDS   How many \$50 savings bonds would have a total value of \$$(50x + 250)$? $x + 5$

SECTION 4.8	*Dividing Polynomials by Polynomials*

Long division is used to divide one polynomial by another. When a division has a remainder, write the answer in the form

$$\text{Quotient} + \frac{\text{remainder}}{\text{divisor}}$$

The division method works best when the exponents of the terms of the divisor and the dividend are written in descending order.

When the dividend is missing a term, write it with a coefficient of zero or leave a blank space.

29. Do each division.

a. $x + 2 \overline{)x^2 + 3x + 5}$ $x + 1 + \dfrac{3}{x + 2}$ **b.** $x - 1 \overline{)x^2 - 6x + 5}$ $x - 5$

c. $\dfrac{2x^2 + 3 + 7x}{x + 3}$ $2x + 1$ **d.** $\dfrac{3x^2 + 14x - 2}{3x - 1}$ $x + 5 + \dfrac{3}{3x - 1}$

e. $2x - 1 \overline{)6x^3 + x^2 + 1}$ **f.** $3x + 1 \overline{)-13x - 4 + 9x^3}$

$\quad 3x^2 + 2x + 1 + \dfrac{2}{2x - 1}$ $\quad 3x^2 - x - 4$

30. Use multiplication to show that the answer when dividing $3y^2 + 11y + 6$ by $y + 3$ is $3y + 2$.

31. ZOOLOGY   The distance in inches traveled by a certain type of snail in $(2x - 1)$ minutes is given by the polynomial $8x^2 + 2x - 3$. At what rate did the snail travel? $(4x + 3)$ in./min

Chapter 4 Test

1. Use exponents to rewrite $2xxxyyyy$. $2x^3y^4$

2. Evaluate $(3 + 5)^2$. 64

Write each expression as an expression containing only one exponent.

3. $y^2(yy^3)$ y^6

4. $(2x^3)^5(x^2)^3$ $32x^{21}$

In Problems 5–8, simplify each expression. Write answers without using parentheses or negative exponents.

5. $3x^0$ 3

6. $2y^{-5}y^2$ $\dfrac{2}{y^3}$

7. $\dfrac{y^2}{yy^{-2}}$ y^3

8. $\left(\dfrac{a^2b^{-1}}{4a^3b^{-2}}\right)^{-3}$ $\dfrac{64a^3}{b^3}$

9. What is the volume of a cube that has sides of length $10y^4$ inches? $1{,}000y^{12}$ in.^{3}

10. Rewrite 4^{-2} using a positive exponent and then evaluate the result. $\dfrac{1}{4^2},\ \dfrac{1}{16}$

11. ELECTRICITY   One ampere (amp) corresponds to the flow of 6,250,000,000,000,000,000 electrons per second past any point in a direct current (DC) circuit. Write this number in scientific notation. 6.25×10^{18}

12. Write 9.3×10^{-5} in standard notation. 0.000093

13. Identify $3x^2 + 2$ as a monomial, binomial, or trinomial. binomial

14. Find the degree of the polynomial $3x^2y^3 + 2x^3y - 5x^2y$. 5th degree

15. If $f(x) = x^2 + x - 2$, find $f(-2)$. 0

16. Simplify $(xy)^2 + 5x^2y^2 - (3x)^2y^2$. $-3x^2y^2$

17. Simplify $-6(x - y) + 2(x + y) - 3(x + 2y)$.
$-7x + 2y$

18. Subtract:
$$\begin{array}{r} 2x^2 - 7x + 3 \\ 3x^2 - 2x - 1 \\ \hline -x^2 - 5x + 4 \end{array}$$

In Problems 19–24, find each product.

19. $(-2x^3)(2x^2y)$ $-4x^5y$

20. $3y^2(y^2 - 2y + 3)$ $3y^4 - 6y^3 + 9y^2$

21. $(x - 9)(x + 9)$ $x^2 - 81$

22. $(3y - 4)^2$ $9y^2 - 24y + 16$

23. $(2x - 5)(3x + 4)$ $6x^2 - 7x - 20$

24. $(2x - 3)(x^2 - 2x + 4)$ $2x^3 - 7x^2 + 14x - 12$

25. Solve $(a + 2)^2 = (a - 3)^2$. $\frac{1}{2}$

26. Simplify $\dfrac{8x^2y^3z^4}{16x^3y^2z^4}$. $\dfrac{y}{2x}$

27. Simplify $\dfrac{6a^2 - 12b^2}{24ab}$. $\dfrac{a}{4b} - \dfrac{b}{2a}$

28. Divide $2x + 3\overline{)2x^2 - x - 6}$. $x - 2$

29. In your own words, explain this rule for exponents:

$$x^{-n} = \frac{1}{x^n}$$

30. A rectangle has an area of $(x^2 - 6x + 5)$ ft^2 and a length of $(x - 1)$ feet. Show how division can be used to find the width of the rectangle. Explain your steps.
$(x - 5)$ ft

Chapters 1-4   Cumulative Review Exercises

1. PERSONAL SAVINGS RATE   The graph in Illustration 1 shows a situation occurring in September of 1998 that hadn't occurred since the Great Depression. Explain what was unusual.

The negative savings rate means that Americans spent more than they earned that month.

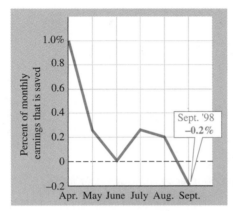

Based on data from the U.S. Department of Commerce

ILLUSTRATION 1

2. Find $\dfrac{3}{4} \div \dfrac{6}{5}$. $\frac{5}{8}$

3. Find $\dfrac{7}{10} - \dfrac{1}{14}$. $\frac{22}{35}$

4. Is π a rational or irrational number?   irrational

5. RACING   Suppose a driver has completed x laps of a 250-lap race. Write an expression for how many more laps he must make to finish the race. $250 - x$

6. CLINICAL TRIALS   In a clinical test of Aricept, a drug to treat Alzheimer's disease, one group of patients took a placebo (a sugar pill) while another group took the actual medication. See Illustration 2. Find the number of patients in each group who experienced nausea. Round to the nearest whole number.   19, 16

Comparison of rates of adverse events in patients		
Adverse event	Group 1—Placebo (number = 315)	Group 2—Aricept (number = 311)
Nausea	6%	5%

ILLUSTRATION 2

Consider the algebraic expression $3x^3 + 5x^2y + 37y$.

7. Find the coefficient of the second term.   5

8. What is the third term? $37y$

Simplify each expression.

9. $3x - 5x + 2y$ $-2x + 2y$

10. $3(x - 7) + 2(8 - x)$ $x - 5$

11. $2x^2y^3 - xy(xy^2)$ x^2y^3

12. $x^2(3 - y) + x(xy + x)$ $4x^2$

Solve each equation.

13. $3(x - 5) + 2 = 2x$ 13   **14.** $\dfrac{x - 5}{3} - 5 = 7$ 41

Solve each formula for the variable indicated.

15. $A = \dfrac{1}{2}h(b + B)$; for h $h = \frac{2A}{b + B}$

16. $y = mx + b$; for x $x = \frac{y - b}{m}$

Evaluate each expression.

17. $4^2 - 5^2$ -9 **18.** $(4 - 5)^2$ 1

19. $\dfrac{-3 - (-7)}{2^2 - 3}$ 4   **20.** $12 - 2[1 - (-8 + 2)]$ -2

Solve each inequality and graph the solution set. Then describe the solution using interval notation

21. $8(4 + x) > 10(6 + x)$
$x < -14, (-\infty, -14)$ $\xleftarrow{\qquad}\!\!)\!\!\xrightarrow{\qquad}$ -14

22. $-9 < 3(x + 2) \le 3$
$-5 < x \le -1, (-5, -1]$ $\xleftarrow{}(\ \ ]\xrightarrow{}$ $-5\quad -1$

Graph each equation.

23. $y = x^2$ **24.** $y = |x|$

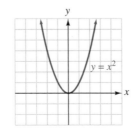

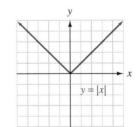

25. $4x - 3y = 12$

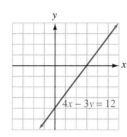

26. $3x = 12$

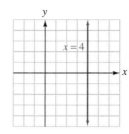

$x = 4$

Find the slope of the line with the given properties.

27. Passing through $(-2, 4)$ and $(6, 8)$ $\frac{1}{2}$

28. A line that is horizontal 0

29. An equation of $y = -4x + 3$ -4

30. An equation of $2x - 3y = 12$ $\frac{2}{3}$

Write the equation of the line with the following properties.

31. Slope $= \dfrac{2}{3}$, y-intercept $= (0, 5)$ $y = \frac{2}{3}x + 5$

32. Passing through $(-2, 4)$ and $(6, 10)$ $3x - 4y = -22$

33. A horizontal line passing through $(2, 4)$ $y = 4$

34. A vertical line passing through $(2, 4)$ $x = 2$

Are the graphs of the lines parallel or perpendicular?

35. $y = -\dfrac{3}{4}x + \dfrac{15}{4}$ perpendicular

$\quad 4x - 3y = 25$

36. $y = -\dfrac{3}{4}x + \dfrac{15}{4}$ parallel

$\quad 6x = 15 - 8y$

Tell whether each equation defines a function.

37. $y = x^3 - 4$ yes   **38.** $x = |y|$ no

In Exercises 35–38, $f(x) = 2x^2 - 3$. Find each value.

39. $f(0)$ -3 **40.** $f(3)$ 15

41. $f(-2)$ 5 **42.** $f(0.5)$ -2.5

43. Find the domain and range of the function $f(x) = |x|$.
D: all real numbers, R: real numbers greater than or equal to 0

44. Tell whether the graph is the graph of a function.   no

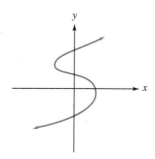

45. Give an example of a positive rate of change and a negative rate of change.
The temperature is rising at a rate of 3°/hr; the temperature is falling at a rate of -3°/hr.

46. Evaluate -3^2. -9

Write each expression using one positive exponent.

47. $(y^3y^5)y^6$ y^{14} **48.** $(x^3x^4)^2$ x^{14}

49. $\dfrac{x^3x^4}{x^2x^3}$ x^2 **50.** $\dfrac{a^4b^0}{a^{-3}}$ a^7

51. x^{-5} $\dfrac{1}{x^5}$ **52.** $(-2y)^{-4}$ $\dfrac{1}{16y^4}$

53. $(x^{-4})^2$ $\dfrac{1}{x^8}$ **54.** $\left(-\dfrac{x^3}{x^{-2}}\right)^3$ $-x^{15}$

Write each number in scientific notation.

55. $615,000$ 6.15×10^5 **56.** 0.0000013 1.3×10^{-6}

Write each number in standard notation.

57. 5.25×10^{-4} 0.000525 **58.** 2.77×10^3 $2,770$

In Exercises 59–60, give the degree of each polynomial.

59. $3x^2 + 2x - 5$ 2 **60.** $-3x^3y^2 + 3x^2y^2 - xy$ 5

61. MUSICAL INSTRUMENTS   The gong shown in Illustration 3 is a percussion instrument used throughout Southeast Asia. The amount of deflection of the horizontal support (in inches) is given by the polynomial function

$$f(x) = 0.01875x^4 - 0.15x^3 + 1.2x$$

where x is the distance (in feet) that the gong is hung from one end of the support. Find the deflection if the gong is hung in the middle of the support.   1.5 in.

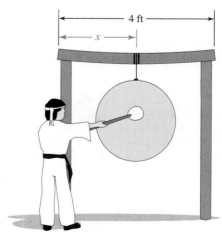

ILLUSTRATION 3

62. Consider the polynomial $2x^2 - 5x + 9$. Determine each of the following.

a. The number of terms   3

b. The leading term $2x^2$

c. The leading coefficient   2

d. The degree of the second term   1

e. The degree of the polynomial   2

f. The constant term   9

Do the operations.

63. $(3x^2 + 2x - 7) - (2x^2 - 2x + 7)$ $x^2 + 4x - 14$

64. $(2x^2 - 3x + 4) + (2x^2 + 2x - 5)$ $4x^2 - x - 1$

65. $-5x^2(7x^3 - 2x^2 - 2)$ $-35x^5 + 10x^4 + 10x^2$

66. $(3x^3y^2)(-4x^2y^3)$ $-12x^5y^5$

67. $(3x - 7)(2x + 8)$ $6x^2 + 10x - 56$

68. $(5x - 4y)(3x + 2y)$ $15x^2 - 2xy - 8y^2$

69. $(3x + 1)^2$ $9x^2 + 6x + 1$

70. $(x - 2)(x^2 + 2x + 4)$ $x^3 - 8$

71. $\dfrac{6x^2 - 8x}{2x}$ $3x - 4$

72. $x - 3 \overline{)2x^2 - 5x - 3}$ $2x + 1$

5

Factoring and Quadratic Equations

IN THIS CHAPTER, WE WILL DISCUSS SOME METHODS FOR FACTORING POLYNOMIALS. FACTORING REVERSES THE PROCESS OF MULTIPLICATION. IT CAN BE USED TO SIMPLIFY EXPRESSIONS AND TO SOLVE EQUATIONS.

5.1 Factoring Out the Greatest Common Factor and Factoring by Grouping

In this section, you will learn about

- Factoring natural numbers • The greatest common factor (GCF)
- Finding the GCF of several monomials
- Factoring out the greatest common factor • Factoring out a negative factor
- Factoring by grouping

INTRODUCTION. Recall that the distributive property provides a way to multiply a monomial and a binomial. For example,

$$4y(3y + 5) = 4y \cdot 3y + 4y \cdot 5$$
$$= 12y^2 + 20y$$

In this section, we will reverse the operation of multiplication. Given a polynomial such as $12y^2 + 20y$, we will ask ourselves, "What factors were multiplied to obtain $12y^2 + 20y$?" The process of finding the individual factors of a known product is called **factoring.**

The multiplication process	**The factoring process**
Given the factors . . . find the product	Given the product . . . find the factors
$4y(3y + 5) = ?$	$12y^2 + 20y = ?(\ ?\ )$

To begin the discussion of factoring, we consider two methods that can be used to factor natural numbers.

Factoring natural numbers

Because 4 divides 12 exactly, 4 is called a **factor** of 12. The numbers 1, 2, 3, 4, 6, and 12 are the natural-number factors of 12, because each divides 12 exactly.

Prime numbers

> A **prime number** is a natural number greater than 1 whose only factors are 1 and itself.

For example, 17 is a prime number, because

1. 17 is a natural number greater than 1, and
2. the only two natural-number factors of 17 are 1 and 17.

The prime numbers less than 50 are

2, 3, 5, 7, 11, 13, 17, 19, 23, 29, 31, 37, 41, 43, and 47

A natural number is said to be in **prime-factored form** if it is written as the product of factors that are prime numbers.

To find the prime-factored form of a natural number, we can use a **factoring tree.** The following examples show two ways to find the prime-factored form of 90 using factoring trees. The factoring process stops when a row of the tree contains only prime-number factors.

1. Start with 90.

2. Factor 90 as $9 \cdot 10$.

3. Factor 9 and 10.

$$90$$
$$9 \quad \cdot \quad 10$$
$$3 \cdot 3 \quad \cdot \quad 2 \cdot 5$$

1. Start with 90.

2. Factor 90 as $6 \cdot 15$.

3. Factor 6 and 15.

$$90$$
$$6 \quad \cdot \quad 15$$
$$2 \cdot 3 \quad \cdot \quad 3 \cdot 5$$

Since the prime factors in either case are $2 \cdot 3 \cdot 3 \cdot 5$, the prime-factored form, or the **prime factorization,** of 90 is $2 \cdot 3^2 \cdot 5$. This example illustrates the **fundamental theorem of arithmetic,** which states that there is only one prime factorization for every natural number greater than 1.

We can also find the prime factorization of a natural number using the **division method.** For example, to find the prime factorization of 42, we begin by choosing the *smallest* prime number that will divide the given number exactly. We continue this process until the result of the division is a prime number.

Step 1: 2 divides 42 exactly. The result is 21, which is not prime. We continue the process.

$$2\,\overline{|\,42}$$
$$21$$

Step 2: We choose the smallest prime number that divides 21. The prime number 2 does not divide 21 exactly, but 3 does. The result is 7, which is prime. We are done.

$$2\,\overline{|\,42}$$
$$3\,\overline{|\,21}$$
$$7$$

The prime factorization of 42 is $2 \cdot 3 \cdot 7$.

EXAMPLE 1 *Prime factorizations.*   Find the prime factorization of 150.

Solution

We can use a factoring tree or the division method to find the prime factorization.

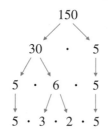

$$\begin{array}{r} 2\,\overline{|\,150} \\ 3\,\overline{|\,\;75} \leftarrow 150 \div 2 \\ 5\,\overline{|\,\;25} \leftarrow 75 \div 3 \\ 5 \leftarrow 25 \div 5 \end{array}$$

Using exponents, we can write the prime factorization of 150 as $2 \cdot 3 \cdot 5^2$.

Self Check

Find the prime factorization of 225.

Answer: $3^2 \cdot 5^2$

The greatest common factor (GCF)

The right-hand sides of the equations

$$90 = 2 \cdot 3 \cdot 3 \cdot 5$$
$$42 = 2 \cdot 3 \cdot 7$$

show the prime-factored forms of 90 and 42. The color highlighting indicates that 90 and 42 have one prime factor of 2 and one prime factor of 3 in common. We can conclude that $2 \cdot 3 = 6$ is the largest natural number that divides 90 and 42 exactly, and we say that 6 is their **greatest common factor (GCF).**

$$\frac{90}{6} = 15 \qquad \text{and} \qquad \frac{42}{6} = 7$$

EXAMPLE 2   *Finding the GCF of three numbers.*   Find the greatest common factor of 24, 60, and 96.

Solution

We write each prime factorization and highlight the prime factors the three numbers have in common.

$24 = 2 \cdot 2 \cdot 2 \cdot 3$

$60 = 2 \cdot 2 \cdot 3 \cdot 5$

$96 = 2 \cdot 2 \cdot 2 \cdot 2 \cdot 2 \cdot 3$

Since 24, 60, and 96 each have two factors of 2 and one factor of 3, their greatest common factor is $2 \cdot 2 \cdot 3 = 12$.

Self Check

Find the GCF for 45, 60, 75.

Answer: $3 \cdot 5 = 15$ ■

Finding the GCF of several monomials

The right-hand sides of the equations

$$12y^2 = 2 \cdot 2 \cdot 3 \cdot y \cdot y$$
$$20y = 2 \cdot 2 \cdot 5 \cdot y$$

show the prime factorizations of $12y^2$ and $20y$. Since the monomials have two factors of 2 and one factor of y in common, their GCF is

$$2 \cdot 2 \cdot y \qquad \text{or} \qquad 4y$$

To find the GCF of several monomials, we follow these steps.

Strategy for finding the greatest common factor (GCF)	1. Find the prime factorization of each monomial. 2. List each common factor the least number of times it appears in any one monomial. 3. Find the product of the factors in the list to obtain the GCF.

EXAMPLE 3   *Finding the GCF of three monomials.*   Find the GCF of $10x^3y^2$, $60x^2y$, and $30xy^2$.

Solution

Step 1: Find the prime factorization of each monomial.

$10x^3y^2 = 2 \cdot 5 \cdot x \cdot x \cdot x \cdot y \cdot y$

$60x^2y = 2 \cdot 2 \cdot 3 \cdot 5 \cdot x \cdot x \cdot y$

$30xy^2 = 2 \cdot 3 \cdot 5 \cdot x \cdot y \cdot y$

Step 2: List each common factor the least number of times it appears in any one monomial: 2, 5, x, and y.

Step 3: Find the product of the factors in the list:

$2 \cdot 5 \cdot x \cdot y = 10xy$ The GCF is $10xy$.

Self Check

Find the GCF of $20a^2b^3$, $12ab^4$, and $8a^3b^2$.

Answer: $4ab^2$ ■

Factoring out the greatest common factor

To factor $12y^2 + 20y$, we find the GCF of $12y^2$ and $20y$ (which is $4y$) and use the distributive property.

$$12y^2 + 20y = \mathbf{4y} \cdot 3y + \mathbf{4y} \cdot 5 \quad \text{Write each term of the polynomial as the product of the GCF, } 4y, \text{ and one other factor.}$$

$$= \mathbf{4y}(3y + 5) \quad \text{4y is a common factor of both terms.}$$

This process is called **factoring out the greatest common factor.**

EXAMPLE 4   *Factoring out the greatest common factor.*   Factor $25 - 5m$.

Solution
To find the GCF of 25 and $5m$, we find their prime factorizations.

$$\left.\begin{array}{l} 25 = \mathbf{5} \cdot 5 \\ 5m = \mathbf{5} \cdot m \end{array}\right\} \quad \text{GCF} = 5$$

We can use the distributive property to factor out the GCF.

$$25 - 5m = \mathbf{5} \cdot 5 - \mathbf{5} \cdot m \quad \text{Factor each monomial using 5 and one other factor.}$$

$$= \mathbf{5}(5 - m) \quad \text{Factor out the common factor of 5.}$$

We check by verifying that $5(5 - m) = 25 - 5m$.

Self Check
Factor $18x - 24$.

Answer: $6(3x - 4)$ ■

EXAMPLE 5   *Factoring out the GCF.*   Factor $35a^3b^2 + 14a^2b^3$.

Solution
To find the GCF, we find the prime factorizations of $35a^3b^2$ and $14a^2b^3$.

$$\left.\begin{array}{l} 35a^3b^2 = \mathbf{5} \cdot \mathbf{7} \cdot \mathbf{a} \cdot \mathbf{a} \cdot a \cdot \mathbf{b} \cdot \mathbf{b} \\ 14a^2b^3 = 2 \cdot \mathbf{7} \cdot \mathbf{a} \cdot \mathbf{a} \cdot \mathbf{b} \cdot \mathbf{b} \cdot b \end{array}\right\} \quad \text{GCF} = 7 \cdot a \cdot a \cdot b \cdot b = 7a^2b^2$$

We factor out the GCF of $7a^2b^2$.

$$35a^3b^2 + 14a^2b^3 = 7a^2b^2 \cdot 5a + 7a^2b^2 \cdot 2b$$

$$= 7a^2b^2(5a + 2b)$$

We check by verifying that $7a^2b^2(5a + 2b) = 35a^3b^2 + 14a^2b^3$.

Self Check
Factor $32x^2y^3 + 12x^3y^2$.

Answer: $4x^2y^2(8y + 3x)$ ■

EXAMPLE 6   *An implied coefficient of 1.*   Factor $4x^3y^2z - 2x^2yz + xz$.

Solution
The expression has three terms. We factor out the GCF, which is xz.

$$4x^3y^2z - 2x^2yz + xz = xz \cdot 4x^2y^2 - xz \cdot 2xy + xz \cdot \mathbf{1}$$

$$= xz(4x^2y^2 - 2xy + \mathbf{1})$$

The last term of $4x^3y^2z - 2x^2yz + xz$ has an implied coefficient of 1. When xz is factored out, we must write this coefficient of 1, as shown in blue. We check by verifying that $xz(4x^2y^2 - 2xy + 1) = 4x^3y^2z - 2x^2yz + xz$.

Self Check
Factor $2ab^2c + 4a^2bc - ab$.

Answer: $ab(2bc + 4ac - 1)$ ■

EXAMPLE 7   *Crayon.*   The amount of colored wax used to make the crayon shown in Figure 5-1 can be found by computing its volume using the formula

$$V = \pi r^2 h_1 + \frac{1}{3}\pi r^2 h_2$$

Factor the expression on the right-hand side of this equation.

FIGURE 5-1

Solution Each term on the right-hand side of the formula contains a factor of π and r^2.

$$V = \pi r^2 h_1 + \frac{1}{3}\pi r^2 h_2$$

$$= \pi r^2 \left(h_1 + \frac{1}{3}h_2\right) \quad \text{Factor out the GCF, } \pi r^2.$$

The formula to find the volume of the crayon can be expressed as $V = \pi r^2 \left(h_1 + \frac{1}{3}h_2\right)$.

EXAMPLE 8 *Factoring out a common binomial.* Factor $x(x + 4) + 3(x + 4)$.

Solution
The given polynomial has two terms:

$$\underbrace{x(x + 4)}_{\text{The first term}} + \underbrace{3(x + 4)}_{\text{The second term}}$$

The GCF of the terms is $x + 4$, which can be factored out.

$$x(x + 4) + 3(x + 4) = (x + 4)(x + 3)$$

Self Check
Factor $2y(y - 1) - 7(y - 1)$.

Answer: $(y - 1)(2y - 7)$

Factoring out a negative factor

It is often useful to factor out a common factor having a negative coefficient.

EXAMPLE 9 *Factoring out -1.* Factor -1 out of $-a^3 + 2a^2 - 4$.

Solution
First, we write each term of the polynomial as the product of -1 and another factor. Then we factor out the common factor of -1.

$$-a^3 + 2a^2 - 4 = (-1)a^3 + (-1)(-2a^2) + (-1)4$$

$$= -1(a^3 - 2a^2 + 4) \quad \text{Factor out } -1.$$

$$= -(a^3 - 2a^2 + 4) \quad \begin{array}{l}\text{The coefficient of 1 need not}\\ \text{be written.}\end{array}$$

We check by verifying that $-(a^3 - 2a^2 + 4) = -a^3 + 2a^2 - 4$.

Self Check
Factor -1 out of $-b^4 - 3b^2 + 2$.

Answer: $-(b^4 + 3b^2 - 2)$

EXAMPLE 10 *Factoring out the negative of the GCF.* Factor out the negative (opposite) of the GCF in $-18a^2b + 6ab^2 - 12a^2b^2$.

Solution
The GCF is $6ab$. To factor out its negative, we write each term of the polynomial as the product of $-6ab$ and another factor. Then we factor out $-6ab$.

$$-18a^2b + 6ab^2 - 12a^2b^2 = (-6ab)3a - (-6ab)b + (-6ab)2ab$$

$$= -6ab(3a - b + 2ab)$$

We check by verifying that $-6ab(3a - b + 2ab) = -18a^2b + 6ab^2 - 12a^2b^2$.

Self Check
Factor out the negative (opposite) of the GCF in $-27xy^2 - 18x^2y + 36x^2y^2$.

Answer: $-9xy(3y + 2x - 4xy)$

Factoring by grouping

Suppose we wish to factor the polynomial

$$ax + ay + cx + cy$$

Although no factor is common to all four terms, there is a common factor of a in $ax + ay$ and a common factor of c in $cx + cy$. We can factor out a and c, and then factor out $x + y$ to obtain

$$
\begin{aligned}
ax + ay + cx + cy &= a(x + y) + c(x + y) \\
&= (x + y)(a + c) \qquad \text{Factor out } x + y.
\end{aligned}
$$

We can check the result by multiplication.

$$
\begin{aligned}
(x + y)(a + c) &= ax + cx + ay + cy \\
&= ax + ay + cx + cy \quad \text{Rearrange the terms.}
\end{aligned}
$$

Thus, $ax + ay + cx + cy$ factors as $(x + y)(a + c)$. This type of factoring is called **factoring by grouping.**

Factoring by grouping	1. Group the terms of the polynomial so that the first two terms have a common factor and the last two terms have a common factor.
	2. Factor out the common factor from each group.
	3. Factor out the resulting common binomial factor. If there is no common binomial factor, regroup the terms of the polynomial and repeat steps 2 and 3.

EXAMPLE 11   *Factoring by grouping.*   Factor $2c - 2d + cd - d^2$.

Solution

Since 2 is a common factor of the first two terms and d is a common factor of the last two terms, we have

$$
\begin{aligned}
2c - 2d + cd - d^2 &= 2(c - d) + d(c - d) \quad \begin{array}{l}\text{Factor out 2 from } 2c - 2d \text{ and } d \\ \text{from } cd - d^2.\end{array} \\
&= (c - d)(2 + d) \qquad \text{Factor out } c - d.
\end{aligned}
$$

We check by verifying that

$$
\begin{aligned}
(c - d)(2 + d) &= 2c + cd - 2d - d^2 \\
&= 2c - 2d + cd - d^2 \quad \text{Rearrange the terms.}
\end{aligned}
$$

Self Check

Factor $7x - 7y + xy - y^2$.

Answer: $(x - y)(7 + y)$ ∎

EXAMPLE 12   *Factoring out -1.*   Factor $x^2y - ax - xy + a$.

Solution

Since x is a common factor of the first two terms, we can factor it out and proceed as follows.

$$x^2y - ax - xy + a = x(xy - a) - xy + a \quad \text{Factor out } x \text{ from } x^2y - ax.$$

If we factor -1 from $-xy + a$, a common binomial factor $(xy - a)$ appears, which we can factor out.

$$
\begin{aligned}
x^2y - ax - xy + a &= x(xy - a) - 1(xy - a) \\
&= (xy - a)(x - 1) \qquad \text{Factor out } xy - a.
\end{aligned}
$$

Check by multiplication.

Self Check

Factor $7b + 3c - 7bt - 3ct$.

Answer: $(7b + 3c)(1 - t)$ ∎

COMMENT   When factoring the expressions in the previous two examples, don't think that $2(c - d) + d(c - d)$ or $x(xy - a) - 1(xy - a)$ are in factored form. For an expression to be in factored form, the result must be a product.

The next example illustrates that when factoring a polynomial, we should always look for a common factor first.

EXAMPLE 13   *Factoring out the GCF first.*   Factor $10k + 10m - 2km - 2m^2$.

Solution

Since the four terms have a common factor of 2, we factor it out first. Then we use factoring by grouping to factor the polynomial within the parentheses. The first two terms have a common factor of 5. The last two terms have a common factor of $-m$.

$$
\begin{aligned}
10k + 10m - 2km - 2m^2 &= 2(5k + 5m - km - m^2) && \text{Factor out the GCF 2.} \\
&= 2[5(k + m) - m(k + m)] \\
&= 2[(k + m)(5 - m)] && \text{Factor out } k + m. \\
&= 2(k + m)(5 - m)
\end{aligned}
$$

Use multiplication to check the result.

Self Check

Factor $-4t - 4s - 4tz - 4sz$.

Answer: $-4(t + s)(1 + z)$ ■

STUDY SET   Section 5.1

VOCABULARY   *Fill in the blanks.*

1. A natural number greater than 1 whose only factors are 1 and itself is called a _____prime_____ number.

2. When we write 24 as $2^3 \cdot 3$, we say that 24 has been written in ___prime-factored___ form.

3. The GCF of several natural numbers is the _____largest_____ number that divides each of the numbers exactly.

4. When we write $15x^2 - 25x$ as $5x(3x - 5)$, we say that we have ___factored out___ the greatest common factor.

5. The process of finding the individual factors of a known product is called ___factoring___.

6. The numbers 1, 2, 3, 4, 6, and 12 are the natural-number _____factors_____ of 12.

CONCEPTS   *In Exercises 7–10, explain what is wrong with each solution.*

7. Factor $6a + 9b + 3$.

$$
\begin{aligned}
6a + 9b + 3 &= 3(2a + 3b + 0) \\
&= 3(2a + 3b)
\end{aligned}
$$

The 0 in the first line should be 1.

8. Prime factor 100.

$$
\begin{array}{r}
10\,|\,100 \\
5\,|\,10 \\
\hline
2
\end{array}
$$

$100 = 2 \cdot 5 \cdot 10$

10 can't be used in the division method; it is not a prime number.

9. Factor out the GCF: $30a^3 - 12a^2$.

$$
30a^3 - 12a^2 = 6a(5a^2 - 2a)
$$

The GCF is $6a^2$, not $6a$.

10. Factor $ab + b + a + 1$.

$$
\begin{aligned}
ab + b + a + 1 &= b(a + 1) + (a + 1) \\
&= (a + 1)b
\end{aligned}
$$

The answer should be $(a + 1)(b + 1)$.

11. What algebraic concept is illustrated in the work shown below?   factoring out the GCF

$$
4 \cdot 5x + 4 \cdot 3 = 4(5x + 3)
$$

12. a. Complete each tree diagram to prime-factor 30.

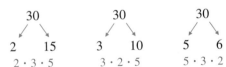

$$
\begin{array}{ccc}
30 & 30 & 30 \\
2 \quad 15 & 3 \quad 10 & 5 \quad 6 \\
2 \cdot 3 \cdot 5 & 3 \cdot 2 \cdot 5 & 5 \cdot 3 \cdot 2
\end{array}
$$

b. Complete the statement: The fundamental theorem of arithmetic states that every natural number greater than 1 has ___exactly one___ prime factorization.

13. The prime factorizations of three monomials are shown here. Find their GCF. $3x$

$$
\begin{aligned}
&3 \cdot 3 \cdot 5 \cdot x \cdot x \\
&2 \cdot 3 \cdot 5 \cdot x \cdot y \\
&2 \cdot 2 \cdot 3 \cdot x \cdot y \cdot y
\end{aligned}
$$

14. Consider the polynomial $2k - 8 + hk - 4h$.
   a. How many terms does the polynomial have? 4
   b. Is there a common factor of all the terms? no
   c. What is the common factor of the first two terms? 2
   d. What is the common factor of the last two terms? h

15. How can we check the answer of the problem shown below?

   Factor $3j^3 + 6j^2 + 2j + 4$.

   $$3j^3 + 6j^2 + 2j + 4 = 3j^2(j + 2) + 2(j + 2)$$
   $$= (j + 2)(3j^2 + 2)$$

   Find $(j + 2)(3j^2 + 2)$. The result, when written in descending powers of j, should be $3j^3 + 6j^2 + 2j + 4$.

16. List the first 12 prime numbers.
   2, 3, 5, 7, 11, 13, 17, 19, 23, 29, 31, 37

NOTATION In Exercises 17–18, complete each factorization.

17. Factor $b^3 - 6b^2 + 2b - 12$.
   $$b^3 - 6b^2 + 2b - 12 = b^2 (b - 6) + 2 (b - 6)$$
   $$= (b - 6) (b^2 + 2)$$

18. Factor $12b^3 - 6b^2 + 2b - 2$.
   $$12b^3 - 6b^2 + 2b - 2 = 2 (6b^3 - 3b^2 + b - 1)$$

19. In the expression $4x^2y + xy$, what is the coefficient of the last term? 1

20. Is the following statement true?
   $$-(x^2 - 3x + 1) = -1(x^2 - 3x + 1)$$ yes

PRACTICE Find the prime factorization of each number.

21. 12 $2^2 \cdot 3$
22. 24 $2^3 \cdot 3$
23. 15 $3 \cdot 5$
24. 20 $2^2 \cdot 5$
25. 40 $2^3 \cdot 5$
26. 62 $2 \cdot 31$
27. 98 $2 \cdot 7^2$
28. 112 $2^4 \cdot 7$
29. 225 $3^2 \cdot 5^2$
30. 144 $2^4 \cdot 3^2$
31. 288 $2^5 \cdot 3^2$
32. 968 $2^3 \cdot 11^2$

Complete each factorization.

33. $4a + 12 = $ 4 $(a + 3)$
34. $r^4 + r^2 = r^2(r^2 + 1)$
35. $4y^2 + 8y - 2xy = 2y(2y + $ 4 $ - x)$
36. $3x^2 - 6xy + 9xy^2 = $ 3x $ (x - 2y + 3y^2)$

Factor out the GCF.

37. $3x + 6$ $3(x + 2)$
38. $2y - 10$ $2(y - 5)$
39. $12x^2 - 6x - 24$ $6(2x^2 - x - 4)$
40. $27a^2 - 9a + 45$ $9(3a^2 - a + 5)$
41. $t^3 + 2t^2$ $t^2(t + 2)$
42. $b^3 - 3b^2$ $b^2(b - 3)$

43. $a^3 - a^2$ $a^2(a - 1)$
44. $r^3 + r^2$ $r^2(r + 1)$
45. $24x^2y^3 + 8xy^2$ $8xy^2(3xy + 1)$
46. $3x^2y^3 - 9x^4y^3$ $3x^2y^3(1 - 3x^2)$
47. $12uvw^3 - 18uv^2w^2$ $6uvw^2(2w - 3v)$
48. $14xyz - 16x^2y^2z$ $2xyz(7 - 8xy)$
49. $3x + 3y - 6z$ $3(x + y - 2z)$
50. $2x - 4y + 8z$ $2(x - 2y + 4z)$
51. $ab + ac - ad$ $a(b + c - d)$
52. $rs - rt + ru$ $r(s - t + u)$
53. $12r^2 - 3rs + 9r^2s^2$ $3r(4r - s + 3rs^2)$
54. $6a^2 - 12a^3b + 36ab$ $6a(a - 2a^2b + 6b)$
55. $\pi R^2 - \pi ab$ $\pi(R^2 - ab)$
56. $\frac{1}{3}\pi R^2h - \frac{1}{3}\pi rh$ $\frac{1}{3}\pi h(R^2 - r)$
57. $3(x + 2) - x(x + 2)$ $(x + 2)(3 - x)$
58. $t(5 - s) + 4(5 - s)$ $(5 - s)(t + 4)$
59. $h^2(14 + r) + 14 + r$ $(14 + r)(h^2 + 1)$
60. $k^2(14 + v) - 7(14 + v)$ $(14 + v)(k^2 - 7)$

Factor out -1 from each polynomial.

61. $-a - b$ $-(a + b)$
62. $-x - 2y$ $-(x + 2y)$
63. $-2x + 5y$ $-(2x - 5y)$
64. $-3x + 8z$ $-(3x - 8z)$
65. $-3m - 4n + 1$ $-(3m + 4n - 1)$
66. $-3r + 2s - 3$ $-(3r - 2s + 3)$
67. $-3ab - 5ac + 9bc$ $-(3ab + 5ac - 9bc)$
68. $-6yz + 12xz - 5xy$ $-(6yz - 12xz + 5xy)$

Factor each polynomial by factoring out the negative of the GCF.

69. $-3x^2 - 6x$ $-3x(x + 2)$
70. $-4a^2 + 6a$ $-2a(2a - 3)$
71. $-4a^2b^3 + 12a^3b^2$ $-4a^2b^2(b - 3a)$
72. $-25x^4y^3 + 30x^2y^3$ $-5x^2y^3(5x^2 - 6)$
73. $-4a^2b^2c^2 + 14a^2b^2c - 10ab^2c^2$
   $-2ab^2c(2ac - 7a + 5c)$
74. $-10x^4y^3z^2 + 8x^3y^2z - 20x^2y$
   $-2x^2y(5x^2y^2z^2 - 4xyz + 10)$

Factor by grouping.

75. $2x + 2y + ax + ay$ $(x + y)(2 + a)$
76. $bx + bz + 5x + 5z$ $(x + z)(b + 5)$
77. $7r + 7s - kr - ks$ $(r + s)(7 - k)$
78. $9p - 9q + mp - mq$ $(p - q)(9 + m)$
79. $xr + xs + yr + ys$ $(r + s)(x + y)$
80. $pm - pn + qm - qn$ $(m - n)(p + q)$
81. $2ax + 2bx + 3a + 3b$ $(2x + 3)(a + b)$
82. $3xy + 3xz - 5y - 5z$ $(y + z)(3x - 5)$
83. $2ab + 2ac + 3b + 3c$ $(b + c)(2a + 3)$

84. $3ac + a + 3bc + b$ $(3c + 1)(a + b)$

85. $6x^2 - 2x - 15x + 5$ $(3x - 1)(2x - 5)$

86. $6x^2 + 2x + 9x + 3$ $(3x + 1)(2x + 3)$

87. $9mp + 3mq - 3np - nq$ $(3p + q)(3m - n)$

88. $ax + bx - a - b$ $(a + b)(x - 1)$

89. $2xy + y^2 - 2x - y$ $(2x + y)(y - 1)$

90. $2xy - 3y^2 + 2x - 3y$ $(2x - 3y)(y + 1)$

91. $8z^5 + 12z^2 - 10z^3 - 15$ $(2z^3 + 3)(4z^2 - 5)$

92. $2a^4 + 2a^3 - 4a - 4$ $(a + 1)(2a^3 - 4)$

Factor by grouping. Factor out the GCF first.

93. $ax^3 + bx^3 + 2ax^2y + 2bx^2y$ $x^2(a + b)(x + 2y)$

94. $x^3y^2 - 2x^2y^2 + 3xy^2 - 6y^2$ $y^2(x - 2)(x^2 + 3)$

95. $4a^2b + 12a^2 - 8ab - 24a$ $4a(b + 3)(a - 2)$

96. $-4abc - 4ac^2 + 2bc + 2c^2$ $-2c(b + c)(2a - 1)$

97. $x^3y - x^2y - xy^2 + y^2$ $y(x^2 - y)(x - 1)$

98. $2x^3z - 4x^2z + 32xz - 64z$ $2z(x - 2)(x^2 + 16)$

APPLICATIONS

99. PICTURE FRAMING   The dimensions of a family portrait and the frame in which it is mounted are given in Illustration 1. Write an algebraic expression that describes

   a. the area of the picture frame. $12x^3$ in.^{2}

   b. the area of the portrait. $20x^2$ in.^{2}

   c. the area of the mat used in the framing. Express the result in factored form. $4x^2(3x - 5)$ in.^{2}

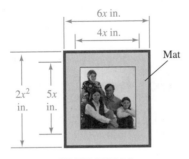

ILLUSTRATION 1

100. REARVIEW MIRRORS   The dimensions of the three rearview mirrors on an automobile are given in Illustration 2. Write an algebraic expression that gives

   a. the area of the rearview mirror mounted on the windshield. $6x^3$ cm^2

   b. the total area of the two side mirrors. $24x^2$ cm^2

   c. the total area of all three mirrors. Express the result in factored form. $6x^2(x + 4)$ cm^2

101. COOKING   See Illustration 3.

   a. What is the length of a side of the square griddle, in terms of r? What is the area of the cooking surface of the griddle, in terms of r?
    $4r$ in.; $16r^2$ in.^{2}

   b. How many square inches of the cooking surface do the pancakes cover, in terms of r? $4\pi r^2$ in.^{2}

   c. Find the amount of cooking surface that is not covered by the pancakes. Express the result in factored form. $16r^2 - 4\pi r^2 = 4r^2(4 - \pi)$ in.^{2}

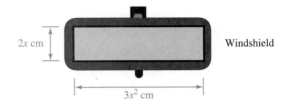

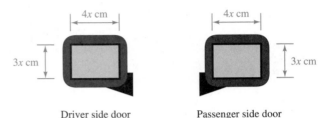

ILLUSTRATION 2

ILLUSTRATION 3

102. U.S. NAVY   Illustration 4 shows the deck of the aircraft carrier *Enterprise.* The rectangular-shaped landing area of $(x^3 + 4x^2 + 5x + 20)$ ft^2 is shaded. What are the length and width of the landing area? (*Hint:* Factor the expression that represents the area.)
$(x^2 + 5)$ ft; $(x + 4)$ ft

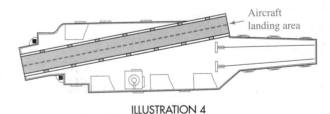

ILLUSTRATION 4

WRITING

103. To add $5x$ and $7x$, we combine like terms: $5x + 7x = 12x$. Explain how this is related to factoring out a common factor.

104. One student commented, "Factoring undoes the distributive property." What do you think she meant? Give an example.

105. If asked to write $ax + ay - bx - by$ in factored form, explain why $a(x + y) - b(x + y)$ is not an acceptable answer.

106. When asked to factor $rx - sy + ry - sx$, a student wrote the expression as $rx + ry - sx - sy$. Then she factored it by grouping. Can the terms be rearranged in this manner? Explain your answer.

REVIEW

107. Simplify $\left(\dfrac{y^3 y}{2yy^2}\right)^3$. $\dfrac{y^3}{8}$

108. Find the slope of the line passing through the points $(3,5)$ and $(-2,-7)$. $\dfrac{12}{5}$

109. Does the point $(3,5)$ lie on the graph of the line $4x - y = 7$? yes

110. Simplify $-5(3a - 2)(2a + 3)$. $-30a^2 - 25a + 30$

5.2 *Factoring Trinomials of the Form $x^2 + bx + c$*

In this section, you will learn about

- Factoring trinomials that have a leading coefficient of 1 • Multistep factoring
- Prime polynomials

INTRODUCTION. Recall that to multiply $x + 2$ and $x + 3$, we proceed as follows:

$$(x + 2)(x + 3) = x^2 + 3x + 2x + 6$$
$$= x^2 + 5x + 6$$

In this section, we will reverse the process. Given a trinomial, such as $x^2 + 5x + 6$, we will ask ourselves, "What factors were multiplied to obtain $x^2 + 5x + 6$?" The process of finding the individual factors of a given trinomial is called *factoring the trinomial.* Since the product of two binomials is often a trinomial, we should not be surprised that many trinomials factor into the product of two binomials.

The multiplication process		**The factoring process**	
Given two binomial factors . . .	find the product	Given the product . . .	find the two binomial factors
$\downarrow \quad \downarrow$	$\downarrow$	$\downarrow$	$\downarrow \quad \downarrow$
$(x + 2)(x + 3)$ =	**?**	$x^2 + 5x + 6$ =	$(\ ?\ )(\ ?\ )$

We will now consider how to factor trinomials of the form $ax^2 + bx + c$, where a (called the **leading coefficient**) is 1.

Factoring trinomials that have a leading coefficient of 1

To develop a method for factoring trinomials, we multiply $(x + a)$ and $(x + b)$.

$$(x + a)(x + b) = x \cdot x + bx + ax + ab \quad \text{Use the FOIL method.}$$
$$= x^2 + ax + bx + ab \quad \text{Write } x \cdot x \text{ as } x^2. \text{ Write } bx + ax \text{ as } ax + bx.$$
$$= x^2 + (a + b)x + ab \quad \text{Factor } x \text{ out of } ax + bx.$$

First term — Middle term — Last term

The result has three terms. We can see that

- the first term is the product of x and x,
- the last term is the product of a and b, and
- the coefficient of the middle term is the sum of a and b.

We can use these facts to factor trinomials with leading coefficients of 1.

EXAMPLE 1   *A positive last term.*   Factor $x^2 + 5x + 6$.

Solution

Self Check
Factor $y^2 + 7y + 6$.

Since the first term of the trinomial is x^2, the first term of each binomial factor must be x. To fill in the blanks, we must find two integers whose product is $+6$ and whose sum is $+5$.

$$x^2 + 5x + 6 = \left(x \qquad\right)\left(x \qquad\right)$$

The positive factorizations of 6 and the sum of the factors are shown in the following table.

Factors of 6	Sum of the factors of 6
1(6)	$1 + 6 = 7$
2(3)	$2 + 3 = 5$

The last row contains the integers $+2$ and $+3$, whose product is $+6$ and whose sum is $+5$. So, we can fill in the blanks with $+2$ and $+3$.

$$x^2 + 5x + 6 = (x + 2)(x + 3)$$

To check the result, we verify that $(x + 2)(x + 3)$ is $x^2 + 5x + 6$.

$$(x + 2)(x + 3) = x^2 + 3x + 2x + 6$$
$$= x^2 + 5x + 6$$

Answer: $(y + 1)(y + 6)$ ∎

COMMENT   When factoring trinomials, the binomial factors can be written in either order. In Example 1, an equivalent factorization is $x^2 + 5x + 6 = (x + 3)(x + 2)$.

EXAMPLE 2   *A positive last term.*   Factor $y^2 - 7y + 12$.

Solution

Self Check
Factor $p^2 - 5p + 6$.

Since the first term of the trinomial is y^2, the first term of each binomial factor must be y. To fill in the blanks, we must find two integers whose product is $+12$ and whose sum is -7.

$$y^2 - 7y + 12 = \left(y \qquad\right)\left(y \qquad\right)$$

The two-integer factorizations of 12 and the sums of the factors are shown in the following table.

Factors of 12	Sum of the factors of 12
1(12)	$1 + 12 = 13$
2(6)	$2 + 6 = 8$
3(4)	$3 + 4 = 7$
$-1(-12)$	$-1 + (-12) = -13$
$-2(-6)$	$-2 + (-6) = -8$
$-3(-4)$	$-3 + (-4) = -7$

The last row contains the integers -3 and -4, whose product is $+12$ and whose sum is -7. So, we can fill in the blanks with -3 and -4.

$$y^2 - 7y + 12 = (y - 3)(y - 4)$$

To check the result, we verify that $(y - 3)(y - 4)$ is $y^2 - 7y + 12$.

$$(y - 3)(y - 4) = y^2 - 4y - 3y + 12$$
$$= y^2 - 7y + 12$$

Answer: $(p - 3)(p - 2)$ ■

EXAMPLE 3   *A negative last term.*   Factor $a^2 + 2a - 15$.
Solution

Self Check
Factor $p^2 + 3p - 18$.

Since the first term of the trinomial is a^2, the first term of each binomial factor must be a. To fill in the blanks, we must find two integers whose product is -15 and whose sum is $+2$.

$$a^2 + 2a - 15 = \left(a \qquad\right)\left(a \qquad\right)$$

The possible factorizations of -15 and the sum of the factors are shown in the following table.

Factors of -15	Sum of the factors of -15
$1(-15)$	$1 + (-15) = -14$
$3(-5)$	$3 + (-5) = -2$
$5(-3)$	$5 + (-3) = 2$
$15(-1)$	$15 + (-1) = 14$

The third row contains the integers $+5$ and -3, whose product is -15 and whose sum is $+2$. So, we can fill in the blanks with $+5$ and -3.

$$a^2 + 2a - 15 = (a + 5)(a - 3)$$

We can check by multiplying.

$$(a + 5)(a - 3) = a^2 - 3a + 5a - 15$$
$$= a^2 + 2a - 15$$

Answer: $(p + 6)(p - 3)$ ■

EXAMPLE 4   *A negative last term.*   Factor $z^2 - 4z - 21$.
Solution

Self Check
Factor $q^2 - 2q - 24$.

Since the first term of the trinomial is z^2, the first term of each binomial factor must be z. To fill in the blanks, we must find two integers whose product is -21 and whose sum is -4.

$$z^2 - 4y - 21 = \left(z \qquad\right)\left(z \qquad\right)$$

The factorizations of -21 and the sums of the factors are shown in the following table.

Factors of -21	Sum of the factors of -21
$1(-21)$	$1 + (-21) = -20$
$3(-7)$	$3 + (-7) = -4$
$7(-3)$	$7 + (-3) = 4$
$21(-1)$	$21 + (-1) = 20$

The second row contains the integers $+3$ and -7, whose product is -21 and whose sum is -4. So, we can fill in the blanks with $+3$ and -7.

$$z^2 - 4z - 21 = (z + 3)(z - 7)$$

We can check by multiplying.

$$(z + 3)(z - 7) = z^2 - 7z + 3z - 21$$
$$= z^2 - 4z - 21$$

Answer: $(q + 4)(q - 6)$ ∎

The following sign patterns can be helpful when factoring trinomials.

Factoring $x^2 + bx + c$

To factor $x^2 + bx + c$, find two integers whose product is c and whose sum is b.

1. If c is positive, the integers have the same sign.
2. If c is negative, the integers have opposite signs.

When factoring out trinomials of the form $ax^2 + bx + c$, where $a = -1$, we begin by factoring out -1.

EXAMPLE 5 *Factoring out -1.* Factor $-h^2 + 2h + 15$.

Solution
We factor out -1 and then factor $h^2 - 2h - 15$.

$$-h^2 + 2h + 15 = -1(h^2 - 2h - 15) \quad \text{Factor out } -1.$$
$$= -(h^2 - 2h - 15)$$
$$= -(h - 5)(h + 3) \quad \begin{array}{l}\text{Use the integers } -5 \text{ and } 3, \text{ because their} \\ \text{product is } -15 \text{ and their sum is } -2.\end{array}$$

We can check by multiplying.

$$-(h - 5)(h + 3) = -(h^2 + 3h - 5h - 15) \quad \text{Multiply the binomials first.}$$
$$= -(h^2 - 2h - 15)$$
$$= -h^2 + 2h + 15$$

Self Check
Factor $-x^2 + 11x - 18$.

Answer: $-(x - 9)(x - 2)$ ∎

The trinomials in the next two examples are of a form similar to $x^2 + bx + c$, and we can use the methods of this section to factor them.

EXAMPLE 6 *Trinomials containing two variables.* Factor $x^2 - 4xy - 5y^2$.

Solution
The trinomial has two variables, x and y. Since the first term is x^2, the first term of each factor must be x.

$$x^2 - 4xy - 5y^2 = \left(x \qquad\right)\left(x \qquad\right)$$

To fill in the blanks, we must find two *expressions* whose product is the last term, $-5y^2$, and that will give a middle term of $-4xy$. Two such expressions are $-5y$ and y.

$$x^2 - 4xy - 5y^2 = (x - 5y)(x + y)$$

We can check by multiplying.

$$(x - 5y)(x + y) = x^2 + xy - 5xy - 5y^2$$
$$= x^2 - 4xy - 5y^2$$

SELF CHECK
Factor $s^2 + 6st - 7t^2$.

Answer: $(s + 7t)(s - t)$ ∎

Multistep factoring

If the terms of a trinomial have a common factor, the GCF should always be factored out before any of the factoring techniques of this section are used. A trinomial is **factored completely** when no factor can be factored further. Always factor completely when you are asked to factor.

EXAMPLE 7   *Factoring completely.*   Factor $2x^4 + 26x^3 + 80x^2$.

Solution

We begin by factoring out the GCF of $2x^2$.

$$2x^4 + 26x^3 + 80x^2 = 2x^2(x^2 + 13x + 40)$$

Next, we factor $x^2 + 13x + 40$. The integers 8 and 5 have a product of 40 and a sum of 13, so the completely factored form of the given trinomial is

$$2x^4 + 26x^3 + 80x^2 = 2x^2(x + 8)(x + 5)$$

Check by multiplying $2x^2$, $x + 8$, and $x + 5$.

Self Check

Factor $4m^5 + 8m^4 - 32m^3$ completely.

Answer: $4m^3(m + 4)(m - 2)$ ■

EXAMPLE 8   *Writing terms in descending powers.*   Factor $-13g^2 + 36g + g^3$ completely.

Solution

Before factoring the trinomial, we write its terms in descending powers of g.

$$\begin{aligned} -13g^2 + 36g + g^3 &= g^3 - 13g^2 + 36g & \text{Rearrange the terms.} \\ &= g(g^2 - 13g + 36) & \text{Factor out } g, \text{ which is the GCF.} \\ &= g(g - 9)(g - 4) & \text{Factor the trinomial.} \end{aligned}$$

Check by multiplying g, $g - 9$, and $g - 4$.

Self Check

Factor $-12t + t^3 + 4t^2$ completely.

Answer: $t(t - 2)(t + 6)$ ■

Prime polynomials

If a trinomial cannot be factored using only integers, it is called a **prime polynomial,** or more specifically, a **prime trinomial.**

EXAMPLE 9   *Trinomials that do not factor.*   Factor $x^2 + 2x + 3$, if possible.

Solution

To factor the trinomial, we must find two integers whose product is 3 and whose sum is 2. The possible factorizations of 3 and the sums of the factors are shown in the following table.

Factors of 3	Sum of the factors of 3
$1(3)$	$1 + 3 = 4$
$-1(-3)$	$-1 + (-3) = -4$

Since two integers whose product is 3 and whose sum is 2 do not exist, $x^2 + 2x + 3$ cannot be factored. It is a prime trinomial.

Self Check

Factor $x^2 - 4x + 6$, if possible.

Answer: not possible; prime trinomial   ■

STUDY SET   Section 5.2

VOCABULARY   *Fill in the blanks.*

1. A polynomial, such as $x^2 - x - 6$, that has exactly three terms is called a ____trinomial____. A polynomial, such as $x - 3$, that has exactly two terms is called a ____binomial____.

2. The statement $x^2 - x - 12 = (x - 4)(x + 3)$ shows that $x^2 - x - 12$ ____factors____ into the product of two binomials.

3. Since $10 = (-5)(-2)$, we say -5 and -2 are ____factors____ of 10.

4. A ____prime____ polynomial cannot be factored by using only integers.

5. The ____leading____ coefficient of the trinomial $x^2 - 3x + 2$ is 1, the ____coefficient____ of the middle term is -3, and the last ____term____ is 2.

6. A trinomial is factored ____completely____ when no factor can be factored further.

CONCEPTS   *In Exercises 7–12, fill in the blanks.*

7. Two factorizations of 4 that involve only positive numbers are $4 \cdot 1$ and $2 \cdot 2$. Two factorizations of 4 that involve only negative numbers are $-4(-1)$ and $-2(-2)$.

8. Before attempting to factor a trinomial, be sure that the exponents are written in ____descending____ order.

9. Before attempting to factor a trinomial into two binomials, always factor out any ____common____ factors first.

10. To factor $x^2 + x - 56$, we must find two integers whose ____product____ is -56 and whose ____sum____ is 1.

11. Two factors of 18 whose sum is -9 are -6 and -3.

12. $x^2 + 5x + 3$ cannot be factored because we cannot find two integers whose product is 3 and whose sum is 5.

13. Complete the table.

Factors of 8	Sum of the factors of 8
1(8)	9
2(4)	6
$-1(-8)$	-9
$-2(-4)$	-6

14. If we use the FOIL method to do the multiplication $(x + 5)(x + 4)$, we obtain $x^2 + 9x + 20$.
    a. What step of the FOIL process produced 20?
       Last: $5 \cdot 4$

b. What steps of the FOIL process produced $9x$?
   Outer: $x \cdot 4$ and Inner: $5 \cdot x$

15. Given $x^2 - 2x - 15$:
    a. What is the coefficient of the x^2-term?   1
    b. What is the last term? The last term is the product of what two integers? -15; -5 and 3
    c. What is the coefficient of the middle term? It is the sum of what two integers? -2; -5 and 3

16. Given $x^2 + 8x + 15$:
    a. What is the coefficient of the x^2-term?   1
    b. What is the last term? The last term is the product of what two integers?   15; 5 and 3
    c. What is the coefficient of the middle term? It is the sum of what two integers?   8; 5 and 3

17. To determine which two integers to use in the factorization of $x^2 + 7x + 10$, a student constructed the following table. Explain why she didn't need to write the last two rows.
    The sum of two negative factors of 10 could not be 7.

Factors of 10	Sum of the factors of 10
1(10)	
2(5)	
$-1(-10)$	
$-2(-5)$	

18. Complete the factorization table.
    The order of the entries may vary.

Factors of -9	Sum of the factors of -9
$1(-9)$	$1 + (-9) = -8$
$3(-3)$	$3 + (-3) = 0$
$-1(9)$	$-1 + 9 = 8$

19. Consider factoring a trinomial of the form $x^2 + bx + c$.
    a. If c is positive, what can be said about the two integers that should be chosen for the factorization?
       They are both positive or they are both negative.
    b. If c is negative, what can be said about the two integers that should be chosen for the factorization?
       One will be positive, the other negative.

20. What trinomial has the factorization of $(x + 8)(x - 2)$?
    $x^2 + 6x - 16$

NOTATION   *Complete each factorization.*

21. $6 + 5x + x^2 = x^2 + \underline{5x} + 6$
$= (x + 3)(x + 2)$

22. $-a^2 - a + 20 = \underline{-}(a^2 + a - 20)$
$= -(a + 5)(a - 4)$

PRACTICE   *Complete each factorization.*

23. $x^2 + 3x + 2 = (x + 2)(x + 1)$
24. $y^2 + 4y + 3 = (y + 3)(y + 1)$
25. $t^2 - 9t + 14 = (t - 7)(t - 2)$
26. $c^2 - 9c + 8 = (c - 8)(c - 1)$
27. $a^2 + 6a - 16 = (a + 8)(a - 2)$
28. $x^2 - 3x - 40 = (x - 8)(x + 5)$

Factor each trinomial. If it can't be factored, write "prime."

29. $z^2 + 12z + 11$ $(z + 11)(z + 1)$
30. $x^2 + 7x + 10$ $(x + 5)(x + 2)$
31. $m^2 - 5m + 6$ $(m - 3)(m - 2)$
32. $n^2 - 7n + 10$ $(n - 5)(n - 2)$
33. $a^2 - 4a - 5$ $(a - 5)(a + 1)$
34. $b^2 + 6b - 7$ $(b + 7)(b - 1)$
35. $x^2 + 5x - 24$ $(x + 8)(x - 3)$
36. $t^2 - 5t - 50$ $(t - 10)(t + 5)$
37. $a^2 - 10a - 39$ $(a - 13)(a + 3)$
38. $r^2 - 9r - 12$ prime
39. $u^2 + 10u + 15$ prime
40. $v^2 + 9v + 15$ prime
41. $s^2 + 11s - 26$ $(s + 13)(s - 2)$
42. $y^2 + 8y + 12$ $(y + 6)(y + 2)$
43. $r^2 - 2r + 4$ prime
44. $m^2 + 3m - 10$ $(m + 5)(m - 2)$
45. $m^2 - m - 12$ $(m - 4)(m + 3)$
46. $u^2 + u - 42$ $(u + 7)(u - 6)$
47. $x^2 + 4xy + 4y^2$ $(x + 2y)(x + 2y)$
48. $a^2 + 10ab + 9b^2$ $(a + 9b)(a + b)$
49. $m^2 + 3mn - 10n^2$ $(m + 5n)(m - 2n)$
50. $m^2 - mn - 12n^2$ $(m - 4n)(m + 3n)$
51. $a^2 - 4ab - 12b^2$ $(a - 6b)(a + 2b)$
52. $p^2 + pq - 6q^2$ $(p + 3q)(p - 2q)$
53. $r^2 - 2rs + 4s^2$ prime
54. $m^2 + 3mn - 20n^2$ prime

Factor each trinomial. Factor out −1 first.

55. $-x^2 - 7x - 10$ $-(x + 5)(x + 2)$
56. $-x^2 + 9x - 20$ $-(x - 5)(x - 4)$

57. $-t^2 - 15t + 34$ $-(t + 17)(t - 2)$
58. $-t^2 - t + 30$ $-(t + 6)(t - 5)$
59. $-r^2 + 14r - 40$ $-(r - 10)(r - 4)$
60. $-r^2 + 14r - 45$ $-(r - 9)(r - 5)$
61. $-a^2 - 4ab - 3b^2$ $-(a + 3b)(a + b)$
62. $-a^2 - 6ab - 5b^2$ $-(a + b)(a + 5b)$
63. $-x^2 + 6xy + 7y^2$ $-(x - 7y)(x + y)$
64. $-x^2 - 10xy + 11y^2$ $-(x + 11y)(x - y)$

Write each trinomial in descending powers of one variable and then factor.

65. $4 - 5x + x^2$ $(x - 4)(x - 1)$
66. $y^2 + 5 + 6y$ $(y + 5)(y + 1)$
67. $10y + 9 + y^2$ $(y + 9)(y + 1)$
68. $x^2 - 13 - 12x$ $(x - 13)(x + 1)$
69. $-r^2 + 2 + r$ $-(r - 2)(r + 1)$
70. $u^2 - 3 + 2u$ $(u + 3)(u - 1)$
71. $4rx + r^2 + 3x^2$ $(r + 3x)(r + x)$
72. $a^2 + 5b^2 + 6ab$ $(a + b)(a + 5b)$
73. $-3ab + a^2 + 2b^2$ $(a - 2b)(a - b)$
74. $-13yz + y^2 - 14z^2$ $(y - 14z)(y + z)$

Completely factor each trinomial. Factor out any common monomials first (including −1 if necessary).

75. $2x^2 + 10x + 12$ $2(x + 3)(x + 2)$
76. $3y^2 - 21y + 18$ $3(y - 6)(y - 1)$
77. $-5a^2 + 25a - 30$ $-5(a - 3)(a - 2)$
78. $-2b^2 + 20b - 18$ $-2(b - 9)(b - 1)$
79. $3z^2 - 15z + 12$ $3(z - 4)(z - 1)$
80. $5m^2 + 45m - 50$ $5(m + 10)(m - 1)$
81. $12xy + 4x^2y - 72y$ $4y(x + 6)(x - 3)$
82. $48xy + 6xy^2 + 96x$ $6x(y + 4)(y + 4)$
83. $-4x^2y - 4x^3 + 24xy^2$ $-4x(x + 3y)(x - 2y)$
84. $3x^2y^3 + 3x^3y^2 - 6xy^4$ $3xy^2(x + 2y)(x - y)$

APPLICATIONS

85. PETS   The cage shown in Illustration 1 is used for transporting dogs. Its volume is $(x^3 + 12x^2 + 27x)$ in.^{3}. The dimensions of the cage can be found by factoring this expression. If the cage is longer than it is tall, and taller than it is wide, determine its length, width, and height.
$(x + 9)$ in., $(x + 3)$ in., x in.

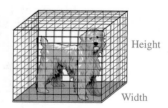

Height
Width
Length

ILLUSTRATION 1

86. CARPOOLING   The average rate at which a carpool van travels and the distance it covers are given in the table in terms of t. Factor the expression representing the distance traveled and then complete the table.

Rate (mi/hr)	Time (hr)	Distance traveled (mi)
$t + 11$	$t + 5$	$t^2 + 16t + 55$

WRITING

87. Explain what it means when we say that a trinomial is the product of two binomials. Give an example.

88. Are $2x^2 - 12x + 16$ and $x^2 - 6x + 8$ factored in the same way? Explain why or why not.

89. When factoring $x^2 - 2x - 3$, one student got $(x - 3)(x + 1)$, and another got $(x + 1)(x - 3)$. Are both answers acceptable? Explain.

90. Explain how to use the FOIL method to check the factorization of a trinomial.

91. In the partial solution shown below, a student began to factor the trinomial and then gave up. Write a brief note to the student explaining his initial mistake.

Factor $x^2 - 2x - 63$.

$$(x - \quad)(x - \quad)$$

???

92. Explain why the given trinomial is not factored completely.

$$3x^2 - 3x - 60 = 3(x^2 - x - 20)$$

REVIEW

Graph the solution of each inequality on a number line.

93. $x - 3 > 5$

94. $x + 4 \le 3$

95. $-3x - 5 \ge 4$

96. $2x - 3 < 7$

5.3 *Factoring Trinomials of the Form $ax^2 + bx + c$*

In this section, you will learn about

- Observations about multiplying binomials
- The trial-and-check factoring method • The grouping method

INTRODUCTION. In this section, we will factor trinomials with leading coefficients that are not 1. Two methods are used to factor these trinomials. With the first method, educated guesses are made. These guesses are checked by multiplication. The correct factorization is determined by a process of elimination. The second method is an extension of factoring by grouping.

Observations about multiplying binomials

In the work below, we find the products $(2x + 1)(x + 3)$ and $(2x + 3)(x + 1)$. There are several observations that can be made when we compare the results.

$$(2x + 1)(x + 3) = 2x^2 + 6x + x + 3 \qquad (2x + 3)(x + 1) = 2x^2 + 2x + 3x + 3$$
$$= 2x^2 + 7x + 3 \qquad\qquad\qquad = 2x^2 + 5x + 3$$

In each case, the result is a trinomial, and

- the first terms are the same ($2x^2$),
- the last terms are the same (3), and
- the middle terms are different ($7x$ and $5x$).

These observations indicate that when the last terms in $(2x + 1)(x + 3)$ are interchanged to form $(2x + 3)(x + 1)$, only the middle terms of the products are different. This fact is helpful when factoring trinomials by using the *trial-and check method*.

The trial-and-check factoring method

To factor a trinomial with a leading coefficient of 1 (say, $x^2 + 4x + 3$), we begin with a factorization of the form

$$x^2 + 4x + 3 = (x \quad\quad)(x \quad\quad)$$

and determine which integers to write in the blanks.

To factor a trinomial with a leading coefficient that is not 1 (say, $2x^2 + 5x + 3$), we begin with a factorization of the form

$$2x^2 + 5x + 3 = (\quad x \quad)(\quad x \cdot \quad)$$

We must determine what numbers to write in the blanks. Because there are four blanks, there are more combinations of factors to consider.

EXAMPLE 1   *A leading coefficient of 2.*   Factor $2x^2 + 5x + 3$.

Solution

Since the first term is $2x^2$, the first terms of the binomial factors must be $2x$ and x. To fill in the blanks, we must find two factors of $+3$ that will give a middle term of $+5x$.

$$(2x \quad\quad)(x \quad\quad)$$

Because each term of the trinomial is positive, we need only consider positive factors of the last term. Since the positive factors of 3 are 1 and 3, there are two possible factorizations.

$$(2x + 1)(x + 3) \qquad \text{or} \qquad (2x + 3)(x + 1)$$

The first possibility is incorrect: When we find the outer and inner products and combine like terms, we obtain an incorrect middle term of $7x$.

Outer: $6x$

$(2x + 1)(x + 3)$ Multiply and add to find the middle term: $6x + x = 7x$.

Inner: x

The second possibility is correct, because it gives a middle term of $5x$.

Outer: $2x$

$(2x + 3)(x + 1)$ Multiply and add to find the middle term: $2x + 3x = 5x$.

Inner: $3x$

Thus,

$$2x^2 + 5x + 3 = (2x + 3)(x + 1)$$

EXAMPLE 2   *A leading coefficient of 6.*   Factor $6x^2 - 17x + 5$.

Solution

Since the first term is $6x^2$, the first terms of the binomial factors must be $6x$ and x or $3x$ and $2x$. To fill in the blanks, we must find two factors of $+5$ that will give a middle term of $-17x$.

$$(6x \quad\quad)(x \quad\quad) \qquad \text{or} \qquad (3x \quad\quad)(2x \quad\quad)$$

Because the sign of the last term is positive and the sign of the middle term is negative, we need only consider negative factors of the last term. Since the negative factors of 5 are -1 and -5, there are four possible factorizations.

Self Check

Factor $3x^2 + 7x + 2$.

Answer: $(3x + 1)(x + 2)$ ∎

Self Check

Factor $6x^2 - 7x + 2$.

$$\overset{\overset{\displaystyle -30a}{\frown}}{(6a - 1)(a - 5)} \quad -30a - a = -31a. \qquad \overset{\overset{\displaystyle -6a}{\frown}}{(6a - 5)(a - 1)} \quad -6a - 5a = -11a.$$
$$\underset{\underset{\displaystyle -a}{\smile}}{} \qquad \qquad \underset{\underset{\displaystyle -5a}{\smile}}{}$$

$$\overset{\overset{\displaystyle -15a}{\frown}}{(3a - 1)(2a - 5)} \quad -15a - 2a = -17a. \qquad \overset{\overset{\displaystyle -3a}{\frown}}{(3a - 5)(2a - 1)} \quad -3a - 10a = -13a.$$
$$\underset{\underset{\displaystyle -2a}{\smile}}{} \qquad \qquad \underset{\underset{\displaystyle -10a}{\smile}}{}$$

Only the possibility shown in blue gives the correct middle term of $-17a$. Thus,

$$6a^2 - 17a + 5 = (3a - 1)(2a - 5)$$

Answer: $(3x - 2)(2x - 1)$ ■

EXAMPLE 3 *Discarding possible factorizations.* Factor $3y^2 - 7y - 6$.

Self Check
Factor $5a^2 - 23a - 10$.

Solution

Since the first term is $3y^2$, the first terms of the binomial factors must be $3y$ and y.

$$(3y \quad)(y \quad)$$

To fill in the blanks, we must find two integers whose product is -6 that produce a middle term of $-7y$. Since the sign of the last term of $3y^2 - 7y - 6$ is negative, we need to find factors of -6 that have opposite signs. There are four such pairs: $-1(6)$, $1(-6)$, $-2(3)$, and $2(-3)$. These four pairs create eight possible factorizations to consider.

Four of the possible factorizations can be discarded because they include a binomial whose terms have a common factor. If $3y^2 - 7y - 6$ does not have a common factor, neither will any of its binomial factors.

For the factors -1 and 6:

$$\overset{\overset{\displaystyle 18y}{\frown}}{(3y - 1)(y + 6)} \quad 18y - y = 17y \qquad \cancel{(3y + 6)(y - 1)}$$
$$\underset{\underset{\displaystyle -y}{\smile}}{} \qquad \qquad \qquad \text{A common factor of 3}$$

For the factors 1 and -6:

$$\overset{\overset{\displaystyle -18y}{\frown}}{(3y + 1)(y - 6)} \quad -18y + y = -17y \qquad \cancel{(3y - 6)(y + 1)}$$
$$\underset{\underset{\displaystyle y}{\smile}}{} \qquad \qquad \qquad \text{A common factor of 3}$$

For the factors -2 and 3:

$$\overset{\overset{\displaystyle 9y}{\frown}}{(3y - 2)(y + 3)} \quad 9y - 2y = 7y \qquad \cancel{(3y + 3)(y - 2)}$$
$$\underset{\underset{\displaystyle -2y}{\smile}}{} \qquad \qquad \qquad \text{A common factor of 3}$$

For the factors 2 and -3:

$$\overset{\overset{\displaystyle -9y}{\frown}}{(3y + 2)(y - 3)} \quad -9y + 2y = -7y \qquad \cancel{(3y - 3)(y + 2)}$$
$$\underset{\underset{\displaystyle 2y}{\smile}}{} \qquad \qquad \qquad \text{A common factor of 3}$$

Only the possibility shown in blue gives the correct middle term of $-7y$. Thus,

$$3y^2 - 7y - 6 = (3y + 2)(y - 3)$$

Check the factorization by multiplication.

Answer: $(5a + 2)(a - 5)$ ■

> **!**   **COMMENT**   If a trinomial does not have a common factor, the terms of each of its binomial factors will not have a common factor.

EXAMPLE 4   *Factoring a trinomial in two variables.*   Factor $4b^2 + 8bc - 45c^2$.

Solution

Since the first term is $4b^2$, the first terms of the factors must be $4b$ and b or $2b$ and $2b$.

$$\left(4b \qquad \right)\left(b \qquad \right) \qquad \text{or} \qquad \left(2b \qquad \right)\left(2b \qquad \right)$$

To fill in the blanks, we must find two factors of $-45c^2$ that will give a middle term of $8bc$.

Since $-45c^2$ has many factors, there are many possible combinations for the last terms of the binomial factors. The signs of the factors must be different, because the last term of the trinomial is negative.

If we pick factors of $4b$ and b for the first terms, and $-c$ and $45c$ for the last terms, the multiplication gives an incorrect middle term of $179bc$. So the factorization is incorrect.

$$\overset{\displaystyle 180bc}{\underset{\displaystyle -bc}{(4b - c)(b + 45c)}} \quad 180bc - bc = 179bc.$$

If we pick factors of $4b$ and b for the first terms and $15c$ and $-3c$ for the last terms, the multiplication gives an incorrect middle term of $3bc$.

$$\overset{\displaystyle -12bc}{\underset{\displaystyle 15bc}{(4b + 15c)(b - 3c)}} \quad -12bc + 15bc = 3bc.$$

If we pick factors of $2b$ and $2b$ for the first terms and $-5c$ and $9c$ for the last terms, we have

$$\overset{\displaystyle 18bc}{\underset{\displaystyle -10bc}{(2b - 5c)(2b + 9c)}} \quad 18bc - 10bc = 8bc.$$

which gives the correct middle term of $8bc$. Thus,

$$4b^2 + 8bc - 45c^2 = (2b - 5c)(2b + 9c)$$

Check by multiplication.

Self Check

Factor $4x^2 + 4xy - 3y^2$.

Answer: $(2x + 3y)(2x - y)$ ∎

Because some guesswork is often necessary, it is difficult to give specific rules for factoring trinomials with a leading coefficient that is not 1. However, the following hints are helpful.

Factoring $ax^2 + bx + c$
$(a \neq 1)$

> 1. Write the trinomial in descending powers of the variable and factor out any GCF (including -1 if that is necessary to make the leading coefficient positive).
>
> 2. Attempt to write the trinomial as *the product of two binomials*. The coefficients of the first terms of each binomial factor must be factors of a, and the last terms must be factors of c.

Factors
of a

$$(\;\;x + \;\;)(\;\;x + \;\;)$$

Factors
of c

3. If the sign of the last term of the trinomial is positive, the signs between the terms of the binomial factors are the same as the sign of the middle term. If the sign of the last term is negative, the signs between the terms of the binomial factors are opposite.

4. Try combinations of coefficients of the first terms and last terms until you find one that gives the middle term of the trinomial. If no combination works, the trinomial is prime.

5. Check the factorization by multiplication.

EXAMPLE 5 *Writing terms in descending powers.* Factor $2x^2 - 8x^3 + 3x$.

Self Check

Factor $12y - 2y^3 - 2y^2$.

Solution

We write the trinomial in descending powers of x

$$-8x^3 + 2x^2 + 3x$$

and we factor out the negative of the GCF, which is $-x$.

$$-8x^3 + 2x^2 + 3x = -x(8x^2 - 2x - 3)$$

We must now factor $8x^2 - 2x - 3$. Its factorization has the form

$$(x\quad)(8x\quad) \qquad \text{or} \qquad (2x\quad)(4x\quad)$$

To fill in the blanks, we find two factors of the last term of the trinomial (-3) that will give a middle term of $-2x$. Because the sign of the last term is negative, the signs within its binomial factors will be different. If we pick factors of $2x$ and $4x$ for the first terms and 1 and -3 for the last terms, we have

$$\overset{-6x}{(2x + 1)(4x - 3)} \quad -6x + 4x = -2x.$$
$$\underset{4x}{}$$

which gives the correct middle term of $-2x$, so it is correct.

$$8x^2 - 2x - 3 = (2x + 1)(4x - 3)$$

We can now give the complete factorization.

$$-8x^3 + 2x^2 + 3x = -x(8x^2 - 2x - 3)$$
$$= -x(2x + 1)(4x - 3)$$

Check by multiplication.

Answer: $-2y(y + 3)(y - 2)$

The grouping method

The method of factoring by grouping can be used to help factor trinomials of the form $ax^2 + bx + c$. For example, to factor $2x^2 + 5x + 3$, we proceed as follows.

1. We find the product ac: In $2x^2 + 5x + 3$, $a = 2$, $b = 5$, and $c = 3$, so $ac = 2(3) = 6$. This number is called the **key number.**

2. Find two factors of the key number 6 whose sum is $b = 5$. Two such numbers are 2 and 3.

$$2(3) = 6 \qquad \text{and} \qquad 2 + 3 = 5$$

3. Use the factors 2 and 3 as coefficients of two terms to be placed between $2x^2$ and 3:

$$2x^2 + 5x + 3 = 2x^2 + 2x + 3x + 3 \quad \text{Express } 5x \text{ as } 2x + 3x.$$

4. Factor by grouping:

$$2x^2 + 2x + 3x + 3 = 2x(x + 1) + 3(x + 1) \quad \begin{array}{l} \text{Factor } 2x \text{ out of } 2x^2 + 2x \\ \text{and 3 out of } 3x + 3. \end{array}$$

$$= (x + 1)(2x + 3) \qquad \text{Factor out } x + 1.$$

So $2x^2 + 5x + 3 = (x + 1)(2x + 3)$. Verify this factorization by multiplication.

EXAMPLE 6   *The grouping method.*   Factor $10x^2 + 13x - 3$.

Solution

Since $a = 10$ and $c = -3$ in the trinomial, $ac = -30$. We now find two factors of -30 whose sum is 13. Two such factors are 15 and -2. We use these factors as coefficients of two terms to be placed between $10x^2$ and -3.

$$10x^2 + 13x - 3 = 10x^2 + 15x - 2x - 3 \quad \text{Express } 13x \text{ as } 15x - 2x.$$

Finally, we factor by grouping.

$$10x^2 + 15x - 2x - 3 = 5x(2x + 3) - 1(2x + 3)$$
$$= (2x + 3)(5x - 1)$$

So $10x^2 + 13x - 3 = (2x + 3)(5x - 1)$. Check the result.

Self Check

Factor $15a^2 + 17a - 4$.

Answer: $(3a + 4)(5a - 1)$ ∎

Factoring $ax^2 + bx + c$ by grouping

1. Write the trinomial in descending powers of the variable and factor out any GCF (including -1 if that is necessary to make the leading coefficient positive).

2. Calculate the key number ac.

3. Find two numbers whose product is the key number found in step 2 and whose sum is the coefficient of the middle term of the trinomial.

4. Write the numbers in the blanks of the form shown below, and then factor the polynomial by grouping.

$$ax^2 + \boxed{}\, x + \boxed{}\, x + c$$

5. Check the factorization using multiplication.

EXAMPLE 7   *Factoring by grouping.*   Factor $12x^5 - 17x^4 + 6x^3$.

Solution

First, we factor out the GCF, which is x^3.

$$12x^5 - 17x^4 + 6x^3 = x^3(12x^2 - 17x + 6)$$

To factor $12x^2 - 17x + 6$, we need to find two integers whose product is $12(6) = 72$ and whose sum is -17. Two such numbers are -8 and -9.

$$12x^2 - 17x + 6 = 12x^2 - 8x - 9x + 6 \quad \text{Express } -17x \text{ as } -8x - 9x.$$
$$= 4x(3x - 2) - 3(3x - 2) \quad \text{Factor out } 4x \text{ and factor out } -3.$$
$$= (3x - 2)(4x - 3) \qquad \text{Factor out } 3x - 2.$$

The complete factorization is

$$12x^5 - 17x^4 + 6x^3 = x^3(3x - 2)(4x - 3)$$

Check the result.

Self Check

Factor $21a^4 - 13a^3 + 2a^2$.

Answer: $a^2(7a - 2)(3a - 1)$ ∎

STUDY SET Section 5.3 ·www·

VOCABULARY *Fill in the blanks.*

1. The trinomial $3x^2 - x - 12$ has a ___leading___ coefficient of 3. The ___last___ term is -12.

2. The numbers 3 and 2 are ___factors___ of the first term of the trinomial $6x^2 + x - 12$.

3. Consider $(x - 2)(5x - 1)$. The product of the ___outer___ terms is $-x$ and the product of the ___inner___ terms is $-10x$.

4. When we write $2x^2 + 7x + 3$ as $(2x + 1)(x + 3)$, we say that we have ___factored___ the trinomial—it has been expressed as the product of two ___binomials___.

5. The ___middle___ term of $4x^2 - 7x + 13$ is $-7x$.

6. The polynomial $6x^2 + 2x + 9x + 3$ has four ___terms___.

7. The ___sum___ of the middle terms of the polynomial $4a^2 - 12a - a + 3$ is $-13a$.

8. The ___GCF___ of the terms of the trinomial $6b^3 - 3b^2 - 12b$ is $3b$.

CONCEPTS *Complete each statement in red.*

9.

These coefficients must be factors of _5_.

$$5x^2 + 6x - 8 = (\quad x + \quad)(\quad x + \quad)$$

These numbers must be factors of _−8_.

10.

The product of these coefficients must be _15_.

$$3x^2 + 16x + 5 = 3x^2 + \quad x + \quad x + 5$$

The sum of these coefficients must be _16_.

A trinomial has been partially factored. Complete each statement that describes the type of integers we should consider for the blanks.

11. $5y^2 - 13y + 6 = (5x \quad)(x \quad)$

Since the last term of the trinomial is ___positive___ and the middle term is ___negative___, the integers must be ___negative___ factors of 6.

12. $5y^2 + 13y + 6 = (5x \quad)(x \quad)$

Since the last term of the trinomial is ___positive___ and the middle term is ___positive___, the integers must be ___positive___ factors of 6.

13. $5y^2 + 7y - 6 = (5x \quad)(x \quad)$

Since the last term of the trinomial is ___negative___, the signs of the integers will be ___different___.

14. $5y^2 - 7y - 6 = (5x \quad)(x \quad)$

Since the last term of the trinomial is ___negative___, the signs of the integers will be ___different___.

A trinomial is to be factored by the grouping method. Complete each statement that describes the type of integers we should consider for the blanks.

15. $8c^2 - 11c + 3 = 8c^2 + \quad c + \quad c + 3$

We need to find two integers whose product is _24_ and whose sum is _−11_.

16. $15c^2 + 4c - 4 = 15c^2 + \quad c + \quad c - 4$

We need to find two integers whose product is _−60_ and whose sum is _4_.

NOTATION

17. Write a trinomial of the form $ax^2 + bx + c$
   a. where $a = 1$ $\quad x^2 + 2x + 3$ (answers may vary)
   b. where $a \neq 1$ $\quad 2x^2 + 2x + 3$ (answers may vary)

18. Write the terms of the trinomial $40 - t - 4t^2$ in descending powers of the variable. $\quad -4t^2 - t + 40$

PRACTICE *Complete each factorization.*

19. $3a^2 + 13a + 4 = (3a + 1)(a + 4)$

20. $2b^2 + 7b + 6 = (2b + 3)(b + 2)$

21. $4z^2 - 13z + 3 = (z - 3)(4z - 1)$

22. $4t^2 - 4t + 1 = (2t - 1)(2t - 1)$

23. $2m^2 + 5m - 12 = (2m - 3)(m + 4)$

24. $10u^2 - 13u - 3 = (2u - 3)(5u + 1)$

Complete each step of the factorization of the trinomial by grouping.

25. $12t^2 + 17t + 6 = 12t^2 + 9\ t + 8\ t + 6$
$$= 3t(4t + 3) + 2(4t + 3)$$
$$= (\ 4t + 3\ )(3t + 2)$$

26. $35t^2 - 11t - 6 = 35t^2 + 10\ t - 21t - 6$
$$= 5t(7t + 2) - 3(7t + 2)$$
$$= (\ 7t + 2\ )(5t - 3)$$

Factor each trinomial, if possible.

27. $2x^2 - 3x + 1$ $\quad (2x - 1)(x - 1)$

28. $2y^2 - 7y + 3$ $\quad (2y - 1)(y - 3)$

29. $3a^2 + 13a + 4$ $\quad (3a + 1)(a + 4)$

30. $2b^2 + 7b + 6$ $\quad (2b + 3)(b + 2)$

31. $4z^2 + 13z + 3$ $\quad (z + 3)(4z + 1)$

32. $4t^2 - 4t + 1$ $\quad (2t - 1)(2t - 1)$

33. $6y^2 + 7y + 2$ $(3y + 2)(2y + 1)$

34. $4x^2 + 8x + 3$ $(2x + 3)(2x + 1)$

35. $6x^2 - 7x + 2$ $(3x - 2)(2x - 1)$

36. $4z^2 - 9z + 2$ $(4z - 1)(z - 2)$

37. $3a^2 - 4a - 4$ $(3a + 2)(a - 2)$

38. $8u^2 - 2u - 15$ $(2u - 3)(4u + 5)$

39. $2x^2 - 3x - 2$ $(2x + 1)(x - 2)$

40. $12y^2 - y - 1$ $(4y + 1)(3y - 1)$

41. $2m^2 + 5m - 10$ prime

42. $10u^2 - 13u - 6$ prime

43. $10y^2 - 3y - 1$ $(5y + 1)(2y - 1)$

44. $6m^2 + 19m + 3$ $(6m + 1)(m + 3)$

45. $12y^2 - 5y - 2$ $(3y - 2)(4y + 1)$

46. $10x^2 + 21x - 10$ $(2x + 5)(5x - 2)$

47. $-5t^2 - 13t - 6$ $-(5t + 3)(t + 2)$

48. $-16y^2 - 10y - 1$ $-(8y + 1)(2y + 1)$

49. $-16m^2 + 14m - 3$ $-(8m - 3)(2m - 1)$

50. $-16x^2 - 16x - 3$ $-(4x + 1)(4x + 3)$

51. $4a^2 - 4ab + b^2$ $(2a - b)(2a - b)$

52. $2b^2 - 5bc + 2c^2$ $(2b - c)(b - 2c)$

53. $6r^2 + rs - 2s^2$ $(3r + 2s)(2r - s)$

54. $3m^2 + 5mn + 2n^2$ $(3m + 2n)(m + n)$

55. $4x^2 + 8xy + 3y^2$ $(2x + 3y)(2x + y)$

56. $4b^2 + 15bc - 4c^2$ $(4b - c)(b + 4c)$

57. $4a^2 - 15ab + 9b^2$ $(4a - 3b)(a - 3b)$

58. $12x^2 + 5xy - 3y^2$ $(4x + 3y)(3x - y)$

59. $-13x + 3x^2 - 10$ $(3x + 2)(x - 5)$

60. $-14 + 3a^2 - a$ $(3a - 7)(a + 2)$

61. $15 + 8a^2 - 26a$ $(2a - 5)(4a - 3)$

62. $16 - 40a + 25a^2$ $(5a - 4)(5a - 4)$

63. $12y^2 + 12 - 25y$ $(4y - 3)(3y - 4)$

64. $12t^2 - 1 - 4t$ $(6t + 1)(2t - 1)$

65. $3x^2 + 6 + x$ prime

66. $25 + 2u^2 + 3u$ prime

67. $2a^2 + 3b^2 + 5ab$ $(2a + 3b)(a + b)$

68. $11uv + 3u^2 + 6v^2$ $(3u + 2v)(u + 3v)$

69. $pq + 6p^2 - q^2$ $(3p - q)(2p + q)$

70. $-11mn + 12m^2 + 2n^2$ $(3m - 2n)(4m - n)$

71. $4x^2 + 10x - 6$ $2(2x - 1)(x + 3)$

72. $9x^2 + 21x - 18$ $3(3x - 2)(x + 3)$

73. $-y^3 - 13y^2 - 12y$ $-y(y + 12)(y + 1)$

74. $-2xy^2 - 8xy + 24x$ $-2x(y + 6)(y - 2)$

75. $6x^3 - 15x^2 - 9x$ $3x(2x + 1)(x - 3)$

76. $9y^3 + 3y^2 - 6y$ $3y(3y - 2)(y + 1)$

77. $30r^5 + 63r^4 - 30r^3$ $3r^3(5r - 2)(2r + 5)$

78. $6s^5 - 26s^4 - 20s^3$ $2s^3(3s + 2)(s - 5)$

79. $-16m^3n - 20m^2n^2 - 6mn^3$ $-2mn(4m + 3n)(2m + n)$

80. $-84x^4 - 100x^3y - 24x^2y^2$ $-4x^2(3x + y)(7x + 6y)$

81. $-28u^3v^3 + 26u^2v^4 - 6uv^5$ $-2uv^3(7u - 3v)(2u - v)$

82. $-16x^4y^3 + 30x^3y^4 + 4x^2y^5$ $-2x^2y^3(8x + y)(x - 2y)$

APPLICATIONS

83. OFFICE FURNITURE   The area of the desktop shown in Illustration 1 is given by the expression $(4x^2 + 20x - 11)$ in.^{2}. Factor this expression to find the expressions that represent its length and width. Then determine the difference in the length and width of the desktop. $(2x + 11)$ in., $(2x - 1)$ in.; 12 in.

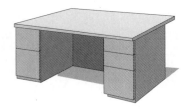

ILLUSTRATION 1

84. STORAGE   The volume of the 8-foot-wide portable storage container shown in Illustration 2 is given by the expression $(72x^2 + 120x - 400)$ ft^3. If its dimensions can be determined by factoring the expression, find the height and the length of the container.
$(3x - 5)$ ft, $(3x + 10)$ ft

ILLUSTRATION 2

WRITING

85. In the work below, a student began to factor the trinomial and then gave up. Explain his initial mistake.

Factor $3x^2 - 5x - 2$.

$(3x - \quad)(x - \quad)$

$???$

86. Two students factor $2x^2 + 20x + 42$ and get two different answers:

$(2x + 6)(x + 7)$ and $(x + 3)(2x + 14)$

Do both answers check? Why don't they agree? Is either answer completely correct? Explain.

87. Why is the process of factoring $6x^2 - 5x - 6$ more complicated than the process of factoring $x^2 - 5x - 6$?

88. How can the factorization shown below be checked?

$$6x^2 - 5x - 6 = (3x + 2)(2x - 3)$$

REVIEW

89. Simplify $(x^2x^5)^2$. x^{14}

90. Simplify $\dfrac{(a^3b^4)^2}{ab^5}$. a^5b^3

91. Evaluate $\dfrac{1}{2^{-3}}$.   8

92. Evaluate 7^0.   1

5.4 *Special Factorizations and a Factoring Strategy*

In this section, you will learn about

- Factoring perfect square trinomials • Factoring the difference of two squares
- Multistep factoring • Factoring the sum and difference of two cubes
- A factoring strategy

INTRODUCTION. We have already studied several methods that can be used to factor trinomials. In this section, we will introduce another method that can be used to factor two specific types of trinomials, called *perfect square trinomials*. We will also develop techniques for factoring three specific types of binomials, called the *difference of two squares,* and the *sum* and *difference of two cubes.*

Factoring perfect square trinomials

In Section 4.6, we saw that the squares of binomials are trinomials.

$$(x + y)^2 \quad = \quad x^2 \quad + \quad 2xy \quad + \quad y^2$$

| This is the square of the first term of the binomial. | This is twice the product of the two terms of the binomial. | This is the square of the last term of the binomial. |

$$(x - y)^2 \quad = \quad x^2 \quad - \quad 2xy \quad + \quad y^2$$

Trinomials that are squares of a binomial are called **perfect square trinomials.** Some examples of perfect square trinomials are

$y^2 + 6y + 9$ — Because it is the square of $(y + 3)$: $(y + 3)^2 = y^2 + 6y + 9$.

$t^2 - 14t + 49$ — Because it is the square of $(t - 7)$: $(t - 7)^2 = t^2 - 14t + 49$.

$4m^2 - 20m + 25$ — Because it is the square of $(2m - 5)$: $(2m - 5)^2 = 4m^2 - 20m + 25$.

EXAMPLE 1 *Recognizing perfect square trinomials.* Determine whether the following trinomials are perfect square trinomials: **a.** $x^2 + 10x + 25$, **b.** $c^2 - 12c - 36$, and **c.** $25y^2 - 30y + 9$.

Solution

a. To determine whether $x^2 + 10x + 25$ is a perfect square trinomial, we note that

- the first term is the square of x,
- the last term is the square of 5, and
- the middle term is twice the product of x and 5.

Thus, $x^2 + 10x + 25$ is a perfect square trinomial.

Self Check

Tell which of the following are perfect square trinomials:

a. $y^2 + 4y + 4$

b. $b^2 - 6b - 9$

c. $4z^2 + 4z + 4$

b. To determine whether $c^2 - 12c - 36$ is a perfect square trinomial, we note that

- the first term is the square of c, but
- the last term is negative.

Thus, $c^2 - 12c - 36$ is not a perfect square trinomial.

c. To determine whether $25y^2 - 30y + 9$ is a perfect square trinomial, we note that

- the first term is the square of $5y$,
- the last term is the square of -3, and
- the middle term is twice the product of $5y$ and -3.

Thus, $25y^2 - 30y + 9$ is a perfect square trinomial.

Answers: **a.** yes, **b.** no,
c. no   ■

Although we can factor perfect square trinomials using techniques discussed earlier in the chapter, we can also factor them by inspecting their terms and applying the special product formulas in reverse.

Factoring perfect square trinomials	$x^2 + 2xy + y^2 = (x + y)^2$ $x^2 - 2xy + y^2 = (x - y)^2$

EXAMPLE 2   *Factoring perfect square trinomials.*   Factor $N^2 + 20N + 100$.

Self Check
Factor $x^2 + 18x + 81$.

Solution
$N^2 + 20N + 100$ is a perfect square trinomial, because:

- The first term N^2 is the square of N: $(N)^2 = N^2$.
- The last term 100 is the square of **10**: $10^2 = 100$.
- The middle term is twice the product of N and 10: $2(N)(10) = 20N$.

The factored form of the trinomial involves the terms N and 10.

$N^2 + 20N + 100 = (N + \mathbf{10})^2$ The sign in the binomial is the sign of the middle term of the trinomial.

Check by multiplication.

Answer: $(x + 9)^2$ ■

EXAMPLE 3   *Perfect square trinomials in two variables.*   Factor $9x^2 - 30xy + 25y^2$.

Self Check
Factor $16x^2 + 8xy + y^2$.

Solution
$9x^2 - 30xy + 25y^2$ is a perfect square trinomial, because:

- The first term $9x^2$ is the square of $3x$: $(3x)^2 = 9x^2$.
- The last term $25y^2$ is the square of $-5y$: $(-5y)^2 = 25y^2$.
- The middle term is twice the product of $3x$ and $-5y$: $2(3x)(-5y) = -30xy$.

The factored form of the trinomial involves the terms $3x$ and $-5y$.

$9x^2 - 30xy + 25y^2 = (\mathbf{3x - 5y})^2$ The sign in the binomial is the sign of the middle term of the trinomial.

Check by multiplication.

Answer: $(4x + y)^2$ ■

Factoring the difference of two squares

Whenever we multiply a binomial of the form $x + y$ by a binomial of the form $x - y$, we obtain a binomial of the form $x^2 - y^2$.

$$(x + y)(x - y) = x^2 - xy + xy - y^2 \quad \text{Use the FOIL method.}$$
$$= x^2 - y^2 \quad \text{Combine like terms: } -xy + xy = 0.$$

The binomial $x^2 - y^2$ is called the **difference of two squares,** because x^2 is the square of x and y^2 is the square of y. The difference of the squares of two quantities always factors into the sum of those two quantities multiplied by the difference of those two quantities.

Factoring the difference of two squares

$$x^2 - y^2 = (x + y)(x - y)$$

If we think of the difference of two squares as the square of a **F**irst quantity minus the square of a **L**ast quantity, we have the formula

$$F^2 - L^2 = (F + L)(F - L)$$

and we say: *To factor the square of a First quantity minus the square of a Last quantity, we multiply the First plus the Last by the First minus the Last.*

To factor $x^2 - 9$, we note that it can be written in the form $x^2 - 3^2$ and use the formula for factoring the difference of two squares:

$$F^2 - L^2 = (F + L)(F - L)$$
$$\downarrow \quad \downarrow \qquad \downarrow \quad \downarrow \downarrow \quad \downarrow$$
$$x^2 - 3^2 = (x + 3)(x - 3) \quad \text{Substitute } x \text{ for F and 3 for L.}$$

We can check by verifying that $(x + 3)(x - 3) = x^2 - 9$. Because of the commutative property of multiplication, we can also write this factorization as $(x - 3)(x + 3)$.

To factor the difference of two squares, it is helpful to know the integers that are perfect squares. The number 400, for example, is a perfect square, because $20^2 = 400$. The perfect integer squares through 400 are

1, 4, 9, 16, 25, 36, 49, 64, 81, 100, 121, 144, 169, 196, 225, 256, 289, 324, 361, 400

Expressions containing variables such as $25x^2$ are also perfect squares, because they can be written as the square of a quantity:

$$25x^2 = (5x)^2$$

EXAMPLE 4   *Factoring the difference of two squares.*   Factor $25x^2 - 49$.

Solution

We can write $25x^2 - 49$ in the form $(5x)^2 - 7^2$ and use the formula for factoring the difference of two squares:

$$F^2 \quad - L^2 = (F \ + L)(F \ - L)$$
$$\downarrow \quad \ \downarrow \qquad \downarrow \quad \ \downarrow \downarrow \quad \ \downarrow$$
$$(5x)^2 - 7^2 = (5x + 7)(5x - 7) \quad \text{Substitute } 5x \text{ for F and 7 for L.}$$

We can check by multiplying.

$$(5x + 7)(5x - 7) = 25x^2 - 35x + 35x - 49$$
$$= 25x^2 - 49$$

Self Check

Factor $16a^2 - 81$.

Answer: $(4a + 9)(4a - 9)$ ■

EXAMPLE 5   *Factoring the difference of two squares.*   Factor
$4y^4 - 121z^2$.

Solution
We can write $4y^4 - 121z^2$ in the form $(2y^2)^2 - (11z)^2$ and use the formula for factoring
the difference of two squares:

$$\begin{array}{ccccccc}
F^2 & - & L^2 & = (F & + & L) & (F & - & L) \\
\downarrow & & \downarrow & \downarrow & & \downarrow & \downarrow & & \downarrow \\
(2y^2)^2 & - & (11z)^2 & = (2y^2 & + & 11z) & (2y^2 & - & 11z)
\end{array}$$

Check by multiplying.

Multistep factoring

When factoring a polynomial, we should always factor out the greatest common factor
first.

EXAMPLE 6   *Factoring out the GCF first.*   Factor $8x^2 - 8$.

Solution
We factor out the GCF of 8, and then factor the resulting difference of two squares.

$$\begin{aligned}
8x^2 - 8 &= 8(x^2 - 1) && \text{The GCF is 8.} \\
&= 8(x + 1)(x - 1) && \text{Think of } x^2 - 1 \text{ as } x^2 - 1^2 \text{ and factor the difference of} \\
& && \text{two squares.}
\end{aligned}$$

We check by multiplying.

$$\begin{aligned}
8(x + 1)(x - 1) &= 8(x^2 - 1) && \text{Multiply the binomials first.} \\
&= 8x^2 - 8 && \text{Distribute the multiplication by 8.}
\end{aligned}$$

Sometimes we must factor a difference of two squares more than once to completely factor a polynomial.

EXAMPLE 7   *Multistep factoring.*   Factor $x^4 - 16$.
Solution

$$\begin{aligned}
x^4 - 16 &= (x^2 + 4)(x^2 - 4) && \text{Factor the difference of two squares.} \\
&= (x^2 + 4)(x + 2)(x - 2) && \text{Factor another difference of two squares: } x^2 - 4.
\end{aligned}$$

COMMENT   In Example 7, the binomial $x^2 + 4$ is the **sum of two squares.** If we are
limited to integer coefficients, binomials that are the sum of two squares cannot be factored.

Factoring the sum and difference of two cubes

We have seen that the sum of two squares, such as $x^2 + 4$ or $25a^2 + 9b^2$, cannot be factored. However, the sum of two cubes and the difference of two cubes can be factored.

The sum of two cubes	The difference of two cubes
$x^3 + 8$	$a^3 - 64b^3$
↑ ↑	↑ ↑
This term is This term is 2	This term is This term is 4b
x cubed. cubed: $2^3 = 8$.	a cubed. cubed: $(4b)^3 = 64b^3$.

To find the formulas for factoring the sum of two cubes and the difference of two cubes, we need to find the following two products:

$$(x + y)(x^2 - xy + y^2) = (x + y)x^2 - (x + y)xy + (x + y)y^2 \quad \text{Use the distributive property.}$$

$$= x^3 + x^2y - x^2y - xy^2 + xy^2 + y^3$$

$$= x^3 + y^3 \quad \text{Combine like terms.}$$

$$(x - y)(x^2 + xy + y^2) = (x - y)x^2 + (x - y)xy + (x - y)y^2 \quad \text{Use the distributive property.}$$

$$= x^3 - x^2y + x^2y - xy^2 + xy^2 - y^3$$

$$= x^3 - y^3 \quad \text{Combine like terms.}$$

These results justify the formulas for factoring the **sum and difference of two cubes.**

Factoring the sum and difference of two cubes

$$x^3 + y^3 = (x + y)(x^2 - xy + y^2)$$
$$x^3 - y^3 = (x - y)(x^2 + xy + y^2)$$

If we think of the sum of two cubes as the cube of a **First** quantity plus the cube of a **Last** quantity, we have the formula

$$F^3 + L^3 = (F + L)(F^2 - FL + L^2)$$

In words, we say, *To factor the cube of a **First** quantity plus the cube of a **Last** quantity, we multiply the **First** plus the **Last** by*

- *the **First** squared*
- *minus the **First** times the **Last***
- *plus the **Last** squared.*

The formula for the difference of two cubes is

$$F^3 - L^3 = (F - L)(F^2 + FL + L^2)$$

In words, we say, *To factor the cube of a **First** quantity minus the cube of a **Last** quantity, we multiply the **First** minus the **Last** by*

- *the **First** squared*
- *plus the **First** times the **Last***
- *plus the **Last** squared.*

To factor the sum or difference of two cubes, it's helpful to know the cubes of the numbers from 1 to 10:

1, 8, 27, 64, 125, 216, 343, 512, 729, 1,000

Expressions containing variables such as $64b^3$ are also perfect cubes, because they can be written as the cube of a quantity:

$$64b^3 = (4b)^3$$

EXAMPLE 8 *Factoring the sum of two cubes.* Factor $x^3 + 8$.

Solution

We think of $x^3 + 8$ as the cube of a **First** quantity, x, plus the cube of a **Last** quantity, 2.

$$x^3 + 8 = x^3 + 2^3$$

Thus, $x^3 + 8$ factors as the product of the sum of x and 2 and the trinomial $x^2 - 2x + 2^2$.

Self Check

Factor $h^3 + 27$.

$$F^3 + L^3 = (F + L)(F^2 - FL + L^2)$$

$$x^3 + 2^3 = (x + 2)(x^2 - x2 + 2^2) \quad \text{Substitute } x \text{ for F and 2 for L.}$$

$$= (x + 2)(x^2 - 2x + 4)$$

We can check by multiplying.

$$(x + 2)(x^2 - 2x + 4) = (x + 2)x^2 - (x + 2)2x + (x + 2)4$$

$$= x^3 + 2x^2 - 2x^2 - 4x + 4x + 8$$

$$= x^3 + 8$$

Answer: $(h + 3)(h^2 - 3h + 9)$ ■

EXAMPLE 9 *Factoring the difference of two cubes.* Factor $a^3 - 64b^3$.

Self Check
Factor $8c^3 - 1$.

Solution

We think of $a^3 - 64b^3$ as the cube of a First quantity, a, minus the cube of a Last quantity, $4b$.

$$a^3 - 64b^3 = a^3 - (4b)^3$$

Thus, its factors are the difference $a - 4b$ and the trinomial $a^2 + a(4b) + (4b)^2$.

$$F^3 - L^3 = (F - L)(F^2 + F\,L + L^2)$$

$$a^3 - (4b)^3 = (a - 4b)[a^2 + a(4b) + (4b)^2]$$

$$= (a - 4b)(a^2 + 4ab + 16b^2)$$

Check by multiplying.

Answer:
$(2c - 1)(4c^2 + 2c + 1)$ ■

Sometimes we must factor out a greatest common factor before factoring a sum or difference of two cubes.

EXAMPLE 10 *Factoring out the GCF first.* Factor $-2t^5 + 250t^2$.

Self Check
Factor $4c^3 + 4d^3$.

Solution

Each term contains the factor $-2t^2$.

$$-2t^5 + 250t^2 = -2t^2(t^3 - 125) \quad \text{Factor out } -2t^2.$$

$$= -2t^2(t - 5)(t^2 + 5t + 25) \quad \text{Factor } t^3 - 125.$$

Check by multiplying.

Answer:
$4(c + d)(c^2 - cd + d^2)$ ■

A factoring strategy

Later, when we solve equations and simplify expressions containing polynomials, we won't be told what type of factoring technique to apply—we will have to determine that ourselves. The following strategy is helpful when factoring a random polynomial.

Steps for factoring a polynomial

1. Factor out all common factors.

2. If a polynomial has two terms, check for the following problem types:
   a. **The difference of two squares:** $x^2 - y^2 = (x + y)(x - y)$
   b. **The sum of two cubes:** $x^3 + y^3 = (x + y)(x^2 - xy + y^2)$
   c. **The difference of two cubes:** $x^3 - y^3 = (x - y)(x^2 + xy + y^2)$

3. If a polynomial has three terms, check for the following problem types:
   a. **A perfect square trinomial:**
      $$x^2 + 2xy + y^2 = (x + y)^2$$
      $$x^2 - 2xy + y^2 = (x - y)^2$$

b. If the trinomial is not a perfect square, attempt to factor it as a general trinomial using the **trial-and-check method** or **factoring by grouping**.

4. If a polynomial has four or more terms, try **factoring by grouping**.

5. Continue until each individual factor is prime.

6. Check the results by multiplying.

STUDY SET Section 5.4

VOCABULARY *Fill in the blanks.*

1. The binomial $x^2 - 25$ is called a ____difference____ of two squares.

2. $x^2 + 6x + 9$ is a ____perfect____ square trinomial because it is the square of the binomial $(x + 3)$.

3. The binomial $x^3 + 27$ is called a sum of two ____cubes____. The binomial $x^3 - 8$ is called a ____difference____ of two cubes.

4. To ____factor____ $4x^2 - 12x + 9$ means to write it as the product of two binomials.

CONCEPTS *In Exercises 5–10, fill in the blanks.*

5. Consider $25x^2 + 30x + 9$.
  a. The first term is the square of $5x$.
  b. The last term is the square of 3 .
  c. The middle term is twice the product of $5x$ and 3 .

6. Consider $49x^2 - 28xy + 4y^2$.
  a. The first term is the square of $7x$.
  b. The last term is the square of $-2y$.
  c. The middle term is twice the product of $7x$ and $-2y$.

7. To factor the square of a First quantity minus the square of a Last quantity, we multiply the ____First____ plus the ____Last____ by the ____First____ minus the ____Last____.

8. If a trinomial is the square of one quantity, plus the square of a second quantity, plus ____twice____ the product of the quantities, it factors into the square of the ____sum____ of the quantities.

9. a. $36x^2 = (6x)^2$ **b.** $100x^4 = (10x^2)^2$
  c. $27m^3 = (3m)^3$ **d.** $a^6 = (a^2)^3$

10. a. $4x^2 - 9 = (2x)^2 - (3)^2$
  b. $8x^3 - 27 = (2x)^3 - (3)^3$
  c. $x^3 + 64y^3 = (x)^3 + (4y)^3$

11. List the first ten perfect integer squares.
  1, 4, 9, 16, 25, 36, 49, 64, 81, 100

12. List the first five perfect integer cubes.   1, 8, 27, 64, 125

13. Explain why each trinomial is not a perfect square trinomial.
  a. $9h^2 - 6h + 7$ 7 is not a perfect square.
  b. $j^2 - 8j - 16$
    The sign of the last term must be positive.
  c. $25r^2 + 20r + 16$
    The middle term is not twice the product of $5r$ and 4.

14. a. Three incorrect factorizations of $x^2 + 36$ are given below. Use the FOIL method to show why each is wrong.

$$(x + 6)(x - 6) \quad x^2 - 36$$
$$(x + 6)(x + 6) \quad x^2 + 12x + 36$$
$$(x - 6)(x - 6) \quad x^2 - 12x + 36$$

  b. Can $x^2 + 36$ be factored using only integers?   no

NOTATION *Write each expression as a polynomial in simpler form.*

15. $(6x)^2 - (5y)^2$ $36x^2 - 25y^2$
16. $(4x)^2 - (9y)^2$ $16x^2 - 81y^2$
17. $(3a)^2 - 2(3a)(5b) + (5b)^2$ $9a^2 - 30ab + 25b^2$
18. $(2s)^2 + 2(2s)(9t) + (9t)^2$ $4s^2 + 36st + 81t^2$

Use an exponent to write each expression in simpler form.

19. $(x + 8)(x + 8)$ **20.** $(x - 8)(x - 8)$
  $(x + 8)^2$ $(x - 8)^2$

PRACTICE *Complete each fractorization.*

21. $a^2 - 6a + 9 = (a - 3)^2$
22. $t^2 + 2t + 1 = (t + 1)^2$
23. $4x^2 + 4x + 1 = (2x + 1)^2$
24. $9y^2 - 12y + 4 = (3y - 2)^2$

Factor each polynomial.

25. $x^2 + 6x + 9$ $(x + 3)^2$
26. $x^2 + 10x + 25$ $(x + 5)^2$
27. $y^2 - 8y + 16$ $(y - 4)^2$
28. $z^2 - 2z + 1$ $(z - 1)^2$

29. $t^2 + 20t + 100$ $(t + 10)^2$

30. $r^2 + 24r + 144$ $(r + 12)^2$

31. $u^2 - 18u + 81$ $(u - 9)^2$

32. $v^2 - 14v + 49$ $(v - 7)^2$

33. $4x^2 + 12x + 9$ $(2x + 3)^2$

34. $4x^2 - 4x + 1$ $(2x - 1)^2$

35. $36x^2 + 12x + 1$ $(6x + 1)^2$

36. $4x^2 - 20x + 25$ $(2x - 5)^2$

37. $a^2 + 2ab + b^2$ $(a + b)^2$

38. $a^2 - 2ab + b^2$ $(a - b)^2$

39. $16x^2 - 8xy + y^2$ $(4x - y)^2$

40. $25x^2 + 20xy + 4y^2$ $(5x + 2y)^2$

Complete each factorization.

41. $y^2 - 49 = \left(y + \boxed{7}\right)\left(y - \boxed{7}\right)$

42. $p^4 - q^2 = (p^2 + q)\left(\boxed{p^2} - q\right)$

43. $t^2 - w^2 = \left(\boxed{t} + \boxed{w}\right)(t - w)$

44. $49u^2 - 64v^2 = \left(\boxed{7u} + 8v\right)\left(7u - \boxed{8v}\right)$

Factor each polynomial, if possible.

45. $x^2 - 16$ $(x + 4)(x - 4)$

46. $x^2 - 25$ $(x + 5)(x - 5)$

47. $4y^2 - 1$ $(2y + 1)(2y - 1)$

48. $9z^2 - 1$ $(3z + 1)(3z - 1)$

49. $9x^2 - y^2$ $(3x + y)(3x - y)$

50. $4x^2 - z^2$ $(2x + z)(2x - z)$

51. $16a^2 - 25b^2$ $(4a + 5b)(4a - 5b)$

52. $36a^2 - 121b^2$ $(6a + 11b)(6a - 11b)$

53. $a^2 + b^2$ prime

54. $121a^2 + 144b^2$ prime

55. $a^4 - 144b^2$ $(a^2 + 12b)(a^2 - 12b)$

56. $81y^4 - 100z^2$ $(9y^2 + 10z)(9y^2 - 10z)$

57. $t^2z^2 - 64$ $(tz + 8)(tz - 8)$

58. $900 - B^2C^2$ $(30 + BC)(30 - BC)$

59. $8x^2 - 32y^2$ $8(x + 2y)(x - 2y)$

60. $2a^2 - 200b^2$ $2(a + 10b)(a - 10b)$

61. $7a^2 - 7$ $7(a + 1)(a - 1)$

62. $20x^2 - 5$ $5(2x + 1)(2x - 1)$

63. $6x^4 - 6x^2y^2$ $6x^2(x + y)(x - y)$

64. $4b^2y - 16c^2y$ $4y(b + 2c)(b - 2c)$

65. $x^4 - 81$ $(x^2 + 9)(x + 3)(x - 3)$

66. $y^4 - 625$ $(y^2 + 25)(y + 5)(y - 5)$

67. $a^4 - 16$ $(a^2 + 4)(a + 2)(a - 2)$

68. $b^4 - 256$ $(b^2 + 16)(b + 4)(b - 4)$

69. $81r^4 - 256s^4$ $(9r^2 + 16s^2)(3r + 4s)(3r - 4s)$

70. $16y^8 - 81z^4$ $(4y^4 + 9z^2)(2y^2 + 3z)(2y^2 - 3z)$

Complete each factorization.

71. $a^3 + 8 = (a + 2)\left(a^2 - \boxed{2a} + 4\right)$

72. $x^3 - 1 = (x - 1)\left(x^2 + \boxed{x} + 1\right)$

73. $b^3 + 27 = \left(\boxed{b + 3}\right)(b^2 - 3b + 9)$

74. $z^3 - 125 = \left(\boxed{z - 5}\right)(z^2 + 5z + 25)$

Factor each polynomial.

75. $y^3 + 1$ $(y + 1)(y^2 - y + 1)$

76. $x^3 - 8$ $(x - 2)(x^2 + 2x + 4)$

77. $a^3 - 27$ $(a - 3)(a^2 + 3a + 9)$

78. $b^3 + 125$ $(b + 5)(b^2 - 5b + 25)$

79. $8 + x^3$ $(2 + x)(4 - 2x + x^2)$

80. $27 - y^3$ $(3 - y)(9 + 3y + y^2)$

81. $s^3 - t^3$ $(s - t)(s^2 + st + t^2)$

82. $8u^3 + w^3$ $(2u + w)(4u^2 - 2uw + w^2)$

83. $a^3 + 8b^3$ $(a + 2b)(a^2 - 2ab + 4b^2)$

84. $27a^3 - b^3$ $(3a - b)(9a^2 + 3ab + b^2)$

85. $64x^3 - 27$ $(4x - 3)(16x^2 + 12x + 9)$

86. $27x^3 + 125$ $(3x + 5)(9x^2 - 15x + 25)$

87. $a^6 - b^3$ $(a^2 - b)(a^4 + a^2b + b^2)$

88. $a^3 + b^6$ $(a + b^2)(a^2 - ab^2 + b^4)$

89. $x^9 + y^6$ $(x^3 + y^2)(x^6 - x^3y^2 + y^4)$

90. $x^3 - y^9$ $(x - y^3)(x^2 + xy^3 + y^6)$

91. $2x^3 + 54$ $2(x + 3)(x^2 - 3x + 9)$

92. $2x^3 - 2$ $2(x - 1)(x^2 + x + 1)$

93. $-x^3 + 216$ $-(x - 6)(x^2 + 6x + 36)$

94. $-x^3 - 125$ $-(x + 5)(x^2 - 5x + 25)$

95. $64m^3x - 8n^3x$ $8x(2m - n)(4m^2 + 2mn + n^2)$

96. $16r^4 + 128rs^3$ $16r(r + 2s)(r^2 - 2rs + 4s^2)$

97. $x^4y + 216xy^4$ $xy(x + 6y)(x^2 - 6xy + 36y^2)$

98. $16a^5 - 54a^2b^3$ $2a^2(2a - 3b)(4a^2 + 6ab + 9b^2)$

99. $81r^4s^2 - 24rs^5$ $3rs^2(3r - 2s)(9r^2 + 6rs + 4s^2)$

100. $4m^5n + 500m^2n^4$ $4m^2n(m + 5n)(m^2 - 5mn + 25n^2)$

APPLICATIONS

101. GENETICS The Hardy–Weinberg equation, one of the fundamental concepts in population genetics, is

$$p^2 + 2pq + q^2 = 1$$

where p represents the frequency of a certain dominant gene and q represents the frequency of a certain recessive gene. Factor the left-hand side of the equation. $(p + q)^2$

102. SPACE TRAVEL The first Soviet manned spacecraft, Vostok, is shown in Illustration 1. The surface area of the spherical part of the craft is given by $(36\pi r^2 - 48\pi r + 16\pi)$ m^2. Factor the expression. $4\pi(3r - 2)^2$ m^2

ILLUSTRATION 1

103. PHYSICS Illustration 2 shows a time-sequence picture of a falling apple. Factor the expression, which gives the difference in the distance fallen by the apple during the time interval from t_1 to t_2 seconds. $0.5g(t_1 + t_2)(t_1 - t_2)$

This distance is $0.5gt_1^2 - 0.5gt_2^2$

ILLUSTRATION 2

104. DARTS A circular dart board has a series of rings around a solid center, called the bullseye. (See Illustration 3.) To find the area of the outer white ring, we can use the formula

$$A = \pi R^2 - \pi r^2$$

Factor the expression on the right-hand side of the equation. $\pi(R + r)(R - r)$

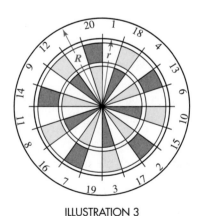

ILLUSTRATION 3

WRITING

105. When asked to factor $x^2 - 25$, one student wrote $(x + 5)(x - 5)$, and another student wrote $(x - 5)(x + 5)$. Are both answers correct? Explain.

106. Write a comment to the student whose work is shown below, explaining the initial error that was made.

Factor $4x^2 - 16y^2$.

$(2x + 4y)(2x - 4y)$

107. Explain why $x^6 - 1$ can be thought of as a difference of two squares or as a difference of two cubes.

108. Why is $a^2 + 2a + 1$ a perfect square trinomial, and why isn't $a^2 + 4a + 1$ a perfect square trinomial?

REVIEW *Do each division.*

109. $\dfrac{5x^2 + 10y^2 - 15xy}{5xy}$ $\frac{x}{y} + \frac{2y}{x} - 3$

110. $\dfrac{-30c^2d^2 - 15c^2d - 10cd^2}{-10cd}$ $3cd + \frac{3c}{2} + d$

111. $2a - 1\overline{)a - 2 + 6a^2}$ $3a + 2$

112. $4b + 3\overline{)4b^3 - 5b^2 - 2b + 3}$ $b^2 - 2b + 1$

ADDITIONAL FACTORING PROBLEMS *Apply the factoring strategy to factor each polynomial completely. If a polynomial is not factorable, write "prime."*

113. $a^2(x - a) - b^2(x - a)$ $(x - a)(a + b)(a - b)$

114. $a^2c + a^2d^2 + bc + bd^2$ $(c + d^2)(a^2 + b)$

115. $70p^4q^3 - 35p^4q^2 + 49p^5q^2$ $7p^4q^2(10q - 5 + 7p)$

116. $a^2b^2 - 144$ $(ab + 12)(ab - 12)$

117. $2ab^2 + 8ab - 24a$ $2a(b + 6)(b - 2)$

118. $t^4 - 16$ $(t^2 + 4)(t + 2)(t - 2)$

119. $-8p^3q^7 - 4p^2q^3$ $-4p^2q^3(2pq^4 + 1)$

120. $8m^2n^3 - 24mn^4$ $8mn^3(m - 3n)$

121. $20m^2 + 100m + 125$ $5(2m + 5)^2$

122. $3rs + 6r^2 - 18s^2$ $3(2r - 3s)(r + 2s)$

123. $x^2 + 7x + 1$ prime

124. $3a^3 + 24b^3$ $3(a + 2b)(a^2 - 2ab + 4b^2)$

125. $-2x^5 + 128x^2$ $-2x^2(x - 4)(x^2 + 4x + 16)$

126. $16 - 40z + 25z^2$ $(5z - 4)^2$

127. $14t^3 - 40t^2 + 6t^4$ $2t^2(3t - 5)(t + 4)$

128. $-9x^2y^2 + 6xy - 1$ $-(3xy - 1)^2$

129. $x^2y^2 - 2x^2 - y^2 + 2$ $(y^2 - 2)(x + 1)(x - 1)$

130. $5x^3y^3z^4 + 25x^2y^3z^2 - 35x^3y^2z^5$
$5x^2y^2z^2(xyz^2 + 5y - 7xz^3)$

131. $8p^6 - 27q^6$ $(2p^2 - 3q^2)(4p^4 + 6p^2q^2 + 9q^4)$

132. $2c^2 - 5cd - 3d^2$ $(2c + d)(c - 3d)$

133. $125p^3 - 64y^3$ $(5p - 4y)(25p^2 + 20py + 16y^2)$

134. $8a^2x^3y - 2b^2xy$ $2xy(2ax + b)(2ax - b)$

135. $-16x^4y^2z + 24x^5y^3z^4 - 15x^2y^3z^7$
$-x^2y^2z(16x^2 - 24x^3yz^3 + 15yz^6)$

136. $2ac + 4ad + bc + 2bd$ $(c + 2d)(2a + b)$

137. $81p^4 - 16q^4$ $(9p^2 + 4q^2)(3p + 2q)(3p - 2q)$

138. $6x^2 - x - 16$ prime

139. $4x^2 + 9y^2$ prime

140. $30a^4 + 5a^3 - 200a^2$ $5a^2(3a + 8)(2a - 5)$

141. $54x^3 + 250y^6$ $2(3x + 5y^2)(9x^2 - 15xy^2 + 25y^4)$

142. $6a^3 + 35a^2 - 6a$ $a(6a - 1)(a + 6)$

143. $10r^2 - 13r - 4$ prime

144. $21t^3 - 10t^2 + t$ $t(7t - 1)(3t - 1)$

145. $49p^2 + 28pq + 4q^2$ $(7p + 2q)^2$

146. $16x^2 - 40x^3 + 25x^4$ $x^2(5x - 4)^2$

5.5 *Quadratic Equations*

In this section, you will learn about

- Quadratic equations • Solving quadratic equations by factoring
- Applications

INTRODUCTION. Equations that involve first-degree polynomials, such as $9x - 6 = 0$, are called *linear equations*. Equations that involve second-degree polynomials, such as $9x^2 - 6x = 0$, are called **quadratic equations.** In this section, we will define quadratic equations and learn how to solve many of them by factoring.

Quadratic equations

If a polynomial contains one variable with an exponent to the second (but no higher) power, it is called a **second-degree polynomial.** Equations in which a second-degree polynomial is equal to zero are called **quadratic equations.** Some examples are

$$9x^2 - 6x = 0, \qquad x^2 - 2x - 63 = 0, \quad \text{and} \quad 2x^2 + 3x - 2 = 0$$

Quadratic equations

> A **quadratic equation** is an equation that can be written in the form
> $$ax^2 + bx + c = 0 \quad (a \neq 0)$$
> where a, b, and c represent real numbers.

To write a quadratic equation such as $21x = 10 - 10x^2$ in $ax^2 + bx + c = 0$ form (called **quadratic form**), we use the addition and subtraction properties of equality to get 0 on the right-hand side.

$$21x = 10 - 10x^2$$
$$10x^2 + 21x = 10 - 10x^2 + 10x^2 \qquad \text{Add } 10x^2 \text{ to both sides.}$$
$$10x^2 + 21x = 10 \qquad\qquad\qquad \text{Combine like terms: } -10x^2 + 10x^2 = 0.$$
$$10x^2 + 21x - 10 = 0 \qquad\qquad \text{Subtract 10 from both sides.}$$

When $21x = 10 - 10x^2$ is written in quadratic form, we see that $a = 10$, $b = 21$, and $c = -10$.

The techniques we have used to solve linear equations cannot be used to solve a quadratic equation, because those techniques cannot isolate x on one side of the equation. However, we can often solve quadratic equations using factoring and the following property of real numbers.

The zero-factor property of real numbers

> Suppose a and b represent two real numbers. Then
> If $ab = 0$, then $a = 0$ or $b = 0$.

In words, the zero-factor property states that when the product of two numbers is zero, at least one of them must be zero.

EXAMPLE 1 *Using the zero-factor property.* Solve $(4y - 1)(y + 6) = 0$.

Self Check
Solve $b(5b - 3) = 0$.

Solution
The left-hand side of the equation is $(4y - 1)(y + 6)$. By the zero-factor property, one of these factors must be 0.

$$4y - 1 = 0 \quad \text{or} \quad y + 6 = 0$$

We can solve each of the linear equations.

$$4y - 1 = 0 \quad \text{or} \quad y + 6 = 0$$
$$4y = 1 \qquad\qquad\quad y = -6$$
$$y = \frac{1}{4}$$

The equation has two solutions, $\frac{1}{4}$ and -6. To check, we substitute the results for y in the original equation and simplify.

For $y = \frac{1}{4}$	**For $y = -6$**
$(4y - 1)(y + 6) = 0$	$(4y - 1)(y + 6) = 0$
$\left[4\left(\frac{1}{4}\right) - 1\right]\left(\frac{1}{4} + 6\right) \stackrel{?}{=} 0$	$[4(-6) - 1](-6 + 6) \stackrel{?}{=} 0$
$(1 - 1)\left(6\frac{1}{4}\right) \stackrel{?}{=} 0$	$(-24 - 1)(0) \stackrel{?}{=} 0$
$0\left(6\frac{1}{4}\right) \stackrel{?}{=} 0$	$-25(0) \stackrel{?}{=} 0$
$0 = 0$	$0 = 0$

Answer: $0, \dfrac{3}{5}$

■

Solving quadratic equations by factoring

In Example 1, the left-hand side of the equation was in factored form, so we were able to use the zero-factor property immediately. However, to solve many quadratic equations, we must first do the factoring.

EXAMPLE 2 *Solving quadratic equations.* Solve $9x^2 - 6x = 0$.

Self Check
Solve $5x^2 + 10x = 0$.

Solution
We begin by factoring the left-hand side of the equation.

$$9x^2 - 6x = 0$$
$$3x(3x - 2) = 0 \quad \text{Factor out the GCF of } 3x.$$

By the zero-factor property, we have

$$3x = 0 \quad \text{or} \quad 3x - 2 = 0$$

We can solve each of the linear equations to get

$$x = 0 \quad \text{or} \quad x = \frac{2}{3}$$

To check, we substitute the results for x in the original equation and simplify.

For x = 0

$$9x^2 - 6x = 0$$

$$9(0)^2 - 6(0) \stackrel{?}{=} 0$$

$$0 - 0 \stackrel{?}{=} 0$$

$$0 = 0$$

For $x = \frac{2}{3}$

$$9x^2 - 6x = 0$$

$$9\left(\frac{2}{3}\right)^2 - 6\left(\frac{2}{3}\right) \stackrel{?}{=} 0$$

$$9\left(\frac{4}{9}\right) - 6\left(\frac{2}{3}\right) \stackrel{?}{=} 0$$

$$4 - 4 \stackrel{?}{=} 0$$

$$0 = 0$$

Answer: $0, -2$ ■

We can use the following steps to solve a quadratic equation by factoring.

Factoring method

1. Write the equation in $ax^2 + bx + c = 0$ form.
2. Factor the left-hand side of the equation.
3. Use the zero-factor property to set each factor equal to zero.
4. Solve each resulting linear equation.
5. Check the results in the original equation.

EXAMPLE 3 *Writing an equation in quadratic form.* Solve $x^2 = 9$.

Solution

Before we can use the zero-factor property, we must subtract 9 from both sides to make the right-hand side zero.

$$x^2 = 9$$

$$x^2 - 9 = 0 \qquad \text{Subtract 9 from both sides.}$$

$$(x + 3)(x - 3) = 0 \qquad \text{Factor the difference of two squares.}$$

$$x + 3 = 0 \quad \text{or} \quad x - 3 = 0 \qquad \text{Set each factor equal to zero.}$$

$$x = -3 \qquad\qquad x = 3 \qquad \text{Solve each linear equation.}$$

Check each possible solution by substituting it into the original equation.

For x = −3

$$x^2 = 9$$

$$(-3)^2 \stackrel{?}{=} 9$$

$$9 = 9$$

For x = 3

$$x^2 = 9$$

$$(3)^2 \stackrel{?}{=} 9$$

$$9 = 9$$

Self Check

Solve $9x^2 - 36 = 0$.

Answer: $2, -2$ ■

EXAMPLE 4 *Solving quadratic equations.* Solve $x^2 - 2x - 63 = 0$.

Solution

In this case, we must factor a trinomial to solve the equation.

$$x^2 - 2x - 63 = 0$$

$$(x + 7)(x - 9) = 0 \qquad \text{Factor the trinomial } x^2 - 2x - 63.$$

$$x + 7 = 0 \quad \text{or} \quad x - 9 = 0 \qquad \text{Set each factor equal to zero.}$$

$$x = -7 \qquad\qquad x = 9 \qquad \text{Solve each linear equation.}$$

The solutions are -7 and 9. Check each one.

Self Check

Solve $x^2 + 5x + 6 = 0$.

Answer: $-2, -3$ ■

EXAMPLE 5 *Writing an equation in quadratic form.* Solve $2x^2 + 3x = 2$.

Solution

We write the equation in the form $ax^2 + bx + c = 0$ and then solve for x.

$$2x^2 + 3x = 2$$

$2x^2 + 3x - 2 = 0$ Subtract 2 from both sides so that the right-hand side is zero.

$(2x - 1)(x + 2) = 0$ Factor $2x^2 + 3x - 2$.

$2x - 1 = 0$ or $x + 2 = 0$ Set each factor equal to zero.

$\quad 2x = 1 \qquad\qquad x = -2$ Solve each linear equation.

$$x = \frac{1}{2}$$

Check each solution.

Self Check

Solve $3x^2 - 6 = -7x$.

Answer: $\dfrac{2}{3}, -3$ ■

EXAMPLE 6 *A repeated solution.* Solve $-4 = x(9x - 12)$.

Solution

First, we need to write the equation in the form $ax^2 + bx + c = 0$.

$$-4 = x(9x - 12)$$

$-4 = 9x^2 - 12x$ Distribute the multiplication by x.

$0 = 9x^2 - 12x + 4$ Add 4 to both sides to make the left-hand side zero.

$0 = (3x - 2)(3x - 2)$ Factor the trinomial

$3x - 2 = 0$ or $3x - 2 = 0$ Set each factor equal to zero.

$\quad 3x = 2 \qquad\qquad 3x = 2$ Add 2 to both sides.

$\quad x = \dfrac{2}{3} \qquad\qquad x = \dfrac{2}{3}$ Divide both sides by 3.

The equation has two solutions that are the same. We call $\frac{2}{3}$ a *repeated solution.* Check by substituting it into the original equation.

Self Check

Solve $x(4x + 12) = -9$.

Answer: $-\dfrac{3}{2}, -\dfrac{3}{2}$ ■

EXAMPLE 7 *An equation with three solutions.* Solve $6x^3 + 12x = 17x^2$.

Solution

This is not a quadratic equation, because it contains the term x^3. However, we can solve it using factoring and an extension of the zero-factor property.

$$6x^3 + 12x = 17x^2$$

$6x^3 - 17x^2 + 12x = 0$ Add $-17x^2$ to both sides to get 0 on the right-hand side.

$x(6x^2 - 17x + 12) = 0$ Factor out the GCF of x.

$x(2x - 3)(3x - 4) = 0$ Factor $6x^2 - 17x + 12$.

$x = 0$ or $2x - 3 = 0$ or $3x - 4 = 0$ Set each factor equal to zero.

$\qquad\qquad\qquad 2x = 3 \qquad\qquad\quad 3x = 4$ Solve the linear equations.

$$x = \frac{3}{2} \qquad\qquad\quad x = \frac{4}{3}$$

This equation has three solutions.

Self Check

Solve $10x^3 + x^2 - 2x = 0$.

Answer: $0, \dfrac{2}{5}, -\dfrac{1}{2}$ ■

Applications

The solutions of many problems involve the use of quadratic equations.

EXAMPLE 8   *Softball.*   A softball pitcher can throw a "fastball" underhand at about 55 mph (80 feet per second). If she throws a ball up into the air with that velocity, as in Figure 5-2, its height h in feet, t seconds after being released, is given by the formula

$$h = 80t - 16t^2$$

After the ball is thrown, in how many seconds will it hit the ground?

Solution   When the ball hits the ground, its height will be zero. Thus, we set h equal to zero and solve for t.

$$h = 80t - 16t^2$$
$$0 = 80t - 16t^2$$
$$0 = 16t(5 - t) \qquad \text{Factor out the GCF of } 16t.$$
$$16t = 0 \quad \text{or} \quad 5 - t = 0 \qquad \text{Set each factor equal to zero.}$$
$$t = 0 \qquad\qquad t = 5 \qquad \text{Solve each linear equation.}$$

FIGURE 5-2

When $t = 0$, the ball's height above the ground is 0 feet. When $t = 5$, the height is again 0 feet, and the object has hit the ground. The solution is 5 seconds. ■

EXAMPLE 9   *Perimeter of a rectangle.*   Assume that the rectangle in Figure 5-3 has an area of 52 square centimeters and that its length is 1 centimeter more than 3 times its width. Find the perimeter of the rectangle.

$3w + 1$

w | $A = 52 \text{ cm}^2$

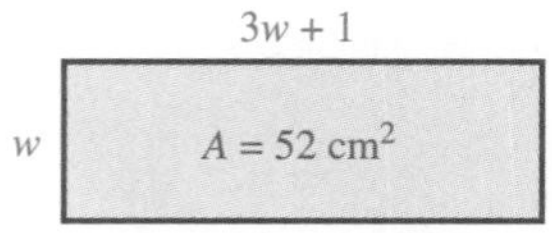

FIGURE 5-3

Analyze the problem   The area of the rectangle is 52 square centimeters. Recall that the formula that gives the area of a rectangle is $A = lw$. To find the perimeter of the rectangle, we need to know its length and width. We are told that its length is related to its width; the length is 1 centimeter more than 3 times the width.

Form an equation   Let w represent the width of the rectangle. Then $3w + 1$ represents its length. Because the area is 52 square centimeters, we substitute 52 for A and $3w + 1$ for l in the formula $A = lw$.

$$A = lw$$
$$52 = (3w + 1)w$$

Solve the equation   Now we solve the equation for w.

$$52 = (3w + 1)w \qquad \text{The equation to solve.}$$
$$52 = 3w^2 + w \qquad \text{Distribute the multiplication by } w.$$
$$0 = 3w^2 + w - 52 \qquad \text{Subtract 52 from both sides to make the left-hand side zero.}$$
$$0 = (3w + 13)(w - 4) \qquad \text{Factor the trinomial.}$$
$$3w + 13 = 0 \qquad \text{or} \quad w - 4 = 0 \qquad \text{Set each factor equal to zero.}$$
$$3w = -13 \qquad\qquad w = 4 \qquad \text{Solve each linear equation.}$$
$$w = -\frac{13}{3}$$

State the conclusion Since the width cannot be negative, we discard the result $w = -\frac{13}{3}$. Thus, the width of the rectangle is 4, and the length is given by

$$3w + 1 = 3(4) + 1 \quad \text{Substitute 4 for } w.$$
$$= 12 + 1$$
$$= 13$$

The dimensions of the rectangle are 4 centimeters by 13 centimeters. We find the perimeter by substituting 13 for l and 4 for w in the formula for the perimeter of a rectangle.

$$P = 2l + 2w$$
$$= 2(13) + 2(4)$$
$$= 26 + 8$$
$$= 34$$

The perimeter of the rectangle is 34 centimeters.

Check the result A rectangle with dimensions of 13 centimeters by 4 centimeters does have an area of 52 square centimeters, and the length is 1 centimeter more than 3 times the width. A rectangle with these dimensions has a perimeter of 34 centimeters. ∎

The next example involves a right triangle. A **right triangle** is a triangle that contains a 90° angle. The longest side of a right triangle is the **hypotenuse,** which is the side opposite the right angle. The remaining two sides are the **legs** of the triangle. (See Figure 5-4.) The **Pythagorean theorem** provides a formula relating the lengths of the three sides of a right triangle.

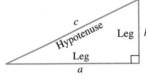

FIGURE 5-4

The Pythagorean theorem

If the length of the hypotenuse of a right triangle is c and the lengths of the two legs are a and b, then
$$c^2 = a^2 + b^2$$

EXAMPLE 10 ***Recording ozone levels.*** Three pollution monitoring stations are shown in Figure 5-5. The east county station is 3 miles farther from the downtown station than is the west county station. The distance between the east and west county stations is 6 miles longer than the distance between the downtown and west stations. How far apart are the stations?

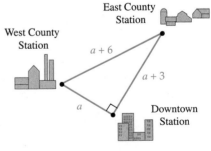

FIGURE 5-5

Analyze the problem To find the distances between the stations, we need to find the lengths of the sides of the right triangle formed by connecting their positions. The Pythagorean theorem gives the relationship between the sides of a right triangle: $a^2 + b^2 = c^2$.

Form an equation We let a represent the distance in miles from the downtown station to the west station, because the other two distances can be expressed in terms of it. The distance between the downtown and east stations is $(a + 3)$ miles, and that between the east and west stations is $(a + 6)$ miles. We substitute these distances into the Pythagorean theorem, noting that the length of the hypotenuse c is $(a + 6)$ miles.

$$a^2 + b^2 = c^2 \qquad \text{The Pythagorean theorem.}$$
$$a^2 + (a + 3)^2 = (a + 6)^2 \qquad \text{Substitute } (a + 3) \text{ for } b \text{ and } (a + 6) \text{ for } c.$$
$$a^2 + a^2 + 6a + 9 = a^2 + 12a + 36 \qquad \text{Find } (a + 3)^2 \text{ and } (a + 6)^2.$$
$$2a^2 + 6a + 9 = a^2 + 12a + 36 \qquad \text{Combine like terms on the left-hand side.}$$
$$a^2 - 6a - 27 = 0 \qquad \text{Subtract } a^2, 12a, \text{ and } 36 \text{ from both sides to make the right-hand side zero.}$$

Solve the equation   Now we solve the equation for a.

$$a^2 - 6a - 27 = 0$$
$$(a - 9)(a + 3) = 0 \qquad \text{Factor.}$$
$$a - 9 = 0 \quad \text{or} \quad a + 3 = 0 \qquad \text{Set each factor to zero.}$$
$$a = 9 \qquad\qquad a = -3 \qquad \text{Solve each linear equation.}$$

State the conclusion   Since a triangle cannot have a negative number for the length of a side, we discard the result $a = -3$. The distance from the downtown station to the west county station is 9 miles. The distance from the downtown station to the east county station is $9 + 3$, or 12 miles. The distance between the east and west stations is $9 + 6$, or 15 miles.

Check the result   The differences in the distances between stations meet the requirements stated in the problem. The distances also satisfy the Pythagorean theorem. So the solutions check.

$$9^2 + 12^2 \overset{?}{=} 15^2$$
$$81 + 144 \overset{?}{=} 225$$
$$225 = 225 \qquad\qquad\qquad ■$$

STUDY SET   Section 5.5   www

VOCABULARY   *Fill in the blanks.*

1. Any equation that can be written in the form $ax^2 + bx + c = 0$ is called a ___quadratic___ equation.

2. To ___factor___ a binomial or trinomial means to write it as a product.

CONCEPTS   *In Exercises 3–6, fill in the blanks.*

3. When the product of two numbers is zero, at least one of them is ___zero___. Symbolically, we can state this: If $ab = 0$, then $a =$ 0 or $b =$ 0.

4. The techniques used to solve linear equations cannot be used to solve quadratic equations, because those techniques cannot ___isolate___ the variable on one side of the equation.

5. To write a quadratic equation in *quadratic form* means that one side of the equation must be ___zero___ and the other side must be in the form $ax^2 + bx + c$.

6. If the length of the hypotenuse of a right triangle is c and the legs are a and b, then $c^2 =$ $a^2 + b^2$.

7. Classify each equation as quadratic or linear.
  a. $3x^2 + 4x + 2 = 0$ **b.** $3x + 7 = 0$
    quadratic   linear
  c. $2 = -16 - 4x$ **d.** $-6x + 2 = x^2$
    linear   quadratic

8. Check to see whether the given number is a solution of the given quadratic equation.
  a. $x^2 - 4x = 0; x = 4$ yes
  b. $x^2 + 2x - 4 = 0; x = -2$ no
  c. $4x^2 - x + 3 = 0; x = 1$ no

9. a. Evaluate $x^2 + 6x - 16$ for $x = 0$. -16
  b. Factor $x^2 + 6x - 16$. $(x - 2)(x + 8)$
  c. Solve $x^2 + 6x - 16 = 0$. $2, -8$

10. The equation $3x^2 - 4x + 5 = 0$ is written in $ax^2 + bx + c = 0$ form. What are a, b, and c?
  $3, -4, 5$

11. What is the first step that should be performed to solve each equation?
  a. $x^2 + 7x = -6$ Add 6 to both sides.
  b. $x(x + 7) = -3$ Distribute the multiplication by x.

12. a. How many solutions does the linear equation $2a + 3 = 2$ have?   1
  b. How many solutions does the quadratic equation $2a^2 + 3a = 2$ have?   2

NOTATION *Complete each solution.*

13. $7y^2 + 14y = 0$

$7y\,(y + 2) = 0$

$7y = 0$ or $y + 2 = 0$

$y = 0$ $\qquad\qquad$ $y = -2$

14. $\qquad 12p^2 - p - 6 = 0$

$\left(\,4p\, - 3\right)\!\left(3p + \,2\,\right) = 0$

$4p - 3 = 0$ or $3p + 2 = 0$

$4p = 3$ $\qquad\qquad$ $3p = -2$

$p = \dfrac{3}{4}$ $\qquad\qquad$ $p = -\dfrac{2}{3}$

PRACTICE *Solve each equation.*

15. $(x - 2)(x + 3) = 0$ $2, -3$

16. $(x - 3)(x - 2) = 0$ $3, 2$

17. $(2s - 5)(s + 6) = 0$ $\frac{5}{2}, -6$

18. $(3h - 4)(h + 1) = 0$ $\frac{4}{3}, -1$

19. $(x - 1)(x + 2)(x - 3) = 0$ $1, -2, 3$

20. $(x + 2)(x + 3)(x - 4) = 0$ $-2, -3, 4$

21. $x(x - 3) = 0$ $0, 3$

22. $x(x + 5) = 0$ $0, -5$

23. $x(2x - 5) = 0$ $0, \frac{5}{2}$

24. $x(5x + 7) = 0$ $0, -\frac{7}{5}$

25. $w^2 - 7w = 0$ $0, 7$

26. $p^2 + 5p = 0$ $0, -5$

27. $3x^2 + 8x = 0$ $0, -\frac{8}{3}$

28. $5x^2 - x = 0$ $0, \frac{1}{5}$

29. $8s^2 - 16s = 0$ $0, 2$

30. $15s^2 - 20s = 0$ $0, \frac{4}{3}$

31. $x^2 - 25 = 0$ $-5, 5$

32. $x^2 - 36 = 0$ $-6, 6$

33. $4x^2 - 1 = 0$ $-\frac{1}{2}, \frac{1}{2}$

34. $9y^2 - 1 = 0$ $-\frac{1}{3}, \frac{1}{3}$

35. $9y^2 - 4 = 0$ $-\frac{2}{3}, \frac{2}{3}$

36. $16z^2 - 25 = 0$ $-\frac{5}{4}, \frac{5}{4}$

37. $x^2 = 100$ $-10, 10$

38. $z^2 = 25$ $-5, 5$

39. $4x^2 = 81$ $-\frac{9}{2}, \frac{9}{2}$

40. $9y^2 = 64$ $-\frac{8}{3}, \frac{8}{3}$

41. $x^2 - 13x + 12 = 0$ $12, 1$

42. $x^2 + 7x + 6 = 0$ $-1, -6$

43. $x^2 - 4x - 21 = 0$ $-3, 7$

44. $x^2 + 2x - 15 = 0$ $3, -5$

45. $x^2 - 9x + 8 = 0$ $8, 1$

46. $x^2 - 14x + 45 = 0$ $9, 5$

47. $a^2 + 8a = -15$ $-3, -5$

48. $a^2 - a = 56$ $8, -7$

49. $2y - 8 = -y^2$ $-4, 2$

50. $-3y + 18 = y^2$ $3, -6$

51. $x^3 + 3x^2 + 2x = 0$ $0, -1, -2$

52. $x^3 - 7x^2 + 10x = 0$ $0, 5, 2$

53. $k^3 - 27k - 6k^2 = 0$ $0, 9, -3$

54. $j^3 - 22j - 9j^2 = 0$ $0, 11, -2$

55. $(x - 1)(x^2 + 5x + 6) = 0$ $1, -2, -3$

56. $(x - 2)(x^2 - 8x + 7) = 0$ $2, 7, 1$

57. $2x^2 - 5x + 2 = 0$ $\frac{1}{2}, 2$

58. $2x^2 + x - 3 = 0$ $-\frac{3}{2}, 1$

59. $5x^2 - 6x + 1 = 0$ $\frac{1}{5}, 1$

60. $6x^2 - 5x + 1 = 0$ $\frac{1}{3}, \frac{1}{2}$

61. $4r^2 + 4r = -1$ $-\frac{1}{2}, -\frac{1}{2}$

62. $9m^2 + 6m = -1$ $-\frac{1}{3}, -\frac{1}{3}$

63. $-15x^2 + 2 = -7x$ $\frac{2}{3}, -\frac{1}{5}$

64. $-8x^2 - 10x = -3$ $\frac{1}{4}, -\frac{3}{2}$

65. $x(2x - 3) = 20$ $-\frac{5}{2}, 4$

66. $x(2x - 3) = 14$ $\frac{7}{2}, -2$

67. $(d + 1)(8d + 1) = 18d$ $\frac{1}{8}, 1$

68. $4h(3h + 2) = h + 12$ $-\frac{4}{3}, \frac{3}{4}$

69. $2x(3x^2 + 10x) = -6x$ $0, -3, -\frac{1}{3}$

70. $2x^3 = 2x(x + 2)$ $0, -1, 2$

71. $x^3 + 7x^2 = x^2 - 9x$ $0, -3, -3$

72. $x^2(x + 10) = 2x(x - 8)$ $0, -4, -4$

APPLICATIONS *In Exercises 73–74, an object has been thrown straight up into the air. The formula $h = vt - 16t^2$ gives the height h of the object above the ground after t seconds, when it is thrown upward with an initial velocity v.*

73. TIME OF FLIGHT   After how many seconds will the object hit the ground if it is thrown with a velocity of 144 feet per second?   9 sec

74. TIME OF FLIGHT   After how many seconds will the object hit the ground if it is thrown with a velocity of 160 feet per second?   10 sec

75. OFFICIATING   Before a football game, a coin toss is used to determine which team will kick off. See Illustration 1. The height h (in feet) of a coin above the ground t seconds after being flipped up into the air is given by $h = -16t^2 + 22t + 3$. How long does a team captain have to call heads or tails if it must be done while the coin is in the air? $\frac{3}{2} = 1.5$ sec

ILLUSTRATION 1

76. DOLPHINS   See Illustration 2. The height h in feet reached by a dolphin t seconds after breaking the surface of the water is given by

$$h = -16t^2 + 32t$$

How long will it take the dolphin to jump out of the water and touch the trainer's hand?   1 sec

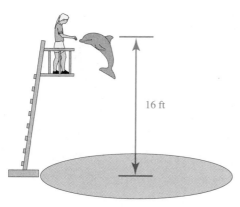

ILLUSTRATION 2

77. EXHIBITION DIVING   In Acapulco, Mexico, men diving from a cliff to the water 64 feet below are quite a tourist attraction. A diver's height h above the water t seconds after diving is given by $h = -16t^2 + 64$. How long does a dive last?   2 sec

78. FORENSIC MEDICINE   The kinetic energy E of a moving object is given by $E = \frac{1}{2}mv^2$, where m is the mass of the object (in kilograms) and v is the object's velocity (in meters per second). Kinetic energy is measured in joules. Examining the damage done to a victim, a police pathologist determines that the energy of a 3-kilogram mass at impact was 54 joules. Find the velocity at impact. (*Hint:* Multiply both sides of the equation by 2.)   6 m/s

79. CHOREOGRAPHY   For the finale of a musical, 36 dancers are to assemble in a triangular-shaped series of rows, where each successive row has one more dancer than the previous row. Illustration 3 shows the beginning of such a formation. The relationship between the number of rows r and the number of dancers d is given by

$$d = \frac{1}{2}r(r + 1)$$

Determine the number of rows in the formation. (*Hint:* Multiply both sides of the equation by 2.)   8

ILLUSTRATION 3

80. CRAFTS   Illustration 4 shows how a geometric wall hanging can be created by stretching yarn from peg to peg across a wooden ring. The relationship between the number of pegs p placed evenly around the ring and the number of yarn segments s that criss-cross the ring is given by the formula

$$s = \frac{p(p - 3)}{2}$$

How many pegs are needed if the designer wants 27 segments to criss-cross the ring? (*Hint:* Multiply both sides of the equation by 2.)   9

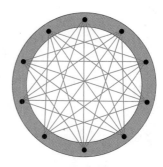

ILLUSTRATION 4

81. INSULATION   The area of the rectangular slab of foam insulation in Illustration 5 is 36 square meters. Find the dimensions of the slab.   4 m by 9 m

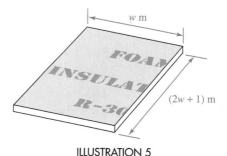

ILLUSTRATION 5

82. SHIPPING PALLETS   The length of a rectangular shipping pallet is 2 feet less than 3 times its width. Its area is 21 square feet. Find the dimensions of the pallet.   3 ft by 7 ft

83. BOATING   The inclined ramp of the boat launch shown in Illustration 6 is 8 meters longer than the "rise" of the ramp. The "run" is 7 meters longer than the "rise." How long are the three sides of the ramp?   5 m, 12 m, 13 m

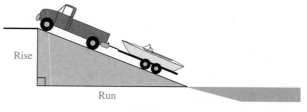

ILLUSTRATION 6

84. CAR REPAIR   To create some space to work under the front end of a car, a mechanic drives it up steel ramps. See Illustration 7. The ramp is 1 foot longer than the back, and the base is 2 feet longer than the back of the ramp. Find the length of each side of the ramp.   3 ft, 4 ft, 5 ft

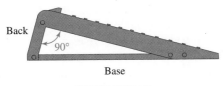

ILLUSTRATION 7

85. GARDENING TOOLS   The dimensions (in millimeters) of the teeth of a pruning saw blade are given in Illustration 8. Find each length.   3 mm, 4 mm, 5 mm

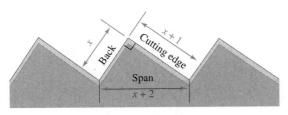

ILLUSTRATION 8

86. HARDWARE   An aluminum brace used to support a wooden shelf has a length that is 2 inches less than twice the width of the shelf. The brace is anchored to the wall 8 inches below the shelf, as shown in Illustration 9. Find the width of the shelf and the length of the brace. $w = 6$ in., $l = 10$ in.

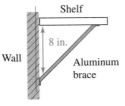

ILLUSTRATION 9

87. DESIGNING A TENT   The length of the base of the triangular sheet of canvas above the door of the tent in Illustration 10 is 2 feet more than twice its height. The area is 30 square feet. Find the height and the length of the base of the triangle. $h = 5$ ft, $b = 12$ ft

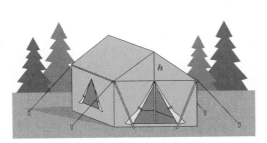

ILLUSTRATION 10

88. DIMENSIONS OF A TRIANGLE   The height of a triangle is 2 inches less than 5 times the length of its base.

The area is 36 square inches. Find the length of the base and the height of the triangle. $b = 4$ in., $h = 18$ in.

89. TUBING   A piece of cardboard in the shape of a parallelogram is twisted to form the tube for a roll of paper towels. (See Illustration 11.) The parallelogram has an area of 60 square inches. If its height h is 7 inches more than the length of the base b, what is the circumference of the tube? (*Hint:* The formula for the area of a parallelogram is $A = bh$.)   5 in.

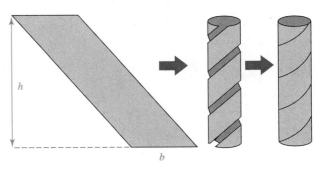

ILLUSTRATION 11

90. SWIMMING POOL BORDER   The owners of the rectangular swimming pool in Illustration 12 want to surround the pool with a crushed-stone border of uniform width. They have enough stone to cover 74 square meters. How wide should they make the border? (*Hint:* The area of the larger rectangle minus the area of the smaller is the area of the border.)   1 m

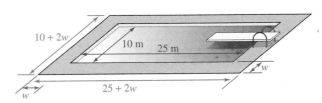

ILLUSTRATION 12

91. HOUSE CONSTRUCTION   The formula for the area of a trapezoid is

$$A = \frac{h(B + b)}{2}$$

The area of the trapezoidal truss in Illustration 13 is 24 square meters. Find the height of the trapezoid if one base is 8 meters and the other base is the same as the height. (*Hint:* Multiply both sides of the equation by 2.)   4 m

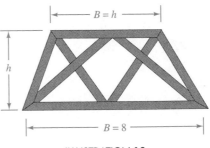

ILLUSTRATION 13

92. VOLUME OF A PYRAMID   The volume of a
pyramid is given by the formula

$$V = \frac{Bh}{3}$$

where *B* is the area of its base and *h* is its height. The
volume of the pyramid in Illustration 14 is 192 cubic
centimeters. Find the dimensions of its rectangular base
if one edge of the base is 2 centimeters longer than the
other and the height of the pyramid is 12 centimeters.
6 cm by 8 cm

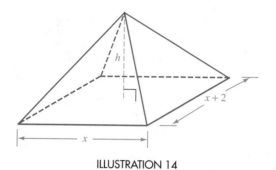

ILLUSTRATION 14

WRITING

93. What is wrong with the logic used by a student to
"solve" $x^2 + x = 6$?

$$x(x + 1) = 6$$
$$x = 6 \quad \text{or} \quad x + 1 = 6$$
$$x = 5$$

So the solutions are 6 or 5.

94. Suppose that to find the length of the base of a triangle,
you write a quadratic equation and solve it to find
$b = 6$ or $b = -8$. Explain why one solution should be
discarded.

REVIEW

95. EXERCISE   A doctor advises one patient to exercise
at least 15 minutes but less than 30 minutes per day.
Use a compound inequality to express the range of
these times in minutes. $15 \text{ min} \leq t < 30 \text{ min}$

96. SNACKS   A bag of peanuts is worth $0.30 less than a
bag of cashews. Equal amounts of peanuts and cashews
are used to make 40 bags of a mixture that is worth
$1.05 per bag. How much is a bag of cashews worth?
$1.20

97. A rectangle is 3 times as long as it is wide, and its
perimeter is 120 centimeters. Find its area. 675 cm^2

98. INVESTING   A woman invests $15,000, part at 7%
annual interest and part at 8% annual interest. If she receives $1,100 interest per year, how much did she
invest at 7%? $10,000

Factoring

Factoring polynomials is the reverse of the process of multiplying polynomials. When we factor a polynomial, we write it as a product of two or more factors.

1. In the following problem, the distributive property is used to multiply a monomial and a binomial.

Find $3(x + 9)$.

$$3(x + 9) = 3 \cdot x + 3 \cdot 9$$
$$= 3x + 27$$

Rewrite this so that it becomes a factoring problem. What would you start with? What would the answer be?

Factor $3x + 27$; $3(x + 9)$

2. In the following problem, we multiply two binomials.

Find $(x + 3)(x + 9)$.

$$(x + 3)(x + 9) = x^2 + 9x + 3x + 27$$
$$= x^2 + 12x + 27$$

Rewrite this so that it becomes a factoring problem. What would you start with? What would the answer be?

Factor $x^2 + 12x + 27$; $(x + 3)(x + 9)$

A factoring strategy

The following flowchart leads you through the correct steps to identify the type(s) of factoring necessary to factor any given polynomial having two or more terms.

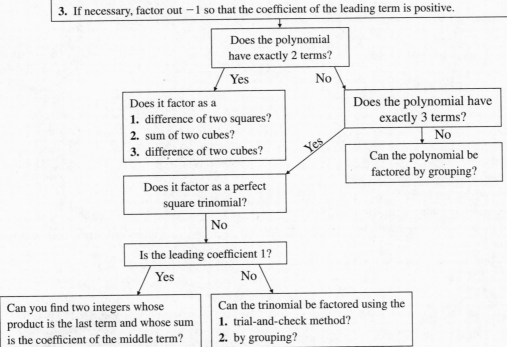

Factor each polynomial completely.

3. $-3a^2 + 21a - 36$ $-3(a - 3)(a - 4)$

4. $x^2 - 121y^2$ $(x + 11y)(x - 11y)$

5. $rt + 2r + st + 2s$ $(r + s)(t + 2)$

6. $v^3 - 8$ $(v - 2)(v^2 + 2v + 4)$

7. $6t^2 - 19t + 15$ $(3t - 5)(2t - 3)$

8. $25y^2 - 20y + 4$ $(5y - 2)^2$

9. $2r^3 - 50r$ $2r(r + 5)(r - 5)$

10. $46w - 6 + 16w^2$ $2(8w - 1)(w + 3)$

381

Section 5.1

PRIME NUMBERS We can use a procedure called the **sieve of Eratosthenes** to find all the prime numbers in the set of the first 100 whole numbers. Give each member in your group a copy of the table shown in Illustration 1. Cross out 1, since it is not a prime number by definition. Cross out any numbers divisible by 2, 3, 5, or 7, because they have a factor of 2, 3, 5, or 7 and thus would not be prime. Don't cross out 2, 3, 5, or 7, because they are prime numbers. At the end of this process, you should end up with the first 25 prime numbers.

1	2	3	4	5	6	7	8	9	10
11	12	13	14	15	16	17	18	19	20
21	22	23	24	25	26	27	28	29	30
31	32	33	34	35	36	37	38	39	40
41	42	43	44	45	46	47	48	49	50
51	52	53	54	55	56	57	58	59	60
61	62	63	64	65	66	67	68	69	70
71	72	73	74	75	76	77	78	79	80
81	82	83	84	85	86	87	88	89	90
91	92	93	94	95	96	97	98	99	100

ILLUSTRATION 1

Section 5.2

FACTORING TRINOMIALS

a. Four squares and four rectangles are shown in Illustration 2. The dimensions of the figures are given in the same units. Find the sum of their areas by combining like terms.

b. Cut out the figures and assemble them into a large rectangle having a length of $(x + 3)$ units and a width of $(x + 1)$ units. Note that these dimensions give the factored form of $x^2 + 4x + 3$, the answer to part a.

c. Make a new model that could be used to find the factored form of $x^2 + 5x + 4$.

Section 5.3

COMPARING METHODS Factor $18x^2 + 3x - 10$ by using the trial-and-check method and by using the grouping method. Which method do you think is better? Explain why.

Section 5.4

COMPARING METHODS Show how $x^6 - 1$ can be factored in two ways: first as a difference of two squares and then as a difference of two cubes.

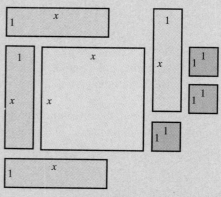

ILLUSTRATION 2

SUMS AND DIFFERENCES OF CUBES Long division can be used to verify the following factoring formulas.

$$x^3 + y^3 = (x + y)(x^2 - xy + y^2)$$
$$x^3 - y^3 = (x - y)(x^2 + xy + y^2)$$

a. Divide: $x + y \overline{)x^3 + y^3}$.

(*Hint:* Write $x^3 + y^3$ as $x^3 + 0x^2y + 0xy^2 + y^3$)

b. Divide: $x - y \overline{)x^3 - y^3}$.

FACTORING Factor each of the following polynomials completely. Begin by factoring out the indicated amount first.

a. Factor out 503 from $44{,}767a - 12{,}072b$.
b. Factor out 0.05 from $0.05t^2 - 0.25t + 0.3$.
c. Factor out -1.8 from $-16.2s^2 - 9s + 7.2$.
d. Factor out 2.375 from $38x^2 - 9.5y^2$.
e. Factor out 6.758 from $182.466b^3 - 54.064c^3$.

Section 5.5

SOLVING QUADRATIC EQUATIONS

a. Write $x^2 = 12x$ in quadratic form and then use factoring to solve it.

b. Divide both sides of $x^2 = 12x$ by x to "solve" it. Why don't you get two answers as you did in part a?

c. Consider the division property of equality and explain how it was inappropriately applied in part b.

QUADRATIC EQUATIONS Find a quadratic equation that has the following solutions. To do this, use the factoring method in reverse.

a. 3, 4

b. $-5, 1$

c. $\dfrac{1}{3}, 9$

d. $-\dfrac{2}{5}, -\dfrac{4}{3}$

Factoring Out the Greatest Common Factor and Factoring by Grouping

CONCEPTS

A *prime number* is a natural number greater than 1 whose only factors are 1 and itself. A natural number is in *prime-factored form* when it is written as the product of prime numbers.

To find the *greatest common factor* (GCF) of several monomials:

1. Prime factor each monomial.
2. List each common factor the least number of times it appears in any one monomial.
3. Find the product of the factors in the list to obtain the GCF.

To *factor by grouping,* arrange the polynomial so that the first two terms have a common factor and the last two terms have a common factor. Factor out the common factor from both groups. Then factor out the resulting common binomial factor.

REVIEW EXERCISES

1. Find the prime factorization of each number.

   a. 35 $5 \cdot 7$ **b.** 45 $3^2 \cdot 5$

   c. 96 $2^5 \cdot 3$ **d.** 99 $3^2 \cdot 11$

   e. 2,050 $2 \cdot 5^2 \cdot 41$ **f.** 4,096 2^{12}

2. Factor each polynomial completely.

   a. $3x + 9y$ $3(x + 3y)$ **b.** $5ax^2 + 15a$ $5a(x^2 + 3)$

   c. $7s^2 + 14s$ $7s(s + 2)$ **d.** $\pi ab - \pi ac$ $\pi a(b - c)$

   e. $2x^3 + 4x^2 - 8x$ $2x(x^2 + 2x - 4)$ **f.** $x^2yz + xy^2z + xyz$ $xyz(x + y + 1)$

   g. $-5ab^2 + 10a^2b - 15ab$ $-5ab(b - 2a + 3)$

   h. $4(x - 2) - x(x - 2)$ $(x - 2)(4 - x)$

3. Factor out -1 from each polynomial.

   a. $-a - 7$ $-(a + 7)$ **b.** $-4t^2 + 3t - 1$ $-(4t^2 - 3t + 1)$

4. Factor by grouping:

   a. $2c + 2d + ac + ad$ **b.** $3xy + 9x - 2y - 6$
       $(c + d)(2 + a)$ $(y + 3)(3x - 2)$

   c. $2a^3 - a + 2a^2 - 1$ **d.** $4m^2n + 12m^2 - 8mn - 24m$
       $(2a^2 - 1)(a + 1)$ $4m(n + 3)(m - 2)$

Factoring Trinomials of the Form $x^2 + bx + c$

To *factor a trinomial* of the form $x^2 + bx + c$ means to write it as the product of two binomials.

To factor $x^2 + bx + c$, find two integers whose product is c and whose sum is b.

$$\left(x \boxed{}\right)\left(x \boxed{}\right)$$

Write the trinomial in descending powers of the variable and factor out -1 when applicable.

5. Complete the table.

Factors of 6	Sum of the factors of 6
1(6)	7
2(3)	5
−1 (−6)	−7
−2(−3)	−5

6. Factor each trinomial, if possible.

a. $x^2 + 2x - 24$ $(x + 6)(x - 4)$ **b.** $x^2 - 4x - 12$ $(x - 6)(x + 2)$

c. $n^2 - 7x + 10$ $(n - 5)(n - 2)$ **d.** $t^2 + 10t + 15$ prime

e. $-y^2 + 9y - 20$ $-(y - 5)(y - 4)$ **f.** $10y + 9 + y^2$ $(y + 9)(y + 1)$

g. $c^2 + 3cd - 10d^2$
$(c + 5d)(c - 2d)$

h. $-3mn + m^2 + 2n^2$
$(m - 2n)(m - n)$

If a trinomial cannot be factored using only integers, it is called a *prime polynomial*.

7. Explain how we can check to see if $(x - 4)(x + 5)$ is the factorization of $x^2 + x - 20$.   Multiply to see if $(x - 4)(x + 5) = x^2 + x - 20$.

The *GCF* should always be factored out first. A trinomial is *factored completely* when it is expressed as a product of prime polynomials.

8. Completely factor each trinomial.

a. $5a^2 + 45a - 50$
$5(a + 10)(a - 1)$

b. $-4x^2y - 4x^3 + 24xy^2$
$-4x(x + 3y)(x - 2y)$

SECTION 5.3

Factoring Trinomials of the Form $ax^2 + bx + c$

To factor $ax^2 + bx + c$ using the *trial-and-check* factoring method, we must determine four integers. Use the FOIL method to check your work.

Factors
of a

$$\left(\boxed{}\, x + \boxed{}\right)\left(\boxed{}\, x + \boxed{}\right)$$

Factors
of c

To factor $ax^2 + bx + c$ using the *grouping* method, we write it as

$$ax^2 + \boxed{}\, x + \boxed{}\, x + c$$

9. Factor each trinomial completely, if possible.

a. $2x^2 - 5x - 3$
$(2x + 1)(x - 3)$

b. $10y^2 + 21y - 10$
$(2y + 5)(5y - 2)$

c. $-3x^2 + 14x + 5$
$-(3x + 1)(x - 5)$

d. $-9p^2 - 6p + 6p^3$
$3p(2p + 1)(p - 2)$

e. $4b^2 - 17bc + 4c^2$ $(4b - c)(b - 4c)$ **f.** $3y^2 + 7y - 11$ prime

10. ENTERTAINING   The rectangular-shaped area occupied by a table setting shown in Illustration 1 is $(12x^2 - x - 1)$ square inches. Factor the expression to find the binomials that represent the length and width of the table setting.
$(4x + 1)$ in., $(3x - 1)$ in.

ILLUSTRATION 1

SECTION 5.4

Special Factorizations and a Factoring Strategy

Special product formulas are used to factor *perfect square trinomials*.

$$x^2 + 2xy + y^2 = (x + y)^2$$

$$x^2 - 2xy + y^2 = (x - y)^2$$

To factor the *difference of two squares*, use the formula

$$F^2 - L^2 = (F + L)(F - L)$$

11. Factor each polynomial completely.

a. $x^2 + 10x + 25$ $(x + 5)^2$ **b.** $9y^2 - 24y + 16$ $(3y - 4)^2$

c. $-z^2 + 2z - 1$ $-(z - 1)^2$ **d.** $25a^2 + 20ab + 4b^2$ $(5a + 2b)^2$

12. Factor each polynomial completely, if possible.

a. $x^2 - 9$ $(x + 3)(x - 3)$ **b.** $49t^2 - 25y^2$ $(7t + 5y)(7t - 5y)$

c. $x^2y^2 - 400$ $(xy + 20)(xy - 20)$ **d.** $8at^2 - 32a$ $8a(t + 2)(t - 2)$

e. $c^4 - 64$ $(c^2 + 16)(c + 4)(c - 4)$ **f.** $h^2 + 36$ prime

To factor the *sum* and *difference of two cubes,* use the formulas

$$F^3 + L^3$$
$$= (F + L)(F^2 - FL + L^2)$$

$$F^3 - L^3$$
$$= (F - L)(F^2 + FL + L^2)$$

To factor a random polynomial, use the *factoring strategy* discussed in Section 5.4.

13. Factor each polynomial completely, if possible.

a. $h^3 + 1$
$(h + 1)(h^2 - h + 1)$

b. $125p^3 + q^3$
$(5p + q)(25p^2 - 5pq + q^2)$

c. $x^3 - 27$
$(x - 3)(x^2 + 3x + 9)$

d. $16x^5 - 54x^2y^3$
$2x^2(2x - 3y)(4x^2 + 6xy + 9y^2)$

14. Factor each polynomial completely, if possible.

a. $14y^3 + 6y^4 - 40y^2$
$2y^2(3y - 5)(y + 4)$

b. $s^2t + s^2u^2 + tv + u^2v$
$(t + u^2)(s^2 + v)$

c. $j^4 - 16$
$(j^2 + 4)(j + 2)(j - 2)$

d. $3j^3 - 24k^3$
$-3(j + 2k)(j^2 - 2jk + 4k^2)$

e. $12w^2 - 36w + 27$ $\quad 3(2w - 3)^2$

f. $121p^2 + 36q^2$ $\quad$ prime

SECTION 5.5 — *Quadratic Equations*

A *quadratic equation* is an equation of the form
$ax^2 + bx + c = 0$ $(a \neq 0)$,
where a, b, and c represent real numbers.

To use the *factoring method* to solve a quadratic equation:

1. Write the equation in $ax^2 + bx + c = 0$ form.
2. Factor the left-hand side.
3. Use the *zero-factor property* (if $ab = 0$, then $a = 0$ or $b = 0$) and set each factor equal to zero.
4. Solve each resulting linear equation.
5. Check the results in the original equation.

The Pythagorean theorem: If the length of the hypotenuse of a right triangle is c and the lengths of the two legs are a and b, then $c^2 = a^2 + b^2$.

15. Solve each quadratic equation by factoring.

a. $x^2 + 2x = 0$ $\quad 0, -2$

b. $x(x - 6) = 0$ $\quad 0, 6$

c. $x^2 - 9 = 0$ $\quad -3, 3$

d. $a^2 - 7a + 12 = 0$ $\quad 3, 4$

e. $t^2 + 4t + 4 = 0$ $\quad -2, -2$

f. $2x - x^2 + 24 = 0$ $\quad 6, -4$

g. $5a^2 - 6a + 1 = 0$ $\quad \frac{1}{5}, 1$

h. $2p^3 = 2p(p + 2)$ $\quad 0, -1, 2$

16. CONSTRUCTION The face of the triangular preformed concrete panel shown in Illustration 2 has an area of 45 square meters, and its base is 3 meters longer than twice its height. How long is its base? 15 m

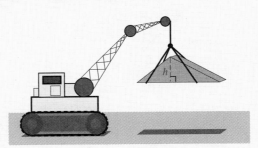

ILLUSTRATION 2

17. GARDENING A rectangular flower bed occupies 27 square feet and is 3 feet longer than twice its width. Find its dimensions. 3 ft by 9 ft

18. TIGHTROPE WALKER
A circus performer intends to walk up a taut cable to a platform atop a pole, as shown in Illustration 3. How high above the ground is the platform?
5 m

ILLUSTRATION 3

Chapter 5 Test

Find the prime factorization of each number.

1. 196 $2^2 \cdot 7^2$ **2.** 111 $3 \cdot 37$

Factor each polynomial completely. If a polynomial cannot be factored, write "prime."

3. $4x + 16$ $4(x + 4)$

4. $30a^2b^3 - 20a^3b^2 + 5abc$ $5ab(6ab^2 - 4a^2b + c)$

5. $q^2 - 81$ $(q + 9)(q - 9)$

6. $x^2 + 9$ prime

7. $16x^4 - 81$ $(4x^2 + 9)(2x + 3)(2x - 3)$

8. $x^2 + 4x + 3$ $(x + 3)(x + 1)$

9. $-x^2 + 9x + 22$ $-(x - 11)(x + 2)$

10. $9a - 9b + ax - bx$ $(a - b)(9 + x)$

11. $2a^2 + 5a - 12$ $(2a - 3)(a + 4)$

12. $18x^2 - 60xy + 50y^2$ $2(3x - 5y)^2$

13. $x^3 + 8$ $(x + 2)(x^2 - 2x + 4)$

14. $2a^3 - 54$ $2(a - 3)(a^2 + 3a + 9)$

15. LANDSCAPING   See Illustration 1. The combined area of the portions of the square lot that the sprinkler doesn't reach is given by $4r^2 - \pi r^2$, where r is the radius of the circular spray. Factor this expression. $r^2(4 - \pi)$

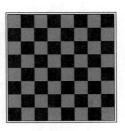

ILLUSTRATION 1

16. CHECKERS   The area of the square checkerboard in Illustration 2 is $25x^2 - 40x + 16$. Find the length of a side. $(5x - 4)$

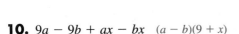

ILLUSTRATION 2

17. What is the greatest common factor of $4a^3b^2$ and $18ab^2$? $2ab^2$

18. Factor $x^2 - 3x - 54$. Show a check of your answer.
$(x - 9)(x + 6)$; Multiply the binomials: $(x - 9)(x + 6) = x^2 + 6x - 9x - 54 = x^2 - 3x - 54$.

Solve each equation.

19. $(x + 3)(x - 2) = 0$ $-3, 2$

20. $x^2 - 25 = 0$ $-5, 5$

21. $6x^2 - x = 0$ $0, \frac{1}{6}$

22. $x^2 + 6x + 9 = 0$ $-3, -3$

23. $6x^2 + x - 1 = 0$ $\frac{1}{3}, -\frac{1}{2}$

24. $x^2 + 7x = -6$ $-1, -6$

25. DRIVING SAFETY   Virtually all cars have a "blind spot" where it is difficult for the driver to see a car behind and to the right. The area of the blind spot shown in Illustration 3 is 54 square feet. Find the width and length of the blind spot.   6 ft by 9 ft

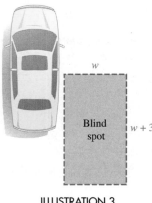

ILLUSTRATION 3

26. What is a quadratic equation? Give an example.
A quadratic equation is an equation that can be written in the form $ax^2 + bx + c = 0$; $x^2 - 2x + 1 = 0$. (Answers may vary.)

27. Find the length of the hypotenuse of the right triangle shown in Illustration 4.   10

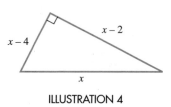

ILLUSTRATION 4

28. If the product of two numbers is 0, what conclusion can be drawn about the numbers?   At least one of them is 0.

Chapters 1–5 Cumulative Review Exercises

1. HEART RATE   Refer to the graph in Illustration 1. Determine the difference in the maximum heart beat rate for a 70-year-old as compared to someone half that age.   about 35 beats/min difference

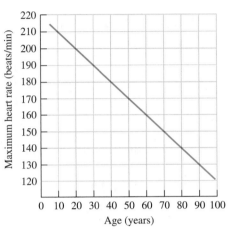

220
210
200
190
180
170
160
150
140
130
120

Maximum heart rate (beats/min)

0 10 20 30 40 50 60 70 80 90 100
Age (years)

Based on data from *Cardiopulmonary Anatomy and Physiology: Essentials for Respiratory Care,* 2nd ed.

ILLUSTRATION 1

2. Give the prime factorization of 250. $2 \cdot 5^3$

3. Write $\frac{124}{125}$ as a decimal.   0.992

4. Tell whether each statement is true or false.
  a. Every integer is a whole number.   false
  b. Every integer is a rational number.   true
  c. π is a real number.   true

5. Find the quotient: $\frac{16}{5} \div \frac{10}{3}$. $\frac{24}{25}$

6. What is -3 cubed? -27

Evaluate each expression.

7. $3 + 2[-1 - 4(5)]$
-39

8. $\dfrac{|-25| - 2(-5)}{9 - 2^4}$
-5

9. Evaluate $\dfrac{-x - a}{y - b}$ for $x = -2$, $y = 1$, $a = 5$, and $b = 2$.   3

10. Which division is undefined, $\dfrac{0}{5}$ or $\dfrac{5}{0}$? $\frac{5}{0}$

Simplify each expression.

11. $-8y^2 - 5y^2 + 6$
$-13y^2 + 6$

12. $3z + 2(y - z) + y$
$3y + z$

Solve each equation.

13. $-(3a + 1) + a = 2$ $-\frac{3}{2}$

14. $2 - (4x + 7) = 3 + 2(x + 2)$ -2

15. $\dfrac{3t - 21}{2} = t - 6$ 9

16. $-\dfrac{1}{3} - \dfrac{x}{5} = \dfrac{3}{2}$ $-\frac{55}{6}$

17. Solve $A = P + Prt$ for t. $t = \frac{A - P}{Pr}$

18. Solve $-\dfrac{x}{2} + 4 > 5$ and graph the solution.

$x < -2$

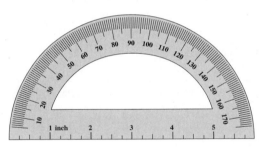

19. GEOMETRY TOOL   Find the total distance around the outside edge of the protractor shown in Illustration 2. Round to the nearest tenth of an inch.   15.4 in.

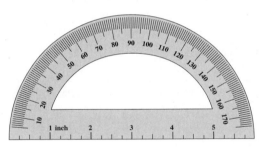

ILLUSTRATION 2

20. What is the formula for simple interest? $I = Prt$

21. What is the value of x twenty-dollar bills? $\$20x$

22. PHOTOGRAPHIC CHEMICALS   A photographer wishes to mix 6 liters of a 5% acetic acid solution with a 10% solution to get a 7% solution. How many liters of 10% solution must be added?   4 L

Graph each equation.

23. $y = (x + 2)^2$

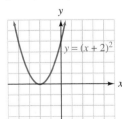

$y = (x + 2)^2$

24. $y = |x| - 2$

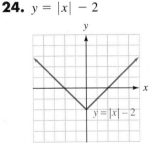

$y = |x| - 2$

25. Find the slope and the y-intercept of the graph of $3x - 3y = 6$. $1; (0, -2)$

26. Write the equation of the line passing through $(-2, 5)$ and $(-3, -2)$. Answer in slope–intercept form.
$y = 7x + 19$

27. Graph the line passing through $(-4, 1)$ that having slope $m = -3$.

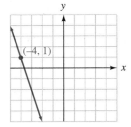

28. Graph $8x + 4y = -24$.

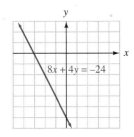

29. If two lines are parallel, what can be said about their slopes? They are the same.

30. BEVERAGES   Illustration 3 shows the annual per-person consumption of coffee and tea in the United States.
   a. What was the rate of change in coffee consumption for 1995–2000? a decrease of 0.86 gal/year
   b. Did the per-person consumption of tea change for 1995–2000? virtually no change

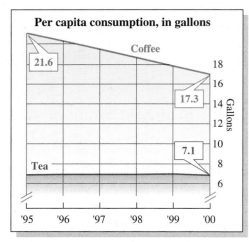

Based on data from Davenport & Co. and the U.S. Department of Agriculture

ILLUSTRATION 3

31. If $g(x) = 3x - x^3$, what is $g(-2)$?   2

32. Write 1,700,000 in scientific notation. 1.7×10^6

Simplify each expression. Write each answer without using parentheses or negative exponents.

33. $-y^2(4y^3)$ $-4y^5$

34. $\dfrac{15(x^2y^5)^5}{21(x^3y)^2}$ $\dfrac{5x^4y^{23}}{7}$

35. $\left(\dfrac{b^5}{b^{-2}}\right)^{-2}$ $\dfrac{1}{b^{14}}$

36. $2x^0$ 2

Do each operation.

37. $(x^2 - 3x + 8) - (3x^2 + x + 3)$ $-2x^2 - 4x + 5$

38. $4b^3(2b^2 - 2b)$ $8b^5 - 8b^4$

39. $(y - 6)^2$ $y^2 - 12y + 36$

40. $(3x - 2)(x + 4)$ $3x^2 + 10x - 8$

41. $\dfrac{12a^2b^2 - 8a^2b - 4ab}{4ab}$ $3ab - 2a - 1$

42. $x - 3\overline{)2x^2 - 5x - 3}$ $2x + 1$

43. PLAYPEN   See Illustration 4.
   a. Find the perimeter of the playpen. $(4x + 8)$ in.
   b. Find the area of the floor of the playpen.
      $(x^2 + 4x + 3)$ in.^{2}
   c. Find the volume of the playpen.
      $(x^3 + 4x^2 + 3x)$ in.^{3}

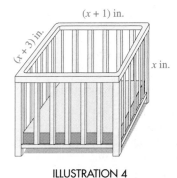

ILLUSTRATION 4

44. What is the degree of the polynomial $7y^3 + 4y^2 + y + 3$?   3

Factor each polynomial completely.

45. $b^3 - 3b^2$
   $b^2(b - 3)$

46. $u^2 - 3 + 2u$
   $(u + 3)(u - 1)$

47. $2x^2 - 3x - 2$
   $(2x + 1)(x - 2)$

48. $9z^2 - 1$
   $(3z + 1)(3z - 1)$

49. $-5a^2 + 25a - 30$
   $-5(a - 3)(a - 2)$

50. $ax + bx + ay + by$
   $(x + y)(a + b)$

51. $t^3 - 8$
   $(t - 2)(t^2 + 2t + 4)$

52. $4a^2 - 12a + 9$
   $(2a - 3)^2$

Solve each equation.

53. $15s^2 - 20s = 0$ $0, \frac{4}{3}$

54. $2x^2 - 5x = -2$ $\frac{1}{2}, 2$

Rational Expressions and Equations

6

6.1 Simplifying Rational Expressions

In this section, you will learn about

- Evaluating rational expressions • Simplifying rational expressions
- Division of opposites

INTRODUCTION. Fractions such as $\frac{1}{2}$ and $\frac{3}{4}$ that are the quotient of two integers are *rational numbers*. Fractions such as

$$\frac{3}{2y}, \qquad \frac{x}{x+2}, \qquad \text{and} \qquad \frac{5a^2+b^2}{3a-b}$$

where the numerators and denominators are polynomials are called **rational expressions.**

Evaluating rational expressions

To evaluate a rational expression, we replace each variable with a given number value and simplify.

EXAMPLE 1 *Evaluating rational expressions.* Find the value of $\frac{2x-1}{x^2+1}$ for $x=-3$.

Solution

We replace each x in the expression with -3 and then evaluate the numerator and denominator separately.

$$\frac{2x-1}{x^2+1} = \frac{2(-3)-1}{(-3)^2+1} \qquad \text{Substitute } -3 \text{ for } x.$$

$$= \frac{-6-1}{9+1} \qquad \text{In the numerator, do the multiplication. In the denominator, evaluate the exponential expression.}$$

$$= -\frac{7}{10}$$

Self Check

Evaluate $\dfrac{3a-7}{a^3+1}$ for $a=1$.

Answer: -2 ∎

Since rational expressions indicate division, we must make sure that the denominator of a rational expression is not 0.

EXAMPLE 2 *Restricted values.* Find the values for x for which each rational expression is undefined: **a.** $\dfrac{7x}{x-5}$ and **b.** $\dfrac{x-1}{x^2-x-6}$.

Solution

a. The denominator of $\dfrac{7x}{x-5}$ will be 0 if we replace x with 5.

$$\frac{7x}{x-5} = \frac{7(5)}{5-5} = \frac{35}{0}$$

Since $\frac{35}{0}$ is undefined, the rational expression is undefined for $x=5$.

b. The expression $\dfrac{x-1}{x^2-x-6}$ will be undefined for values of x that make the denominator 0. To find these values, we solve $x^2-x-6=0$.

Self Check

Find the values for x for which each expression is undefined.

a. $\dfrac{x}{x+9}$

b. $\dfrac{x+7}{x^2-25}$

$$x^2 - x - 6 = 0$$ Set the denominator of the rational expression equal to 0.

$$(x - 3)(x + 2) = 0$$ Factor the trinomial.

$$x - 3 = 0 \quad \text{or} \quad x + 2 = 0$$ Set each factor equal to 0.

$$x = 3 \qquad\qquad x = -2$$ Solve each equation.

Since the values 3 and -2 make the denominator 0, the expression is undefined for $x = 3$ or $x = -2$.

Answers: **a.** -9,   **b.** 5 or -5

■

Simplifying rational expressions

A fraction can be simplified by factoring the numerator and denominator and dividing out common factors shared by the numerator and denominator. For example, to simplify $\frac{18}{30}$ and $\frac{6}{15}$, we proceed as follows:

$$\frac{18}{30} = \frac{3 \cdot 6}{5 \cdot 6} = \frac{3 \cdot \overset{1}{\cancel{6}}}{5 \cdot \underset{1}{\cancel{6}}} = \frac{3}{5} \qquad \text{and} \qquad \frac{6}{15} = \frac{3 \cdot 2}{3 \cdot 5} = \frac{\overset{1}{\cancel{3}} \cdot 2}{\underset{1}{\cancel{3}} \cdot 5} = -\frac{2}{5}$$

When all common factors have been divided out, we say that the fraction has been **expressed in lowest terms.** The generalization of this idea is called the *fundamental property of fractions.*

Fundamental property of fractions

If a represents a real number and b and c represent nonzero real numbers,

$$\frac{ac}{bc} = \frac{a}{b}$$

The fundamental property of fractions enables us to divide out common factors of the numerator and denominator of a fraction. The resulting fraction is equivalent to the original fraction.

Simplifying rational expressions is similar to simplifying fractions. We use the following process.

Simplifying a rational expression to lowest terms

To simplify a rational expression to lowest terms,

1. Completely factor the numerator and denominator.

2. Divide out the common factors of the numerator and denominator.

EXAMPLE 3   *Simplifying rational expressions.*   Simplify $\dfrac{21x^2y}{14xy^2}$.

Solution

We look for common factors in the numerator and denominator and divide them out.

$$\frac{21x^2y}{14xy^2} = \frac{3 \cdot 7 \cdot x \cdot x \cdot y}{2 \cdot 7 \cdot x \cdot y \cdot y}$$ Factor the numerator and denominator.

$$= \frac{3 \cdot \overset{1}{\cancel{7}} \cdot \overset{1}{\cancel{x}} \cdot x \cdot \overset{1}{\cancel{y}}}{2 \cdot \underset{1}{\cancel{7}} \cdot \underset{1}{\cancel{x}} \cdot y \cdot \underset{1}{\cancel{y}}}$$ Divide out the common factors, 7, x, and y.

$$= \frac{3x}{2y}$$ Do the multiplications in the numerator and in the denominator: $3 \cdot 1 \cdot 1 \cdot x \cdot 1 = 3x$ and $2 \cdot 1 \cdot 1 \cdot y \cdot 1 = 2y$.

Self Check

Simplify $\dfrac{32a^3b^2}{24ab^4}$.

Answer: $\dfrac{4a^2}{3b^2}$

■

To simplify rational expressions, we often make use of the factoring techniques discussed in the preceding chapter.

EXAMPLE 4 *Factoring to simplify rational expressions.* Write $\dfrac{x^2 + 3x}{3x + 9}$ in lowest terms.

Solution

We note that the terms of the numerator have a common factor of x and the terms of the denominator have a common factor of 3.

$$\frac{x^2 + 3x}{3x + 9} = \frac{x(x + 3)}{3(x + 3)} \qquad \text{Factor the numerator and the denominator.}$$

$$= \frac{x\cancel{(x + 3)}^{1}}{3\cancel{(x + 3)}_{1}} \qquad \text{Divide out the common factor, } x + 3.$$

$$= \frac{x}{3} \qquad \begin{array}{l}\text{Simplify the numerator: } x \cdot 1 = x.\\ \text{Simplify the denominator: } 3 \cdot 1 = 3.\end{array}$$

Self Check

Write
$$\frac{x^2 - 5x}{5x - 25}$$
in lowest terms.

Answer: $\dfrac{x}{5}$ ∎

EXAMPLE 5 *Factoring to simplify rational expressions.* Simplify $\dfrac{x^2 + 13x + 12}{x^2 - 144}$.

Solution

The numerator is a trinomial, and the denominator is a difference of two squares.

$$\frac{x^2 + 13x + 12}{x^2 - 144} = \frac{(x + 1)(x + 12)}{(x + 12)(x - 12)} \qquad \text{Factor the numerator and the denominator.}$$

$$= \frac{(x + 1)\cancel{(x + 12)}^{1}}{\cancel{(x + 12)}_{1}(x - 12)} \qquad \text{Divide out the common factor, } x + 12.$$

$$= \frac{x + 1}{x - 12}$$

Self Check

Simplify $\dfrac{3x^2 - 8x - 3}{x^2 - 9}$.

Answer: $\dfrac{3x + 1}{x + 3}$ ∎

 COMMENT When simplifing a fraction, remember that only *factors* that are common to the *entire numerator* and the *entire denominator* can be divided out. For example, consider the correct simplification

$$\frac{5 + 8}{5} = \frac{13}{5}$$

It would be incorrect to divide out the common *term* of 5 in this simplification. Doing so would give an incorrect answer of 9.

$$\frac{5 + 8}{5} = \frac{\cancel{5}^{1} + 8}{\cancel{5}_{1}} = \frac{1 + 8}{1} = 9$$

When simplifying algebraic fractions, it is also incorrect to divide out terms common to both the numerator and denominator.

$$\require{cancel}\cancel{\dfrac{\overset{1}{\cancel{x}} + 5}{\underset{1}{\cancel{x}} + 6}} \qquad\qquad \cancel{\dfrac{a^2 - 3\overset{1}{\cancel{a}} + \overset{1}{\cancel{2}}}{\underset{1}{\cancel{a}} + \underset{1}{\cancel{2}}}} \qquad\qquad \cancel{\dfrac{\overset{1}{\cancel{y}}^2 - 36}{\underset{1}{\cancel{y}}^2 - y - 7}}$$

Any number or algebraic expression divided by 1 remains unchanged. For example,

$$\dfrac{37}{1} = 37, \qquad \dfrac{5x}{1} = 5x, \qquad \text{and} \qquad \dfrac{3x + y}{1} = 3x + y.$$

In general, we have the following.

Division by 1

For any real number a, $\dfrac{a}{1} = a$.

EXAMPLE 6 *Simplifying rational expressions.* Simplify $\dfrac{x^3 + x^2}{x + 1}$.

Solution

$$\dfrac{x^3 + x^2}{x + 1} = \dfrac{x^2(x + 1)}{x + 1} \qquad \text{Factor the numerator.}$$

$$= \dfrac{x^2\cancel{(x + 1)}}{\cancel{x + 1}} \qquad \text{Divide out the common factor, } x + 1.$$

$$= \dfrac{x^2}{1} \qquad\qquad \text{Simplify.}$$

$$= x^2 \qquad\qquad \text{Denominators of 1 need not be written.}$$

Self Check

Simplify $\dfrac{a^2 + a - 2}{a - 1}$.

Answer: $a + 2$

EXAMPLE 7 *Dividing out common factors.* Simplify $\dfrac{5(x + 3) - 5}{7(x + 3) - 7}$.

Solution

We cannot divide out $x + 3$, because it is not a factor of the entire numerator, nor is it a factor of the entire denominator. Instead, we simplify the numerator and denominator, factor them, and then divide out any common factors.

$$\dfrac{5(x + 3) - 5}{7(x + 3) - 7} = \dfrac{5x + 15 - 5}{7x + 21 - 7} \qquad \text{Use the distributive property twice.}$$

$$= \dfrac{5x + 10}{7x + 14} \qquad\qquad \text{Combine like terms.}$$

$$= \dfrac{5(x + 2)}{7(x + 2)} \qquad\qquad \text{Factor the numerator and the denominator.}$$

$$= \dfrac{5\cancel{(x + 2)}}{7\cancel{(x + 2)}} \qquad\qquad \text{Divide out the common factor, } x + 2.$$

$$= \dfrac{5}{7}$$

Self Check

Simplify:

$$\dfrac{4(x - 2) + 4}{3(x - 2) + 3}$$

Answer: $\dfrac{4}{3}$

EXAMPLE 8   *Combining like terms.*   Simplify $\dfrac{x(x + 3) - 3(x - 1)}{x^2 + 3}$.

Solution

We begin by simplifying the numerator. Then we look for any common factors to divide out in the numerator and denominator.

$$\frac{x(x + 3) - 3(x - 1)}{x^2 + 3} = \frac{x^2 + 3x - 3x + 3}{x^2 + 3}$$ Use the distributive property twice in the numerator.

$$= \frac{x^2 + 3}{x^2 + 3}$$ Combine like terms in the numerator: $3x - 3x = 0$.

$$= \frac{\overset{1}{\cancel{x^2 + 3}}}{\underset{1}{\cancel{x^2 + 3}}}$$ Divide out the common factor, $x^2 + 3$.

$$= 1$$

Self Check
Simplify:
$$\frac{a(a + 2) - 2(a - 1)}{a^2 + 2}$$

Answer: 1

Sometimes a fraction does not simplify. For example, to attempt to simplify

$$\frac{x^2 + x - 2}{x^2 + x}$$

we factor the numerator and the denominator.

$$\frac{x^2 + x - 2}{x^2 + x} = \frac{(x + 2)(x - 1)}{x(x + 1)}$$

Because there are no factors common to the numerator and denominator, this fraction is already in lowest terms.

Division of opposites

If the terms of two polynomials are the same, except for sign, the polynomials are called **opposites (negatives)** of each other. For example, the following pairs of polynomials are opposites of each other:

$$x - y \qquad \text{and} \qquad -x + y$$
$$2a - 1 \qquad \text{and} \qquad -2a + 1$$
$$-3x^2 - 2x + 5 \qquad \text{and} \qquad 3x^2 + 2x - 5$$

Example 9 shows why the quotient of two binomials that are opposites is always -1.

EXAMPLE 9   *Division of opposites.*   Simplify $\dfrac{2a - 1}{1 - 2a}$.

Solution

We can rearrange terms in each numerator, factor out -1, and proceed as follows:

$$\frac{2a - 1}{1 - 2a} = \frac{-1 + 2a}{1 - 2a}$$ In the numerator, think of $2a - 1$ as $2a + (-1)$. Then change the order of the terms: $2a + (-1) = -1 + 2a$.

$$= \frac{-(1 - 2a)}{1 - 2a}$$ In the numerator, factor out -1: $-1 + 2a = -(1 - 2a)$.

$$= \frac{-\overset{1}{\cancel{(1 - 2a)}}}{\underset{1}{\cancel{1 - 2a}}}$$ Divide out the common factor, $1 - 2a$.

$$= -1$$

Self Check
Simplify $\dfrac{3p - 2}{2 - 3p}$.

Answer: -1

In general, we have this important fact.

D pposites | The quotient of any nonzero expression and its opposite is -1.

 COMMENT Apply the preceding rule only to expressions that are opposites. For example, it would be incorrect to use this rule to simplify $\frac{x+1}{1+x}$. Since $x + 1$ equals $1 + x$ by the commutative property of addition, this is the quotient of a number and itself. The result is 1, not -1.

$$\frac{x+1}{1+x} = \frac{\overset{1}{\cancel{x+1}}}{\underset{1}{\cancel{x+1}}} = 1$$

STUDY SET Section 6.1

VOCABULARY *Fill in the blanks.*

1. In a fraction, the part above the fraction bar is called the ___numerator___, and the part below the fraction bar is called the ___denominator___.

2. A fraction that has polynomials in its numerator and denominator, such as $\frac{x+2}{x-3}$, is called a ___rational___ expression.

3. Division by 0 is ___undefined___.

4. A fraction is in ___lowest___ terms when all common factors of the numerator and denominator have been divided out.

5. To ___simplify___ a rational expression means to factor the numerator and denominator completely and divide out common factors.

6. If the terms of two polynomials are the same, except for sign, the polynomials are called ___opposites___ of each other.

CONCEPTS

7. What value of x makes each rational expression undefined?

a. $\dfrac{x+2}{x}$ 0   **b.** $\dfrac{x+2}{x-6}$ 6   **c.** $\dfrac{x+2}{x+6}$ -6

8. Fill in the blank: When a ___common___ factor of the numerator and the denominator of a fraction is divided out, the resulting fraction is equivalent to the original fraction.

9. In the following work, what common factor has been divided out? $x + 1$

$$\frac{x^2+2x+1}{x^2+4x+3} = \frac{\overset{1}{\cancel{(x+1)}}(x+1)}{(x+3)\underset{1}{\cancel{(x+1)}}} = \frac{x+1}{x+3}$$

10. Simplify each rational expression.

a. $\dfrac{x-8}{x-8}$ 1   **b.** $\dfrac{x-8}{-x+8}$ -1 **c.** $\dfrac{x-8}{1}$ $x-8$

11. Explain the error in the following work.

$$\frac{x}{x+2} = \frac{\overset{1}{\cancel{x}}}{\underset{1}{\cancel{x}}+2} = \frac{1}{3}$$

x is not a common factor of the numerator and denominator. It cannot be divided out.

12. What is the first step in the process of simplifying $\dfrac{3(x+1)-2x}{x+3}$?

In the numerator, distribute the multiplication by 3.

NOTATION *Complete each solution.*

13. $\dfrac{x^2+5x-6}{x^2-1} = \dfrac{(x+\boxed{6})(x-1)}{(x+1)(x-\boxed{1})}$

$\qquad\qquad = \dfrac{x+6}{x+1}$

14. $\dfrac{5(x+2)-5}{4(x+2)-4} = \dfrac{5x+\boxed{10}-5}{4x+\boxed{8}-4}$

$\qquad\qquad = \dfrac{5x+\boxed{5}}{4x+\boxed{4}}$

$\qquad\qquad = \dfrac{5\,(x+\boxed{1})}{4(x+1)}$

$\qquad\qquad = \dfrac{5}{4}$

PRACTICE Evaluate each expression for $x = 6$.

15. $\dfrac{x - 2}{x - 5}$ 4

16. $\dfrac{3x - 2}{x - 2}$ 4

17. $\dfrac{-2x - 3}{x^2 - 1}$ $-\frac{3}{7}$

18. $\dfrac{x^2 - 11}{-x - 4}$ $-\frac{5}{2}$

19. $\dfrac{x^2 - 4x - 12}{x^2 + x - 2}$ 0

20. $\dfrac{x^2 - 1}{x^3 - 1}$ $\frac{7}{43}$

Which value(s) of x make each rational expression undefined?

21. $\dfrac{15}{x - 2}$ 2

22. $\dfrac{5x}{x + 5}$ -5

23. $\dfrac{15x + 2}{16}$ none

24. $\dfrac{x^2 - 4x}{25}$ none

25. $\dfrac{x + 1}{2x - 1}$ $\frac{1}{2}$

26. $\dfrac{-6x}{3x - 1}$ $\frac{1}{3}$

27. $\dfrac{30}{x^2 - 36}$ $-6, 6$

28. $\dfrac{2x - 15}{x^2 - 49}$ $-7, 7$

29. $\dfrac{15}{x^2 + x - 2}$ $-2, 1$

30. $\dfrac{x - 20}{x^2 + 2x - 8}$ $-4, 2$

Write each fraction in lowest terms.

31. $\dfrac{28}{35}$ $\frac{4}{5}$

32. $\dfrac{14}{20}$ $\frac{7}{10}$

33. $\dfrac{9}{27}$ $\frac{1}{3}$

34. $\dfrac{15}{45}$ $\frac{1}{3}$

35. $-\dfrac{36}{48}$ $-\frac{3}{4}$

36. $-\dfrac{32}{40}$ $-\frac{4}{5}$

Simplify each expression. If it is already in lowest terms, so indicate. Assume that no denominators are zero.

37. $\dfrac{45}{9a}$ $\frac{5}{a}$

38. $\dfrac{48}{16y}$ $\frac{3}{y}$

39. $\dfrac{5 + 5}{5z}$ $\frac{2}{z}$

40. $\dfrac{(3 - 18)k}{25}$ $-\frac{3k}{5}$

41. $\dfrac{(3 + 4)a}{24 - 3}$ $\frac{a}{3}$

42. $\dfrac{x + x}{2}$ x

43. $\dfrac{2x}{3x}$ $\frac{2}{3}$

44. $\dfrac{5y}{7y}$ $\frac{5}{7}$

45. $\dfrac{6x^2}{4x^2}$ $\frac{3}{2}$

46. $\dfrac{9xy}{6xy}$ $\frac{3}{2}$

47. $\dfrac{2x^2}{3y}$ in lowest terms

48. $\dfrac{5y^2}{2y^2}$ $\frac{5}{2}$

49. $\dfrac{15x^2y}{5xy^2}$ $\frac{3x}{y}$

50. $\dfrac{12xz}{4xz^2}$ $\frac{3}{z}$

51. $\dfrac{6x + 3}{3y}$ $\frac{2x + 1}{y}$

52. $\dfrac{4x + 12}{2y}$ $\frac{2x + 6}{y}$

53. $\dfrac{x + 3}{3x + 9}$ $\frac{1}{3}$

54. $\dfrac{2x + 14}{x - 7}$ in lowest terms

55. $\dfrac{x - 7}{7 - x}$ -1

56. $\dfrac{18 - d}{d - 18}$ -1

57. $\dfrac{6x - 30}{5 - x}$ -6

58. $\dfrac{6t - 42}{7 - t}$ -6

59. $\dfrac{12 - 3x^2}{x^2 - x - 2}$ $\dfrac{-3(x + 2)}{x + 1}$

60. $\dfrac{-5x + 10}{x^2 - 4x + 4}$ $-\dfrac{5}{x - 2}$

61. $\dfrac{x^2 + 3x + 2}{x^2 + x - 2}$ $\dfrac{x + 1}{x - 1}$

62. $\dfrac{x^2 + x - 6}{x^2 - x - 2}$ $\dfrac{x + 3}{x + 1}$

63. $\dfrac{x^2 - 8x + 15}{x^2 - x - 6}$ $\dfrac{x - 5}{x + 2}$

64. $\dfrac{x^2 - 6x - 7}{x^2 + 8x + 7}$ $\dfrac{x - 7}{x + 7}$

65. $\dfrac{2x^2 - 8x}{x^2 - 6x + 8}$ $\dfrac{2x}{x - 2}$

66. $\dfrac{3y^2 - 15y}{y^2 - 3y - 10}$ $\dfrac{3y}{y + 2}$

67. $\dfrac{2 - a}{a^2 - a - 2}$ $-\dfrac{1}{a + 1}$

68. $\dfrac{4 - b}{b^2 - 5b + 4}$ $-\dfrac{1}{b - 1}$

69. $\dfrac{x^2 + 3x + 2}{x^3 + x^2}$ $\dfrac{x + 2}{x^2}$

70. $\dfrac{6x^2 - 13x + 6}{3x^2 + x - 2}$ $\dfrac{2x - 3}{x + 1}$

71. $\dfrac{x^2 - 8x + 16}{x^2 - 16}$ $\dfrac{x - 4}{x + 4}$

72. $\dfrac{3x + 15}{x^2 - 25}$ $\dfrac{3}{x - 5}$

73. $\dfrac{2x^2 - 8}{x^2 - 3x + 2}$ $\dfrac{2(x + 2)}{x - 1}$

74. $\dfrac{3x^2 - 27}{x^2 + 3x - 18}$ $\dfrac{3(x + 3)}{x + 6}$

75. $\dfrac{5x^2 + 2x - 3}{x^2 + 2x - 15}$ in lowest terms

76. $\dfrac{x^2 + 4x - 77}{x^2 - 4x - 21}$ $\dfrac{x + 11}{x + 3}$

77. $\dfrac{x^2 - 3(2x - 3)}{9 - x^2}$ $\dfrac{3 - x}{3 + x}$ or $-\dfrac{x - 3}{x + 3}$

78. $\dfrac{x(x - 8) + 16}{16 - x^2}$ $\dfrac{4 - x}{4 + x}$ or $-\dfrac{x - 4}{x + 4}$

79. $\dfrac{4(x + 3) + 4}{3(x + 2) + 6}$ $\frac{4}{3}$

80. $\dfrac{4 + 2(x - 5)}{3x - 5(x - 2)}$ $\dfrac{x - 3}{5 - x}$

81. $\dfrac{x^2 - 9}{(2x + 3) - (x + 6)}$ $x + 3$

82. $\dfrac{x^2 + 5x + 4}{2(x + 3) - (x + 2)}$ $x + 1$

83. $\dfrac{y - xy}{xy - x}$ in lowest terms

84. $\dfrac{x^2 + y^2}{x + y}$ in lowest terms

85. $\dfrac{6a - 6b + 6c}{9a - 9b + 9c}$ $\frac{2}{3}$

86. $\dfrac{3a - 3b - 6}{2a - 2b - 4}$ $\frac{3}{2}$

87. $\dfrac{15x - 3x^2}{25y - 5xy}$ $\frac{3x}{5y}$

88. $\dfrac{xz - 2x}{yz - 2y}$ $\frac{x}{y}$

89. $\dfrac{a + b - c}{c - a - b}$ -1

90. $\dfrac{x - y - z}{z + y - x}$ -1

APPLICATIONS

91. ROOFING   The *pitch* of a roof is a measure of how steep or how flat the roof is. If pitch $= \frac{\text{rise}}{\text{run}}$, find the pitch of the roof of the cabin shown in Illustration 1. Express the result in lowest terms. $\frac{x+2}{x-2}$

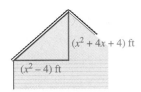

$(x^2 + 4x + 4)$ ft

$(x^2 - 4)$ ft

ILLUSTRATION 1

92. GRAPHIC DESIGN   A chart of the basic food groups, in the shape of an equilateral triangle, is to be enlarged and distributed to schools for display in their health classes. (See Illustration 2.) What is the length of a side of the original design divided by the length of a side of the enlargement? Express the result in lowest terms. $\frac{2}{x+1}$

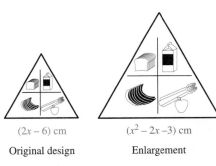

$(2x - 6)$ cm $(x^2 - 2x - 3)$ cm

Original design   Enlargement

ILLUSTRATION 2

93. WORD PROCESSOR   For the word processor shown in Illustration 3, the number of words w that can be typed on a piece of paper is given by the formula

$$w = \frac{8{,}000}{x}$$

where x is the font size used. Find the number of words that can be typed on a page for each font size choice shown.   1,000; 800; about 667; 500; about 333; about 222

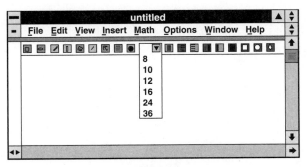

ILLUSTRATION 3

94. ORGAN PIPE   The number of vibrations n per second of an organ pipe is given by the formula

$$n = \frac{512}{L}$$

where L is the length of the pipe in feet. (See Illustration 4.) How many times per second will a 6-foot pipe vibrate? $85\frac{1}{3}$

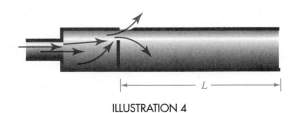

L

ILLUSTRATION 4

WRITING

95. Explain why $\dfrac{x-7}{7-x} = -1$.

96. Explain the difference between a factor and a term. Give several examples.

97. Explain the error.

$$\frac{3(\overset{1}{\cancel{x+1}}) - x}{\underset{1}{\cancel{x+1}}} = 3 - x$$

98. Explain why there are no values for x for which $\dfrac{x-7}{x^2 + 49}$ is undefined.

REVIEW

99. State the associative property of addition using the variables a, b, and c. $(a+b)+c = a+(b+c)$

100. State the distributive property using the variables x, y, and z. $x(y+z) = xy + xz$

101. If $ab = 0$, what must be true about a or b?
One of them is zero.

102. What is the product of a number and 1?   the number

103. What is the opposite of $-\dfrac{5}{3}$? $\frac{5}{3}$

104. What is the cube of 2 squared?   64

6.2 *Multiplying and Dividing Rational Expressions*

In this section, you will learn about

- Multiplying rational expressions
- Multiplying a rational expression by a polynomial
- Dividing rational expressions • Dividing a rational expression by a polynomial
- Combined operations

INTRODUCTION. In this section, we extend the rules for multiplying and dividing numerical fractions to problems involving multiplication and division of rational expressions.

Multiplying rational expressions

To multiply fractions, we multiply their numerators and multiply their denominators. For example,

$$\frac{4}{7} \cdot \frac{3}{5} = \frac{4 \cdot 3}{7 \cdot 5} \quad \text{Multiply the numerators and multiply the denominators.}$$

$$= \frac{12}{35} \quad \begin{array}{l}\text{Do the multiplication in the numerator: } 4 \cdot 3 = 12.\\ \text{Do the multiplication in the denominator: } 7 \cdot 5 = 35.\end{array}$$

In general, we have the following rule.

Rule for multiplying fractions

> If a, b, c, and d represent real numbers and $b \neq 0$ and $d \neq 0$,
>
> $$\frac{a}{b} \cdot \frac{c}{d} = \frac{ac}{bd}$$

We use the same procedure to multiply rational expressions.

EXAMPLE 1 *Multiplying rational expressions.*   Multiply: **a.** $\dfrac{x}{3} \cdot \dfrac{2}{5}$,
b. $\dfrac{7}{9} \cdot \dfrac{-5}{3x}$,   **c.** $\dfrac{x^2}{2} \cdot \dfrac{3}{y^2}$,   and   **d.** $\dfrac{t+1}{t} \cdot \dfrac{t-1}{t-2}$.

Solution

a. $\dfrac{x}{3} \cdot \dfrac{2}{5} = \dfrac{x \cdot 2}{3 \cdot 5}$

$\qquad = \dfrac{2x}{15}$

b. $\dfrac{7}{9} \cdot \dfrac{-5}{3x} = \dfrac{7(-5)}{9 \cdot 3x}$

$\qquad = \dfrac{-35}{27x}$

$\qquad = -\dfrac{35}{27x}$

c. $\dfrac{x^2}{2} \cdot \dfrac{3}{y^2} = \dfrac{x^2 \cdot 3}{2 \cdot y^2}$

$\qquad = \dfrac{3x^2}{2y^2}$

d. $\dfrac{t+1}{t} \cdot \dfrac{t-1}{t-2} = \dfrac{(t+1)(t-1)}{t(t-2)}$

Self Check

Multiply: $\dfrac{3x}{4} \cdot \dfrac{x-3}{5}$.

Answer: $\dfrac{3x(x-3)}{20}$

EXAMPLE 2 *Multiplying rational expressions.*

Multiply: $\dfrac{35x^2y}{7y^2z} \cdot \dfrac{z}{5xy}$.

Solution

$$\dfrac{35x^2y}{7y^2z} \cdot \dfrac{z}{5xy} = \dfrac{35x^2y \cdot z}{7y^2z \cdot 5xy}$$

Multiply the numerators and multiply the denominators.

$$= \dfrac{5 \cdot 7 \cdot x \cdot x \cdot y \cdot z}{7 \cdot y \cdot y \cdot z \cdot 5 \cdot x \cdot y}$$

Factor $35x^2$ and factor y^2.

$$= \dfrac{\overset{1}{\cancel{5}} \cdot \overset{1}{\cancel{7}} \cdot \overset{1}{\cancel{x}} \cdot x \cdot \overset{1}{\cancel{y}} \cdot \overset{1}{\cancel{z}}}{\underset{1}{\cancel{7}} \cdot \underset{1}{\cancel{y}} \cdot y \cdot \underset{1}{\cancel{z}} \cdot \underset{1}{\cancel{5}} \cdot \underset{1}{\cancel{x}} \cdot y}$$

Divide out the common factors: 5, 7, x, y, and z.

$$= \dfrac{x}{y^2}$$

Do the multiplications in the numerator and the denominator.

Self Check

Multiply:

$$\dfrac{a^2b^2}{2a} \cdot \dfrac{9a^3}{3b^3}$$

Answer: $\dfrac{3a^4}{2b}$ ∎

EXAMPLE 3 *Factoring to simplify a product.*

Multiply: $\dfrac{x^2 - x}{2x + 4} \cdot \dfrac{x + 2}{x}$.

Solution

$$\dfrac{x^2 - x}{2x + 4} \cdot \dfrac{x + 2}{x} = \dfrac{(x^2 - x)(x + 2)}{(2x + 4)(x)}$$

Multiply the numerators and multiply the denominators.

We now factor the numerator and denominator to see if this product can be simplified.

$$\dfrac{x^2 - x}{2x + y} \cdot \dfrac{x + 2}{x} = \dfrac{x(x - 1)(x + 2)}{2(x + 2)x}$$

Factor the numerator: $(x^2 - x) = x(x - 1)$.
Factor the denominator: $(2x + 4) = 2(x + 2)$.

$$= \dfrac{x(x - 1)\overset{1}{\cancel{(x + 2)}}}{2\underset{1}{\cancel{(x + 2)}}x}$$

Divide out common factors.

$$= \dfrac{x - 1}{2}$$

Self Check

Multiply:

$$\dfrac{x^2 + x}{3x + 6} \cdot \dfrac{x + 2}{x + 1}$$

Answer: $\dfrac{x}{3}$ ∎

EXAMPLE 4 *Factoring to simplify a product.*

Multiply: $\dfrac{x^2 - 3x}{x^2 - x - 6} \cdot \dfrac{x^2 + x - 2}{x^2 - x}$.

Solution

$$\dfrac{x^2 - 3x}{x^2 - x - 6} \cdot \dfrac{x^2 + x - 2}{x^2 - x}$$

$$= \dfrac{(x^2 - 3x)(x^2 + x - 2)}{(x^2 - x - 6)(x^2 - x)}$$

Multiply the numerators and multiply the denominators.

$$= \dfrac{x(x - 3)(x + 2)(x - 1)}{(x + 2)(x - 3)x(x - 1)}$$

Factor the numerator and denominator to see if the result can be simplified.

$$= \dfrac{\overset{1}{\cancel{x}}\overset{1}{\cancel{(x - 3)}}\overset{1}{\cancel{(x + 2)}}\overset{1}{\cancel{(x - 1)}}}{\underset{1}{\cancel{(x + 2)}}\underset{1}{\cancel{(x - 3)}}\underset{1}{\cancel{x}}\underset{1}{\cancel{(x - 1)}}}$$

Divide out common factors.

$$= 1$$

Self Check

Multiply:

$$\dfrac{a^2 + a}{a^2 - 4} \cdot \dfrac{a^2 - a - 2}{a^2 + 2a + 1}$$

Answer: $\dfrac{a}{a + 2}$ ∎

Multiplying a rational expression by a polynomial

Since any number divided by 1 remains unchanged, we can write any polynomial as a fraction by inserting a denominator of 1.

EXAMPLE 5   *Multiplying a rational expression by a monomial.*
Multiply: **a.** $\dfrac{4}{x} \cdot x$,   **b.** $63x\left(\dfrac{1}{7x}\right)$,   and   **c.** $5a\left(\dfrac{3a-1}{a}\right)$.

Solution

a. $\dfrac{4}{x} \cdot x = \dfrac{4}{x} \cdot \dfrac{x}{1}$

Write x as a fraction: $x = \frac{x}{1}$.

$$= \dfrac{4 \cdot \overset{1}{\cancel{x}}}{\underset{1}{\cancel{x}} \cdot 1}$$

Multiply the numerators and the denominators. Then divide out the common factor in the numerator and denominator.

$$= 4$$

Simplify.

b. $63x\left(\dfrac{1}{7x}\right) = \dfrac{63x}{1}\left(\dfrac{1}{7x}\right)$

Write $63x$ as a fraction: $63x = \frac{63x}{1}$.

$$= \dfrac{63x \cdot 1}{1 \cdot 7 \cdot x}$$

Multiply the numerators and the denominators.

$$= \dfrac{9 \cdot \overset{1}{\cancel{7}} \cdot \overset{1}{\cancel{x}} \cdot 1}{1 \cdot \underset{1}{\cancel{7}} \cdot \underset{1}{\cancel{x}}}$$

Write $63x$ in factored form as $9 \cdot 7 \cdot x$. Then divide out the common factors, 7 and x.

$$= 9$$

Simplify.

c. $5a\left(\dfrac{3a-1}{a}\right) = \dfrac{5a}{1}\left(\dfrac{3a-1}{a}\right)$

Write $5a$ as a fraction: $5a = \frac{5a}{1}$.

$$= \dfrac{5\overset{1}{\cancel{a}}(3a-1)}{1 \cdot \underset{1}{\cancel{a}}}$$

Multiply the numerators and the denominators. Then divide out the common factor, a, in the numerator and denominator.

$$= 5(3a - 1)$$

Simplify.

$$= 15a - 5$$

Distribute the multiplication by 5.

Self Check
Multiply:

a. $\dfrac{9}{7y} \cdot 7y$

b. $36b\left(\dfrac{1}{6b}\right)$

c. $4x\left(\dfrac{x+3}{x}\right)$

Answers: a. 9,   **b.** 6,
c. $4x + 12$

EXAMPLE 6   *Multiplying a rational expression by a binomial.*
Multiply: $\dfrac{x^2 + x}{x^2 + 8x + 7} \cdot (x + 7)$.

Solution

$$\dfrac{x^2 + x}{x^2 + 8x + 7} \cdot (x + 7)$$

$$= \dfrac{x^2 + x}{x^2 + 8x + 7} \cdot \dfrac{x + 7}{1}$$

Write $x + 7$ as a fraction with a denominator of 1.

$$= \dfrac{x(x + 1)(x + 7)}{(x + 1)(x + 7)1}$$

Multiply the numerators and multiply the denominators. Factor where possible.

$$= \dfrac{x\overset{1}{\cancel{(x + 1)}}\overset{1}{\cancel{(x + 7)}}}{\underset{1}{\cancel{(x + 1)}}\underset{1}{\cancel{(x + 7)}}1}$$

Divide out common factors.

$$= x$$

Self Check
Multiply:

$(a - 7) \cdot \dfrac{a^2 - a}{a^2 - 8a + 7}$

Answer: a

Dividing rational expressions

Division by a nonzero number is equivalent to multiplying by its reciprocal. Thus, to divide two fractions, we can invert the divisor (the fraction following the ÷ sign) and multiply. For example,

$$\frac{4}{7} \div \frac{3}{5} = \frac{4}{7} \cdot \frac{5}{3} \qquad \text{Invert } \tfrac{3}{5} \text{ and change the division to a multiplication.}$$

$$= \frac{20}{21} \qquad \text{Multiply the numerators and multiply the denominators.}$$

In general, we have the following rule.

Division of fractions

> If a represents a real number and b, c, and d represent nonzero real numbers,
>
> $$\frac{a}{b} \div \frac{c}{d} = \frac{a}{b} \cdot \frac{d}{c}$$

We use the same procedures to divide rational expressions.

EXAMPLE 7   *Dividing rational expressions.*   Divide: a. $\dfrac{a}{13} \div \dfrac{17}{26}$ and   **b.** $-\dfrac{9x}{35y} \div \dfrac{15x^2}{14}$.

Self Check

Divide:

$$-\frac{8a}{3b} \div \frac{16a^2}{9b^2}$$

Solution

a. $\dfrac{a}{13} \div \dfrac{17}{26} = \dfrac{a}{13} \cdot \dfrac{26}{17}$ Invert the divisor, which is $\tfrac{17}{26}$, and change the division to a multiplication.

$$= \frac{a \cdot 2 \cdot 13}{13 \cdot 17} \qquad \text{Multiply. Then factor where possible.}$$

$$= \frac{a \cdot 2 \cdot \overset{1}{\cancel{13}}}{\underset{1}{\cancel{13}} \cdot 17} \qquad \text{Divide out common factors.}$$

$$= \frac{2a}{17}$$

b. $-\dfrac{9x}{35y} \div \dfrac{15x^2}{14} = -\dfrac{9x}{35y} \cdot \dfrac{14}{15x^2}$ Multiply by the reciprocal of $\dfrac{15x^2}{14}$.

$$= -\frac{3 \cdot 3 \cdot x \cdot 2 \cdot 7}{5 \cdot 7 \cdot y \cdot 3 \cdot 5 \cdot x \cdot x} \qquad \text{Multiply. Then factor where possible.}$$

$$= -\frac{3 \cdot \overset{1}{\cancel{3}} \cdot \overset{1}{\cancel{x}} \cdot 2 \cdot \overset{1}{\cancel{7}}}{5 \cdot \underset{1}{\cancel{7}} \cdot y \cdot \underset{1}{\cancel{3}} \cdot 5 \cdot \underset{1}{\cancel{x}} \cdot x} \qquad \text{Divide out common factors.}$$

$$= -\frac{6}{25xy} \qquad \text{Multiply the remaining factors.}$$

Answer: $-\dfrac{3b}{2a}$

EXAMPLE 8 *Dividing rational expressions.* Divide:

$\dfrac{x^2 + x}{3x - 15} \div \dfrac{x^2 + 2x + 1}{6x - 30}.$

Solution

$\dfrac{x^2 + x}{3x - 15} \div \dfrac{x^2 + 2x + 1}{6x - 30}$

$= \dfrac{x^2 + x}{3x - 15} \cdot \dfrac{6x - 30}{x^2 + 2x + 1}$ Invert the divisor and change the division to multiplication.

$= \dfrac{x(x + 1) \cdot 2 \cdot 3(x - 5)}{3(x - 5)(x + 1)(x + 1)}$ Multiply. Then factor.

$= \dfrac{x(\cancel{x + 1}) \cdot 2 \cdot \cancel{3}(\cancel{x - 5})}{\cancel{3}(\cancel{x - 5})(\cancel{x + 1})(x + 1)}$ Divide out common factors.

$= \dfrac{2x}{x + 1}$

Self Check

Divide:

$\dfrac{z^2 - 1}{z^2 + 4z + 3} \div \dfrac{z - 1}{z^2 + 2z - 3}$

Answer: $z - 1$ ∎

Dividing a rational expression by a polynomial

To divide a rational expression by a polynomial, we write the polynomial as a fraction by inserting a denominator of 1, and then we divide the fractions.

EXAMPLE 9 *Dividing by a polynomial.* Divide:

$\dfrac{2x^2 - 3x - 2}{2x + 1} \div (4 - x^2).$

Solution

$\dfrac{2x^2 - 3x - 2}{2x + 1} \div (4 - x^2)$

$= \dfrac{2x^2 - 3x - 2}{2x + 1} \div \dfrac{4 - x^2}{1}$ Write $4 - x^2$ as a fraction with a denominator of 1.

$= \dfrac{2x^2 - 3x - 2}{2x + 1} \cdot \dfrac{1}{4 - x^2}$ Invert the divisor and change the division to multiplication.

$= \dfrac{(2x + 1)(x - 2) \cdot 1}{(2x + 1)(2 + x)(2 - x)}$ Multiply. Then factor where possible.

$= \dfrac{\cancel{(2x + 1)}\overset{-1}{\cancel{(x - 2)}} \cdot 1}{\cancel{(2x + 1)}(2 + x)\cancel{(2 - x)}}$ Divide out common factors. The binomials $x - 2$ and $2 - x$ are opposites. $\frac{x - 2}{2 - x} = -1$.

$= \dfrac{-1}{2 + x}$

$= -\dfrac{1}{2 + x}$

Self Check

Divide:

$(b - a) \div \dfrac{a^2 - b^2}{a^2 + ab}$

Answer: $-a$ ∎

Combined operations

Unless parentheses indicate otherwise, we do multiplication and divisions in order from left to right.

EXAMPLE 10 *Multiplying and dividing rational expressions.*

Simplify $\dfrac{x^2 - x - 6}{x - 2} \div \dfrac{x^2 - 4x}{x^2 - x - 2} \cdot \dfrac{x - 4}{x^2 + x}$.

Solution

Since there are no parentheses to indicate otherwise, we do the division first.

$$\dfrac{x^2 - x - 6}{x - 2} \div \dfrac{x^2 - 4x}{x^2 - x - 2} \cdot \dfrac{x - 4}{x^2 + x}$$

$$= \dfrac{x^2 - x - 6}{x - 2} \cdot \dfrac{x^2 - x - 2}{x^2 - 4x} \cdot \dfrac{x - 4}{x^2 + x}$$

Invert the divisor, which is $\dfrac{x^2 - 4x}{x^2 - x - 2}$, and change the division to a multiplication.

$$= \dfrac{(x + 2)(x - 3)(x + 1)(x - 2)(x - 4)}{(x - 2)x(x - 4)x(x + 1)}$$

Multiply. Then factor.

$$= \dfrac{(x + 2)(x - 3)\cancel{(x + 1)}\cancel{(x - 2)}\cancel{(x - 4)}}{\cancel{(x - 2)}x\cancel{(x - 4)}x\cancel{(x + 1)}}$$

Divide out common factors.

$$= \dfrac{(x + 2)(x - 3)}{x^2}$$

Self Check

Simplify:

$$\dfrac{a^2 + ab}{ab - b^2} \cdot \dfrac{a^2 - b^2}{a^2 + ab} \div \dfrac{a + b}{b}$$

Answer: 1

EXAMPLE 11 *Multiplying and dividing rational expressions.*

Simplify $\dfrac{x^2 + 6x + 9}{x^2 - 2x}\left(\dfrac{x^2 - 4}{x^2 + 3x} \div \dfrac{x + 2}{x} \right)$.

Solution

We do the division within the parentheses first.

$$\dfrac{x^2 + 6x + 9}{x^2 - 2x}\left(\dfrac{x^2 - 4}{x^2 + 3x} \div \dfrac{x + 2}{x} \right)$$

$$= \dfrac{x^2 + 6x + 9}{x^2 - 2x}\left(\dfrac{x^2 - 4}{x^2 + 3x} \cdot \dfrac{x}{x + 2} \right)$$

Invert the divisor and change the division to multiplication.

$$= \dfrac{(x + 3)(x + 3)(x - 2)(x + 2)x}{x(x - 2)x(x + 3)(x + 2)}$$

Multiply and factor where possible.

$$= \dfrac{\cancel{(x + 3)}(x + 3)\cancel{(x - 2)}\cancel{(x + 2)}x}{x\cancel{(x - 2)}x\cancel{(x + 3)}\cancel{(x + 2)}}$$

Divide out common factors.

$$= \dfrac{x + 3}{x}$$

Self Check

Simplify:

$$\dfrac{x^2 - 2x}{x^2 + 6x + 9} \div \left(\dfrac{x^2 - 4}{x^2 + 3x} \cdot \dfrac{x}{x + 2} \right)$$

Answer: $\dfrac{x}{x + 3}$

STUDY SET   Section 6.2

VOCABULARY   *Fill in the blanks.*

1. In a fraction, the part above the fraction bar is called the ____numerator____.

2. In a fraction, the part below the fraction bar is called the ____denominator____.

CONCEPTS   *Fill in the blanks.*

3. To multiply fractions, we multiply their ____numerators____ and multiply their ____denominators____.

4. $\dfrac{a}{b} \cdot \dfrac{c}{d} = \dfrac{ac}{bd}$

5. To write a polynomial in fractional form, we insert a denominator of 1.

6. $\dfrac{a}{b} \div \dfrac{c}{d} = \dfrac{a}{b} \cdot \dfrac{d}{c}$

7. To divide fractions, we invert the ____divisor____ and ____multiply____.

8. The ____reciprocal____ of $\dfrac{x}{x+2}$ is $\dfrac{x+2}{x}$.

NOTATION   *Complete each solution.*

9. $\dfrac{x^2 + x}{3x - 6} \cdot \dfrac{x - 2}{x + 1} = \dfrac{(x^2 + x)\,(x - 2)}{(3x - 6)\,(x + 1)}$

$= \dfrac{x(x + 1)\,(x - 2)}{3(x - 2)\,(x + 1)}$

$= \dfrac{x}{3}$

10. $\dfrac{x^2 - x}{4x + 12} \div \dfrac{x - 1}{x + 3} = \dfrac{x^2 - x}{4x + 12} \cdot \dfrac{x + 3}{x - 1}$

$= \dfrac{(x^2 - x)\,(x + 3)}{(4x + 12)\,(x - 1)}$

$= \dfrac{x(x - 1)\,(x + 3)}{4(x + 3)\,(x - 1)}$

$= \dfrac{x}{4}$

PRACTICE   *Do the multiplications. Simplify answers if possible.*

11. $\dfrac{3}{y} \cdot \dfrac{y}{2}$ $\dfrac{3}{2}$

12. $\dfrac{2}{z} \cdot \dfrac{z}{3}$ $\dfrac{2}{3}$

13. $\dfrac{5y}{7} \cdot \dfrac{7}{5}$ y

14. $\dfrac{4x}{3y} \cdot \dfrac{3y}{7x}$ $\dfrac{4}{7}$

15. $\dfrac{7z}{9z} \cdot \dfrac{4z}{2z}$ $\dfrac{14}{9}$

16. $\dfrac{8}{2x} \cdot \dfrac{16x}{3x}$ $\dfrac{64}{3x}$

17. $\dfrac{2x^2 y}{3xy} \cdot \dfrac{3xy^2}{2}$ $x^2 y^2$

18. $\dfrac{2x^2 z}{z} \cdot \dfrac{5x}{z}$ $\dfrac{10x^3}{z}$

19. $\dfrac{8x^2 y^2}{4x^2} \cdot \dfrac{2xy}{2y}$ $2xy^2$

20. $\dfrac{9x^2 y}{3x} \cdot \dfrac{3xy}{3y}$ $3x^2 y$

21. $-\dfrac{2xy}{x^2} \cdot \dfrac{3xy}{2}$ $-3y^2$

22. $-\dfrac{3x}{x^2} \cdot \dfrac{2xz}{3}$ $-2z$

23. $\dfrac{ab^2}{a^2 b} \cdot \dfrac{b^2 c^2}{abc} \cdot \dfrac{abc^2}{a^3 c^2}$ $\dfrac{b^3 c}{a^4}$

24. $\dfrac{x^3 y}{z} \cdot \dfrac{xz^3}{x^2 y^2} \cdot \dfrac{yz}{xyz}$ $\dfrac{xz^2}{y}$

25. $\dfrac{10r^2 st^3}{6rs^2} \cdot \dfrac{3r^3 t}{2rst} \cdot \dfrac{2s^3 t^4}{5s^2 t^3}$ $\dfrac{r^3 t^4}{s}$

26. $\dfrac{3a^3 b}{25cd^3} \cdot \dfrac{-5cd^2}{6ab} \cdot \dfrac{10abc^2}{2bc^2 d}$ $-\dfrac{a^3}{2d^2}$

27. $\dfrac{z + 7}{7} \cdot \dfrac{z + 2}{z}$ $\dfrac{(z + 7)(z + 2)}{7z}$

28. $\dfrac{a - 3}{a} \cdot \dfrac{a + 3}{5}$ $\dfrac{(a - 3)(a + 3)}{5a}$

29. $\dfrac{x - 2}{2} \cdot \dfrac{2x}{x - 2}$ x

30. $\dfrac{y + 3}{y} \cdot \dfrac{3y}{y + 3}$ 3

31. $\dfrac{x + 5}{5} \cdot \dfrac{x}{x + 5}$ $\dfrac{x}{5}$

32. $\dfrac{y - 9}{y + 9} \cdot \dfrac{y}{9}$ $\dfrac{y(y - 9)}{9(y + 9)}$

33. $\dfrac{5}{m} \cdot m$ 5

34. $p \cdot \dfrac{10}{p}$ 10

35. $4d \cdot \dfrac{3}{2d}$ 6

36. $9x \cdot \dfrac{25}{3x}$ 75

37. $15x\left(\dfrac{x + 1}{15x}\right)$ $x + 1$

38. $30t\left(\dfrac{t - 7}{30t}\right)$ $t - 7$

39. $12y\left(\dfrac{y + 8}{6y}\right)$ $2y + 16$

40. $16x\left(\dfrac{3x + 8}{4x}\right)$ $12x + 32$

41. $(x + 8)\dfrac{x + 5}{x + 8}$ $x + 5$

42. $(y - 2)\dfrac{y + 3}{y - 2}$ $y + 3$

43. $10(h + 9)\dfrac{h - 3}{h + 9}$

$10h - 30$

44. $r(r - 25)\dfrac{r + 4}{r - 25}$

$r^2 + 4r$

45. $\dfrac{(x + 1)^2}{x + 1} \cdot \dfrac{x + 2}{x + 1}$

$x + 2$

46. $\dfrac{(y - 3)^2}{y - 3} \cdot \dfrac{y - 3}{y - 3}$

$y - 3$

47. $\dfrac{2x + 6}{x + 3} \cdot \dfrac{3}{4x}$ $\dfrac{3}{2x}$

48. $\dfrac{3y - 9}{y - 3} \cdot \dfrac{y}{3y^2}$ $\dfrac{1}{y}$

49. $\dfrac{x^2 - x}{x} \cdot \dfrac{3x - 6}{3x - 3}$

$x - 2$

50. $\dfrac{5z - 10}{z + 2} \cdot \dfrac{3}{3z - 6}$

$\dfrac{5}{z + 2}$

51. $\dfrac{7y - 14}{y - 2} \cdot \dfrac{x^2}{7x}$ x

52. $\dfrac{y^2 + 3y}{9} \cdot \dfrac{3x}{y + 3}$ $\dfrac{xy}{3}$

53. $\dfrac{x^2 + x - 6}{5x} \cdot \dfrac{5x - 10}{x + 3}$ $\dfrac{(x - 2)^2}{x}$

54. $\dfrac{z^2 + 4z - 5}{5z - 5} \cdot \dfrac{5z}{z + 5}$ z

55. $\dfrac{m^2 - 2m - 3}{2m + 4} \cdot \dfrac{m^2 - 4}{m^2 + 3m + 2}$ $\dfrac{(m - 2)(m - 3)}{2(m + 2)}$

56. $\dfrac{p^2 - p - 6}{3p - 9} \cdot \dfrac{p^2 - 9}{p^2 + 6p + 9}$ $\dfrac{(p + 2)(p - 3)}{3(p + 3)}$

57. $\dfrac{3x^2 + 5x + 2}{x^2 - 9} \cdot \dfrac{x - 3}{x^2 - 4} \cdot \dfrac{x^2 + 5x + 6}{6x + 4}$ $\dfrac{x + 1}{2(x - 2)}$

58. $\dfrac{x^2 - 25}{3x + 6} \cdot \dfrac{x^2 + x - 2}{2x + 10} \cdot \dfrac{6x}{3x^2 - 18x + 15}$ $\dfrac{x}{3}$

Do each division. Simplify answers when possible.

59. $\dfrac{2}{y} \div \dfrac{4}{3}$ $\dfrac{3}{2y}$

60. $\dfrac{3}{a} \div \dfrac{a}{9}$ $\dfrac{27}{a^2}$

61. $\dfrac{3x}{2} \div \dfrac{x}{2}$ 3

62. $\dfrac{y}{6} \div \dfrac{2}{3y}$ $\dfrac{y^2}{4}$

63. $\dfrac{3x}{y} \div \dfrac{2x}{4}$ $\dfrac{6}{y}$

64. $\dfrac{3y}{8} \div \dfrac{2y}{4y}$ $\dfrac{3y}{4}$

65. $\dfrac{4x}{3x} \div \dfrac{2y}{9y}$ 6

66. $\dfrac{14}{7y} \div \dfrac{10}{5z}$ $\dfrac{z}{y}$

67. $\dfrac{x^2}{3} \div \dfrac{2x}{4}$ $\dfrac{2x}{3}$

68. $\dfrac{z^2}{z} \div \dfrac{z}{3z}$ $3z$

69. $\dfrac{x^2 y}{3xy} \div \dfrac{xy^2}{6y}$ $\dfrac{2}{y}$

70. $\dfrac{2xz}{z} \div \dfrac{4x^2}{z^2}$ $\dfrac{z^2}{2x}$

71. $\dfrac{x + 2}{3x} \div \dfrac{x + 2}{2}$ $\dfrac{2}{3x}$

72. $\dfrac{z - 3}{3z} \div \dfrac{z + 3}{z}$ $\dfrac{z - 3}{3(z + 3)}$

73. $\dfrac{(z - 2)^2}{3z^2} \div \dfrac{z - 2}{6z}$ $\dfrac{2(z - 2)}{z}$

74. $\dfrac{(x + 7)^2}{x + 7} \div \dfrac{(x - 3)^2}{x + 7}$ $\dfrac{(x + 7)^2}{(x - 3)^2}$

75. $\dfrac{(z - 7)^2}{z + 2} \div \dfrac{z(z - 7)}{5z^2}$ $\dfrac{5z(z - 7)}{z + 2}$

76. $\dfrac{y(y + 2)}{y^2(y - 3)} \div \dfrac{y^2(y + 2)}{(y - 3)^2}$ $\dfrac{y - 3}{y^3}$

77. $\dfrac{x^2 - 4}{3x + 6} \div \dfrac{x - 2}{x + 2}$ $\dfrac{x + 2}{3}$

78. $\dfrac{x^2 - 9}{5x + 15} \div \dfrac{x - 3}{x + 3}$ $\dfrac{x + 3}{5}$

79. $\dfrac{x^2 - 1}{3x - 3} \div \dfrac{x + 1}{3}$ 1

80. $\dfrac{x^2 - 16}{x - 4} \div \dfrac{3x + 12}{x}$ $\dfrac{x}{3}$

81. $\dfrac{x^2 - 2x - 35}{3x^2 + 27x} \div \dfrac{x^2 + 7x + 10}{6x^2 + 12x}$ $\dfrac{2(x - 7)}{x + 9}$

82. $\dfrac{x^2 - x - 6}{2x^2 + 9x + 10} \div \dfrac{x^2 - 25}{2x^2 + 15x + 25}$ $\dfrac{x - 3}{x - 5}$

83. $\dfrac{2d^2 + 8d - 42}{d - 3} \div \dfrac{2d^2 + 14d}{d^2 + 5d}$ $d + 5$

84. $\dfrac{5x^2 + 13x - 6}{x + 3} \div \dfrac{5x^2 - 17x + 6}{x - 2}$ $\dfrac{x - 2}{x - 3}$

Do the operations.

85. $\dfrac{x}{3} \cdot \dfrac{9}{4} \div \dfrac{x^2}{6}$ $\dfrac{9}{2x}$

86. $\dfrac{y^2}{2} \div \dfrac{4}{y} \cdot \dfrac{y^2}{8}$ $\dfrac{y^5}{64}$

87. $\dfrac{x^2}{18} \div \dfrac{x^3}{6} \div \dfrac{12}{x^2}$ $\dfrac{x}{36}$

88. $\dfrac{y^3}{3y} \cdot \dfrac{3y^2}{4} \div \dfrac{15}{20}$ $\dfrac{y^4}{3}$

89. $\dfrac{z^2 - 4}{2z + 6} \div \dfrac{z + 2}{4} \cdot \dfrac{z + 3}{z - 2}$ 2

90. $\dfrac{2}{3x - 3} \div \dfrac{2x + 2}{x - 1} \cdot \dfrac{5}{x + 1}$ $\dfrac{5}{3(x + 1)^2}$

91. $\dfrac{x - x^2}{x^2 - 4}\left(\dfrac{2x + 4}{x + 2} \div \dfrac{5}{x + 2}\right)$ $\dfrac{2x(1 - x)}{5(x - 2)}$

92. $\dfrac{2}{3x - 3} \div \left(\dfrac{2x + 2}{x - 1} \cdot \dfrac{5}{x + 1}\right)$ $\dfrac{1}{15}$

93. $\dfrac{y^2}{x + 1} \cdot \dfrac{x^2 + 2x + 1}{x^2 - 1} \div \dfrac{3y}{xy - y}$ $\dfrac{y^2}{3}$

94. $\dfrac{x^2 - y^2}{x^4 - x^3} \div \dfrac{x - y}{x^2} \div \dfrac{x^2 + 2xy + y^2}{x + y}$ $\dfrac{1}{x(x - 1)}$

95. $\dfrac{x^2 + x - 6}{x^2 - 4} \cdot \dfrac{x^2 + 2x}{x - 2} \div \dfrac{x^2 + 3x}{x + 2}$ $\dfrac{x + 2}{x - 2}$

96. $\dfrac{x^2 - x - 6}{x^2 + 6x - 7} \cdot \dfrac{x^2 + x - 2}{x^2 + 2x} \div \dfrac{x^2 + 7x}{x^2 - 3x}$ $\dfrac{(x - 3)^2(x + 2)}{x(x + 7)^2}$

APPLICATIONS

97. INTERNATIONAL ALPHABET   The symbols representing the letters A, B, C, D, E, and F in an international code used at sea are printed six to a sheet and then cut into separate cards. If each card is a square, find the area of the large printed sheet shown in Illustration 1.

$\dfrac{12x^2 + 12x + 3}{2}$ in.^{2}

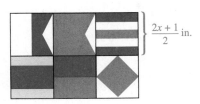

ILLUSTRATION 1

98. PHYSICS EXPERIMENT   The table in Illustration 2 contains algebraic expressions for the rate an object travels, and the time traveled at that rate, in terms of a constant k. Complete the table.

Rate (mph)	Time (hr)	Distance (mi)
$\dfrac{k^2 + k - 6}{k - 3}$	$\dfrac{k^2 - 9}{k^2 - 4}$	$\dfrac{(k + 3)^2}{k + 2}$

ILLUSTRATION 2

WRITING

99. Explain how to multiply two fractions and how to simplify the result.

100. Explain why any mathematical expression can be written as a fraction.

101. To divide fractions, you must first know how to multiply fractions. Explain.

102. Explain how to do the division $\dfrac{a}{b} \div \dfrac{c}{d} \div \dfrac{e}{f}$.

REVIEW   *Simplify each expression. Write all answers without using negative exponents.*

103. $2x^3y^2(-3x^2y^4)$ $-6x^5y^6$ **104.** $\dfrac{8x^4y^5}{-2x^3y^2}$ $-4xy^3$

105. $(3y)^{-4}$ $\dfrac{1}{81y^4}$ **106.** $x^{3m} \cdot x^{4m}$ x^{7m}

Do the operations and simplify.

107. $-4(y^3 - 4y^2 + 3y - 2) - 4(-2y^3 - y)$
$4y^3 + 16y^2 - 8y + 8$

108. $y - 5\overline{)5y^3 - 3y^2 + 4y - 1}$
$5y^2 + 22y + 114 + \dfrac{569}{y - 5}$

6.3 *Adding and Subtracting Rational Expressions*

In this section, you will learn about

- Adding and subtracting rational expressions with like denominators
- Combined operations • The LCD
- Adding and subtracting rational expressions with unlike denominators
- Combined operations

INTRODUCTION. In this section, we extend the rules for adding and subtracting numerical fractions to problems involving addition and subtraction of rational expressions.

Adding and subtracting rational expressions with like denominators

To add (or subtract) fractions with a common denominator, we add (or subtract) their numerators and keep the common denominator. For example,

$$\frac{3}{7} + \frac{2}{7} = \frac{3 + 2}{7} \qquad\qquad \frac{3}{7} - \frac{2}{7} = \frac{3 - 2}{7}$$
$$= \frac{5}{7} \qquad\qquad\qquad = \frac{1}{7}$$

In general, we have the following rule.

Adding and subtracting fractions with like denominators

If a, b, and d represent real numbers,

$$\frac{a}{d} + \frac{b}{d} = \frac{a + b}{d} \qquad \text{and} \qquad \frac{a}{d} - \frac{b}{d} = \frac{a - b}{d} \qquad (d \neq 0)$$

We use the same procedure to add and subtract rational expressions with like denominators.

EXAMPLE 1 *Adding rational expressions.* Do each addition.

a. $\dfrac{x}{8} + \dfrac{3x}{8} = \dfrac{x + 3x}{8}$ Add the numerators and keep the common denominator.

$\qquad\qquad = \dfrac{4x}{8}$ Combine like terms: $x + 3x = 4x$.

$\qquad\qquad = \dfrac{\overset{1}{\cancel{4}} \cdot x}{\underset{1}{\cancel{4}} \cdot 2}$ Factor the numerator and denominator and divide out the common factor, 4.

$\qquad\qquad = \dfrac{x}{2}$ Simplify.

b. $\dfrac{3x + y}{5x} + \dfrac{x + y}{5x} = \dfrac{3x + y + x + y}{5x}$ Add the numerators and keep the common denominator.

$\qquad\qquad\qquad = \dfrac{4x + 2y}{5x}$ Combine like terms.

EXAMPLE 2 *Adding rational expressions.* Add:

$\dfrac{3x + 21}{5x + 10} + \dfrac{8x + 1}{5x + 10}$

Solution

Because the fractions have the same denominator, we add their numerators and keep the common denominator.

$\dfrac{3x + 21}{5x + 10} + \dfrac{8x + 1}{5x + 10} = \dfrac{3x + 21 + 8x + 1}{5x + 10}$ Add.

$\qquad\qquad\qquad\qquad = \dfrac{11x + 22}{5x + 10}$ Combine like terms.

$\qquad\qquad\qquad\qquad = \dfrac{11\overset{1}{\cancel{(x + 2)}}}{5\underset{1}{\cancel{(x + 2)}}}$ Simplify the result by factoring the numerator and denominator. Divide out the common factor, $x + 2$.

$\qquad\qquad\qquad\qquad = \dfrac{11}{5}$

EXAMPLE 3 *Subtracting rational expressions.* Subtract:

a. $\dfrac{5x}{3} - \dfrac{2x}{3}$ and   **b.** $\dfrac{5x + 1}{x - 3} - \dfrac{4x - 2}{x - 3}$.

Solution

In each part, the fractions have the same denominator. To subtract them, we subtract their numerators and keep the common denominator.

a. $\dfrac{5x}{3} - \dfrac{2x}{3} = \dfrac{5x - 2x}{3}$

$\qquad\qquad = \dfrac{3x}{3}$ Combine like terms: $5x - 2x = 3x$.

$\qquad\qquad = \dfrac{x}{1}$ Divide out the common factor, 3.

$\qquad\qquad = x$ Denominators of 1 need not be written.

b. $\dfrac{5x + 1}{x - 3} - \dfrac{4x - 2}{x - 3} = \dfrac{(5x + 1) - (4x - 2)}{x - 3}$ Subtract. Write each numerator in parentheses.

$\qquad = \dfrac{5x + 1 - 4x + 2}{x - 3}$ Distribute the multiplication by -1: $-(4x - 2) = -4x + 2$.

$\qquad = \dfrac{x + 3}{x - 3}$ Combine like terms.

Answer: 1   ■

Combined operations

To add and/or subtract three or more rational expressions, we follow the rules for the order of operations.

EXAMPLE 4   *Combined operations.*   Simplify

$\dfrac{3x + 1}{x^2 + x + 1} - \dfrac{5x + 2}{x^2 + x + 1} + \dfrac{2x + 1}{x^2 + x + 1}$.

Solution

This example combines addition and subtraction. Unless parentheses indicate otherwise, we do additions and subtractions from left to right.

$\dfrac{3x + 1}{x^2 + x + 1} - \dfrac{5x + 2}{x^2 + x + 1} + \dfrac{2x + 1}{x^2 + x + 1}$

$= \dfrac{(3x + 1) - (5x + 2) + (2x + 1)}{x^2 + x + 1}$ Combine the numerators and keep the common denominator.

$= \dfrac{3x + 1 - 5x - 2 + 2x + 1}{x^2 + x + 1}$ Distribute the multiplication by -1: $-(5x + 2) = -5x - 2$.

$= \dfrac{0}{x^2 + x + 1}$ Combine like terms.

$= 0$ If the numerator of a fraction is zero and the denominator is not zero, the fraction's value is zero.

Self Check

Simplify:

$\dfrac{2a^2 - 3}{a - 5} + \dfrac{3a^2 + 2}{a - 5} - \dfrac{5a^2}{a - 5}$

Answer: $-\dfrac{1}{a - 5}$ ■

The LCD

Since the denominators of the fractions in the addition $\frac{4}{7} + \frac{3}{5}$ are different, we cannot add the fractions in their present form.

four-sevenths   +   three-fifths

└ Different denominators ┘

To add these fractions, we need to find a common denominator. The smallest common denominator (called the **least** or **lowest common denominator**) is usually the easiest one to work with.

Least common denominator

> The **least common denominator (LCD)** for a set of fractions is the smallest number that each denominator will divide exactly.

In the addition $\frac{4}{7} + \frac{3}{5}$, the denominators are 7 and 5. The smallest number that 7 and 5 will divide exactly is 35. This is the LCD. We now **build** each fraction into an equivalent fraction with a denominator of 35. To do so, we use the fundamental property of fractions to multiply both the numerator and the denominator of each fraction by some appropriate number.

$$\frac{4}{7} + \frac{3}{5} = \frac{4 \cdot 5}{7 \cdot 5} + \frac{3 \cdot 7}{5 \cdot 7} \qquad \text{Multiply the numerator and denominator of } \tfrac{4}{7} \text{ by 5, and}$$
$$\text{multiply the numerator and denominator of } \tfrac{3}{5} \text{ by 7.}$$
$$= \frac{20}{35} + \frac{21}{35} \qquad \text{Do the multiplications.}$$

Now that the fractions have a common denominator, we can add them.

$$\frac{20}{35} + \frac{21}{35} = \frac{20 + 21}{35} = \frac{41}{35}$$

EXAMPLE 5 *Building fractions.* Change each fraction into one with a denominator of $30y$: **a.** $\dfrac{1}{2y}$, **b.** $\dfrac{3y}{5}$, and **c.** $\dfrac{7 + x}{10y}$.

Self Check

Change $\dfrac{5}{6b}$ into a fraction with a denominator of $30ab$.

Solution

To build each fraction, we multiply the numerator and denominator by the factor that makes the denominator $30y$.

a. $\dfrac{1}{2y} = \dfrac{1 \cdot 15}{2y \cdot 15} = \dfrac{15}{30y}$ Multiply numerator and denominator by 15, because $2y \cdot 15 = 30y$.

b. $\dfrac{3y}{5} = \dfrac{3y \cdot 6y}{5 \cdot 6y} = \dfrac{18y^2}{30y}$ Multiply numerator and denominator by $6y$, because $5 \cdot 6y = 30y$.

c. $\dfrac{7 + x}{10y} = \dfrac{(7 + x)3}{(10y)3} = \dfrac{21 + 3x}{30y}$ Multiply numerator and denominator by 3, because $10y \cdot 3 = 30y$.

Answer: $\dfrac{25a}{30ab}$ ■

There is a process that we can use to find the least common denominator of several fractions.

Finding the least common denominator (LCD)

1. List the different denominators that appear in the fraction.
2. Completely factor each denominator.
3. Form a product using each different factor obtained in Step 2. Use each different factor the *greatest* number of times it appears in any one factorization. The product formed by multiplying these factors is the LCD.

EXAMPLE 6 *Finding the LCD.* Find the LCD of $\dfrac{5}{24b}$ and $\dfrac{11}{18b}$.

Self Check

Find the LCD of $\dfrac{3}{28z}$ and $\dfrac{5}{21z}$.

Solution

We list and factor each denominator into the product of prime numbers.

$$24b = 2 \cdot 2 \cdot 2 \cdot 3 \cdot b$$
$$18b = 2 \cdot 3 \cdot 3 \cdot b$$

To find the LCD, we use each of these factors the greatest number of times it appears in any one factorization. We use 2 three times, because it appears three times as a factor of 24. We use 3 twice, because it occurs twice as a factor of 18. We use b once.

$$\text{LCD} = 2 \cdot 2 \cdot 2 \cdot 3 \cdot 3 \cdot b$$
$$= 8 \cdot 9 \cdot b$$
$$= 72b$$

Answer: $84z$ ■

Adding and subtracting rational expressions with unlike denominators

The following steps summarize how to add (or subtract) fractions that have unlike denominators.

Adding or subtracting fractions with unlike denominators

To add (or subtract) fractions with unlike denominators,

1. Find the LCD.

2. Write each fraction as an equivalent fraction whose denominator is the LCD.

3. Add (or subtract) the resulting fractions and simplify the result, if possible.

EXAMPLE 7 *Adding rational expressions.* Add: $\dfrac{4x}{7} + \dfrac{3x}{5}$.

Self Check

Add:

$$\frac{y}{2} + \frac{6y}{7}$$

Solution

The LCD is 35. We build each fraction so that it has a denominator of 35 and then add the resulting fractions.

$$\frac{4x}{7} + \frac{3x}{5} = \frac{4x \cdot 5}{7 \cdot 5} + \frac{3x \cdot 7}{5 \cdot 7}$$ Multiply the numerator and the denominator of $\frac{4x}{7}$ by 5 and the numerator and denominator of $\frac{3x}{5}$ by 7.

$$= \frac{20x}{35} + \frac{21x}{35}$$ Do the multiplications.

$$= \frac{41x}{35}$$ Add the numerators and keep the common denominator.

Answer: $\dfrac{19y}{14}$

EXAMPLE 8 *Adding rational expressions.* Add: $\dfrac{5}{24b} + \dfrac{11}{18b}$.

Self Check

Add:

$$\frac{3}{28z} + \frac{5}{21z}$$

Solution

In Example 6, we saw that the LCD of these fractions is $2 \cdot 2 \cdot 2 \cdot 3 \cdot 3 \cdot b = 72b$. To add them, we first factor each denominator:

$$\frac{5}{24b} + \frac{11}{18b} = \frac{5}{2 \cdot 2 \cdot 2 \cdot 3 \cdot b} + \frac{11}{2 \cdot 3 \cdot 3 \cdot b}$$

In each resulting fraction, we multiply the numerator and the denominator by whatever it takes to build the denominator to the LCD of $2 \cdot 2 \cdot 2 \cdot 3 \cdot 3 \cdot b$.

$$= \frac{5 \cdot 3}{2 \cdot 2 \cdot 2 \cdot 3 \cdot b \cdot 3} + \frac{11 \cdot 2 \cdot 2}{2 \cdot 3 \cdot 3 \cdot b \cdot 2 \cdot 2}$$

$$= \frac{15}{72b} + \frac{44}{72b}$$ Do the multiplications.

$$= \frac{59}{72b}$$ Add the numerators and keep the common denominator.

Answer: $\dfrac{29}{84z}$

EXAMPLE 9 *Adding rational expressions.* Add: $\dfrac{x+4}{x^2} + \dfrac{x-5}{4x}$.

Solution

First we find the LCD.

$$\left.\begin{array}{l} x^2 = x \cdot x \\ 4x = 2 \cdot 2 \cdot x \end{array}\right\} \qquad \text{LCD} = x \cdot x \cdot 2 \cdot 2 = 4x^2$$

$$\dfrac{x+4}{x^2} + \dfrac{x-5}{4x} = \dfrac{(x+4)4}{(x^2)4} + \dfrac{(x-5)x}{(4x)x} \qquad \text{Build the fractions to get the common denominator, } 4x^2.$$

$$= \dfrac{4x+16}{4x^2} + \dfrac{x^2-5x}{4x^2} \qquad \text{Do the multiplications.}$$

$$= \dfrac{4x+16+x^2-5x}{4x^2} \qquad \text{Add the numerators and keep the common denominator.}$$

$$= \dfrac{x^2-x+16}{4x^2} \qquad \text{Combine like terms.}$$

Self Check
Add:

$$\dfrac{a-1}{9a} + \dfrac{2-a}{a^2}$$

Answer: $\dfrac{a^2-10a+18}{9a^2}$ ■

EXAMPLE 10 *Subtracting rational expressions.*   Subtract: $\dfrac{x}{x+1} - \dfrac{3}{x}$.

Solution

By inspection, the least common denominator is $(x+1)x$.

$$\dfrac{x}{x+1} - \dfrac{3}{x} = \dfrac{x(x)}{(x+1)x} - \dfrac{3(x+1)}{x(x+1)} \qquad \text{Build the fractions to get the common denominator.}$$

$$= \dfrac{x(x) - 3(x+1)}{x(x+1)} \qquad \text{Subtract the numerators and keep the common denominator.}$$

$$= \dfrac{x^2 - 3x - 3}{x(x+1)} \qquad \text{Do the multiplications in the numerator.}$$

Self Check
Subtract:

$$\dfrac{a}{a-1} - \dfrac{5}{a}$$

Answer: $\dfrac{a^2-5a+5}{a(a-1)}$ ■

EXAMPLE 11 *Simplifying after subtracting.*   Subtract: $\dfrac{a}{a-1} - \dfrac{2}{a^2-1}$.

Solution

We factor $a^2 - 1$ to see that the LCD is $(a+1)(a-1)$.

$$\dfrac{a}{a-1} - \dfrac{2}{a^2-1}$$

$$= \dfrac{a(a+1)}{(a-1)(a+1)} - \dfrac{2}{(a+1)(a-1)} \qquad \text{Build the first fraction to get the LCD.}$$

$$= \dfrac{a(a+1)-2}{(a-1)(a+1)} \qquad \text{Subtract the numerators and keep the common denominator.}$$

$$= \dfrac{a^2+a-2}{(a-1)(a+1)} \qquad \text{Distribute the multiplication by } a.$$

$$= \dfrac{(a+2)\overset{1}{\cancel{(a-1)}}}{\underset{1}{\cancel{(a-1)}}(a+1)} \qquad \text{Simplify the result by factoring } a^2+a-2. \text{ Divide out the common factor, } a-1.$$

$$= \dfrac{a+2}{a+1}$$

Self Check
Subtract:

$$\dfrac{b}{b-2} - \dfrac{8}{b^2-4}$$

Answer: $\dfrac{b+4}{b+2}$ ■

EXAMPLE 12   *Factoring to find the LCD.*   Subtract:

$$\frac{2a}{a^2 + 4a + 4} - \frac{1}{2a + 4}.$$

Solution

Find the least common denominator by factoring each denominator.

$$\left. \begin{array}{l} a^2 + 4a + 4 = (a + 2)(a + 2) \\ 2a + 4 = 2(a + 2) \end{array} \right\} \qquad \text{LCD} = (a + 2)(a + 2)2$$

We build each fraction into a new fraction with a denominator of $2(a + 2)(a + 2)$.

$$\frac{2a}{a^2 + 4a + 4} - \frac{1}{2a + 4}$$

$$= \frac{2a}{(a + 2)(a + 2)} - \frac{1}{2(a + 2)} \qquad \text{Write the denominators in factored form.}$$

$$= \frac{2a \cdot 2}{(a + 2)(a + 2)2} - \frac{1(a + 2)}{2(a + 2)(a + 2)} \qquad \text{Build each fraction to get a common denominator.}$$

$$= \frac{4a - 1(a + 2)}{2(a + 2)^2} \qquad \begin{array}{l}\text{Subtract the numerators and keep} \\ \text{the common denominator. Write} \\ (a + 2)(a + 2) \text{ as } (a + 2)^2.\end{array}$$

$$= \frac{4a - a - 2}{2(a + 2)^2} \qquad \text{Distribution the multiplication by } -1.$$

$$= \frac{3a - 2}{2(a + 2)^2} \qquad \text{Combine like terms.}$$

EXAMPLE 13   *Denominators that are opposites.*   Subtract:

$$\frac{3}{x - y} - \frac{x}{y - x}.$$

Solution

We note that the second denominator is the opposite (negative) of the first. So we can multiply the numerator and denominator of the second fraction by -1 to get

$$\frac{3}{x - y} - \frac{x}{y - x} = \frac{3}{x - y} - \frac{-1x}{-1(y - x)} \qquad \text{Multiply numerator and denominator by } -1.$$

$$= \frac{3}{x - y} - \frac{-x}{-y + x} \qquad \begin{array}{l}\text{Distribution the multiplication by } -1\text{:} \\ -1(y - x) = -y + x.\end{array}$$

$$= \frac{3}{x - y} - \frac{-x}{x - y} \qquad \begin{array}{l}-y + x = x - y. \text{ The fractions now} \\ \text{have a common denominator of } x - y.\end{array}$$

$$= \frac{3 - (-x)}{x - y} \qquad \begin{array}{l}\text{Subtract the numerators and keep the} \\ \text{common denominator.}\end{array}$$

$$= \frac{3 + x}{x - y} \qquad -(-x) = x.$$

Combined operations

To add and/or subtract three or more rational expressions, we follow the rules for the order of operations.

EXAMPLE 14   *Combined operations.*   Do the operations:

$\dfrac{3}{x^2y} + \dfrac{2}{xy} - \dfrac{1}{xy^2}$.

Solution

Find the least common denominator.

$$\left.\begin{array}{l} x^2y = x \cdot x \cdot y \\ xy = x \cdot y \\ xy^2 = x \cdot y \cdot y \end{array}\right\} \quad \text{Factor each denominator.}$$

In any one of these denominators, the factor x occurs at most twice, and the factor y occurs at most twice. Thus,

$$\begin{aligned} \text{LCD} &= x \cdot x \cdot y \cdot y \\ &= x^2y^2 \end{aligned}$$

We build each fraction into one with a denominator of x^2y^2.

$$\dfrac{3}{x^2y} + \dfrac{2}{xy} - \dfrac{1}{xy^2}$$

$$= \dfrac{3 \cdot y}{x \cdot x \cdot y \cdot y} + \dfrac{2 \cdot x \cdot y}{x \cdot y \cdot x \cdot y} - \dfrac{1 \cdot x}{x \cdot y \cdot y \cdot x} \qquad \text{Factor each denominator and build each fraction.}$$

$$= \dfrac{3y + 2xy - x}{x^2y^2} \qquad \text{Do the multiplications and combine the numerators. Write the result over the LCD.}$$

Self Check

Combine: $\dfrac{5}{ab^2} - \dfrac{b}{a} + \dfrac{a}{b}$.

Answer: $\dfrac{5 - b^3 + a^2b}{ab^2}$ ∎

STUDY SET   Section 6.3

VOCABULARY   *Fill in the blanks.*

1. The _____LCD_____ for a set of fractions is the smallest number that each denominator divides exactly.

2. When we multiply the numerator and denominator of a fraction by some number to get a common denominator, we say that we are ____building____ the fraction.

CONCEPTS   *Fill in the blanks.*

3. To add two fractions with like denominators, we add their ____numerators____ and keep the ____common denominator____.

4. To subtract two fractions with ____unlike____ denominators, we need to find a common denominator.

NOTATION   *Complete each solution.*

5.
$$\dfrac{6a - 1}{4a + 1} + \dfrac{2a + 3}{4a + 1} = \dfrac{6a - 1 + \; 2a + 3}{4a + 1}$$

$$= \dfrac{8a + \; 2}{4a + 1}$$

$$= \dfrac{2 \; (4a + 1)}{4a + 1}$$

$$= 2$$

6.
$$\dfrac{x}{2x + 1} - \dfrac{1}{3x} = \dfrac{x \,(3x)}{(2x + 1)(3x)} - \dfrac{1(2x + 1)}{3x \,(2x + 1)}$$

$$= \dfrac{x(3x) - 1 \,(2x + 1)}{3x(2x + 1)}$$

$$= \dfrac{3x^2 - \; 2x \; - \; 1}{3x(2x + 1)}$$

$$= \dfrac{(3x + 1)(x - 1)}{3x(2x + 1)}$$

PRACTICE   *Do each addition. Simplify answers, if possible.*

7. $\dfrac{x}{9} + \dfrac{2x}{9} \quad \dfrac{x}{3}$

8. $\dfrac{5x}{7} + \dfrac{9x}{7} \quad 2x$

9. $\dfrac{2x}{y} + \dfrac{2x}{y} \quad \dfrac{4x}{y}$

10. $\dfrac{4y}{3x} + \dfrac{2y}{3x} \quad \dfrac{2y}{x}$

11. $\dfrac{4}{7y} + \dfrac{10}{7y} \quad \dfrac{2}{y}$

12. $\dfrac{x^2}{4y} + \dfrac{x^2}{4y} \quad \dfrac{x^2}{2y}$

13. $\dfrac{y + 2}{10z} + \dfrac{y + 4}{10z} \quad \dfrac{y + 3}{5z}$

14. $\dfrac{x + 3}{2x^2} + \dfrac{x + 5}{2x^2} \quad \dfrac{x + 4}{x^2}$

15. $\dfrac{3x - 5}{x - 2} + \dfrac{6x - 13}{x - 2} \quad 9$

16. $\dfrac{8x - 7}{x + 3} + \dfrac{2x + 37}{x + 3} \quad 10$

17. $\dfrac{a}{a^2 + 5a + 6} + \dfrac{3}{a^2 + 5a + 6}$ $\dfrac{1}{a + 2}$

18. $\dfrac{b}{b^2 - 4} + \dfrac{2}{b^2 - 4}$ $\dfrac{1}{b - 2}$

Do each subtraction. Simplify answers, if possible.

19. $\dfrac{35y}{72} - \dfrac{44y}{72}$ $-\dfrac{y}{8}$

20. $\dfrac{13t}{99} - \dfrac{35t}{99}$ $-\dfrac{2t}{9}$

21. $\dfrac{2x}{y} - \dfrac{x}{y}$ $\dfrac{x}{y}$

22. $\dfrac{7y}{5} - \dfrac{4y}{5}$ $\dfrac{3y}{5}$

23. $\dfrac{9y}{3x} - \dfrac{6y}{3x}$ $\dfrac{y}{x}$

24. $\dfrac{5r^2}{2r} - \dfrac{r^2}{2r}$ $2r$

25. $\dfrac{6x - 5}{3xy} - \dfrac{3x - 5}{3xy}$ $\dfrac{1}{y}$

26. $\dfrac{7x + 7}{5y} - \dfrac{2x + 7}{5y}$ $\dfrac{x}{y}$

27. $\dfrac{3y - 2}{2y + 6} - \dfrac{2y - 5}{2y + 6}$ $\dfrac{1}{2}$

28. $\dfrac{5x + 8}{3x + 15} - \dfrac{3x - 2}{3x + 15}$ $\dfrac{2}{3}$

29. $\dfrac{2c}{c^2 - d^2} - \dfrac{2d}{c^2 - d^2}$ $\dfrac{2}{c + d}$

30. $\dfrac{3t}{t^2 - 8t + 7} - \dfrac{3}{t^2 - 8t + 7}$ $\dfrac{3}{t - 7}$

Do the operations. Simplify answers if possible.

31. $\dfrac{13x}{15} + \dfrac{12x}{15} - \dfrac{5x}{15}$ $\dfrac{4x}{3}$

32. $\dfrac{13y}{32} + \dfrac{13y}{32} - \dfrac{10y}{32}$ $\dfrac{y}{2}$

33. $-\dfrac{x}{y} + \dfrac{2x}{y} - \dfrac{x}{y}$ 0

34. $\dfrac{5y}{8x} + \dfrac{4y}{8x} - \dfrac{9y}{8x}$ 0

35. $\dfrac{3x}{y + 2} - \dfrac{3y}{y + 2} + \dfrac{x + y}{y + 2}$ $\dfrac{4x - 2y}{y + 2}$

36. $\dfrac{3y}{x - 5} + \dfrac{x}{x - 5} - \dfrac{y - x}{x - 5}$ $\dfrac{2(y + x)}{x - 5}$

37. $\dfrac{x + 1}{x - 2} - \dfrac{2(x - 3)}{x - 2} + \dfrac{3(x + 1)}{x - 2}$ $\dfrac{2x + 10}{x - 2}$

38. $\dfrac{3xy}{x - y} - \dfrac{x(3y - x)}{x - y} - \dfrac{x(x - y)}{x - y}$ $\dfrac{xy}{x - y}$

Build each fraction into an equivalent fraction with the indicated denominator.

39. $\dfrac{25}{4}; 20x$ $\dfrac{125x}{20x}$

40. $\dfrac{5}{y}; y^2$ $\dfrac{5y}{y^2}$

41. $\dfrac{8}{x}; x^2y$ $\dfrac{8xy}{x^2y}$

42. $\dfrac{7}{y}; xy^2$ $\dfrac{7xy}{xy^2}$

43. $\dfrac{3x}{x + 1}; (x + 1)^2$ $\dfrac{3x(x + 1)}{(x + 1)^2}$

44. $\dfrac{5y}{y - 2}; (y - 2)^2$ $\dfrac{5y(y - 2)}{(y - 2)^2}$

45. $\dfrac{2y}{x}; x^2 + x$ $\dfrac{2y(x + 1)}{x^2 + x}$

46. $\dfrac{3x}{y}; y^2 - y$ $\dfrac{3x(y - 1)}{y^2 - y}$

47. $\dfrac{z}{z - 1}; z^2 - 1$ $\dfrac{z(z + 1)}{z^2 - 1}$

48. $\dfrac{y}{y + 2}; y^2 - 4$ $\dfrac{y(y - 2)}{y^2 - 4}$

49. $\dfrac{2}{x + 1}; x^2 + 3x + 2$ $\dfrac{2(x + 2)}{x^2 + 3x + 2}$

50. $\dfrac{3}{x - 1}; x^2 + x - 2$ $\dfrac{3(x + 2)}{x^2 + x - 2}$

Several denominators are given. Find the LCD.

51. $2x, 6x$ $6x$

52. $3y, 9y$ $9y$

53. $6y, 9xy^2$ $18xy^2$

54. $6y, 3x^2y$ $6x^2y$

55. $x^2 - 1, x + 1$ $x^2 - 1$

56. $y^2 - 9, y - 3$ $y^2 - 9$

57. $x^2 + 6x, x + 6, x$ $x^2 + 6x$

58. $xy^2 - xy, xy, y - 1$ $xy^2 - xy$

59. $x^2 - 4x - 5, x^2 - 25$ $(x + 1)(x + 5)(x - 5)$

60. $x^2 - x - 6, x^2 - 9$ $(x - 3)(x + 2)(x + 3)$

Do the operations. Simplify answers, if possible.

61. $\dfrac{2y}{9} + \dfrac{y}{3}$ $\dfrac{5y}{9}$

62. $\dfrac{8a}{15} - \dfrac{5a}{12}$ $\dfrac{7a}{60}$

63. $\dfrac{21x}{14} - \dfrac{5x}{21}$ $\dfrac{53x}{42}$

64. $\dfrac{7y}{6} + \dfrac{10y}{9}$ $\dfrac{41y}{18}$

65. $\dfrac{4x}{3} + \dfrac{2x}{y}$ $\dfrac{4xy + 6x}{3y}$

66. $\dfrac{2y}{5x} - \dfrac{y}{2}$ $\dfrac{4y - 5xy}{10x}$

67. $\dfrac{2}{x} - 3x$ (Hint: $3x = \frac{3x}{1}$) $\dfrac{2 - 3x^2}{x}$

68. $14 + \dfrac{10}{y^2}$ (Hint: $14 = \frac{14}{1}$) $\dfrac{14y^2 + 10}{y^2}$

69. $\dfrac{y + 2}{5y^2} + \dfrac{y + 4}{15y}$ $\dfrac{y^2 + 7y + 6}{15y^2}$

70. $\dfrac{x + 3}{x^2} + \dfrac{x + 5}{2x}$ $\dfrac{x^2 + 7x + 6}{2x^2}$

71. $\dfrac{x + 5}{xy} - \dfrac{x - 1}{x^2y}$ $\dfrac{x^2 + 4x + 1}{x^2y}$

72. $\dfrac{x - 7}{y^2} - \dfrac{y + 7}{2y}$ $-\dfrac{y^2 + 5y + 14}{2y^2}$

73. $\dfrac{x}{x + 1} + \dfrac{x - 1}{x}$ $\dfrac{2x^2 - 1}{x(x + 1)}$

74. $\dfrac{3x}{xy} + \dfrac{x + 1}{y - 1}$ $\dfrac{4y - 3 + xy}{y(y - 1)}$

75. $\dfrac{x - 1}{x} + \dfrac{y + 1}{y}$ $\dfrac{2xy + x - y}{xy}$

76. $\dfrac{a+2}{b} + \dfrac{b-2}{a}$ $\dfrac{a^2 + 2a + b^2 - 2b}{ab}$

77. $\dfrac{x}{x-2} + \dfrac{4+2x}{x^2-4}$ $\dfrac{x+2}{x-2}$

78. $\dfrac{y}{y+3} - \dfrac{2y-6}{y^2-9}$ $\dfrac{y-2}{y+3}$

79. $\dfrac{x+1}{x-1} + \dfrac{x-1}{x+1}$ $\dfrac{2x^2+2}{(x-1)(x+1)}$

80. $\dfrac{2x}{x+2} + \dfrac{x+1}{x-3}$ $\dfrac{3x^2-3x+2}{(x-3)(x+2)}$

81. $\dfrac{5}{a-4} + \dfrac{7}{4-a}$ $-\dfrac{2}{a-4}$

82. $\dfrac{4}{b-6} - \dfrac{b}{6-b}$ $\dfrac{b+4}{b-6}$

83. $\dfrac{t+1}{t-7} - \dfrac{t+1}{7-t}$ $\dfrac{2t+2}{t-7}$

84. $\dfrac{r+2}{r^2-4} + \dfrac{4}{4-r^2}$ $\dfrac{1}{r+2}$

85. $\dfrac{2x+2}{x-2} - \dfrac{2x}{2-x}$ $\dfrac{4x+2}{x-2}$

86. $\dfrac{y+3}{y-1} - \dfrac{y+4}{1-y}$ $\dfrac{2y+7}{y-1}$

87. $\dfrac{b}{b+1} - \dfrac{b+1}{2b+2}$ $\dfrac{b-1}{2(b+1)}$

88. $\dfrac{4x+1}{8x-12} + \dfrac{x-3}{2x-3}$ $\dfrac{8x-11}{4(2x-3)}$

89. $\dfrac{2}{a^2+4a+3} + \dfrac{1}{a+3}$ $\dfrac{1}{a+1}$

90. $\dfrac{1}{c+6} - \dfrac{-4}{c^2+8a+12}$ $\dfrac{1}{c+2}$

91. $\dfrac{x+1}{2x+4} - \dfrac{x^2}{2x^2-8}$ $-\dfrac{1}{2(x-2)}$

92. $\dfrac{x+1}{x+2} - \dfrac{x^2+1}{x^2-x-6}$ $-\dfrac{2}{x-3}$

93. $\dfrac{2x}{x^2-3x+2} + \dfrac{2x}{x-1} - \dfrac{x}{x-2}$ $\dfrac{x}{x-2}$

94. $\dfrac{4a}{a-2} - \dfrac{3a}{a-3} + \dfrac{4a}{a^2-5a+6}$ $\dfrac{a}{a-3}$

95. $\dfrac{2x}{x-1} + \dfrac{3x}{x+1} - \dfrac{x+3}{x^2-1}$ $\dfrac{5x+3}{x+1}$

96. $\dfrac{a}{a-1} - \dfrac{2}{a+2} + \dfrac{3(a-2)}{a^2+a-2}$ $\dfrac{a+4}{a+2}$

APPLICATIONS *Refer to Illustration 1.*

97. Find the total height of the funnel. $\dfrac{20x+9}{6x^2}$ cm

98. What is the difference between the diameter of the opening at the top of the funnel and the diameter of its spout? $\dfrac{16x^2-3}{6x^3}$ cm

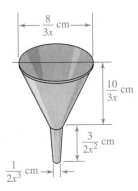

ILLUSTRATION 1

WRITING

99. Explain how to add fractions with the same denominator.

100. Explain how to find a lowest common denominator.

101. Explain what is wrong with the following solution:

$$\frac{2x+3}{x+5} - \frac{x+2}{x+5} = \frac{2x+3-x+2}{x+5}$$

$$= \frac{x+5}{x+5}$$

$$= 1$$

102. Explain what is wrong with the following solution:

$$\frac{5x-4}{y} + \frac{x}{y} = \frac{5x-4+x}{y+y}$$

$$= \frac{6x-4}{2y}$$

$$= \frac{2(3x-2)}{2y}$$

$$= \frac{3x-2}{y}$$

REVIEW   *Write each number in prime-factored form.*

103. 49 7^2

104. 64 2^6

105. 136 $2^3 \cdot 17$

106. 315 $3^2 \cdot 5 \cdot 7$

6.4 *Complex Fractions*

In this section, you will learn about

- Simplifying complex fractions
- Simplifying fractions with terms containing negative exponents

INTRODUCTION. Rational expressions such as

$$\frac{\dfrac{5x}{3}}{\dfrac{2y}{9}}, \qquad \frac{x + \dfrac{1}{2}}{3 - x}, \qquad \text{and} \qquad \frac{\dfrac{x + 1}{2}}{x + \dfrac{1}{x}}$$

which contain fractions in their numerators and/or denominators, are called **complex fractions.** In this section, we will show how to use the properties of algebra to simplify complex fractions.

Simplifying complex fractions

Complex fractions can often be simplified.

$$\frac{\dfrac{5x}{3}}{\dfrac{2y}{9}} \quad \longleftarrow \text{The main fraction bar indicates division.}$$

We can simplify the complex fraction by doing the division:

$$\frac{\dfrac{5x}{3}}{\dfrac{2y}{9}} = \frac{5x}{3} \div \frac{2y}{9} = \frac{5x}{3} \cdot \frac{9}{2y} = \frac{5x \cdot 3 \cdot \overset{1}{\cancel{3}}}{\underset{1}{\cancel{3}} \cdot 2y} = \frac{15x}{2y}$$

There are two ways to simplify complex fractions.

Methods for simplifying complex fractions

> **Method 1:** Write the numerator and denominator of the complex fraction as single fractions. Then divide the fractions and simplify.
>
> **Method 2:** Multiply the numerator and denominator of the complex fraction by the LCD of the fractions in its numerator and denominator. Then simplify the results, if possible.

To simplify the complex fraction

$$\frac{\dfrac{3x}{5} + 1}{2 - \dfrac{x}{5}}$$

using method 1, we proceed as follows:

$$\frac{\dfrac{3x}{5} + 1}{2 - \dfrac{x}{5}} = \frac{\dfrac{3x}{5} + \dfrac{5}{5}}{\dfrac{10}{5} - \dfrac{x}{5}}$$

Change 1 to $\frac{5}{5}$ and 2 to $\frac{10}{5}$ so that we can write the numerator and denominator as single fractions.

$$= \frac{\dfrac{3x + 5}{5}}{\dfrac{10 - x}{5}}$$

Add the fractions in the numerator and subtract the fractions in the denominator.

$$= \frac{3x + 5}{5} \div \frac{10 - x}{5}$$

Write the complex fraction as an equivalent division problem.

$$= \frac{3x + 5}{5} \cdot \frac{5}{10 - x}$$

Invert the divisor and multiply.

$$= \frac{(3x + 5)5}{5(10 - x)}$$

Multiply the fractions.

$$= \frac{3x + 5}{10 - x}$$

Divide out the common factor, 5.

To use method 2, we proceed as follows:

$$\frac{\dfrac{3x}{5} + 1}{2 - \dfrac{x}{5}} = \frac{5\left(\dfrac{3x}{5} + 1\right)}{5\left(2 - \dfrac{x}{5}\right)}$$

Multiply both the numerator and denominator of the complex fraction by 5, the LCD of $\frac{3x}{5}$ and $\frac{x}{5}$.

$$= \frac{5 \cdot \dfrac{3x}{5} + 5 \cdot 1}{5 \cdot 2 - 5 \cdot \dfrac{x}{5}}$$

Distribute the multiplication by 5.

$$= \frac{3x + 5}{10 - x}$$

Distribute the multiplication by 5.

In this example, method 2 is easier than method 1. Either method can be used to simplify complex fractions. With practice, you will be able to see which method is best in a given situation.

EXAMPLE 1 *Simplifying complex fractions.* Simplify $\dfrac{\dfrac{x}{3}}{\dfrac{y}{3}}$.

Self Check

Simplify $\dfrac{\dfrac{a}{4}}{\dfrac{5}{b}}$.

Solution

Method 1

$$\frac{\dfrac{x}{3}}{\dfrac{y}{3}} = \frac{x}{3} \div \frac{y}{3}$$

$$= \frac{x}{3} \cdot \frac{3}{y}$$

$$= \frac{3x}{3y}$$

$$= \frac{x}{y}$$

Method 2

$$\frac{\dfrac{x}{3}}{\dfrac{y}{3}} = \frac{3\left(\dfrac{x}{3}\right)}{3\left(\dfrac{y}{3}\right)}$$

The LCD for the fractions in the given complex fraction is 3.

$$= \frac{x}{y}$$

Answer: $\dfrac{ab}{20}$

EXAMPLE 2   *Simplifying complex fractions.*   Simplify $\dfrac{\dfrac{x}{x+1}}{\dfrac{y}{x}}$.

Solution

Method 1

$$\dfrac{\dfrac{x}{x+1}}{\dfrac{y}{x}} = \dfrac{x}{x+1} \div \dfrac{y}{x}$$

$$= \dfrac{x}{x+1} \cdot \dfrac{x}{y}$$

$$= \dfrac{x^2}{y(x+1)}$$

Method 2

$$\dfrac{\dfrac{x}{x+1}}{\dfrac{y}{x}} = \dfrac{x(x+1)\left(\dfrac{x}{x+1}\right)}{x(x+1)\left(\dfrac{y}{x}\right)}$$

$$= \dfrac{x^2}{y(x+1)}$$

The LCD for the fractions in the given complex fraction is $x(x+1)$.

Self Check

Simplify $\dfrac{\dfrac{x}{y}}{\dfrac{x}{y+1}}$.

Answer: $\dfrac{y+1}{y}$ ■

EXAMPLE 3   *Simplifying complex fractions.*   Simplify $\dfrac{1+\dfrac{1}{x}}{1-\dfrac{1}{x}}$.

Solution

Method 1

$$\dfrac{1+\dfrac{1}{x}}{1-\dfrac{1}{x}} = \dfrac{\dfrac{x}{x}+\dfrac{1}{x}}{\dfrac{x}{x}-\dfrac{1}{x}}$$

$$= \dfrac{\dfrac{x+1}{x}}{\dfrac{x-1}{x}}$$

$$= \dfrac{x+1}{x} \div \dfrac{x-1}{x}$$

$$= \dfrac{x+1}{x} \cdot \dfrac{x}{x-1}$$

$$= \dfrac{(x+1)\overset{1}{\cancel{x}}}{\underset{1}{\cancel{x}}(x-1)}$$

$$= \dfrac{x+1}{x-1}$$

Method 2

$$\dfrac{1+\dfrac{1}{x}}{1-\dfrac{1}{x}} = \dfrac{x\left(1+\dfrac{1}{x}\right)}{x\left(1-\dfrac{1}{x}\right)}$$

$$= \dfrac{x \cdot 1 + x \cdot \dfrac{1}{x}}{x \cdot 1 - x \cdot \dfrac{1}{x}}$$

$$= \dfrac{x+1}{x-1}$$

Self Check

Simplify $\dfrac{\dfrac{1}{x}+1}{\dfrac{1}{x}-1}$.

Answer: $\dfrac{1+x}{1-x}$ ■

EXAMPLE 4   *Simplifying complex fractions.*   Simplify $\dfrac{1}{1+\dfrac{1}{x+1}}$.

Self Check

Simplify $\dfrac{2}{\dfrac{1}{x+2}-2}$.

Solution

We use method 2.

$$\cfrac{1}{1 + \cfrac{1}{x + 1}} = \cfrac{(x + 1) \cdot 1}{(x + 1)\left(1 + \cfrac{1}{x + 1}\right)}$$

Multiply the numerator and the denominator of the complex fraction by $x + 1$.

$$= \frac{x + 1}{(x + 1)1 + 1}$$

In the denominator, distribute $x + 1$.

$$= \frac{x + 1}{x + 2}$$

Simplify.

Answer: $\dfrac{2(x + 2)}{-2x - 3}$ ∎

Simplifying fractions with terms containing negative exponents

Many fractions with terms containing negative exponents are complex fractions in disguise.

EXAMPLE 5 *Simplifying complex fractions.* Simplify $\dfrac{x^{-1} + y^{-2}}{x^{-2} - y^{-1}}$.

Self Check

Simplify $\dfrac{x^{-2} - y^{-1}}{x^{-1} + y^{-2}}$.

Solution

Write the fraction as a complex fraction and simplify using method 2.

$$\frac{x^{-1} + y^{-2}}{x^{-2} - y^{-1}} = \cfrac{\cfrac{1}{x} + \cfrac{1}{y^2}}{\cfrac{1}{x^2} - \cfrac{1}{y}}$$

$$= \cfrac{x^2 y^2 \left(\cfrac{1}{x} + \cfrac{1}{y^2}\right)}{x^2 y^2 \left(\cfrac{1}{x^2} - \cfrac{1}{y}\right)}$$

Multiply the numerator and denominator by $x^2 y^2$, which is the LCD of the fractions in the numerator and the denominator of the complex fraction.

$$= \frac{xy^2 + x^2}{y^2 - x^2 y}$$

Distribute the multiplication by $x^2 y^2$ and simplify.

$$= \frac{x(y^2 + x)}{y(y - x^2)}$$

Attempt to simplify the fraction by factoring the numerator and the denominator. The result cannot be simplified.

Answer: $\dfrac{y(y - x^2)}{x(y^2 + x)}$ ∎

STUDY SET Section 6.4

VOCABULARY *Fill in the blanks.*

1. If a fraction has a fraction in its numerator or denominator, it is called a ___complex fraction___.

2. The denominator of the complex fraction $\dfrac{\dfrac{3}{x} + \dfrac{x}{y}}{\dfrac{1}{x} + 2}$ is $\dfrac{1}{x} + 2$.

CONCEPTS *Fill in the blanks.*

3. To simplify a complex fraction using method 1, we write the numerator and denominator of a complex fraction as ___single___ fractions and then ___divide___.

4. To simplify a complex fraction using method 2, we multiply the numerator and denominator of the complex fraction by the ___LCD___ of the fractions in its numerator and denominator.

NOTATION *Complete each solution.*

5. $\dfrac{\dfrac{2}{a}-\dfrac{1}{b}}{\dfrac{1}{a}+\dfrac{2}{b}}=\dfrac{\dfrac{2b-a}{ab}}{\dfrac{b+2a}{ab}}$

$$=\dfrac{2b-a}{ab}\div\dfrac{b+2a}{ab}$$

$$=\dfrac{2b-a}{ab}\cdot\dfrac{ab}{b+2a}$$

$$=\dfrac{(2b-a)\,ab}{ab\,(b+2a)}$$

$$=\dfrac{2b-a}{b+2a}$$

6. $\dfrac{\dfrac{2}{a}-\dfrac{1}{b}}{\dfrac{1}{a}+\dfrac{2}{b}}=\dfrac{ab\left(\dfrac{2}{a}-\dfrac{1}{b}\right)}{ab\left(\dfrac{1}{a}+\dfrac{2}{b}\right)}$

$$=\dfrac{2b-a}{b+2a}$$

PRACTICE *Simplify each complex fraction.*

7. $\dfrac{\dfrac{2}{3}}{\dfrac{3}{4}}$ $\dfrac{8}{9}$

8. $\dfrac{\dfrac{3}{5}}{\dfrac{2}{7}}$ $\dfrac{21}{10}$

9. $\dfrac{\dfrac{4}{5}}{\dfrac{32}{15}}$ $\dfrac{3}{8}$

10. $\dfrac{\dfrac{7}{8}}{\dfrac{49}{4}}$ $\dfrac{1}{14}$

11. $\dfrac{\dfrac{2}{3}+1}{\dfrac{1}{3}+1}$ $\dfrac{5}{4}$

12. $\dfrac{\dfrac{3}{5}-2}{\dfrac{2}{5}-2}$ $\dfrac{7}{8}$

13. $\dfrac{\dfrac{1}{2}+\dfrac{3}{4}}{\dfrac{3}{2}+\dfrac{1}{4}}$ $\dfrac{5}{7}$

14. $\dfrac{\dfrac{2}{3}-\dfrac{5}{2}}{\dfrac{2}{3}-\dfrac{3}{2}}$ $\dfrac{11}{5}$

15. $\dfrac{\dfrac{x}{y}}{\dfrac{1}{x}}$ $\dfrac{x^2}{y}$

16. $\dfrac{\dfrac{y}{x}}{\dfrac{x}{xy}}$ $\dfrac{y^2}{x}$

17. $\dfrac{\dfrac{5t^2}{9x^2}}{\dfrac{3t}{x^2t}}$ $\dfrac{5t^2}{27}$

18. $\dfrac{\dfrac{5w^2}{4tz}}{\dfrac{15wt}{z^2}}$ $\dfrac{wz}{12t^2}$

19. $\dfrac{\dfrac{1}{x}-3}{\dfrac{5}{x}+2}$ $\dfrac{1-3x}{5+2x}$

20. $\dfrac{\dfrac{1}{y}+3}{\dfrac{3}{y}-2}$ $\dfrac{1+3y}{3-2y}$

21. $\dfrac{\dfrac{2}{x}+2}{\dfrac{4}{x}+2}$ $\dfrac{1+x}{2+x}$

22. $\dfrac{\dfrac{3}{x}-3}{\dfrac{9}{x}-3}$ $\dfrac{1-x}{3-x}$

23. $\dfrac{\dfrac{3y}{x}-y}{y-\dfrac{y}{x}}$ $\dfrac{3-x}{x-1}$

24. $\dfrac{\dfrac{y}{x}+3y}{y+\dfrac{2y}{x}}$ $\dfrac{3x+1}{x+2}$

25. $\dfrac{\dfrac{1}{x+1}}{1+\dfrac{1}{x+1}}$ $\dfrac{1}{x+2}$

26. $\dfrac{\dfrac{1}{x-1}}{1-\dfrac{1}{x-1}}$ $\dfrac{1}{x-2}$

27. $\dfrac{\dfrac{x}{x+2}}{\dfrac{x}{x+2}+x}$ $\dfrac{1}{x+3}$

28. $\dfrac{\dfrac{2}{x-2}}{\dfrac{2}{x-2}-1}$ $\dfrac{2}{4-x}$

29. $\dfrac{1}{\dfrac{1}{x}+\dfrac{1}{y}}$ $\dfrac{xy}{y+x}$

30. $\dfrac{1}{\dfrac{b}{a}-\dfrac{a}{b}}$ $\dfrac{ab}{b^2-a^2}$

31. $\dfrac{\dfrac{2}{x}}{\dfrac{2}{y}-\dfrac{4}{x}}$ $\dfrac{y}{x-2y}$

32. $\dfrac{\dfrac{2y}{3}}{\dfrac{2y}{3}-\dfrac{8}{y}}$ $\dfrac{y^2}{y^2-12}$

33. $\dfrac{3+\dfrac{3}{x-1}}{3-\dfrac{3}{x}}$ $\dfrac{x^2}{(x-1)^2}$

34. $\dfrac{2-\dfrac{2}{x+1}}{2+\dfrac{2}{x}}$ $\dfrac{x^2}{(x+1)^2}$

35. $\dfrac{\dfrac{3}{x}+\dfrac{4}{x+1}}{\dfrac{2}{x+1}-\dfrac{3}{x}}$ $\dfrac{7x+3}{-x-3}$

36. $\dfrac{\dfrac{5}{y-3}-\dfrac{2}{y}}{\dfrac{1}{y}+\dfrac{2}{y-3}}$ $\dfrac{y+2}{y-1}$

37. $\dfrac{\dfrac{2}{x}-\dfrac{3}{x+1}}{\dfrac{2}{x+1}-\dfrac{3}{x}}$ $\dfrac{x-2}{x+3}$

38. $\dfrac{\dfrac{5}{y}+\dfrac{4}{y+1}}{\dfrac{4}{y}-\dfrac{5}{y+1}}$ $\dfrac{9y+5}{4-y}$

39. $\dfrac{\dfrac{1}{y^2+y}-\dfrac{1}{xy+x}}{\dfrac{1}{xy+x}-\dfrac{1}{y^2+y}}$ -1

40. $\dfrac{\dfrac{2}{b^2-1}-\dfrac{3}{ab-a}}{\dfrac{3}{ab-a}-\dfrac{2}{b^2-1}}$ -1

41. $\dfrac{x^{-2}}{y^{-1}}$ $\dfrac{y}{x^2}$

42. $\dfrac{a^{-4}}{b^{-2}}$ $\dfrac{b^2}{a^4}$

43. $\dfrac{1 + x^{-1}}{x^{-1} - 1}$ $\dfrac{x + 1}{1 - x}$

44. $\dfrac{y^{-2} + 1}{y^{-2} - 1}$ $\dfrac{1 + y^2}{1 - y^2}$

45. $\dfrac{a^{-2} + a}{a}$ $\dfrac{1 + a^3}{a^3}$

46. $\dfrac{t - t^{-2}}{t^{-1}}$ $\dfrac{t^3 - 1}{t}$

47. $\dfrac{2x^{-1} + 4x^{-2}}{2x^{-2} + x^{-1}}$ 2

48. $\dfrac{x^{-2} - 3x^{-3}}{3x^{-2} - 9x^{-3}}$ $\dfrac{1}{3}$

49. $\dfrac{1 - 25y^{-2}}{1 + 10y^{-1} + 25y^{-2}}$ $\dfrac{y - 5}{y + 5}$

50. $\dfrac{1 - 9x^{-2}}{1 - 6x^{-1} + 9x^{-2}}$ $\dfrac{x + 3}{x - 3}$

APPLICATIONS

51. GARDENING TOOL   In Illustration 1, what is the result when the opening of the cutting blades is divided by the opening of the handles? Express the result in simplest form. $\frac{3}{14}$

ILLUSTRATION 1

52. EARNED RUN AVERAGE   The earned run average (ERA) is a statistic that gives the average number of earned runs a pitcher allows. For a softball pitcher, this is based on a six-inning game. The formula for ERA is

$$\text{ERA} = \dfrac{\dfrac{\text{earned runs}}{\text{innings pitched}}}{6}$$

Simplify the complex fraction on the right-hand side of the equation. $\text{ERA} = \dfrac{6 \cdot \text{earned runs}}{\text{innings pitched}}$

53. ELECTRONICS   In electronic circuits, resistors oppose the flow of an electric current. To find the total resistance of a parallel combination of two resistors (see Illustration 2), we can use the formula

$$\text{Total resistance} = \dfrac{1}{\dfrac{1}{R_1} + \dfrac{1}{R_2}}$$

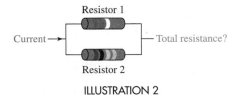

ILLUSTRATION 2

where R_1 is the resistance of the first resistor and R_2 is the resistance of the second. Simplify the complex fraction on the right-hand side of the formula. $\dfrac{R_1 R_2}{R_2 + R_1}$

54. DATA ANALYSIS   Use the data in Illustration 3 to find the average measurement for the three-trial experiment. $\frac{4k}{9}$

	Trial 1	Trial 2	Trial 3
Measurement	$\frac{k}{2}$	$\frac{k}{3}$	$\frac{k}{2}$

ILLUSTRATION 3

WRITING

55. Explain how to use method 1 to simplify

$$\dfrac{1 + \dfrac{1}{x}}{3 - \dfrac{1}{x}}$$

56. Explain how to use method 2 to simplify the expression in Exercise 55.

REVIEW   *Write each expression as an expression involving only one exponent.*

57. $t^3 t^4 t^2$ t^9

58. $(a^0 a^2)^3$ a^6

59. $-2r(r^3)^2$ $-2r^7$

60. $(s^3)^2 (s^4)^0$ s^6

Write each expression without using parentheses or negative exponents.

61. $\left(\dfrac{3r}{4r^3}\right)^4$ $\dfrac{81}{256r^8}$

62. $\left(\dfrac{12y^{-3}}{3y^2}\right)^{-2}$ $\dfrac{y^{10}}{16}$

63. $\left(\dfrac{6r^{-2}}{2r^3}\right)^{-2}$ $\dfrac{r^{10}}{9}$

64. $\left(\dfrac{4x^3}{5x^{-3}}\right)^{-2}$ $\dfrac{25}{16x^{12}}$

6.5 *Rational Equations and Problem Solving*

In this section, you will learn about

- Solving rational equations • Extraneous solutions
- Solving formulas • Applications

INTRODUCTION. In this section, we will solve problems from banking, petroleum engineering, business, electronics, and travel. We will encounter a new type of equation when we write mathematical models of such situations. These equations will contain one or more rational expressions; they are called **rational equations.**

Solving rational equations

Recall that to solve an equation such as $\frac{x}{6} + \frac{5}{2} = \frac{1}{3}$, we can multiply both sides of the equation by the LCD of the fractions to clear the equation of fractions.

$$\frac{x}{6} + \frac{5}{2} = \frac{1}{3}$$

$$6\left(\frac{x}{6} + \frac{5}{2}\right) = 6\left(\frac{1}{3}\right) \qquad \text{Multiply both sides of the equation by the LCD of } \frac{x}{6}, \frac{5}{2}, \text{and } \frac{1}{3}, \text{which is 6.}$$

$$6 \cdot \frac{x}{6} + 6 \cdot \frac{5}{2} = 6 \cdot \frac{1}{3} \qquad \text{Distribute the multiplication by 6.}$$

$$x + 15 = 2 \qquad \text{Do the multiplications.}$$

$$x + 15 - 15 = 2 - 15 \qquad \text{To undo the addition of 15, subtract 15 from both sides.}$$

$$x = -13 \qquad \text{Do the subtractions.}$$

This method can be used to solve rational equations.

EXAMPLE 1 *Solving rational equations.* Solve $\frac{4}{x} + 1 = \frac{6}{x}$.

Solution

To clear the equation of fractions, we multiply both sides by the LCD of $\frac{4}{x}$ and $\frac{6}{x}$, which is x.

$$\frac{4}{x} + 1 = \frac{6}{x}$$

$$x\left(\frac{4}{x} + 1\right) = x\left(\frac{6}{x}\right)$$

$$x \cdot \frac{4}{x} + x \cdot 1 = x \cdot \frac{6}{x} \qquad \text{Distribute the multiplication by } x.$$

$$4 + x = 6 \qquad \text{Do each multiplication.}$$

$$x = 2 \qquad \text{Subtract 4 from both sides.}$$

Check:
$$\frac{4}{x} + 1 = \frac{6}{x}$$

$$\frac{4}{2} + 1 \stackrel{?}{=} \frac{6}{2} \qquad \text{Substitute 2 for } x.$$

$$2 + 1 \stackrel{?}{=} 3 \qquad \text{Simplify.}$$

$$3 = 3$$

Self Check

Solve $\frac{6}{x} - 1 = \frac{3}{x}$.

Answer: 3

EXAMPLE 2   *Solving rational equations.*   Solve $\dfrac{22}{5} - \dfrac{3a - 1}{a} = \dfrac{8}{a}$.

Self Check

Solve $\dfrac{7}{6} - \dfrac{2r - 11}{r} = \dfrac{1}{r}$.

Solution

We multiply both sides by $5a$, the LCD of the rational expressions in the equation.

$$\frac{22}{5} - \frac{3a - 1}{a} = \frac{8}{a}$$

$$5a\left(\frac{22}{5} - \frac{3a - 1}{a}\right) = 5a\left(\frac{8}{a}\right)$$

$$5a\left(\frac{22}{5}\right) - 5a\left(\frac{3a - 1}{a}\right) = 5a\left(\frac{8}{a}\right) \quad \text{Distribute the multiplication by } 5a.$$

$$22a - 5(3a - 1) = 40 \quad \begin{array}{l}\text{Simplify. Note that } 3a - 1 \text{ must be} \\ \text{written within parentheses.}\end{array}$$

$$22a - 15a + 5 = 40 \quad \text{Distribute the multiplication by } -5.$$

$$7a + 5 = 40 \quad \text{Combine like terms: } 22a - 15a = 7a.$$

$$7a = 35 \quad \text{Subtract 5 from both sides.}$$

$$a = 5 \quad \text{Divide both sides by 7.}$$

Check: $\dfrac{22}{5} - \dfrac{3a - 1}{a} = \dfrac{8}{a}$

$$\frac{22}{5} - \frac{3(5) - 1}{5} \overset{?}{=} \frac{8}{5} \quad \text{Substitute 5 for } a.$$

$$\frac{22}{5} - \frac{14}{5} \overset{?}{=} \frac{8}{5}$$

$$\frac{8}{5} = \frac{8}{5}$$

Answer: 12

$\blacksquare$

EXAMPLE 3   *Factoring to find the LCD.*   Solve

$$\frac{x + 2}{x + 3} + \frac{1}{x^2 + 2x - 3} = 1.$$

Self Check

Solve $\dfrac{1}{x + 3} + \dfrac{1}{x - 3} = \dfrac{10}{x^2 - 9}$.

Solution

To find the LCD, we must factor the second denominator.

$$\frac{x + 2}{x + 3} + \frac{1}{x^2 + 2x - 3} = 1$$

$$\frac{x + 2}{x + 3} + \frac{1}{(x + 3)(x - 1)} = 1 \quad \text{Factor } x^2 + 2x - 3.$$

To clear the equation of fractions, we multiply both sides by the LCD, which is $(x + 3)(x - 1)$.

$$(x + 3)(x - 1)\left[\frac{x + 2}{x + 3} + \frac{1}{(x + 3)(x - 1)}\right] = (x + 3)(x - 1)1$$

Next, we distribute the multiplication by $(x + 3)(x - 1)$.

$$(x + 3)(x - 1)\frac{x + 2}{x + 3} + (x + 3)(x - 1)\frac{1}{(x + 3)(x - 1)} = (x + 3)(x - 1)1$$

$$(x - 1)(x + 2) + 1 = (x + 3)(x - 1) \quad \text{Simplify.}$$
$$x^2 + x - 2 + 1 = x^2 + 2x - 3 \quad \text{Multiply the pairs of binomials.}$$
$$x^2 + x - 1 = x^2 + 2x - 3 \quad \text{Combine like terms.}$$
$$x - 1 = 2x - 3 \quad \text{Subtract } x^2 \text{ from both sides.}$$
$$-x - 1 = -3 \quad \text{Subtract } 2x \text{ from both sides.}$$
$$-x = -2 \quad \text{Add 1 to both sides.}$$
$$x = 2 \quad \text{Divide both sides by } -1.$$

Verify that 2 is a solution of the given equation.

Answer: 5

EXAMPLE 4 *A rational equation that leads to a quadratic equation.* Solve $\dfrac{4}{5} + y = \dfrac{4y - 50}{5y - 25}$.

Self Check

Solve:

$$\frac{x - 6}{3x - 9} - \frac{1}{3} = \frac{x}{2}$$

Solution

To find the LCD, we must factor $5y - 25$.

$$\frac{4}{5} + y = \frac{4y - 50}{5y - 25}$$

$$\frac{4}{5} + y = \frac{4y - 50}{5(y - 5)}$$

$$5(y - 5)\left[\frac{4}{5} + y\right] = 5(y - 5)\left[\frac{4y - 50}{5(y - 5)}\right] \quad \begin{array}{l}\text{Multiply both sides by the LCD,}\\ \text{which is } 5(y - 5).\end{array}$$

$$4(y - 5) + 5y(y - 5) = 4y - 50 \quad \text{Distribute } 5(y - 5).$$

$$4y - 20 + 5y^2 - 25y = 4y - 50 \quad \text{Distribute 4 and } 5y.$$

$$5y^2 - 25y - 20 = -50 \quad \begin{array}{l}\text{Subtract } 4y \text{ from both sides and}\\ \text{rearrange terms.}\end{array}$$

$$5y^2 - 25y + 30 = 0 \quad \text{Add 50 to both sides.}$$

$$y^2 - 5y + 6 = 0 \quad \text{Divide both sides by 5.}$$

$$(y - 3)(y - 2) = 0 \quad \text{Factor } y^2 - 5y + 6.$$

$$y - 3 = 0 \quad \text{or} \quad y - 2 = 0 \quad \text{Set each factor equal to zero.}$$

$$y = 3 \qquad\qquad y = 2 \quad \text{Solve each equation.}$$

Verify that 3 and 2 satisfy the original equation.

Answer: 1, 2

Extraneous solutions

If we multiply both sides of an equation by an expression that involves a variable, as we did in the previous examples, we must check the apparent solutions. The next example shows why.

EXAMPLE 5 *Checking apparent solutions.* Solve $\dfrac{x + 3}{x - 1} = \dfrac{4}{x - 1}$.

Self Check

Solve $\dfrac{x + 5}{x - 2} = \dfrac{7}{x - 2}$.

Solution

To clear the equation of fractions, we multiply both sides by the LCD, which is $x - 1$.

$$\frac{x + 3}{x - 1} = \frac{4}{x - 1}$$

$$(x - 1)\frac{x + 3}{x - 1} = (x - 1)\frac{4}{x - 1} \qquad \text{Multiply both sides by } x - 1.$$

$$x + 3 = 4 \qquad\qquad \text{Simplify.}$$

$$x = 1 \qquad\qquad \text{Subtract 3 from both sides.}$$

Because both sides were multiplied by an expression containing a variable, we must check the apparent solution.

$$\frac{x + 3}{x - 1} = \frac{4}{x - 1}$$

$$\frac{1 + 3}{1 - 1} \stackrel{?}{=} \frac{4}{1 - 1} \qquad \text{Substitute 1 for } x.$$

$$\frac{4}{0} \stackrel{?}{=} \frac{4}{0} \qquad \text{Simplify.}$$

Since zeros appear in the denominators, the fractions are undefined. Thus, 1 is a false solution, and the equation has no solutions. Such false solutions are often called **extraneous solutions.**

Answer: 2 is extraneous. ■

Solving formulas

Many formulas are equations that contain rational expressions.

EXAMPLE 6 *Solving formulas.*

The formula $\dfrac{1}{r} = \dfrac{1}{r_1} + \dfrac{1}{r_2}$

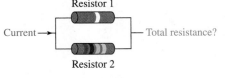

FIGURE 6-1

is used in electronics to calculate parallel resistances. Solve the equation for r.

Self Check
Solve the formula in Example 6 for r_1.

Solution
Clear the equation of fractions by multiplying both sides by the LCD, which is rr_1r_2.

$$\frac{1}{r} = \frac{1}{r_1} + \frac{1}{r_2}$$

$$rr_1r_2\left(\frac{1}{r}\right) = rr_1r_2\left(\frac{1}{r_1} + \frac{1}{r_2}\right) \qquad \text{Multiply both sides by } rr_1r_2.$$

$$\frac{rr_1r_2}{r} = \frac{rr_1r_2}{r_1} + \frac{rr_1r_2}{r_2} \qquad \text{Distribute the multiplication by } rr_1r_2.$$

$$r_1r_2 = rr_2 + rr_1 \qquad \text{Simplify each fraction.}$$

$$r_1r_2 = r(r_2 + r_1) \qquad \text{Factor out } r.$$

$$\frac{r_1r_2}{r_2 + r_1} = r \qquad \text{To isolate } r, \text{ divide both sides by } r_2 + r_1.$$

or

$$r = \frac{r_1r_2}{r_2 + r_1}$$

Answer: $r_1 = \dfrac{rr_2}{r_2 - r}$ ■

Applications

EXAMPLE 7   ***A number problem.***   If the same number is added to both the numerator and the denominator of the fraction $\frac{3}{5}$, the result is $\frac{4}{5}$. Find the number.

Analyze the problem   We are asked to find a number. If we add it to both the numerator and the denominator of a fraction, we will get $\frac{4}{5}$.

Form an equation   Let n represent the unknown number and add n to both the numerator and the denominator of $\frac{3}{5}$. Then set the result equal to $\frac{4}{5}$ to get the equation

$$\frac{3 + n}{5 + n} = \frac{4}{5}$$

Solve the equation   To solve the equation, we proceed as follows:

$$\frac{3 + n}{5 + n} = \frac{4}{5}$$

$$5(5 + n)\frac{3 + n}{5 + n} = 5(5 + n)\frac{4}{5} \qquad \text{Multiply both sides by } 5(5 + n), \text{ which is the LCD of the fractions appearing in the equation.}$$

$$5(3 + n) = (5 + n)4 \qquad \text{Simplify.}$$

$$15 + 5n = 20 + 4n \qquad \text{Distribute the multiplications by 5 and by 4.}$$

$$15 + n = 20 \qquad \text{Subtract } 4n \text{ from both sides.}$$

$$n = 5 \qquad \text{Subtract 15 from both sides.}$$

State the conclusion   The number is 5.

Check the result   When we add 5 to both the numerator and denominator of $\frac{3}{5}$, we get

$$\frac{3 + 5}{5 + 5} = \frac{8}{10} = \frac{4}{5}$$

The result checks. ■

We can use rational equations to model shared-work problems. In this case, we assume that the work is being performed at a constant rate by all of those involved.

EXAMPLE 8   ***Filling an oil tank.***   An inlet pipe can fill an oil tank in 7 days, and a second inlet pipe can fill the same tank in 9 days. If both pipes are used, how long will it take to fill the tank?

Analyze the problem   The key is to determine what each pipe can do in 1 day. If we add what the first pipe can do in 1 day to what the second pipe can do in 1 day, the sum is what they can do together in 1 day.

Since the first pipe can fill the tank in 7 days, it can do $\frac{1}{7}$ of the job in 1 day. Since the second pipe can fill the tank in 9 days, it can do $\frac{1}{9}$ of the job in 1 day. If it takes x days for both pipes to fill the tank, together they can do $\frac{1}{x}$ of the job in 1 day.

Form an equation   Let x represent the number of days it will take to fill the tank if both inlet pipes are used. Then form the equation.

What the first inlet pipe can do in 1 day	plus	what the second inlet pipe can do in 1 day	equals	what they can do together in 1 day.
$\dfrac{1}{7}$	$+$	$\dfrac{1}{9}$	$=$	$\dfrac{1}{x}$

Solve the equation   To solve the equation, we proceed as follows:

$$\frac{1}{7} + \frac{1}{9} = \frac{1}{x}$$

$$63x\left(\frac{1}{7} + \frac{1}{9}\right) = 63x\left(\frac{1}{x}\right)$$ Multiply both sides by $63x$ to clear the equation of fractions.

$$9x + 7x = 63$$ Distribute the multiplication by $63x$ and simplify.

$$16x = 63$$ Combine like terms.

$$x = \frac{63}{16}$$ Divide both sides by 16.

State the conclusion   It will take $\frac{63}{16}$ or $3\frac{15}{16}$ days for both inlet pipes to fill the tank.

Check the result   In $\frac{63}{16}$ days, the first pipe fills $\frac{1}{7}\left(\frac{63}{16}\right)$ of the tank and the second pipe fills $\frac{1}{9}\left(\frac{63}{16}\right)$ of the tank. The sum of these efforts, $\frac{9}{16} + \frac{7}{16}$, is equal to one full tank.   ∎

EXAMPLE 9   ***Track and field.***   A coach can run 10 miles in the same amount of time as his best student-athlete can run 12 miles. If the student can run 1 mile per hour faster than the coach, how fast can the student run?

Analyze the problem   We can use the formula $d = rt$, where d is the distance traveled, r is the rate, and t is the time. If we solve this formula for t, we obtain

$$t = \frac{d}{r}$$

Form an equation   It will take $\frac{10}{r}$ hours for the coach to run 10 miles at some unknown rate of r mph. It will take $\frac{12}{r+1}$ hours for the student to run 12 miles at some unknown rate of $(r + 1)$ mph. We can organize the information of the problem in a table, as shown in Figure 6-2.

	r	$\cdot$	t	$=$	d
Student	$r + 1$		$\dfrac{12}{r+1}$		12
Coach	r		$\dfrac{10}{r}$		10

FIGURE 6-2

The time it takes the student to run 12 miles	equals	the time it takes the coach to run 10 miles.
$\dfrac{12}{r+1}$	$=$	$\dfrac{10}{r}$

Solve the equation   We can solve the equation as follows:

$$\frac{12}{r+1} = \frac{10}{r}$$

$$r(r+1)\frac{12}{r+1} = r(r+1)\frac{10}{r}$$ Multiply both sides by $r(r+1)$.

$$12r = 10(r + 1)$$ Simplify.

$$12r = 10r + 10$$ Distribute the multiplication by 10.

$$2r = 10$$ Subtract $10r$ from both sides.

$$r = 5$$ Divide both sides by 2.

State the conclusion The coach can run 5 mph. The student, running 1 mph faster, can run 6 mph.

Check the result Verify that these results check. ■

EXAMPLE 10 ***Banking.*** At one bank, a sum of money invested for one year will earn $96 interest. If invested in bonds, that money would earn $108, because the interest rate paid by the bonds is 1% greater than that paid by the bank. Find the bank's rate.

Analyze the problem This interest problem is based on the formula $I = Pr$, where I is the interest earned in 1 year, P is the principal (the amount invested), and r is the annual rate of interest. If we solve this formula for P, we obtain

$$P = \frac{I}{r}$$

Form an equation If we let r represent the bank's rate of interest, then $r + 0.01$ represents the rate paid by the bonds. If a person earns $96 interest at a bank at some unknown rate r, the principal invested was $\frac{96}{r}$. If a person earns $108 interest in bonds at some unknown rate $(r + 0.01)$, the principal invested was $\frac{108}{r + 0.01}$. We can organize the information of the problem in a table, as shown in Figure 6-3.

	Principal ·	Rate	= Interest
Bank	$\dfrac{96}{r}$	r	96
Bonds	$\dfrac{108}{r + 0.01}$	$r + 0.01$	108

FIGURE 6-3

Because the same principal would be invested in either account, we can set up the following equation:

$$\frac{96}{r} = \frac{108}{r + 0.01}$$

Solve the equation We can solve the equation as follows:

$$\frac{96}{r} = \frac{108}{r + 0.01}$$

$$r(r + 0.01) \cdot \frac{96}{r} = r(r + 0.01) \cdot \frac{108}{r + 0.01} \qquad \text{Multiply both sides by } r(r + 0.01).$$

$$96(r + 0.01) = 108r$$

$$96r + 0.96 = 108r \qquad\qquad \text{Distribute.}$$

$$0.96 = 12r \qquad\qquad \text{Subtract } 96r \text{ from both sides.}$$

$$0.08 = r \qquad\qquad \text{Divide both sides by 12.}$$

State the conclusion The bank's interest rate is 0.08, or 8%. The bonds pay 9% interest, a rate 1% greater than that paid by the bank.

Check the result Verify that these rates check. ■

STUDY SET Section 6.5

VOCABULARY *Fill in the blanks.*

1. Equations that contain one or more rational expressions, such as

$$\frac{x+2}{x+3} + \frac{1}{x^2+2x-3} = 1$$

are called <u>rational equations</u>.

2. To clear an equation of fractions, we multiply both sides by the <u>LCD</u> of the fractions in the equation.

3. If you multiply both sides of an equation by an expression that involves a variable, you must <u>check</u> the solution.

4. False solutions that result from multiplying both sides of an equation by a variable are called <u>extraneous</u> solutions.

5. In the formula $I = Pr$, I stands for the amount of <u>interest</u> earned in one year, P stands for the <u>principal</u>, and r stands for the annual interest <u>rate</u>.

6. In the formula $d = rt$, d stands for the <u>distance</u> traveled, r is the <u>rate</u>, and t is the <u>time</u>.

CONCEPTS

7. Is $x = 5$ a solution of the following equations?

a. $\dfrac{1}{x-1} = 1 - \dfrac{3}{x-1}$ yes

b. $\dfrac{x}{x-5} = 3 + \dfrac{5}{x-5}$ no

8. By what should we multiply both sides of each equation to clear it of fractions?

a. $\dfrac{1}{x} + \dfrac{2}{x} = 5$ **b.** $\dfrac{x}{x-2} - \dfrac{x}{x-1} = 5$
      x $(x-2)(x-1)$

9. Illustration 1 shows the length of time it takes each of two hardware store employees to assemble a metal storage shed, working alone.

a. Complete the table.

	Time to assemble the shed (hr)	Amount of the shed assembled in 1 hr
Marvin	6	$\frac{1}{6}$
Kyla	5	$\frac{1}{5}$

ILLUSTRATION 1

b. If we assume that working together would not change their individual rates, how much of the shed could they assemble in one hour if they worked together? $\frac{11}{30}$

10. When two ice machines are both running, they can fill a supermarket's order in x hours. At this rate, how much of the order do they fill in 1 hour? $\frac{1}{x}$

11. If the exits at the front of a theater are opened, a full theater can be emptied of all occupants in 6 minutes. How much of the theater is emptied in 1 minute? $\frac{1}{6}$

12. Solve $d = rt$

a. for r $r = \frac{d}{t}$ **b.** for t $t = \frac{d}{r}$

13. Solve $I = Pr$

a. for r $r = \frac{I}{P}$ **b.** for P $P = \frac{I}{r}$

14. a. Complete the table in Illustration 2.

	r	$\cdot$	t	$=$	d
Snowmobile	r		$\frac{4}{r}$		4
4×4 truck	$r-5$		$\frac{3}{r-5}$		3

ILLUSTRATION 2

b. Complete the table in Illustration 3.

	P	$\cdot$	r	$=$	I
City Savings	$\frac{50}{r}$		r		50
Credit Union	$\frac{75}{r-0.02}$		$r-0.02$		75

ILLUSTRATION 3

NOTATION *In Exercises 15–16, a rational equation is solved. Complete each solution.*

15.
$$\frac{2}{a} + \frac{1}{2} = \frac{7}{2a}$$

$$2a\left(\frac{2}{a} + \frac{1}{2}\right) = 2a\left(\frac{7}{2a}\right)$$

$$2a \cdot \frac{2}{a} + 2a \cdot \frac{1}{2} = 2a \cdot \frac{7}{2a}$$

$$4 + a = 7$$

$$4 + a - 4 = 7 - 4$$

$$a = 3$$

16.
$$\frac{3}{5} + \frac{7}{a + 2} = 2$$

$$5(a + 2)\left(\frac{3}{5} + \frac{7}{a + 2}\right) = 5(a + 2) \cdot 2$$

$$5(a + 2) \cdot \frac{3}{5} + 5(a + 2) \cdot \frac{7}{a + 2} = 5(a + 2) \cdot 2$$

$$3(a + 2) + 35 = 10(a + 2)$$

$$3a + 6 + 35 = 10a + 20$$

$$3a + 41 = 10a + 20$$

$$-7a = -21$$

$$a = 3$$

17. The following work shows both sides of an equation being multiplied by the LCD to clear it of fractions. What was the original equation? $\frac{3}{5} + \frac{7}{x + 2} = 2$

$$5(x + 2)\left(\frac{3}{5}\right) + 5(x + 2)\left(\frac{7}{x + 2}\right) = 5(x + 2) \cdot 2$$

18. After solving a rational equation, a student checked her answer and obtained the following:

$$\frac{-1}{0} + \frac{1}{0} = 0$$

What conclusion can be drawn?
The answer is an extraneous solution.

PRACTICE *Solve each equation and check the result. If an equation has no solution, so indicate.*

19. $\dfrac{x}{2} + 4 = \dfrac{3x}{2}$ 4

20. $\dfrac{2y}{5} - 8 = \dfrac{4y}{5}$ -20

21. $\dfrac{x + 1}{3} + \dfrac{x - 1}{5} = \dfrac{2}{15}$ 0

22. $\dfrac{3x - 1}{6} - \dfrac{x + 3}{2} = \dfrac{3x + 4}{3}$ -3

23. $\dfrac{3}{x} + 2 = 3$ 3   **24.** $\dfrac{2}{x} + 9 = 11$ 1

25. $\dfrac{5}{a} - \dfrac{4}{a} = 8 + \dfrac{1}{a}$ **26.** $\dfrac{11}{b} + \dfrac{13}{b} = 12$
no solution; 0 is extraneous   2

27. $\dfrac{3}{4h} + \dfrac{2}{h} = 1$ $\frac{11}{4}$ **28.** $\dfrac{5}{3k} + \dfrac{1}{k} = -2$ $-\frac{4}{3}$

29. $\dfrac{a}{4} - \dfrac{4}{a} = 0$ $-4, 4$ **30.** $0 = \dfrac{t}{3} - \dfrac{12}{t}$ $-6, 6$

31. $\dfrac{2}{y + 1} + 5 = \dfrac{12}{y + 1}$ **32.** $\dfrac{3}{p + 6} - 2 = \dfrac{7}{p + 6}$
1   -8

33. $\dfrac{x}{x - 5} - \dfrac{5}{x - 5} = 3$ no solution; 5 is extraneous

34. $\dfrac{3}{y - 2} + 1 = \dfrac{3}{y - 2}$ no solution; 2 is extraneous

35. $\dfrac{3r}{2} - \dfrac{3}{r} = \dfrac{3r}{2} + 3$ -1 **36.** $\dfrac{2p}{3} - \dfrac{1}{p} = \dfrac{2p - 1}{3}$ 3

37. $\dfrac{1}{3} + \dfrac{2}{x - 3} = 1$ 6   **38.** $\dfrac{3}{5} + \dfrac{7}{x + 2} = 2$ 3

39. $\dfrac{z - 4}{z - 3} = \dfrac{z + 2}{z + 1}$ 1   **40.** $\dfrac{a + 2}{a + 8} = \dfrac{a - 3}{a - 2}$ 4

41. $\dfrac{v}{v + 2} + \dfrac{1}{v - 1} = 1$ 4   **42.** $\dfrac{x}{x - 2} = 1 + \dfrac{1}{x - 3}$ 4

43. $\dfrac{a^2}{a + 2} - \dfrac{4}{a + 2} = a$ no solution; -2 is extraneous

44. $\dfrac{z^2}{z + 1} + 2 = \dfrac{1}{z + 1}$ no solution; -1 is extraneous

45. $\dfrac{7}{q^2 - q - 2} + \dfrac{1}{q + 1} = \dfrac{3}{q - 2}$ 1

46. $\dfrac{3}{x - 1} - \dfrac{1}{x + 9} = \dfrac{18}{x^2 + 8x - 9}$ -5

47. $\dfrac{u}{u - 1} + \dfrac{1}{u} = \dfrac{u^2 + 1}{u^2 - u}$ 2

48. $\dfrac{3}{x - 2} + \dfrac{1}{x} = \dfrac{2(3x + 2)}{x^2 - 2x}$ -3

49. $\dfrac{n}{n^2 - 9} + \dfrac{n + 8}{n + 3} = \dfrac{n - 8}{n - 3}$ 0

50. $\dfrac{7}{x - 5} - \dfrac{3}{x + 5} = \dfrac{40}{x^2 - 25}$ $-\frac{5}{2}$

51. $\dfrac{5}{x + 4} + \dfrac{1}{x + 4} = x - 1$ $2, -5$

52. $\dfrac{7}{x - 3} + \dfrac{1}{x - 3} = x - 5$ $7, 1$

53. $\dfrac{3}{x + 1} - \dfrac{x - 2}{2} = \dfrac{x - 2}{x + 1}$ $-4, 3$

54. $\dfrac{2}{x - 1} + \dfrac{x - 2}{3} = \dfrac{4}{x - 1}$ $4, -1$

55. $\dfrac{b + 2}{b + 3} + 1 = \dfrac{-7}{b - 5}$ $-2, 1$

56. $\dfrac{x - 4}{x - 3} + \dfrac{x - 2}{x - 3} = x - 3$ 5; 3 is extraneous

57. $\dfrac{x}{x - 1} - \dfrac{12}{x^2 - x} = \dfrac{-1}{x - 1}$ $3, -4$

58. $y + \dfrac{2}{3} = \dfrac{2y - 12}{3y - 9}$ $1, 2$

59. $1 - \dfrac{3}{b} = \dfrac{-8b}{b^2 + 3b}$ $1, -9$

60. $\dfrac{5}{4y + 12} - \dfrac{3}{4} = \dfrac{5}{4y + 12} - \dfrac{y}{4}$ 3; -3 is extraneous

Solve each formula for the indicated variable.

61. $\dfrac{1}{a} + \dfrac{1}{b} = 1$ for a $a = \dfrac{b}{b-1}$

62. $\dfrac{1}{a} - \dfrac{1}{b} = 1$ for b $b = \dfrac{a}{1-a}$

63. $I = \dfrac{E}{R+r}$ for r $r = \dfrac{E-1R}{1}$

64. $h = \dfrac{2A}{b+d}$ for A $A = \dfrac{h(b+d)}{2}$

65. $\dfrac{a}{b} = \dfrac{c}{d}$ for d $d = \dfrac{bc}{a}$

66. $F = \dfrac{L^2}{6d} + \dfrac{d}{2}$ for L^2 $L^2 = 6dF - 3d^2$

Use the given information to find the number or numbers.

67. If the denominator of $\frac{3}{4}$ is increased by a number and the numerator of the fraction is doubled, the result is 1.   2

68. If a number is added to the numerator of $\frac{7}{8}$ and the same number is subtracted from the denominator, the result is 2.   3

69. If a number is added to the numerator of $\frac{3}{4}$ and twice as much is added to the denominator, the result is $\frac{4}{7}$.   5

70. If a number is added to the numerator of $\frac{5}{7}$ and twice as much is subtracted from the denominator, the result is 8.   3

71. The sum of a number and its reciprocal is $\frac{13}{6}$. $\frac{2}{3}, \frac{3}{2}$

72. The sum of the reciprocals of two consecutive even integers is $\frac{7}{24}$. (*Hint:* Let $x =$ the first integer and $x + 2 =$ the second integer.)   6 and 8

APPLICATIONS

73. OPTICS   The focal length f of a lens is given by the formula

$$\frac{1}{f} = \frac{1}{d_1} + \frac{1}{d_2}$$

where d_1 is the distance from the object to the lens and d_2 is the distance from the lens to the image.

Solve the formula for f. $f = \dfrac{d_1 d_2}{d_1 + d_2}$

74. OPTICS   Solve the formula in Exercise 73 for d_1.

$d_1 = \dfrac{f d_2}{d_2 - f}$

75. MEDICINE   Radioactive tracers are used for diagnostic work in nuclear medicine. The **effective half-life** H of a radioactive material in an organism is given by the formula

$$H = \frac{RB}{R+B}$$

where R is the radioactive half-life and B is the biological half-life of the tracer. Solve the formula for R.

$R = \dfrac{HB}{B-H}$

76. CHEMISTRY   Charles's Law describes the relationship between the volume and the temperature of a gas that is kept at a constant pressure. It states that as the temperature of the gas increases, the volume of the gas will increase:

$$\frac{V_1}{V_2} = \frac{T_1}{T_2}$$

Solve the equation for V_2. $V_2 = \dfrac{V_1 T_2}{T_1}$

77. FILLING A POOL   An inlet pipe can fill an empty swimming pool in 5 hours, and another inlet pipe can fill the pool in 4 hours. How long will it take both pipes to fill the pool? $2\frac{2}{9}$ hr

78. FILLING A POOL   One inlet pipe can fill an empty pool in 4 hours, and a drain can empty the pool in 8 hours. How long will it take the pipe to fill the pool if the drain is left open?   8 hr

79. ROOFING A HOUSE   A homeowner estimates that it will take her 7 days to roof her house. A professional roofer estimates that he could roof the house in 4 days. How long will it take if the homeowner helps the roofer? $2\frac{6}{11}$ days

80. SEWAGE TREATMENT   A sludge pool is filled by two inlet pipes. One pipe can fill the pool in 15 days, and the other can fill it in 21 days. However, if no sewage is added, continuous waste removal will empty the pool in 36 days. How long will it take the two inlet pipes to fill an empty sludge pool? $11\frac{61}{109}$ days

81. TOURING   A woman can bicycle 28 miles in the same time as it takes her to walk 8 miles. If she can ride 10 mph faster than she can walk, how much time should she allow to walk a 30-mile trail? See Illustration 4. (*Hint:* How fast can she walk?) $7\frac{1}{2}$ hr

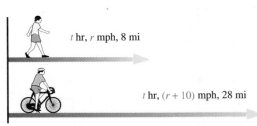

t hr, r mph, 8 mi

t hr, $(r+10)$ mph, 28 mi

ILLUSTRATION 4

82. COMPARING TRAVEL   A plane can fly 300 miles in the same time as it takes a car to go 120 miles. If the car travels 90 mph slower than the plane, find the speed of the plane.   150 mph

83. BOATING   A boat that travels 18 mph in still water can travel 22 miles downstream in the same time as it takes to travel 14 miles upstream. Find the speed of the current in the river. (See Illustration 5.)   4 mph

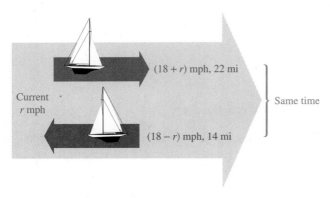

Current
r mph

$(18 + r)$ mph, 22 mi

$(18 - r)$ mph, 14 mi

Same time

ILLUSTRATION 5

84. WIND SPEED   A plane can fly 300 miles downwind in the same time as it can travel 210 miles upwind. Find the velocity of the wind if the plane can fly 255 mph in still air.   45 mph

85. COMPARING INVESTMENTS   Two certificates of deposit (CDs) pay interest at rates that differ by 1%. Money invested for one year in the first CD earns $175 interest. The same principal invested in the second CD earns $200. Find the two rates of interest.   7% and 8%

86. COMPARING INTEREST RATES   Two bond funds pay interest at rates that differ by 2%. Money invested for one year in the first fund earns $315 interest. The same amount invested in the second fund earns $385. Find the lower rate of interest.   9%

87. SHARING COSTS   Several office workers bought a $35 gift for their boss. If there had been two more employees to contribute, everyone's cost would have been $2 less. How many workers contributed to the gift?   5

88. SALES   A dealer bought some radios for a total of $1,200. She gave away 6 radios as gifts, sold the rest for $10 more than she paid for each radio, and broke even. How many radios did she buy?   30

89. SALES   A bookstore can purchase several calculators for a total cost of $120. If each calculator cost $1 less, the bookstore could purchase 10 additional calculators at the same total cost. How many calculators can be purchased at the regular price?   30

90. FURNACE REPAIR   A repairman purchased several furnace-blower motors for a total cost of $210. If his cost per motor had been $5 less, he could have purchased one additional motor. How many motors did he buy at the regular rate?   6

91. RIVER TOUR   A river boat tour begins by going 60 miles upstream against a 5-mph current. There, the boat turns around and returns with the current. What still-water speed should the captain use to complete the tour in 5 hours?   25 mph

92. TRAVEL TIME   A company president flew 680 miles one way in the corporate jet but returned in a smaller plane that could fly only half as fast. If the total travel time was 6 hours, find the speeds of the planes.   340 mph and 170 mph

WRITING

93. Explain how you would decide what to do first to solve an equation that involves fractions.

94. Why is it important to check your solutions of an equation that contains fractions with variables in the denominator?

95. In Example 8, one inlet pipe could fill an oil tank in 7 days, and another could fill the same tank in 9 days. We were asked to find how long it would take if both pipes were used. Explain why each of the following approaches is incorrect.

The time it would take to fill the tank

- is the *sum* of the lengths of time it takes each pipe to fill the tank: 7 days + 9 days = 16 days.

- is the *difference* in the lengths of time it takes each pipe to fill the tank: 9 days − 7 days = 2 days.

- is the *average* of the lengths of time it takes each pipe to fill the tank:

$$\frac{7 \text{ days} + 9 \text{ days}}{2} = \frac{16 \text{ days}}{2} = 8 \text{ days}$$

96. Explain the difference between the procedure used to simplify

$$\frac{1}{x} + \frac{1}{3}$$

and the procedure used to solve

$$\frac{1}{x} + \frac{1}{3} = \frac{1}{2}$$

REVIEW   *Factor each expression.*

97. $x^2 + 4x$ $x(x + 4)$

98. $x^2 - 16y^2$ $(x + 4y)(x - 4y)$

99. $2x^2 + x - 3$ $(2x + 3)(x - 1)$

100. $6a^2 - 5a - 6$ $(3a + 2)(2a - 3)$

101. $x^4 - 16$ $(x^2 + 4)(x + 2)(x - 2)$

102. $4x^2 + 10x - 6$ $2(x + 3)(2x - 1)$

6.6 *Proportions and Similar Triangles*

In this section, you will learn about

- Ratios and rates • Proportions • Solving proportions
- Problem solving • Similar triangles

INTRODUCTION. In this section, we will discuss a problem-solving tool called a *proportion*. A proportion is a type of rational equation that involves two *ratios* or two *rates*.

Ratios and rates

Ratios enable us to compare numerical quantities.

- To prepare fuel for a Lawnboy lawnmower, gasoline must be mixed with oil in the ratio of 50 to 1.
- To make 14-karat jewelry, gold is mixed with other metals in the ratio of 14 to 10.
- In the stock market, winning stocks might outnumber losing stocks in the ratio of 7 to 4.

Ratios

> A **ratio** is the quotient of two numbers or the quotient of two quantities that have the same units.

There are three common ways to write a ratio: as a fraction, with the word *to,* or with a colon. For example, the ratio describing the ratio of the number of winning stocks to the number of losing stocks mentioned earlier can be written as

$$\frac{7}{4}, \quad 7 \text{ to } 4, \quad \text{or} \quad 7:4$$

Each of these forms can be read as "the ratio of 7 to 4."

When ratios are used to compare quantities with different units, they are called *rates.* For example, if the 495-mile drive from New Orleans to Dallas takes 9 hours, the average rate of speed is the ratio of the miles driven to the length of time the trip takes.

$$\text{Average rate of speed} = \frac{495 \text{ miles}}{9 \text{ hours}} = \frac{55 \text{ miles}}{1 \text{ hour}} \qquad \frac{495}{9} = \frac{\overset{1}{\cancel{9}} \cdot 55}{\underset{1}{\cancel{9}} \cdot 1} = \frac{55}{1}.$$

Rates

> A **rate** is a quotient of two quantities that have different units.

Proportions

Consider the following table, in which we are given the costs of various numbers of gallons of gasoline.

Number of gallons	Cost
2	$3.72
5	$9.30
8	$14.88
12	$22.32
20	$37.20

If we compare the costs to the numbers of gallons purchased, we see that they are equal. In this example, each quotient represents the cost of 1 gallon of gasoline, which is $1.86.

$$\frac{\$3.72}{2} = \$1.86, \qquad \frac{\$9.30}{5} = \$1.86, \qquad \frac{\$14.88}{8} = \$1.86,$$

$$\frac{\$22.32}{12} = \$1.86, \quad \text{and} \quad \frac{\$37.20}{20} = \$1.86$$

When two ratios or rates $\left(\text{such as } \frac{\$3.72}{2} \text{ and } \frac{\$9.30}{5}\right)$ are equal, they form a *proportion*.

Proportions

> A **proportion** is a statement that two ratios or two rates are equal.

Some examples of proportions are

$$\frac{1}{2} = \frac{3}{6}, \qquad \frac{3 \text{ waiters}}{7 \text{ tables}} = \frac{9 \text{ waiters}}{21 \text{ tables}}, \quad \text{and} \quad \frac{a}{b} = \frac{c}{d}$$

- The proportion $\frac{1}{2} = \frac{3}{6}$ can be read as "1 is to 2 as 3 is to 6."
- The proportion $\frac{3 \text{ waiters}}{7 \text{ tables}} = \frac{9 \text{ waiters}}{21 \text{ tables}}$ can be read as "3 waiters is to 7 tables as 9 waiters is to 21 tables."
- The proportion $\frac{a}{b} = \frac{c}{d}$ can be read as "a is to b as c is to d."

In the proportion $\frac{a}{b} = \frac{c}{d}$, a and d are called the **extremes,** and b and c are called the **means.** We can show that the product of the extremes (ad) is equal to the product of the means (bc) by multiplying both sides of the proportion by bd and observing that $ad = bc$.

$$\frac{a}{b} = \frac{c}{d}$$

$bd \cdot \dfrac{a}{b} = bd \cdot \dfrac{c}{d}$ To clear the equation of fractions, multiply both sides by the LCD, which is bd.

$\qquad ad = bc$ Do each multiplication and simplify.

Since $ad = bc$, the product of the extremes equals the product of the means.

The fundamental property of proportions

> In a proportion, the product of the extremes is equal to the product of the means.

To determine whether an equation is a proportion, we can check to see whether the product of the extremes is equal to the product of the means.

EXAMPLE 1 *Proportions.* Determine whether each equation is a proportion: **a.** $\frac{3}{7} = \frac{9}{21}$ and **b.** $\frac{8}{3} = \frac{13}{5}$.

Solution

In each case, we check to see whether the product of the extremes is equal to the product of the means.

a. The product of the extremes is $3 \cdot 21 = 63$. The product of the means is $7 \cdot 9 = 63$. Since the products are equal, the equation is a proportion: $\frac{3}{7} = \frac{9}{21}$.

$$3 \cdot 21 = 63 \qquad 7 \cdot 9 = 63$$

$$\frac{3}{7} = \frac{9}{21}$$

The product of the extremes and the product of the means are also known as **cross products**.

b. The product of the extremes is $8 \cdot 5 = 40$. The product of the means is $3 \cdot 13 = 39$. Since the cross products are not equal, the equation is not a proportion: $\frac{8}{3} \neq \frac{13}{5}$.

$$8 \cdot 5 = 40 \qquad 3 \cdot 13 = 39$$

$$\frac{8}{3} = \frac{13}{5}$$

Self Check
Determine whether the equation is a proportion:

$$\frac{6}{13} = \frac{24}{53}$$

Answer: no ∎

Solving proportions

Suppose that we know three terms in the proportion

$$\frac{x}{5} = \frac{24}{20}$$

To find the unknown term, we can multiply both sides of the equation by 20 to clear it of fractions, and then solve for x. However, with proportions, it is often easier to simply compute the cross products, set them equal, and solve for the variable.

$$\frac{x}{5} = \frac{24}{20}$$

$20 \cdot x = 5 \cdot 24$ In a proportion, the product of the extremes equals the product of the means.

$20x = 120$ Do the multiplication: $5 \cdot 24 = 120$.

$\dfrac{20x}{20} = \dfrac{120}{20}$ To undo the multiplication by 20, divide both sides by 20.

$x = 6$ Do the divisions.

The first term is 6. To check this result, we substitute 6 for x in $\frac{x}{5} = \frac{24}{20}$ and find the cross products.

$$\frac{6}{5} \overset{?}{=} \frac{24}{20} \qquad \begin{array}{l} 6 \cdot 20 = 120 \\ 5 \cdot 24 = 120 \end{array}$$

Since the cross products are equal, this is a proportion. The result, 6, is correct.

EXAMPLE 2 *Solving proportions.* Solve $\dfrac{12}{18} = \dfrac{3}{x}$.

Solution

$$\frac{12}{18} = \frac{3}{x}$$

$12 \cdot x = 18 \cdot 3$ In a proportion, the product of the extremes equals the product of the means.

$12x = 54$ Multiply: $18 \cdot 3 = 54$.

$\dfrac{12x}{12} = \dfrac{54}{12}$ To undo the multiplication by 12, divide both sides by 12.

Self Check
Solve $\dfrac{15}{x} = \dfrac{25}{40}$.

$$x = \frac{9}{2} \qquad \text{Simplify:} \quad \frac{54}{12} = \frac{9 \cdot \cancel{6}^{\,1}}{\cancel{6}_{\,1} \cdot 2} = \frac{9}{2}.$$

Thus, $x = \frac{9}{2}$. Check the result.

Answer: 24   ■

 COMMENT   Remember that a cross product is the product of the means or extremes of a *proportion*. For example, it would be incorrect to try to compute "cross products" to solve the rational equation $\frac{12}{18} = \frac{3}{x} + \frac{1}{2}$. The right-hand side is not a ratio, so the equation not a proportion.

Accent on Technology: **Solving proportions with a calculator**

To solve the proportion $\dfrac{3.5}{7.2} = \dfrac{x}{15.84}$ with a calculator, we can proceed as follows.

$$\frac{3.5}{7.2} = \frac{x}{15.84}$$

$$\frac{3.5(15.84)}{7.2} = x \qquad \begin{array}{l}\text{To undo the division by 15.84 and isolate } x \text{, multiply both sides}\\ \text{of the equation by 15.84.}\end{array}$$

We can find x by entering these numbers into a scientific calculator.

Keystrokes   3.5 $\boxed{\times}$ 15.84 $\boxed{\div}$ 7.2 $\boxed{=}$ $\boxed{ 7.7}$

Using a graphing calculator, we enter these numbers and press these keys.

Keystrokes   3.5 $\boxed{\times}$ 15.84 $\boxed{\div}$ 7.2 $\boxed{\text{ENTER}}$ $\boxed{\begin{array}{l}\texttt{3.5*15.84/7.2}\\ \qquad\qquad\qquad \texttt{7.7}\end{array}}$

Thus, $x = 7.7$.

EXAMPLE 3   *Solving proportions.*   Solve $\dfrac{2a + 1}{4} = \dfrac{10}{8}$.

Solution

$$\frac{2a + 1}{4} = \frac{10}{8}$$

$$8(2a + 1) = 40 \qquad \begin{array}{l}\text{In a proportion, the product of the extremes equals the}\\ \text{product of the means.}\end{array}$$

$$16a + 8 = 40 \qquad \text{Distribute the multiplication by 8.}$$

$$16a + 8 - 8 = 40 - 8 \qquad \text{To undo the addition of 8, subtract 8 from both sides.}$$

$$16a = 32 \qquad \text{Combine like terms.}$$

$$\frac{16a}{16} = \frac{32}{16} \qquad \text{To undo the multiplication by 16, divide both sides by 16.}$$

$$x = 2 \qquad \text{Do the divisions.}$$

Thus, $a = 2$. Check the result.

Self Check

Solve $\dfrac{3x - 1}{2} = \dfrac{12.5}{5}$.

Answer: 2   ■

Problem solving

We can use proportions to solve many real-world problems. If we are given a ratio (or rate) comparing two quantities, the words of the problem can be translated to a proportion, and we can solve it to find the unknown.

EXAMPLE 4   *Grocery shopping.*   If 6 apples cost $1.38, how much will 16 apples cost?

Solution

Analyze the problem   We know the cost of 6 apples; we are to find the cost of 16 apples.

Form a proportion   Let c represent the cost of 16 apples. If we compare the number of apples to their cost, we know that the two rates are equal.

6 apples is to $1.38 as 16 apples is to $c.

$$\underset{\text{Cost of 6 apples} \longrightarrow}{\overset{\text{6 apples} \longrightarrow}{\frac{6}{1.38}}} = \underset{\longleftarrow \text{Cost of 16 apples}}{\overset{\longleftarrow \text{16 apples}}{\frac{16}{c}}}$$

Solve the proportion

$6 \cdot c = 1.38(16)$ In a proportion, the product of the extremes equals the product of the means.

$6c = 22.08$ Do the multiplication: $1.38(16) = 22.08$.

$\dfrac{6c}{6} = \dfrac{22.08}{6}$ To undo the multiplication by 6, divide both sides by 6.

$c = 3.68$ Simplify: $\frac{22.08}{6} = 3.68$.

State the conclusion   Sixteen apples will cost $3.68.

Check the result   If 16 apples are bought, this is about 3 times as many as 6 apples, which cost $1.38. If we multiply $1.38 by 3, we get an estimate of the cost of 16 apples: $1.38 \cdot 3 = \$4.14$. The result, $3.68, seems reasonable.

Self Check
If 9 tickets to a concert cost $112.50, how much will 15 tickets cost?

Answer: $187.50   ∎

In Example 4, we could have compared the cost of the apples to the number of apples: $1.38 is to 6 apples as c is to 16 apples. This would have led to the proportion

$$\underset{\text{6 apples} \longrightarrow}{\overset{\text{Cost of 6 apples} \longrightarrow}{\frac{1.38}{6}}} = \underset{\longleftarrow \text{16 apples}}{\overset{\longleftarrow \text{Cost of 16 apples}}{\frac{c}{16}}}$$

If we solve this proportion for c, we will obtain the same result: $c = 3.68$.

 COMMENT   When solving problems using proportions, we must make sure that the units of both numerators are the same and the units of both denominators are the same. For Example 4, it would be incorrect to write

$$\underset{\text{6 apples} \longrightarrow}{\overset{\text{Cost of 6 apples} \longrightarrow}{\frac{1.38}{6}}} \times \underset{\longleftarrow \text{Cost of 16 apples}}{\overset{\longleftarrow \text{16 apples}}{\frac{16}{c}}}$$

EXAMPLE 5   *Miniature.*   A **scale** is a ratio (or rate) that compares the size of a model, drawing, or map to the size of an actual object. The scale shown in Figure 6-4 indicates that 1 inch on the model carousel is equivalent to 160 inches on the actual carousel. How wide should the model be if the actual carousel is 35 feet wide?

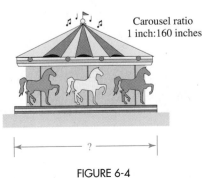

Carousel ratio
1 inch:160 inches

FIGURE 6-4

Solution

Analyze the problem   We are asked to determine the width of the miniature carousel, if a ratio of 1 inch to 160 inches is used. We would like the width of the model to be given in inches, not feet, so we will express the 35-foot width of the actual carousel as $35 \cdot 12 = 420$ inches.

Form a proportion   Let w represent the width of the model. The ratios of the dimensions of the model to the corresponding dimensions of the actual carousel are equal.

1 inch is to 160 inches as w inches is to 420 inches.

$$\text{model} \longrightarrow \frac{1}{160} = \frac{w}{420} \longleftarrow \text{model}$$
$$\text{actual} \longrightarrow \qquad \qquad \longleftarrow \text{actual}$$

Solve the proportion

$420 = 160w$ In a proportion, the product of the extremes is equal to the product of the means.

$\dfrac{420}{160} = \dfrac{160w}{160}$ To undo the multiplication by 160, divide both sides by 160.

$2.625 = w$ Do the division: $\frac{420}{160} = 2.625$.

State the conclusion   The width of the miniature carousel should be 2.625 in., or $2\frac{5}{8}$ in.

Check the result   A width of $2\frac{5}{8}$ in. is approximately 3 in. When we write the ratio of the model's approximate width to the width of the actual carousel, we get $\frac{3}{420} = \frac{1}{140}$, which is about $\frac{1}{160}$. The answer seems reasonable. ∎

EXAMPLE 6   *Baking.*   A recipe for rhubarb cake calls for $1\frac{1}{4}$ cups of sugar for every $2\frac{1}{2}$ cups of flour. How many cups of flour are needed if the baker intends to use 3 cups of sugar?

Solution

Analyze the problem   The baker needs to maintain the same ratio between the amounts of sugar and flour as is called for in the original recipe.

Form a proportion   Let f represent the number of cups of flour to be mixed with the 3 cups of sugar. The ratios of the cups of sugar to the cups of flour are equal.

$1\frac{1}{4}$ cups sugar is to $2\frac{1}{2}$ cups flour as 3 cups sugar is to f cups flour.

$$\text{Cups sugar} \longrightarrow \frac{1\frac{1}{4}}{2\frac{1}{2}} = \frac{3}{f} \longleftarrow \text{Cups sugar}$$
$$\text{Cups flour} \longrightarrow \qquad \qquad \longleftarrow \text{Cups flour}$$

Solve the proportion

$\dfrac{1.25}{2.5} = \dfrac{3}{f}$ Change the fractions to decimals.

$1.25f = 2.5 \cdot 3$ In a proportion, the product of the extremes equals the product of the means.

$1.25f = 7.5$ Do the multiplication: $2.5 \cdot 3 = 7.5$.

$\dfrac{1.25f}{1.25} = \dfrac{7.5}{1.25}$ To undo the multiplication by 1.25, divide both sides by 1.25.

$f = 6$ Divide: $\frac{7.5}{1.25} = 6$.

State the conclusion   The baker should use 6 cups of flour.

Check the result   The recipe calls for about 2 cups of flour for about 1 cup of sugar. If 3 cups of sugar are used, 6 cups of flour seems reasonable.

Self Check

How many cups of sugar will be needed to make several cakes that will require a total of 25 cups of flour?

Answer: $12\frac{1}{2}$ ∎

Similar triangles

If two angles of one triangle have the same measures as two angles of a second triangle, the triangles will have the same shape. Triangles with the same shape are called **similar triangles.** In Figure 6-5, $\triangle ABC \sim \triangle DEF$. (Read the symbol ~ as "is similar to.")

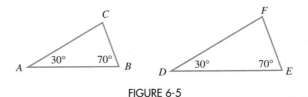

FIGURE 6-5

Property of similar triangles

If two triangles are **similar,** all pairs of corresponding sides are in proportion.

In the similar triangles shown in Figure 6-5, the following proportions are true.

$$\frac{AB}{DE} = \frac{BC}{EF}, \quad \frac{BC}{EF} = \frac{CA}{FD}, \quad \text{and} \quad \frac{CA}{FD} = \frac{AB}{DE}$$ Read AB as "the length of segment AB."

EXAMPLE 7   *Finding the height of a tree.*   A tree casts a shadow 18 feet long at the same time as a woman 5 feet tall casts a shadow 1.5 feet long. Find the height of the tree.

Solution

Analyze the problem   Figure 6-6 shows the triangles determined by the tree and its shadow and the woman and her shadow. Since the triangles have the same shape, they are similar, and the lengths of their corresponding sides are in proportion.

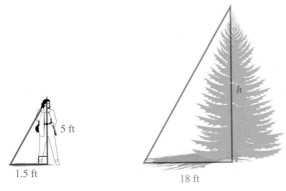

FIGURE 6-6

Form a proportion   If we let h represent the height of the tree, we can find h by solving the following proportion.

$$\frac{h}{5} = \frac{18}{1.5} \qquad \frac{\text{Height of the tree}}{\text{Height of the woman}} = \frac{\text{Length of shadow of the tree}}{\text{Length of shadow of the woman}}$$

Solve the proportion

$1.5h = 5(18)$ In a proportion, the product of the extremes equals the product of the means.

$1.5h = 90$ Do the multiplication.

$h = 60$ To undo the multiplication by 1.5, divide both sides by 1.5 and simplify.

State the conclusion   The tree is 60 feet tall.

Check the result $\frac{18}{1.5} = 12$ and $\frac{60}{5} = 12$. The ratios are the same. The result checks.

Self Check

Find the height of the tree in Example 7 if the woman is 5 feet 6 inches tall.

Answer: 66 ft

STUDY SET   Section 6.6

VOCABULARY   *Fill in the blanks.*

1. A _____ratio_____ is the quotient of two numbers or the quotient of two quantities with the same units. A _____rate_____ is a quotient of two quantities that have different units.

2. A _____proportion_____ is a statement that two ratios or two rates are equal.

3. In the proportion $\frac{a}{b} = \frac{c}{d}$, a and d are called the _____extremes_____ of the proportion. The second and third terms of a proportion are called the _____means_____ of the proportion.

4. The product of the extremes and the product of the means of a proportion are also known as _____cross_____ products.

5. If two triangles have the same _____shape_____, they are said to be *similar*.

6. If two triangles are _____similar_____, their corresponding sides are in proportion.

CONCEPTS   *In Exercises 7–8, fill in the blanks.*

7. The equation $\frac{a}{b} = \frac{c}{d}$ is a proportion if the cross product *ad* is equal to the cross product *bc* .

8. If $3 \cdot 10 = x \cdot 17$, then $\frac{3}{x} = \frac{17}{10}$ is a proportion.

9. Is $x = 45$ a solution of $\frac{5}{3} = \frac{75}{x}$?   yes

10. Consider $\frac{2}{3} = \frac{x}{15}$.

   a. Solve the proportion by multiplying both sides by the LCD.   10

   b. Solve the proportion by setting the cross products equal.   10

11. MINIATURES   A "high wheeler" bicycle is shown in Illustration 1. A model of it is to be made using a scale of 2 inches to 15 inches. The following proportion was set up to determine the height of the front wheel of the model. Explain the error.   The ratio on the right-hand side should be $\frac{h}{48}$.

$$\frac{2}{15} = \frac{48}{h}$$

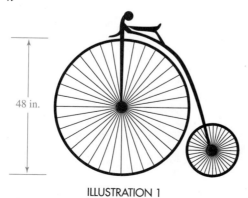

ILLUSTRATION 1

12. Two similar triangles are shown in Illustration 2. Fill in the blanks to make the proportions true.

$$\frac{AB}{DE} = \frac{BC}{EF} \qquad \frac{BC}{EF} = \frac{CA}{FD} \qquad \frac{CA}{FD} = \frac{AB}{DE}$$

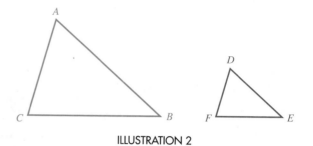

ILLUSTRATION 2

NOTATION   *In Exercises 13–14, complete each solution.*

13. Solve for x: $\frac{12}{18} = \frac{x}{24}$.

$$12 \cdot 24 = 18 \cdot x$$
$$288 = 18x$$
$$\frac{288}{18} = \frac{18x}{18}$$
$$16 = x$$

14. Solve for x: $\frac{14}{x} = \frac{49}{17.5}$.

$$14 \cdot 17.5 = 49x$$
$$245 = 49x$$
$$\frac{245}{49} = \frac{49x}{49}$$
$$5 = x$$

15. We read "$\triangle ABC$" as "_____triangle_____ ABC."

16. The symbol ~ is read as "_____is similar to_____."

PRACTICE   *Tell whether each statement is a proportion.*

17. $\frac{9}{7} = \frac{81}{70}$ no

18. $\frac{5}{2} = \frac{20}{8}$ yes

19. $\frac{7}{3} = \frac{14}{6}$ yes

20. $\frac{13}{19} = \frac{65}{95}$ yes

21. $\frac{9}{19} = \frac{38}{80}$ no

22. $\frac{40}{29} = \frac{29}{22}$ no

23. $\frac{10.4}{3.6} = \frac{41.6}{14.4}$ yes

24. $\frac{13.23}{3.45} = \frac{39.96}{11.35}$ no

Solve each proportion.

25. $\dfrac{2}{3} = \dfrac{x}{6}$ 4

26. $\dfrac{3}{6} = \dfrac{x}{8}$ 4

27. $\dfrac{5}{10} = \dfrac{3}{c}$ 6

28. $\dfrac{7}{14} = \dfrac{2}{x}$ 4

29. $\dfrac{6}{x} = \dfrac{8}{4}$ 3

30. $\dfrac{4}{x} = \dfrac{2}{8}$ 16

31. $\dfrac{x}{3} = \dfrac{9}{3}$ 9

32. $\dfrac{x}{2} = \dfrac{18}{6}$ 6

33. $\dfrac{x+1}{5} = \dfrac{3}{15}$ 0

34. $\dfrac{x-1}{7} = \dfrac{2}{21}$ $\frac{5}{3}$

35. $\dfrac{x+3}{12} = \dfrac{-7}{6}$ -17

36. $\dfrac{x+7}{-4} = \dfrac{1}{4}$ -8

37. $\dfrac{4-x}{13} = \dfrac{11}{26}$ $-\frac{3}{2}$

38. $\dfrac{5-x}{17} = \dfrac{13}{34}$ $-\frac{3}{2}$

39. $\dfrac{2x+1}{18} = \dfrac{14}{3}$ $\frac{83}{2}$

40. $\dfrac{2x-1}{18} = \dfrac{9}{54}$ 2

41. $\dfrac{y}{4} = \dfrac{4}{y}$ $4, -4$

42. $\dfrac{2}{3x} = \dfrac{6x}{36}$ $2, -2$

43. $\dfrac{2}{c} = \dfrac{c-3}{2}$ $4, -1$

44. $\dfrac{b-5}{3} = \dfrac{2}{b}$ $6, -1$

45. $\dfrac{2}{x+6} = \dfrac{-2x}{5}$ $-5, -1$ **46.** $\dfrac{x-1}{x+1} = \dfrac{2}{3x}$ $-\frac{1}{3}, 2$

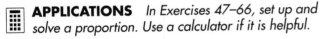 **APPLICATIONS** *In Exercises 47–66, set up and solve a proportion. Use a calculator if it is helpful.*

47. GROCERY SHOPPING   If 3 pints of yogurt cost $1, how much will 51 pints cost? $17

48. SHOPPING FOR CLOTHES   If shirts are on sale at two for $25, how much will five shirts cost? $62.50

49. ADVERTISING   In 1997, a 30-second TV ad during the Super Bowl telecast cost $1.2 million. At this rate, what was the cost of a 45-second ad? $1.8 million

50. COOKING   A recipe for spaghetti sauce requires four 16-ounce bottles of ketchup to make two gallons of sauce. How many bottles of ketchup are needed to make 10 gallons of sauce?   20

51. MIXING PERFUME   A perfume is to be mixed in the ratio of 3 drops of pure essence to 7 drops of alcohol. How many drops of pure essence should be mixed with 56 drops of alcohol?   24

52. CPR   A first aid handbook states that when performing cardiopulmonary resuscitation on an adult, the ratio of chest compressions to breaths should be 5 : 2. If 210 compressions were administered to an adult patient, how many breaths should have been given?   84

53. COOKING   A recipe for wild rice soup is shown in Illustration 3. Find the amounts of chicken broth, rice, and flour needed to make 15 servings. $7\frac{1}{2}, 1\frac{2}{3}, 5$

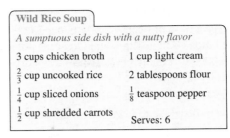

Wild Rice Soup

A sumptuous side dish with a nutty flavor

3 cups chicken broth	1 cup light cream
$\frac{2}{3}$ cup uncooked rice	2 tablespoons flour
$\frac{1}{4}$ cup sliced onions	$\frac{1}{8}$ teaspoon pepper
$\frac{1}{2}$ cup shredded carrots	Serves: 6

ILLUSTRATION 3

54. QUALITY CONTROL   In a manufacturing process, 95% of the parts made are to be within specifications. How many defective parts would be expected in a run of 940 pieces?   47

55. QUALITY CONTROL   Out of a sample of 500 men's shirts, 17 were rejected because of crooked collars. How many crooked collars would you expect to find in a run of 15,000 shirts?   510

56. GAS CONSUMPTION   If a car can travel 42 miles on 1 gallon of gas, how much gas is needed to travel 315 miles? $7\frac{1}{2}$ gal

57. HIP-HOP   According to the *Guinness Book of World Records 1998,* Rebel X.D. of Chicago rapped 674 syllables in 54.9 seconds. At this rate, how many syllables could he rap in 1 minute? Round to the nearest syllable.   737

58. BANKRUPTCY   After filing for bankruptcy, a company was able to pay its creditors only 15 cents on the dollar. If the company owed a lumberyard $9,712, how much could the lumberyard expect to be paid? $1,456.80

59. COMPUTING A PAYCHECK   Billie earns $412 for a 40-hour week. If she missed 10 hours of work last week, how much did she get paid? $309

60. MODEL RAILROAD   A model railroad engine is 9 inches long. If the scale is 87 feet to 1 foot, how long is a real engine?   65 ft, 3 in.

61. MODEL RAILROAD   A model railroad caboose is 3.5 inches long. If the scale is 169 feet to 1 foot, how long is a real caboose?   49 ft, $3\frac{1}{2}$ in.

62. NUTRITION   Illustration 4 shows the nutritional facts about a 10-oz chocolate milkshake sold by a fast-food restaurant. Use the information to complete the table for the 16-oz shake. Round to the nearest unit when an answer is not exact.

	Calories	Fat (gm)	Protein (gm)
10-oz chocolate milkshake	355	8	9
16-oz chocolate milkshake	568	13	14

ILLUSTRATION 4

63. DRIVER'S LICENSE Of the 50 states, Oregon has the largest ratio of licensed drivers per 1,000 residents. If the ratio is 824 to 1,000 and Oregon's population is 3,282,000, how many Oregonians have a driver's license?   2,704,368

64. MIXING FUEL The instructions on a can of oil intended to be added to lawnmower gasoline read as follows:

Recommended	Gasoline	Oil
50 to 1	6 gal	16 oz

Are these instructions correct? (*Hint:* There are 128 ounces in 1 gallon.)   not exactly, but close

65. PHOTO ENLARGEMENT In Illustration 5, the 3-by-5 photo is to be blown up to the larger size. Find *x*.
$3\frac{3}{4}$ in.

5 in. $6\frac{1}{4}$ in.

3 in.   *x* in.

ILLUSTRATION 5

66. BLUEPRINT The scale for the drawing in Illustration 6 tells the reader that a $\frac{1}{4}$-inch length $\left(\frac{1}{4}''\right)$ on the drawing corresponds to an actual size of 1 foot (1′0″). Suppose the length of the kitchen is $2\frac{1}{2}$ inches on the drawing. How long is the actual kitchen?   10 ft

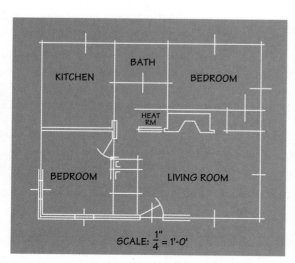

SCALE: $\frac{1''}{4}$ = 1′-0′

ILLUSTRATION 6

In Exercises 67–72, use similar triangles to solve each problem.

67. HEIGHT OF A TREE A tree casts a shadow of 26 feet at the same time as a 6-foot man casts a shadow of 4 feet. (See Illustration 7.) Find the height of the tree.   39 ft

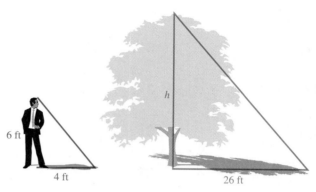

6 ft   *h*

4 ft   26 ft

ILLUSTRATION 7

68. HEIGHT OF A BUILDING A man places a mirror on the ground and sees the reflection of the top of a building, as shown in Illustration 8. The two triangles in the illustration are similar. Find the height, *h*, of the building.   25 ft

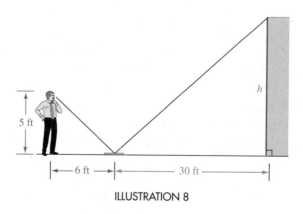

5 ft   *h*

6 ft   30 ft

ILLUSTRATION 8

69. WIDTH OF A RIVER Use the dimensions in Illustration 9 to find *w*, the width of the river. (The two triangles in the illustration are similar.) $46\frac{7}{8}$ ft

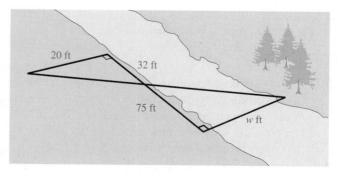

20 ft   32 ft

75 ft

w ft

ILLUSTRATION 9

70. FLIGHT PATH   An airplane ascends 100 feet as it flies a horizontal distance of 1,000 feet. How much altitude will it gain as it flies a horizontal distance of 1 mile? See Illustration 10. (*Hint:* 5,280 feet = 1 mile.)   528 ft

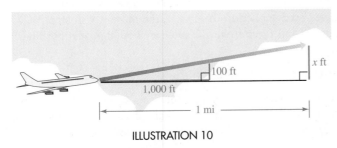

ILLUSTRATION 10

71. FLIGHT PATH   An airplane descends 1,350 feet as it flies a horizontal distance of 1 mile. How much altitude is lost as it flies a horizontal distance of 5 miles?   6,750 ft

72. SKI RUN   A ski course falls 100 feet in every 300 feet of horizontal run. If the total horizontal run is $\frac{1}{2}$ mile, find the height of the hill.   880 ft

WRITING

73. Explain the difference between a ratio and a proportion.

74. Explain how to tell whether $\frac{3.2}{3.7} = \frac{5.44}{6.29}$ is a proportion.

75. Explain why the concept of cross products cannot be used to solve the equation

$$\frac{x}{3} - \frac{3x}{4} = \frac{1}{12}$$

76. Write a problem about a situation you encounter in your daily life that could be solved by using a proportion.

REVIEW

77. Change $\frac{9}{10}$ to a percent.   90%

78. Change $33\frac{1}{3}\%$ to a fraction. $\frac{1}{3}$

79. Find 30% of 1,600.   480

80. SHOPPING   Maria bought a dress for 25% off the original price of $98. How much did the dress cost? $73.50

81. Find the slope of the line passing through $(-2, -2)$ and $(-12, -8)$. $\frac{3}{5}$

82. What are the slope and the y-intercept of the graph of $y = 2x - 3$? $2; (0, -3)$

6.7 Variation

In this section, you will learn about

• Direct variation   • Inverse variation

INTRODUCTION. If the value of one quantity depends on the value of another quantity, we can often describe that relationship using the language of variation:

• The sales tax on an item varies with the price.
• The intensity of light varies with the distance from its source.
• The pressure exerted by water on an object varies with the depth of the object beneath the surface.

In this section, we will discuss two types of variation, and we will see how to represent them algebraically using equations.

Direct variation

One type of variation, called **direct variation,** is represented by an equation of the form $y = kx$, where k is a constant (a number). Two variables are said to *vary directly* if one is a constant multiple of the other.

Direct variation

> The words *y varies directly with x* mean that
>
> $$y = kx$$
>
> for some constant k, called the **constant of variation.**

Scientists have found that the distance a spring will stretch varies directly with the force applied to it. The more force applied to the spring, the more it will stretch. If d represents the distance stretched and f represents the force applied, this relationship can be expressed by the equation

$$d = kf \qquad \text{where } k \text{ is the constant of variation}$$

Suppose that a 150-pound wooden garage door stretches a spring 18 inches when the door is closed. (See Figure 6-7.) We can find the constant of variation for the spring by substituting 150 for f and 18 for d in the equation $d = kf$ and solving for k:

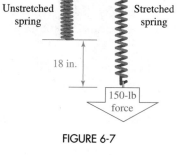

FIGURE 6-7

$$d = kf$$

$$18 = k(150)$$

$$\frac{18}{150} = k \qquad \text{Divide both sides by 150 to isolate } k.$$

$$\frac{3}{25} = k \qquad \text{Simplify the fraction: } \frac{18}{150} = \frac{\overset{1}{\cancel{6}} \cdot 3}{\underset{1}{\cancel{6}} \cdot 25} = \frac{3}{25}.$$

Therefore, the equation describing the relationship between the distance the spring will stretch and the amount of force applied to it is $d = \frac{3}{25}f$. To find the distance that the same spring will stretch when a new, 50-pound aluminum garage door is installed, we proceed as follows:

$$d = \frac{3}{25}f \qquad \text{The equation describing the direct variation.}$$

$$d = \frac{3}{25}(50) \qquad \text{Substitute 50 for } f.$$

$$d = 6 \qquad \text{Do the multiplication.}$$

The spring will stretch 6 inches when the 50-pound aluminum door is closed.

The table in Figure 6-8 shows some other possible values for f and d as determined by the equation $d = \frac{3}{25}f$. When these ordered pairs are graphed and a straight line is drawn through them, it is apparent that as the force f applied to a spring increases, the distance d it stretches increases. Furthermore, the slope of the graph is $\frac{3}{25}$, the constant of variation.

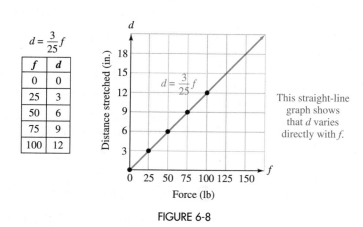

$d = \dfrac{3}{25}f$

f	d
0	0
25	3
50	6
75	9
100	12

This straight-line graph shows that d varies directly with f.

FIGURE 6-8

We can use the following steps to solve variation problems.

Solving variation problems

To solve a variation problem:

1. Translate the verbal model into an equation.
2. Substitute the first set of values into the equation from Step 1 to determine the value of k.
3. Substitute the value of k into the equation from Step 1.
4. Substitute the remaining set of values into the equation from Step 3 and solve for the unknown variable.

EXAMPLE 1 *Direct variation.* The weight of an object on Earth varies directly with its weight on the moon. If a rock weighs 5 pounds on the moon and 30 pounds on Earth, what would be the weight on Earth of a larger rock weighing 26 pounds on the moon?

Solution

Step 1: We let e represent the weight of the object on Earth and m the weight of the object on the moon. Translating the words *weight on Earth varies directly with weight on the moon,* we get the equation

$e = km$

Step 2: To find the constant of variation, k, we substitute 30 for e and 5 for m.

$e = km$
$30 = k(5)$
$6 = k$ To undo the multiplication by 5, divide both sides by 5.

Step 3: The equation describing the relationship between the weight of an object on Earth and on the moon is

$e = 6m$

Step 4: We can find the weight of the larger rock on Earth by substituting 26 for m in the equation from Step 3.

$e = 6m$
$e = 6(26)$
$e = 156$

The rock would weigh 156 pounds on Earth.

Self Check

The cost of a bus ticket varies directly with the number of miles traveled. If a ticket for a 180-mile trip cost $45, what would a ticket for a 1,500-mile trip cost?

Answer: $375 ■

Inverse variation

Another type of variation, called **inverse variation,** is represented by an equation of the form $y = \frac{k}{x}$, where k is a constant. Two variables are said to *vary inversely* if one is a constant multiple of the reciprocal of the other.

Inverse variation

The words *y varies inversely with x* mean that

$$y = \frac{k}{x}$$

for some constant k, called the **constant of variation.**

Suppose that the time (in hours) it takes to paint a house varies inversely with the size of the painting crew. As the number of painters increases, the time that it takes to paint the house decreases. If n represents the number of painters and t represents the time it takes to paint the house, this relationship can be expressed by the equation

$$t = \frac{k}{n} \qquad \text{where } k \text{ is the constant of variation}$$

If we know that a crew of 8 can paint the house in 12 hours, we can find the constant of variation by substituting 8 for n and 12 for t in the equation $t = \frac{k}{n}$ and solving for k:

$$t = \frac{k}{n}$$

$$12 = \frac{k}{8}$$

$12 \cdot 8 = k \qquad$ Multiply both sides by 8 to isolate k.

$96 = k$

The equation describing the relationship between the size of the painting crew and the time it takes to paint the house is $t = \frac{96}{n}$. We can use this equation to find the time it will take a crew of any size to paint the house. For example, to find the time it would take a four-person crew, we substitute 4 for n in the equation $t = \frac{96}{n}$.

$t = \dfrac{96}{n} \qquad$ The equation describing the inverse variation.

$t = \dfrac{96}{4} \qquad$ Substitute 4 for n.

$t = 24$

It would take a four-person crew 24 hours to paint the house.

The table in Figure 6-9 shows some possible values for n and t as determined by the equation $t = \frac{96}{n}$. When these ordered pairs are graphed and a smooth curve is drawn through them, it is clear that as the number of painters n increases, the time t decreases.

$t = \dfrac{96}{n}$

n	t
2	48
3	32
4	24
6	16
8	12
12	8
16	6
24	4

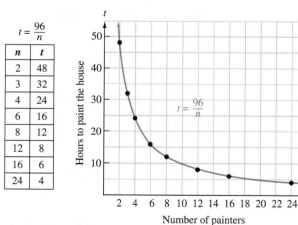

This curved graph shows that t varies directly with n.

FIGURE 6-9

EXAMPLE 2 *Gas law.* The volume occupied by a gas varies inversely with the pressure placed on it. That is, the volume decreases as the pressure increases. If a gas occupies a volume of 15 cubic inches when placed under 4 pounds per square inch (psi) of pressure, how much pressure is needed to compress the gas into a volume of 10 cubic inches?

Self Check

How much pressure is needed to compress the gas in Example 2 into a volume of 8 cubic inches?

Solution

Step 1: We let V represent the volume occupied by the gas and p represent the pressure. Translating the words *volume occupied by a gas varies inversely with the pressure,* we get the equation

$$V = \frac{k}{p}$$

Step 2: To find the constant of variation, k, we substitute 15 for V and 4 for p.

$$V = \frac{k}{p}$$

$$15 = \frac{k}{4}$$

$$60 = k \qquad \text{Multiply both sides by 4.}$$

Step 3: The equation describing the relationship between the volume occupied by the gas and the pressure placed on it is

$$V = \frac{60}{p}$$

Step 4: We can now find the pressure needed to compress the gas into a volume of 10 cubic inches by substituting 10 for V in the equation and solving for p.

$$V = \frac{60}{p}$$

$$10 = \frac{60}{p}$$

$$10p = 60 \qquad \text{To clear the equation of the fraction, multiply both sides by } p.$$

$$p = 6 \qquad \text{To undo the multiplication by 10, divide both sides by 6.}$$

It will take 6 psi of pressure to compress the gas into a volume of 10 cubic inches.

Answer: 7.5 psi ∎

STUDY SET Section 6.7

VOCABULARY *Fill in the blanks.*

1. The equation $y = kx$ defines _____direct_____ variation.

2. The equation $y = \frac{k}{x}$ defines _____inverse_____ variation.

3. In $y = kx$, the _____constant_____ of variation is k.

4. A constant is a _____number_____.

CONCEPTS *Exercises 5–8 illustrate two types of variation. Tell whether each graph represents direct variation or inverse variation.*

5.

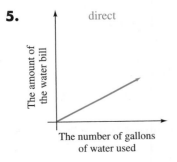

direct

The amount of the water bill / The number of gallons of water used

6.

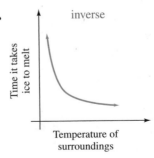

inverse

Time it takes ice to melt / Temperature of surroundings

7.

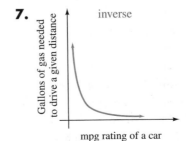

inverse

Gallons of gas needed to drive a given distance / mpg rating of a car

8.

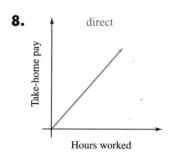

9. Tell whether the equation defines direct variation.

   a. $y = kx$ yes   **b.** $y = k + x$ no

   c. $y = \dfrac{k}{x}$ no   **d.** $m = kc$ yes

10. a. Translate to mathematical symbols: $h = ka$

> | A farmer's harvest h | varies directly | with the number of acres planted a. |

   b. If the constant of variation for part a is $k = 10,000$, what will happen to the size of the harvest as the number of acres planted increases?   It will increase.

11. Express this relationship using an equation: The number of gallons g of paint needed to paint a room varies directly with the number of square feet f to be painted. $g = kf$

12. Express this relationship using an equation: The amount of sales tax t varies directly with the purchase price p of a new car. $t = kp$

13. Assume that t varies directly with s and $t = ks$. If $t = 21$ when $s = 6$, find k. $\frac{7}{2}$

14. Assume that y varies directly with x and $y = kx$. If $y = 10$ when $x = 2$, find k.   5

15. Tell whether each equation defines inverse variation.

   a. $y = kx$ no   **b.** $y = \dfrac{k}{x}$ yes

   c. $y = \dfrac{x}{k}$ no   **d.** $d = \dfrac{k}{g}$ yes

16. a. Translate to mathematical symbols: $t = \dfrac{k}{s}$

> | The time t (in hours) it takes a commuter to drive from her home to her office | varies inversely | with her average speed s (in mph). |

   b. If the constant of variation for part a is $k = 30$, what will happen to the time her commute takes her as her average speed increases?   It will decrease.

17. Express this relationship using an equation: The number of hot dogs n that a street vendor sells varies inversely with the price p that he charges. $n = \frac{k}{p}$

18. a. If y varies directly with x and $k > 0$, what happens to y as x increases?   It increases.

b. If y varies inversely with x and $k > 0$, what happens to y as x increases?   It decreases.

19. Assume that y varies inversely with x and $y = \frac{k}{x}$. If $y = 15$ when $x = 10$, find k.   150

20. Assume that c varies inversely with d and $c = \frac{k}{d}$. If $c = 9$ when $d = 5$, find k.   45

NOTATION   *Complete each solution.*

21. Find f if $d = 21$ and $k = \frac{7}{5}$.

$$d = kf$$
$$21 = \tfrac{7}{5}\, f$$
$$\tfrac{5}{7} \cdot 21 = \tfrac{5}{7} \cdot \frac{7}{5}f$$
$$15 = f$$

22. Find f if $d = 20$ and $k = 0.75$.

$$d = \frac{k}{f}$$
$$20 = \frac{0.75}{f}$$
$$f \cdot 20 = f \cdot \frac{0.75}{f}$$
$$20f = 0.75$$
$$f = \frac{0.75}{20}$$
$$f = 0.0375$$

PRACTICE

23. Assume that y varies directly with x. If $y = 10$ when $x = 2$, find y when $x = 7$.   35

24. Assume that r varies directly with s. If $r = 21$ when $s = 6$, find r when $s = 12$.   42

25. Assume that l varies directly with m. If $l = 50$ when $m = 200$, find l when $m = 25$.   6.25

26. Assume that g varies directly with t. If $g = 3,616$ when $t = 8,000$, find g when $t = 2,405$.   1,087.06

27. Assume that x and y vary directly. If $x = 30$ when $y = 2$, find y when $x = 45$.   3

28. Assume that n_1 and n_2 vary directly. If $n_1 = 315$ when $n_2 = 3$, find n_2 when $n_1 = 10.5$.   0.1

29. Assume that y varies inversely with x. If $y = 8$ when $x = 1$, find y when $x = 8$.   1

30. Assume that r varies inversely with s. If $r = 40$ when $s = 10$, find r when $s = 15$. $\frac{80}{3}$

31. Assume that a varies inversely with t. If $a = 600$ when $t = 300$, find a when $t = 15$.   12,000

32. Assume that b varies inversely with c. If $b = 0.45$ when $c = 1.6$, find b when $c = 80$.   0.009

33. Assume that t_1 and t_2 vary inversely. If $t_1 = 4$ when $t_2 = 5$, find t_2 when $t_1 = 3\frac{1}{3}$.   6

34. Assume that a and r vary inversely. If $a = 9$ when $r = 7$, find r when $a = \frac{1}{9}$.   567

APPLICATIONS

35. COMMUTING DISTANCE   The distance that a car can travel without refueling varies directly with the number of gallons of gasoline in the tank. If a car can go 360 miles on a full tank of gas (15 gallons), how far can it go on 7 gallons?   168 mi

36. COMPUTING FORCES   The force of gravity acting on an object varies directly with the mass of the object. The force on a mass of 5 kilograms is 49 newtons. What is the force acting on a mass of 12 kilograms?   117.6 newtons

37. DOSAGE   The recommended dose (in milligrams) of Demerol, a preoperative medication given to children, varies directly with the child's weight in pounds. The proper dosage for a child weighing 30 pounds is 18 milligrams. What would be the correct dosage for a child weighing 45 pounds?   27 mg

38. MEDICATION   To fight ear infections in children, doctors often prescribe Ceclor. The recommended dose in milligrams varies directly with the child's body weight in pounds. The correct dosage for a 20-pound child is 124 milligrams. What would be the correct dosage for a 28-pound child?   173.6 mg

39. CIDER   For the recipe shown in Illustration 1, the number of inches of stick cinnamon to use varies directly with the number of servings of spiced cider to be made. How many inches of stick cinnamon are needed to make $2\frac{1}{2}$ dozen servings? $22\frac{1}{2}$

> **Hot Spiced Cider**
>
> 8 cups apple cider or apple juice
> $\frac{1}{4}$ to $\frac{1}{2}$ cup packed brown sugar
> 6 inches stick cinnamon
> 1 teaspoon whole allspice
> 1 teaspoon whole cloves
> 8 thin orange wedges or slices (optional)
> 8 whole cloves (optional)   Makes 8 servings

ILLUSTRATION 1

40. LUNAR GRAVITY   The weight of an object on the moon varies directly with its weight on Earth; six pounds on Earth weighs 1 pound on the moon. What would the scale shown in Illustration 2 register if the astronaut were weighed on the moon?   55 lb

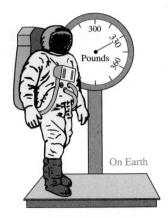

ILLUSTRATION 2

41. COMMUTING TIME   The time it takes a car to travel a certain distance varies inversely with its rate of speed. If a certain trip takes 3 hours at 50 miles per hour, how long will the trip take at 60 miles per hour? $2\frac{1}{2}$ hr

42. GEOMETRY   For a fixed area, the length of a rectangle is inversely proportional to its width. A rectangle has a width of 12 feet and a length of 20 feet. If its length is increased to 24 feet, find the width that will maintain the same area.   10 ft

43. ELECTRICITY   The current in an electric circuit varies inversely with the resistance. If the current in the circuit shown in Illustration 3 is 30 amps when the resistance is 4 ohms, what will the current be for a resistance of 15 ohms?   8 amps

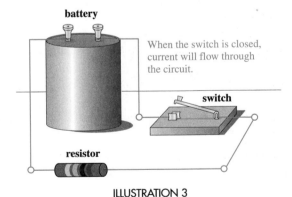

ILLUSTRATION 3

44. FARMING   The length of time a given number of bushels of corn will last when feeding cattle varies inversely with the number of animals. If a certain number of bushels will feed 25 cows for 10 days, how long will the feed last for 10 cows?   25 days

45. COMPUTING PRESSURES   If the temperature of a gas is constant, the volume occupied varies inversely with the pressure. If a gas occupies a volume of 40 cubic meters under a pressure of 8 atmospheres, find the volume when the pressure is changed to 6 atmospheres. $55\frac{1}{3}$ m^3

46. COMPUTING DEPRECIATION   Assume that the value of a machine varies inversely with its age. If a drill press is worth \$300 when it is 2 years old, find its value when it is 6 years old. How much has the machine depreciated over that 4-year period? \$100; \$200

WRITING

47. Give two examples of quantities that vary directly and two that do not.

48. What is the difference between direct variation and inverse variation?

49. What is a constant of variation?

50. Is there a direct variation or an inverse variation between each pair of quantities? Explain why.

   a. The time it takes to type a term paper and the speed at which you type

   b. The time it takes to type a term paper (working at a constant rate) and the length of the term paper

REVIEW   *Solve each equation.*

51. $x^2 - 5x - 6 = 0$ $-1, 6$

52. $x^2 - 25 = 0$ $5, -5$

53. $(t + 2)(t^2 + 7t + 12) = 0$ $-2, -3, -4$

54. $2(y - 4) = -y^2$ $2, -4$

55. $y^3 - y^2 = 0$ $0, 0, 1$

56. $5a^3 - 125a = 0$ $0, 5, -5$

57. $(x^2 - 1)(x^2 - 4) = 0$ $1, -1, 2, -2$

58. $6t^3 + 35t^2 = 6t$ $0, -6, \frac{1}{6}$

Expressions and Equations

In this chapter, we have discussed procedures for working with **rational expressions** and procedures for solving **rational equations.**

Rational expressions

The **fundamental property of fractions** is used when simplifying rational expressions and when multiplying and dividing rational expressions: *We can divide out factors that are common to the numerator and the denominator of a fraction.*

1. a. Simplify $\dfrac{2x^2 - 8x}{x^2 - 6x + 8} \cdot \dfrac{2x}{x - 2}$.

   b. What common factor was divided out? $x - 4$

2. a. Multiply: $\dfrac{x^2 + 2x + 1}{x} \cdot \dfrac{x^2 - x}{x^2 - 1}$. $x + 1$

   b. What common factors were divided out?
     $x, x - 1, x + 1$

The fundamental property of fractions also states that *multiplying the numerator and denominator of a fraction by the same nonzero number does not change the value of the fraction.* We use this concept to "build" fractions when adding or subtracting rational expressions with unlike denominators, and when simplifying complex fractions.

3. a. Add: $\dfrac{x}{x + 1} + \dfrac{x - 1}{x}$. $\dfrac{2x^2 - 1}{x(x + 1)}$

   b. By what did you multiply the first fraction to rewrite it in terms of the LCD? The second fraction?
     $\dfrac{x}{x}, \dfrac{x + 1}{x + 1}$

4. a. Simplify $\dfrac{n - 1 - \dfrac{2}{n}}{\dfrac{n}{3}}$. $\dfrac{3(n^2 - n - 2)}{n^2}$

   b. By what did you multiply the numerator and denominator to simplify the complex fraction? $3n$

Rational equations

The multiplication property of equality states that *if equal quantities are multiplied by the same nonzero number, the results will be equal quantities.* We use this property when solving rational equations. If we multiply both sides of the equation by the LCD of the rational expressions in the equation, we can clear it of fractions.

5. a. Solve $\dfrac{11}{b} + \dfrac{13}{b} = 12$. 2

   b. By what did you multiply both sides to clear the equation of fractions? b

6. a. Solve $\dfrac{-5}{s^2 + s - 2} + \dfrac{3}{s + 2} = \dfrac{1}{s - 1}$. 5

   b. By what did you multiply both sides to clear the equation of fractions? $(s + 2)(s - 1)$

7. a. Solve $y + \dfrac{3}{4} = \dfrac{3y - 50}{4y - 24}$. $2, 4$

   b. By what did you multiply both sides to clear the equation of fractions? $4(y - 6)$

8. a. Solve $\dfrac{1}{a} - \dfrac{1}{b} = 1$ for b. $b = \dfrac{a}{1 - a}$

   b. By what did you multiply both sides to clear the equation of fractions? ab

Section 6.1

CHECKING A SIMPLIFICATION   We can use evaluation to check a simplification. To check whether

$$\frac{x^2 - 16}{x + 4} = x - 4$$

have each member of your group evaluate

$$\frac{x^2 - 16}{x + 4} \quad \text{and} \quad x - 4$$

for a given value of x. That is, have one person evaluate both expressions for $x = -5$, have another person evaluate both for $x = -3$, and so on. (Don't use $x = -4$, because the original expression is undefined for this value of x.) The expressions should give identical values of x. If the evaluations differ for any number, the original expression was not simplified correctly.

Use evaluation to check each of the following simplifications. If an expression was incorrectly simplified, find the correct answer.

a. $\dfrac{x^2 - 4}{x^3 + 8} \overset{?}{=} \dfrac{x - 2}{x^2 + 2x + 2}$ **b.** $\dfrac{x^2 + 2x + 1}{x^2 + 4x + 3} \overset{?}{=} \dfrac{x + 1}{x + 3}$

c. $\dfrac{x^2 + 2x - 15}{x^2 - 25} \overset{?}{=} \dfrac{x - 3}{x - 5}$ **d.** $\dfrac{6x^2 - 13x + 6}{3x^2 + x - 2} \overset{?}{=} \dfrac{2x - 3}{x + 2}$

Section 6.2

COMBINED OPERATIONS   Insert a $\cdot$ sign or a $\div$ sign in each blank so that the answer is 1.

$$\frac{x^2 - 2x - 15}{3x^2 - 27} \quad\rule{1cm}{0.4pt}\quad \frac{x^2 - 25}{6x^2 + 45x + 75} \quad\rule{1cm}{0.4pt}\quad \frac{x^2 - x - 6}{2x^2 + 9x + 10}$$

Section 6.3

First, add $\dfrac{1}{2x^2} + \dfrac{1}{8x}$

by expressing each fraction in terms of a common denominator $16x^3$. (This is the *product* of their denominators.) Then add the fractions again by expressing each of them in terms of their lowest common denominator. What is one advantage and one disadvantage of each method?

Section 6.4

UNIT ANALYSIS   Simplify each complex fraction. The units can be divided out just as in the case of common factors.

$$\cfrac{\dfrac{36 \text{ inches}}{3 \text{ feet}}}{\dfrac{1 \text{ yard}}{3 \text{ feet}}} \qquad \cfrac{\dfrac{60 \text{ minutes}}{1 \text{ hour}}}{\dfrac{3{,}600 \text{ seconds}}{1 \text{ hour}}} \qquad \cfrac{\dfrac{4 \text{ quarts}}{1 \text{ gallon}}}{\dfrac{8 \text{ pints}}{1 \text{ gallon}}}$$

Section 6.5

SIMPLIFY AND SOLVE   The two problems below look similar. Explain why their one-word instructions can't be switched. Write a solution for each problem and then identify the major similarity and the major difference in the solution methods.

Simplify	Solve
$\dfrac{2}{4x - 4} + \dfrac{3}{x - 1}$	$\dfrac{2}{4x - 4} + \dfrac{3}{x - 1} = \dfrac{7}{4}$

Section 6.6

PROBLEM SOLVING   Problems such as the filling of a water tank are often called *shared-work problems*. For each of the following equations, write a shared-work problem that could be solved using it.

$$\frac{1}{3} + \frac{1}{8} = \frac{1}{x}$$

$$\frac{1}{3} - \frac{1}{8} = \frac{1}{x}$$

$$\frac{1}{3} + \frac{1}{8} - \frac{1}{16} = \frac{1}{x}$$

Section 6.7

PI   The Greek letter pi (π) represents the ratio of the circumference C of any circle to its diameter d. That is, $\pi = \frac{C}{d}$. Use a tape measure to find the circumference and the diameter of various objects that are circular in shape. You can measure anything round: for example, a swimming pool spa, the top of a can, or a ring. Enter your results in a table like that in Illustration 1. Convert each measurement to a decimal and use a calculator to compute the ratio of C to d. Make some observations about your results.

Object	Circumference	Diameter	$\dfrac{C}{d}$
A quarter	$2\frac{15}{16}$ in. 2.9375 in.	$\frac{15}{16}$ in. 0.9375 in.	3.13333. . .

ILLUSTRATION 1

COOKING   Find a simple recipe for a treat that you can make for your class. Use a proportion to determine the amount of each ingredient needed to make enough for the exact number of people in your class. Write the old recipe and the new recipe on separate pieces of poster board. Did the recipe serve the correct number of people? Share with the class how you made the calculations, as well as any difficulties you encountered.

CHAPTER REVIEW

| **SECTION 6.1** | *Simplifying Rational Expressions* |

CONCEPTS

A *rational expression* is a fraction in which the numerator and denominator are polynomials.

Since division by 0 is undefined, we must make sure that the denominator of a rational expression is not 0.

The fundamental property of fractions:
If b and c are not zero, then

$$\frac{ac}{bc} = \frac{a}{b}$$

When all common factors have been divided out, a fraction is in *lowest terms.*

The quotient of any nonzero expression and its opposite is -1.

REVIEW EXERCISES

1. Find the values of x for which the rational expression $\dfrac{x-1}{x^2-16}$ is undefined. $4, -4$

2. Write each fraction in lowest terms. If it is already in lowest terms, so indicate.

   a. $\dfrac{10}{25}$ $\frac{2}{5}$ **b.** $-\dfrac{12}{18}$ $-\frac{2}{3}$

3. Simplify each rational expression. If it is already in lowest terms, so indicate. Assume that no denominators are zero.

   a. $\dfrac{3x^2}{6x^3}$ $\frac{1}{2x}$ **b.** $\dfrac{5xy^2}{2x^2y^2}$ $\frac{5}{2x}$

   c. $\dfrac{x^2}{x^2+x}$ $\frac{x}{x+1}$ **d.** $\dfrac{a^2-4}{a+2}$ $a-2$

   e. $\dfrac{3p-2}{2-3p}$ -1 **f.** $\dfrac{8-x}{x^2-5x-24}$ $-\frac{1}{x+3}$

   g. $\dfrac{2x^2-16x}{2x^2-18x+16}$ $\frac{x}{x-1}$ **h.** $\dfrac{x^2+x-2}{x^2-x-2}$ in lowest terms

4. Evaluate $\dfrac{x^2-1}{x-5}$ for $x=-2$. $-\frac{3}{7}$

5. Explain why it would be incorrect to divide out the common x's in $\frac{x+1}{x}$.

   x is not a common factor of the numerator and the denominator.

6. Simplify $\dfrac{4(t+3)+4}{3(t+2)+6}$. $\frac{4}{3}$

| *Multiplying and Dividing Rational Expressions* |

Rule for multiplying fractions:

$$\frac{a}{b} \cdot \frac{c}{d} = \frac{ac}{bd} \quad (b, d \neq 0)$$

Rule for dividing fractions:

$$\frac{a}{b} \div \frac{c}{d} = \frac{a}{b} \cdot \frac{d}{c} \, (b, c, d \neq 0)$$

To write the *reciprocal* of a fraction, we invert the fraction.

7. Do each multiplication and simplify.

   a. $\dfrac{3xy}{2x} \cdot \dfrac{4x}{2y^2}$ $\frac{3x}{y}$ **b.** $56x\left(\dfrac{12}{7x}\right)$ 96

   c. $\dfrac{x^2-1}{x^2+2x} \cdot \dfrac{x}{x+1}$ $\frac{x-1}{x+2}$ **d.** $\dfrac{x^2+x}{3x-15} \cdot \dfrac{6x-30}{x^2+2x+1}$ $\frac{2x}{x+1}$

8. Do each division and simplify.

   a. $\dfrac{3x^2}{5x^2y} \div \dfrac{6x}{15xy^2}$ $\frac{3y}{2}$ **b.** $\dfrac{x^2+5x}{x^2+4x-5} \div \dfrac{x^2}{x-1}$ $\frac{1}{x}$

   c. $\dfrac{x^2-x-6}{2x-1} \div \dfrac{x^2-2x-3}{2x^2+x-1}$ $x+2$

9. Simplify $\dfrac{b^2 + 4b + 4}{b^2 + b - 6}\left(\dfrac{b - 2}{b - 1} \div \dfrac{b + 2}{b^2 + 2b - 3}\right).$ $b + 2$

Adding and Subtracting Rational Expressions

Adding and subtracting fractions with like denominators:

$$\dfrac{a}{d} + \dfrac{b}{d} = \dfrac{a + b}{d} \quad (d \ne 0)$$

$$\dfrac{a}{d} - \dfrac{b}{d} = \dfrac{a - b}{d} \quad (d \ne 0)$$

To find the *LCD*, factor each denominator completely. Form a product using each different factor the greatest number of times it appears in any one factorization.

To add or subtract fractions with unlike denominators, first find the LCD of the fractions. Then express each fraction in equivalent form with a common denominator. Finally, add or subtract the fractions.

10. Do each operation. Simplify all answers.

a. $\dfrac{x}{x + y} + \dfrac{y}{x + y}$ 1

b. $\dfrac{3x}{x - 7} - \dfrac{x - 2}{x - 7}$ $\dfrac{2x + 2}{x - 7}$

c. $\dfrac{a}{a^2 - 2a - 8} + \dfrac{2}{a^2 - 2a - 8}$ $\dfrac{1}{a - 4}$

11. Several denominators are given. Find the lowest common denominator (LCD).

a. $2x^2, 4x$ $4x^2$

b. $3y^2, 9x, 6x$ $18xy^2$

c. $x + 1, x + 2$ $(x + 1)(x + 2)$

d. $y^2 - 25, y - 5$ $y^2 - 25$

12. Do each operation. Simplify all answers.

a. $\dfrac{x}{x - 1} + \dfrac{1}{x}$ $\dfrac{x^2 + x - 1}{x(x - 1)}$

b. $\dfrac{1}{7} - \dfrac{1}{c}$ $\dfrac{c - 7}{7c}$

c. $\dfrac{x + 2}{2x} - \dfrac{2 - x}{x^2}$ $\dfrac{x^2 + 4x - 4}{2x^2}$

d. $\dfrac{2t + 2}{t^2 + 2t + 1} - \dfrac{1}{t + 1}$ $\dfrac{1}{t + 1}$

e. $\dfrac{x}{x + 2} + \dfrac{3}{x} - \dfrac{4}{x^2 + 2x}$ $\dfrac{x + 1}{x}$

f. $\dfrac{6}{b - 1} - \dfrac{b}{1 - b}$ $\dfrac{b + 6}{b - 1}$

13. VIDEO CAMERA   See Illustration 1. Find the perimeter and the area of the LED screen of the camera. $\dfrac{14x + 28}{(x + 6)(x - 1)}$ units, $\dfrac{12}{(x + 6)(x - 1)}$ square units

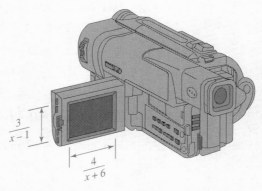

ILLUSTRATION 1

Complex Fractions

Complex fractions contain fractions in their numerators and/or their denominators.

14. Simplify each complex fraction.

a. $\dfrac{\frac{3}{2}}{\frac{2}{3}}$ $\dfrac{9}{4}$

b. $\dfrac{\frac{3}{2} + 1}{\frac{2}{3} + 1}$ $\dfrac{3}{2}$

To simplify a complex fraction, use either of these methods:

1. Write the numerator and denominator of the complex fraction as single fractions, do the division of the fractions, and simplify.

2. Multiply both the numerator and the denominator of the complex fraction by the LCD of the fractions that appear in the numerator and denominator, then simplify.

c. $\dfrac{\dfrac{1}{y} + 1}{\dfrac{1}{y} - 1}$ $\dfrac{1+y}{1-y}$

d. $\dfrac{1 + \dfrac{3}{x}}{2 - \dfrac{1}{x^2}}$ $\dfrac{x(x+3)}{2x^2-1}$

e. $\dfrac{\dfrac{2}{x-1} + \dfrac{x-1}{x+1}}{\dfrac{1}{x^2-1}}$ $x^2 + 3$

f. $\dfrac{x^{-2}+1}{x^{-2}-1}$ $\dfrac{1+x^2}{1-x^2}$

Rational Equations and Problem Solving

To solve an equation that contains fractions, change it to an equivalent equation without fractions. Do so by multiplying both sides by the LCD of the fractions. Check all solutions.

An apparent solution that does not satisfy the original equation is called an *extraneous* solution.

15. Solve each equation and check all answers.

a. $\dfrac{3}{x} = \dfrac{2}{x-1}$ 3

b. $\dfrac{a}{a-5} = 3 + \dfrac{5}{a-5}$ no solution; 5 is extraneous

c. $\dfrac{2}{3t} + \dfrac{1}{t} = \dfrac{5}{9}$ 3

d. $a = \dfrac{3a-50}{4a-24} - \dfrac{3}{4}$ 2, 4

e. $\dfrac{4}{x+2} - \dfrac{3}{x+3} = \dfrac{6}{x^2+5x+6}$ 0

16. The efficiency E of a Carnot engine is given by the formula

$$E = 1 - \frac{T_2}{T_1}$$

Solve the formula for T_1. $T_1 = \dfrac{T_2}{1-E}$

17. Solve for r_1: $\dfrac{1}{r} = \dfrac{1}{r_1} + \dfrac{1}{r_2}$. $r_1 = \dfrac{rr_2}{r_2-r}$

18. NUMBER PROBLEM If a number is subtracted from the denominator of $\frac{4}{5}$ and twice as much is added to the numerator, the result is 5. Find the number. 3

19. If a maid can clean a house in 4 hours, how much of the house does she clean in 1 hour? $\frac{1}{4}$

20. HOUSE PAINTING If a homeowner can paint a house in 14 days and a professional painter can paint it in 10 days, how long will it take if they work together? $5\frac{5}{6}$ days

21. INVESTMENTS In one year, a student earned $100 interest on money she deposited at a savings and loan. She later learned that the money would have earned $120 if she had deposited it at a credit union, because the credit union paid 1% more interest at the time. Find the rate she received from the savings and loan. 5%

22. EXERCISE A jogger can bicycle 30 miles in the same time that it takes her to jog 10 miles. If she can ride 10 mph faster than she can jog, how fast can she jog? 5 mph

23. WIND SPEED A plane flies 400 miles downwind in the same amount of time as it takes to travel 320 miles upwind. If the plane can fly at 360 mph in still air, find the velocity of the wind. 40 mph

To solve a problem, follow these steps:

1. Analyze the problem.
2. Form an equation.
3. Solve the equation.
4. State the conclusion.
5. Check the result.

Interest = principal · rate · time

Distance = rate · time

Proportions and Similar Triangles

A *proportion* is a statement that two ratios or two rates are equal.

In the proportion $\frac{a}{b} = \frac{c}{d}$, *a* and *d* are the *extremes,* and *b* and *c* are the *means.*

In any proportion, the product of the extremes is equal to the product of the means.

24. Determine whether each equation is a proportion.

   a. $\dfrac{4}{7} = \dfrac{20}{34}$ no   **b.** $\dfrac{5}{7} = \dfrac{30}{42}$ yes

25. Solve each proportion.

   a. $\dfrac{3}{x} = \dfrac{6}{9}$ $\frac{9}{2}$ **b.** $\dfrac{x}{3} = \dfrac{x}{5}$ 0

   c. $\dfrac{x-2}{5} = \dfrac{x}{7}$ 7   **d.** $\dfrac{2x}{x+4} = \dfrac{3}{x-1}$ $4, -\frac{3}{2}$

26. DENTISTRY   The diagram in Illustration 2 was displayed in a dentist's office. According to the diagram, if the dentist has 340 adult patients, how many will develop gum disease?   255

3 out of 4 adults will develop gum disease.

ILLUSTRATION 2

The measures of corresponding sides of *similar triangles* are in proportion.

27. A telephone pole casts a shadow 12 feet long at the same time that a man 6 feet tall casts a shadow of 3.6 feet. How tall is the pole?   20 ft

Variation

Direct variation: As one variable gets larger, the other gets larger as described by the equation $y = kx$, where *k* is the *constant of variation.*

Inverse variation: As one variable gets larger, the other gets smaller as described by the equation

$$y = \frac{k}{x} \quad (k \text{ is a constant})$$

28. PROFIT   The profit made by a strawberry farm varies directly with the number of baskets of strawberries sold. If a profit of $500 was made from the sale of 750 baskets, what is the profit when 1,250 baskets are sold? $833.33

29. *l* varies inversely with *w*. Find the constant of variation if $l = 30$ when $w = 20$.   600

30. ELECTRICITY   For a fixed voltage, the current in an electrical circuit varies inversely with the resistance in the circuit. If a certain circuit has a current of $2\frac{1}{2}$ amps when the resistance is 150 ohms, find the current in the circuit when the resistance is doubled.   1.25 amps

31. The graph in Illustration 3 shows a type of variation. Does it show direct or inverse variation?   inverse variation

ILLUSTRATION 3

32. Give an example of two quantities that vary directly.

1. Find the values of x for which $\dfrac{x}{x^2 + x - 6}$ is undefined. $-3, 2$

2. Simplify $\dfrac{48x^2y}{54xy^2}.$ $\dfrac{8x}{9y}$

3. Simplify $\dfrac{2x^2 - x - 3}{4x^2 - 9}.$ $\dfrac{x + 1}{2x + 3}$

4. Simplify $\dfrac{3(x + 2) - 3}{2x - 4 - (x - 5)}.$ 3

5. Multiply and simplify: $-\dfrac{12x^2y}{15xy} \cdot \dfrac{25y^2}{16x}.$ $-\dfrac{5y^2}{4}$

6. Multiply and simplify: $\dfrac{x^2 + 3x + 2}{3x + 9} \cdot \dfrac{x + 3}{x^2 - 4}.$ $\dfrac{x + 1}{3(x - 2)}$

7. Divide and simplify: $\dfrac{8x^2}{25x} \div \dfrac{16x^2}{30x}.$ $\dfrac{3}{5}$

8. Divide and simplify: $\dfrac{x - x^2}{3x^2 + 6x} \div \dfrac{3x - 3}{3x^3 + 6x^2}.$ $-\dfrac{x^2}{3}$

9. Simplify $\dfrac{x^2 + x}{x - 1} \cdot \dfrac{x^2 - 1}{x^2 - 2x} \div \dfrac{x^2 + 2x + 1}{x^2 - 4}.$ $x + 2$

10. Add: $\dfrac{5x - 4}{x - 1} + \dfrac{5x + 3}{x - 1}.$ $\dfrac{10x - 1}{x - 1}$

11. Subtract: $\dfrac{3y + 7}{2y + 3} - \dfrac{3(y - 2)}{2y + 3}.$ $\dfrac{13}{2y + 3}$

12. Add: $\dfrac{x + 1}{x} + \dfrac{x - 1}{x + 1}.$ $\dfrac{2x^2 + x + 1}{x(x + 1)}$

13. Subtract: $\dfrac{a + 3}{a - 1} - \dfrac{a + 4}{1 - a}.$ $\dfrac{2a + 7}{a - 1}$

14. Subtract: $\dfrac{2n}{5m} - \dfrac{n}{2}.$ $\dfrac{4n - 5mn}{10m}$

15. Simplify $\dfrac{1 + \dfrac{y}{x}}{\dfrac{y}{x} - 1}.$ $\dfrac{x + y}{y - x}$

16. Solve for q: $\dfrac{7}{q^2 - q - 2} + \dfrac{1}{q + 1} = \dfrac{3}{q - 2}.$ 1

17. Solve for c: $\dfrac{2}{3} = \dfrac{2c - 12}{3c - 9} - c.$ $1, 2$

18. Solve for B: $H = \dfrac{RB}{R + B}.$ $B = \dfrac{HR}{R - H}$

19. Is the equation $\dfrac{3}{5} = \dfrac{6xt}{10xt}$ a proportion?   yes

20. Solve the proportion for y: $\dfrac{y}{y - 1} = \dfrac{y - 2}{y}.$ $\dfrac{2}{3}$

21. HEALTH RISK   A medical newsletter states that a "healthy" waist-to-hip ratio for men is 19:20 or less. Does the patient shown in Illustration 1 fall within the "healthy" range?   yes

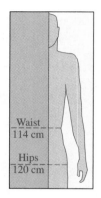

Waist
114 cm

Hips
120 cm

ILLUSTRATION 1

22. FLIGHT PATH   A plane drops 575 feet as it flies a horizontal distance of $\frac{1}{2}$ mile, as shown in Illustration 2. How much altitude will it lose as it flies a horizontal distance of 7 miles?   8,050 ft

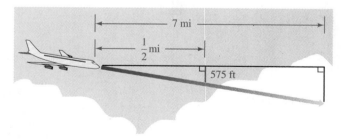

7 mi

$\frac{1}{2}$ mi

575 ft

ILLUSTRATION 2

23. POGO STICK   See Illustration 3. The force required to compress a spring varies directly with the change in the length of the spring. If a force of 130 pounds compresses the spring on the pogo stick 6.5 inches, how much force is required to compress the spring 5 inches?   100 lb

ILLUSTRATION 3

24. If i varies inversely with d, find the constant of variation if $i = 100$ when $d = 2$.   200

25. CLEANING HIGHWAYS   One highway worker can pick up all the trash on a strip of highway in 7 hours, and his helper can pick up the trash in 9 hours. How long will it take them if they work together? $3\frac{15}{16}$ hr

26. BOATING   A boat can motor 28 miles downstream in the same amount of time as it can motor 18 miles upstream. Find the speed of the current if the boat can motor at 23 mph in still water.   5 mph

27. Explain why we can divide out the 5's in $\frac{5x}{5}$ and why we can't divide them out in $\frac{5+x}{5}$.
We can divide out only common factors, as in the first expression. We can't divide out common terms, as in the second expression.

28. Explain what it means to clear the following equation of fractions.

$$\frac{u}{u-1} + \frac{1}{u} = \frac{u^2+1}{u^2-u}$$

Why is this a helpful first step in solving the equation?
We multiply both sides of the equation by the LCD of the rational expressions appearing in the equation. The resulting equation is easier to solve.

Chapters 1-6   Cumulative Review Exercises

1. Evaluate $9^2 - 3[45 - 3(6 + 4)]$.   36

2. PAIN RELIEVER   For the 12-month period ending August 16, 1998, Tylenol had sales of $567,600,000. Use the information in Illustration 1 to determine the total amount of money spent on pain-relieving tablets for that 12-month period. $2,580,000,000

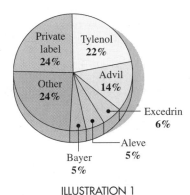

ILLUSTRATION 1

Based on information from *Los Angeles Times* (Sept. 24, 1998)

3. Find the average (mean) test score of a student in a history class with scores of 80, 73, 61, 73, and 98.   77

4. What is the value in cents of x 35¢ stamps? $35x$¢

5. Solve $\dfrac{3}{4} = \dfrac{1}{2} + \dfrac{x}{5}$. $\frac{5}{4}$

6. Change $40°C$ to degrees Fahrenheit. $104°F$

7. Find the volume of a pyramid that has a square base, measuring 6 feet on a side, and whose height is 20 feet. 240 ft^3

8. Tell whether each statement is true or false.
  a. Every integer is a whole number.   false
  b. 0 is not a rational number.   false
  c. π is an irrational number.   true
  d. The set of integers is the set of whole numbers and their opposites.   true

9. Solve $2 - 3(x - 5) = 4(x - 1)$.   3

10. Simplify $8(c + 7) - 2(c - 3)$. $6c + 62$

11. Solve $A - c = 2B + r$ for B. $B = \frac{A - c - r}{2}$

12. Solve $7x + 2 \geq 4x - 1$ and graph the solution. Then describe the graph using interval notation.
  $x \geq -1, [-1, \infty]$

13. Solve $\dfrac{4}{5}d = -4$. -5

14. BLENDING TEA   One grade of tea (worth $3.20 per pound) is to be mixed with another grade (worth $2 per pound) to make 20 pounds of a mixture that will be worth $2.72 per pound. How much of each grade of tea must be used?   12 lb of the $3.20 tea and 8 lb of the $2 tea

15. SPEED OF A PLANE   Two planes are 6,000 miles apart, and their speeds differ by 200 mph. If they travel toward each other and meet in 5 hours, find the speed of the slower plane.   500 mph

16. Graph $y = 2x - 3$.   **17.** Graph $y = (x + 2)^3$.

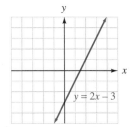   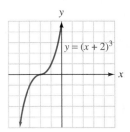

18. Find the slope of the line passing through $(-1, 3)$ and $(3, -1)$. -1

19. Write the equation of a line that has slope 3 and passes through the point $(1, 5)$. $y = 3x + 2$

20. Graph $3x - 2y = 6$.   **21.** Graph $y = \dfrac{5}{2}$.

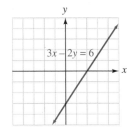   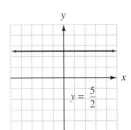

22. What is the slope of a line perpendicular to the line $y = -\dfrac{7}{8}x - 6$? $\frac{8}{7}$

23. Is this the graph of a function?   no

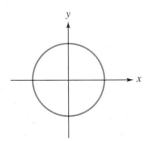

24. CUTTING STEEL The graph in Illustration 2 shows the amount of wear (in mm) on a cutting blade for a given length of a cut (in m). Find the rate of change in the length of the cutting blade. 0.008 mm/m

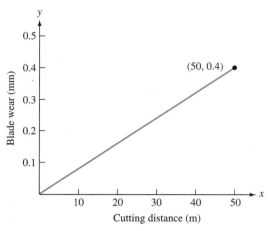

ILLUSTRATION 2

25. Find $f(-4)$ if $f(x) = \dfrac{x^2 - 2x}{2}$. 12

26. Evaluate -5^2. -25

Simplify each expression. Write each answer without using negative exponents.

27. $x^4 x^3$ x^7

28. $(x^2 x^3)^5$ x^{25}

29. $\left(\dfrac{y^3 y}{2yy^2}\right)^3$ $\dfrac{y^3}{8}$

30. $\left(\dfrac{-2a}{b}\right)^5$ $-\dfrac{32a^5}{b^5}$

31. $(a^{-2}b^3)^{-4}$ $\dfrac{a^8}{b^{12}}$

32. $\dfrac{9b^0 b^3}{3b^{-3}b^4}$ $3b^2$

33. Write 290,000 in scientific notation. 2.9×10^5

34. What is the degree of the polynomial $5x^3 - 4x + 16$? 3

Do the operations.

35. $(3x^2 - 3x - 2) + (3x^2 + 4x - 3)$ $6x^2 + x - 5$

36. $(2x^2 y^3)(3x^3 y^2)$ $6x^5 y^5$

37. $(2y - 5)(3y + 7)$ $6y^2 - y - 35$

38. $-4x^2 z(3x^2 - z)$ $-12x^4 z + 4x^2 z^2$

39. $\dfrac{6x + 9}{3}$ $2x + 3$

40. $\dfrac{15(r^2 s^3)^2}{-5(rs^5)^3}$ $-\dfrac{3r}{s^9}$

41. LICENSE PLATES The number of different license plates of the form three digits followed by three letters, as shown in Illustration 3, is

$10 \cdot 10 \cdot 10 \cdot 26 \cdot 26 \cdot 26$. Write this expression using exponents. Then evaluate it.
$10^3 \cdot 26^3$; 17,576,000

ILLUSTRATION 3

42. CONCENTRIC CIRCLES See Illustration 4. The area of the ring between the two concentric circles of radius r and R is given by the formula

$$A = \pi(R + r)(R - r)$$

Do the multiplication on the right-hand side of the equation. $A = \pi R^2 - \pi r^2$

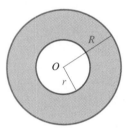

ILLUSTRATION 4

Factor each polynomial completely, if possible.

43. $k^3 t - 3k^2 t$ $k^2 t(k - 3)$

44. $2ab + 2ac + 3b + 3c$ $(b + c)(2a + 3)$

45. $2a^2 - 200b^2$ $2(a + 10b)(a - 10b)$

46. $b^3 + 125$ $(b + 5)(b^2 - 5b + 25)$

47. $u^2 - 18u + 81$ $(u - 9)^2$

48. $6x^2 - 63 - 13x$ $(2x - 9)(3x + 7)$

49. $-r^2 + 2 + r$ $-(r - 2)(r + 1)$

50. $u^2 + 10u + 15$ prime

Solve each equation by factoring.

51. $5x^2 + x = 0$ $0, -\frac{1}{5}$

52. $6x^2 - 5x = -1$ $\frac{1}{3}, \frac{1}{2}$

53. COOKING The electric griddle shown in Illustration 5 has a cooking surface of 160 square inches. Find the length and the width of the griddle. 10 in., 16 in.

ILLUSTRATION 5

54. For what values of x is the rational expression $\dfrac{3x^2}{x^2 - 25}$ undefined? $5, -5$

Do the operations and simplify, if possible.

55. $\dfrac{x^2 - 16}{x - 4} \div \dfrac{3x + 12}{x}$ $\dfrac{x}{3}$

56. $\dfrac{4}{x - 3} + \dfrac{5}{3 - x}$ $-\dfrac{1}{x - 3}$

57. $\dfrac{2 - \dfrac{2}{x + 1}}{2 + \dfrac{2}{x}}$ $\dfrac{x^2}{(x + 1)^2}$

58. $\dfrac{4a}{a - 2} - \dfrac{3a}{a - 3} + \dfrac{4a}{a^2 - 5a + 6}$ $\dfrac{a}{a - 3}$

Solve each equation.

59. $\dfrac{7}{5x} - \dfrac{1}{2} = \dfrac{5}{6x} + \dfrac{1}{3}$ $\dfrac{17}{25}$

60. $\dfrac{3}{5} + \dfrac{7}{x + 2} = 2$ 3

61. COMPUTING INTEREST   For a fixed rate and principal, the interest earned in a bank account paying simple interest varies directly with the length of time the principal is left on deposit. If an investment earns $700 in 2 years, how much will it earn in 7 years? $2,450

62. HEIGHT OF A TREE   A tree casts a shadow of 29 feet at the same time as a vertical yardstick casts a shadow of 2.5 feet. (See Illustration 6.) Find the height of the tree.   34.8 ft

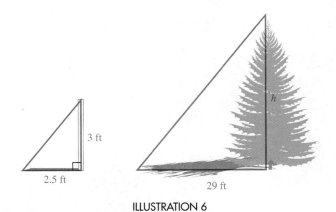

3 ft

2.5 ft

29 ft

h

ILLUSTRATION 6

63. DRAINING A TANK   If one outlet pipe can drain a tank in 24 hours, and another pipe can drain the tank in 36 hours, how long will it take for both pipes to drain the tank? $14\frac{2}{5}$ hr

64. Explain what it means for two variables to vary inversely.

One variable is a constant multiple of the reciprocal of the other; $y = \dfrac{k}{x}$.

7

Solving Systems of Equations and Inequalities

TO SOLVE MANY PROBLEMS, WE MUST USE TWO VARIABLES. THIS REQUIRES THAT WE SOLVE A SYSTEM OF EQUATIONS.

7.1 *Solving Systems of Equations by Graphing*

In this section, you will learn about

- Systems of equations • The graphing method • Inconsistent systems
- Dependent equations

INTRODUCTION. The lines graphed in Figure 7-1 approximate the per-person consumption of chicken and beef in the United States for the years 1990–1997. We can see that consumption of chicken increased, while that of beef decreased.

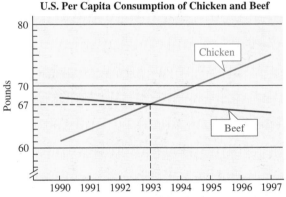

U.S. Per Capita Consumption of Chicken and Beef

Based on data from the National Broiler Council

FIGURE 7-1

By graphing this *pair* of lines on the same coordinate system, it is apparent that Americans consumed equal amounts of chicken and beef in 1993—about 67 pounds of each. In this section, we will work with pairs of linear equations whose graphs are straight lines. We call such a pair of equations a *system of equations*.

Systems of equations

We have previously discussed equations that contain two variables, such as $x + y = 3$. Because there are infinitely many pairs of numbers whose sum is 3, there are infinitely many pairs (x, y) that satisfy this equation. Some of these pairs are

$$x + y = 3$$

x	y	(x, y)
0	3	(0, 3)
1	2	(1, 2)
2	1	(2, 1)
3	0	(3, 0)

Likewise, there are infinitely many pairs (x, y) that satisfy the equation $3x - y = 1$. Some of these pairs are

$$3x - y = 1$$

x	y	(x, y)
0	-1	$(0, -1)$
1	2	$(1, 2)$
2	5	$(2, 5)$
3	8	$(3, 8)$

Although there are infinitely many pairs that satisfy each of these equations, only the pair $(1, 2)$ satisfies both equations at the same time. The pair of equations

$$\begin{cases} x + y = 3 \\ 3x - y = 1 \end{cases}$$

is called a **system of equations.** Because the ordered pair $(1, 2)$ satisfies both equations simultaneously (at the same time), it is called a **simultaneous solution,** or a **solution of the system of equations.** In this chapter, we will discuss three methods for finding the solution of a system of equations.

The graphing method

To use the graphing method to solve

$$\begin{cases} x + y = 3 \\ 3x - y = 1 \end{cases}$$

we graph both equations on one set of coordinate axes using the intercept method, as shown in Figure 7-2.

$$x + y = 3 \qquad\qquad 3x - y = 1$$

x	y	(x, y)		x	y	(x, y)
0	3	$(0, 3)$		0	-1	$(0, -1)$
3	0	$(3, 0)$		$\frac{1}{3}$	0	$\left(\frac{1}{3}, 0\right)$
2	1	$(2, 1)$		2	5	$(2, 5)$

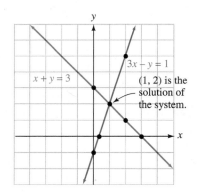

$(1, 2)$ is the solution of the system.

FIGURE 7-2

Although there are infinitely many pairs (x, y) that satisfy $x + y = 3$, and infinitely many pairs (x, y) that satisfy $3x - y = 1$, only the coordinates of the point where their graphs intersect satisfy both equations simultaneously. Thus, the solution of the system is $x = 1$ and $y = 2$, or $(1, 2)$.

To check this solution, we substitute 1 for x and 2 for y in each equation and verify that the pair $(1, 2)$ satisfies each equation.

First equation	**Second equation**
$x + y = 3$	$3x - y = 1$
$1 + 2 \stackrel{?}{=} 3$	$3(1) - 2 \stackrel{?}{=} 1$
$3 = 3$	$3 - 2 \stackrel{?}{=} 1$
	$1 = 1$

When the graphs of two equations in a system are different lines, the equations are called **independent equations.** When a system of equations has a solution, the system is called a **consistent system.**

To solve a system of equations in two variables by graphing, we follow these steps.

The graphing method	1. Carefully graph each equation.
	2. When possible, find the coordinates of the point where the graphs intersect.
	3. Check the solution in the equations of the original system.

EXAMPLE 1   *Solving systems by graphing.* Using graphing to solve
$$\begin{cases} 2x + 3y = 2 \\ 3x = 2y + 16 \end{cases}$$

Solution
Using the intercept method, we graph both equations on one set of coordinate axes, as shown in Figure 7-3.

$2x + 3y = 2$

x	y	(x, y)
0	$\frac{2}{3}$	$(0, \frac{2}{3})$
1	0	$(1, 0)$
-2	2	$(-2, 2)$

$3x = 2y + 16$

x	y	(x, y)
0	-8	$(0, -8)$
$\frac{16}{3}$	0	$(\frac{16}{3}, 0)$
2	-5	$(2, -5)$

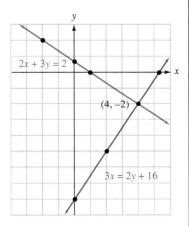

FIGURE 7-3

Although there are infinitely many pairs (x, y) that satisfy $2x + 3y = 2$, and infinitely many pairs (x, y) that satisfy $3x = 2y + 16$, only the coordinates of the point where the graphs intersect satisfy both equations at the same time. The solution is $x = 4$ and $y = -2$, or $(4, -2)$.

To check, we substitute 4 for x and -2 for y in each equation and verify that the pair $(4, -2)$ satisfies each equation.

$$2x + 3y = 2 \qquad\qquad 3x = 2y + 16$$
$$2(4) + 3(-2) \stackrel{?}{=} 2 \qquad 3(4) \stackrel{?}{=} 2(-2) + 16$$
$$8 - 6 \stackrel{?}{=} 2 \qquad\qquad 12 \stackrel{?}{=} -4 + 16$$
$$2 = 2 \qquad\qquad\qquad 12 = 12$$

The equations in this system are independent equations, and the system is a consistent system of equations.

EXAMPLE 2   *Solving an equivalent system.* Solve
$$\begin{cases} -\dfrac{x}{2} - 1 = \dfrac{y}{2} \\ \dfrac{1}{3}x - \dfrac{1}{2}y = -4 \end{cases}$$

Solution
We can multiply both sides of the first equation by 2 to clear it of fractions.

Self Check

Solve $\begin{cases} 2x = y - 5 \\ x + y = -1 \end{cases}$

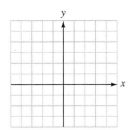

Answer: $(-2, 1)$

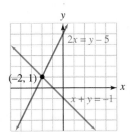

Self Check

Solve $\begin{cases} -\dfrac{x}{2} = \dfrac{y}{4} \\ \dfrac{1}{4}x - \dfrac{3}{8}y = -2 \end{cases}$

$$-\frac{x}{2} - 1 = \frac{y}{2}$$

$$2\left(-\frac{x}{2} - 1\right) = 2\left(\frac{y}{2}\right)$$

(1) $\quad -x - 2 = y \qquad$ We will call this Equation 1.

We then multiply both sides of the second equation by 6 to clear it of fractions.

$$\frac{1}{3}x - \frac{1}{2}y = -4$$

$$6\left(\frac{1}{3}x - \frac{1}{2}y\right) = 6(-4)$$

(2) $\quad 2x - 3y = -24 \qquad$ We will call this Equation 2.

Equations 1 and 2 form the following **equivalent system,** which has the same solutions as the original system:

$$\begin{cases} -x - 2 = y \\ 2x - 3y = -24 \end{cases}$$

In Figure 7-4, we graph $-x - 2 = y$ by plotting the y-intercept $(0, -2)$ and then drawing a slope of -1. We graph $2x - 3y = -24$ using the intercept method. We find that $(-6, 4)$ is the point of intersection. The solution is $x = -6$ and $y = 4$, or $(-6, 4)$.

$$y = -x - 2 \qquad\qquad 2x - 3y = -24$$

so $m = -1 = \dfrac{-1}{1}$

and $b = -2$

x	y	(x, y)
0	8	$(0, 8)$
-12	0	$(-12, 0)$
-3	6	$(-3, 6)$

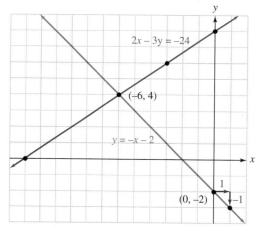

FIGURE 7-4

A check will show that when the coordinates of $(-6, 4)$ are substituted into the two original equations, true statements result. Therefore, the equations are independent and the system is consistent.

Answer: $(-2, 4)$

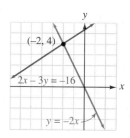

 COMMENT When solving a system of equations, always check your answer by substituting into the *original* equations. Do not check by substituting into the equations of an equivalent system. If an algebraic error was made while finding the equivalent system, an answer that would not satisfy the original system might appear to be correct.

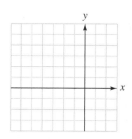

Accent on Technology: *Solving systems with a graphing calculator*

We can use a graphing calculator to solve the system

$$\begin{cases} 2x + y = 12 \\ 2x - y = -2 \end{cases}$$

However, before we can enter the equations into the calculator, we must solve them for y.

$$2x + y = 12 \qquad\qquad 2x - y = -2$$
$$y = -2x + 12 \qquad\qquad -y = -2x - 2$$
$$\qquad\qquad\qquad\qquad y = 2x + 2$$

We enter the resulting equations and graph them on the same coordinate axes. If we use the standard window settings, their graphs will look like Figure 7-5(a).

To find the solution of the system, we use the INTERSECT feature that is found on most graphing calculators. With this option, the cursor automatically moves to the point of intersection of the graphs and displays the coordinates of that point. In Figure 7-5(b), we see that the solution is $(2.5, 7)$. Consult your owner's manual for specific keystrokes to use INTERSECT.

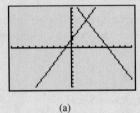
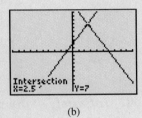

(a)   (b)

FIGURE 7-5

Inconsistent systems

Sometimes a system of equations has no solution. Such systems are called **inconsistent systems**.

EXAMPLE 3   *A system having no solution.*   Solve $\begin{cases} y = -2x - 6 \\ 4x + 2y = 8 \end{cases}$

Self Check

Solve $\begin{cases} y = \dfrac{3}{2}x \\ 3x - 2y = 6 \end{cases}$

Solution

Since $y = -2x - 6$ is written in slope–intercept form, we can graph it by plotting the y-intercept $(0, -6)$ and then drawing a slope of -2. (The run is 1, and the rise is -2.) We graph $4x + 2y = 8$ using the intercept method.

$y = -2x - 6$

so $m = -2 = \dfrac{-2}{1}$

and $b = -6$

$$4x + 2y = 8$$

x	y	(x, y)
0	4	$(0, 4)$
2	0	$(2, 0)$
1	2	$(1, 2)$

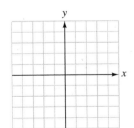

The system is graphed in Figure 7-6. Since the lines in the figure are parallel, they have the same slope. We can verify this by writing the second equation in slope–intercept form and observing that the coefficients of x in each equation are equal.

$$y = -2x - 6 \qquad 4x + 2y = 8$$
$$2y = -4x + 8$$
$$y = -2x + 4$$

Because parallel lines do not intersect, this system has no solution and is inconsistent. Since the graphs are different lines, the equations of the system are independent.

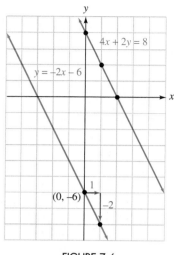

FIGURE 7-6

Answer: The lines are parallel; therefore, the system has no solution.

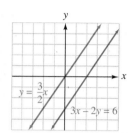

Dependent equations

Sometimes a system has an infinite number of solutions. In this case, we say that the equations of the system are **dependent equations.**

EXAMPLE 4   *Infinitely many solutions.*   Solve $\begin{cases} y - 4 = 2x \\ 4x + 8 = 2y \end{cases}$

Solution

We graph both equations on one set of axes, using the intercept method. See Figure 7-7.

$y - 4 = 2x$		
x	y	(x, y)
0	4	$(0, 4)$
-2	0	$(-2, 0)$
-1	2	$(-1, 2)$

$4x + 8 = 2y$		
x	y	(x, y)
0	4	$(0, 4)$
-2	0	$(-2, 0)$
-3	-2	$(-3, -2)$

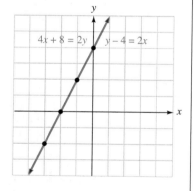

FIGURE 7-7

Self Check

Solve $\begin{cases} 6x - 2y = 4 \\ y + 2 = 3x \end{cases}$

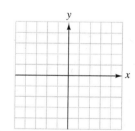

Answer: The graphs are the same line. There is an infinite number of solutions.

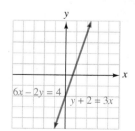

The lines in Figure 7-7 coincide (they are the same line). Because the lines intersect at infinitely many points, there is an infinite number of solutions. Any pair (x, y) that satisfies one of the equations also satisfies the other.

From the graph, we can see that some possible solutions are $(0, 4)$, $(-1, 2)$, and $(-3, -2)$, since each of these points lies on the one line that is the graph of both equations.

The possibilities that can occur when graphing two linear equations, each with two variables, are summarized as follows.

Possible graph	If the	Then
	lines are different and intersect,	the equations are independent and the system is consistent. One solution exists.
	lines are different and parallel,	the equations are independent and the system is inconsistent. No solutions exist.
	lines are the same,	the equations are dependent and the system is consistent. Infinitely many solutions exist.

STUDY SET Section 7.1

VOCABULARY *Fill in the blanks.*

1. The pair of equations $\begin{cases} x - y = -1 \\ 2x - y = 1 \end{cases}$ is called a _____system_____ of equations.

2. Because the ordered pair (2, 3) satisfies both equations in Exercise 1, it is called a _____solution_____ of the system of equations.

3. When the graphs of two equations in a system are different lines, the equations are called _____independent_____ equations.

4. When a system of equations has a solution, the system is called a _____consistent_____ system.

5. Systems of equations that have no solution are called _____inconsistent_____ systems.

6. When a system has infinitely many solutions, the equations of the system are said to be _____dependent_____ equations.

CONCEPTS *Refer to Illustration 1. Tell whether a true or false statement would be obtained when the coordinates of*

7. point A are substituted into the equation for line l_1.   true

8. point B are substituted into the equation for line l_2.   true

9. point A are substituted into the equation for line l_2.   false

10. point B are substituted into the equation for line l_1.   false

11. point C are substituted into the equation for line l_1.   true

12. point C are substituted into the equation for line l_2.   true

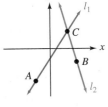

ILLUSTRATION 1

In Exercises 13–14, a furniture company is considering manufacturing a new line of oak chairs. Graphs showing the cost to make the chairs and the revenue the company will receive from their sale are given in Illustration 2.

13. a. What will it cost to make 30 chairs? $2,000

  b. What revenue will the sale of 30 chairs bring? $1,200

  c. How much money will the company make or lose in this case?   lose $800

14. a. How many chairs must be built and sold so that the costs and the revenue are the same?   70

  b. Why do you think (70, 2,800) is called the "break-even point"?   costs = revenue

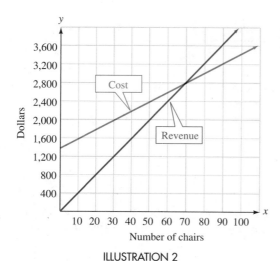

ILLUSTRATION 2

15. How many solutions does the system of equations graphed in Illustration 3 have? Is the system consistent or inconsistent?
1 solution; consistent

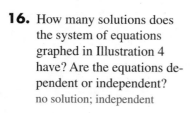

ILLUSTRATION 3

16. How many solutions does the system of equations graphed in Illustration 4 have? Are the equations dependent or independent?
no solution; independent

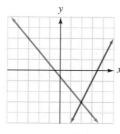

ILLUSTRATION 4

17. The solution of the system of equations graphed in Illustration 5 is $\left(\frac{2}{5}, -\frac{1}{3}\right)$. Knowing this, can you see any disadvantages to the graphing method?
The method is not accurate enough to find a solution such as $\left(\frac{2}{5}, -\frac{1}{3}\right)$.

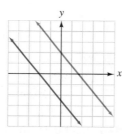

ILLUSTRATION 5

18. Draw the graphs of two linear equations so that the system has
a. one solution $(-3, -2)$.
    Answers may vary.

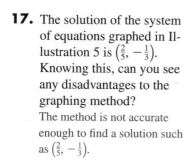

b. infinitely many solutions, three of which are $(-2, 0)$, $(1, 2)$, and $(4, 4)$.

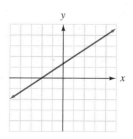

NOTATION   *Clear each equation of fractions.*

19.
$$\frac{1}{6}x - \frac{1}{3}y = \frac{11}{2}$$
$$6\left(\frac{1}{6}x - \frac{1}{3}y\right) = 6\left(\frac{11}{2}\right)$$
$$6\left(\frac{1}{6}x\right) - 6\left(\frac{1}{3}y\right) = 6\left(\frac{11}{2}\right)$$
$$x - 2y = 33$$

20.
$$\frac{3x}{5} - \frac{4y}{5} = -1$$
$$5\left(\frac{3x}{5} - \frac{4y}{5}\right) = 5(-1)$$
$$5\left(\frac{3x}{5}\right) - 5\left(\frac{4y}{5}\right) = 5(-1)$$
$$3x - 4y = -5$$

PRACTICE   *Tell whether the ordered pair is a solution of the given system.*

21. $(1, 1)$, $\begin{cases} x + y = 2 \\ 2x - y = 1 \end{cases}$ yes

22. $(1, 3)$, $\begin{cases} 2x + y = 5 \\ 3x - y = 0 \end{cases}$ yes

23. $(3, -2)$, $\begin{cases} 2x + y = 4 \\ y = 1 - x \end{cases}$ yes

24. $(-2, 4)$, $\begin{cases} 2x + 2y = 4 \\ 3y = 10 - x \end{cases}$ yes

25. $(-2, -4)$, $\begin{cases} 4x + 5y = -23 \\ -3x + 2y = 0 \end{cases}$ no

26. $(-5, 2)$, $\begin{cases} -2x + 7y = 17 \\ 3x - 4y = -19 \end{cases}$ no

27. $\left(\frac{1}{2}, 3\right)$, $\begin{cases} 2x + y = 4 \\ 4x - 11 = 3y \end{cases}$ no

28. $\left(2, \frac{1}{3}\right)$, $\begin{cases} x - 3y = 1 \\ -2x + 6 = -6y \end{cases}$ no

29. $\left(-\frac{2}{5}, \frac{1}{4}\right)$, $\begin{cases} x - 4y = -6 \\ 8y = 10x + 12 \end{cases}$ no

30. $\left(-\frac{1}{3}, \frac{3}{4}\right)$, $\begin{cases} 3x + 4y = 2 \\ 12y = 3(2 - 3x) \end{cases}$ yes

31. $(0.2, 0.3)$, $\begin{cases} 20x + 10y = 7 \\ 20y = 15x + 3 \end{cases}$ yes

32. $(2.5, 3.5)$, $\begin{cases} 4x - 3 = 2y \\ 4y + 1 = 6x \end{cases}$ yes

Solve each system by the graphing method. If the equations of a system are dependent or if a system is inconsistent, so indicate.

33. $\begin{cases} x + y = 2 \\ x - y = 0 \end{cases}$

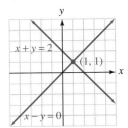

34. $\begin{cases} x + y = 4 \\ x - y = 0 \end{cases}$

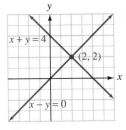

35. $\begin{cases} x + y = 2 \\ y = x - 4 \end{cases}$

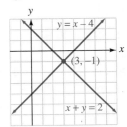

36. $\begin{cases} x + y = 1 \\ y = x + 5 \end{cases}$

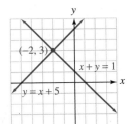

37. $\begin{cases} 3x + 2y = -8 \\ 2x - 3y = -1 \end{cases}$

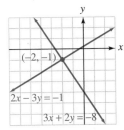

38. $\begin{cases} x + 4y = -2 \\ y = -x - 5 \end{cases}$

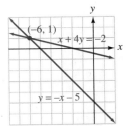

39. $\begin{cases} 4x - 2y = 8 \\ y = 2x - 4 \end{cases}$

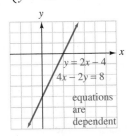

40. $\begin{cases} 3x - 6y = 18 \\ x = 2y + 3 \end{cases}$

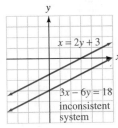

41. $\begin{cases} 2x - 3y = -18 \\ 3x + 2y = -1 \end{cases}$

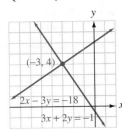

42. $\begin{cases} -x + 3y = -11 \\ 3x - y = 17 \end{cases}$

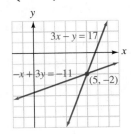

43. $\begin{cases} x = 4 \\ 2y = 12 - 4x \end{cases}$

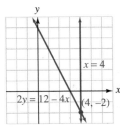

44. $\begin{cases} x = 3 \\ 3y = 6 - 2x \end{cases}$

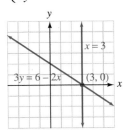

45. $\begin{cases} x + 2y = -4 \\ x - \frac{1}{2}y = 6 \end{cases}$

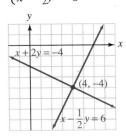

46. $\begin{cases} \frac{2}{3}x - y = -3 \\ 3x + y = 3 \end{cases}$

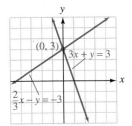

47. $\begin{cases} -\frac{3}{4}x + y = 3 \\ \frac{1}{4}x + y = -1 \end{cases}$

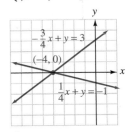

48. $\begin{cases} \frac{1}{3}x + y = 7 \\ \frac{2x}{3} - y = -4 \end{cases}$

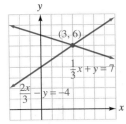

49. $\begin{cases} 2y = 3x + 2 \\ \frac{3}{2}x - y = 3 \end{cases}$

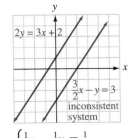

50. $\begin{cases} -\frac{3}{5}x - \frac{1}{5}y = \frac{6}{5} \\ x + \frac{y}{3} = -2 \end{cases}$

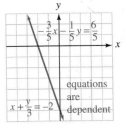

51. $\begin{cases} \frac{1}{3}x - \frac{1}{2}y = \frac{1}{6} \\ \frac{2x}{5} + \frac{y}{2} = \frac{13}{10} \end{cases}$

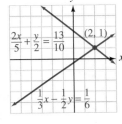

52. $\begin{cases} \frac{3x}{4} + \frac{2y}{3} = -\frac{19}{6} \\ 3y = -x \end{cases}$

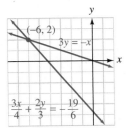

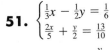 *Use a graphing calculator to solve each system, if possible.*

53. $\begin{cases} y = 4 - x \\ y = 2 + x \end{cases}$ $(1, 3)$

54. $\begin{cases} 3x - 6y = 4 \\ 2x + y = 1 \end{cases}$ $\left(\frac{2}{3}, -\frac{1}{3}\right)$

55. $\begin{cases} 6x - 2y = 5 \\ 3x = y + 10 \end{cases}$ **56.** $\begin{cases} x - 3y = -2 \\ 5x + y = 10 \end{cases}$

no solution   (1.75, 1.25)

APPLICATIONS

57. TRANSPLANTS   See Illustration 6.
  a. What was the relationship between the number of donors and those awaiting a transplant in 1989?
  Donors outnumbered those needing a transplant.
  b. In what year were the number of donors and the number waiting for a transplant the same? Estimate the number.   1994; 4,100

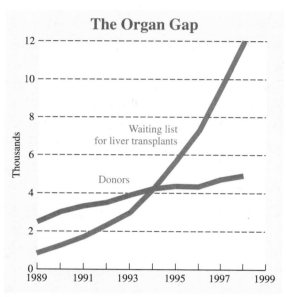

The Organ Gap

Based on data from United Network for Organ Sharing

ILLUSTRATION 6

58. DAILY TRACKING POLL   See Illustration 7.
  a. Which political candidate was ahead on October 28 and by how much?   the incumbent; 7%
  b. On what day did the challenger pull even with the incumbent?   November 2
  c. If the election was held November 4, who did the poll predict would win, and by how many percentage points?   the challenger; 3

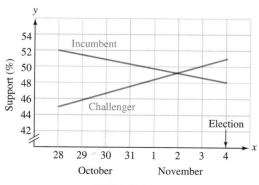

ILLUSTRATION 7

59. LATITUDE AND LONGITUDE   See Illustration 8.
  a. Name three American cities that lie on a latitude line of 30° north.
  Houston, New Orleans, St. Augustine
  b. Name three American cities that lie on a longitude line of 90° west.   St. Louis, Memphis, New Orleans
  c. What city lies on both lines?   New Orleans

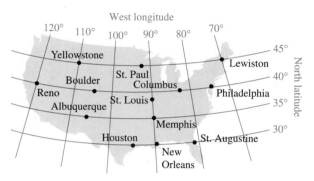

ILLUSTRATION 8

60. ECONOMICS   The graph in Illustration 9 illustrates the law of supply and demand.
  a. Complete this sentence: As the price of an item increases, the *supply* of the item _____increases_____.
  b. Complete this sentence: As the price of an item increases, the *demand* for the item _____decreases_____.
  c. For what price will the supply equal the demand? How many items will be supplied for this price?
  $6; 30,000

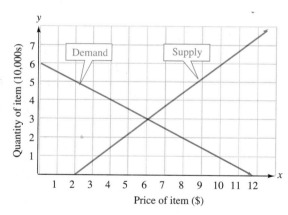

ILLUSTRATION 9

61. AIR TRAFFIC CONTROL   The equations describing the paths of two airplanes are $y = -\frac{1}{2}x + 3$ and $3y = 2x + 2$. Graph each equation on the radar screen shown in Illustration 10. Is there a possibility of a mid-air collision? If so, where?   yes, (2, 2)

62. TV COVERAGE   A television camera is located at $(-2, 0)$ and will follow the launch of a space shuttle, as shown in Illustration 11. (Each unit in the illustration is 1 mile.) As the shuttle rises vertically on a path described by $x = 2$, the farthest the camera can tilt back is a line of sight given by $y = \frac{5}{2}x + 5$. For how many miles of the shuttle's flight will it be in view of the camera?   10 mi

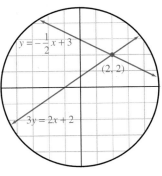

ILLUSTRATION 10

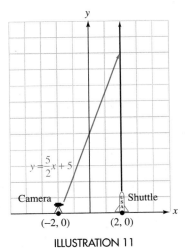

ILLUSTRATION 11

WRITING

63. Look up the word *simultaneous* in a dictionary and give its definition. In mathematics, what is meant by a simultaneous solution of a system of equations?

64. Suppose the solution of a system is $\left(\frac{1}{3}, -\frac{3}{5}\right)$. Do you think you would be able to find the solution using the graphing method? Explain.

REVIEW

65. What is the slope and the y-intercept of the graph of the line $y = -3x + 4$? $-3; (0, 4)$

66. Are the graphs of the lines $y = 5x$ and $y = -\frac{1}{5}x$ parallel, perpendicular, or neither? perpendicular

67. If $f(x) = -4x - x^2$, find $f(3)$. -21

68. In what quadrant does $(-12, 15)$ lie? quadrant II

69. Write the equation for the y-axis. $x = 0$

70. Does $(1, 2)$ lie on the line $2x + y = 4$? yes

71. What point does the line with equation $y - 2 = 7(x - 5)$ pass through? $(5, 2)$

72. Is the word *domain* associated with the inputs or the outputs of a function? inputs

---

7.2 *Solving Systems of Equations by Substitution*

In this section, you will learn about

- The substitution method • Inconsistent systems • Dependent equations

INTRODUCTION. When solving a system of equations by the graphing method, it is often difficult to determine the exact coordinates of the point of intersection. For example, it would be virtually impossible to distinguish that two lines intersect at the point $\left(\frac{1}{16}, -\frac{3}{5}\right)$. In this section, we introduce an algebraic method that finds *exact* solutions. It is called the *substitution method*. This method is based on the **substitution principle**: If $a = b$, then a may replace b or b may replace a in any statement.

The substitution method

To solve the system

$$\begin{cases} y = 3x - 2 \\ 2x + y = 8 \end{cases}$$

by the **substitution method**, we note that the first equation, $y = 3x - 2$, is *solved for y* (or *y is expressed in terms of x*). Because $y = 3x - 2$, we can substitute $3x - 2$ for y in the equation $2x + y = 8$ to get

$$2x + y = 8 \quad \text{The second equation of the system.}$$
$$2x + 3x - 2 = 8 \quad \text{Substitute } 3x - 2 \text{ for } y.$$

The resulting equation has only one variable and can be solved for x.

$$2x + 3x - 2 = 8$$
$$5x - 2 = 8 \quad \text{Combine like terms: } 2x + 3x = 5x.$$
$$5x = 10 \quad \text{Add 2 to both sides.}$$
$$x = 2 \quad \text{Divide both sides by 5.}$$

We can find y by substituting 2 for x in either equation of the given system. Because $y = 3x - 2$ is already solved for y, it is easier to substitute into this equation.

$$y = 3x - 2 \quad \text{The first equation of the system.}$$
$$= 3(2) - 2 \quad \text{Substitute 2 for } x.$$
$$= 6 - 2$$
$$y = 4$$

The solution to the given system is $x = 2$ and $y = 4$, or $(2, 4)$.

Check: **First equation**   **Second equation**

$$y = 3x - 2 \qquad\qquad 2x + y = 8$$
$$4 \stackrel{?}{=} 3(2) - 2 \qquad\qquad 2(2) + 4 \stackrel{?}{=} 8$$
$$4 \stackrel{?}{=} 6 - 2 \qquad\qquad 4 + 4 \stackrel{?}{=} 8$$
$$4 = 4 \qquad\qquad\qquad 8 = 8$$

If we graphed the lines represented by the equations of the given system, they would intersect at the point $(2, 4)$. The equations of this system are independent, and the system is consistent.

To solve a system of equations in x and y by the substitution method, we follow these steps.

The substitution method

1. Solve one of the equations for either x or y. (This step will not be necessary if an equation is already solved for x or y.)

2. Substitute the resulting expression for the variable obtained in Step 1 into the remaining equation and solve that equation.

3. Find the value of the other variable by substituting the solution found in Step 2 into any equation containing both variables.

4. Check the solution in the equations of the original system.

EXAMPLE 1   *Solving systems by substitution.*   Solve $\begin{cases} 2x + y = -10 \\ x = -3y \end{cases}$

Self Check

Solve $\begin{cases} y = -2x \\ 3x - 2y = -7 \end{cases}$

Solution

The second equation, $x = -3y$, tells us that x and $-3y$ have the same value. Therefore, we may substitute $-3y$ for x in the first equation.

$$2x + y = -10 \quad \text{The first equation of the system.}$$
$$2(-3y) + y = -10 \quad \text{Replace } x \text{ with } -3y.$$
$$-6y + y = -10 \quad \text{Do the multiplication.}$$
$$-5y = -10 \quad \text{Combine like terms.}$$
$$y = 2 \quad \text{Divide both sides by } -5.$$

We can find x by substituting 2 for y in the equation $x = -3y$.

$x = -3y$ The second equation of the system.

$= -3(2)$ Substitute 2 for y.

$= -6$

The solution is $x = -6$ and $y = 2$, or $(-6, 2)$.

Check: **First equation**   **Second equation**

$$2x + y = -10 \qquad x = -3y$$
$$2(-6) + 2 \overset{?}{=} -10 \qquad -6 \overset{?}{=} -3(2)$$
$$-12 + 2 \overset{?}{=} -10 \qquad -6 = -6$$
$$-10 = -10$$

Answer: $(-1, 2)$ ■

EXAMPLE 2   *Solving for a variable first.*   Solve $\begin{cases} 2x + y = -5 \\ 3x + 5y = -4 \end{cases}$

Self Check

Solve $\begin{cases} 2x - 3y = 13 \\ 3x + y = 3 \end{cases}$

Solution

We solve one of the equations for one of the variables. Since the term y in the first equation has a coefficient of 1, we solve the first equation for y.

$2x + y = -5$ The first equation of the system.

$y = -5 - 2x$ Subtract $2x$ from both sides to isolate y.

We then substitute $-5 - 2x$ for y in the second equation and solve for x.

$3x + 5y = -4$ The second equation of the system.

$3x + 5(-5 - 2x) = -4$ Substitute $-5 - 2x$ for y.

$3x - 25 - 10x = -4$ Distribute the multiplication by 5.

$-7x - 25 = -4$ Combine like terms: $3x - 10x = -7x$.

$-7x = 21$ Add 25 to both sides.

$x = -3$ Divide both sides by -7.

We can find y by substituting -3 for x in the equation $y = -5 - 2x$.

$y = -5 - 2x$

$= -5 - 2(-3)$ Substitute -3 for x.

$= -5 + 6$

$= 1$

The solution is $(-3, 1)$. Check it in the original equations.

Answer: $(2, -3)$ ■

Systems of equations are sometimes written in variables other than x and y. For example, the system

$$\begin{cases} 3a - 3b = 5 \\ 3 - a = -2b \end{cases}$$

is written in a and b. Regardless of the variables used, the procedures used to solve the system remain the same. The solution should be expressed in the form (a, b).

EXAMPLE 3   *Solving for a variable first.*   Solve $\begin{cases} 3a - 3b = 5 \\ 3 - a = -2b \end{cases}$

Self Check

Solve $\begin{cases} 2s - t = 4 \\ 3s - 5t = 2 \end{cases}$

Solution

Since the coefficient of a in the second equation is -1, we will solve that equation for a.

$$3 - a = -2b \qquad \text{The second equation of the system.}$$
$$-a = -2b - 3 \qquad \text{Subtract 3 from both sides.}$$

To obtain a on the left-hand side, we can multiply (or divide) both sides of the equation by -1.

$$-1(-a) = -1(-2b - 3) \qquad \text{Multiply both sides by } -1.$$
$$a = 2b + 3 \qquad \text{Do the multiplications.}$$

We then substitute $2b + 3$ for a in the first equation and proceed as follows:

$$3a - 3b = 5$$
$$3(2b + 3) - 3b = 5 \qquad \text{Substitute.}$$
$$6b + 9 - 3b = 5 \qquad \text{Distribute the multiplication by 3.}$$
$$3b + 9 = 5 \qquad \text{Combine like terms.}$$
$$3b = -4 \qquad \text{Subtract 9 from both sides: } 5 - 9 = -4.$$
$$b = -\frac{4}{3} \qquad \text{Divide both sides by 3.}$$

To find a, we substitute $-\frac{4}{3}$ for b in $a = 2b + 3$ and simplify.

$$a = 2b + 3$$
$$= 2\left(-\frac{4}{3}\right) + 3 \qquad \text{Substitute.}$$
$$= -\frac{8}{3} + \frac{9}{3} \qquad \text{Do the multiplication: } 2\left(-\frac{4}{3}\right) = -\frac{8}{3}. \text{ Write 3 as } \frac{9}{3}.$$
$$= \frac{1}{3} \qquad \text{Add the numerators and keep the common denominator.}$$

The solution is $\left(\frac{1}{3}, -\frac{4}{3}\right)$. Check it in the original equations.

Answer: $\left(\dfrac{18}{7}, \dfrac{8}{7}\right)$ ■

EXAMPLE 4   *Solving an equivalent system.*   Solve

$$\begin{cases} \dfrac{x}{2} + \dfrac{y}{4} = -\dfrac{1}{4} \\ 2x - y = 2 + y - x \end{cases}$$

Self Check

Solve $\begin{cases} \dfrac{1}{3}x - \dfrac{1}{6}y = -\dfrac{1}{3} \\ x + y = -3 - 2x - y \end{cases}$

Solution
It is helpful to rewrite each equation in simpler form before performing a substitution. We begin by clearing the first equation of fractions.

$$\frac{x}{2} + \frac{y}{4} = -\frac{1}{4}$$
$$4\left(\frac{x}{2} + \frac{y}{4}\right) = 4\left(-\frac{1}{4}\right) \qquad \text{Multiply both sides by the LCD, which is 4.}$$
$$2x + y = -1$$

We can write the second equation in general form ($Ax + By = C$) by adding x and subtracting y from both sides.

$$2x - y = 2 + y - x$$
$$2x - y + x - y = 2 + y - x + x - y$$
$$3x - 2y = 2 \qquad \text{Combine like terms.}$$

The two results form the following equivalent system, which has the same solution as the original one.

(1) $\begin{cases} 2x + y = -1 \\ 3x - 2y = 2 \end{cases}$
(2)

To solve this system, we solve Equation 1 for y.

$$2x + y = -1$$
$$2x + y - 2x = -1 - 2x \quad \text{Subtract } 2x \text{ from both sides.}$$
$$\textbf{(3)} \qquad y = -1 - 2x \quad \text{Combine like terms.}$$

To find x, we substitute $-1 - 2x$ for y in Equation 2 and proceed as follows:

$$3x - 2y = 2$$
$$3x - 2(-1 - 2x) = 2 \quad \text{Substitute.}$$
$$3x + 2 + 4x = 2 \quad \text{Distribute the multiplication by } -2.$$
$$7x + 2 = 2 \quad \text{Combine like terms.}$$
$$7x = 0 \quad \text{Subtract 2 from both sides.}$$
$$x = 0 \quad \text{Divide both sides by 7.}$$

To find y, we substitute 0 for x in Equation 3.

$$y = -1 - 2x$$
$$y = -1 - 2(\mathbf{0})$$
$$y = -1$$

The solution is $(0, -1)$. Check it in the original equations.

Answer: $(-1, 0)$

Inconsistent systems

EXAMPLE 5 *A system with no solution.* Solve $\begin{cases} 0.01x = 0.12 - 0.04y \\ 2x = 4(3 - 2y) \end{cases}$

Self Check

Solve $\begin{cases} 0.1x - 0.4 = 0.1y \\ -2y = 2(2 - x) \end{cases}$

Solution

The first equation contains decimal coefficients. We can clear the equation of decimals by multiplying both sides by 100.

$$\begin{cases} x = 12 - 4y \\ 2x = 4(3 - 2y) \end{cases}$$

Since $x = 12 - 4y$, we can substitute $12 - 4y$ for x in the second equation and solve for y.

$$2x = 4(3 - 2y) \quad \text{The second equation.}$$
$$2(\mathbf{12 - 4y}) = 4(3 - 2y) \quad \text{Substitute.}$$
$$24 - 8y = 12 - 8y \quad \text{Distribute.}$$
$$24 \neq 12 \quad \text{Add } 8y \text{ to both sides.}$$

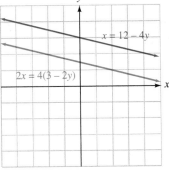

FIGURE 7-8

Here, the terms involving y drop out, and a false result of $24 = 12$ is obtained. This result indicates that the equations are independent and also that the system is inconsistent. As we see in Figure 7-8, when the equations are graphed, the graphs are parallel lines. This system has no solution.

Answer: no solution

Dependent equations

EXAMPLE 6 *Infinitely many solutions.* Solve $\begin{cases} x = -3y + 6 \\ 2x + 6y = 12 \end{cases}$

Self Check

Solve $\begin{cases} y = 2 - x \\ 3x + 3y = 6 \end{cases}$

Solution

We can substitute $-3y + 6$ for x in the second equation and proceed as follows:

$$2x + 6y = 12 \quad \text{The second equation of the system.}$$
$$2(-3y + 6) + 6y = 12 \quad \text{Substitute.}$$
$$-6y + 12 + 6y = 12 \quad \text{Distribute the multiplication by 2.}$$
$$12 = 12 \quad \text{Combine like terms.}$$

Although $12 = 12$ is true, we did not find y. This indicates that the equations are dependent. As we see in Figure 7-9, when these equations are graphed, their graphs are identical.

Because any ordered pair that satisfies one equation of the system also satisfies the other, the system has infinitely many solutions. To find some, we substitute 0, 3, and 6 for x in either equation and solve for y. The pairs $(0, 2)$, $(3, 1)$, and $(6, 0)$ are some of the solutions.

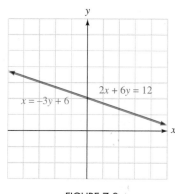

FIGURE 7-9

Answer: infinitely many solutions

Study Set Section 7.2

VOCABULARY *Fill in the blanks.*

1. We say that the equation $y = 2x + 4$ is solved for __y__ or that y is expressed in ____terms____ of x.

2. "To ____check____ a solution of a system" means to see whether the coordinates of the ordered pair satisfy both equations.

3. When we write $2(x - 6)$ as $2x - 12$, we are applying the ____distributive____ property.

4. In mathematics, "to ____substitute____" means to replace an expression with one that is equivalent to it.

5. A dependent system has ____infinitely____ many solutions.

6. In the term y, the ____coefficient____ is understood to be 1.

CONCEPTS

7. Consider the system $\begin{cases} 2x + 3y = 12 \\ y = 2x + 4 \end{cases}$

a. How many variables does each equation of the system contain?   2

b. Substitute $2x + 4$ for y in the first equation. How many variables does the resulting equation contain?   1

8. For each equation, solve for y.

a. $y + 2 = x$ $y = x - 2$

b. $2 - y = x$ $y = 2 - x$

c. $2 + x + y = 0$ $y = -x - 2$

9. Given the equation $x - 2y = -10$,

a. solve it for x. $x = 2y - 10$

b. solve it for y. $y = \frac{x}{2} + 5$

c. which variable was easier to solve for, x or y? Explain. x; it involved only one step.

10. Which variable in which equation should be solved for in step 1 of the substitution method?

a. $\begin{cases} x - 2y = 2 \\ 2x + 3y = 11 \end{cases}$ Solve for x in the first equation.

b. $\begin{cases} 2x - 3y = 2 \\ 2x - y = 11 \end{cases}$ Solve for y in the second equation.

c. $\begin{cases} 7x - 3y = 2 \\ 2x - 8y = 0 \end{cases}$ Solve for x in the second equation.

11. a. Find the error in the following work when $x - 4$ is substituted for y.

$$x + 2y = 5 \quad \text{The first equation of the system.}$$
$$x + 2x - 4 = 5 \quad \text{Substitute for } y: y = x - 4.$$
$$3x - 4 = 5 \quad \text{Combine like terms.}$$
$$3x = 9 \quad \text{Add 4 to both sides.}$$
$$x = 3 \quad \text{Do the divisions.}$$

Parentheses must be written around $x - 4$ in line 2.

b. Rework the problem to find the correct value of x. $\frac{13}{3}$

12. A student uses the substitution method to solve the system $\begin{cases} 4a + 5b = 2 \\ b = 3a - 11 \end{cases}$. She finds that $a = 3$. What is the easiest way for her to determine the value of b?

Substitute 3 for a in the second equation.

13. Consider the system $\begin{cases} x - 2y = 0 \\ 6x + 3y = 5 \end{cases}$

  a. Graph the equations on the same coordinate system. Why is it difficult to determine the solution of the system?
  The coordinates of the intersection point are not integers.

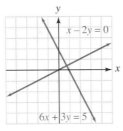

  b. Solve the system by the substitution method. $\left(\frac{2}{3}, \frac{1}{3}\right)$

14. The equation $-2 = 1$ is the result when a system is solved by the substitution method. Which graph in Illustration 1 is a possible graph of the system?
  the second graph

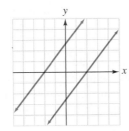

ILLUSTRATION 1

NOTATION *Complete the solution of each system.*

15. Solve $\begin{cases} y = 3x \\ x - y = 4 \end{cases}$

$\quad\quad x - y = 4 \quad\quad$ The second equation.

$\quad x - \left(3x\right) = 4$

$\quad\quad -2x = 4$

$\quad\quad x = -2$

$\quad\quad y = 3x \quad\quad$ The first equation.

$\quad\quad y = 3\left(-2\right)$

$\quad\quad y = -6$

The solution is $(-2, -6)$.

16. Solve $\begin{cases} 2x + y = -5 \\ 2 - 2y = x \end{cases}$

$\quad 2x + y = -5 \quad\quad$ The first equation.

$2\left(2 - 2y\right) + y = -5$

$\quad 4 - 4y + y = -5$

$\quad 4 - 3y = -5$

$\quad\quad -3y = -9$

$\quad\quad y = 3$

$\quad 2 - 2y = x \quad\quad$ The second equation.

$\quad 2 - 2\left(3\right) = x$

$\quad 2 - 6 = x$

$\quad -4 = x$

The solution is $(-4, 3)$.

PRACTICE *Use the substitution method to solve each system. If the equations of a system are dependent or if a system is inconsistent, so indicate.*

17. $\begin{cases} y = 2x \\ x + y = 6 \end{cases}$ $(2, 4)$
18. $\begin{cases} y = 3x \\ x + y = 4 \end{cases}$ $(1, 3)$

19. $\begin{cases} y = 2x - 6 \\ 2x + y = 6 \end{cases}$ $(3, 0)$
20. $\begin{cases} y = 2x - 9 \\ x + 3y = 8 \end{cases}$ $(5, 1)$

21. $\begin{cases} y = 2x + 5 \\ x + 2y = -5 \end{cases}$ $(-3, -1)$
22. $\begin{cases} y = -2x \\ 3x + 2y = -1 \end{cases}$ $(1, -2)$

23. $\begin{cases} 2a + 4b = -24 \\ a = 20 - 2b \end{cases}$ inconsistent system
24. $\begin{cases} 3a + 6b = -15 \\ a = -2b - 5 \end{cases}$ dependent equations

25. $\begin{cases} 2a = 3b - 13 \\ -b = -2a - 7 \end{cases}$ $(-2, 3)$
26. $\begin{cases} a = 3b - 1 \\ -b = -2a - 2 \end{cases}$ $(-1, 0)$

27. $\begin{cases} r + 3s = 9 \\ 3r + 2s = 13 \end{cases}$ $(3, 2)$
28. $\begin{cases} x - 2y = 2 \\ 2x + 3y = 11 \end{cases}$ $(4, 1)$

29. $\begin{cases} 0.4x + 0.5y = 0.2 \\ 3x - y = 11 \end{cases}$ $(3, -2)$
30. $\begin{cases} 0.5u + 0.3v = 0.5 \\ 4u - v = 4 \end{cases}$ $(1, 0)$

31. $\begin{cases} 6x - 3y = 5 \\ 2y + x = 0 \end{cases}$ $\left(\frac{2}{3}, -\frac{1}{3}\right)$
32. $\begin{cases} 5s + 10t = 3 \\ 2s + t = 0 \end{cases}$ $\left(-\frac{1}{5}, \frac{2}{5}\right)$

33. $\begin{cases} 3x + 4y = -7 \\ 2y - x = -1 \end{cases}$ $(-1, -1)$
34. $\begin{cases} 4x + 5y = -2 \\ x + 2y = -2 \end{cases}$ $(2, -2)$

35. $\begin{cases} 9x = 3y + 12 \\ 4 = 3x - y \end{cases}$ dependent equations
36. $\begin{cases} 8y = 15 - 4x \\ x + 2y = 4 \end{cases}$ inconsistent system

37. $\begin{cases} 0.02x + 0.05y = -0.02 \\ -\frac{x}{2} = y \end{cases}$ $(4, -2)$

38. $\begin{cases} y = -\frac{x}{2} \\ 0.02x - 0.03y = -0.07 \end{cases}$ $(-2, 1)$

39. $\begin{cases} b = \frac{2}{3}a \\ 8a - 3b = 3 \end{cases}$ $\left(\frac{1}{2}, \frac{1}{3}\right)$
40. $\begin{cases} a = \frac{2}{3}b \\ 9a + 4b = 5 \end{cases}$ $\left(\frac{1}{3}, \frac{1}{2}\right)$

41. $\begin{cases} y - x = 3x \\ 2x + 2y = 14 - y \end{cases}$ $(1, 4)$
42. $\begin{cases} y + x = 2x + 2 \\ 6x - 4y = 21 - y \end{cases}$ $(9, 11)$

43. $\begin{cases} 2x - y = x + y \\ -2x + 4y = 6 \end{cases}$ inconsistent system
44. $\begin{cases} x = -3y + 6 \\ 2x + 4y = 6 + x + y \end{cases}$ dependent equations

45. $\begin{cases} 3(x - 1) + 3 = 8 + 2y \\ 2(x + 1) = 8 + y \end{cases}$ $(4, 2)$

46. $\begin{cases} 4(x - 2) = 19 - 5y \\ 3(x - 2) - 2y = -y \end{cases}$ $(3, 3)$

47. $\begin{cases} \frac{1}{2}x + \frac{1}{2}y = -1 \\ \frac{1}{3}x - \frac{1}{2}y = -4 \end{cases}$ $(-6, 4)$
48. $\begin{cases} \frac{2}{3}y + \frac{1}{5}z = 1 \\ \frac{1}{3}y - \frac{2}{5}z = 3 \end{cases}$ $(3, -5)$

49. $\begin{cases} 5x = \frac{1}{2}y - 1 \\ \frac{1}{4}y = 10x - 1 \end{cases}$ $\left(\frac{1}{5}, 4\right)$
50. $\begin{cases} \frac{2}{3}x = 1 - 2y \\ 2(5y - x) + 11 = 0 \end{cases}$ $\left(3, -\frac{1}{2}\right)$

51. $\begin{cases} \dfrac{6x-1}{3} - \dfrac{5}{3} = \dfrac{3y+1}{2} \\ \dfrac{1+5y}{4} + \dfrac{x+3}{4} = \dfrac{17}{2} \end{cases}$ (5, 5)

52. $\begin{cases} \dfrac{5x-2}{4} + \dfrac{1}{2} = \dfrac{3y+2}{2} \\ \dfrac{7y+3}{3} = \dfrac{x}{2} + \dfrac{7}{3} \end{cases}$ (2, 1)

APPLICATIONS

53. DINING   See the breakfast menu in Illustration 2. What substitution from the a la carte menu will the restaurant owner allow customers to make if they don't want hash browns with their country breakfast? Why?

melon, because it's the same price as hash browns

Village Vault Restaurant			
Country Breakfast $5.95			
Includes 2 eggs, 3 pancakes, sausage, bacon, hash browns, and coffee			
A la Carte Menu–Single Servings			
Strawberries	$1.25	Melon	$0.95
Croissant	$1.70	Orange juice	$1.65
Hash browns	$0.95	Oatmeal	$1.95
Muffin	$1.30	Ham	$1.80

ILLUSTRATION 2

54. DISCOUNT COUPON   In mathematics, the substitution property states:

If a = b, then a may replace b or b may replace a in any statement.

Where on the coupon in Illustration 3 is there an application of the substitution property? Explain.

An entree of equal value may be substituted for the second roast beef dinner.

WRITING

55. Explain how to use substitution to solve a system of equations.

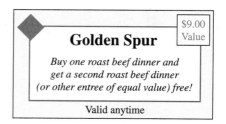

Golden Spur

$9.00 Value

Buy one roast beef dinner and get a second roast beef dinner (or other entree of equal value) free!

Valid anytime

ILLUSTRATION 3

56. If the equations of a system are written in general form, why is it to your advantage to solve for a variable whose coefficient is 1 when using the substitution method?

57. When solving a system, what advantages and disadvantages are there with the graphing method? With the substitution method?

58. In this section, the substitution method for solving a system of two equations was discussed. List some other uses of the word *substitution,* or *substitute,* that you encounter in everyday life.

REVIEW

59. What is the slope of the line $y = -\dfrac{5}{8}x - 12$? $-\frac{5}{8}$

60. If $g(x) = -3x + 9$, find $g(-3)$.   18

61. Find the y-intercept of $2x - 3y = 18$.   (0, −6)

62. Write the equation of the line passing through $(-1, 5)$ with a slope of -3. $y = -3x + 2$

63. Can a circle represent the graph of a function?   no

64. What is the range of the function $f(x) = |x|$?
all real numbers greater than or equal to 0

65. A bowler has found that his score s varies directly with the time t in minutes he practices. Write an equation describing this relationship. $s = kt$

66. On what axis does $(0, -2)$ lie?   y-axis

7.3 *Solving Systems of Equations by Addition*

In this section, you will learn about

- The addition method • Inconsistent systems • Dependent equations

INTRODUCTION. In step 1 of the substitution method for solving a system of equations, we solve one equation for one of the variables. At times, this can be difficult—especially if neither variable has a coefficient of 1 or −1. In cases such as these, we can use another algebraic method called the *addition* or *elimination method* to find the exact solution of the system. This method is based on the addition property of equality: *When equal quantities are added to both sides of an equation, the results are equal.*

The addition method

To solve the system

$$\begin{cases} x + y = 8 \\ x - y = -2 \end{cases}$$

by the **addition method,** we see that the coefficients of y are opposites and then add the left- and right-hand sides of the equations to eliminate the variable y.

$$\begin{array}{ll} x + y = 8 & \text{Equal quantities, } x - y \text{ and } -2, \text{ are added to both sides of the equation} \\ \underline{x - y = -2} & x + y = 8. \text{ By the addition property of equality, the results will be equal.} \end{array}$$

Now, column by column, we add like terms. The terms y and $-y$ are eliminated.

$$\begin{array}{ll} \downarrow\downarrow\downarrow & \\ x + y = 8 & \text{Combine like terms: } x + x = 2x, y + (-y) = 0, \text{ and } 8 + (-2) = 6. \\ \underline{x - y = -2} & \\ 2x = 6 & \leftarrow \text{Write each result here.} \end{array}$$

We can then solve the resulting equation for x.

$$2x = 6$$
$$x = 3 \quad \text{Divide both sides by 2.}$$

To find y, we substitute 3 for x in either equation and solve it for y.

$$\begin{array}{ll} x + y = 8 & \text{The first equation of the system.} \\ 3 + y = 8 & \text{Substitute 3 for } x. \\ y = 5 & \text{Subtract 3 from both sides.} \end{array}$$

We check the solution by verifying that $(3, 5)$ satisfies each equation of the system.

To solve an equation in x and y by the addition method, we follow these steps.

The addition method

> 1. Write both equations in general form: $Ax + By = C$.
> 2. If necessary, multiply one or both of the equations by nonzero quantities to make the coefficients of x (or the coefficients of y) opposites.
> 3. Add the equations to eliminate the terms involving x (or y).
> 4. Solve the equation resulting from Step 3.
> 5. Find the value of the other variable by substituting the solution found in Step 4 into any equation containing both variables.
> 6. Check the solution in the equations of the original system.

EXAMPLE 1 *Solving systems by addition.* Solve $\begin{cases} 5x + y = -4 \\ -5x + 2y = 7 \end{cases}$

Self Check

Solve $\begin{cases} x + 3y = 7 \\ 2x - 3y = -22 \end{cases}$

Solution

When the equations are added, the terms $5x$ and $-5x$ drop out. We can then solve the resulting equation for y.

$$\begin{array}{ll} 5x + y = -4 & \text{Combine like terms: } 5x + (-5x) = 0, y + 2y = 3y, \text{ and } -4 + 7 = 3. \\ \underline{-5x + 2y = 7} & \\ 3y = 3 & \\ y = 1 & \text{Divide both sides by 3.} \end{array}$$

To find *x*, we substitute 1 for *y* in either equation. If we use $5x + y = -4$, we have

$5x + y = -4$ The first equation of the system.

$5x + 1 = -4$ Substitute 1 for *y*.

$5x = -5$ Subtract 1 from both sides.

$x = -1$ Divide both sides by 5.

Verify that $(-1, 1)$ satisfies each original equation.

EXAMPLE 2   *Solving systems by addition.*   Solve $\begin{cases} 3x + y = 7 \\ x + 2y = 4 \end{cases}$

Self Check

Solve $\begin{cases} 3x + 4y = 25 \\ 2x + y = 10 \end{cases}$

Solution

If we add the equations as they are, neither variable will be eliminated. We must write the equations so that the coefficients of one of the variables are opposites. To eliminate *x*, we can multiply both sides of the second equation by -3 to get

$$\begin{cases} 3x + y = 7 \\ -3(x + 2y) = -3(4) \end{cases} \longrightarrow \begin{cases} 3x + y = 7 \\ -3x - 6y = -12 \end{cases}$$

The coefficients of the terms $3x$ and $-3x$ are now opposites. When the equations are added, *x* is eliminated.

$$\begin{array}{r} 3x + y = 7 \\ -3x - 6y = -12 \\ \hline -5y = -5 \\ y = 1 \end{array}$$ Divide both sides by -5.

To find *x*, we substitute 1 for *y* in the equation $x + 2y = 4$.

$x + 2y = 4$ The second equation of the original system.

$x + 2(1) = 4$ Substitute 1 for *y*.

$x + 2 = 4$ Do the multiplication.

$x = 2$ Subtract 2 from both sides.

Check the solution $(2, 1)$ in the original system of equations.

EXAMPLE 3   *Solving systems by addition.*   Solve $\begin{cases} 2a - 5b = 10 \\ 3a - 2b = -7 \end{cases}$

Self Check

Solve $\begin{cases} 2a + 3b = 7 \\ 5a + 2b = 1 \end{cases}$

Solution

The equations in the system must be written so that one of the variables will be eliminated when the equations are added. To eliminate *a*, we can multiply the first equation by **3** and the second equation by -2 to get

$$\begin{cases} 3(2a - 5b) = 3(10) \\ -2(3a - 2b) = -2(-7) \end{cases} \longrightarrow \begin{cases} 6a - 15b = 30 \\ -6a + 4b = 14 \end{cases}$$

When these equations are added, the terms $6a$ and $-6a$ are eliminated.

$$\begin{array}{r} 6a - 15b = 30 \\ -6a + 4b = 14 \\ \hline -11b = 44 \\ b = -4 \end{array}$$ Divide both sides by -11.

To find *a*, we substitute -4 for *b* in the equation $2a - 5b = 10$.

$2a - 5b = 10$ The first equation of the original system.

$2a - 5(-4) = 10$ Substitute -4 for *b*.

$2a + 20 = 10$ Simplify.

$$2a = -10 \quad \text{Subtract 20 from both sides.}$$
$$a = -5 \quad \text{Divide both sides by 2.}$$

Check the solution $(-5, -4)$ in the original equations.

Answer: $(-1, 3)$ ∎

EXAMPLE 4 *Equations containing fractions.* Solve $\begin{cases} \frac{5}{6}x + \frac{2}{3}y = \frac{7}{6} \\ \frac{10}{7}x - \frac{4}{9}y = \frac{17}{21} \end{cases}$

Solution

To clear the equations of fractions, we multiply both sides of the first equation by 6 and both sides of the second equation by 63. This gives the equivalent system

(1) $\begin{cases} 5x + 4y = 7 \\ 90x - 28y = 51 \end{cases}$
(2)

We can solve for x by eliminating the terms involving y. To do so, we multiply Equation 1 by 7 and add the result to Equation 2.

$$\begin{array}{r} 35x + 28y = 49 \\ 90x - 28y = 51 \\ \hline 125x = 100 \end{array}$$

$$x = \frac{100}{125} \quad \text{Divide both sides by 125.}$$

$$x = \frac{4}{5} \quad \text{Simplify } \tfrac{100}{125}: \text{ Divide out the common factor of 25.}$$

To solve for y, we substitute $\frac{4}{5}$ for x in Equation 1 and simplify.

$$5x + 4y = 7$$
$$5\left(\frac{4}{5}\right) + 4y = 7$$
$$4 + 4y = 7 \quad \text{Simplify.}$$
$$4y = 3 \quad \text{Subtract 4 from both sides.}$$
$$y = \frac{3}{4} \quad \text{Divide both sides by 4.}$$

Check the solution of $\left(\frac{4}{5}\right), \left(\frac{3}{4}\right)$ in the original equations.

Self Check

Solve $\begin{cases} \frac{1}{3}x + \frac{1}{6}y = 1 \\ \frac{1}{2}x - \frac{1}{4}y = 0 \end{cases}$

Answer: $\left(\frac{3}{2}, 3\right)$ ∎

EXAMPLE 5 *Writing equations in general form.* Solve

$\begin{cases} 2(2x + y) = 13 \\ 8x = 2y - 16 \end{cases}$

Solution

We begin by writing each equation in $Ax + By = C$ form. For the first equation, we need only apply the distributive property. To write the second equation in general form, we subtract $2y$ from both sides.

$$2(2x + y) = 13 \qquad\qquad 8x = 2y - 16$$
$$4x + 2y = 13 \qquad\qquad 8x - 2y = 2y - 16 - 2y$$
$$ 8x - 2y = -16$$

The two resulting equations form the following system.

(1) $\begin{cases} 4x + 2y = 13 \\ 8x - 2y = -16 \end{cases}$
(2)

When the equations are added, the terms involving y are eliminated.

Self Check

Solve $\begin{cases} -3y = -5 - x \\ 3(x - y) = -11 \end{cases}$

$$4x + 2y = 13$$
$$\underline{8x - 2y = -16}$$
$$12x = -3$$

$$x = -\frac{1}{4} \qquad \text{\small Divide both sides by 12 and simplify the fraction: } -\frac{3}{12} = -\frac{1}{4}.$$

We can use Equation 1 to find y.

$$4x + 2y = 13$$

$$4\left(-\frac{1}{4}\right) + 2y = 13 \qquad \text{\small Substitute } -\frac{1}{4} \text{ for } x.$$

$$-1 + 2y = 13 \qquad \text{\small Do the multiplication.}$$

$$2y = 14 \qquad \text{\small Add 1 to both sides.}$$

$$y = 7 \qquad \text{\small Divide both sides by 2.}$$

Verify that $\left(-\frac{1}{4}, 7\right)$ satisfies each original equation.

Answer: $\left(-3, \dfrac{2}{3}\right)$

Inconsistent systems

EXAMPLE 6   *A system with no solutions.*   Solve $\begin{cases} 3x - 2y = 8 \\ -3x + 2y = -12 \end{cases}$

Solution
We can add the equations to eliminate the term involving x.

$$3x - 2y = 8$$
$$\underline{-3x + 2y = -12}$$
$$0 = -4$$

Here the terms involving both x and y drop out, and a false result of $0 = -4$ is obtained. This indicates that the equations of the system are independent and that the system is inconsistent. This system has no solution.

Self Check

Solve $\begin{cases} 2t - 7v = 5 \\ -2t + 7v = 3 \end{cases}$

Answer: no solution

Dependent equations

EXAMPLE 7   *Infinitely many solutions.*   Solve $\begin{cases} \dfrac{2x - 5y}{2} = \dfrac{19}{2} \\ -0.2x + 0.5y = -1.9 \end{cases}$

Solution
We can multiply both sides of the first equation by **2** to clear it of fractions and both sides of the second equation by **10** to clear it of decimals.

$$\begin{cases} 2\left(\dfrac{2x - 5y}{2}\right) = 2\left(\dfrac{19}{2}\right) \\ 10(-0.2x + 0.5y) = 10(-1.9) \end{cases} \longrightarrow \begin{cases} 2x - 5y = 19 \\ -2x + 5y = -19 \end{cases}$$

We add the resulting equations to get

$$2x - 5y = 19$$
$$\underline{-2x + 5y = -19}$$
$$0 = 0$$

As in Example 6, both x and y drop out. However, this time a true result is obtained. This indicates that the equations are dependent and that the system has infinitely many solutions.

Any ordered pair that satisfies one equation also satisfies the other equation. Some solutions are $(2, -3)$, $(12, 1)$, and $\left(0, -\frac{19}{5}\right)$.

Self Check

Solve $\begin{cases} \dfrac{3x + y}{6} = \dfrac{1}{3} \\ -0.3x - 0.1y = -0.2 \end{cases}$

Answer: infinitely many solutions

STUDY SET Section 7.3

VOCABULARY *Fill in the blanks.*

1. The _____coefficient_____ of the term $-3x$ is -3.

2. The _____opposite_____ of 4 is -4.

3. $Ax + By = C$ is the _____general_____ form of the equation of a line.

4. When adding the equations

$$5x - 6y = 10$$
$$-3x + 6y = 24$$

the variable y will be _____eliminated_____.

CONCEPTS

5. If the addition method is to be used to solve this system, what is wrong with the form in which it is written?

$$\begin{cases} 2x - 5y = -3 \\ -2y + 3x = 10 \end{cases}$$

The second equation should be written in general form:
$3x - 2y = 10$.

6. Can the system

$$\begin{cases} 2x + 5y = -13 \\ -2x - 3y = -5 \end{cases}$$

be solved more easily using the addition method or the substitution method? Explain.

addition; the coefficients of x are opposites

7. What algebraic step should be performed to clear this equation of fractions?

$$\frac{2}{3}x + 4y = -\frac{4}{5} \quad \text{Multiply both sides by 15.}$$

8. If the addition method is used to solve

$$\begin{cases} 3x + 12y = 4 \\ 6x - 4y = 8 \end{cases}$$

a. By what would we multiply the first equation to eliminate x? -2

b. By what would we multiply the second equation to eliminate y? 3

9. Solve $\begin{cases} 4x + 2y = 2 \\ 3x - 2y = 12 \end{cases}$

a. by the graphing method. $(2, -3)$

b. by the substitution method. $(2, -3)$

c. by the addition method. $(2, -3)$

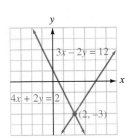

10. The addition method was used to solve three different systems. The results after x was eliminated in each case are listed here. Match each result with a possible graph of the system.

Result when solving

a. System 1:   **b.** System 2:   **c.** System 3:
$-1 = -1$ ii $y = -1$ iii $-1 = -2$ i

Possible graph of the system

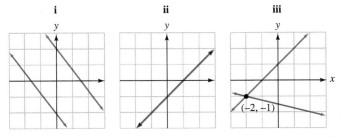

NOTATION *Complete the solution of each system.*

11. Solve $\begin{cases} x + y = 5 \\ x - y = -3 \end{cases}$

$$\begin{array}{rcl} x + y &=& 5 \\ x - y &=& -3 \\ \hline 2x &=& 2 \end{array}$$

$$x = 1$$

$$x + y = 5 \quad \text{The first equation.}$$
$$\left(1 \right) + y = 5$$
$$y = 4$$

The solution is $(1, 4)$.

12. Solve $\begin{cases} x - 2y = 8 \\ -x + 5y = -17 \end{cases}$

$$\begin{array}{rcl} x - 2y &=& 8 \\ -x + 5y &=& -17 \\ \hline 3y &=& -9 \end{array}$$

$$y = -3$$

$$x - 2y = 8 \quad \text{The first equation.}$$
$$x - 2\left(-3 \right) = 8$$
$$x + 6 = 8$$
$$x = 2$$

The solution is $(2, -3)$.

PRACTICE *Use the addition method to solve each system.*

13. $\begin{cases} x - y = -5 \\ x + y = 1 \end{cases}$ $(-2, 3)$ **14.** $\begin{cases} x + y = 1 \\ x - y = 5 \end{cases}$ $(3, -2)$

15. $\begin{cases} 2r + s = -1 \\ -2r + s = 3 \end{cases}$
$(-1, 1)$

16. $\begin{cases} 3m + n = -6 \\ m - n = -2 \end{cases}$
$(-2, 0)$

17. $\begin{cases} 2x + y = -2 \\ -2x - 3y = -6 \end{cases}$
$(-3, 4)$

18. $\begin{cases} 3x + 4y = 8 \\ 5x - 4y = 24 \end{cases}$
$(4, -1)$

19. $\begin{cases} 4x + 3y = 24 \\ 4x - 3y = -24 \end{cases}$
$(0, 8)$

20. $\begin{cases} 5x - 4y = 8 \\ -5x - 4y = 8 \end{cases}$
$(0, -2)$

Use the addition method to solve each system of equations. If the equations of a system are dependent or if a system is inconsistent, so indicate.

21. $\begin{cases} x + y = 5 \\ x + 2y = 8 \end{cases}$ $(2, 3)$

22. $\begin{cases} x + 2y = 0 \\ x - y = -3 \end{cases}$ $(-2, 1)$

23. $\begin{cases} 2x + y = 4 \\ 2x + 3y = 0 \end{cases}$
$(3, -2)$

24. $\begin{cases} 2x + 5y = -13 \\ 2x - 3y = -5 \end{cases}$
$(-4, -1)$

25. $\begin{cases} 3x - 5y = -29 \\ 3x + 4y = 34 \end{cases}$
$(2, 7)$

26. $\begin{cases} 3x - 5y = 16 \\ 4x + 5y = 33 \end{cases}$
$(7, 1)$

27. $\begin{cases} 2a - 3b = -6 \\ 2a - 3b = 8 \end{cases}$
inconsistent system

28. $\begin{cases} 3a - 4b = 6 \\ 2(2b + 3) = 3a \end{cases}$
dependent equations

29. $\begin{cases} 8x - 4y = 18 \\ 3x - 2y = 8 \end{cases}$
$\left(1, -\frac{5}{2}\right)$

30. $\begin{cases} 4x + 6y = 5 \\ 8x - 9y = 3 \end{cases}$
$\left(\frac{3}{4}, \frac{1}{3}\right)$

31. $\begin{cases} 2x + y = 10 \\ 0.1x + 0.2y = 1.0 \end{cases}$
$\left(\frac{10}{3}, \frac{10}{3}\right)$

32. $\begin{cases} 0.3x + 0.2y = 0 \\ 2x - 3y = -13 \end{cases}$
$(-2, 3)$

33. $\begin{cases} 2x - y = 16 \\ 0.03x + 0.02y = 0.03 \end{cases}$ $(5, -6)$

34. $\begin{cases} -5y + 2x = 4 \\ -0.02y + 0.03x = 0.04 \end{cases}$ $\left(\frac{12}{11}, -\frac{4}{11}\right)$

35. $\begin{cases} 6x + 3y = 0 \\ 5y = 2x + 12 \end{cases}$ $(-1, 2)$

36. $\begin{cases} 0 = 4x - 3y \\ 5x = 4y - 2 \end{cases}$ $(6, 8)$

37. $\begin{cases} -2(x + 1) = 3y - 6 \\ 3(y + 2) = 10 - 2x \end{cases}$ dependent equations

38. $\begin{cases} 3x + 2y + 1 = 5 \\ 3(x - 1) = -2y - 4 \end{cases}$ inconsistent system

39. $\begin{cases} 4(x + 1) = 17 - 3(y - 1) \\ 2(x + 2) + 3(y - 1) = 9 \end{cases}$ $(4, 0)$

40. $\begin{cases} 5(x - 1) = 8 - 3(y + 2) \\ 4(x + 2) - 7 = 3(2 - y) \end{cases}$ $(2, -1)$

41. $\begin{cases} \frac{3}{5}s + \frac{4}{5}t = 1 \\ -\frac{1}{4}s + \frac{3}{8}t = 1 \end{cases}$
$(-1, 2)$

42. $\begin{cases} \frac{1}{2}s - \frac{1}{4}t = 1 \\ \frac{1}{3}s + t = 3 \end{cases}$
$(3, 2)$

43. $\begin{cases} \frac{3}{5}x + y = 1 \\ \frac{4}{5}x - y = -1 \end{cases}$
$(0, 1)$

44. $\begin{cases} \frac{1}{2}x + \frac{4}{7}y = -1 \\ 5x - \frac{4}{5}y = -10 \end{cases}$
$(-2, 0)$

45. $\begin{cases} \dfrac{x}{2} - \dfrac{y}{3} = -2 \\ \dfrac{2x - 3}{2} + \dfrac{6y + 1}{3} = \dfrac{17}{6} \end{cases}$
$(-2, 3)$

46. $\begin{cases} \dfrac{x + 2}{4} + \dfrac{y - 1}{3} = \dfrac{1}{12} \\ \dfrac{x + 4}{5} - \dfrac{y - 2}{2} = \dfrac{5}{2} \end{cases}$
$(1, -1)$

47. $\begin{cases} \dfrac{x - 3}{2} + \dfrac{y + 5}{3} = \dfrac{11}{6} \\ \dfrac{x + 3}{3} - \dfrac{5}{12} = \dfrac{y + 3}{4} \end{cases}$
$(2, 2)$

48. $\begin{cases} \dfrac{x + 2}{3} = \dfrac{3 - y}{2} \\ \dfrac{x + 3}{2} = \dfrac{2 - y}{3} \end{cases}$
$(-5, 5)$

WRITING

49. Why is it usually to your advantage to write the equations of a system in general form before using the addition method to solve it?

50. How would you decide whether to use substitution or addition to solve a system of equations?

51. In this section, we discussed the addition method for solving a system of two equations. Some instructors call it the *elimination method*. Why do you think it would be known by this name?

52. Explain the error in the work shown below.

Solve $\begin{cases} x + y = 1 \\ x - y = 5 \end{cases}$

$\begin{array}{r} x + y = 1 \\ +\quad x - y = 5 \\ \hline 2x \quad\quad = 6 \end{array}$

$\dfrac{2x}{2} = \dfrac{6}{2}$

$\boxed{x = 3}$ —Done—

REVIEW

53. Solve $8(3x - 5) - 12 = 4(2x + 3)$.   4

54. Solve $3y + \dfrac{y + 2}{2} = \dfrac{2(y + 3)}{3} + 16$.   6

55. Simplify $x - x$.   0

56. Simplify $3.2m - 4.4 + 2.1m + 16$. $5.3m - 11.6$

57. Find the area of a triangular-shaped sign with a base of 4 feet and a height of 3.75 feet. 7.5 ft^2

58. Translate to mathematical symbols: *the product of the sum of x and y and the difference of x and y.*
$(x + y)(x - y)$

59. What is 10 less than x? $x - 10$

60. Factor $6x^2 + 7x - 20$. $(3x - 4)(2x + 5)$

7.4 *Applications of Systems of Equations*

In this section, you will learn about

• Solving problems using two variables

INTRODUCTION. We have previously formed equations involving one variable to solve problems. In this section, we consider ways to solve problems using two variables.

Solving problems using two variables

The following steps are helpful when solving problems involving two unknown quantities.

Problem-solving strategy

> 1. Read the problem several times and *analyze* the facts. Occasionally, a sketch, table, or diagram will help you visualize the facts of the problem.
> 2. Pick different variables to represent two unknown quantities. *Form* two equations involving each of the two variables. This will give a system of two equations in two variables.
> 3. *Solve* the system of equations using the most convenient method: graphing, substitution, or addition.
> 4. *State* the conclusion.
> 5. *Check* the result in the words of the problem.

EXAMPLE 1   *Farming.*   A farmer raises wheat and soybeans on 215 acres. He wants to plant fewer acres in soybeans than in wheat—31 acres less, to be exact. How many acres of each should he plant?

Analyze the problem   We know that the number of acres of wheat planted plus the number of acres of soybeans planted will equal a total of 215 acres. We also know that there are 31 fewer acres of soybeans than of wheat.

Form two equations   If w represents the number of acres of wheat and s the number of acres of soybeans to be planted, we can form the two equations.

The number of acres planted in wheat	plus	the number of acres planted in soybeans	is	215 acres.
w	$+$	s	$=$	215

Since the farmer wants to plant 31 fewer acres in soybeans than in wheat, we have

The number of acres planted in wheat	less	the number of acres planted in soybeans	is	31 acres.
w	$-$	s	$=$	31

Solve the system   We can now solve the system

$$(1) \quad \begin{cases} w + s = 215 \\ w - s = 31 \end{cases}$$
$$(2)$$

using the addition method.

$$w + s = 215$$
$$\underline{w - s = 31}$$
$$2w = 246$$

$\qquad\qquad w = 123$ Divide both sides by 2.

To find *s*, we substitute 123 for *w* in Equation 1.

$$w + s = 215$$
$$123 + s = 215$$ Substitute.
$$s = 92$$ Subtract 123 from both sides.

State the conclusion   The farmer should plant 123 acres of wheat and 92 acres of soybeans.

Check the result   The total acreage planted is $123 + 92$, or 215 acres. The area planted in soybeans is 31 fewer acres than that planted in wheat, because $123 - 92 = 31$. The answers check.   ■

     EXAMPLE 2   *Lawn care.*   An installer of underground irrigation systems wants to cut a 20-foot length of plastic tubing into two pieces. The longer piece is to be 2 feet longer than twice the shorter piece. Find the length of each piece.

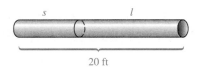

FIGURE 7-10

Analyze the problem   Refer to Figure 7-10, which shows the pipe.

Form two equations   We can let *s* represent the length of the shorter piece and *l* the length of the longer piece. Then we can form the two equations.

The length of the shorter piece	plus	the length of the longer piece	is	20 feet.
s	$+$	l	$=$	20

Since the longer piece is 2 feet longer than twice the shorter piece, we have

The length of the longer piece	is	2	times	the length of the shorter piece	plus	2 feet.
l	$=$	2	$\cdot$	s	$+$	2

Solve the system   We can use the substitution method to solve the system.

(1) $\begin{cases} s + l = 20 \\ l = 2s + 2 \end{cases}$
(2)

$s + 2s + 2 = 20$ Substitute $2s + 2$ for *l* in Equation 1.
$3s + 2 = 20$ Combine like terms.
$3s = 18$ Subtract 2 from both sides.
$s = 6$ Divide both sides by 3.

The shorter piece should be 6 feet long. To find the length of the longer piece, we substitute 6 for *s* in Equation 2 and find *l*.

$$l = 2s + 2$$
$$= 2(6) + 2$$ Substitute.
$$= 12 + 2$$ Simplify.
$$l = 14$$

State the conclusion   The longer piece should be 14 feet long, and the shorter piece 6 feet long.

Check the result   The sum of 6 and 14 is 20, and 14 is 2 more than twice 6. The answers check.   ■

EXAMPLE 3   *Gardening.*   Tom has 150 feet of fencing to enclose a rectangular garden. If the garden's length is to be 5 feet less than 3 times its width, find the area of the garden.

FIGURE 7-11

Analyze the problem   To find the area of a rectangle, we need to know its length and width.

Form two equations   We can let *l* represent the length of the garden and *w* its width, as shown in Figure 7-11. Since the perimeter of a rectangle is two lengths plus two widths, we have

2	times	the length of the garden	plus	2	times	the width of the garden	is	150 feet.
2	$\cdot$	*l*	+	2	$\cdot$	*w*	=	150

Since the length is 5 feet less than 3 times the width,

The length of the garden	is	3	times	the width of the garden	minus	5 feet.
l	=	3	$\cdot$	*w*	−	5

Solve the system   We can use the substitution method to solve this system.

$$\begin{align}
(1) \quad & \begin{cases} 2l + 2w = 150 \\ l = 3w - 5 \end{cases} \\
(2) \quad &
\end{align}$$

$$2(3w - 5) + 2w = 150 \quad \text{Substitute } 3w - 5 \text{ for } l \text{ in Equation 1.}$$
$$6w - 10 + 2w = 150 \quad \text{Distribute the multiplication by 2.}$$
$$8w - 10 = 150 \quad \text{Combine like terms.}$$
$$8w = 160 \quad \text{Add 10 to both sides.}$$
$$w = 20 \quad \text{Divide both sides by 8.}$$

The width of the garden is 20 feet. To find the length, we substitute 20 for *w* in Equation 2 and simplify.

$$l = 3w - 5$$
$$= 3(20) - 5 \quad \text{Substitute.}$$
$$= 60 - 5$$
$$l = 55 \quad \text{The length of the garden is 55 feet.}$$

Now we find the area of the rectangle with dimensions 55 feet by 20 feet.

$$A = lw \quad \text{The formula for the area of a rectangle.}$$
$$= 55 \cdot 20 \quad \text{Substitute 55 for } l \text{ and 20 for } w.$$
$$A = 1{,}100$$

State the conclusion   The garden covers an area of 1,100 square feet.

Check the result   Because the dimensions of the garden are 55 feet by 20 feet, the perimeter is

$$P = 2l + 2w$$
$$= 2(55) + 2(20) \quad \text{Substitute for } l \text{ and } w.$$
$$= 110 + 40$$
$$P = 150$$

It is also true that 55 feet is 5 feet less than 3 times 20 feet. The answers check. ■

EXAMPLE 4   *Manufacturing.*   The setup cost of a machine that mills brass plates is $750. After setup, it costs $0.25 to mill each plate. Management is considering the purchase of a larger machine that can produce the same plate at a cost of $0.20 per plate. If the setup cost of the larger machine is $1,200, how many plates would the company have to produce to make the purchase worthwhile?

Analyze the problem   We need to find the number of plates (called the **break point**) that will cost equal amounts to produce on either machine.

Form two equations   We can let c represent the cost of milling p plates. If we call the machine currently being used machine 1, and the new, larger one machine 2, we can form the two equations.

The cost of making p plates on machine 1	is	the setup cost of machine 1	plus	the cost per plate on machine 1	times	the number of plates p to be made.
c	$=$	750	$+$	0.25	$\cdot$	p

The cost of making p plates on machine 2	is	the setup cost of machine 2	plus	the cost per plate on machine 2	times	the number of plates p to be made.
c	$=$	1,200	$+$	0.20	$\cdot$	p

Solve the system   Since the costs are equal, we can use the substitution method to solve the system

$$\textbf{(1)} \quad \begin{cases} c = 750 + 0.25p \\ c = 1{,}200 + 0.20p \end{cases}$$
$$\textbf{(2)}$$

$750 + 0.25p = 1{,}200 + 0.20p$	Substitute $750 + 0.25p$ for c in the second equation.
$0.25p = 450 + 0.20p$	Subtract 750 from both sides.
$0.05p = 450$	Subtract $0.20p$ from both sides.
$p = 9{,}000$	Divide both sides by 0.05.

State the conclusion   If 9,000 plates are milled, the cost will be the same on either machine. If more than 9,000 plates are milled, the cost will be cheaper on the larger machine, because it mills the plates less expensively than the smaller machine.

Check the result   We check the solution by substituting 9,000 for p in Equations 1 and 2 and verifying that 3,000 is the value of c in both cases.

     If we graph the two equations, we can illustrate the break point. (See Figure 7-12.)

Machine 1
$c = 750 + 0.25p$

p	c
0	750
1,000	1,000
5,000	2,000

Machine 2
$c = 1,200 + 0.20p$

p	c
0	1,200
4,000	2,000
12,000	3,600

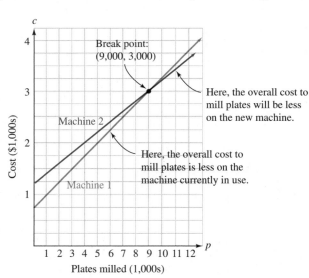

FIGURE 7-12

EXAMPLE 5   ***White-collar crime.***   Federal investigators discovered that a company secretly moved $150,000 out of the country to avoid paying corporate income tax on it. Some of the money was invested in a Swiss bank account that paid 8% interest annually. The remainder was deposited in a Cayman Islands account, paying 7% annual interest. The investigation also revealed that the combined interest earned the first year was $11,500. How much money was invested in each account?

Analyze the problem   We are told that an unknown part of the $150,000 was invested at an annual rate of 8% and the rest at 7%. Together, the accounts earned $11,500 in interest.

Form two equations   We can let x represent the amount invested in the Swiss bank account and y represent the amount invested in the Cayman Islands account. Because the total investment was $150,000, we have

The amount invested in the Swiss account	+	the amount invested in the Cayman Is. account	is	$150,000.
x	+	y	=	150,000

Since the annual income on x dollars invested at 8% is $0.08x$, the income on y dollars invested at 7% is $0.07y$, and the combined income is $11,500, we have

The income on the 8% investment	+	the income on the 7% investment	is	$11,500.
$0.08x$	+	$0.07y$	=	11,500

The resulting system is

(1) $\qquad \begin{cases} x + y = 150,000 \\ 0.08x + 0.07y = 11,500 \end{cases}$
(2)

Solve the system   To solve the system, we use the addition method to eliminate x.

$$\begin{array}{ll} -8x - 8y = -1,200,000 & \text{Multiply both sides of Equation 1 by } -8. \\ \underline{8x + 7y = 1,150,000} & \text{Multiply both sides of Equation 2 by 100.} \\ -y = -50,000 \\ y = 50,000 & \text{Multiply (or divide) both sides by } -1. \end{array}$$

To find x, we substitute 50,000 for y in Equation 1 and simplify.

$$\begin{array}{ll} x + y = 150,000 \\ x + \mathbf{50,000} = 150,000 & \text{Substitute.} \\ x = 100,000 & \text{Subtract 50,000 from both sides.} \end{array}$$

State the conclusion $100,000 was invested in the Swiss bank account, and $50,000 was invested in the Cayman Islands account.

Check the result
$$\begin{array}{ll} \$100,000 + \$50,000 = \$150,000 & \text{The two investments total } \$150,000. \\ 0.08(\$100,000) = \$8,000 & \text{The Swiss bank account earned } \$8,000. \\ 0.07(\$50,000) = \$3,500 & \text{The Cayman Islands account earned } \$3,500. \end{array}$$

The combined interest is $8,000 + $3,500 = $11,500. The answers check.   ∎

EXAMPLE 6   ***Boating.***   A boat traveled 30 kilometers downstream in 3 hours and made the return trip in 5 hours. Find the speed of the boat in still water.

Analyze the problem   Traveling downstream, the speed of the boat will be faster than it would be in still water. Traveling upstream, the speed of the boat will be less than it would be in still water.

Form two equations   We can let s represent the speed of the boat in still water and c the speed of the current. Then the rate of the boat going downstream is $s + c$, and its rate going upstream is $s - c$. We can organize the information as shown in Figure 7-13.

	Rate	·	Time	=	Distance
Downstream	$s + c$		3		$3(s + c)$
Upstream	$s - c$		5		$5(s - c)$

FIGURE 7-13

Since each trip is 30 miles long, the Distance column of the table gives two equations in two variables.

$$\begin{cases} 3(s + c) = 30 \\ 5(s - c) = 30 \end{cases}$$

After using the distributive property, we have

(1)
(2)
$$\begin{cases} 3s + 3c = 30 \\ 5s - 5c = 30 \end{cases}$$

Solve the system   To solve this system by addition, we multiply Equation 1 by 5, multiply Equation 2 by 3, add the equations, and solve for s.

$$\begin{aligned} 15s + 15c &= 150 \\ 15s - 15c &= 90 \\ \hline 30s &= 240 \end{aligned}$$

$$s = 8 \qquad \text{Divide both sides by 30.}$$

State the conclusion   The speed of the boat in still water is 8 kilometers per hour.

Check the result   We leave the check to the reader.   ■

EXAMPLE 7   *Medical technology.*   A laboratory technician has one batch of antiseptic that is 40% alcohol and a second batch that is 60% alcohol. She would like to make 8 liters of solution that is 55% alcohol. How many liters of each batch should she use?

Analyze the problem   Some 60% solution must be added to some 40% solution to make a 55% solution.

Form two equations   We can let x represent the number of liters to be used from batch 1 and y the number of liters to be used from batch 2. We then organize the information as shown in Figure 7-14.

	% of concentration	·	Number of liters of solution	=	Number of liters of alcohol
Batch 1	0.40		x		$0.40x$
Batch 2	0.60		y		$0.60y$
Mixture	0.55		8		$0.55(8)$

40%, 60%, and 55% have been expressed as decimals.   One equation comes from information in this column.   Another equation comes from information in this column.

FIGURE 7-14

The information in Figure 7-14 provides two equations.

(1)
(2)
$$\begin{cases} x + y = 8 \\ 0.40x + 0.60y = 0.55(8) \end{cases}$$

The number of liters of batch 1 plus the number of liters of batch 2 equals the total number of liters in the mixture.

The amount of alcohol in batch 1 plus the amount of alcohol in batch 2 equals the amount of alcohol in the mixture.

Solve the system We can use addition to solve this system.

$$-40x - 40y = -320 \quad \text{Multiply both sides of Equation 1 by } -40.$$
$$\underline{40x + 60y = 440} \quad \text{Multiply both sides of Equation 2 by 100.}$$
$$20y = 120$$
$$y = 6 \qquad \text{Divide both sides by 20.}$$

To find x, we substitute 6 for y in Equation 1 and simplify.

$$x + y = 8$$
$$x + 6 = 8 \quad \text{Substitute.}$$
$$x = 2 \quad \text{Subtract 6 from both sides.}$$

State the conclusion The technician should use 2 liters of the 40% solution and 6 liters of the 60% solution.

Check the result The check is left to the reader. ■

STUDY SET Section 7.4

VOCABULARY *Fill in the blanks.*

1. A _____variable_____ is a letter that stands for a number.

2. An _____equation_____ is a statement indicating that two quantities are equal.

3. $\begin{cases} a + b = 20 \\ a = 2b + 4 \end{cases}$ is a _____system_____ of linear equations.

4. A _____solution_____ of a system of linear equations satisfies both equations simultaneously.

CONCEPTS

5. For each case in Illustration 1, write an algebraic expression that represents the speed of the canoe in miles per hour if its speed in still water is x miles per hour.
$x - c, x + c$

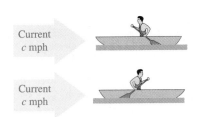

Current
c mph

Current
c mph

ILLUSTRATION 1

6. See Illustration 2.
  a. If the contents of the two test tubes are poured into a third test tube, how much solution will the third test tube contain? (mL means milliliters.) $(x + y)$ mL

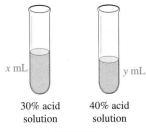

x mL

y mL

30% acid
solution

40% acid
solution

ILLUSTRATION 2

  b. Which is the best estimate of the concentration of the solution in the third test tube—25%, 35%, or 45% acid solution? 35%

7. Use the information in the table to answer the questions about two investments.

	Principal ·	Rate ·	Time =	Interest
City Bank	x	5%	1 yr	$0.05x$
USA Savings	y	11%	1 yr	$0.11y$

  a. How much money was deposited in the USA Savings account? $\$y$
  b. What interest rate did the City Bank account earn? 5%
  c. Complete the table.

8. Use the information in the table to answer the questions about a plane flying in windy conditions.

	Rate ·	Time =	Distance
With	$x + y$	3 hr	450 mi
Against	$x - y$	5 hr	450 mi

  a. For how long did the plane fly against the wind? 5 hr
  b. At what rate did the plane travel when flying with the wind? $(x + y)$ mph
  c. Write two equations that could be used to solve for x and y. $3(x + y) = 450, 5(x - y) = 450$

9. a. If a problem contains two unknowns, and if two variables are used to represent them, how many equations must be written to find the unknowns? two

b. Name three methods that can be used to solve a system of linear equations.
graphing, substitution, addition

10. Put the steps of the five-step problem-solving strategy listed below in the correct order.

State the conclusion   Form two equations
Analyze the problem   Check the result
Solve the system

analyze, form, solve, state, check

NOTATION   *Write a formula that relates the given quantities.*

11. length, width, area of a rectangle $A = lw$

12. length, width, perimeter of a rectangle $P = 2l + 2w$

13. rate, time, distance traveled $d = rt$

14. principal, rate, time, interest earned $I = Prt$

Translate each verbal model into mathematical symbols. Use variables to represent any unknowns.

15. $2 \cdot \begin{array}{c}\text{length}\\\text{of pool}\end{array} + 2 \cdot \begin{array}{c}\text{width}\\\text{of pool}\end{array}$ is $\begin{array}{c}90\\\text{yards.}\end{array}$

$2l + 2w = 90$

16. $\$6 \cdot \begin{array}{c}\text{number}\\\text{of adults}\end{array} + \$2 \cdot \begin{array}{c}\text{number}\\\text{of children}\end{array}$ is $\$26.$

$6a + 2c = 26$

PRACTICE   *Use two equations in two variables to find the integers.*

17. One integer is twice another. Their sum is 96.   32, 64

18. The sum of two integers is 38. Their difference is 12.   13, 25

19. Three times one integer plus another integer is 29. The first integer plus twice the second is 18.   8, 5

20. Twice one integer plus another integer is 21. The first integer plus 3 times the second is 33.   6, 9

APPLICATIONS   *Use two equations in two variables to solve each problem.*

21. TREE TRIMMING
When fully extended, the arm on the tree service truck shown in Illustration 3 is 51 feet long. If the upper part of the arm is 7 feet shorter than the lower part, how long is each part of the arm?
22 ft, 29 ft

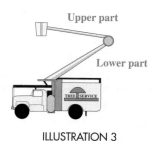

Upper part
Lower part
TREE SERVICE
ILLUSTRATION 3

22. TV PROGRAMMING   The producer of a 30-minute TV documentary about World War I divided it into two parts. Four times as much program time was devoted to the causes of the war as to the outcome. How long is each part of the documentary?
causes: 24 min; outcome: 6 min

23. EXECUTIVE BRANCH   The salaries of the president and vice president of the United States total $581,000 a year. If the president makes $219,000 more than the vice president, find each of their salaries.
president: $400,000; vice president: $181,000

24. CAUSES OF DEATH   In 1993, the number of Americans dying from cancer was 6 times the number who died from accidents. If the number of deaths from these two causes totaled 630,000, how many Americans died from each cause?
90,000 in accidents; 540,000 from cancer

25. BUYING PAINTING SUPPLIES   Two partial receipts for paint supplies are shown in Illustration 4. How much does each gallon of paint and each brush cost? $30, $10

Colorfu
Paint an
Wallpape

8 latex @
gallon
3 brushes @
Total $ 270.00

Colorful
Paint and
Wallpape

6 latex @
gallon
2 brushes @
Total $ 200.00

ILLUSTRATION 4

26. WEDDING PICTURES   A photographer sells the two wedding picture packages shown in Illustration 5.

Package #1	Package #2
One 10 x 14	One 10 x 14
Ten 8 x 10	Five 8 x 10
color photos	color photos
Cost $239.50	Cost $134.50

ILLUSTRATION 5

How much does a 10×14 photo cost? An 8×10 photo?
$29.50, $21

27. BUYING TICKETS   If receipts for the movie advertised in Illustration 6 were $1,440 for an audience of 190 people, how many senior citizens attended?   40

28. SELLING ICE CREAM   At a store, ice cream cones cost $0.90 and sundaes cost $1.65. One day the receipts for a total of 148 cones and sundaes were $180.45. How many cones were sold?   85

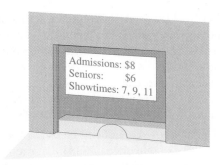

ILLUSTRATION 6

29. MARINE CORPS   The Marine Corps War Memorial in Arlington, Virginia, portrays the raising of the U.S. flag on Iwo Jima during World War II. Find the two angles shown in Illustration 7 if the measure of one of the angles is 15° less than twice the other.   65°, 115°

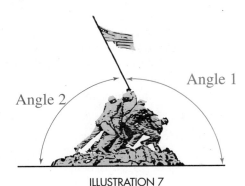

ILLUSTRATION 7

30. PHYSICAL THERAPY   To rehabilitate her knee, an athlete does leg extensions. Her goal is to regain a full 90° range of motion in this exercise. Use the information in Illustration 8 to determine her current range of motion in degrees.   72°

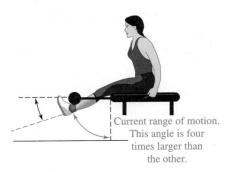

Current range of motion. This angle is four times larger than the other.

ILLUSTRATION 8

31. THEATER SCREEN   At an IMAX theater, the giant rectangular movie screen has a width 26 feet less than its length. If its perimeter is 332 feet, find the area of the screen.   6,720 ft²

32. GEOMETRY   A 50-meter path surrounds the rectangular garden shown in Illustration 9. The width of the garden is two-thirds its length. Find its area.   150 m²

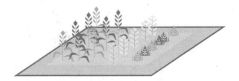

ILLUSTRATION 9

33. MAKING TIRES   A company has two molds to form tires. One mold has a setup cost of $1,000, and the other has a setup cost of $3,000. The cost to make each tire with the first mold is $15, and the cost to make each tire with the second mold is $10.
   a. Find the break point.   400 tires
   b. Check your result by graphing both equations on the coordinate system in Illustration 10.

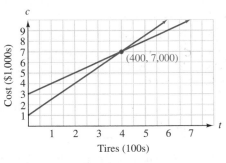

ILLUSTRATION 10

   c. If a production run of 500 tires is planned, determine which mold should be used.   the second mold

34. CHOOSING A FURNACE   A high-efficiency 90+ furnace can be purchased for $2,250 and costs an average of $412 per year to operate in Rockford, Illinois. An 80+ furnace can be purchased for only $1,715, but it costs $446 per year to operate.
   a. Find the break point.   about 9.9 yr
   b. If you intended to live in a Rockford house for 7 years, which furnace would you choose?   80+

35. STUDENT LOANS   A college used a $5,000 gift from an alumnus to make two student loans. The first was at 5% annual interest to a nursing student. The second was at 7% to a business major. If the college collected $310 in interest the first year, how much was loaned to each student?   nursing: $2,000; business: $3,000

36. FINANCIAL PLANNING   In investing $6,000 of a couple's money, a financial planner put some of it into a savings account paying 6% annual interest. The rest was invested in a riskier mini-mall development plan paying 12% annually. The combined interest earned for the first year was $540. How much money was invested at each rate?   6%: $3,000; 12%: $3,000

37. GULF STREAM   The Gulf Stream is a warm ocean current of the North Atlantic Ocean that flows northward, as shown in Illustration 11. Heading north with the Gulf Stream, a cruise ship traveled 300 miles in 10 hours. Against the current, it took 15 hours to make the return trip. Find the speed of the current.   5 mph

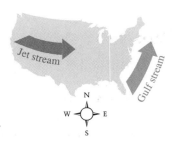

ILLUSTRATION 11

38. JET STREAM   The jet stream is a strong wind current that flows across the United States, as shown in Illustration 11. Flying with the jet stream, a plane flew 3,000 miles in 5 hours. Against the same wind, the trip took 6 hours. Find the airspeed of the plane (the speed in still air).   550 mph

39. AVIATION   An airplane can fly downwind a distance of 600 miles in 2 hours. However, the return trip against the same wind takes 3 hours. Find the speed of the wind.   50 mph

40. BOATING   A boat can travel 24 miles downstream in 2 hours and can make the return trip in 3 hours. Find the speed of the boat in still water.   10 mph

41. MARINE BIOLOGY   A marine biologist wants to set up an aquarium containing 3% salt water. He has two tanks on hand that contain 6% and 2% salt water. How much water from each tank must he use to fill a 16-liter aquarium with a 3% saltwater mixture?
4 L 6% salt water, 12 L 2% salt water

42. COMMEMORATIVE COINS   A foundry has been commissioned to make souvenir coins. The coins are to be made from an alloy that is 40% silver. The foundry has on hand two alloys, one with 50% silver content and one with a 25% silver content. How many kilograms of each alloy should be used to make 20 kilograms of the 40% silver alloy?
12 kg 50% alloy, 8 kg 25% alloy

43. MIXING NUTS   A merchant wants to mix peanuts with cashews, as shown in Illustration 12, to get 48 pounds of mixed nuts that will be sold at $4 per pound. How many pounds of each should the merchant use?
32 lb peanuts, 16 lb cashews

ILLUSTRATION 12

44. COFFEE SALES   A coffee supply store waits until the orders for its special coffee blend reach 100 pounds before making up a batch. Coffee selling for $8.75 a pound is blended with coffee selling for $3.75 a pound to make a product that sells for $6.35 a pound. How much of each type of coffee should be used to make the blend that will fill the orders?   52 lb $8.75, 48 lb $3.75

45. MARKDOWN   A set of golf clubs has been marked down 40% to a sale price of $384. Let r represent the retail price and d the discount. Then use the following equations to find the original retail price. $640

Retail price	$-$	discount	$=$	sale price

Discount	$=$	discount rate	$\cdot$	retail price

46. MARKUP   A stereo system retailing at $565.50 has been marked up 45% from wholesale. Let w represent the wholesale cost and m the markup. Then use the following equations to find the wholesale cost. $390

Wholesale cost	$+$	markup	$=$	retail price

Markup	$=$	markup rate	$\cdot$	wholesale cost

WRITING

47. When solving a problem using two variables, why isn't one equation sufficient to find the two unknown quantities?

48. Describe an everyday situation in which you might need to make a mixture.

REVIEW   *Graph each inequality.*

49. $x < 4$

50. $x \geq -3$

51. $-1 < x \leq 2$

52. $-2 \leq x \leq 0$

Solve each equation.

53. $x^2 - 4 = 0$ $-2, 2$

54. $x^2 - 4x = 0$ $0, 4$

55. $x^2 - 4x + 4 = 0$ $2, 2$

56. $2x^2 + 3x = 2$ $\frac{1}{2}, -2$

7.5 *Graphing Linear Inequalities*

In this section, you will learn about

- Solving linear inequalities • Graphing linear inequalities
- An application of linear inequalities

INTRODUCTION. We have seen that the solutions of a linear *equation* in x and y can be expressed as ordered pairs (x, y) and that when graphed, the ordered pairs form a line. In this section, we consider linear *inequalities*. Solutions of linear inequalities can also be expressed as ordered pairs and graphed.

Solving linear inequalities

A linear equation in x and y is an equation that can be written in the form $Ax + By = C$. A **linear inequality** in x and y is an inequality that can be written in one of four forms:

$$Ax + By > C, \qquad Ax + By < C, \qquad Ax + By \geq C, \qquad \text{or} \qquad Ax + By \leq C$$

where A, B, and C represent real numbers and A and B are not both zero. Some examples of linear inequalities are

$$2x - y > -3, \qquad y < 3, \qquad x + 4y \geq 6, \qquad \text{and} \qquad x \leq -2$$

As with linear equations, an ordered pair (x, y) is a solution of an inequality in x and y if a true statement results when the variables in the inequality are replaced by the coordinates of the ordered pair.

EXAMPLE 1   *Verifying a solution.*   Determine whether each ordered pair is a solution of $x - y \leq 5$. Then graph each solution: **a.** $(4, 2)$,   **b.** $(0, -6)$,   and   **c.** $(1, -4)$.

Solution

In each case, we substitute the x-coordinate for x and the y-coordinate for y in the inequality $x - y \leq 5$. If the ordered pair is a solution, a true statement will be obtained.

a. For $(4, 2)$:

$x - y \leq 5$ The original inequality.

$4 - 2 \leq 5$ Replace x with 4 and y with 2.

$2 \leq 5$ True.

Because $2 \leq 5$ is true, $(4, 2)$ is a solution of the inequality, and we graph it in Figure 7-15.

b. For $(0, -6)$:

$x - y \leq 5$ The original inequality.

$0 - (-6) \leq 5$ Replace x with 0 and y with -6.

$6 \leq 5$ False.

Because $6 \leq 5$ is false, $(0, -6)$ is not a solution.

c. For $(1, -4)$:

$x - y \leq 5$ The original inequality.

$1 - (-4) \leq 5$ Replace x with 1 and y with -4.

$5 \leq 5$ True.

Because $5 \leq 5$ is true, $(1, -4)$ is a solution, and we graph it in Figure 7-15.

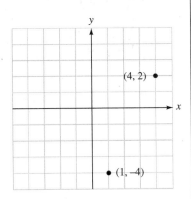

FIGURE 7-15

Self Check

Using the inequality in Example 1, determine whether each ordered pair is a solution. If it is, graph that solution on the coordinate system in Figure 7-15.   **a.** $(8, 2)$,   **b.** $(4, -1)$,   **c.** $(-2, 4)$,   and   **d.** $(-3, -5)$.

Answers: **a.** not a solution,   **b.** solution,   **c.** solution,   **d.** solution

The graph in Figure 7-15 contains some solutions of the inequality $x - y \leq 5$. Intuition tells us that there are many more ordered pairs (x, y) such that $x - y$ is less than or equal to 5. How then do we get a complete graph of the solutions of $x - y \leq 5$? We address this question in the following discussion.

Graphing linear inequalities

The graph of $x - y = 5$ is a line consisting of the points whose coordinates satisfy the equation. The graph of the inequality $x - y \leq 5$ is not a line, but an area bounded by a line, called a **half-plane.** The half-plane consists of the points whose coordinates satisfy the inequality.

    EXAMPLE 2   *Graphing a linear inequality.*   Graph $x - y \leq 5$.

Solution

Since the inequality symbol $\leq$ includes an equals sign, the graph of $x - y \leq 5$ includes the graph of $x - y = 5$. So we begin by graphing the equation $x - y = 5$, using the intercept method. See Figure 7-16(a).

$$x - y = 5$$

x	y	(x, y)
0	−5	(0, −5)
5	0	(5, 0)
6	1	(6, 1)

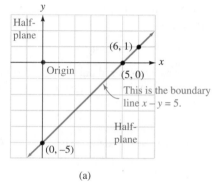

(a)

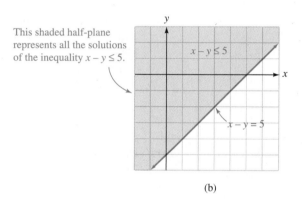

(b)

FIGURE 7-16

Since the inequality $x - y \leq 5$ allows $x - y$ to be less than 5, the coordinates of points other than those shown on the line in Figure 7-16(a) satisfy the inequality. For example, the coordinates of the origin $(0, 0)$ satisfy the inequality. We can verify this by letting x and y be zero in the given inequality:

$$x - y \leq 5$$
$$\mathbf{0 - 0} \leq 5 \quad \text{Substitute 0 for } x \text{ and 0 for } y.$$
$$0 \leq 5$$

Because $0 \leq 5$, the coordinates of the origin satisfy the original inequality. In fact, the coordinates of every point on the *same side* of the line as the origin satisfy the inequality. The graph of $x - y \leq 5$ is the half-plane that is shaded in Figure 7-16(b). Since the **boundary line** $x - y = 5$ is included, we draw it with a solid line.   ∎

EXAMPLE 3   *Graphing a linear inequality.*   Graph $2(x - 3) - (x - y) \geq -3$.

Solution

We begin by simplifying the inequality as follows:

$$2(x - 3) - (x - y) \geq -3$$
$$2x - 6 - x + y \geq -3 \quad \text{Use the distributive property.}$$
$$x - 6 + y \geq -3 \quad \text{Combine like terms.}$$
$$x + y \geq 3 \quad \text{Add 6 to both sides.}$$

Self Check

Graph $3(x - 1) - (2x + y) \leq -5$.

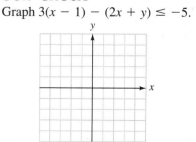

To graph the inequality $x + y \geq 3$, we graph the boundary line whose equation is $x + y = 3$. Since the graph of $x + y \geq 3$ includes the line $x + y = 3$, we draw the boundary with a solid line. Note that it divides the coordinate plane into two half-planes. See Figure 7-17(a).

To decide which half-plane to shade, we substitute the coordinates of some point that lies on one side of the boundary line into the inequality. If we use the origin $(0, 0)$ for the **test point,** we have

$$x + y \geq 3$$
$$\mathbf{0} + \mathbf{0} \geq 3 \quad \text{Substitute 0 for } x \text{ and 0 for } y.$$
$$0 \geq 3 \quad \text{This statement is false.}$$

Since $0 \geq 3$ is a false statement, the origin is not in the graph. In fact, the coordinates of *every* point on the origin's side of the boundary line will not satisfy the inequality. However, every point on the other side of the boundary line will satisfy the inequality. We shade that half-plane. The graph of $x + y \geq 3$ is the half-plane that appears in color in Figure 7-17(b).

$x + y = 3$

x	y	(x, y)
0	3	$(0, 3)$
3	0	$(3, 0)$
1	2	$(1, 2)$

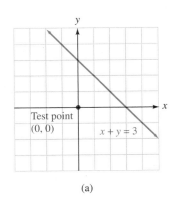

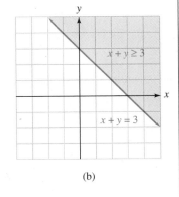

(a)   (b)

FIGURE 7-17

Answer:

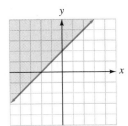

EXAMPLE 4   *Graphing a linear inequality.*   Graph $y > 2x$.

Solution

To find the boundary line, we graph $y = 2x$. Since the symbol $>$ does not include an equals sign, the points on the graph of $y = 2x$ are not part of the graph of $y > 2x$. We draw the boundary line as a broken line to show this, as in Figure 7-18(a).

To determine which half-plane to shade, we substitute the coordinates of some point that lies on one side of the boundary line into $y > 2x$. Since the origin is on the boundary, we cannot use it as a test point. Point $T(2, 0)$, for example, is below the boundary line. See Figure 7-18(a). To see whether point $T(2, 0)$ satisfies $y > 2x$, we substitute 2 for x and 0 for y in the inequality.

$$y > 2x$$
$$\mathbf{0} > 2(\mathbf{2}) \quad \text{Substitute 2 for } x \text{ and 0 for } y.$$
$$0 > 4 \quad \text{This statement is false.}$$

Since $0 > 4$ is a false statement, the coordinates of point T do not satisfy the inequality, and point T is not on the side of the broken line we wish to shade. Instead, we shade the other side of the boundary line. The graph of the solution set of $y > 2x$ is shown in Figure 7-18(b).

Self Check

Graph $y < 3x$.

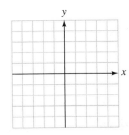

	$y = 2x$	
x	y	(x, y)
0	0	(0, 0)
−1	−2	(−1, −2)
1	2	(1, 2)

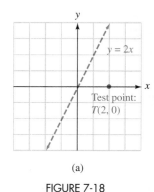
(a)

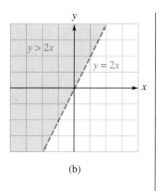
(b)

FIGURE 7-18

Answer:

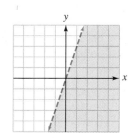

EXAMPLE 5   *Graphing a linear inequality.*   Graph $x + 2y < 6$.

Solution

We find the boundary by graphing the equation $x + 2y = 6$. We draw the boundary as a broken line to show that it is not part of the solution. We then choose a test point not on the boundary and see whether its coordinates satisfy $x + 2y < 6$. The origin is a convenient choice.

$$x + 2y < 6$$
$$0 + 2(0) < 6 \quad \text{Substitute 0 for } x \text{ and 0 for } y.$$
$$0 < 6$$

Since $0 < 6$ is a true statement, we shade the side of the line that includes the origin. The graph is shown in Figure 7-19.

	$x + 2y = 6$	
x	y	(x, y)
0	3	(0, 3)
6	0	(6, 0)
4	1	(4, 1)

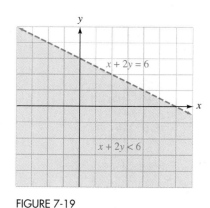

FIGURE 7-19

Self Check

Graph $2x - y < 4$.

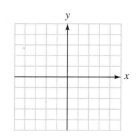

Answer:

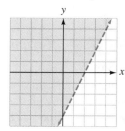

EXAMPLE 6   *Graphing a linear inequality.*   Graph $y \geq 0$.

Solution

We find the boundary by graphing the equation $y = 0$. We draw the boundary as a solid line to show that it is part of the solution. We then choose a test point not on the boundary and see whether its coordinates satisfy $y \geq 0$. The point $T(0, 1)$ is a convenient choice.

$$y \geq 0$$
$$1 \geq 0 \quad \text{Substitute 1 for } y.$$

Since $1 \geq 0$ is a true statement, we shade the side of the line that includes point T. The graph is shown in Figure 7-20.

Self Check

Graph $x \geq 2$.

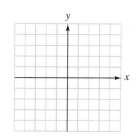

$y = 0$

x	y	(x, y)
1	0	$(1, 0)$
2	0	$(2, 0)$
3	0	$(3, 0)$

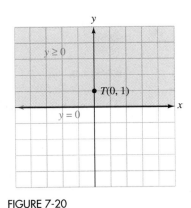

FIGURE 7-20

Answer:

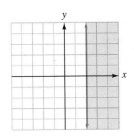

The following is a summary of the procedure for graphing linear inequalities.

Graphing linear inequalities in two variables

1. Graph the boundary line of the region. If the inequality allows the possibility of equality (the symbol is either $\leq$ or $\geq$), draw the boundary line as a solid line. If equality is not allowed ($<$ or $>$), draw the boundary line as a broken line.

2. Pick a test point that is on one side of the boundary line. (Use the origin if possible.) Replace x and y in the inequality with the coordinates of that point. If the inequality is satisfied, shade the side that contains that point. If the inequality is not satisfied, shade the other side of the boundary.

An application of linear inequalities

 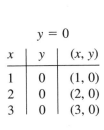 **EXAMPLE 7** *Earning money.* Carlos has two part-time jobs, one paying $10 per hour and another paying $12 per hour. He must earn at least $240 per week to pay his expenses while attending college. Write an inequality that shows the various ways he can schedule his time to achieve his goal.

Solution
If we let x represent the number of hours Carlos works on the first job and y the number of hours he works on the second job, we have

The hourly rate on the first job	times	the hours worked on the first job	plus	the hourly rate on the second job	times	the hours worked on the second job	is at least	$240.
10	$\cdot$	x	$+$	12	$\cdot$	y	$\geq$	240

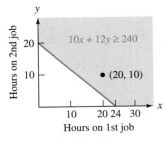

FIGURE 7-21

The graph of the inequality $10x + 12y \geq 240$ is shown in Figure 7-21. Any point in the shaded region indicates a possible way Carlos can schedule his time and earn $240 or more per week. For example, if he works 20 hours on the first job and 10 hours on the second job, he will earn

$$\$10(20) + \$12(10) = \$200 + \$120$$
$$= \$320$$

Since Carlos cannot work a negative number of hours, a graph showing negative values of x or y would have no meaning.

STUDY SET   Section 7.5

VOCABULARY   *Fill in the blanks.*

1. $2x - y \leq 4$ is a linear ___inequality___ in x and y.

2. The symbol $\leq$ means ___is less than___ or ___equal to___.

3. In the graph in Illustration 1, the line $2x - y = 4$ is the ___boundary___.

4. In Illustration 1, the line $2x - y = 4$ divides the rectangular coordinate system into two ___half-planes___.

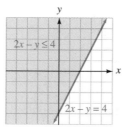

ILLUSTRATION 1

CONCEPTS

5. Tell whether each ordered pair is a solution of $5x - 3y \geq 0$.
  a. $(1, 1)$ yes   **b.** $(-2, -3)$ no
  c. $(0, 0)$ yes   **d.** $\left(\dfrac{1}{5}, \dfrac{4}{3}\right)$ no

6. Tell whether each ordered pair is a solution of $x + 4y < -1$.
  a. $(3, 1)$ no   **b.** $(-2, 0)$ yes
  c. $(-0.5, 0.2)$ no   **d.** $\left(-2, \dfrac{1}{4}\right)$ no

7. Tell whether the graph of each linear inequality includes the boundary line.
  a. $y > -x$ no   **b.** $5x - 3y \leq -2$ yes

8. If a false statement results when the coordinates of a test point are substituted into a linear inequality, which half-plane should be shaded to represent the solution of the inequality?
  the half-plane opposite that in which the test point lies

9. A linear inequality has been graphed in Illustration 2. Tell whether each point satisfies the inequality.
  a. $(1, -3)$ no
  b. $(-2, -1)$ yes
  c. $(2, 3)$ yes
  d. $(3, -4)$ no

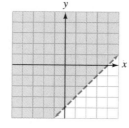

ILLUSTRATION 2

10. A linear inequality has been graphed in Illustration 3. Tell whether each point satisfies the inequality.
  a. $(2, 1)$ yes
  b. $(-2, -4)$ no
  c. $(4, -2)$ no
  d. $(-3, 4)$ yes

ILLUSTRATION 3

11. The boundary for the graph of a linear inequality is shown in Illustration 4. Why can't the origin be used as a test point to decide which side to shade?
  The test point must be on one side of the boundary.

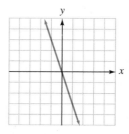

ILLUSTRATION 4

12. To decide how many pallets (x) and barrels (y) a delivery truck can hold, a dispatcher refers to the loading sheet in Illustration 5. Can a truck make a delivery of 4 pallets and 10 barrels in one trip?   no

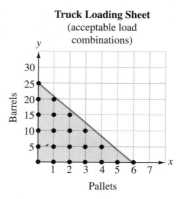

Truck Loading Sheet
(acceptable load combinations)

Barrels / Pallets

ILLUSTRATION 5

PRACTICE   *Complete the graph by shading the correct side of the boundary.*

13. $y \leq x + 2$

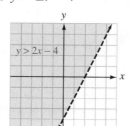

14. $y > x - 3$

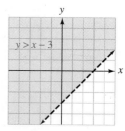

15. $y > 2x - 4$

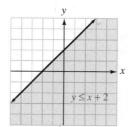

16. $y \leq -x + 1$

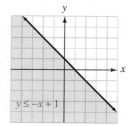

17. $x - 2y \geq 4$

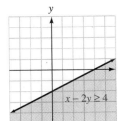

18. $3x + 2y > 12$

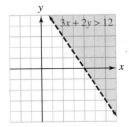

29. $y - x \geq 0$

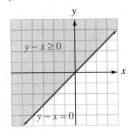

30. $y + x < 0$

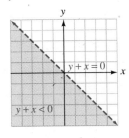

19. $y \leq 4x$

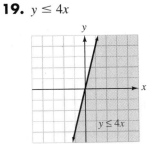

20. $y + 2x < 0$

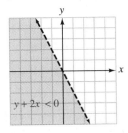

31. $2x + y > 2$

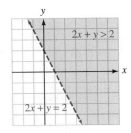

32. $3x - 2y > 6$

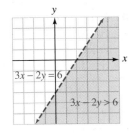

Graph each inequality.

21. $y \geq 3 - x$

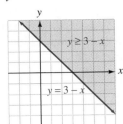

22. $y < 2 - x$

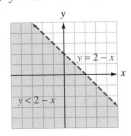

33. $3x - 4y > 12$

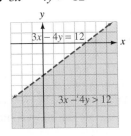

34. $4x + 3y \leq 12$

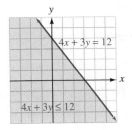

23. $y < 2 - 3x$

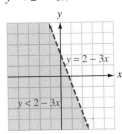

24. $y \geq 5 - 2x$

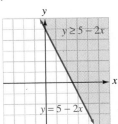

35. $5x + 4y \geq 20$

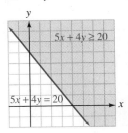

36. $7x - 2y < 21$

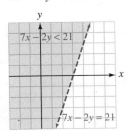

25. $y \geq 2x$

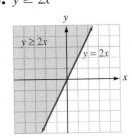

26. $y < 3x$

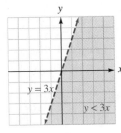

37. $x < 2$

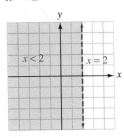

38. $y > -3$

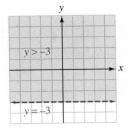

27. $2y - x < 8$

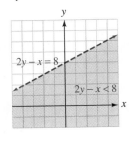

28. $y + 9x \geq 3$

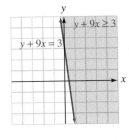

39. $y \leq 1$

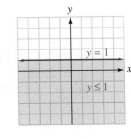

40. $x \geq -4$

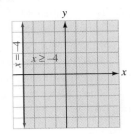

Simplify each inequality and then graph it.

41. $3(x + y) + x < 6$

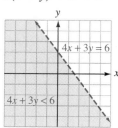

42. $2(x - y) - y \geq 4$

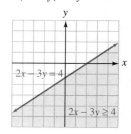

43. $4x - 3(x + 2y) \geq -6y$

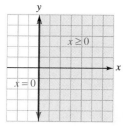

44. $3y + 2(x + y) < 5y$

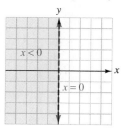

APPLICATIONS

45. NATO In March of 1999, NATO aircraft and cruise missiles targeted Serbian military forces that were south of the 44th parallel in Yugoslavia, Montenegro, and Kosovo. See Illustration 6. Shade the geographic area that NATO was trying to rid of Serbian forces.

Based on data from *Los Angeles Times* (March 24, 1999)

ILLUSTRATION 6

46. U.S. HISTORY When he ran for president in 1844, the campaign slogan of James K. Polk was "54-40 or fight!" It meant that Polk was willing to fight Great Britain for the possession of the Oregon Territory north to the 54°40′ parallel, as shown in Illustration 7. In 1846, Polk accepted a compromise to establish the 49th parallel as the permanent boundary of the United States. Shade the area of land that Polk conceded to the British.

ILLUSTRATION 7

Write an inequality and graph it for nonnegative values of x and y. Then give three ordered pairs that satisfy the inequality.

47. PRODUCTION PLANNING It costs a bakery $3 to make a cake and $4 to make a pie. Production costs cannot exceed $120 per day. Use Illustration 8 to graph an inequality that shows the possible combinations of cakes (x) and pies (y) that can be made.
(10, 10), (20, 10), (10, 20)

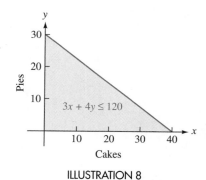

ILLUSTRATION 8

48. HIRING BABYSITTERS Mary has a choice of two babysitters. Sitter 1 charges $6 per hour, and sitter 2 charges $7 per hour. If Mary can afford no more than $42 per week for sitters, use Illustration 9 to graph an inequality that shows the possible ways that she can hire sitter 1 (x) and sitter 2 (y). (2, 2), (4, 2), (3, 3)

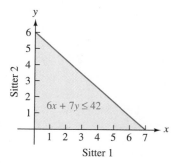

ILLUSTRATION 9

49. INVENTORY   A clothing store advertises that it maintains an inventory of at least $4,400 worth of men's jackets. If a leather jacket costs $100 and a nylon jacket costs $88, use Illustration 10 to graph an inequality that shows the possible ways that leather jackets (x) and nylon jackets (y) can be stocked.
(50, 50), (30, 40), (40, 40)

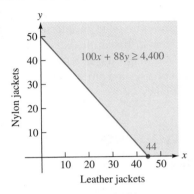

ILLUSTRATION 10

50. MAKING SPORTING GOODS   To keep up with demand, a sporting goods manufacturer allocates at least 2,400 units of production time per day to make baseballs and footballs. If it takes 20 units of time to make a baseball and 30 units of time to make a football, use Illustration 11 to graph an inequality that shows the possible ways to schedule the production time to make baseballs (x) and footballs (y).
(60, 80), (100, 60), (120, 40)

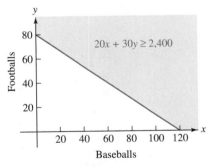

ILLUSTRATION 11

51. INVESTING IN STOCKS   Robert has up to $8,000 to invest in two companies. If stock in Robotronics sells for $40 per share and stock in Macrocorp sells for $50 per share, use Illustration 12 to graph an inequality that shows the possible ways that he can buy shares of Robotronics (x) and Macrocorp (y).
(80, 40), (80, 80), (120, 40)

52. BUYING BASEBALL TICKETS   Tickets to the Rockford Rox baseball games cost $6 for reserved seats and $4 for general admission. If nightly receipts must average at least $10,200 to meet expenses, use Illustration 13 to graph an inequality that shows the possible ways that the Rox can sell reserved seats (x) and general admission tickets (y).
(1,200, 2000), (1,600, 1,200), (800, 2,400)

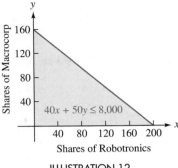

ILLUSTRATION 12

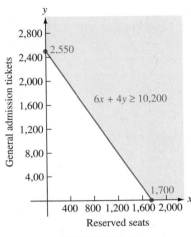

ILLUSTRATION 13

WRITING

53. Explain how to find the boundary for the graph of a linear inequality in two variables.

54. Explain how to decide which side of the boundary line to shade when graphing a linear inequality in two variables.

REVIEW

55. Let $g(x) = 3x^2 - 4x + 3$. Find $g(2)$.   7

56. Solve $2(x - 4) \le -12$. $x \le -2$

57. Factor $x^3 + 27$. $(x + 3)(x^2 - 3x + 9)$

58. Factor $9p - 9q + mp - mq$. $(p - q)(9 + m)$

59. Write a formula relating distance, rate, and time. $d = rt$

60. What is the slope of the line $2x - 3y = 2$? $\frac{2}{3}$

61. Solve $A = P + Prt$ for t. $t = \frac{A - P}{Pr}$

62. What is the sum of the measures of the three angles of any triangle?   180°

7.6 *Solving Systems of Linear Inequalities*

In this section, you will learn about

- Systems of linear inequalities • An application of systems of linear inequalities

INTRODUCTION. We have previously solved systems of linear *equations* by the graphing method. The solution of such a system is the point of intersection of the straight lines. We now consider how to solve systems of linear *inequalities* graphically. When the solution of a linear inequality is graphed, the result is a half-plane. Therefore, we would expect to find the graphical solution of a system of inequalities by looking for the intersection, or "overlap," of shaded half-planes.

Systems of linear inequalities

To solve the **system of linear inequalities**

$$\begin{cases} x + y \ge 1 \\ x - y \ge 1 \end{cases}$$

we first graph each inequality. For instructional purposes, we will initially graph each inequality on a separate set of axes, although in practice we will draw them on the same axes.

The graph of $x + y \ge 1$ includes the graph of the equation $x + y = 1$ and all points above it. Because the boundary line is included, we draw it with a solid line, as shown in Figure 7-22(a).

The graph of $x - y \ge 1$ includes the graph of the equation $x - y = 1$ and all points below it. Because the boundary line is included here also, it is drawn with a solid line, as shown in Figure 7-22(b).

$x + y = 1$

x	y	(x, y)
0	1	(0, 1)
1	0	(1, 0)
2	−1	(2, −1)

$x - y = 1$

x	y	(x, y)
0	−1	(0, −1)
1	0	(1, 0)
2	1	(2, 1)

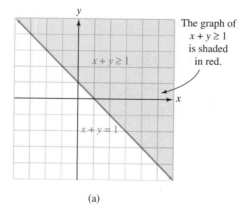

The graph of $x + y \ge 1$ is shaded in red.

(a)

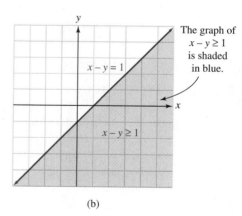

The graph of $x - y \ge 1$ is shaded in blue.

(b)

FIGURE 7-22

In Figure 7-23, we show the result when the inequalities $x + y \ge 1$ and $x - y \ge 1$ are graphed one at a time on the same coordinate axes. The area that is shaded twice represents the set of simultaneous solutions of the given system of inequalities. Any point in the doubly shaded region (shown in purple) has coordinates that satisfy both inequalities of the system.

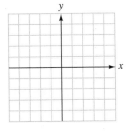

FIGURE 7-23

To see whether this is true, we can pick a point, such as point A, that lies in the doubly shaded region and show that its coordinates satisfy both inequalities. Because point A has coordinates $(4, 1)$, we have

$$x + y \geq 1 \qquad \text{and} \qquad x - y \geq 1$$
$$4 + 1 \geq 1 \qquad\qquad\qquad 4 - 1 \geq 1$$
$$5 \geq 1 \qquad\qquad\qquad\qquad 3 \geq 1$$

Since the coordinates of point A satisfy each inequality, point A is a solution of the system. If we pick a point that is not in the doubly shaded region, its coordinates will fail to satisfy at least one of the inequalities.

In general, to solve systems of linear inequalities, we will follow these steps.

Solving systems of inequalities

1. Graph each inequality in the system on the same coordinate axes.
2. Find the region that is common to every graph.
3. Pick a test point from the region to verify the solution.

EXAMPLE 1 *Solving systems of inequalities.* Graph the solution of
$$\begin{cases} 2x + y < 4 \\ -2x + y > 2 \end{cases}$$

Self Check
Graph the solution of
$$\begin{cases} x + 3y < 3 \\ -x + 3y > 3 \end{cases}$$

Solution
First, we graph each inequality on one set of axes, as shown in Figure 7-24.

	$2x + y = 4$			$-2x + y = 2$	
x	y	(x, y)	x	y	(x, y)
0	4	(0, 4)	−1	0	(−1, 0)
2	0	(2, 0)	0	2	(0, 2)
1	2	(1, 2)	2	6	(2, 6)

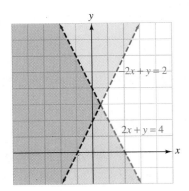

FIGURE 7-24

We note that

- The graph of $2x + y < 4$ includes all points below the line $2x + y = 4$. Since the boundary is not included, we draw it as a broken line.

• The graph of $-2x + y > 2$ includes all points above the line $-2x + y = 2$. Since the boundary is not included, we also draw it as a broken line.

The area that is shaded twice (the region in purple) is the solution of the given system of inequalities. Any point in the doubly shaded region has coordinates that will satisfy both inequalities of the system.

Pick a point in the doubly shaded region and show that it satisfies both inequalities.

Answer:

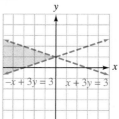

EXAMPLE 2   *Solving systems of inequalities.*   Graph the solution of $\begin{cases} x \le 2 \\ y > 3 \end{cases}$

Solution

We graph each inequality on one set of axes, as shown in Figure 7-25.

$x = 2$				$y = 3$		
x	y	(x, y)		x	y	(x, y)
2	0	(2, 0)		0	3	(0, 3)
2	2	(2, 2)		1	3	(1, 3)
2	4	(2, 4)		4	3	(4, 3)

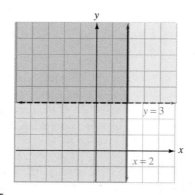

FIGURE 7-25

Self Check

Graph the solution of $\begin{cases} y \le 1 \\ x > 2 \end{cases}$

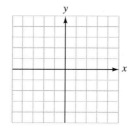

We note that

• The graph of $x \le 2$ includes all points to the left of the line $x = 2$. Since the boundary line is included, we draw it as a solid line.

• The graph $y > 3$ includes all points above the line $y = 3$. Since the boundary is not included, we draw it as a broken line.

The area that is shaded twice is the solution of the given system of inequalities. Any point in the doubly shaded region (purple) has coordinates that will satisfy both inequalities of the system. Pick a point in the doubly shaded region and show that this is true.

Answer:

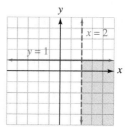

EXAMPLE 3   *Solving systems of inequalities.*   Graph the solution of $\begin{cases} y < 3x - 1 \\ y \ge 3x + 1 \end{cases}$

Solution

We graph each inequality as shown in Figure 7-26 and make the following observations:

• The graph of $y < 3x - 1$ includes all points below the broken line $y = 3x - 1$.

• The graph of $y \ge 3x + 1$ includes all points on and above the solid line $y = 3x + 1$.

Self Check

Graph the solution of

$\begin{cases} y \ge -\frac{1}{2}x + 1 \\ y < -\frac{1}{2}x - 1 \end{cases}$

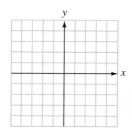

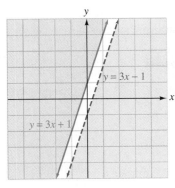

FIGURE 7-26

Because the graphs of these inequalities do not intersect, the solution set is empty. There are no solutions.

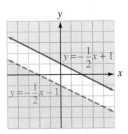

EXAMPLE 4   *Solving systems of inequalities.*   Graph the solution of

$$\begin{cases} x \ge 0 \\ y \ge 0 \\ x + 2y \le 6 \end{cases}$$

Solution

We graph each inequality as shown in Figure 7-27 and make the following observations:

- The graph of $x \ge 0$ includes all points on the y-axis and to the right.
- The graph of $y \ge 0$ includes all points on the x-axis and above.
- The graph of $x + 2y \le 6$ includes all points on the line $x + 2y = 6$ and below.

The solution is the region that is shaded three times. This includes triangle OPQ and the triangular region it encloses.

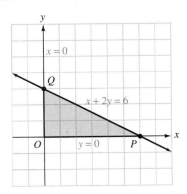

FIGURE 7-27

Self Check

Graph the solution of $\begin{cases} x \le 1 \\ y \le 2 \\ 2x - y \le 4 \end{cases}$

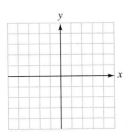

Answer:

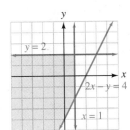

An application of systems of linear inequalities

EXAMPLE 5   *Landscaping.*   A homeowner budgets from $300 to $600 for trees and bushes to landscape his yard. After shopping around, he finds that good trees cost $150 and mature bushes cost $75. What combinations of trees and bushes can he afford to buy?

Analyze the problem   The homeowner wants to spend *at least* $300 but *not more than* $600 for trees and bushes.

Form two inequalities   We can let x represent the number of trees purchased and y the number of bushes purchased. We then form the following system of inequalities:

The cost of a tree	times	the number of trees purchased	plus	the cost of a bush	times	the number of bushes purchased	should at least be	$300.
$150	$\cdot$	x	$+$	$75	$\cdot$	y	$\geq$	$300

The cost of a tree	times	the number of trees purchased	plus	the cost of a bush	times	the number of bushes purchased	should not be more than	$600.
$150	$\cdot$	x	$+$	$75	$\cdot$	y	$\leq$	$600

Solve the system   We graph the system

$$\begin{cases} 150x + 75y \geq 300 \\ 150x + 75y \leq 600 \end{cases}$$

as shown in Figure 7-28. The coordinates of each point shown in the graph give a possible combination of the number of trees (x) and the number of bushes (y) that can be purchased. These possibilities are

$(0, 4), (0, 5), (0, 6), (0, 7), (0, 8)$

$(1, 2), (1, 3), (1, 4), (1, 5), (1, 6)$

$(2, 0), (2, 1), (2, 2), (2, 3), (2, 4)$

$(3, 0), (3, 1), (3, 2), (4, 0)$

Only these points can be used, because the homeowner cannot buy a portion of a tree or a bush.

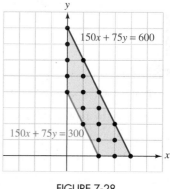

FIGURE 7-28

STUDY SET Section 7.6

VOCABULARY   *Fill in the blanks.*

1. $\begin{cases} x + y > 2 \\ x + y < 4 \end{cases}$ is a system of linear ___inequalities___.

2. The ___solution___ of a system of linear inequalities is all the ordered pairs that make all inequalities of the system true at the same time.

3. Any point in the ___doubly shaded___ region of the graph of the solution of a system of two linear inequalities has coordinates that satisfy both inequalities of the system.

4. To graph a linear inequality such as $x + y > 2$, first graph the boundary. Then pick a test ___point___ to determine which half-plane to shade.

CONCEPTS

5. In Illustration 1, the solution of linear inequality 1 was shaded in red, and the solution of linear inequality 2 was shaded in blue. The overlap of the red and the blue regions is shown in purple. Tell whether a true or a false statement results when the coordinates of the given point are substituted into the given inequality.

a. A, inequality 1   true
b. A, inequality 2   false
c. B, inequality 1   false
d. B, inequality 2   true
e. C, inequality 1   true
f. C, inequality 2   true

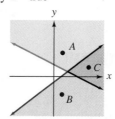

ILLUSTRATION 1

6. Match each equation, inequality, or system with the graph of its solution.

a. $x + y = 2$ ii   **b.** $x + y \geq 2$ iii

c. $\begin{cases} x + y = 2 \\ x - y = 2 \end{cases}$ iv   **d.** $\begin{cases} x + y \geq 2 \\ x - y \leq 2 \end{cases}$ i

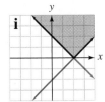
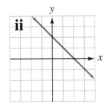

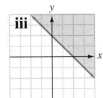
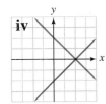

7. The graph of the solution of a system of linear inequalities is shown in Illustration 2. Tell whether each point is a part of the solution set.

a. $(4, -2)$ yes
b. $(1, 3)$ no
c. the origin   no

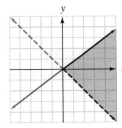

ILLUSTRATION 2

8. Use a system of inequalities to describe the shaded region in Illustration 3.

$\begin{cases} x \leq -2 \\ y > 2 \end{cases}$

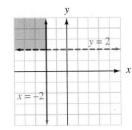

ILLUSTRATION 3

NOTATION

9. Fill in the blank to make the statement true: The graph of the solution of a system of linear inequalities shown in Illustration 4 can be described as the triangle ___ABC___ and the triangular region it encloses.

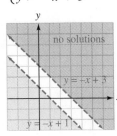

ILLUSTRATION 4

10. Represent each phrase using either $>$, $<$, $\geq$, or $\leq$.
a. is not more than $\leq$
b. must be at least $\geq$

c. should not surpass $\leq$
d. cannot go below $\geq$

PRACTICE   *Graph the solution set of each system of inequalities, when possible.*

11. $\begin{cases} x + 2y \leq 3 \\ 2x - y \geq 1 \end{cases}$ **12.** $\begin{cases} 2x + y \geq 3 \\ x - 2y \leq -1 \end{cases}$

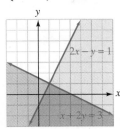
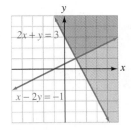

13. $\begin{cases} x + y < -1 \\ x - y > -1 \end{cases}$ **14.** $\begin{cases} x + y > 2 \\ x - y < -2 \end{cases}$

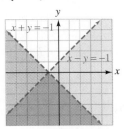
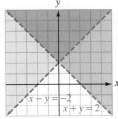

15. $\begin{cases} x \geq 2 \\ y \leq 3 \end{cases}$ **16.** $\begin{cases} x \geq -1 \\ y > -2 \end{cases}$

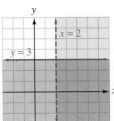
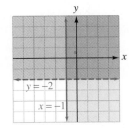

17. $\begin{cases} 2x - 3y \leq 0 \\ y \geq x - 1 \end{cases}$ **18.** $\begin{cases} y > 2x - 4 \\ y \geq -x - 1 \end{cases}$

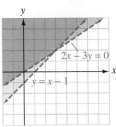
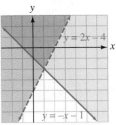

19. $\begin{cases} y < -x + 1 \\ y > -x + 3 \end{cases}$ **20.** $\begin{cases} y > -x + 2 \\ y < -x + 4 \end{cases}$

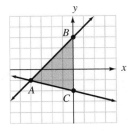
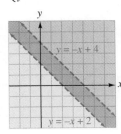

21. $\begin{cases} x > 0 \\ y > 0 \end{cases}$

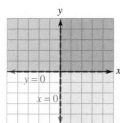

22. $\begin{cases} x \le 0 \\ y < 0 \end{cases}$

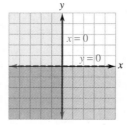

31. $\begin{cases} \frac{x}{2} + \frac{y}{3} \ge 2 \\ \frac{x}{2} - \frac{y}{2} < -1 \end{cases}$

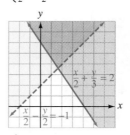

32. $\begin{cases} \frac{x}{3} - \frac{y}{2} < -3 \\ \frac{x}{3} + \frac{y}{2} > -1 \end{cases}$

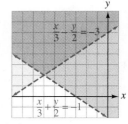

23. $\begin{cases} 3x + 4y \ge -7 \\ 2x - 3y \ge 1 \end{cases}$

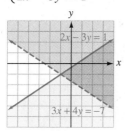

24. $\begin{cases} 3x + y \le 1 \\ 4x - y \ge -8 \end{cases}$

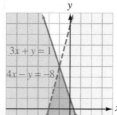

33. $\begin{cases} x \ge 0 \\ y \ge 0 \\ x + y \le 3 \end{cases}$

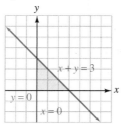

34. $\begin{cases} x - y \le 6 \\ x + 2y \le 6 \\ x \ge 0 \end{cases}$

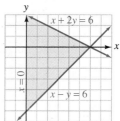

25. $\begin{cases} 2x + y < 7 \\ y > 2(1 - x) \end{cases}$

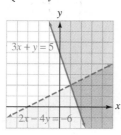

26. $\begin{cases} 2x + y \ge 6 \\ y \le 2(2x - 3) \end{cases}$

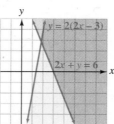

APPLICATIONS

35. BIRDS OF PREY   Parts a and b of Illustration 5 show the individual fields of vision for each eye of an owl. In part c, shade the area where the fields of vision overlap—that is, the area that is seen by both eyes.

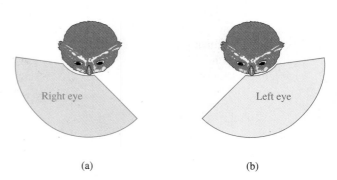

(a)   (b)

27. $\begin{cases} 2x - 4y > -6 \\ 3x + y \ge 5 \end{cases}$

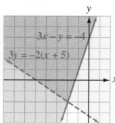

28. $\begin{cases} 2x - 3y < 0 \\ 2x + 3y \ge 12 \end{cases}$

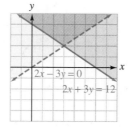

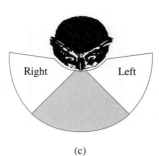

(c)

ILLUSTRATION 5

29. $\begin{cases} 3x - y \le -4 \\ 3y > -2(x + 5) \end{cases}$

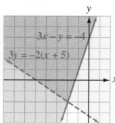

30. $\begin{cases} 3x + y < -2 \\ y > 3(1 - x) \end{cases}$

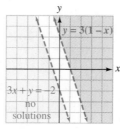

36. EARTH SCIENCE   In Illustration 6, shade the area of the earth's surface that is north of the Tropic of Capricorn and south of the Tropic of Cancer.

ILLUSTRATION 6

In Exercises 37–40, graph each system of inequalities and give two possible solutions.

37. BUYING COMPACT DISCS
Melodic Music has compact discs on sale for either $10 or $15. If a customer wants to spend at least $30 but no more than $60 on CDs, use Illustration 7 to graph a system of inequalities showing the possible combinations of $10 CDs ($x$) and $15 CDs ($y$) that the customer can buy.
1 $10 CD and 2 $15 CDs; 4 $10 CDs and 1 $15 CD

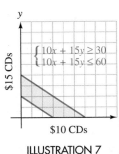

$$\begin{cases} 10x + 15y \geq 30 \\ 10x + 15y \leq 60 \end{cases}$$

$15 CDs / $10 CDs

ILLUSTRATION 7

38. BUYING BOATS   Dry Boatworks wholesales aluminum boats for $800 and fiberglass boats for $600. Northland Marina wants to make a purchase totaling at least $2,400, but no more than $4,800. Use Illustration 8 to graph a system of inequalities showing the possible combinations of aluminum boats (x) and fiberglass boats (y) that can be ordered.
4 alum. and 1 glass; 1 alum. and 4 glass

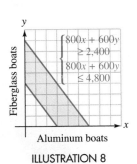

$$\begin{cases} 800x + 600y \geq 2,400 \\ 800x + 600y \leq 4,800 \end{cases}$$

Fiberglass boats / Aluminum boats

ILLUSTRATION 8

39. BUYING FURNITURE   A distributor wholesales desk chairs for $150 and side chairs for $100. Best Furniture wants its order to total no more than $900; Best also wants to order more side chairs than desk chairs. Use Illustration 9 to graph a system of inequalities showing the possible combinations of desk chairs (x) and side chairs (y) that can be ordered.
2 desk chairs and 4 side chairs; 1 desk chair and 5 side chairs

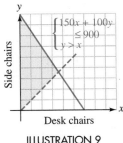

$$\begin{cases} 150x + 100y \leq 900 \\ y > x \end{cases}$$

Side chairs / Desk chairs

ILLUSTRATION 9

40. ORDERING FURNACE EQUIPMENT   J. Bolden Heating Company wants to order no more than $2,000 worth of electronic air cleaners and humidifiers from a wholesaler that charges $500 for air cleaners and $200 for humidifiers. If Bolden wants more humidifiers than air cleaners, use Illustration 10 to graph a system of inequalities showing the possible combinations of air cleaners (x) and humidifiers (y) that can be ordered.
1 air cleaner and 2 humidifiers; 2 air cleaners and 3 humidifiers

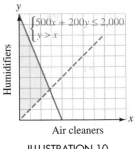

$$\begin{cases} 500x + 200y \leq 2,000 \\ y > x \end{cases}$$

Humidifiers / Air cleaners

ILLUSTRATION 10

41. PESTICIDE   To eradicate a fruit fly infestation, helicopters sprayed an area of a city that can be described by $y \geq -2x + 1$ (within the city limits). Two weeks later, more spraying was ordered over the area described by $y \geq \frac{1}{4}x - 4$ (within the city limits). In Illustration 11, show the part of the city that was sprayed twice.

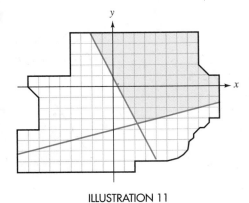

ILLUSTRATION 11

42. REDEVELOPMENT   A government agency has declared an area of a city east of First Street, north of Second Avenue, south of Sixth Avenue, and west of Fifth Street as eligible for federal redevelopment funds. See Illustration 12. Describe this area of the city mathematically using a system of four inequalities, if the corner of Central Avenue and Main Street is considered the origin.
$$\begin{cases} x > 1 \\ x < 5 \\ y > 2 \\ y < 6 \end{cases}$$

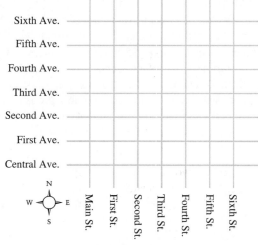

ILLUSTRATION 12

WRITING

43. Explain how to use graphing to solve a system of inequalities.

44. Explain when a system of inequalities will have no solutions.

45. Describe how the graphs of the solutions of these systems are similar and how they differ.

$$\begin{cases} x + y = 4 \\ x - y = 4 \end{cases} \quad \text{and} \quad \begin{cases} x + y \geq 4 \\ x - y \geq 4 \end{cases}$$

46. When a solution of a system of linear inequalities is graphed, what does the shading represent?

REVIEW *Complete each table of values.*

47. $y = 2x^2$

x	y
8	128
-2	8

48. $t = -|s + 2|$

s	t
-3	-1
-10	-8

49. $f(x) = 4 + x^3$

Input	Output
0	4
-3	-23

50. $g(x) = 2x - x^2$

x	$g(x)$
5	-15
-5	-35

Systems of Equations and Inequalities

In Chapter 7, we have solved problems that required the use of two variables to represent two unknown quantities. To find the unknowns, we write a pair of equations (or inequalities) called a **system.**

Solving systems of equations by graphing

A system of linear equations can be solved by graphing both equations and locating the point of intersection of the two lines.

1. FOOD SERVICE   The two equations in the table give the fees two different catering companies charge a Hollywood studio for on-location meal service.

Caterer	Setup fee	Cost per meal	Equation
Sunshine	$1,000	$4	$y = 4x + 1,000$
Lucy's	$500	$5	$y = 5x + 500$

Complete Illustration 1, using the graphing method to find the break point. That is, find the number of meals and the corresponding fee for which the two caterers will charge the studio the same amount. (500, 3,000)

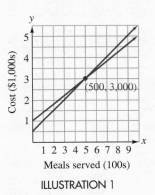

ILLUSTRATION 1

Solving systems of equations by substitution

The substitution method for solving a system of equations works well when a variable in either equation has a coefficient of 1 or -1.

2. Solve by substitution: $\begin{cases} y = 2x - 9 \\ x + 3y = 8 \end{cases}$ (5, 1)

3. Solve by substitution: $\begin{cases} 3x + 4y = -7 \\ 2y - x = -1 \end{cases}$ $(-1, -1)$

Solving systems of equations by addition

With the addition method, equal quantities are added to both sides of an equation to eliminate one of the variables. Then we solve for the other variable.

4. Solve by addition: $\begin{cases} x + y = 1 \\ x - y = 5 \end{cases}$ (3, -2)

5. Solve by addition: $\begin{cases} 2x - 3y = -18 \\ 3x + 2y = -1 \end{cases}$ $(-3, 4)$

Solving systems of inequalities

To solve a system of two linear inequalities, we graph the inequalities on the same coordinate axes. The area that is shaded twice represents the set of solutions.

6. This system of inequalities describes the number of $20 shirts ($x$) and $40 pants ($y$) a person can buy if he or she plans to spend not less than $80 but not more than $120. Using Illustration 2, graph the system. Then give three solutions.   (1, 2), (2, 2), (3, 1) (answers may vary)

$$\begin{cases} 20x + 40y \geq 80 \\ 20x + 40y \leq 120 \end{cases}$$

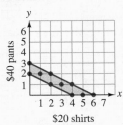

ILLUSTRATION 2

517

Section 7.1

SOLVING SYSTEMS GRAPHICALLY The graphing method was used to solve a system of linear equations. The work is shown in Illustration 1. What are the two equations of the system?

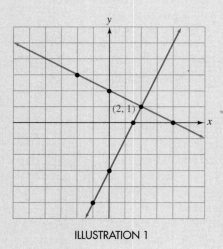

ILLUSTRATION 1

WRITING SYSTEMS OF EQUATIONS In your group, pick a specific ordered pair (x, y) where the x-coordinate and the y-coordinate are integers between -5 and 5. Write a system of two linear equations whose solution is the ordered pair that you picked. Then exchange systems with another group and solve the system that they wrote.

Section 7.2

SUBSTITUTIONS The word *substitution* is used in several ways. Explain how it is used in the context of a sporting event such as a basketball game. Explain how it is sometimes used when ordering food at a restaurant. Explain what is meant by a *substitute* teacher. Finally, explain how the substitution method is used to solve a system such as

$$\begin{cases} y = -2x - 5 \\ 3x + 5y = -4 \end{cases}$$

What is the difference in the mathematical meaning of the word *substitution* as opposed to the everyday usage of the word?

Section 7.3

SOLVING SYSTEMS Solve the system

$$\begin{cases} 2x + y = 4 \\ 2x + 3y = 0 \end{cases}$$

using the graphing method, the substitution method, and the addition method. Which method do you think is the best to use in this case? Why?

Section 7.4

TWO UNKNOWNS Consider the following problem: A man paid $89 for two white shirts and four pairs of black socks. Find the cost of a white shirt.

If we let x represent the cost of a white shirt and y represent the cost of a pair of black socks, an equation describing the situation is $2x + 4y = 89$. Explain why there is not enough information to solve the problem.

Section 7.5

MATCHING GAME Have a student in your group write ten linear inequalities on 3×5 note cards, one inequality per card. Then have him or her graph each of the inequalities on separate cards. Mix up the cards and put all the inequality cards on one side of a table and all the cards with graphs on the other side. Work together to match each inequality with its proper graph.

Section 7.6

SYSTEMS OF INEQUALITIES The points A, B, C, D, E, F, and G are labeled in the graph of the solution of a system of inequalities in Illustration 2. Tell whether the coordinates of each point make the first inequality (whose solution was shown in red) and the second inequality (whose solution was shown in blue) true or false. Use a table of the following form to keep track of your results.

Point	Coordinates	1st inequality	2nd inequality
A			

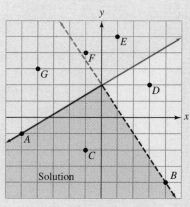

ILLUSTRATION 2

| SECTION 7.1 | *Solving Systems of Equations by Graphing* |

CONCEPTS

An ordered pair that satisfies both equations simultaneously is a *solution* of the system.

REVIEW EXERCISES

1. Tell whether the ordered pair is a solution of the system.

a. $(2, -3)$, $\begin{cases} 3x - 2y = 12 \\ 2x + 3y = -5 \end{cases}$ yes   **b.** $\left(\frac{7}{2}, -\frac{2}{3}\right)$, $\begin{cases} 4x - 6y = 18 \\ \frac{x}{3} + \frac{y}{2} = \frac{5}{6} \end{cases}$ yes

2. INJURY COMPARISON   Illustration 1 shows the number of skiing and snow-boarding injuries nationally for the years 1993–1997. If the number of injuries continued to occur at the 1996–1997 rates, estimate when they would be the same for skiing and snowboarding. About how many injuries would that be?   2000; 60,000 per year

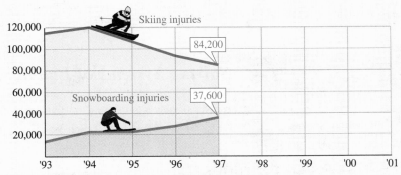

Based on data from *Los Angeles Times* (March 23, 1999)

ILLUSTRATION 1

To *solve a system graphically:*

1. Carefully graph each equation.

2. If the lines intersect, the coordinates of the point of intersection give the solution of the system.

3. Check the solution in the original equations.

When a system of equations has a solution, it is a *consistent* system. Systems with no solutions are *inconsistent*.

When the graphs of two equations in a system are different lines, the equations are *independent* equations.

The equations of a system with infinitely many solutions are *dependent*.

3. Use the graphing method to solve each system.

a. $\begin{cases} x + y = 7 \\ 2x - y = 5 \end{cases}$

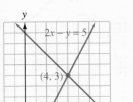

b. $\begin{cases} y = -\frac{x}{3} \\ 2x + y = 5 \end{cases}$

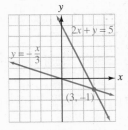

c. $\begin{cases} 3x + 6y = 6 \\ x + 2y = 2 \end{cases}$

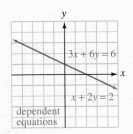

dependent equations

d. $\begin{cases} 6x + 3y = 12 \\ 2x + y = 2 \end{cases}$

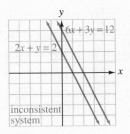

inconsistent system

SECTION 7.2

Solving Systems of Equations by Substitution

To solve a system of equations in x and y by the *substitution method:*

1. Solve one of the equations for either x or y.

2. Substitute the resulting expression for the variable in step 1 into the other equation, and solve the equation.

3. Find the value of the other variable by substituting the solution found in step 2 in any equation containing x and y.

4. Check the solution in the original equations.

4. Use the substitution method to solve each system.

a. $\begin{cases} x = y \\ 5x - 4y = 3 \end{cases}$ $(3, 3)$

b. $\begin{cases} y = 15 - 3x \\ 7y + 3x = 15 \end{cases}$ $(5, 0)$

c. $\begin{cases} 0.2x + 0.2y = 0.6 \\ 3x = 2 - y \end{cases}$ $\left(-\frac{1}{2}, \frac{7}{2}\right)$

d. $\begin{cases} 6(r + 2) = s - 1 \\ r - 5s = -7 \end{cases}$ $(-2, 1)$

e. $\begin{cases} 9x + 3y = 5 \\ 3x + y = \dfrac{5}{3} \end{cases}$ dependent equations

f. $\begin{cases} \dfrac{x}{6} + \dfrac{y}{10} = 3 \\ \dfrac{5x}{16} - \dfrac{3y}{16} = \dfrac{15}{8} \end{cases}$ $(12, 10)$

5. In solving a system using the substitution method, suppose you obtain the result of $8 = 9$.

    a. How many solutions does the system have?   no solutions

    b. Describe the graph of the system.   two parallel lines

    c. What term is used to describe the system?   inconsistent system

SECTION 7.3

Solving Systems of Equations by Addition

To solve a system of equations using the *addition method:*

1. Write each equation in $Ax + By = C$ form.

2. Multiply one or both equations by nonzero quantities to make the coefficients of x (or y) opposites.

3. Add the equations to eliminate the terms involving x (or y).

4. Solve the equation resulting from step 3.

5. Find the value of the other variable by substituting the value of the variable found in step 4 into any equation containing both variables.

6. Check the solution in the original equations.

6. Solve each system using the addition method.

a. $\begin{cases} 2x + y = 1 \\ 5x - y = 20 \end{cases}$ $(3, -5)$

b. $\begin{cases} x + 8y = 7 \\ x - 4y = 1 \end{cases}$ $\left(3, \frac{1}{2}\right)$

c. $\begin{cases} 5a + b = 2 \\ 3a + 2b = 11 \end{cases}$ $(-1, 7)$

d. $\begin{cases} 11x + 3y = 27 \\ 8x + 4y = 36 \end{cases}$ $(0, 9)$

e. $\begin{cases} 9x + 3y = 15 \\ 3x = 5 - y \end{cases}$ dependent equations

f. $\begin{cases} \dfrac{x}{3} + \dfrac{y + 2}{2} = 1 \\ \dfrac{x + 8}{8} + \dfrac{y - 3}{3} = 0 \end{cases}$ $(0, 0)$

g. $\begin{cases} 0.02x + 0.05y = 0 \\ 0.3x - 0.2y = -1.9 \end{cases}$

$(-5, 2)$

h. $\begin{cases} -\dfrac{1}{4}x = 1 - \dfrac{2}{3}y \\ 6(x - 3y) + 2y = 5 \end{cases}$

inconsistent system

7. For each system, tell which method, substitution or addition, would be easier to use to solve the system and why.

a. $\begin{cases} 6x + 2y = 5 \\ 3x - 3y = -4 \end{cases}$
   Addition; no variables have a coefficient of 1 or -1.

b. $\begin{cases} x = 5 - 7y \\ 3x - 3y = -4 \end{cases}$
   Substitution; equation 1 is solved for x.

SECTION 7.4

Applications of Systems of Equations

In this section, we considered ways to solve problems by using *two* variables.

In Exercises 8–16, use two equations in two variables to solve each problem.

8. CAUSE OF DEATH   In 1998, the number of Americans dying from heart disease was about 4.5 times more than the number dying from a stroke. If the total number of deaths from these causes was 880,000, how many deaths were attributed to each? stroke: 160,000; heart disease: 720,000

To solve problems involving two unknown quantities:

1. *Analyze* the facts of the problem. Make a table or diagram if necessary.
2. Pick different variables to represent two unknown quantities. *Form* two equations involving the variables.
3. *Solve* the system of equations.
4. *State* the conclusion.
5. *Check* the results.

The *break point* of a linear system is the point of intersection of the graph.

9. PAINTING EQUIPMENT   When fully extended, the ladder shown in Illustration 2 is 35 feet in length. If the extension is 7 feet shorter than the base, how long is each part of the ladder?   base: 21 ft; extension: 14 ft

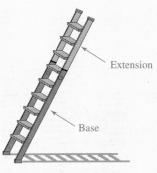

Extension

Base

ILLUSTRATION 2

10. CRASH INVESTIGATION   In an effort to protect evidence, investigators used 420 yards of yellow "Police Line—Do Not Cross" tape to seal off a large rectangular-shaped area around an airplane crash site. How much area will the investigators have to search if the width of the rectangle is three-fourths of the length?   10,800 yd^2

11. CELEBRITY ENDORSEMENT   A company selling a home juicing machine is contemplating hiring either an athlete or an actor to serve as a spokesperson for a product. The terms of each contract would be as follows:

Celebrity	Base pay	Commission per item sold
Athlete	$30,000	$5
Actor	$20,000	$10

a. For each celebrity, write an equation giving the money ($y) the celebrity would earn if x juicers were sold.
   $y = 5x + 30,000$, $y = 10x + 20,000$

b. For what number of juicers would the athlete and the actor earn the same amount?   2,000

c. Using Illustration 3, graph the equations from part a. The company expects to sell over 3,000 juicers. Which celebrity would cost the company the least money to serve as a spokesperson?   the athlete

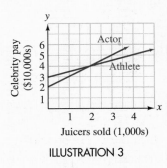

ILLUSTRATION 3

12. CANDY OUTLET STORE   A merchant wants to mix gummy worms worth $3 per pound and gummy bears worth $1.50 per pound to make 30 pounds of a mixture worth $2.10 per pound. How many pounds of each type of candy should he use?   12 lb worms, 18 lb bears

13. BOATING   It takes a motorboat 4 hours to travel 56 miles down a river, and 3 hours longer to make the return trip. Find the speed of the current.   3 mph

14. SHOPPING   Packages containing two bottles of contact lens cleaner and three bottles of soaking solution cost $63.40, and packages containing three bottles of cleaner and two bottles of soaking solution cost $69.60. Find the cost of a bottle of cleaner and a bottle of soaking solution. $16.40, $10.20

15. INVESTING   Carlos invested part of $3,000 in a 10% certificate account and the rest in a 6% passbook account. The total annual interest from both accounts is $270. How much did he invest at 6%? $750

16. ANTIFREEZE   How much of a 40% antifreeze solution must a mechanic mix with a 70% antifreeze solution if he needs 20 gallons of a 50% antifreeze solution?
$13\frac{1}{3}$ gal 40%, $6\frac{2}{3}$ gal 70%

SECTION 7.5

Graphing Linear Inequalities

An ordered pair (x, y) is a *solution* of an inequality in x and y if a true statement results when the variables are replaced by the coordinates of the ordered pair.

To graph a linear inequality:

1. Graph the *boundary line*. Draw a solid line if the inequality contains $\leq$ or $\geq$ and a broken line if it contains $<$ or $>$.

2. Pick a *test point* on one side of the boundary. Use the origin if possible. Replace x and y with the coordinates of that point. If the inequality is satisfied, shade the side that contains the point. If the inequality is not satisfied, shade the other side.

17. Determine whether each ordered pair is a solution of $2x - y \leq -4$.

  a. $(0, 5)$ yes

  b. $(2, 8)$ yes

  c. $(-3, -2)$ yes

  d. $\left(\frac{1}{2}, -5\right)$ no

18. Graph each inequality.

  a. $x - y < 5$

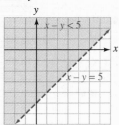

  b. $2x - 3y \geq 6$

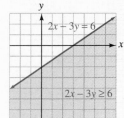

  c. $y \leq -2x$

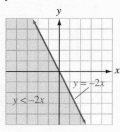

  d. $y < -4$

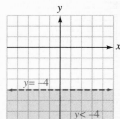

19. In Illustration 4, the graph of a linear inequality is shown. Would a true or a false statement result if the coordinates of

  a. point A were substituted into the inequality?   true

  b. point B were substituted into the inequality?   false

  c. point C were substituted into the inequality?   false

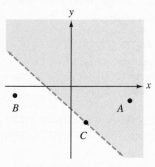

ILLUSTRATION 4

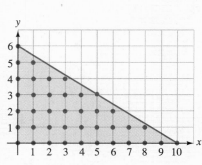

ILLUSTRATION 5

20. WORK SCHEDULE   A student told her employer that during the school year, she would be available for up to 30 hours a week, working either 3- or 5-hour shifts. Find an inequality that shows the possible ways to schedule the number of 3-hour (x) and 5-hour shifts (y) she can work, and graph it in Illustration 5. Give three ordered pairs that satisfy the inequality.
$3x + 5y \leq 30$; $(2, 4)$, $(5, 3)$, $(6, 2)$ (answers may vary)

SECTION 7.6 — *Solving Systems of Linear Inequalities*

To graph a system of linear inequalities:

1. Graph the individual inequalities of the system on the same coordinate axes.

2. The final solution, if one exists, is that region where all individual graphs intersect.

Systems of linear inequalities can be used to solve application problems.

21. Solve each system of inequalities.

a. $\begin{cases} 5x + 3y < 15 \\ 3x - y > 3 \end{cases}$

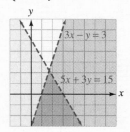

b. $\begin{cases} x \geq 3y \\ y < 3x \end{cases}$

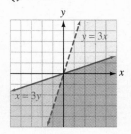

22. GIFT SHOPPING   A grandmother wants to spend at least $40 but no more than $60 on school clothes for her grandson. If T-shirts sell for $10 and pants sell for $20, write a system of inequalities that describes the possible combinations of T-shirts (x) and pants (y) she can buy. Graph the system in Illustration 6. Give two possible solutions.

$10x + 20y \geq 40$, $10x + 20y \leq 60$; (3, 1): 3 shirts and 1 pair of pants; (1, 2): 1 shirt and 2 pairs of pants (answers may vary)

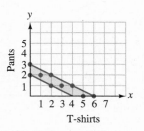

ILLUSTRATION 6

In Problems 1–2, tell whether the given ordered pair is a solution of the given system.

1. $(5, 3)$, $\begin{cases} 3x + 2y = 21 \\ x + y = 8 \end{cases}$ yes

2. $(-2, -1)$, $\begin{cases} 4x + y = -9 \\ 2x - 3y = -7 \end{cases}$ no

3. Solve the system by graphing: $\begin{cases} 3x + y = 7 \\ x - 2y = 0 \end{cases}$ $(2, 1)$

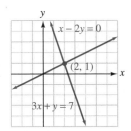

4. To solve a system of two linear equations in x and y, a student used a graphing calculator. From the calculator display in Illustration 1, determine whether the system has a solution. Explain your answer.

The lines appear to be parallel. Since the lines do not intersect, the system does not have a solution.

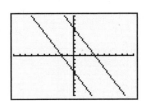

ILLUSTRATION 1

In Problems 5–6, solve each system by substitution.

5. $\begin{cases} y = x - 1 \\ 2x + y = -7 \end{cases}$ **6.** $\begin{cases} 3a + 4b = -7 \\ 2b - a = -1 \end{cases}$
$(-2, -3)$ $(-1, -1)$

In Problems 7–8, solve each system by addition.

7. $\begin{cases} 3x - y = 2 \\ 2x + y = 8 \end{cases}$ **8.** $\begin{cases} 4x + 3y = -3 \\ -3x = -4y + 21 \end{cases}$
$(2, 4)$ $(-3, 3)$

In Problems 9–10, classify each system as consistent or inconsistent.

9. $\begin{cases} x + y = 4 \\ x + y = 6 \end{cases}$ **10.** $\begin{cases} \dfrac{x}{3} + y = 4 \\ x + 3y = 12 \end{cases}$
inconsistent   consistent

11. Which method would be most efficient to solve the following system?
$$\begin{cases} 5x - 3y = 5 \\ 3x + 3y = 3 \end{cases}$$
Explain your answer. (You do not need to solve the system.)

Addition method; the terms involving y can be eliminated easily.

12. FINANCIAL PLANNING   A woman invested some money at 8% and some at 9%. The interest for 1 year on the combined investment of $10,000 was $840. How much was invested at 9%? Use a system of equations in two variables to solve this problem. $4,000

In Problems 13–14, tell whether the given ordered pair is a solution of $2x - 4y > 8$.

13. $(7, 1)$ yes

14. $(0, -2)$ no

15. Graph the inequality $x - y > -2$.

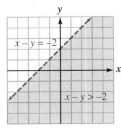

16. Solve the system by graphing.

$$\begin{cases} 2x + 3y \leq 6 \\ x \geq 2 \end{cases}$$

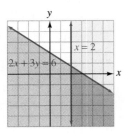

For Problems 17–18, see the graph in Illustration 2, which shows two different ways in which a salesperson can be paid according to the number of items he or she sells.

17. What is the point of intersection of the graphs? Explain its significance.

(30, 3); if 30 items are sold, the salesperson gets paid the same by both plans, $3,000.

18. Which plan do you think is better for the salesperson? Explain why.

If sales of less than 30 items are anticipated, Plan 1 is better. Otherwise, Plan 2 is more profitable.

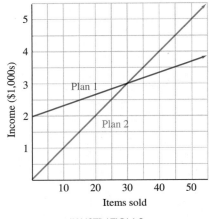

ILLUSTRATION 2

Chapters 1-7   Cumulative Review Exercises

1. STUDY ABROAD   Complete the table in Illustration 1, which shows the number of U.S. college students who studied abroad in Israel and Mexico. Round to the nearest tenth of one percent.

Country	'97–'98	'98–'99	% change
Israel	1,988	3,302	66.1%
Mexico	7,574	7,363	−2.8%

Based on data from the Institute of International Education

ILLUSTRATION 1

2. List the set of integers.
$\{\ldots, -3, -2, -1, 0, 1, 2, 3, \ldots\}$

Evaluate each expression.

3. $3 - 4[-10 - 4(-5)]$ **4.** $\dfrac{|-45| - 2(-5) + 1^5}{2 \cdot 9 - 2^4}$

-37 28

5. AIR CONDITIONING   Find the volume of air contained in the duct shown in Illustration 2. Round to the nearest tenth of a cubic foot. 1.2 ft^3

6 in.

6 ft

ILLUSTRATION 2

6. Simplify $3x^2 + 2x^2 - 5x^2$. 0

Solve each equation.

7. $2 - (4x + 7) = 3 + 2(x + 2)$ -2

8. $\dfrac{2}{5}y + 3 = 9$ 15

9. Solve $-4x + 6 > 17$ and graph the solution set. Then describe the graph using interval notation.

$x < -\frac{11}{4}$ $\qquad$ $\left(-\infty, -\frac{11}{4}\right)$

$-11/4$

10. ANGLE OF ELEVATION   Refer to Illustration 3. Find x. 30

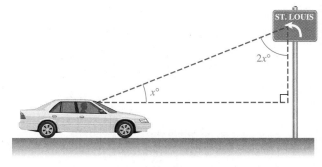

$2x°$

$x°$

ILLUSTRATION 3

11. STOCK MARKET   An investment club invested part of $45,000 in a high-yield mutual fund that earned 12% annual simple interest. The remainder of the money was invested in Treasury bonds that earned 6.5% simple annual interest. The two investments earned $4,300 in one year. How much was invested in each account?   mutual fund: $25,000; bonds: $20,000

12. Give the formula for
 a. the perimeter of a rectangle $P = 2l + 2w$
 b. the area of a rectangle $A = lw$
 c. the area of a circle $A = \pi r^2$
 d. the distance traveled $d = rt$

Graph each equation.

13. $y = -x^3$ **14.** $y = -3x + 2$

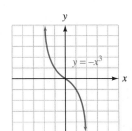

$y = -x^3$

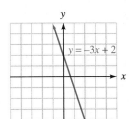

$y = -3x + 2$

15. $3x + 4y = 8$ **16.** $x = -2$

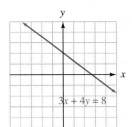

$3x + 4y = 8$

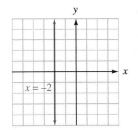

$x = -2$

17. Find the slope and *y*-intercept of the line graphed in Illustration 4. Then write the equation of the line.
$m = 3, (0, -2); y = 3x - 2$

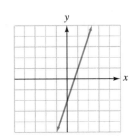

ILLUSTRATION 4

18. Find the slope of the line passing through $(6, -2)$ and $(-3, 2)$. $-\frac{4}{9}$

19. If $f(x) = 4x - 2x^2$, what is $f(-5)$? -70

20. Write 3,890,000,000 in scientific notation. 3.89×10^9

Simplify each expression. Write each answer without using parentheses or negative exponents.

21. $(x^5)^2(x^7)^3$ x^{31}

22. $\dfrac{16(aa^2)^3}{2a^2a^3}$ $8a^4$

23. $\dfrac{2^{-4}}{3^{-1}}$ $\frac{3}{16}$

24. $(2x)^0$ 1

Perform the indicated operation(s).

25. $(5x - 8y) - (-2x + 5y)$ $7x - 13y$

26. $2x^2(3x^2 + 4x - 7)$ $6x^4 + 8x^3 - 14x^2$

27. $(c + 16)^2$
$c^2 + 32c + 256$

28. $(x + 3)(2x - 3)$
$2x^2 + 3x - 9$

29. $\dfrac{2x - 32}{16x}$
$\frac{1}{8} - \frac{2}{x}$

30. $3x + 1\overline{)9x^2 + 6x + 1}$
$3x + 1$

31. Prime factor 288. $2^5 \cdot 3^2$

32. Write a polynomial that is a difference of two squares.
$x^2 - 9$ (answers may vary)

Factor each polynomial completely.

33. $12r^2 - 3rs + 9r^2s^2$
$3r(4r - s + 3rs^2)$

34. $u^2 - 18u + 81$
$(u - 9)^2$

35. $2y^2 - 7y + 3$
$(2y - 1)(y - 3)$

36. $x^4 - 81$
$(x^2 + 9)(x + 3)(x - 3)$

37. $t^3 - v^3$
$(t - v)(t^2 + tv + v^2)$

38. $xy - ty + xs - ts$
$(x - t)(y + s)$

Solve each equation.

39. $8s^2 - 16s = 0$
$0, 2$

40. $x^2 + 2x - 15 = 0$
$3, -5$

41. Simplify $\dfrac{x^2 - 25}{5x + 25} \cdot \dfrac{x - 5}{5}$.

42. Add: $\dfrac{3x}{2y} + \dfrac{5x}{2y}$. $\dfrac{4x}{y}$

43. Divide: $\dfrac{x^2 - x - 2}{x^2 + x} \div \dfrac{2 - x}{x}$. -1

44. Subtract: $\dfrac{x + 5}{xy} - \dfrac{x - 1}{x^2y}$. $\dfrac{x^2 + 4x + 1}{x^2y}$

45. Simplify $\dfrac{\frac{y}{x} + 3y}{y + \frac{2y}{x}}$. $\dfrac{3x + 1}{x + 2}$

46. Solve $\dfrac{3r}{2} - \dfrac{3}{r} = 3 + \dfrac{3r}{2}$. -1

47. The triangles shown in Illustration 5 are similar. Find *a* and *b*. 16, 8

ILLUSTRATION 5

48. Is $(-5, 2)$ a solution of $\begin{cases} -2x + 7y = 24 \\ 3x - 4y = -19 \end{cases}$? no

Solve each system by graphing.

49. $\begin{cases} x + 4y = -2 \\ y = -x - 5 \end{cases}$

50. $\begin{cases} 2x - 3y < 0 \\ y > x - 1 \end{cases}$

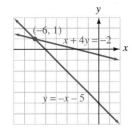

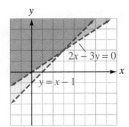

51. Solve $\begin{cases} x - 2y = 2 \\ 2x + 3y = 11 \end{cases}$ by substitution. $(4, 1)$

52. NUTRITION Illustration 6 shows per serving nutritional information for egg noodles and rice pilaf. How many servings of each food should be eaten to consume exactly 22 grams of protein and 21 grams of fat?
noodles: 2 servings, rice: 3 servings

	Protein (g)	Fat (g)
Egg noodles	5	3
Rice pilaf	4	5

ILLUSTRATION 6

Roots and *Radicals*

8

To solve many applied problems, we must determine what number x must be squared to obtain another number n. We call x the square root of n.

8.1 Square Roots

In this section, you will learn about

- Square roots • Approximating square roots
- Rational, irrational, and imaginary numbers • The square root function
- The Pythagorean theorem

INTRODUCTION. To find the area A of the square shown in Figure 8-1, we multiply its length by its width.

$$A = l \cdot w$$
$$A = 5 \cdot 5$$
$$= 25$$

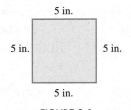

5 in.

5 in. 5 in.

5 in.

FIGURE 8-1

The area is 25 square inches.

We have seen that the product $5 \cdot 5$ can be denoted by the exponential expression 5^2, where 5 is raised to the second power. Whenever we raise a number to the second power, we are squaring it, or finding its **square.** This example illustrates that the formula for the area of a square with sides of length s is $A = s^2$.

Here are some more squares of numbers:

- The square of 3 is 9, because $3^2 = 9$.
- The square of -3 is 9, because $(-3)^2 = 9$.
- The square of 12 is 144, because $12^2 = 144$.
- The square of -12 is 144, because $(-12)^2 = 144$.
- The square of $\frac{1}{8}$ is $\frac{1}{64}$, because $\left(\frac{1}{8}\right)^2 = \frac{1}{8} \cdot \frac{1}{8} = \frac{1}{64}$.
- The square of $-\frac{1}{8}$ is $\frac{1}{64}$, because $\left(-\frac{1}{8}\right)^2 = \left(-\frac{1}{8}\right)\left(-\frac{1}{8}\right) = \frac{1}{64}$.
- The square of 0 is 0, because $0^2 = 0$.

In this section, we will reverse the squaring process and find **square roots** of numbers. We will consider the square root function and introduce the Pythagorean theorem. Finally, we will solve several application problems.

Square roots

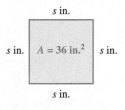

s in.

s in. $A = 36$ in.^{2} s in.

s in.

FIGURE 8-2

Suppose we know that the area of the square shown in Figure 8-2 is 36 square inches. To find the length of each side, we substitute 36 for A in the formula $A = s^2$ and solve for s.

$$A = s^2$$
$$36 = s^2$$

To solve for s, we must find a positive number whose square is 36. Since 6 is such a number, the sides of the square are 6 inches long. The number 6 is called a *square root* of 36, because 6 is the positive number that we square to get 36.

Here are some more square roots of numbers:

- 3 is a square root of 9, because $3^2 = 9$.
- -3 is a square root of 9, because $(-3)^2 = 9$.
- 12 is a square root of 144, because $12^2 = 144$.
- -12 is a square root of 144, because $(-12)^2 = 144$.
- $\frac{1}{8}$ is a square root of $\frac{1}{64}$, because $\left(\frac{1}{8}\right)^2 = \left(\frac{1}{8}\right)\left(\frac{1}{8}\right) = \frac{1}{64}$.
- $-\frac{1}{8}$ is a square root of $\frac{1}{64}$, because $\left(-\frac{1}{8}\right)^2 = \left(-\frac{1}{8}\right)\left(-\frac{1}{8}\right) = \frac{1}{64}$.
- 0 is a square root of 0, because $0^2 = 0$.

In general, we have the following definition.

Square root

> The number b is a **square root** of a if $b^2 = a$.

All positive numbers have two square roots, one that is positive and one that is negative. The two square roots of 9 are 3 and -3, and the two square roots of 144 are 12 and -12. The number 0 is the only number that has one square root, which is 0.

The **principal square root** of a positive number is its positive square root. Although 3 and -3 are both square roots of 9, only 3 is the principal square root. The symbol $\sqrt{}$, called a **radical sign,** is used to represent the principal square root of a number, and $-\sqrt{}$ is used to represent the negative square root of a number. For example, $\sqrt{9} = 3$ and $-\sqrt{9} = -3$. Likewise, $\sqrt{144} = 12$ and $-\sqrt{144} = -12$.

Principal square root

> If $a > 0$, the expression $\sqrt{a}$ represents the **principal** (or positive) **square root** of a.
> The principal square root of 0 is 0: $\sqrt{0} = 0$.

The number (or expression) under a radical sign is called the **radicand.** In $\sqrt{9}$, the number 9 is the radicand, and the entire symbol $\sqrt{9}$ is called a **radical.** We read $\sqrt{9}$ as either "the square root of 9" or as "radical 9."

An algebraic expression containing a radical is called a **radical expression.** In this chapter, we will consider radical expressions such as

$$\sqrt{49}, \qquad \frac{5}{\sqrt{3}}, \qquad -2\sqrt{x+1}, \qquad \text{and} \qquad \sqrt{28y^2} - 2y\sqrt{63}$$

EXAMPLE 1 *Finding square roots.* Find each square root.

a. $\sqrt{0} = 0$ **b.** $\sqrt{1} = 1$ **c.** $\sqrt{225} = 15$ **d.** $\sqrt{1.44} = 1.2$

e. $\sqrt{576} = 24$ **f.** $-\sqrt{4} = -2$ **g.** $-\sqrt{900} = -30$ **h.** $\sqrt{\frac{4}{9}} = \frac{2}{3}$

Self Check

Find each square root:

a. $\sqrt{121}$,   **b.** $-\sqrt{49}$,
c. $\sqrt{0.64}$,   **d.** $\sqrt{256}$,
e. $\sqrt{\frac{1}{25}}$,   **f.** $\sqrt{\frac{9}{49}}$

Answers: a. 11,   **b.** -7,
c. 0.8,   **d.** 16,   **e.** $\frac{1}{5}$,   **f.** $\frac{3}{7}$ ■

Square roots of certain numbers, such as 7, are hard to compute by hand. However, we can find $\sqrt{7}$ with a calculator.

Approximating square roots

To find the principal square root of 7, we can enter 7 into a scientific calculator and press the $\sqrt{x}$ key. The approximate value of $\sqrt{7}$ will appear on the display.

$$\sqrt{7} \approx 2.6457513 \qquad \text{Read } \approx \text{ as "is approximately equal to."}$$

Since $\sqrt{7}$ represents the number that, when squared, gives 7, we would expect squares of approximations of $\sqrt{7}$ to be close to 7.

- Rounded to one decimal place, $\sqrt{7} \approx 2.6$ and $(2.6)^2 = 6.76$.
- Rounded to two decimal places, $\sqrt{7} \approx 2.65$ and $(2.65)^2 = 7.0225$.
- Rounded to three decimal places, $\sqrt{7} \approx 2.646$ and $(2.646)^2 = 7.001316$.

Accent on Technology: **Freeway road sign:**

The sign shown in Figure 8-3 is in the shape of an equilateral triangle, and we can find its height h using the formula

$$h = \frac{\sqrt{3}s}{2}$$

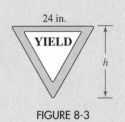

FIGURE 8-3

where s is the length of a side of the triangle. In this case, $s = 24$ inches, so we have

$$h = \frac{\sqrt{3}(24)}{2} \qquad \sqrt{3}(24) \text{ means } \sqrt{3} \cdot 24.$$

To evaluate this expression with a scientific calculator, we enter these numbers and press these keys.

Keystrokes $(\ \ 3\ \ \boxed{\sqrt{x}}\ \ \boxed{\times}\ \ 24\ \ )\ \ \boxed{\div}\ \ 2\ \ \boxed{=}$ $\boxed{20.784609}$

To evaluate this expression using a graphing calculator, we press these keys.

Keystrokes $\boxed{\text{2nd}}\ \ \boxed{\sqrt{}}\ \ 3\ \ \boxed{)}\ \ \boxed{\times}\ \ 24\ \ \boxed{\div}\ \ 2\ \ \boxed{\text{ENTER}}$ $\boxed{\begin{array}{l}\sqrt{\ }(3)*24/2 \\ \quad\quad\quad 20.78460969\end{array}}$

The height of the sign is approximately 21 inches.

Rational, irrational, and imaginary numbers

Whole numbers such as 4, 9, 16, and 49 are called **integer squares,** because each one is the square of an integer. The square root of any integer square is an integer and therefore a rational number:

$$\sqrt{4} = 2, \qquad \sqrt{9} = 3, \qquad \sqrt{16} = 4, \quad \text{and} \quad \sqrt{49} = 7$$

The square root of any whole number that is not an integer square is an **irrational number.** For example, $\sqrt{7}$ is an irrational number. Recall that the set of rational numbers and the set of irrational numbers together make up the set of real numbers.

 COMMENT   Square roots of negative numbers are not real numbers. For example, $\sqrt{-4}$ is nonreal, because the square of no real number is -4. The number $\sqrt{-4}$ is an example from a set of numbers called **imaginary numbers.** Remember: *The square root of a negative number is not a real number.*

If we attempt to evaluate $\sqrt{-4}$ using a calculator, an error message like the ones shown below will be displayed.

$$\boxed{\text{Error}} \qquad\qquad \boxed{\begin{array}{l}\text{ERR:NONREAL ANS} \\ \blacksquare\text{:Quit} \\ 2\text{:Goto}\end{array}}$$

       Scientific calculator   **Graphing calculator**

In this chapter, we will assume that *all radicands under the square root symbols are either positive or zero.* Thus, all square roots will be real numbers.

The square root function

Since there is one principal square root for every nonnegative real number x, the equation $f(x) = \sqrt{x}$ determines a square root function. For example, the value that is determined by $f(x) = \sqrt{x}$ when $x = 4$ is denoted by $f(4)$, and we have $f(4) = \sqrt{4} = 2$.

To graph this function, we make a table of values and plot each ordered pair. In the table, we chose five values for x that are integer squares. This made computing $f(x)$ quite simple. The graph appears in Figure 8-4.

$$f(x) = \sqrt{x}$$

x	$f(x)$	$(x, f(x))$
0	0	(0, 0)
1	1	(1, 1)
4	2	(4, 2)
9	3	(9, 3)
16	4	(16, 4)

Values to be input into $\sqrt{x}$ | Output values | Ordered pairs to plot

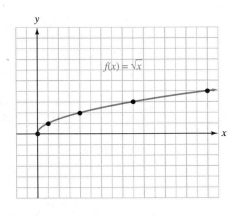

FIGURE 8-4

EXAMPLE 2   *Period of a pendulum.*

The *period* of a pendulum is the time required for the pendulum to swing back and forth to complete one cycle. (See Figure 8-5.) The period (in seconds) of a pendulum having length L (in feet) is approximated by the function

$$f(L) = 1.11\sqrt{L}$$

Find the period of a pendulum that is 5 feet long.

Solution

We substitute 5 for L in the formula and multiply using a calculator.

$$f(L) = 1.11\sqrt{L}$$
$$f(5) = 1.11\sqrt{5} \qquad 1.11\sqrt{5} \text{ means } 1.11 \cdot \sqrt{5}.$$
$$\approx 2.482035455$$

The period is approximately 2.5 seconds.

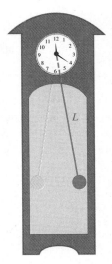

FIGURE 8-5

Self Check

Find the period of a pendulum that is 3 feet long.

Answer: about 1.9 sec

The Pythagorean theorem

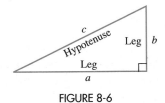

FIGURE 8-6

The longest side of a right triangle is the **hypotenuse,** which is the side opposite the right angle. The remaining two sides are the **legs** of the triangle. See Figure 8-6. Recall that the **Pythagorean theorem** provides a formula relating the lengths of the three sides of a right triangle.

The Pythagorean theorem

If the length of the hypotenuse of a right triangle is c and the lengths of the two legs are a and b,
$$c^2 = a^2 + b^2$$

Since the lengths of the sides of a triangle are positive numbers, we can use the **square root property of equality** and the Pythagorean theorem to find the length of the third side of any right triangle when the measures of two sides are given.

Square root property of equality	If a and b represent positive numbers, and if $a = b$, $$\sqrt{a} = \sqrt{b}$$

EXAMPLE 3   *Picture frame.*   After gluing and nailing together two pieces of picture frame molding, a frame maker checks her work by making a diagonal measurement. (See Figure 8-7.) If the sides of the frame form a right angle, what measurement should the frame maker read on the yardstick?

Solution   If the sides of the frame form a right angle, the sides and the diagonal form a right triangle. The lengths of the legs of the right triangle are 15 inches and 20 inches. We can find c, the length of the hypotenuse, using the Pythagorean theorem.

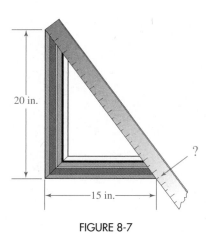

FIGURE 8-7

$$c^2 = a^2 + b^2 \qquad \text{The Pythagorean theorem.}$$
$$c^2 = 15^2 + 20^2 \qquad \text{Substitute 15 for } a \text{ and 20 for } b.$$
$$c^2 = 225 + 400 \qquad 15^2 = 225 \text{ and } 20^2 = 400.$$
$$c^2 = 625 \qquad \text{Do the addition: } 225 + 400 = 625.$$

To find c, we must find a number that, when squared, is 625. There are two such numbers, one positive and one negative. They are called the *square roots* of 625. Since c represents the length of the hypotenuse, c cannot be negative. Thus, we need only determine the positive square root of 625.

$$c^2 = 625 \qquad \text{The equation to solve.}$$
$$\sqrt{c^2} = \sqrt{625} \qquad \text{To find } c, \text{ we undo the operation performed on it by taking the positive}$$
square root of both sides. Recall that a radical symbol $\sqrt{}$ is used to indicate the positive square root of a number.
$$c = 25 \qquad \sqrt{c^2} = c \text{ because } (c)^2 = c^2, \text{ and } \sqrt{625} = 25 \text{ because } 25^2 = 625.$$

The diagonal distance should measure 25 inches. If it does not, the sides of the frame do not form a right angle.   ∎

COMMENT   When using the Pythagorean theorem $c^2 = a^2 + b^2$, we can let a represent the length of either leg of the right triangle in question. We then let b represent the length of the other leg. The variable c must always represent the length of the hypotenuse.

EXAMPLE 4   *Building a high ropes adventure course.*   The builder of a high ropes course wants to use a 25-foot cable to stabilize the pole shown in Figure 8-8. To be safe, the ground anchor stake must be farther than 18 feet from the base of the pole. Is the cable long enough to use?

Solution   We can use the Pythagorean theorem, with $b = 16$ and $c = 25$, to find a.

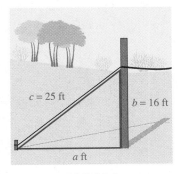

FIGURE 8-8

$$c^2 = a^2 + b^2$$
$$25^2 = a^2 + 16^2 \quad \text{Substitute 25 for } c \text{ and 16 for } b.$$
$$625 = a^2 + 256 \quad 25^2 = 625 \text{ and } 16^2 = 256.$$
$$369 = a^2 \quad \text{To isolate } a^2, \text{ subtract 256 from both sides.}$$
$$\sqrt{369} = \sqrt{a^2} \quad \begin{array}{l} \text{To find } a, \text{ we undo the operation that is performed on it} \\ \text{(squaring) by taking the positive square root of both sides.} \end{array}$$
$$19.209372 \approx a \quad \text{Use a calculator to approximate } \sqrt{369}.$$

Since the anchor stake will be more than 18 feet from the base, the 25-foot cable is long enough to use.   ■

EXAMPLE 5   ***Reach of a ladder.***   A 26-foot ladder rests against the side of a building. If the base of the ladder is 10 feet from the wall, how far up the building will the ladder reach?

Analyze the problem   The wall, the ground, and the ladder form a right triangle, as shown in Figure 8-9. In this triangle, the hypotenuse is 26 feet, and one of the legs is the base-to-wall distance of 10 feet. We can let x represent the length of the other leg, which is the distance that the ladder will reach up the wall.

Form an equation   We can use the Pythagorean theorem to form the equation.

The hypotenuse squared	is	one leg squared	plus	the other leg squared.
26^2	$=$	10^2	$+$	x^2

Solve the equation
$$26^2 = 10^2 + x^2$$
$$676 = 100 + x^2 \quad 26^2 = 676 \text{ and } 10^2 = 100.$$
$$676 - 100 = x^2 \quad \begin{array}{l} \text{To isolate } x^2, \text{ subtract 100} \\ \text{from both sides.} \end{array}$$
$$576 = x^2 \quad 676 - 100 = 576.$$
$$\sqrt{576} = \sqrt{x^2} \quad \begin{array}{l} \text{Take the positive square root} \\ \text{of both sides.} \end{array}$$
$$24 = x \quad \begin{array}{l} \sqrt{576} = 24 \text{ and } \sqrt{x^2} = x, \\ \text{because } x \cdot x = x^2. \end{array}$$

FIGURE 8-9

State the conclusion   The ladder will reach 24 feet up the side of the building.

Check the result   If the ladder reaches 24 feet up the side of the building, we have $10^2 + 24^2 = 100 + 576 = 676$, which is 26^2. The answer, 24, checks.   ■

EXAMPLE 6   ***Roof design.***   The gable end of the roof shown in Figure 8-10 is an isosceles right triangle with a span of 48 feet. Find the distance from the eaves to the peak.

Analyze the problem   The two equal sides of the isosceles triangle are the two legs of the right triangle, and the span of 48 feet is the length of the hypotenuse. We can let x represent the length of each leg, which is the distance from eaves to peak.

Form an equation   We can use the Pythagorean theorem to form the equation.

The hypotenuse squared	is	one leg squared	plus	the other leg squared.
48^2	$=$	x^2	$+$	x^2

Solve the equation

$$48^2 = x^2 + x^2$$
$$2,304 = 2x^2$$
$$1,152 = x^2$$
$$\sqrt{1,152} = \sqrt{x^2}$$
$$33.9411255 \approx x$$

$48^2 = 2,304$ and $x^2 + x^2 = 2x^2$.

To isolate x^2, divide both sides by 2.

Take the positive square root of both sides.

Use a calculator to find the approximate value of $\sqrt{1,152}$.

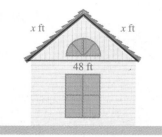

FIGURE 8-10

State the conclusion The eaves-to-peak distance of the roof is approximately 34 feet.

Check the result If the eaves-to-peak distance is approximately 34 feet, we have $34^2 + 34^2 = 1,156 + 1,156 = 2,312$, which is approximately 48^2. The answer, 34, seems reasonable. ∎

STUDY SET Section 8.1

VOCABULARY *Fill in the blanks.*

1. b is a ___square___ root of a if $b^2 = a$.

2. The symbol $\sqrt{}$ is called a ___radical___ sign.

3. The principal square root of a positive number is a ___positive___ number.

4. The number under the radical sign is called the ___radicand___.

5. If a triangle has a right angle, it is called a ___right___ triangle.

6. The longest side of a right triangle is called the ___hypotenuse___, and the other two sides are called ___legs___.

CONCEPTS *In Exercises 7–12, fill in the blanks.*

7. The number 25 has ___two___ square roots. They are 5 and -5.

8. $\sqrt{-11}$ is not a ___real___ number.

9. If the length of the hypotenuse of a right triangle is c and the legs are a and b, then $c^2 = a^2 + b^2$.

10. The hypotenuse squared is one leg squared plus the other leg squared.

11. If a and b are positive numbers and $a = b$, then $\sqrt{a} = \sqrt{b}$.

12. The ___square___ of 2 is 4, because $2^2 = 4$, and 2 is a square ___root___ of 4, because $2^2 = 4$.

13. To isolate x, what step should be used to "undo" the operation performed on it? (Assume that x is a positive number.)
  a. $2x = 16$ Divide both sides by 2.
  b. $x^2 = 16$ Take the positive square root of both sides.

14. 🧮 Graph each number on the number line.
$$\left\{ \sqrt{16},\ -\sqrt{\tfrac{9}{4}},\ \sqrt{1.8},\ \sqrt{6},\ -\sqrt{23} \right\}$$

15. Complete the table of values. *Do not use a calculator.*

x	$\sqrt{x}$
0	0
$\frac{1}{81}$	$\frac{1}{9}$
0.16	0.4
36	6
400	20

16. If $f(x) = \sqrt{x}$, find each value. *Do not use a calculator.*
  a. $f\left(\frac{1}{121}\right)$ $\frac{1}{11}$
  b. $f(1)$ 1
  c. $f(0.25)$ 0.5
  d. $f(81)$ 9
  e. $f(900)$ 30

17. a. What do the dashed lines in the graph in Illustration 1 help to approximate? $\sqrt{5} \approx 2.2$
  b. Use the graph to approximate $\sqrt{3}$ and $\sqrt{8}$.
  $\sqrt{3} \approx 1.7;\ \sqrt{8} \approx 2.8$

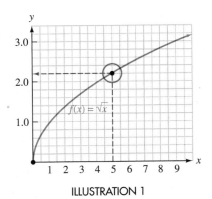

ILLUSTRATION 1

18. A calculator was used to find $\sqrt{-16}$. Explain the message shown on the calculator display in Illustration 2.

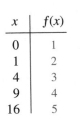

ILLUSTRATION 2

There is an error: $\sqrt{-16}$ is not a real number.

NOTATION *Complete each solution.*

19. If the legs of a right triangle measure 5 and 12 centimeters, find the length of the hypotenuse.

$$c^2 = a^2 + b^2$$
$$c^2 = 5^2 + 12^2$$
$$c^2 = 25 + 144$$
$$c^2 = 169$$
$$\sqrt{c^2} = \sqrt{169}$$
$$c = 13$$

20. If the hypotenuse of a right triangle measures 25 centimeters and one leg measures 24 centimeters, find the length of the other leg.

$$c^2 = a^2 + b^2$$
$$25^2 = 24^2 + b^2$$
$$625 = 576 + b^2$$
$$49 = b^2$$
$$\sqrt{49} = \sqrt{b^2}$$
$$7 = b$$

21. Is the statement $-\sqrt{9} = \sqrt{-9}$ true or false? Explain your answer.

False; $-\sqrt{9} = -3$, $\sqrt{-9}$ is not a real number.

22. Consider the statement $\sqrt{26} \approx 5.1$. Explain why an $\approx$ symbol is used instead of an $=$ sign.

Since $(5.1)^2$ is 26.01, rather than exactly 26, we write $\sqrt{26} \approx 5.1$.

PRACTICE *Find each square root without using a calculator.*

23. $\sqrt{25}$ 5

24. $\sqrt{49}$ 7

25. $-\sqrt{81}$ -9

26. $-\sqrt{36}$ -6

27. $\sqrt{1.21}$ 1.1

28. $\sqrt{1.69}$ 1.3

29. $\sqrt{196}$ 14

30. $\sqrt{169}$ 13

31. $\sqrt{\dfrac{9}{256}}$ $\frac{3}{16}$

32. $\sqrt{\dfrac{49}{225}}$ $\frac{7}{15}$

33. $-\sqrt{289}$ -17

34. $-\sqrt{324}$ -18

35. $-\sqrt{2,500}$ -50

36. $-\sqrt{625}$ -25

37. $\sqrt{3,600}$ 60

38. $\sqrt{1,600}$ 40

 *Use a calculator to evaluate each expression to three decimal places.*

39. $\sqrt{2}$ 1.414

40. $\sqrt{3}$ 1.732

41. $\sqrt{11}$ 3.317

42. $\sqrt{53}$ 7.280

43. $\sqrt{95}$ 9.747

44. $\sqrt{99}$ 9.950

45. $\sqrt{428}$ 20.688

46. $\sqrt{844}$ 29.052

47. $-\sqrt{9,876}$ -99.378

48. $-\sqrt{3,619}$ -60.158

49. $\sqrt{21.35}$ 4.621

50. $\sqrt{13.78}$ 3.712

51. $\sqrt{0.3588}$ 0.599

52. $\sqrt{0.9999}$ 1.000

53. $-\sqrt{0.8372}$ -0.915

54. $-\sqrt{0.4279}$ -0.654

55. $2\sqrt{3}$ 3.464

56. $3\sqrt{2}$ 4.243

57. $\dfrac{2 + \sqrt{3}}{2}$ 1.866

58. $\dfrac{2 - \sqrt{3}}{2}$ 0.134

Tell whether each number in each set is rational, irrational, or imaginary.

59. $\left\{\sqrt{9}, \sqrt{17}, \sqrt{49}, \sqrt{-49}\right\}$

rational; irrational; rational; imaginary

60. $\left\{-\sqrt{5}, \sqrt{0}, \sqrt{-100}, -\sqrt{225}\right\}$

irrational; rational; imaginary; rational

Complete the table and then graph the function.

61. $f(x) = 1 + \sqrt{x}$

x	$f(x)$
0	1
1	2
4	3
9	4
16	5

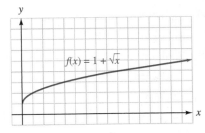

62. $f(x) = -1 + \sqrt{x}$

x	$f(x)$
0	-1
1	0
4	1
9	2
16	3

$f(x) = -1 + \sqrt{x}$

63. $f(x) = -\sqrt{x}$

x	$f(x)$
0	0
1	-1
4	-2
9	-3
16	-4

$f(x) = -\sqrt{x}$

64. $f(x) = 1 - \sqrt{x}$

x	$f(x)$
0	1
1	0
4	-1
9	-2
16	-3

$f(x) = 1 - \sqrt{x}$

Refer to the right triangle in Illustration 3. Find the length of the unknown side.

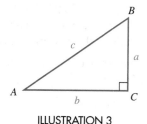

ILLUSTRATION 3

65. Find c if $a = 4$ and $b = 3$. 5
66. Find c if $a = 5$ and $b = 12$. 13
67. Find b if $a = 15$ and $c = 17$. 8
68. Find b if $a = 21$ and $c = 29$. 20
69. Find a if $b = 16$ and $c = 34$. 30
70. Find a if $b = 45$ and $c = 53$. 28
71. Find b if $c = 125$ and $a = 44$. 117
72. Find c if $a = 176$ and $b = 57$. 185

APPLICATIONS *Use a calculator to help solve each problem. If an answer is not exact, give it to the nearest tenth.*

73. ADJUSTING A LADDER   A 20-foot ladder reaches a window 16 feet above the ground. How far from the wall is the base of the ladder?   12 ft

74. LINE OF SIGHT   A movie viewer in a car parked at a drive-in theater sits 600 feet from the base of the vertical screen. What is the line-of-sight distance for the viewer to the middle of the screen, which is 35 feet above the base?   601.0 ft

75. QUALITY CONTROL   How can a tool manufacturer use the Pythagorean theorem to verify that the two sides of the carpenter's square shown in Illustration 4 meet to form a 90° angle?
The diagonal measurement should be $\sqrt{16^2 + 30^2} = 34$ in.

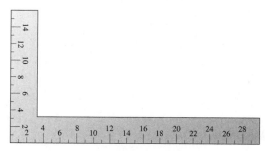

ILLUSTRATION 4

76. GARDENING   A rectangular garden has sides of 28 and 45 feet. Find the length of a path that extends from one corner to the opposite corner.   53 ft

77. BASEBALL   A baseball diamond is a square, with each side 90 feet long, as shown in Illustration 5. How far is it from home plate to second base?   127.3 ft

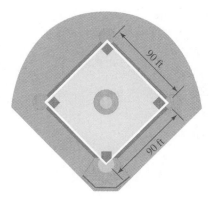

ILLUSTRATION 5

78. TELEVISION   The *size* of a television screen is the diagonal distance from the upper left to the lower right corner. What is the size of the screen shown in Illustration 6?   27.0 in.

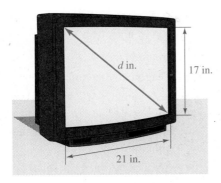

ILLUSTRATION 6

79. FINDING LOCATION   A team of archaeologists travels 4.2 miles east and then 4.0 miles north of their base camp to explore some ancient ruins. "As the crow flies," how far from their base camp are they?   5.8 mi

80. TAKING A SHORTCUT   Instead of walking on the sidewalk, students take a diagonal shortcut across the rectangular vacant lot shown in Illustration 7. How much distance do they save?   44 ft

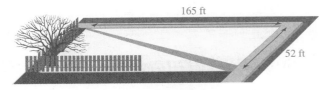

ILLUSTRATION 7

81. FOOTBALL   On first down and ten, a quarterback tells his tight end to go out 6 yards, cut 45° to the right, and run 5 yards, as shown in Illustration 8. The tight end follows instructions, catches a pass, and is tackled immediately. Does he gain the necessary 10 yards for a first down?   no

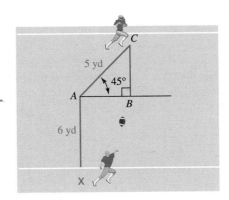

ILLUSTRATION 8

82. GEOMETRY   The legs of a right triangle are equal, and the hypotenuse is 2.82843 units long. Find the length of each leg.   2.0 units

83. PROFESSIONAL WRESTLING   The sides of a square wrestling ring are 18 feet long. Find the distance from one corner to the opposite corner.   25.5 ft

84. PERIMETER OF A SQUARE   The diagonal of a square is 3 feet long. Find its perimeter.   8.5 ft

85. HEIGHT OF A TRIANGLE   Find the area of the isosceles triangle shown in Illustration 9.   240 in.^{2}

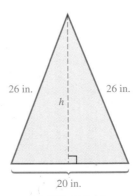

ILLUSTRATION 9

86. INTERIOR DECORATING   The square table in Illustration 10 is covered by a circular tablecloth. If the sides of the table are 2 feet long, find the area of the tablecloth.   6.3 ft^2

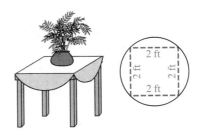

ILLUSTRATION 10

87. DRAFTING   Among the tools used in drafting are the 30–60–90 and the 45–45–90 triangles shown in Illustration 11.
  a. Find the length of the hypotenuse of the 45–45–90 triangle if it is $\sqrt{2}$ times as long as a leg.   8.5 in.
  b. Find the length of the side opposite the 60° angle of the other triangle if it is $\frac{\sqrt{3}}{2}$ times as long as the hypotenuse.   7.8 in.

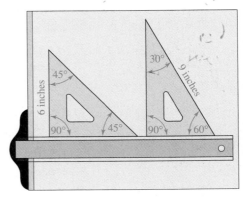

ILLUSTRATION 11

88. ORGAN PIPES   The design for a set of brass pipes for a church organ is shown in Illustration 12. Find the length of each pipe (to the nearest tenth of a foot), and then find the total length of pipe needed to construct this set.   2, 2.8, 3.5, 4, 4.5, 4.9, 5.3, 5.7, and 6 ft; 38.7 ft

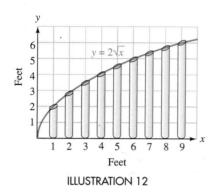

ILLUSTRATION 12

WRITING

89. Explain why the square root of a negative number cannot be a real number.

90. Explain the Pythagorean theorem.

91. Suppose you are told that $\sqrt{10} \approx 3.16$. Explain how another key on your calculator (besides the square root key $\sqrt{}$) could be used to see whether this is a reasonable approximation.

92. Explain the difference between the *square* of a number and the *square root* of a number.

REVIEW

93. Add: $(3s^2 - 3s - 2) + (3s^2 + 4s - 3)$. $6s^2 + s - 5$

94. Subtract: $(3c^2 - 2c + 4) - (c^2 - 3c + 7)$. $2c^2 + c - 3$

95. Multiply: $(3x - 2)(x + 4)$. $3x^2 + 10x - 8$

96. Divide: $x^2 + 13x + 12$ by $x + 1$. $x + 12$

8.2 *Higher-Order Roots; Radicands That Contain Variables*

In this section, you will learn about

- Cube roots • Approximating cube roots • The cube root function
- Higher-order roots • Radicands that contain variables

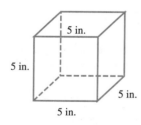

FIGURE 8-11

INTRODUCTION.   To find the volume V of the cube shown in Figure 8-11, we multiply its length, width, and height.

$$V = l \cdot w \cdot h$$
$$V = 5 \cdot 5 \cdot 5$$
$$= 125$$

The volume is 125 cubic inches.

We have seen that $5 \cdot 5 \cdot 5$ can be denoted by the exponential expression 5^3, where 5 is raised to the third power. Whenever we raise a number to the third power, we are cubing it, or finding its **cube.** This example illustrates that the formula for the volume of a cube with each side of length s is $V = s^3$.

Here are some more cubes of numbers:

- The cube of 3 is 27, because $3^3 = 27$.
- The cube of -3 is -27, because $(-3)^3 = -27$.
- The cube of 12 is 1,728, because $12^3 = 1,728$.
- The cube of -12 is $-1,728$, because $(-12)^3 = -1,728$.
- The cube of $\frac{1}{4}$ is $\frac{1}{64}$, because $\left(\frac{1}{4}\right)^3 = \frac{1}{4} \cdot \frac{1}{4} \cdot \frac{1}{4} = \frac{1}{64}$.
- The cube of $-\frac{1}{4}$ is $-\frac{1}{64}$, because $\left(-\frac{1}{4}\right)^3 = \left(-\frac{1}{4}\right)\left(-\frac{1}{4}\right)\left(-\frac{1}{4}\right) = -\frac{1}{64}$.
- The cube of 0 is 0, because $0^3 = 0$.

In this section, we will reverse the cubing process and find **cube roots** of numbers. We will also consider fourth roots, fifth roots, and so on. After graphing the cube root function, we will work with radical expressions having radicands containing variables.

Cube roots

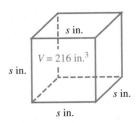

FIGURE 8-12

Suppose we know that the volume of the cube shown in Figure 8-12 is 216 cubic inches. To find the length of each side, we substitute 216 for V in the formula $V = s^3$ and solve for s.

$$V = s^3$$
$$216 = s^3$$

To solve for s, we must find a number whose cube is 216. Since 6 is such a number, the sides of the cube are 6 inches long. The number 6 is called a *cube root* of 216, because $6^3 = 216$.

Here are more examples of cube roots:

- 3 is a cube root of 27, because $3^3 = 27$.
- -3 is a cube root of -27, because $(-3)^3 = -27$.
- 12 is a cube root of 1,728, because $12^3 = 1,728$.
- -12 is a cube root of $-1,728$, because $(-12)^3 = -1,728$.
- $\frac{1}{4}$ is a cube root of $\frac{1}{64}$, because $\left(\frac{1}{4}\right)^3 = \left(\frac{1}{4}\right)\left(\frac{1}{4}\right)\left(\frac{1}{4}\right) = \frac{1}{64}$.
- $-\frac{1}{4}$ is a cube root of $-\frac{1}{64}$, because $\left(-\frac{1}{4}\right)^3 = \left(-\frac{1}{4}\right)\left(-\frac{1}{4}\right)\left(-\frac{1}{4}\right) = -\frac{1}{64}$.
- 0 is a cube root of 0, because $0^3 = 0$.

In general, we have the following definition.

Cube root

> The number b is a **cube root** of a if $b^3 = a$.

All real numbers have one real cube root. As the preceding examples show, a positive number has a positive cube root, a negative number has a negative cube root, and the cube root of 0 is 0.

Cube root notation

> The **cube root of a** is denoted by $\sqrt[3]{a}$. By definition,
> $$\sqrt[3]{a} = b \qquad \text{if} \qquad b^3 = a$$

EXAMPLE 1 *Finding cube roots.* Find each cube root.

a. $\sqrt[3]{8} = 2$, because $2^3 = 8$

b. $\sqrt[3]{343} = 7$, because $7^3 = 343$

c. $\sqrt[3]{-8} = -2$, because $(-2)^3 = -8$

d. $\sqrt[3]{-125} = -5$, because $(-5)^3 = -125$

Self Check

Find each cube root:

a. $\sqrt[3]{64}$, **b.** $\sqrt[3]{-64}$, **c.** $\sqrt[3]{216}$

Answers: a. 4, **b.** -4, **c.** 6

EXAMPLE 2 *Finding cube roots.* Find each cube root.

a. $\sqrt[3]{\frac{1}{8}} = \frac{1}{2}$, because $\left(\frac{1}{2}\right)^3 = \frac{1}{2} \cdot \frac{1}{2} \cdot \frac{1}{2} = \frac{1}{8}$

b. $\sqrt[3]{-\frac{125}{27}} = -\frac{5}{3}$, because $\left(-\frac{5}{3}\right)^3 = \left(-\frac{5}{3}\right)\left(-\frac{5}{3}\right)\left(-\frac{5}{3}\right) = -\frac{125}{27}$

Self Check

Find each cube root:

a. $\sqrt[3]{\frac{1}{27}}$ **b.** $\sqrt[3]{-\frac{8}{125}}$

Answers: a. $\frac{1}{3}$, **b.** $-\frac{2}{5}$

Cube roots of numbers such as 7 are hard to compute by hand. However, we can find $\sqrt[3]{7}$ with a calculator.

Approximating cube roots

To find $\sqrt[3]{7}$, we can enter 7 into a scientific calculator, press the root key $\sqrt[x]{y}$, enter 3, and press the $=$ key. The approximate value of $\sqrt[3]{7}$ will appear on the calculator's display.

$$\sqrt[3]{7} \approx 1.912931183$$

If your scientific calculator doesn't have a $\sqrt[x]{y}$ key, you can use the y^x key. We will see later that $\sqrt[3]{7} = 7^{1/3}$. To find the value of $7^{1/3}$, we enter 7 into the calculator and press these keys:

$$7 \; y^x \; (\; 1 \; \div \; 3 \;) \; =$$

The display will read 1.912931183.

Since $\sqrt[3]{7}$ represents the number that, when cubed, gives 7, we would expect cubes of approximations of $\sqrt[3]{7}$ to be close to 7.

- Rounded to one decimal place, $\sqrt[3]{7} \approx 1.9$, and $(1.9)^3 = 6.859$.
- Rounded to two decimal places, $\sqrt[3]{7} \approx 1.91$, and $(1.91)^3 = 6.967871$.
- Rounded to three decimal places, $\sqrt[3]{7} \approx 1.913$, and $(1.913)^3 = 7.000755497$.

Numbers such as 8, -27, -64, and 125 are called **integer cubes,** because each one is the cube of an integer. The cube root of any integer cube is an integer and therefore a rational number:

$$\sqrt[3]{8} = 2, \qquad \sqrt[3]{-27} = -3, \qquad \sqrt[3]{-64} = -4, \quad \text{and} \quad \sqrt[3]{125} = 5$$

Cube roots of integers such as 7 and -10, which are not integer cubes, are irrational numbers. For example, $\sqrt[3]{7}$ and $\sqrt[3]{-10}$ are irrational numbers.

COMMENT   Recall that the square root of a negative number $\left(\text{for instance } \sqrt{-27}\right)$ is not a real number, because no real number squared is equal to a negative number. However, the cube root of a negative number is a real number. For example, $\sqrt[3]{-27} = -3$.

Accent on Technology: **Radius of a water tank**

Engineers want to design a spherical tank that will hold 33,500 cubic feet of water, as shown in Figure 8-13. They know that the formula for the radius r of a sphere with volume V is given by the formula

$$r = \sqrt[3]{\frac{3V}{4\pi}} \quad \text{Where } \pi = 3.14159. \ldots$$

To use a scientific calculator to find the radius r, we substitute 33,500 for V and enter these numbers and press these keys.

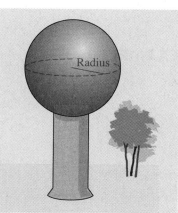

FIGURE 8-13

Keystrokes $3 \; \boxed{\times} \; 33500 \; \boxed{\div} \; \boxed{(} \; 4 \; \boxed{\times} \; \boxed{\pi} \; \boxed{)} \; \boxed{=} \; \boxed{\sqrt[n]{x}} \; 3 \; \boxed{=}$

$$\boxed{19.99794636}$$

To evaluate this expression using a graphing calculator, we press the $\boxed{\text{MATH}}$ key. In this mode, arrow down $\boxed{\blacktriangledown}$ to highlight the option $\sqrt[3]{}$ (and $\boxed{\text{ENTER}}$. Then we press the following keys.

Keystrokes   3 $\boxed{\times}$ 33500 $\boxed{\div}$ $\boxed{(}$ 4 $\boxed{\times}$ $\boxed{\text{2nd}}$ $\boxed{\pi}$ $\boxed{)}$ $\boxed{)}$ $\boxed{\text{ENTER}}$

```
³√(3*33500/(4*π)
)
            19.99794636
```

The result is 19.99794636, so the engineers should design a tank with a radius of 20 feet.

The cube root function

Since every real number has one real-number cube root, there is a cube root function $f(x) = \sqrt[3]{x}$. For example, the value that is determined by $f(x) = \sqrt[3]{x}$ when $x = 8$ is denoted as $f(8)$, and we have $f(8) = \sqrt[3]{8} = 2$.

To graph this function, we substitute numbers for x, compute $f(x)$, plot the resulting ordered pairs, and connect them with a smooth curve, as shown in Figure 8-14.

$$f(x) = \sqrt[3]{x}$$

x	$f(x)$	$(x, f(x))$
-8	-2	$(-8, -2)$
-1	-1	$(-1, -1)$
0	0	$(0, 0)$
1	1	$(1, 1)$
8	2	$(8, 2)$

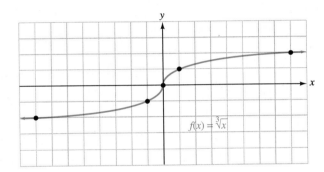

FIGURE 8-14

Higher-order roots

Just as there are square roots and cube roots, there are also fourth roots, fifth roots, sixth roots, and so on. In general, we have this definition.

n*th roots of *a

> The ***n*th root of *a*** is denoted by $\sqrt[n]{a}$, and
> $$\sqrt[n]{a} = b \qquad \text{if} \qquad b^n = a$$
> The number n is called the **index** of the radical. If n is an even natural number, a must be positive or zero, and b must be positive.

In the square root symbol $\sqrt{}$, the unwritten index is understood to be 2.
$$\sqrt{a} = \sqrt[2]{a}$$

EXAMPLE 3 *Finding fourth and fifth roots.*   Find each root.

a. $\sqrt[4]{81} = 3$, because $3^4 = 81$.

b. $\sqrt[5]{32} = 2$, because $2^5 = 32$.

c. $\sqrt[5]{-32} = -2$, because $(-2)^5 = -32$.

d. $\sqrt[4]{-81}$ is not a real number, because no real number raised to the fourth power is -81.

Self Check

Find each root:

a. $\sqrt[4]{16}$, **b.** $\sqrt[5]{243}$,

c. $\sqrt[5]{-1,024}$

Answers: **a.** 2, **b.** 3,

c. -4 ∎

EXAMPLE 4 *Finding fourth and fifth roots.*   Find each root.

a. $\sqrt[4]{\dfrac{1}{81}} = \dfrac{1}{3}$, because $\left(\dfrac{1}{3}\right)^4 = \dfrac{1}{81}$.

b. $\sqrt[5]{-\dfrac{32}{243}} = -\dfrac{2}{3}$, because $\left(-\dfrac{2}{3}\right)^5 = -\dfrac{32}{243}$.

Self Check

Find each root:

a. $\sqrt[4]{\dfrac{1}{16}}$ **b.** $\sqrt[5]{-\dfrac{243}{32}}$

Answers: **a.** $\dfrac{1}{2}$, **b.** $-\dfrac{3}{2}$ ∎

Radicands that contain variables

When n is even and $x \geq 0$, we say that the radical $\sqrt[n]{x}$ represents an **even root**. We can find even roots of many quantities that contain variables, provided that these variables represent positive numbers or zero.

EXAMPLE 5 *Finding even roots.*   Find each root. Assume that each variable represents a positive number.

a. $\sqrt{x^2} = x$, because $(x)^2 = x^2$.

b. $\sqrt{x^4} = x^2$, because $(x^2)^2 = x^4$.

c. $\sqrt{x^4 y^2} = x^2 y$, because $(x^2 y)^2 = x^4 y^2$.

d. $\sqrt[4]{81x^{12}} = 3x^3$, because $(3x^3)^4 = 81x^{12}$.

Self Check

Find each root:

a. $\sqrt{a^4}$, **b.** $\sqrt{m^6 n^8}$, **c.** $\sqrt[4]{16y^8}$

Answers: **a.** a^2, **b.** $m^3 n^4$,

c. $2y^2$ ∎

When n is odd, we say that the radical expression $\sqrt[n]{x}$ represents an **odd root.**

EXAMPLE 6 *Finding odd roots.*   Find each root.

a. $\sqrt[3]{y^3} = y$, because $(y)^3 = y^3$.

b. $\sqrt[3]{64x^6} = 4x^2$, because $(4x^2)^3 = 64x^6$.

c. $\sqrt[5]{x^{10}} = x^2$, because $(x^2)^5 = x^{10}$.

Self Check

Find each root:

a. $\sqrt[3]{p^6}$, **b.** $\sqrt[3]{-27p^9}$,

c. $\sqrt[5]{\frac{1}{32}n^{15}}$

Answers: **a.** p^2, **b.** $-3p^3$,

c. $\frac{1}{2}n^3$ ∎

STUDY SET Section 8.2

VOCABULARY   *Fill in the blanks.*

1. If $p^3 = q$, p is called a ___cube___ root of q.

2. If $p^4 = q$, p is called a ___fourth___ root of q.

3. We denote the cube root ___function___ with the notation $f(x) = \sqrt[3]{x}$.

4. If the index of a radical is an even number, the root is called an ___even___ root.

CONCEPTS   *In Exercises 5–8, fill in the blanks.*

5. The _____cube_____ of -4 is -64, because $(-4)^3 = -64$. The number -3 is a cube _____root_____ of -27, because $(-3)^3 = -27$.

6. $\sqrt[3]{a} = b$ if $b^3 = a$.

7. $\sqrt[3]{-216} = -6$, because $(-6)^3 = -216$.

8. $\sqrt[5]{32x^5} = 2x$, because $(2x)^5 = 32x^5$.

9. Find each value, if possible.

   a. $\sqrt{-125}$ **b.** $\sqrt[3]{-125}$

     not a real number -5

10. 🔲 Graph each number on the number line.

$$\left\{ \sqrt[3]{16},\ -\sqrt[4]{100},\ \sqrt[3]{-1.8},\ \sqrt[4]{0.6} \right\}$$

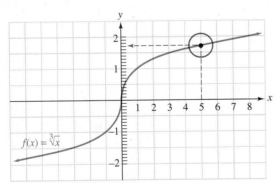

11. If $f(x) = \sqrt[3]{x}$, find each value. *Do not use a calculator.*

   a. $f(1)$ 1   **b.** $f\left(-\dfrac{1}{27}\right)$ $-\frac{1}{3}$

   c. $f(125)$ 5   **d.** $f(0.008)$ 0.2

   e. $f(1,000)$ 10

12. a. What do the dashed lines in the graph in Illustration 1 help to approximate? $\sqrt[3]{5} \approx 1.7$

   b. Use the graph to approximate $\sqrt[3]{4}$ and $\sqrt[3]{-6}$.
     $\sqrt[3]{4} \approx 1.6$; $\sqrt[3]{-6} \approx -1.8$

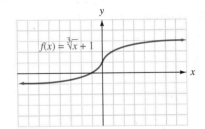

ILLUSTRATION 1

NOTATION   *Fill in the blanks.*

13. In the notation $\sqrt[3]{x^6}$, 3 is called the _____index_____ and x^6 is called the _____radicand_____.

14. $\sqrt{}$ is called a _____radical_____ symbol.

15. The "understood" index of the radical expression $\sqrt{55}$ is 2.

16. In reading $f(x) = \sqrt[3]{x}$, we say "f __of__ x equals the cube root __of__ x."

PRACTICE   *Find each value without using a calculator.*

17. $\sqrt[3]{8}$ 2   **18.** $\sqrt[3]{27}$ 3

19. $\sqrt[3]{0}$ 0   **20.** $\sqrt[3]{1}$ 1

21. $\sqrt[3]{-8}$ -2 **22.** $\sqrt[3]{-1}$ -1

23. $\sqrt[3]{-64}$ -4 **24.** $\sqrt[3]{-27}$ -3

25. $\sqrt[3]{\dfrac{1}{125}}$ $\frac{1}{5}$ **26.** $\sqrt[3]{\dfrac{1}{1,000}}$ $\frac{1}{10}$

27. $-\sqrt[3]{-1}$ 1   **28.** $-\sqrt[3]{-27}$ 3

29. $-\sqrt[3]{64}$ -4 **30.** $-\sqrt[3]{343}$ -7

31. $\sqrt[3]{729}$ 9   **32.** $\sqrt[3]{512}$ 8

33. $\sqrt[3]{1,000}$ 10   **34.** $\sqrt[3]{125}$ 5

🔲 Use a calculator to find each cube root to the nearest hundredth.

35. $\sqrt[3]{32,100}$ 31.78   **36.** $\sqrt[3]{-25,713}$ -29.52

37. $\sqrt[3]{-0.11324}$ -0.48 **38.** $\sqrt[3]{0.875}$ 0.96

Complete the table and then graph the function.

39. $f(x) = \sqrt[3]{x} + 1$

x	$f(x)$
-8	-1
-1	0
0	1
1	2
8	3

40. $f(x) = \sqrt[4]{x}$

x	$f(x)$
0	0
1	1
16	2

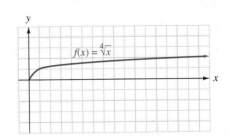

41. $f(x) = -\sqrt[3]{x}$

x	$f(x)$
-8	2
-1	1
0	0
1	-1
8	-2

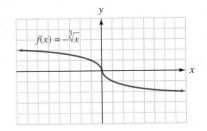

42. $f(x) = \sqrt[4]{x} - 1$

x	$f(x)$
0	-1
1	0
16	1

$f(x) = \sqrt[4]{x} - 1$

Find each value without using a calculator.

43. $\sqrt[4]{16}$ 2

44. $\sqrt[4]{81}$ 3

45. $-\sqrt[5]{32}$ -2

46. $-\sqrt[5]{243}$ -3

47. $\sqrt[6]{1}$ 1

48. $\sqrt[6]{0}$ 0

49. $\sqrt[5]{-32}$ -2

50. $\sqrt[7]{-1}$ -1

Use a calculator to find each root to the nearest hundredth.

51. $\sqrt[4]{125}$ 3.34

52. $\sqrt[5]{12,450}$ 6.59

53. $\sqrt[5]{-6,000}$ -5.70

54. $\sqrt[6]{0.5}$ 0.89

Find each root. All variables represent positive numbers.

55. $\sqrt{x^2}$ x

56. $\sqrt{y^4}$ y^2

57. $\sqrt{x^6}$ x^3

58. $\sqrt{b^8}$ b^4

59. $\sqrt{x^{10}}$ x^5

60. $\sqrt{y^{12}}$ y^6

61. $\sqrt{4z^2}$ $2z$

62. $\sqrt{9t^6}$ $3t^3$

63. $-\sqrt{x^4y^2}$ $-x^2y$

64. $-\sqrt{x^2y^4}$ $-xy^2$

65. $-\sqrt{0.04y^2}$ $-0.2y$

66. $-\sqrt{0.81b^6}$ $-0.9b^3$

67. $-\sqrt{25x^4z^{12}}$ $-5x^2z^6$

68. $-\sqrt{100a^6b^4}$ $-10a^3b^2$

69. $\sqrt{36z^{36}}$ $6z^{18}$

70. $\sqrt{64y^{64}}$ $8y^{32}$

71. $-\sqrt{625z^2}$ $-25z$

72. $-\sqrt{729x^8}$ $-27x^4$

73. $\sqrt[3]{y^6}$ y^2

74. $\sqrt[3]{c^3}$ c

75. $\sqrt[5]{f^5}$ f

76. $\sqrt[5]{y^{20}}$ y^4

77. $\sqrt[3]{27y^3}$ $3y$

78. $\sqrt[3]{64y^6}$ $4y^2$

79. $\sqrt[3]{-p^6q^3}$ $-p^2q$

80. $\sqrt[3]{-r^{12}t^6}$ $-r^4t^2$

81. $\sqrt[4]{x^4}$ x

82. $\sqrt[4]{x^8}$ x^2

APPLICATIONS   *Use a calculator to help solve each problem. Give your answers to the nearest hundredth.*

83. PACKAGING   A cubical box has a volume of 2 cubic feet. Substitute 2 for V in the formula $V = s^3$ and solve for s to find the length of each side of the box.   1.26 ft

84. HOT-AIR BALLOON   If a hot-air balloon is in the shape of a sphere and has a volume of 15,000 cubic feet, what is its radius? (*Hint:* See the Accent on Technology feature in this section.)   15.30 ft

85. WINDMILL   The power generated by a windmill is related to the speed of the wind by the formula

$$S = \sqrt[3]{\frac{P}{0.02}}$$

where S is the speed of the wind (in mph) and P is the power (in watts). Find the speed of the wind when the windmill is producing 400 watts of power.   27.14 mph

86. ASTRONOMY   In the early 17th century, Johannes Kepler, a German astronomer, discovered that a planet's mean distance R from the sun (in millions of miles) is related to the time T (in years) it takes the planet to orbit the sun by the formula

$$R = 93\sqrt[3]{\frac{T^2}{1.002}}$$

Use the information in Illustration 2 to find R for Mercury, Earth, and Jupiter.
Mercury, 35.89; Earth, 92.94; Jupiter, 483.34

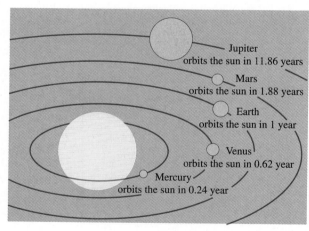

ILLUSTRATION 2

87. DEPRECIATION   The formula

$$r = 1 - \sqrt[n]{\frac{S}{C}}$$

gives the annual depreciation rate r (in percent) of an item that had an original cost of C dollars and has a useful life of n years and a salvage value of S dollars. Use the information in Illustration 3 to find the annual depreciation rate for the new piece of sound equipment.   26.22%

OFFICE MEMO

To: Purchasing Dept.
From: Bob Kinsell, Engineering Dept. BK
Re: New sound board

We recommend you purchase the new Sony sound board @ $27K. This equipment does become obsolete quickly but we figure we can use it for 4 yrs. A college would probably buy it from us then. I bet we could get around $8K for it.

ILLUSTRATION 3

88. SAVINGS ACCOUNT   The interest rate r (in percent) earned by a savings account after n compoundings is given by the formula

$$\sqrt[n]{\frac{V}{P}} - 1 = r$$

where V is the current value and P is the original principal. What interest rate r was paid on an account in which a deposit of $1,000 grew to $1,338.23 after 5 compoundings?   6.00%

WRITING

89. Explain why a negative number can have a real number for its cube root yet cannot have a real number for its fourth root.

90. To find $\sqrt[3]{15}$, we can use the $\sqrt[n]{x}$ key on a calculator to obtain 2.466212074. Explain how a key other than $\sqrt[n]{x}$ can be used to check the validity of this result.

REVIEW   *Simplify each expression.*

91. $m^5 m^2$ m^7

92. $(-5x^3)(-5x)$ $25x^4$

93. $(3^2)^4$ 3^8 or 9^4

94. $r^3 r r^5$ r^9

95. $(x^2 x^3)^5$ x^{25}

96. $(3aa^2 a^3)^5$ $243a^{30}$

97. $4x^3(6x^5)$ $24x^8$

98. $-2x(5x^3)$ $-10x^4$

8.3 *Simplifying Radical Expressions*

In this section, you will learn about

- The multiplication property of radicals • Simplifying square root radicals
- The division property of radicals • Simplifying cube roots

INTRODUCTION. Square dancing is a traditional American folk dance in which four couples, arranged in a square, perform various moves. Figure 8-15 shows a group as they promenade around a square.

If the square shown in the figure has an area of 12 square yards, the length of a side is $\sqrt{12}$ yards. We can use the formula for the area of a square and the concept of square root to show that this is so.

FIGURE 8-15

$A = s^2$	s is the length of a side of the square.
$12 = s^2$	Substitute 12 for A, the area of the square.
$\sqrt{12} = \sqrt{s^2}$	Take the positive square root of both sides.
$\sqrt{12} = s$	The length of a side of the square is $\sqrt{12}$ yards.

The form in which we express the length of a side of the square depends on the situation. If an approximation is acceptable, we can use a calculator to find that $\sqrt{12} \approx 3.464101615$, and we can then round to a specified degree of accuracy. For example, to the nearest tenth, each side is 3.5 yards long.

If the situation calls for the *exact* length, we must use a radical expression. As you will see in this section, it is common practice to write a radical expression such as $\sqrt{12}$ in *simplified form*. To simplify radicals, we will use the multiplication and division properties of radicals.

The multiplication property of radicals

We introduce the first of two properties of radicals with the following examples:

$$\sqrt{4 \cdot 25} = \sqrt{100} \qquad \text{and} \qquad \sqrt{4}\sqrt{25} = 2 \cdot 5 \qquad \text{Read as "the square root of 4}$$
$$= 10 \qquad\qquad\qquad\qquad = 10 \qquad \text{times the square root of 25."}$$

In each case, the answer is 10. Thus, $\sqrt{4 \cdot 25} = \sqrt{4}\sqrt{25}$. Likewise,

$$\sqrt{9 \cdot 16} = \sqrt{144} \qquad \text{and} \qquad \sqrt{9}\sqrt{16} = 3 \cdot 4$$
$$= 12 \qquad\qquad\qquad\qquad = 12$$

In each case, the answer is 12. Thus, $\sqrt{9 \cdot 16} = \sqrt{9}\sqrt{16}$. These results illustrate the **multiplication property of radicals.**

The multiplication property of radicals

> If a and b represent nonnegative real numbers,
>
> $$\sqrt{ab} = \sqrt{a}\sqrt{b}$$

In words, *the square root of the product of two nonnegative numbers is equal to the product of their square roots.*

Simplifying square root radicals

A square root radical is in **simplified form** when each of the following statements is true.

Simplified form of a radical

> **1.** Except for 1, the radicand has no perfect square factors.
>
> **2.** No fraction appears in a radicand.
>
> **3.** No radical appears in the denominator of a fraction.

We can use the multiplication property of radicals to simplify square roots whose radicands have perfect square factors. For example, we can simplify $\sqrt{12}$ as follows:

$$\sqrt{12} = \sqrt{4 \cdot 3} \qquad \text{Factor 12 as } 4 \cdot 3.$$
$$= \sqrt{4}\sqrt{3} \qquad \text{The square root of } 4 \cdot 3 \text{ is equal to the square root of 4 times the}$$
$$\qquad\qquad\qquad \text{square root of 3.}$$
$$= 2\sqrt{3} \qquad \text{Write } \sqrt{4} \text{ as 2. Read as "2 times the square root of 3" or as "2}$$
$$\qquad\qquad\qquad \text{radical 3."}$$

The square in Figure 8-15, which we considered in the introduction to this section, has a side length of $\sqrt{12}$ yards. We now see that the *exact* length of a side can be expressed in simplified form as $2\sqrt{3}$ yards.

To simplify more difficult square roots, we need to know the integers that are **integer squares.** For example, 81 is an integer square, because it is the square of the integer 9: $9^2 = 81$. The first 20 integer squares are

1, 4, 9, 16, 25, 36, 49, 64, 81, 100, 121, 144, 169, 196, 225, 256, 289, 324, 361, 400

EXAMPLE 1 *Simplifying square roots.* Simplify $\sqrt{27}$.

Solution

Since the greatest perfect square that divides 27 exactly is 9, we will factor 27 as $9 \cdot 3$ and apply the multiplication property of radicals.

$$\sqrt{27} = \sqrt{9 \cdot 3}$$
$$= \sqrt{9}\sqrt{3} \quad \text{The square root of a product} \left(\text{that is, } \sqrt{9 \cdot 3}\right) \text{ is equal to the}$$
$$\qquad \qquad \text{product of the square roots, } \sqrt{9}\sqrt{3}.$$
$$= 3\sqrt{3} \quad \text{Simplify: } \sqrt{9} = 3.$$

As a check, recall that $\sqrt{27}$ is the number that, when squared, gives 27. If $3\sqrt{3} = \sqrt{27}$, then $\left(3\sqrt{3}\right)^2$ should be equal to 27.

$$\left(3\sqrt{3}\right)^2 = (3)^2\left(\sqrt{3}\right)^2 \quad \text{Use the "power of a product" rule for exponents: Raise each}$$
$$\qquad \qquad \qquad \text{factor of the product } 3\sqrt{3} \text{ to the 2nd power.}$$
$$= 9(3) \qquad \sqrt{3} \text{ is the number that, when squared, gives 3.}$$
$$= 27$$

Self Check

Simplify $\sqrt{45}$.

Answer: $3\sqrt{5}$ ∎

EXAMPLE 2 *Simplifying square roots.* Simplify $\sqrt{600}$.

Solution

Since the greatest perfect square that divides 600 is 100, we will factor 600 as $100 \cdot 6$ and apply the multiplication property of radicals.

$$\sqrt{600} = \sqrt{100 \cdot 6}$$
$$= \sqrt{100}\sqrt{6} \quad \text{The square root of a product is equal to the product of the}$$
$$\qquad \qquad \text{square roots.}$$
$$= 10\sqrt{6} \quad \sqrt{100} = 10.$$

Check the result.

Self Check

Simplify $\sqrt{200}$.

Answer: $10\sqrt{2}$ ∎

Expressions containing variables can also be perfect squares. For example, $36x^2$ is a perfect square, because

$$36x^2 = (6x)^2 \quad \text{Think, "What was squared to obtain } 36x^2\text{?"}$$

We can use this observation to help simplify radicals involving variable radicands. We will assume that all of the variables in the following examples represent positive numbers.

EXAMPLE 3 *Simplifying radicals involving variable radicands.*

Simplify $\sqrt{b^3}$.

Solution

To write $\sqrt{b^3}$ in simplified form, we factor b^3 into two factors, one of which is the greatest perfect square that divides b^3. The greatest perfect square that divides b^3 is b^2, so such a factorization is $b^3 = b^2 \cdot b$. We then proceed as follows:

$$\sqrt{b^3} = \sqrt{b^2 \cdot b}$$
$$= \sqrt{b^2}\sqrt{b} \quad \text{The square root of a product is equal to the product of the square}$$
$$\qquad \qquad \text{roots.}$$
$$= b\sqrt{b} \qquad \sqrt{b^2} = b.$$

As a check, recall that $\sqrt{b^3}$, when squared, gives b^3. If $b\sqrt{b} = \sqrt{b^3}$, then $\left(b\sqrt{b}\right)^2$ should be equal to b^3.

$$\left(b\sqrt{b}\right)^2 = (b)^2\left(\sqrt{b}\right)^2 \quad \text{Raise each factor of the product } b\sqrt{b} \text{ to the 2nd power.}$$
$$= b^2(b) \qquad \sqrt{b}, \text{ when squared, gives } b.$$
$$= b^3 \qquad \text{Keep the base } b \text{ and add the exponents.}$$

Self Check

Simplify $\sqrt{y^5}$.

Answer: $y^2\sqrt{y}$ ∎

EXAMPLE 4   *Simplifying radicals involving variable radicands.*
Simplify $-7\sqrt{8m}$.

Self Check
Simplify $2\sqrt{18c}$.

Solution
We first write $\sqrt{8m}$ in simplified form, and then we multiply the result by -7. By inspection, we see that the radicand, $8m$, has a perfect square factor of 4. We can write $8m$ in factored form as $4 \cdot 2m$.

$$
\begin{aligned}
-7\sqrt{8m} &= -7\sqrt{4 \cdot 2m} \\
&= -7\sqrt{4}\sqrt{2m} && \text{The square root of a product is equal to the product of the} \\
&&& \text{square roots.} \\
&= -7(2)\sqrt{2m} && \sqrt{4} = 2. \\
&= -14\sqrt{2m} && -7(2) = -14.
\end{aligned}
$$

Answer: $6\sqrt{2c}$ ∎

COMMENT   When writing radical expressions such as $-14\sqrt{2m}$, be sure to extend the radical symbol completely over $2m$, because the expressions $-14\sqrt{2m}$ and $-14\sqrt{2}m$ are not the same. Similar care should be taken when writing expressions such as $\sqrt{3x}$. To avoid any misinterpretation, $\sqrt{3}x$ can be written as $x\sqrt{3}$.

EXAMPLE 5   *Simplifying radicals involving variable radicands.*
Simplify $\sqrt{72x^3}$.

Self Check
Simplify $\sqrt{48y^3}$.

Solution
We factor $72x^3$ into two factors, one of which is the greatest perfect square that divides $72x^3$. Since the greatest perfect square that divides $72x^3$ is $36x^2$, such a factorization is $72x^3 = 36x^2 \cdot 2x$. We now use the multiplication property of radicals to get

$$
\begin{aligned}
\sqrt{72x^3} &= \sqrt{36x^2 \cdot 2x} \\
&= \sqrt{36x^2}\sqrt{2x} && \text{The square root of a product is equal to the product of the} \\
&&& \text{square roots.} \\
&= 6x\sqrt{2x} && \sqrt{36x^2} = 6x.
\end{aligned}
$$

Answer: $4y\sqrt{3y}$ ∎

EXAMPLE 6   *Simplifying radicals involving variable radicands.*
Simplify $3a\sqrt{288a^4b^7}$.

Self Check
Simplify $5q\sqrt{63p^5q^4}$.

Solution
We first simplify $\sqrt{288a^4b^7}$. Then we multiply the result by $3a$. To simplify $\sqrt{288a^4b^7}$, we look for the greatest perfect square that divides $288a^4b^7$. Because

- 144 is the greatest perfect square that divides 288,
- a^4 is the greatest perfect square that divides a^4, and
- b^6 is the greatest perfect square that divides b^7,

the factor $144a^4b^6$ is the greatest perfect square that divides $288a^4b^7$.
    We can now use the multiplication property of radicals to simplify the radical.

$$
\begin{aligned}
3a\sqrt{288a^4b^7} &= 3a\sqrt{144a^4b^6 \cdot 2b} \\
&= 3a\sqrt{144a^4b^6}\sqrt{2b} && \text{The square root of a product is equal to the} \\
&&& \text{product of the square roots.} \\
&= 3a(12a^2b^3)\sqrt{2b} && \sqrt{144a^4b^6} = 12a^2b^3. \\
&= 36a^3b^3\sqrt{2b} && \text{Multiply: } 3a(12a^2b^3) = 36a^3b^3.
\end{aligned}
$$

Answer: $15p^2q^3\sqrt{7p}$ ∎

COMMENT   The multiplication property of radicals applies to the square root of the product of two numbers. There is no such property for sums or differences. To illustrate this, we consider these correct simplifications:

$$\sqrt{9 + 16} = \sqrt{25} = 5 \quad \text{and} \quad \sqrt{25 - 16} = \sqrt{9} = 3$$

It is incorrect to write

$$\sqrt{9 + 16} = \sqrt{9} + \sqrt{16} \quad \text{or} \quad \sqrt{25 - 16} = \sqrt{25} - \sqrt{16}$$
$$= 3 + 4 \qquad\qquad\qquad\qquad = 5 - 4$$
$$= 7 \qquad\qquad\qquad\qquad\qquad = 1$$

Thus, $\sqrt{a + b} \neq \sqrt{a} + \sqrt{b}$ and $\sqrt{a - b} \neq \sqrt{a} - \sqrt{b}$.

The division property of radicals

To introduce the second property of radicals, we consider these examples.

$$\sqrt{\frac{100}{25}} = \sqrt{4} \quad \text{and} \quad \frac{\sqrt{100}}{\sqrt{25}} = \frac{10}{5} \qquad \text{Read as "the square root of 100 divided by the square root of 25."}$$
$$= 2 \qquad\qquad\qquad\qquad = 2$$

Since the answer is 2 in each case,

$$\sqrt{\frac{100}{25}} = \frac{\sqrt{100}}{\sqrt{25}}$$

Likewise,

$$\sqrt{\frac{36}{4}} = \sqrt{9} \quad \text{and} \quad \frac{\sqrt{36}}{\sqrt{4}} = \frac{6}{2}$$
$$= 3 \qquad\qquad\qquad\qquad = 3$$

Since the answer is 3 in each case,

$$\sqrt{\frac{36}{4}} = \frac{\sqrt{36}}{\sqrt{4}}$$

These results illustrate the **division property of radicals.**

The division property of radicals

> If a and b represent real numbers, with $a \geq 0$ and $b > 0$,
>
> $$\sqrt{\frac{a}{b}} = \frac{\sqrt{a}}{\sqrt{b}}$$

In words, *the square root of the quotient of two numbers is the quotient of their square roots.*

We can use the division property of radicals to simplify radicals that have fractions in their radicands. For example,

$$\sqrt{\frac{59}{49}} = \frac{\sqrt{59}}{\sqrt{49}}$$

$$= \frac{\sqrt{59}}{7} \qquad \text{Simplify the denominator: } \sqrt{49} = 7.$$

EXAMPLE 7 *Simplifying radicals involving fractions.*

Simplify $\sqrt{\dfrac{108}{25}}$.

Solution

$$\sqrt{\frac{108}{25}} = \frac{\sqrt{108}}{\sqrt{25}}$$ The square root of a quotient is equal to the quotient of the square roots.

$$= \frac{\sqrt{36 \cdot 3}}{5}$$ Factor 108 using the largest perfect square factor of 108, which is 36. Write $\sqrt{25}$ as 5.

$$= \frac{\sqrt{36}\sqrt{3}}{5}$$ The square root of a product is equal to the product of the square roots.

$$= \frac{6\sqrt{3}}{5}$$ $\sqrt{36} = 6$. This result can also be written as $\frac{6}{5}\sqrt{3}$.

Self Check

Simplify $\sqrt{\dfrac{20}{81}}$.

Answer: $\dfrac{2\sqrt{5}}{9}$

EXAMPLE 8 *Simplifying radicals involving fractions.*

Simplify $\sqrt{\dfrac{44x^3}{9xy^2}}$.

Solution

$$\sqrt{\frac{44x^3}{9xy^2}} = \sqrt{\frac{44x^2}{9y^2}}$$ Simplify the fraction by dividing out the common factor of x: $\dfrac{44x^3}{9xy^2} = \dfrac{44x^2\overset{1}{\cancel{x}}}{9\cancel{x}y^2} = \dfrac{44x^2}{9y^2}$.

$$= \frac{\sqrt{44x^2}}{\sqrt{9y^2}}$$ The square root of a quotient is equal to the quotient of the square roots.

$$= \frac{\sqrt{4x^2}\sqrt{11}}{\sqrt{9y^2}}$$ Factor $44x^2$ as $4x^2 \cdot 11$. The square root of a product is equal to the product of the square roots.

$$= \frac{2x\sqrt{11}}{3y}$$ $\sqrt{4x^2} = 2x$ and $\sqrt{9y^2} = 3y$.

Self Check

Simplify $\sqrt{\dfrac{99b^3}{16a^2b}}$.

Answer: $\dfrac{3b\sqrt{11}}{4a}$

Simplifying cube roots

The multiplication and division properties of radicals are also true for cube roots and higher. To simplify cube roots, we must know the following **integer cubes:**

8, 27, 64, 125, 216, 343, 512, 729, 1,000

EXAMPLE 9 *Simplifying cube roots.* Simplify $\sqrt[3]{54}$.

Solution

The greatest perfect cube that divides 54 is 27.

$$\sqrt[3]{54} = \sqrt[3]{27 \cdot 2}$$ Factor 54: $54 = 27 \cdot 2$.

$$= \sqrt[3]{27}\sqrt[3]{2}$$ The square root of a product is equal to the product of the square roots.

$$= 3\sqrt[3]{2}$$ $\sqrt[3]{27} = 3$.

As a check, we note that $\sqrt[3]{54}$ is the number that, when cubed, gives 54. If $3\sqrt[3]{2} = \sqrt[3]{54}$, then $\left(3\sqrt[3]{2}\right)^3$ will be equal to 54.

$$\left(3\sqrt[3]{2}\right)^3 = (3)^3\left(\sqrt[3]{2}\right)^3$$ Raise each factor of the product $3\sqrt[3]{2}$ to the 3rd power.

Self Check

Simplify $\sqrt[3]{250}$.

$= 27(2)$ $\sqrt[3]{2}$, when cubed, gives 2.

$= 54$

Answer: $5\sqrt[3]{2}$ ■

Expressions containing variables can also be perfect cubes. For example, $8x^3y^3$ is a perfect cube, because

$$8x^3y^3 = (2xy)^3 \quad \text{Think, "What was cubed to obtain } 8x^3y^3\text{?"}$$

EXAMPLE 10   *Simplifying cube roots involving variables.*

Simplify   **a.** $\sqrt[3]{16x^3y^4}$ and   **b.** $\sqrt[3]{\dfrac{64n^4}{27m^3}}$.

Self Check

Simplify:

a. $\sqrt[3]{54a^3b^5}$

b. $\sqrt[3]{\dfrac{27q^5}{64p^3}}$

Solution

a. We factor $16x^3y^4$ into two factors, one of which is the greatest perfect cube that divides $16x^3y^4$. Since $8x^3y^3$ is the greatest perfect cube that divides $16x^3y^4$, the factorization is $16x^3y^4 = 8x^3y^3 \cdot 2y$.

$$\sqrt[3]{16x^3y^4} = \sqrt[3]{8x^3y^3 \cdot 2y}$$

$$= \sqrt[3]{8x^3y^3}\sqrt[3]{2y} \quad \text{The cube root of a product is equal to the product of the cube roots.}$$

$$= 2xy\sqrt[3]{2y} \quad \sqrt[3]{8x^3y^3} = 2xy.$$

b. $\sqrt[3]{\dfrac{64n^4}{27m^3}} = \dfrac{\sqrt[3]{64n^4}}{\sqrt[3]{27m^3}}$ The cube root of a quotient is equal to the quotient of the cube roots.

$$= \dfrac{\sqrt[3]{64n^3}\sqrt[3]{n}}{3m} \quad \text{In the numerator, use the multiplication property of radicals. In the denominator, } \sqrt[3]{27m^3} = 3m.$$

$$= \dfrac{4n\sqrt[3]{n}}{3m} \quad \sqrt[3]{64n^3} = 4n.$$

Answers: **a.** $3ab\sqrt[3]{2b^2}$,

b. $\dfrac{3q\sqrt[3]{q^2}}{4p}$ ■

STUDY SET   Section 8.3

VOCABULARY   *Fill in the blanks.*

1. Squares of integers such as 4, 9, and 16 are called ___perfect___ squares.

2. Cubes of integers such as 8, 27, and 64 are called perfect ___cubes___.

3. "To ___simplify___ $\sqrt{8}$" means to write it as $2\sqrt{2}$.

4. The word *product* is associated with the operation of ___multiplication___ and the word *quotient* with ___division___.

CONCEPTS

5. Fill in the blanks.
  a. The square root of the product of two positive numbers is equal to the ___product___ of their square roots. In symbols,
  $$\sqrt{ab} = \sqrt{a}\sqrt{b}$$

  b. The square root of the quotient of two positive numbers is equal to the ___quotient___ of their square roots. In symbols,
  $$\sqrt{\dfrac{a}{b}} = \dfrac{\sqrt{a}}{\sqrt{b}}$$

6. Which of the integer squares 1, 4, 9, 16, 25, 36, 49, 64, 81, and 100 is the *largest* factor of the given number?
  a. 20   4
  b. 45   9
  c. 72   36
  d. 98   49

In Exercises 7–8, tell what is wrong with each solution.

7. Simplify $\sqrt{20}$.

$$\sqrt{20} = \sqrt{16 + 4}$$

$$= \sqrt{16} + \sqrt{4} \quad \text{Line 2 is not true. There is no addition property of radicals.}$$

$$= 4 + 2$$

$$= 6$$

8. Simplify $\sqrt{27}$.

$$\sqrt{27} = \sqrt{36 - 9}$$
$$= \sqrt{36} - \sqrt{9} \quad \text{Line 2 is not true. There is}$$
$$= 6 - 3 \quad \text{no subtraction property of}$$
$$\text{radicals.}$$
$$= 3$$

9. A crossword puzzle in a newspaper occupies an area of 28 square inches. See Illustration 1.

a. Express the exact length of a side of the square-shaped puzzle in simplified radical form. $2\sqrt{7}$ in.

ILLUSTRATION 1

b. What is the length of a side to the nearest tenth of an inch? 5.3 in.

10. See Illustration 2.

a. What is the exact length of a side of the cube written in simplified radical form? $2\sqrt[3]{5}$ ft

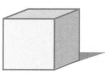

b. What is the length of a side to the nearest tenth of a foot?
3.4 ft

Volume = 40 ft³

ILLUSTRATION 2

Evaluate the expression $\sqrt{b^2 - 4ac}$ for the given values. Do the operations within the radical first, and then simplify the radical.

11. $a = 5, b = 10, c = 3$ $2\sqrt{10}$
12. $a = 2, b = 6, c = 1$ $2\sqrt{7}$
13. $a = -1, b = 6, c = 9$ $6\sqrt{2}$
14. $a = 1, b = -2, c = -11$ $4\sqrt{3}$

NOTATION *In Exercises 15–16, a radical is simplified. Complete each solution.*

15. $\sqrt{80a^3b^2} = \sqrt{16 \cdot 5 \cdot a^2 \cdot a \cdot b^2}$
$$= \sqrt{16a^2b^2 \cdot 5a}$$
$$= \sqrt{16a^2b^2}\sqrt{5a}$$
$$= 4ab\sqrt{5a}$$

16. $\sqrt[3]{\dfrac{27a^4b^2}{64}} = \dfrac{\sqrt[3]{27a^4b^2}}{\sqrt[3]{64}}$
$$= \dfrac{\sqrt[3]{27a^3 \cdot ab^2}}{\sqrt[3]{64}}$$
$$= \dfrac{\sqrt[3]{27a^3}\sqrt[3]{ab^2}}{\sqrt[3]{64}}$$
$$= \dfrac{3a\sqrt[3]{ab^2}}{4}$$

17. What operation is indicated between the two radicals in the expression $\sqrt{4}\sqrt{3}$? multiplication

18. Fill in each blank to make a true statement.
a. $16x^2 = (\;4x\;)^2$ **b.** $27a^3b^6 = (\;3ab^2\;)^3$

19. Write each expression in a better form.
a. $\sqrt{5} \cdot 2$ $2\sqrt{5}$ **b.** $\sqrt{7}a$ $a\sqrt{7}$
c. $9\sqrt{x^2}\sqrt{6}$ $9x\sqrt{6}$ **d.** $\sqrt{y}\sqrt{25z^4}$ $5z^2\sqrt{y}$

20. a. Explain the difference between $\sqrt{5x}$ and $\sqrt{5}x$.
$\sqrt{5x} = \sqrt{5 \cdot x}$; $\sqrt{5}x = \sqrt{5} \cdot x$
b. Why do you think it is better to write $\sqrt{5}x$ as $x\sqrt{5}$? $\sqrt{5}x$ could be mistaken for $\sqrt{5x}$.

PRACTICE *Simplify each radical. Assume that all variables represent positive numbers.*

21. $\sqrt{20}$ $2\sqrt{5}$ **22.** $\sqrt{18}$ $3\sqrt{2}$
23. $\sqrt{50}$ $5\sqrt{2}$ **24.** $\sqrt{75}$ $5\sqrt{3}$
25. $\sqrt{45}$ $3\sqrt{5}$ **26.** $\sqrt{54}$ $3\sqrt{6}$
27. $\sqrt{98}$ $7\sqrt{2}$ **28.** $\sqrt{147}$ $7\sqrt{3}$
29. $\sqrt{48}$ $4\sqrt{3}$ **30.** $\sqrt{128}$ $8\sqrt{2}$
31. $-\sqrt{200}$ $-10\sqrt{2}$ **32.** $-\sqrt{300}$ $-10\sqrt{3}$
33. $\sqrt{192}$ $8\sqrt{3}$ **34.** $\sqrt{88}$ $2\sqrt{22}$
35. $\sqrt{250}$ $5\sqrt{10}$ **36.** $\sqrt{1,000}$ $10\sqrt{10}$
37. $2\sqrt{24}$ $4\sqrt{6}$ **38.** $3\sqrt{32}$ $12\sqrt{2}$
39. $-2\sqrt{28}$ $-4\sqrt{7}$ **40.** $-3\sqrt{72}$ $-18\sqrt{2}$
41. $\sqrt{n^3}$ $n\sqrt{n}$ **42.** $\sqrt{x^5}$ $x^2\sqrt{x}$
43. $\sqrt{4k}$ $2\sqrt{k}$ **44.** $\sqrt{9p}$ $3\sqrt{p}$
45. $\sqrt{12x}$ $2\sqrt{3x}$ **46.** $\sqrt{20y}$ $2\sqrt{5y}$
47. $6\sqrt{75t}$ $30\sqrt{3t}$ **48.** $2\sqrt{24s}$ $4\sqrt{6s}$
49. $\sqrt{25x^3}$ $5x\sqrt{x}$ **50.** $\sqrt{36y^3}$ $6y\sqrt{y}$
51. $\sqrt{a^2b}$ $a\sqrt{b}$ **52.** $\sqrt{rs^4}$ $s^2\sqrt{r}$
53. $\sqrt{9x^4y}$ $3x^2\sqrt{y}$ **54.** $\sqrt{16xy^2}$ $4y\sqrt{x}$

55. $\dfrac{1}{5}x^2y\sqrt{50x^2y^2}$ $x^3y^2\sqrt{2}$

56. $\dfrac{1}{5}x^5y\sqrt{75x^3y^2}$ $x^6y^2\sqrt{3x}$

57. $-12x\sqrt{16x^2y^3}$ $-48x^2y\sqrt{y}$

58. $-4x^5y^3\sqrt{36x^3y^3}$ $-24x^6y^4\sqrt{xy}$

59. $-\dfrac{2}{5}\sqrt{80mn^4}$ $-\dfrac{8n^2\sqrt{5m}}{5}$

60. $\dfrac{5}{6}\sqrt{180ab^6}$ $5b^3\sqrt{5a}$

Write each quotient as the quotient of two radicals and simplify.

61. $\sqrt{\dfrac{25}{9}}$ $\dfrac{5}{3}$ **62.** $\sqrt{\dfrac{36}{49}}$ $\dfrac{6}{7}$

63. $\sqrt{\dfrac{81}{64}}$ $\dfrac{9}{8}$ **64.** $\sqrt{\dfrac{121}{144}}$ $\dfrac{11}{12}$

65. $\sqrt{\dfrac{26}{25}}$ $\dfrac{\sqrt{26}}{5}$ **66.** $\sqrt{\dfrac{17}{169}}$ $\dfrac{\sqrt{17}}{13}$

67. $-\sqrt{\dfrac{20}{49}}$ $-\dfrac{2\sqrt{5}}{7}$ **68.** $-\sqrt{\dfrac{50}{9}}$ $-\dfrac{5\sqrt{2}}{3}$

69. $\sqrt{\dfrac{48}{81}}$ $\dfrac{4\sqrt{3}}{9}$ **70.** $\sqrt{\dfrac{27}{64}}$ $\dfrac{3\sqrt{3}}{8}$

71. $\sqrt{\dfrac{32}{25}}$ $\dfrac{4\sqrt{2}}{5}$ **72.** $\sqrt{\dfrac{75}{16}}$ $\dfrac{5\sqrt{3}}{4}$

Simplify each expression. All variables represent positive numbers.

73. $\sqrt{\dfrac{72x^3}{y^2}}$ $\dfrac{6x\sqrt{2x}}{y}$ **74.** $\sqrt{\dfrac{108b^2}{d^4}}$ $\dfrac{6b\sqrt{3}}{d^2}$

75. $\sqrt{\dfrac{125n^5}{64n}}$ $\dfrac{5n^2\sqrt{5}}{8}$ **76.** $\sqrt{\dfrac{72q^7}{25q^3}}$ $\dfrac{6q^2\sqrt{2}}{5}$

77. $\sqrt{\dfrac{128m^3n^5}{81mn^7}}$ $\dfrac{8m\sqrt{2}}{9n}$ **78.** $\sqrt{\dfrac{75p^3q^2}{p^5q^4}}$ $\dfrac{5\sqrt{3}}{pq}$

79. $\sqrt{\dfrac{12r^7s^7}{r^5s^2}}$ $2rs^2\sqrt{3s}$ **80.** $\sqrt{\dfrac{m^2n^9}{100mn^3}}$ $\dfrac{n^3\sqrt{m}}{10}$

Simplify each cube root.

81. $\sqrt[3]{24}$ $2\sqrt[3]{3}$ **82.** $\sqrt[3]{32}$ $2\sqrt[3]{4}$

83. $\sqrt[3]{-128}$ $-4\sqrt[3]{2}$ **84.** $\sqrt[3]{-250}$ $-5\sqrt[3]{2}$

85. $\sqrt[3]{8x^3}$ $2x$ **86.** $\sqrt[3]{27x^3}$ $3x$

87. $\sqrt[3]{-64x^5}$ $-4x\sqrt[3]{x^2}$ **88.** $\sqrt[3]{-16x^4}$ $-2x\sqrt[3]{2x}$

89. $\sqrt[3]{54x^3z^6}$ $3xz^2\sqrt[3]{2}$ **90.** $\sqrt[3]{-24x^3y^5}$ $-2xy\sqrt[3]{3y^2}$

91. $\sqrt[3]{-81x^2y^3}$ $-3y\sqrt[3]{3x^2}$ **92.** $\sqrt[3]{81y^2z^3}$ $3z\sqrt[3]{3y^2}$

93. $\sqrt[3]{\dfrac{27m^3}{8n^6}}$ $\dfrac{3m}{2n^2}$ **94.** $\sqrt[3]{\dfrac{125t^9}{27s^6}}$ $\dfrac{5t^3}{3s^2}$

95. $\sqrt[3]{\dfrac{r^4s^5}{1,000t^3}}$ $\dfrac{rs\sqrt[3]{rs^2}}{10t}$ **96.** $\sqrt[3]{\dfrac{54m^4n^3}{r^3s^6}}$ $\dfrac{3mn\sqrt[3]{2m}}{rs^2}$

🔲 **APPLICATIONS**   *Use a calculator to help solve each problem.*

97. AMUSEMENT PARK RIDE   Illustration 3 shows the "Swashbuckler" pirate ship ride. The time (in seconds) it takes to swing from one extreme to the other is given by

$$t = \pi\sqrt{\dfrac{L}{32}}$$

   a. Find t and express it in simplified radical form. Leave π in your answer. $\dfrac{3\pi\sqrt{3}}{4}$ sec

b. Express your answer to part a as a decimal. Round to the nearest tenth of a second.   4.1 sec

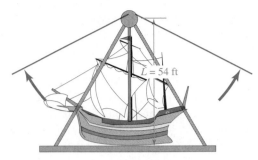

ILLUSTRATION 3

98. HERB GARDEN   The perimeter of the herb garden shown in Illustration 4 is given by

$$p = 2\pi\sqrt{\dfrac{a^2 + b^2}{2}}$$

   a. Find the length of fencing (in meters) needed to enclose the garden. Express the result in simplified radical form. Leave π in your answer. $10\pi\sqrt{2}$ m

   b. Express the result from part a as a decimal. Round to the nearest tenth of a meter.   44.4 m

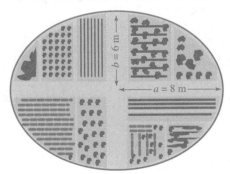

ILLUSTRATION 4

99. ARCHAEOLOGY   Framed grids, made up of 20 cm × 20 cm squares, are often used to record the location of artifacts found during an excavation. (See Illustration 5.)

   a. Use the distance formula to determine the *exact* distance between a piece of pottery found at point A and a cooking utensil found at point B. $60\sqrt{2}$ cm

   b. Approximate the distance to the nearest tenth of a centimeter.   84.9 cm

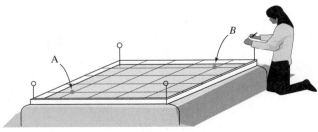

ILLUSTRATION 5

100. ENVIRONMENTAL PROTECTION   A new campground is to be constructed 2 miles from a major highway, as shown in Illustration 6. The proposed entrance, although longer than the direct route, bypasses a grove of old-growth redwood trees.

  a. Use the Pythagorean theorem to find the length of the proposed entrance road. Express the result as a radical in simplified form. $2\sqrt{5}$ mi
  b. Express the result from part a as a decimal. Round to the nearest hundredth of a mile.   4.47 mi
  c. How much longer is the proposed entrance as compared to the direct route into the campground?   about 2.47 mi

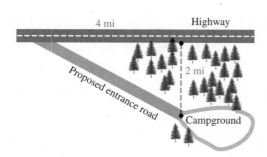

ILLUSTRATION 6

WRITING

101. State the multiplication property of radicals.
102. When comparing $\sqrt{8}$ and $2\sqrt{2}$, why is $2\sqrt{2}$ called simplified radical form?

REVIEW

103. Multiply: $(-2a^3)(3a^2)$. $-6a^5$
104. Find the slope of the line passing through $(-6, 0)$ and $(0, -4)$. $-\frac{2}{3}$
105. Write the equation of the line passing through $(0, 3)$ with slope -2. $y = -2x + 3$
106. Solve $-x = -5$. 5
107. Solve $-x > -5$. $x < 5$
108. What is the slope of a line perpendicular to a line with a slope of 2? $-\frac{1}{2}$

8.4 *Adding and Subtracting Radical Expressions*

In this section, you will learn about

• Combining like radicals • Combining expressions containing cube roots

INTRODUCTION. We have previously discussed how to add and subtract like terms. In this section, we will introduce a similar topic: how to add and subtract expressions that contain like radicals.

Combining like radicals

When adding monomials, we can often combine **like terms.** For example,

$$3x + 5x = (3 + 5)x \quad \text{Use the distributive property.}$$
$$= 8x \quad \text{Do the addition.}$$

 COMMENT   The expression $3x + 5y$ cannot be simplified, because $3x$ and $5y$ are not like terms.

It is often possible to combine terms that contain *like radicals.*

Like radicals	Radicals are called **like radicals** when they have the same index and the same radicand.

Like radicals	**Unlike radicals**
$3\sqrt{2}$ and $5\sqrt{2}$	$3\sqrt{2}$ and $5\sqrt{3}$
The same index and the same radicand	The same index but different radicands
$5x\sqrt{3y}$ and $-2x\sqrt{3y}$	$5x\sqrt[3]{3y}$ and $-2x\sqrt{3y}$
The same index and the same radicand	The same radicands but a different index

Expressions that contain like radicals can be combined by addition and subtraction. For example, we have

$$3\sqrt{2} + 5\sqrt{2} = (3 + 5)\sqrt{2} \quad \text{Use the distributive property.}$$
$$= 8\sqrt{2} \qquad \text{Do the addition.}$$

Likewise, we can simplify the expression $5x\sqrt{3y} - 2x\sqrt{3y}$.

$$5x\sqrt{3y} - 2x\sqrt{3y} = (5x - 2x)\sqrt{3y} \quad \text{Use the distributive property.}$$
$$= 3x\sqrt{3y} \qquad \text{Do the subtraction: } 5x - 2x = 3x.$$

 COMMENT The expression $3\sqrt{2} + 5\sqrt{3}$ cannot be simplified, because the radicals are unlike. For the same reason, we cannot simplify $5x\sqrt[3]{3y} - 2x\sqrt{3y}$.

EXAMPLE 1   *Combining like radicals.* Simplify **a.** $\sqrt{6} + 6 + 5\sqrt{6}$ and **b.** $-2\sqrt{m} - 3\sqrt{m}$.

Solution

a. The expression contains three terms: $\sqrt{6}$, 6, and $5\sqrt{6}$. The first and third terms have like radicals, and they can be combined.

$$\sqrt{6} + 6 + 5\sqrt{6} = 6 + \left(1\sqrt{6} + 5\sqrt{6}\right) \quad \begin{array}{l}\text{Group the expressions with like}\\ \text{radicals. Write } \sqrt{6} \text{ as } 1\sqrt{6}.\end{array}$$
$$= 6 + (1 + 5)\sqrt{6} \qquad \text{Use the distributive property.}$$
$$= 6 + 6\sqrt{6} \qquad \text{Do the addition.}$$

Note that 6 and $6\sqrt{6}$ do not contain like radicals and cannot be combined.

b. The expressions $-2\sqrt{m}$ and $-3\sqrt{m}$ contain like radicals. We can combine them.

$$-2\sqrt{m} - 3\sqrt{m} = (-2 - 3)\sqrt{m} \quad \text{Use the distributive property.}$$
$$= -5\sqrt{m} \qquad \text{Do the subtraction: } -2 - 3 = -5.$$

Self Check

Simplify:

a. $\sqrt{7} + 7 + 7\sqrt{7}$

b. $24\sqrt{m} - 25\sqrt{m}$

Answers: **a.** $8\sqrt{7} + 7$,

b. $-\sqrt{m}$

Radical expressions such as $3\sqrt{18}$ and $5\sqrt{8}$ can be simplified so that they contain like radicals. They can then be combined.

EXAMPLE 2   *Adding radicals.* Simplify $3\sqrt{18} + 5\sqrt{8}$.

Solution

The radical $\sqrt{18}$ is not in simplified form, because 18 has a perfect square factor of 9. The radical $\sqrt{8}$ is not in simplified form either, because 8 has a perfect square factor of 4. To simplify the radicals and add the expressions, we proceed as follows.

$3\sqrt{18} + 5\sqrt{8}$

$$= 3\sqrt{9 \cdot 2} + 5\sqrt{4 \cdot 2} \quad \text{Factor 18 and 8 using perfect square factors.}$$
$$= 3\sqrt{9}\sqrt{2} + 5\sqrt{4}\sqrt{2} \quad \begin{array}{l}\text{The square root of a product is equal to the product}\\ \text{of the square roots.}\end{array}$$
$$= 3(3)\sqrt{2} + 5(2)\sqrt{2} \quad \sqrt{9} = 3 \text{ and } \sqrt{4} = 2.$$
$$= 9\sqrt{2} + 10\sqrt{2} \quad 3(3) = 9 \text{ and } 5(2) = 10.$$
$$= 19\sqrt{2} \qquad \begin{array}{l}\text{To combine like radicals, combine their coefficients:}\\ 9 + 10 = 19.\end{array}$$

Self Check

Simplify $2\sqrt{50} + \sqrt{32}$.

Answer: $14\sqrt{2}$

EXAMPLE 3 *Orthopedics.*   Doctors sometimes use traction to help align a broken bone so that a fracture can heal properly. Figure 8-16 shows how traction is applied by fixing a weight, two pulleys, and some stainless steel cable to a broken leg. How many feet of cable are used in the setup shown in the figure?

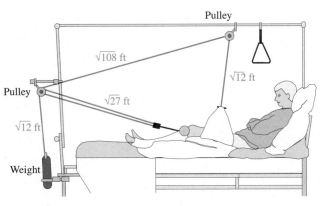

FIGURE 8-16

Solution   Two segments of the cable are $\sqrt{12}$ feet long, another is $\sqrt{108}$ feet long, and two others are $\sqrt{27}$ feet long. The total number of feet of cable can be found by adding

$$2\sqrt{12} + \sqrt{108} + 2\sqrt{27}$$

Since $\sqrt{12}$, $\sqrt{108}$, and $\sqrt{27}$ are not like radicals, we cannot do the addition at this time. First, we need to write each radical in simplified form. Then we can add any expressions that contain like radicals.

$$2\sqrt{12} + \sqrt{108} + 2\sqrt{27}$$

$= 2\sqrt{4 \cdot 3} + \sqrt{36 \cdot 3} + 2\sqrt{9 \cdot 3}$	Factor 12, 108, and 27 using perfect squares.
$= 2\sqrt{4}\sqrt{3} + \sqrt{36}\sqrt{3} + 2\sqrt{9}\sqrt{3}$	The square root of a product is equal to the product of the square roots.
$= 2(2)\sqrt{3} + 6\sqrt{3} + 2(3)\sqrt{3}$	Simplify: $\sqrt{4} = 2$, $\sqrt{36} = 6$, and $\sqrt{9} = 3$.
$= 4\sqrt{3} + 6\sqrt{3} + 6\sqrt{3}$	Do the multiplications.
$= 16\sqrt{3}$	To combine like radicals, combine their coefficients: $4 + 6 + 6 = 16$.

The traction setup uses $16\sqrt{3}$ feet of cable.   ■

EXAMPLE 4   *Adding radicals.*   Simplify $\sqrt{44x^2y} + x\sqrt{99y}$.

Solution

We simplify each radical and then add the expressions containing like radicals.

$$\sqrt{44x^2y} + x\sqrt{99y}$$

$= \sqrt{4x^2 \cdot 11y} + x\sqrt{9 \cdot 11y}$	Factor $44x^2y$ and $99y$.
$= \sqrt{4x^2}\sqrt{11y} + x\sqrt{9}\sqrt{11y}$	The square root of a product is equal to the product of the square roots.
$= 2x\sqrt{11y} + 3x\sqrt{11y}$	Simplify: $\sqrt{4x^2} = 2x$ and $\sqrt{9} = 3$.
$= 5x\sqrt{11y}$	To combine like radicals, combine their coefficients: $2x + 3x = 5x$.

Self Check

Simplify $\sqrt{12xy^2} + \sqrt{27xy^2}$.

Answer: $5y\sqrt{3x}$ ■

EXAMPLE 5 *Subtracting radicals.* Simplify $\sqrt{28x^2y} - 2\sqrt{63y^3}$.

Solution

We begin by simplifying each radical.

$$\sqrt{28x^2y} - 2\sqrt{63y^3}$$
$$= \sqrt{4x^2 \cdot 7y} - 2\sqrt{9y^2 \cdot 7y} \qquad \text{Factor } 28x^2y \text{ and } 63y^3.$$
$$= \sqrt{4x^2}\sqrt{7y} - 2\sqrt{9y^2}\sqrt{7y} \qquad \text{The square root of a product is equal to the product of the square roots.}$$
$$= 2x\sqrt{7y} - 2(3y)\sqrt{7y} \qquad \sqrt{4x^2} = 2x \text{ and } \sqrt{9y^2} = 3y.$$
$$= 2x\sqrt{7y} - 6y\sqrt{7y}$$

Since $2x$ and $6y$ are not like terms and therefore cannot be subtracted, the expression does not simplify further.

Self Check

Simplify $\sqrt{20mn^2} - \sqrt{80m^3}$.

Answer: $2n\sqrt{5m} - 4m\sqrt{5m}$ ∎

EXAMPLE 6 *Adding radicals.* Simplify $\sqrt{27xy} + \sqrt{20xy}$.

Solution

$$\sqrt{27xy} + \sqrt{20xy} = \sqrt{9 \cdot 3xy} + \sqrt{4 \cdot 5xy} \qquad \text{Factor } 27xy \text{ and } 20xy.$$
$$= \sqrt{9}\sqrt{3xy} + \sqrt{4}\sqrt{5xy} \qquad \text{The square root of a product is equal to the product of the square roots.}$$
$$= 3\sqrt{3xy} + 2\sqrt{5xy} \qquad \sqrt{9} = 3 \text{ and } \sqrt{4} = 2.$$

Since the terms have unlike radicals, the expression does not simplify further.

Self Check

Simplify $\sqrt{75ab} + \sqrt{72ab}$.

Answer: $5\sqrt{3ab} + 6\sqrt{2ab}$ ∎

EXAMPLE 7 *Adding and subtracting radicals.* Simplify $\sqrt{8x} + \sqrt{3y} - \sqrt{50x} + \sqrt{27y}$.

Solution

We simplify the radicals and then combine like radicals, where possible.

$$\sqrt{8x} + \sqrt{3y} - \sqrt{50x} + \sqrt{27y}$$
$$= \sqrt{4 \cdot 2x} + \sqrt{3y} - \sqrt{25 \cdot 2x} + \sqrt{9 \cdot 3y} \qquad \text{Factor } 8x, 50x, \text{ and } 27y.$$
$$= \sqrt{4}\sqrt{2x} + \sqrt{3y} - \sqrt{25}\sqrt{2x} + \sqrt{9}\sqrt{3y}$$
$$= 2\sqrt{2x} + \sqrt{3y} - 5\sqrt{2x} + 3\sqrt{3y}$$
$$= -3\sqrt{2x} + 4\sqrt{3y} \qquad \text{Combine like radicals.}$$

Self Check

Simplify $\sqrt{32x} - \sqrt{5y} - \sqrt{200x} + \sqrt{125y}$.

Answer: $-6\sqrt{2x} + 4\sqrt{5y}$ ∎

Combining expressions containing cube roots

We can extend the concepts used to combine square roots to radicals with higher order.

 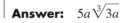

EXAMPLE 8 *Subtracting cube roots.* Simplify $\sqrt[3]{81x^4} - x\sqrt[3]{24x}$.

Solution

We simplify each radical and then combine like radicals.

$$\sqrt[3]{81x^4} - x\sqrt[3]{24x} = \sqrt[3]{27x^3 \cdot 3x} - x\sqrt[3]{8 \cdot 3x} \qquad \text{Factor } 81x^4 \text{ and } 24x.$$
$$= \sqrt[3]{27x^3}\sqrt[3]{3x} - x\sqrt[3]{8}\sqrt[3]{3x}$$
$$= 3x\sqrt[3]{3x} - 2x\sqrt[3]{3x}$$
$$= x\sqrt[3]{3x} \qquad \text{Combine like radicals.}$$

Self Check

Simplify $\sqrt[3]{24a^4} + a\sqrt[3]{81a}$.

Answer: $5a\sqrt[3]{3a}$ ∎

STUDY SET Section 8.4

VOCABULARY *Fill in the blanks.*

1. Like _____radicals_____ have the same index and the same radicand.

2. Like _____terms_____ have the same variables with the same exponents.

3. Radical expressions such as $\sqrt{8}$ and $\sqrt{18}$ can be _____simplified_____ so that they contain like radicals.

4. The expression $3\sqrt{2} + \sqrt{8} - 2$ contains three _____terms_____.

CONCEPTS *Tell whether the expressions contain like radicals.*

5. $5\sqrt{2}$ and $2\sqrt{3}$ no

6. $7\sqrt{3x}$ and $3\sqrt{3x}$ yes

7. $125\sqrt[3]{13a}$ and $-\sqrt[3]{13a}$ yes

8. $-17\sqrt[4]{5x}$ and $25\sqrt[3]{5x}$ no

Tell what is wrong with the following work.

9. $7\sqrt{5} - 3\sqrt{2} = 4\sqrt{3}$

The radicals don't have the same radicand, so they can't be combined.

10. $12\sqrt{7} + 20\sqrt{11} = 32\sqrt{18}$

The radicals don't have the same radicand, so they can't be combined.

11. $7 - 3\sqrt{2} = 4\sqrt{2}$

The two terms are not like terms—they cannot be combined.

12. $12 + 20\sqrt{11} = 32\sqrt{11}$

The two terms are not like terms—they cannot be combined.

Complete each table of values.

13.

x	$\sqrt{x} + \sqrt{3}$
3	$2\sqrt{3}$
12	$3\sqrt{3}$
27	$4\sqrt{3}$
48	$5\sqrt{3}$

14.

x	$3\sqrt{x} - \sqrt{2}$
2	$2\sqrt{2}$
8	$5\sqrt{2}$
18	$8\sqrt{2}$
32	$11\sqrt{2}$

NOTATION *Complete each solution.*

15. Add: $3\sqrt{80} + 4\sqrt{125}$.

$$3\sqrt{80} + 4\sqrt{125} = 3\sqrt{16 \cdot 5} + 4\sqrt{25 \cdot 5}$$
$$= 3\sqrt{16}\,\sqrt{5} + 4\sqrt{25}\,\sqrt{5}$$
$$= 3(4)\sqrt{5} + 4(5)\sqrt{5}$$
$$= 12\sqrt{5} + 20\,\sqrt{5}$$
$$= 32\sqrt{5}$$

16. Subtract: $3\sqrt{125} - 2\sqrt{80}$.

$$3\sqrt{125} - 2\sqrt{80} = 3\sqrt{25 \cdot 5} - 2\sqrt{16 \cdot 5}$$
$$= 3\sqrt{25}\,\sqrt{5} - 2\sqrt{16}\sqrt{5}$$
$$= 3(5)\sqrt{5} - 2(4)\sqrt{5}$$
$$= 15\sqrt{5} - 8\sqrt{5}$$
$$= 7\sqrt{5}$$

PRACTICE *Simplify each expression. All variables represent positive numbers.*

17. $5\sqrt{7} + 4\sqrt{7}$ $9\sqrt{7}$ **18.** $3\sqrt{10} + 4\sqrt{10}$ $7\sqrt{10}$

19. $\sqrt{x} - 4\sqrt{x}$ $-3\sqrt{x}$ **20.** $\sqrt{t} - 9\sqrt{t}$ $-8\sqrt{t}$

21. $5 + 3\sqrt{3} + 3\sqrt{3}$ $5 + 6\sqrt{3}$

22. $\sqrt{5} + 2 + 3\sqrt{5}$ $2 + 4\sqrt{5}$

23. $-1 + 2\sqrt{r} - 3\sqrt{r}$ $-1 - \sqrt{r}$

24. $-8 - 5\sqrt{c} + 4\sqrt{c}$ $-8 - \sqrt{c}$

25. $\sqrt{12} + \sqrt{27}$ $5\sqrt{3}$ **26.** $\sqrt{20} + \sqrt{45}$ $5\sqrt{5}$

27. $\sqrt{18} - \sqrt{8}$ $\sqrt{2}$ **28.** $\sqrt{32} - \sqrt{18}$ $\sqrt{2}$

29. $2\sqrt{45} + 2\sqrt{80}$ $14\sqrt{5}$

30. $3\sqrt{80} + 3\sqrt{125}$ $27\sqrt{5}$

31. $2\sqrt{80} - 3\sqrt{125}$ $-7\sqrt{5}$

32. $3\sqrt{245} - 2\sqrt{180}$ $9\sqrt{5}$

33. $\sqrt{20} + \sqrt{180}$ $8\sqrt{5}$ **34.** $2\sqrt{28} + 7\sqrt{63}$ $25\sqrt{7}$

35. $\sqrt{12} - \sqrt{48}$ $-2\sqrt{3}$ **36.** $\sqrt{48} - \sqrt{75}$ $-\sqrt{3}$

37. $\sqrt{288} - 3\sqrt{200}$ $-18\sqrt{2}$

38. $\sqrt{80} - \sqrt{245}$ $-3\sqrt{5}$

39. $2\sqrt{28} + 2\sqrt{112}$ $12\sqrt{7}$

40. $4\sqrt{63} + 6\sqrt{112}$ $36\sqrt{7}$

41. $\sqrt{20} + \sqrt{45} + \sqrt{80}$ $9\sqrt{5}$

42. $\sqrt{48} + \sqrt{27} + \sqrt{75}$ $12\sqrt{3}$

43. $\sqrt{200} - \sqrt{75} + \sqrt{48}$ $10\sqrt{2} - \sqrt{3}$

44. $\sqrt{20} + \sqrt{80} - \sqrt{125}$ $\sqrt{5}$

45. $8\sqrt{6} - 5\sqrt{2} - 3\sqrt{6}$ $5\sqrt{6} - 5\sqrt{2}$

46. $3\sqrt{2} - 3\sqrt{15} - 4\sqrt{15}$ $3\sqrt{2} - 7\sqrt{15}$

47. $\sqrt{24} + \sqrt{150} + \sqrt{240}$ $7\sqrt{6} + 4\sqrt{15}$

48. $\sqrt{28} + \sqrt{63} + \sqrt{18}$ $5\sqrt{7} + 3\sqrt{2}$

49. $\sqrt{48} - \sqrt{8} + \sqrt{27} - \sqrt{32}$ $7\sqrt{3} - 6\sqrt{2}$

50. $\sqrt{162} + \sqrt{50} - \sqrt{75} - \sqrt{108}$ $14\sqrt{2} - 11\sqrt{3}$

51. $\sqrt{2x^2} + \sqrt{8x^2}$ $3x\sqrt{2}$

52. $\sqrt{3y^2} - \sqrt{12y^2}$ $-y\sqrt{3}$

53. $\sqrt{2d^3} + \sqrt{8d^3}$ $3d\sqrt{2d}$

54. $\sqrt{3a^3} - \sqrt{12a^3}$ $-a\sqrt{3a}$

55. $\sqrt{18x^2y} - \sqrt{27x^2y}$ $3x\sqrt{2y} - 3x\sqrt{3y}$

56. $\sqrt{49xy} + \sqrt{xy}$ $8\sqrt{xy}$

57. $\sqrt{32x^5} - \sqrt{18x^5}$ **58.** $\sqrt{27xy^3} - \sqrt{48xy^3}$
    $x^2\sqrt{2x}$ $-y\sqrt{3xy}$

59. $3\sqrt{54b^2} + 5\sqrt{24b^2}$ **60.** $3\sqrt{24x^4y^3} + 2\sqrt{54x^4y^3}$
    $19b\sqrt{6}$ $12x^2y\sqrt{6y}$

61. $y\sqrt{490y} - 2\sqrt{360y^3}$ **62.** $3\sqrt{20x} + 2\sqrt{63y}$
    $-5y\sqrt{10y}$ $6\sqrt{5x} + 6\sqrt{7y}$

63. $\sqrt{20x^3y} + \sqrt{45x^5y^3} - \sqrt{80x^7y^5}$
    $2x\sqrt{5xy} + 3x^2y\sqrt{5xy} - 4x^3y^2\sqrt{5xy}$

64. $x\sqrt{48xy^2} - y\sqrt{27x^3} + \sqrt{75x^3y^2}$ $6xy\sqrt{3x}$

65. $\sqrt[3]{3} + \sqrt[3]{3}$ $2\sqrt[3]{3}$ **66.** $\sqrt[3]{2} + 5\sqrt[3]{2}$ $6\sqrt[3]{2}$

67. $2\sqrt[3]{x} - 3\sqrt[3]{x}$ $-\sqrt[3]{x}$ **68.** $4\sqrt[3]{s} - 5\sqrt[3]{s}$ $-\sqrt[3]{s}$

69. $\sqrt[3]{16} + \sqrt[3]{54}$ $5\sqrt[3]{2}$ **70.** $\sqrt[3]{24} - \sqrt[3]{81}$ $-\sqrt[3]{3}$

71. $\sqrt[3]{81} - \sqrt[3]{24}$ $\sqrt[3]{3}$ **72.** $\sqrt[3]{32} + \sqrt[3]{108}$ $5\sqrt[3]{4}$

73. $\sqrt[3]{40} + \sqrt[3]{125}$ **74.** $\sqrt[3]{3,000} - \sqrt[3]{192}$
    $2\sqrt[3]{5} + 5$ $6\sqrt[3]{3}$

75. $\sqrt[3]{x^4} - \sqrt[3]{x^7}$ $x\sqrt[3]{x} - x^2\sqrt[3]{x}$

76. $\sqrt[3]{8x^5} + \sqrt[3]{27x^8}$ $2x\sqrt[3]{x^2} + 3x^2\sqrt[3]{x^2}$

77. $\sqrt[3]{192x^4y^5} - \sqrt[3]{24x^4y^5}$ $2xy\sqrt[3]{3xy^2}$

78. $\sqrt[3]{24a^5b^4} + \sqrt[3]{81a^5b^4}$ $5ab\sqrt[3]{3a^2b}$

79. $\sqrt[3]{135x^7y^4} - \sqrt[3]{40x^7y^4}$ $x^2y\sqrt[3]{5xy}$

80. $\sqrt[3]{56a^4b^5} + \sqrt[3]{7a^4b^5}$ $3ab\sqrt[3]{7ab^2}$

APPLICATIONS

81. ANATOMY   See Illustration 1. Determine the length of the patient's arm if he lets it fall to his side. $18\sqrt{3}$ in.

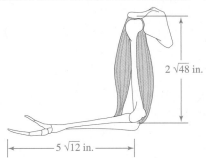

ILLUSTRATION 1

82. PLAYGROUND EQUIPMENT   Find the total length of pipe necessary to construct the frame of the swing set shown in Illustration 2. $\left(16 + 24\sqrt{5}\right)$ ft

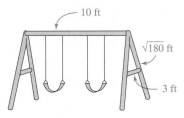

ILLUSTRATION 2

83. READING BLUEPRINTS   What is the length of the motor on the machine shown in Illustration 3? $27\sqrt{2}$ cm

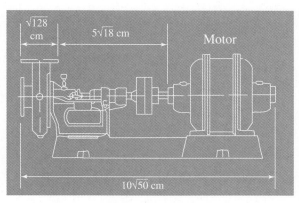

ILLUSTRATION 3

84. TENTS   The length of a center support pole for the tents shown in Illustration 4 is given by the formula

$$l = 0.5s\sqrt{3}$$

where s is the length of the side of the tent. Find the total length of the four poles needed for the parents' and children's tents. $10\sqrt{3}$ ft

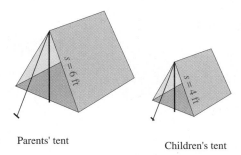

Parents' tent   Children's tent

ILLUSTRATION 4

85. FENCING   Find the number of feet of fencing needed to enclose the swimming pool complex shown in Illustration 5. $133\sqrt{6}$ ft

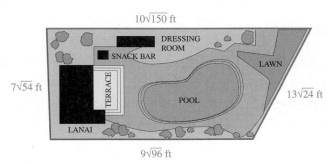

ILLUSTRATION 5

86. HARDWARE Find the difference in the lengths of the "arms" of the door-closing device shown in Illustration 6. $4\sqrt{3}$ in.

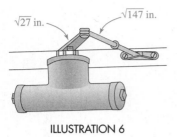

$\sqrt{27}$ in. $\sqrt{147}$ in.

ILLUSTRATION 6

WRITING

87. Explain why $\sqrt{3} + \sqrt{2}$ cannot be combined.

88. Explain why $\sqrt{4x}$ and $\sqrt[3]{4x}$ cannot be combined.

REVIEW *Simplify each expression. Write each answer without using negative exponents.*

89. 3^{-2} $\frac{1}{9}$

90. $\dfrac{1}{3^{-2}}$ 9

91. -3^2 -9

92. -3^{-2} $-\frac{1}{9}$

93. x^{-3} $\dfrac{1}{x^3}$

94. $\dfrac{1}{x^{-3}}$ x^3

95. 3^0 1

96. x^0 1

8.5 *Multiplying and Dividing Radical Expressions*

In this section, you will learn about

- Multiplying radical expressions • Dividing radical expressions
- Rationalizing denominators

INTRODUCTION. In this section, we will discuss the methods used to multiply and divide radical expressions.

Multiplying radical expressions

Recall that the *product of the square roots of two nonnegative numbers is equal to the square root of the product of those numbers.* For example,

$$\sqrt{2}\sqrt{8} = \sqrt{2 \cdot 8} \qquad \sqrt{3}\sqrt{27} = \sqrt{3 \cdot 27} \qquad \sqrt{x}\sqrt{x^3} = \sqrt{x \cdot x^3}$$
$$= \sqrt{16} \qquad\qquad = \sqrt{81} \qquad\qquad = \sqrt{x^4}$$
$$= 4 \qquad\qquad = 9 \qquad\qquad = x^2$$

Likewise, the *product of the cube roots of two numbers is equal to the cube root of the product of those numbers.* For example,

$$\sqrt[3]{2}\sqrt[3]{4} = \sqrt[3]{2 \cdot 4} \qquad \sqrt[3]{4}\sqrt[3]{16} = \sqrt[3]{4 \cdot 16} \qquad \sqrt[3]{3x^2}\sqrt[3]{9x} = \sqrt[3]{3x^2 \cdot 9x}$$
$$= \sqrt[3]{8} \qquad\qquad = \sqrt[3]{64} \qquad\qquad = \sqrt[3]{27x^3}$$
$$= 2 \qquad\qquad = 4 \qquad\qquad = 3x$$

These examples illustrate that radical expressions with the same index can be multiplied.

EXAMPLE 1 *Multiplying radicals.* Multiply **a.** $\sqrt{3}\sqrt{2}$, **b.** $\sqrt{6}\sqrt{8}$, and **c.** $\sqrt[3]{4}\sqrt[3]{10}$.

Solution

a. $\sqrt{3}\sqrt{2} = \sqrt{3 \cdot 2}$ The product of the square roots of two numbers is equal to the square root of the product of those numbers.

$\qquad\quad = \sqrt{6}$ Do the multiplication within the radical.

Self Check

Multiply:

a. $\sqrt{5}\sqrt{3}$

b. $\sqrt{8}\sqrt{9}$

c. $\sqrt[3]{6}\sqrt[3]{9}$

b. $\sqrt{6}\sqrt{8} = \sqrt{6 \cdot 8}$ The product of two square roots is equal to the square root of the product.

$\quad\quad\quad = \sqrt{48}$ Do the multiplication within the radical. Note that this radical can be simplified.

$\quad\quad\quad = \sqrt{16}\sqrt{3}$ Factor 48 as 16 · 3.

$\quad\quad\quad = 4\sqrt{3}$ Simplify: $\sqrt{16} = 4$.

c. $\sqrt[3]{4}\sqrt[3]{10} = \sqrt[3]{4 \cdot 10}$ The product of two cube roots is equal to the cube root of the product.

$\quad\quad\quad = \sqrt[3]{40}$ Do the multiplication within the radical.

$\quad\quad\quad = \sqrt[3]{8}\sqrt[3]{5}$ $\sqrt[3]{40} = \sqrt[3]{8 \cdot 5} = \sqrt[3]{8}\sqrt[3]{5}$.

$\quad\quad\quad = 2\sqrt[3]{5}$ Simplify: $\sqrt[3]{8} = 2$.

Answers: **a.** $\sqrt{15}$,   **b.** $6\sqrt{2}$,   **c.** $3\sqrt[3]{2}$.   ■

To multiply radical expressions having only one term, we multiply the coefficients and multiply the radicals separately and then simplify the result, when possible.

EXAMPLE 2   *Multiplying radical expressions.*   Multiply

a. $3\sqrt{6}$ by $4\sqrt{3}$ and   **b.** $-2\sqrt[3]{7x}$ by $6\sqrt[3]{49x^2}$.

Solution

The commutative and associative properties enable us to multiply the coefficients and the radicals separately.

a. $3\sqrt{6} \cdot 4\sqrt{3} = 3(4)\sqrt{6}\sqrt{3}$ Write the coefficients together and the radicals together.

$\quad\quad\quad = 12\sqrt{18}$ Multiply the coefficients and multiply the radicals.

$\quad\quad\quad = 12\sqrt{9}\sqrt{2}$ $\sqrt{18} = \sqrt{9 \cdot 2} = \sqrt{9}\sqrt{2}$.

$\quad\quad\quad = 12(3)\sqrt{2}$ Simplify: $\sqrt{9} = 3$.

$\quad\quad\quad = 36\sqrt{2}$ Do the multiplication: $12(3) = 36$.

b. $-2\sqrt[3]{7x} \cdot 6\sqrt[3]{49x^2} = -2(6)\sqrt[3]{7x}\sqrt[3]{49x^2}$ Write the coefficients together and the radicals together.

$\quad\quad\quad = -12\sqrt[3]{7x \cdot 49x^2}$ Multiply the coefficients and multiply the radicals.

$\quad\quad\quad = -12\sqrt[3]{343x^3}$ Do the multiplication within the radical.

$\quad\quad\quad = -12(7x)$ Simplify: $\sqrt[3]{343x^3} = 7x$.

$\quad\quad\quad = -84x$ Multiply.

Self Check

Multiply:

a. $\left(2\sqrt{2x}\right)\left(-3\sqrt{3x}\right)$

b. $\left(5\sqrt[3]{2}\right)\left(2\sqrt[3]{4}\right)$

Answers: **a.** $-6x\sqrt{6}$,   **b.** 20   ■

EXAMPLE 3   *Powers of radical expressions.*   Find $\left(2\sqrt{5}\right)^2$.

Solution

Recall that a power is used to indicate repeated multiplication.

$\left(2\sqrt{5}\right)^2 = 2\sqrt{5} \cdot 2\sqrt{5}$ Write $2\sqrt{5}$ as a factor two times.

$\quad\quad\quad = 2(2)\sqrt{5}\sqrt{5}$ Multiply the coefficients and the radicals separately.

$\quad\quad\quad = 4\sqrt{5 \cdot 5}$ The product of two square roots is equal to the square root of the product.

$\quad\quad\quad = 4\sqrt{25}$ Do the multiplication within the radical.

$\quad\quad\quad = 4 \cdot 5$ $\sqrt{25} = 5$

$\quad\quad\quad = 20$

Self Check

Find $\left(3\sqrt[3]{-2}\right)^3$.

Answer: -54 ■

Recall that to multiply a polynomial by a monomial, we use the distributive property. We use the same technique to multiply a radical expression that has two or more terms by a radical expression that has only one term.

EXAMPLE 4   *Using the distributive property.*   Multiply

a. $\sqrt{2x}(\sqrt{6x} + \sqrt{8x})$ and   **b.** $\sqrt[3]{3}(\sqrt[3]{9} - 2)$.

Solution

a. $\sqrt{2x}(\sqrt{6x} + \sqrt{8x}) = \sqrt{2x}\sqrt{6x} + \sqrt{2x}\sqrt{8x}$ Distribute the multiplication by $\sqrt{2x}$.

$\qquad = \sqrt{12x^2} + \sqrt{16x^2}$ The product of two square roots is equal to the square root of the product.

$\qquad = \sqrt{4x^2 \cdot 3} + \sqrt{16x^2}$ Factor $12x^2$ as $4x^2 \cdot 3$.

$\qquad = \sqrt{4x^2}\sqrt{3} + \sqrt{16x^2}$ The square root of a product is equal to the product of the square roots.

$\qquad = 2x\sqrt{3} + 4x$ Simplify: $\sqrt{4x^2} = 2x$ and $\sqrt{16x^2} = 4x$.

b. $\sqrt[3]{3}(\sqrt[3]{9} - 2) = \sqrt[3]{3}\sqrt[3]{9} - 2\sqrt[3]{3}$ Distribute the multiplication by $\sqrt[3]{3}$.

$\qquad = \sqrt[3]{27} - 2\sqrt[3]{3}$ The product of two cube roots is equal to the cube root of the product.

$\qquad = 3 - 2\sqrt[3]{3}$ Simplify: $\sqrt[3]{27} = 3$.

Self Check

Multiply:

a. $\sqrt{3}(3\sqrt{6} - \sqrt{3})$

b. $\sqrt[3]{2x}(3 - \sqrt[3]{4x^2})$

Answers: **a.** $9\sqrt{2} - 3$,

b. $3\sqrt[3]{2x} - 2x$ ■

To multiply two binomials, we multiply each term of one binomial by each term of the other binomial and simplify. We multiply two radical expressions, each having two terms, in the same way.

EXAMPLE 5   *Using the FOIL method.*   Multiply:

$(\sqrt{3x} + 1)(\sqrt{3x} + 2)$.

Solution

$$(\sqrt{3x} + 1)(\sqrt{3x} + 2)$$

$\qquad = \sqrt{3x}\sqrt{3x} + 2\sqrt{3x} + \sqrt{3x} + 2$ Use the FOIL method.

$\qquad = \sqrt{3x}\sqrt{3x} + 3\sqrt{3x} + 2$ Combine like radicals.

$\qquad = 3x + 3\sqrt{3x} + 2$ Simplify: $\sqrt{3x}\sqrt{3x} = (\sqrt{3x})^2 = 3x$.

Self Check

Multiply: $(\sqrt{5a} - 2)(\sqrt{5a} + 3)$.

Answer: $5a + \sqrt{5a} - 6$ ■

EXAMPLE 6   *Special products.*   Multiply: $(\sqrt{7} + \sqrt{2})(\sqrt{7} - \sqrt{2})$.

Solution

Recall from Chapter 4 that the product of two binomials which differ only in sign between the terms is the square of the first term minus the square of the second term: $(x + y)(x - y) = x^2 - y^2$. We can use this special product formula to multiply the given radical expressions.

$$(\sqrt{7} + \sqrt{2})(\sqrt{7} - \sqrt{2}) = (\sqrt{7})^2 - (\sqrt{2})^2$$

$$= 7 - 2$$

$$= 5$$

Self Check

Multiply:

$(\sqrt{5} + \sqrt{11})(\sqrt{5} - \sqrt{11})$

Answer: -6 ■

COMMENT Note that the answers to Example 6 and the Self Check did not contain any radicals. This will be the case whenever we find the product of radical expressions (containing *square* roots) of this form, which differ only in the sign between the terms.

EXAMPLE 7 *Multiplying radical expressions.* Multiply:
$(\sqrt[3]{4x} - 3)(\sqrt[3]{2x^2} + 1)$.

Solution

$(\sqrt[3]{4x} - 3)(\sqrt[3]{2x^2} + 1)$

$= \sqrt[3]{4x}\sqrt[3]{2x^2} + \sqrt[3]{4x} - 3\sqrt[3]{2x^2} - 3$ Use the FOIL method.

$= \sqrt[3]{8x^3} + \sqrt[3]{4x} - 3\sqrt[3]{2x^2} - 3$ The product of two cube roots is equal to the cube root of the product.

$= 2x + \sqrt[3]{4x} - 3\sqrt[3]{2x^2} - 3$ Simplify: $\sqrt[3]{8x^3} = 2x$.

Self Check
Multiply:

$(\sqrt[3]{3x} + 1)(\sqrt[3]{9x^2} - 2)$

Answer:

$3x - 2\sqrt[3]{3x} + \sqrt[3]{9x^2} - 2$ ∎

Dividing radical expressions

To divide radical expressions, we use the division property of radicals. For example, to divide $\sqrt{108}$ by $\sqrt{36}$, we proceed as follows:

$$\frac{\sqrt{108}}{\sqrt{36}} = \sqrt{\frac{108}{36}}$$ The quotient of two square roots is the square root of the quotient.

$$= \sqrt{3}$$ Do the division within the radical: $108 \div 36 = 3$.

EXAMPLE 8 *Dividing radical expressions.* Divide: $\frac{\sqrt{22a^2}}{\sqrt{99a^4}}$ $(a > 0)$.

Solution

$$\frac{\sqrt{22a^2}}{\sqrt{99a^4}} = \sqrt{\frac{22a^2}{99a^4}}$$

$$= \sqrt{\frac{2}{9a^2}}$$ Simplify the radicand: $\frac{22a^2}{99a^4} = \frac{\overset{1}{\cancel{11}} \cdot 2 \cdot \overset{1}{\cancel{a^2}}}{\underset{1}{\cancel{11}} \cdot 9 \cdot \underset{1}{\cancel{a^2}} \cdot a^2} = \frac{2}{9a^2}$.

$$= \frac{\sqrt{2}}{\sqrt{9a^2}}$$ The square root of a quotient is equal to the quotient of the square roots.

$$= \frac{\sqrt{2}}{3a}$$ Simplify: $\sqrt{9a^2} = 3a$.

Self Check
Divide:

$$\frac{\sqrt{30y^9}}{\sqrt{160y^5}}$$ $(y > 0)$

Answer: $\frac{y^2\sqrt{3}}{4}$ ∎

Rationalizing denominators

The length of a diagonal of one of the square adobe tiles shown in Figure 8-17 is 1 foot. Using the Pythagorean theorem, it can be shown that the length of a side of a tile is $\frac{1}{\sqrt{2}}$ feet. Because the expression $\frac{1}{\sqrt{2}}$ contains a radical in its denominator, it is not in simplified radical form. Since it is often easier to work with a radical expression if the denominator does not contain a radical, we now consider a process in which we change the denominator from a radical that represents an irrational number to a rational number. The process is called **rationalizing the denominator.**

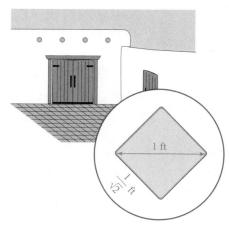

FIGURE 8-17

To rationalize the denominator of $\frac{1}{\sqrt{2}}$, we multiply both the numerator and the denominator by $\sqrt{2}$. Because the expression is multiplied by $\frac{\sqrt{2}}{\sqrt{2}}$, which is 1, the value of $\frac{1}{\sqrt{2}}$ is not changed—only its form.

$$\frac{1}{\sqrt{2}} = \frac{1\sqrt{2}}{\sqrt{2}\sqrt{2}} \qquad \text{Multiply both numerator and denominator by } \sqrt{2}.$$

$$= \frac{\sqrt{2}}{2} \qquad \text{In the numerator, } 1\sqrt{2} = \sqrt{2}. \text{ In the denominator,}$$
$$\sqrt{2}\sqrt{2} = \left(\sqrt{2}\right)^2 = 2. \text{ The denominator is now a rational number.}$$

The length of a side of a patio tile is $\frac{1}{\sqrt{2}} = \frac{\sqrt{2}}{2}$ feet.

This example suggests the following procedure for rationalizing square root denominators.

Rationalizing square root denominators	Multiply the numerator and the denominator by the smallest factor that gives a perfect square radicand in the denominator.

EXAMPLE 9   *Rationalizing the denominator.*   Rationalize each

denominator: **a.** $\sqrt{\dfrac{5}{3}}$ and   **b.** $\dfrac{2}{\sqrt[3]{3}}$.

Self Check
Rationalize each denominator:

a. $\sqrt{\dfrac{2}{7}}$

b. $\dfrac{5}{\sqrt[3]{5}}$

Solution

a. The expression $\sqrt{\frac{5}{3}}$ is not in simplified form, because the radicand is a fraction. To write it in simplified form, we use the division property of radicals. Then we use the fundamental property of fractions to rationalize the denominator by multiplying the numerator and the denominator by $\sqrt{3}$.

$$\sqrt{\frac{5}{3}} = \frac{\sqrt{5}}{\sqrt{3}} \qquad \text{The square root of a quotient is the quotient of the square roots. Note that the denominator is the irrational number } \sqrt{3}.$$

$$= \frac{\sqrt{5}\sqrt{3}}{\sqrt{3}\sqrt{3}} \qquad \text{Multiply the numerator and the denominator by } \sqrt{3}.$$

$$= \frac{\sqrt{15}}{3} \qquad \text{In the numerator, do the multiplication. Simplify in the denominator: } \sqrt{3}\sqrt{3} = \left(\sqrt{3}\right)^2 = 3.$$

b. The denominator contains a cube root. We multiply by the smallest factor that gives an integer cube radicand in the denominator. Since $\sqrt[3]{3}\sqrt[3]{9} = \sqrt[3]{27}$ and 27 is a perfect integer cube, we multiply the numerator and denominator by $\sqrt[3]{9}$ and simplify.

$$\frac{2}{\sqrt[3]{3}} = \frac{2\sqrt[3]{9}}{\sqrt[3]{3}\sqrt[3]{9}}$$

$$= \frac{2\sqrt[3]{9}}{\sqrt[3]{27}} \qquad \text{Multiply: } \sqrt[3]{3}\sqrt[3]{9} = \sqrt[3]{27}.$$

$$= \frac{2\sqrt[3]{9}}{3} \qquad \text{Simplify: } \sqrt[3]{27} = 3. \text{ The denominator is now a rational number.}$$

Answers: a. $\dfrac{\sqrt{14}}{7}$,

b. $\sqrt[3]{25}$ ∎

EXAMPLE 10 *Rationalizing denominators.* Rationalize the denominator and simplify: $\dfrac{5\sqrt{y}}{\sqrt{20x}}$ $(x > 0)$.

Self Check

Rationalize the denominator and simplify:

$\dfrac{6\sqrt{z}}{\sqrt{50y}}$ $(y > 0)$

Solution

To rationalize the denominator, we don't need to multiply the numerator and denominator by $\sqrt{20x}$. To keep the numbers small, we can multiply by $\sqrt{5x}$, because $5x \cdot 20x = 100x^2$, which is a perfect square.

$$\frac{5\sqrt{y}}{\sqrt{20x}} = \frac{5\sqrt{y}\sqrt{5x}}{\sqrt{20x}\sqrt{5x}} \qquad \text{Multiply the numerator and denominator by } \sqrt{5x}.$$

$$= \frac{5\sqrt{5xy}}{\sqrt{100x^2}} \qquad \text{Multiply: } \sqrt{y}\sqrt{5x} = \sqrt{5xy} \text{ and } \sqrt{20x}\sqrt{5x} = \sqrt{100x^2}.$$

$$= \frac{5\sqrt{5xy}}{10x} \qquad \text{Simplify: } \sqrt{100x^2} = 10x.$$

$$= \frac{\overset{1}{\cancel{5}}\sqrt{5xy}}{\underset{1}{\cancel{5}} \cdot 2x} \qquad \text{Factor } 10x \text{ and then divide out a common factor of 5.}$$

$$= \frac{\sqrt{5xy}}{2x} \qquad \text{Simplify.}$$

Answer: $\dfrac{3\sqrt{2yz}}{5y}$ ∎

At times, we will encounter fractions such as $\dfrac{2}{\sqrt{3}-1}$, whose denominator has two terms. Note that $\sqrt{3}-1$ is an irrational number. Because $\sqrt{3}-1$ has two terms, multiplying it by $\sqrt{3}$ will not make it a rational number. The key to rationalizing this denominator is to multiply the numerator and denominator by $\sqrt{3}+1$, because the product $(\sqrt{3}+1)(\sqrt{3}-1)$ has no radicals. Radical expressions such as $\sqrt{3}+1$ and $\sqrt{3}-1$ are called **conjugates** of each other.

EXAMPLE 11 *Multiplying by the conjugate.* Rationalize the denominator and simplify: $\dfrac{2}{\sqrt{3}-1}$.

Self Check

Rationalize the denominator and simplify:

$\dfrac{3}{\sqrt{2}+1}$

Solution

We rationalize the denominator by multiplying the numerator and denominator by the conjugate of the denominator.

$$\frac{2}{\sqrt{3}-1} = \frac{2(\sqrt{3}+1)}{(\sqrt{3}-1)(\sqrt{3}+1)} \qquad \begin{array}{l}\text{Multiply the numerator and denominator by the}\\\text{conjugate of the denominator, which is } \sqrt{3}+1.\end{array}$$

$$= \frac{2(\sqrt{3}+1)}{3-1} \qquad \begin{array}{l}\text{Use a special product formula:}\\(\sqrt{3}-1)(\sqrt{3}+1) = 3 - 1.\end{array}$$

$$= \frac{2(\sqrt{3}+1)}{2} \qquad \begin{array}{l}\text{Subtract. The denominator is now a rational}\\\text{number.}\end{array}$$

$$= \sqrt{3}+1 \qquad \text{Divide out the common factor of 2.}$$

Answer: $3(\sqrt{2}-1)$ ∎

EXAMPLE 12 *Multiplying by the conjugate.* Rationalize the denominator and simplify: $\dfrac{\sqrt{x}+1}{\sqrt{x}-1}$ ($x>0$ and $x \neq 1$).

Self Check
Rationalize the denominator and simplify:

$$\dfrac{\sqrt{x}-1}{\sqrt{x}+1}$$

Solution
We multiply the numerator and denominator by the conjugate of the denominator, which is $\sqrt{x}+1$.

$$\dfrac{\sqrt{x}+1}{\sqrt{x}-1} = \dfrac{\left(\sqrt{x}+1\right)\left(\sqrt{x}+1\right)}{\left(\sqrt{x}-1\right)\left(\sqrt{x}+1\right)}$$

Multiply the numerator and denominator by $\sqrt{x}+1$.

$$= \dfrac{\sqrt{x}\sqrt{x}+\sqrt{x}(1)+1\left(\sqrt{x}\right)+1}{\sqrt{x}\sqrt{x}+\sqrt{x}(1)-1\left(\sqrt{x}\right)-1}$$

Do the multiplications.

$$= \dfrac{x+2\sqrt{x}+1}{x-1}$$

Simplify: $\sqrt{x}\sqrt{x}=\left(\sqrt{x}\right)^2=x$.
Combine like radicals.

Answer: $\dfrac{x-2\sqrt{x}+1}{x-1}$ ■

STUDY SET Section 8.5 ◄www

VOCABULARY *Fill in the blanks.*

1. The method of changing a radical denominator of a fraction into a rational number is called ___rationalizing___ the denominator.

2. The ___numerator___ of the fraction $\frac{4}{\sqrt{3}}$ is 4 and the ___denominator___ is $\sqrt{3}$.

3. $3+\sqrt{2}$ is the ___conjugate___ of $3-\sqrt{2}$.

4. Radical expressions with the same ___index___ can be multiplied.

5. In the radical expression $3\sqrt{7}$, the number 3 is the ___coefficient___ of the radical.

6. Nonterminating, nonrepeating decimals such as $\sqrt{2}=1.414213562\ldots$ and $\sqrt{3}=1.732050808\ldots$ are ___irrational___ numbers.

CONCEPTS *In Exercises 7–12, fill in the blanks.*

7. To change $\sqrt{11}$ into a perfect integer square, we multiply it by $\sqrt{11}$

8. To change $\sqrt[3]{11}$ into a perfect integer cube, we multiply it by $\sqrt[3]{121}$.

9. To rationalize the denominator of
$$\dfrac{x}{\sqrt{7}}$$
we multiply the numerator and denominator by $\sqrt{7}$.

10. To rationalize the denominator of
$$\dfrac{x}{\sqrt{x}+1}$$
we multiply the numerator and denominator by $\sqrt{x}-1$.

11. Explain why each expression is not in simplified radical form.

   a. $\sqrt{\dfrac{3}{4}}$ The radicand is a fraction.   b. $\dfrac{1}{\sqrt{10}}$ There is a radical in the denominator.

12. To multiply $2\sqrt{x}$ and $6\sqrt{x}$, we first multiply the ___coefficients___, then multiply the ___radicals___, and simplify the result.

13. Which fractions have a rational denominator and which have an irrational denominator?
$$\dfrac{\sqrt{5}}{3}, \quad \dfrac{2}{\sqrt{6}}, \quad -\dfrac{\sqrt{2}}{8}, \quad \dfrac{1+\sqrt{3}}{4}, \quad \dfrac{9}{7-\sqrt{10}}$$
rational: $\frac{\sqrt{5}}{3}, -\frac{\sqrt{2}}{8}, \frac{1+\sqrt{3}}{4}$; irrational: $\frac{2}{\sqrt{6}}, \frac{9}{7-\sqrt{10}}$

14. To multiply $\left(\sqrt{3}+\sqrt{2}\right)\left(\sqrt{7}+\sqrt{5}\right)$, we use the FOIL method. What are the
   a. First terms? $\sqrt{3}, \sqrt{7}$
   b. Outer terms? $\sqrt{3}, \sqrt{5}$
   c. Inner terms? $\sqrt{2}, \sqrt{7}$
   d. Last terms? $\sqrt{2}, \sqrt{5}$

Do each operation if possible.

15. a. $\sqrt{2}+\sqrt{3}$ not possible
   b. $\sqrt{2}\cdot\sqrt{3}$ $\sqrt{6}$
   c. $\sqrt{2}-\sqrt{3}$ not possible
   d. $\dfrac{\sqrt{2}}{\sqrt{3}}$ $\dfrac{\sqrt{6}}{3}$
   e. $\sqrt{2}+3\sqrt{2}$ $4\sqrt{2}$
   f. $\sqrt{2}\cdot3\sqrt{2}$ 6
   g. $\sqrt{2}-3\sqrt{2}$ $-2\sqrt{2}$
   h. $\dfrac{\sqrt{2}}{3\sqrt{2}}$ $\frac{1}{3}$

16. Find each special product.

    a. $\left(\sqrt{6} + \sqrt{3}\right)\left(\sqrt{6} - \sqrt{3}\right)$ 3

    b. $\left(\sqrt{a} + \sqrt{7}\right)\left(\sqrt{a} - \sqrt{7}\right)$ $a - 7$

NOTATION *Complete each solution.*

17. $\left(\sqrt{x} + \sqrt{2}\right)\left(\sqrt{x} - 3\sqrt{2}\right)$

$$= \sqrt{x}\,\sqrt{x} - \sqrt{x}\left(3\sqrt{2}\right) + \sqrt{2}\,\sqrt{x} - \sqrt{2}\left(3\sqrt{2}\right)$$

$$= x - 3\,\sqrt{2x} + \sqrt{2x} - 3\sqrt{2}\sqrt{2}$$

$$= x - 2\sqrt{2x} - 3(2)$$

$$= x - 2\sqrt{2x} - 6$$

18. $\dfrac{x}{\sqrt{x} - 2} = \dfrac{x\left(\sqrt{x} + 2\right)}{\left(\sqrt{x} - 2\right)\left(\sqrt{x} + 2\right)}$

$$= \dfrac{x\left(\sqrt{x} + 2\right)}{\left(\sqrt{x}\right)^2 - 2^2}$$

$$= \dfrac{x\left(\sqrt{x} + 2\right)}{x - 4}$$

PRACTICE *Do each multiplication. All variables represent positive numbers.*

19. $\left(\sqrt{5}\right)^2$ 5   **20.** $\left(\sqrt{11}\right)^2$ 11

21. $\left(3\sqrt{6}\right)^2$ 54   **22.** $\left(-7\sqrt{2}\right)^2$ 98

23. $\sqrt{2}\sqrt{8}$ 4   **24.** $\sqrt{27}\sqrt{3}$ 9

25. $\sqrt{7}\sqrt{3}$ $\sqrt{21}$ **26.** $\sqrt{2}\sqrt{11}$ $\sqrt{22}$

27. $\sqrt{8}\sqrt{7}$ $2\sqrt{14}$ **28.** $\sqrt{6}\sqrt{8}$ $4\sqrt{3}$

29. $3\sqrt{2}\sqrt{x}$ $3\sqrt{2x}$ **30.** $4\sqrt{3x}\sqrt{5y}$ $4\sqrt{15xy}$

31. $\sqrt{x^3}\sqrt{x^5}$ x^4 **32.** $\sqrt{a^7}\sqrt{a^3}$ a^5

33. $\left(-5\sqrt{6}\right)\left(4\sqrt{3}\right)$ **34.** $\left(6\sqrt{3}\right)\left(-7\sqrt{2}\right)$
     $-60\sqrt{2}$ $-42\sqrt{6}$

35. $\left(4\sqrt{x}\right)\left(-2\sqrt{x}\right)$ $-8x$ **36.** $\left(3\sqrt{y}\right)\left(15\sqrt{y}\right)$ $45y$

37. $\sqrt{8x}\sqrt{2x^3}$ $4x^2$ **38.** $\sqrt{27y}\sqrt{3y^3}$ $9y^2$

39. $\sqrt{2}\left(\sqrt{2} + 1\right)$ $2 + \sqrt{2}$

40. $\sqrt{5}\left(\sqrt{5} + 2\right)$ $5 + 2\sqrt{5}$

41. $3\sqrt{3}\left(\sqrt{27} - 1\right)$ $27 - 3\sqrt{3}$

42. $2\sqrt{2}\left(\sqrt{8} - 1\right)$ $8 - 2\sqrt{2}$

43. $\sqrt{3}\left(\sqrt{6} + 1\right)$ $3\sqrt{2} + \sqrt{3}$

44. $\sqrt{2}\left(\sqrt{6} - 2\right)$ $2\sqrt{3} - 2\sqrt{2}$

45. $\sqrt{x}\left(\sqrt{3x} - 2\right)$ $x\sqrt{3} - 2\sqrt{x}$

46. $\sqrt{y}\left(\sqrt{y} + 5\right)$ $y + 5\sqrt{y}$

47. $2\sqrt{x}\left(\sqrt{9x} + 3\right)$ $6x + 6\sqrt{x}$

48. $3\sqrt{z}\left(\sqrt{4z} - \sqrt{z}\right)$ $3z$

49. $\left(\sqrt{2} + 1\right)\left(\sqrt{2} - 1\right)$ 1

50. $\left(\sqrt{3} - 1\right)\left(\sqrt{3} + 1\right)$ 2

51. $\left(2\sqrt{7} - x\right)\left(3\sqrt{2} + x\right)$ $6\sqrt{14} + 2x\sqrt{7} - 3x\sqrt{2} - x^2$

52. $\left(4\sqrt{2} - \sqrt{x}\right)\left(\sqrt{x} + 2\sqrt{3}\right)$
     $4\sqrt{2x} + 8\sqrt{6} - x - 2\sqrt{3x}$

53. $\left(\sqrt{6} + 1\right)^2$ $7 + 2\sqrt{6}$

54. $\left(3 - \sqrt{3}\right)^2$ $12 - 6\sqrt{3}$

55. $\left(\sqrt{2x} + 3\right)\left(\sqrt{8x} - 6\right)$ $4x - 18$

56. $\left(\sqrt{5y} - 3\right)\left(\sqrt{20y} + 6\right)$ $10y - 18$

57. $\left(-\sqrt[3]{9}\right)^3$ -9 **58.** $\left(\sqrt[3]{3}\right)^3$ 3

59. $\left(2\sqrt[3]{4}\right)\left(3\sqrt[3]{3}\right)$ **60.** $\left(-3\sqrt[3]{3}\right)\left(\sqrt[3]{5}\right)$
     $6\sqrt[3]{12}$ $-3\sqrt[3]{15}$

61. $\sqrt[3]{7}\left(\sqrt[3]{49} - 2\right)$ $7 - 2\sqrt[3]{7}$

62. $\sqrt[3]{5}\left(\sqrt[3]{25} + 3\right)$ $5 + 3\sqrt[3]{5}$

63. $\left(\sqrt[3]{2} + 1\right)\left(\sqrt[3]{2} + 3\right)$ $\sqrt[3]{4} + 4\sqrt[3]{2} + 3$

64. $\left(\sqrt[3]{5} - 2\right)\left(\sqrt[3]{5} - 1\right)$ $\sqrt[3]{25} - 3\sqrt[3]{5} + 2$

Simplify each expression. Assume that all variables represent positive numbers.

65. $\dfrac{\sqrt{12x^3}}{\sqrt{27x}}$ $\dfrac{2x}{3}$ **66.** $\dfrac{\sqrt{32}}{\sqrt{98x^2}}$ $\dfrac{4}{7x}$

67. $\dfrac{\sqrt{18x}}{\sqrt{25x}}$ $\dfrac{3\sqrt{2}}{5}$ **68.** $\dfrac{\sqrt{27y}}{\sqrt{75y}}$ $\dfrac{3}{5}$

69. $\dfrac{\sqrt{196x}}{\sqrt{49x^3}}$ $\dfrac{2}{x}$ **70.** $\dfrac{\sqrt{50}}{\sqrt{98z^2}}$ $\dfrac{5}{7z}$

71. $\dfrac{\sqrt[3]{16x^6}}{\sqrt[3]{54x^3}}$ $\dfrac{2x}{3}$ **72.** $\dfrac{\sqrt[3]{128a^6}}{\sqrt[3]{16a^3}}$ $2a$

Rationalize each denominator and simplify. All variables represent positive numbers.

73. $\dfrac{1}{\sqrt{3}}$ $\dfrac{\sqrt{3}}{3}$ **74.** $\dfrac{1}{\sqrt{5}}$ $\dfrac{\sqrt{5}}{5}$

75. $\sqrt{\dfrac{13}{7}}$ $\dfrac{\sqrt{91}}{7}$ **76.** $\sqrt{\dfrac{3}{11}}$ $\dfrac{\sqrt{33}}{11}$

77. $\dfrac{9}{\sqrt{27}}$ $\sqrt{3}$ **78.** $\dfrac{4}{\sqrt{20}}$ $\dfrac{2\sqrt{5}}{5}$

79. $\dfrac{3}{\sqrt{32}}$ $\dfrac{3\sqrt{2}}{8}$ **80.** $\dfrac{5}{\sqrt{18}}$ $\dfrac{5\sqrt{2}}{6}$

81. $\sqrt{\dfrac{12}{5}}$ $\dfrac{2\sqrt{15}}{5}$ **82.** $\sqrt{\dfrac{24}{7}}$ $\dfrac{2\sqrt{42}}{7}$

83. $\dfrac{10}{\sqrt{x}}$ $\dfrac{10\sqrt{x}}{x}$ **84.** $\dfrac{12}{\sqrt{y}}$ $\dfrac{12\sqrt{y}}{y}$

85. $\dfrac{\sqrt{9y}}{\sqrt{2x}}$ $\dfrac{3\sqrt{2xy}}{2x}$ **86.** $\dfrac{\sqrt{4t}}{\sqrt{3z}}$ $\dfrac{2\sqrt{3tz}}{3z}$

87. $\dfrac{3}{\sqrt{3} - 1}$ $\dfrac{3\sqrt{3} + 3}{2}$ **88.** $\dfrac{3}{\sqrt{5} - 2}$ $3\sqrt{5} + 6$

89. $\dfrac{3}{\sqrt{7} + 2}$ $\sqrt{7} - 2$ **90.** $\dfrac{5}{\sqrt{8} + 3}$ $15 - 10\sqrt{2}$

91. $\dfrac{12}{3 - \sqrt{3}}$ $6 + 2\sqrt{3}$ **92.** $\dfrac{10}{5 - \sqrt{5}}$ $\dfrac{5 + \sqrt{5}}{2}$

93. $\dfrac{-\sqrt{3}}{\sqrt{3}+1}$ $\dfrac{\sqrt{3}-3}{2}$ **94.** $\dfrac{-\sqrt{2}}{\sqrt{2}-1}$ $-2-\sqrt{2}$

95. $\dfrac{5}{\sqrt{3}+\sqrt{2}}$ $5\sqrt{3}-5\sqrt{2}$

96. $\dfrac{3}{\sqrt{3}-\sqrt{2}}$ $3\sqrt{3}+3\sqrt{2}$

97. $\dfrac{\sqrt{x}+2}{\sqrt{x}-2}$ $\dfrac{x+4\sqrt{x}+4}{x-4}$

98. $\dfrac{\sqrt{x}-3}{\sqrt{x}+3}$ $\dfrac{x-6\sqrt{x}+9}{x-9}$

99. $\dfrac{5}{\sqrt[3]{5}}$ $\sqrt[3]{25}$ **100.** $\dfrac{7}{\sqrt[3]{7}}$ $\sqrt[3]{49}$

101. $\dfrac{4}{\sqrt[3]{4}}$ $2\sqrt[3]{2}$ **102.** $\dfrac{7}{\sqrt[3]{10}}$ $\dfrac{7\sqrt[3]{100}}{10}$

103. $\dfrac{\sqrt[3]{5}}{\sqrt[3]{2}}$ $\dfrac{\sqrt[3]{20}}{2}$ **104.** $\dfrac{\sqrt[3]{2}}{\sqrt[3]{5}}$ $\dfrac{\sqrt[3]{50}}{5}$

APPLICATIONS

105. ROTARY LAWNMOWER   See Illustration 1, which shows the blade of a rotary lawnmower. Use the formula for the area of a circle, $A = \pi r^2$, to find the area of lawn covered by one rotation of the blade. Leave π in your answer. 108π in.^{2}

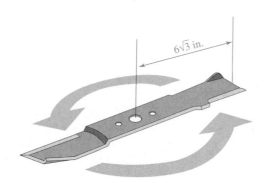

ILLUSTRATION 1

106. AWARDS PLATFORMS   Find the total number of cubic feet of concrete needed to construct the Olympic Games awards platforms shown in Illustration 2. $24\sqrt{2}$ ft^3

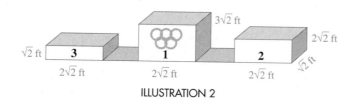

ILLUSTRATION 2

107. AIR HOCKEY GAME   Find the area of the playing surface of the air hockey game in Illustration 3. $1{,}800\sqrt{2}$ in.^{2}

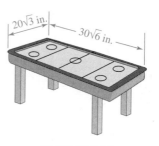

ILLUSTRATION 3

108. PROJECTOR SCREEN   To find the length l of a rectangle, we can use the formula

$$l = \dfrac{A}{w}$$

where A is the area of the rectangle and w is its width. Find the length of the screen shown in Illustration 4 if its area is 54 square feet. $\dfrac{9\sqrt{3}}{2}$ ft

ILLUSTRATION 4

109. COSTUME DESIGN   The pattern for one panel of an 1870s English dress is printed on the 1 in. × 1 in. grid shown in Illustration 5. Find the number of square inches of fabric in the trapezoidal-shaped panel. (*Hint:* Use the Pythagorean theorem to determine the lengths of the sides.)   90 in.^{2}

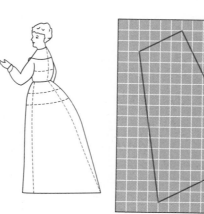

ILLUSTRATION 5

110. SET DESIGN   The director of a stage play requested bright downlighting over the portion of the set shown in Illustration 6. Find the area of the rectangle. (*Hint:* Use the Pythagorean theorem to determine the lengths of the sides.)   34 ft²

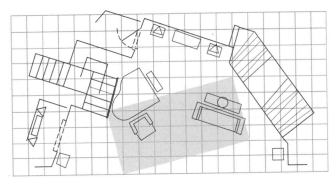

ILLUSTRATION 6

WRITING

111. When rationalizing the denominator of $\dfrac{5}{\sqrt{6}}$, why must we multiply both the numerator *and* denominator by $\sqrt{6}$?

112. A calculator is used to find decimal approximations for the expressions $\dfrac{2}{\sqrt{6}}$ and $\dfrac{\sqrt{6}}{3}$. In each case, the calculator display reads 0.816496581. Explain why the results are the same.

REVIEW

113. Is $x = -2$ a solution of $3x - 7 = 5x + 1$?   no

114. The graph of a line passes through the point (2, 0). Is this the *x*- or *y*-intercept?   *x*-intercept

115. To evaluate the expression $2 - (-3 + 4)^2$, which operation should be performed first?   addition

116. The graph of a straight line rises from left to right. Is the slope of the line positive or negative?   positive

117. Find $(x - 4)(x + 4)$. $x^2 - 16$

118. How far will a car traveling 55 mph go in 3.5 hours?   192.5 mi

---

8.6 *Solving Radical Equations; the Distance Formula*

In this section, you will learn about

- The squaring property of equality • Checking solutions
- Solving equations containing one square root
- Solving equations containing two square roots
- Solving equations containing cube roots • The distance formula

INTRODUCTION. Many situations can be modeled mathematically by equations that contain radicals. In this section, we will develop techniques to solve such equations. Then we will consider a special formula called the *distance formula*.

The squaring property of equality

The equation $\sqrt{x} = 6$ is called a **radical equation,** because it contains a radical expression with a variable radicand. To solve this equation, we isolate x by undoing the operation performed on it. Recall that $\sqrt{x}$ represents the number that, when squared, gives x. Therefore, if we *square* $\sqrt{x}$, we will obtain x.

$$\left(\sqrt{x}\right)^2 = x$$

Using this observation, we can eliminate the radical on the left-hand side of $\sqrt{x} = 6$ by squaring that side. Intuition tells us that we should also square the right-hand side. This is a valid step, because if two numbers are equal, their squares are equal.

Squaring property of equality	If a and b represent real numbers, with $a = b$, then $a^2 = b^2$.

We can now solve $\sqrt{x} = 6$ by applying the squaring property of equality.

$$\sqrt{x} = 6$$
$$\left(\sqrt{x}\right)^2 = (6)^2 \quad \text{Square both sides of the equation to eliminate the radical.}$$
$$x = 36 \quad \text{Simplify each side: } \left(\sqrt{x}\right)^2 = x \text{ and } (6)^2 = 36.$$

Checking this result, we have

$$\sqrt{x} = 6$$
$$\sqrt{36} \stackrel{?}{=} 6 \quad \text{Substitute 36 for } x.$$
$$6 = 6 \quad \text{Simplify the left-hand side: } \sqrt{36} = 6.$$

We obtain a true statement, so $x = 36$ is a solution.

Checking solutions

If we square both sides of an equation, the resulting equation may or may not have the same solutions as the original one. For example, if we square both sides of the equation

(1) $x = 2$

with the solution 2, we obtain $(x)^2 = 2^2$, which simplifies to

(2) $x^2 = 4$

with solutions 2 and -2, since $2^2 = 4$ and $(-2)^2 = 4$.

    Equations 1 and 2 are not equivalent, because they have a different set of solutions. The solution -2 of Equation 2 does not satisfy Equation 1. Because squaring both sides of an equation can produce an equation with solutions that don't satisfy the original one, we must always check each potential solution in the original equation.

Solving equations containing one square root

To solve an equation containing square root radicals, we follow these steps.

Solving radical equations	1. Whenever possible, isolate a single radical expression on one side of the equation.
	2. Square both sides of the equation and solve the resulting equation.
	3. Check the solution in the original equation. This step is required.

EXAMPLE 1   *Solving radical equations.*   Solve $\sqrt{x + 2} = 3$.

Solution

To solve the equation $\sqrt{x + 2} = 3$, we note that the radical is already isolated on one side. We proceed to step 2 and square both sides to eliminate the radical. Since this might produce an equation with more solutions than the original one, we must check each solution.

$$\sqrt{x + 2} = 3$$
$$\left(\sqrt{x + 2}\right)^2 = (3)^2 \quad \text{Square both sides.}$$
$$x + 2 = 9 \quad \text{Simplify each side: } \left(\sqrt{x + 2}\right)^2 = x + 2 \text{ and } 3^2 = 9.$$
$$x = 7 \quad \text{Subtract 2 from both sides.}$$

Self Check

Solve $\sqrt{x - 4} = 9$.

We check by substituting 7 for x in the original equation.

$$\sqrt{x + 2} = 3$$
$$\sqrt{7 + 2} \stackrel{?}{=} 3 \quad \text{Substitute 7 for } x.$$
$$\sqrt{9} \stackrel{?}{=} 3 \quad \text{Do the addition within the radical symbol.}$$
$$3 = 3$$

The answer $x = 7$ checks. It is a solution.

Answer: 85 ■

EXAMPLE 2 *A radical equation with no solution.* Solve $\sqrt{x + 1} + 5 = 3$.

Self Check
Solve $\sqrt{x - 2} + 5 = 2$.

Solution

We isolate the radical on one side and proceed as follows:

$$\sqrt{x + 1} + 5 = 3$$
$$\sqrt{x + 1} = -2 \quad \text{Subtract 5 from both sides.}$$
$$\left(\sqrt{x + 1}\right)^2 = (-2)^2 \quad \text{Square both sides to eliminate the radical.}$$
$$x + 1 = 4 \quad \text{Simplify: } \left(\sqrt{x + 1}\right)^2 = x + 1 \text{ and } (-2)^2 = 4.$$
$$x = 3 \quad \text{Subtract 1 from both sides.}$$

We check by substituting 3 for x in the original equation.

$$\sqrt{x + 1} + 5 = 3$$
$$\sqrt{3 + 1} + 5 \stackrel{?}{=} 3 \quad \text{Substitute 3 for } x.$$
$$\sqrt{4} + 5 \stackrel{?}{=} 3 \quad \text{Do the addition within the radical symbol.}$$
$$2 + 5 \stackrel{?}{=} 3$$
$$7 \neq 3$$

Since $7 \neq 3$, 3 is not a solution. In fact, the equation has no solution. This result was obvious in Step 2 of the solution. There is no real number x that could make the non-negative number $\sqrt{x + 1}$ equal to -2.

Answer: no solution ■

Example 2 shows that squaring both sides of an equation can lead to false solutions, called **extraneous solutions.** These potential solutions do not satisfy the original equation and must be discarded.

EXAMPLE 3 *Height of a bridge.* The distance d (in feet) that an object will fall in t seconds is given by the formula

$$t = \sqrt{\frac{d}{16}}$$

To find the height of the bridge shown in Figure 8-18, a man drops a stone into the water. If it takes the stone 3 seconds to hit the water, how high is the bridge?

Self Check
If it takes 4 seconds for the stone in Example 3 to hit the water, how high is the bridge?

FIGURE 8-18

Solution
We substitute 3 for t in the formula and solve for d.

$$t = \sqrt{\frac{d}{16}}$$

$$3 = \sqrt{\frac{d}{16}} \qquad \text{Substitute 3 for } t.$$

$$(3)^2 = \left(\sqrt{\frac{d}{16}}\right)^2 \qquad \text{Square both sides to eliminate the radical.}$$

$$9 = \frac{d}{16} \qquad \text{Simplify: } 3^2 = 9 \text{ and } \left(\sqrt{\frac{d}{16}}\right)^2 = \frac{d}{16}.$$

$$144 = d \qquad \text{Multiply both sides by 16.}$$

The bridge is 144 feet above the water. Check this result in the original equation.

Answer: 256 feet

EXAMPLE 4 *Solving radical equations.* Solve
$a + 2 = \sqrt{a^2 + 3a + 3}$.

Self Check
Solve:
$b + 4 = \sqrt{b^2 + 6b + 12}$

Solution
The radical is isolated on the right-hand side, so we proceed by squaring both sides to eliminate it.

$$a + 2 = \sqrt{a^2 + 3a + 3}$$

$$(a + 2)^2 = \left(\sqrt{a^2 + 3a + 3}\right)^2 \qquad \text{Square both sides.}$$

$$a^2 + 4a + 4 = a^2 + 3a + 3 \qquad \begin{array}{l}\text{Use a special product formula:} \\ (a + 2)^2 = a^2 + 4a + 4. \text{ Simplify:} \\ \left(\sqrt{a^2 + 3a + 3}\right)^2 = a^2 + 3a + 3.\end{array}$$

$$a^2 + 4a + 4 - a^2 = a^2 + 3a + 3 - a^2 \qquad \begin{array}{l}\text{To eliminate } a^2, \text{ subtract } a^2 \text{ from both} \\ \text{sides.}\end{array}$$

$$4a + 4 = 3a + 3 \qquad \text{Combine like terms: } a^2 - a^2 = 0.$$

$$a + 4 = 3 \qquad \text{Subtract } 3a \text{ from both sides.}$$

$$a = -1 \qquad \text{Subtract 4 from both sides.}$$

We check by substituting -1 for x in the original equation.

$$a + 2 = \sqrt{a^2 + 3a + 3}$$

$$-1 + 2 \overset{?}{=} \sqrt{(-1)^2 + 3(-1) + 3} \qquad \text{Substitute } -1 \text{ for } a.$$

$$1 \overset{?}{=} \sqrt{1 - 3 + 3} \qquad \begin{array}{l}\text{Within the radical symbol, first find the power,} \\ \text{then do the multiplication.}\end{array}$$

$$1 \overset{?}{=} \sqrt{1} \qquad \text{Simplify within the radical symbol.}$$

$$1 = 1$$

The solution checks.

Answer: -2

Solving equations containing two square roots

In the next example, the equation contains two square roots.

EXAMPLE 5 *Solving an equation containing two square roots.*
Solve $\sqrt{x + 12} = 3\sqrt{x + 4}$.

Self Check
Solve:
$$\sqrt{x - 4} = 2\sqrt{x - 16}$$

Solution

Note that each radical is isolated on one side of the equation. We begin by squaring both sides to eliminate them.

$$\sqrt{x + 12} = 3\sqrt{x + 4}$$

$$\left(\sqrt{x + 12}\right)^2 = \left(3\sqrt{x + 4}\right)^2 \quad \text{Square both sides.}$$

$$x + 12 = 9(x + 4) \qquad \left(\sqrt{x + 12}\right)^2 = x + 12.$$
$$\left(3\sqrt{x + 4}\right)^2 = 3^2\left(\sqrt{x + 4}\right)^2 = 9(x + 4).$$

$$x + 12 = 9x + 36 \qquad \text{Distribute the multiplication by 9.}$$

$$-8x = 24 \qquad \text{Subtract } 9x \text{ and 12 from both sides.}$$

$$x = -3 \qquad \text{Divide both sides by } -8.$$

We check the solution by substituting -3 for x in the original equation.

$$\sqrt{x + 12} = 3\sqrt{x + 4}$$

$$\sqrt{-3 + 12} \overset{?}{=} 3\sqrt{-3 + 4} \quad \text{Substitute } -3 \text{ for } x.$$

$$\sqrt{9} \overset{?}{=} 3\sqrt{1} \qquad \text{Simplify within the radical symbols.}$$

$$3 = 3$$

The solution checks.

Answer: 20 ◼

Solving equations containing cube roots

In the next example, we cube both sides of an equation to eliminate a cube root.

EXAMPLE 6 *Solving an equation containing a cube root.* Solve $\sqrt[3]{2x + 10} = 2$.

Self Check

Solve $\sqrt[3]{3x - 3} = 3$.

Solution

To undo the operation performed on $2x + 10$, we cube both sides and proceed as follows:

$$\sqrt[3]{2x + 10} = 2$$

$$\left(\sqrt[3]{2x + 10}\right)^3 = (2)^3 \quad \text{Cube both sides.}$$

$$2x + 10 = 8 \qquad \text{Simplify: } \left(\sqrt[3]{2x + 10}\right)^3 = 2x + 10 \text{ and } (2)^3 = 8.$$

$$2x = -2 \qquad \text{Subtract 10 from both sides.}$$

$$x = -1 \qquad \text{Divide both sides by 2.}$$

Check the result.

Answer: 10 ◼

The distance formula

We can use the Pythagorean theorem to derive a formula for finding the distance between two points $P(x_1, y_1)$ and $Q(x_2, y_2)$ on a rectangular coordinate system. The distance d between points P and Q is the length of the hypotenuse of the triangle in Figure 8-19. The two legs have lengths $x_2 - x_1$ and $y_2 - y_1$.

By the Pythagorean theorem, we have

$$d^2 = (x_2 - x_1)^2 + (y_2 - y_1)^2$$

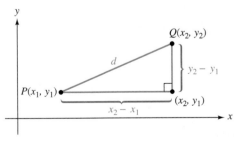

FIGURE 8-19

We can take the positive square root of both sides of this equation to get the **distance formula.**

$$d = \sqrt{(x_2 - x_1)^2 + (y_2 - y_1)^2}$$

The distance formula

> The distance d between points $P(x_1, y_1)$ and $Q(x_2, y_2)$ is given by
> $$d = \sqrt{(x_2 - x_1)^2 + (y_2 - y_1)^2}$$

EXAMPLE 7 ***Using the distance formula.*** Find the distance between points $P(1, 5)$ and $Q(4, 9)$. (See Figure 8-20.)

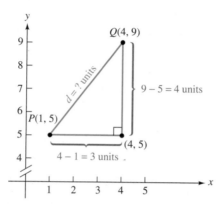

FIGURE 8-20

Solution

We use the distance formula and substitute 1 for x_1, 5 for y_1, 4 for x_2, and 9 for y_2. Then we evaluate the expression under the radical symbol.

$$\begin{aligned} d &= \sqrt{(x_2 - x_1)^2 + (y_2 - y_1)^2} \\ &= \sqrt{(4 - 1)^2 + (9 - 5)^2} && \text{Substitute.} \\ &= \sqrt{3^2 + 4^2} && \text{Do the subtractions within the parentheses first.} \\ &= \sqrt{9 + 16} && \text{Evaluate the powers.} \\ &= \sqrt{25} && \text{Do the addition.} \\ &= 5 && \text{Find the square root.} \end{aligned}$$

The distance between points P and Q is 5 units.

Self Check

Find the distance between $(-2, 1)$ and $(4, 9)$.

Answer: 10 ■

EXAMPLE 8 ***Finding the distance between two points.*** Plot the points $A(-4, 5)$ and $B(3, -1)$ on the graph in Figure 8-21 and find the distance between them.

FIGURE 8-21

Solution

We use the distance formula and substitute -4 for x_1, 5 for y_1, 3 for x_2, and -1 for y_2.

$$\begin{aligned} d &= \sqrt{(x_2 - x_1)^2 + (y_2 - y_1)^2} \\ &= \sqrt{[(3 - (-4)]^2 + (-1 - 5)^2} && \text{Substitute.} \\ &= \sqrt{7^2 + (-6)^2} && \text{Do the subtractions.} \\ &= \sqrt{49 + 36} && \text{Evaluate the powers.} \\ &= \sqrt{85} && \text{Do the addition.} \\ &\approx 9.219544457 && \text{Use a calculator.} \end{aligned}$$

The distance between points A and B is approximately 9.22 units.

Self Check

Plot the points $M(4, 3)$ and $N(-2, -3)$ on the graph in Figure 8-21 and find the distance between them.

Answer: about 8.49 units ■

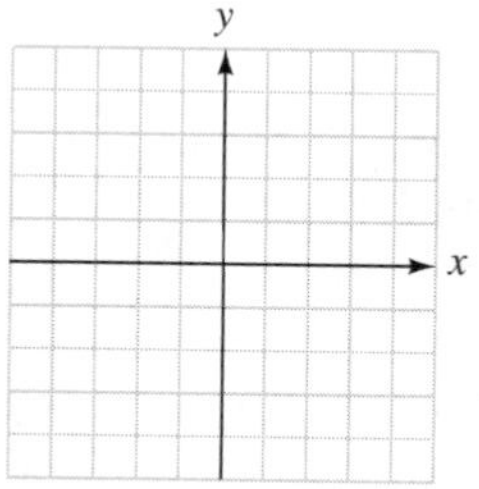

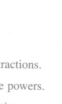

EXAMPLE 9   *Freeway design.*   In a large city, the streets run north and south, and the avenues run east and west. Streets and avenues are 750 feet apart. The city plans to construct a freeway from the intersection of 21st Street and 4th Avenue to the intersection of 111th Street and 60th Avenue. How long will it be?

Solution   We can represent the roads of the city using the coordinate system shown in Figure 8-22. Each unit on each axis represents 750 feet. We represent one end of the freeway at 21st Street and 4th Avenue by the point $(x_1, y_1) = (21, 4)$. The other end is $(x_2, y_2) = (111, 60)$.

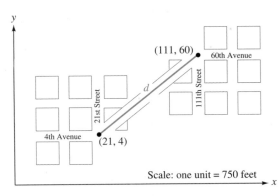

FIGURE 8-22

We can now use the distance formula to find the length of the freeway.

$$d = \sqrt{(x_2 - x_1)^2 + (y_2 - y_1)^2}$$
$$= \sqrt{(111 - 21)^2 + (60 - 4)^2} \quad \text{Substitute for } x_2, x_1, y_2, \text{ and } y_1.$$
$$= \sqrt{90^2 + 56^2} \quad \text{Do the subtractions.}$$
$$= \sqrt{8,100 + 3,136} \quad \text{Evaluate the powers.}$$
$$= \sqrt{11,236} \quad \text{Do the addition.}$$
$$= 106 \quad \text{Use a calculator to find the square root.}$$

Because each unit represents 750 feet, the length of the freeway will be $106 \cdot 750 = 79,500$ feet. Since there are 5,280 feet in 1 mile, we can divide 79,500 by 5,280 to convert 79,500 feet to 15.056818 miles. The freeway will be about 15 miles long. ■

STUDY SET   Section 8.6

VOCABULARY   *Fill in the blanks.*

1. A ____radical____ equation contains one or more radical expressions with a variable radicand.

2. "To ____isolate____ the radical expression" in $\sqrt{x} + 1 = 10$ means to get $\sqrt{x}$ all by itself on one side of the equation.

3. A false solution that occurs when you square both sides of an equation is called an ____extraneous____ solution.

4. The squaring property of equality states that if two numbers are equal, their ____squares____ are equal.

CONCEPTS   *In Exercises 5–6, fill in the blanks.*

5. The squaring property of equality states that
If $a = b$, then $a^2 = b^2$.

6. The distance formula states that
$$d = \sqrt{(x_2 - x_1)^2 + (y_2 - y_1)^2}$$

7. To isolate x, what step should be used to undo the operation performed on it? (Assume that x is a positive number.)
   a. $x^2 = 4$ Take the positive square root of both sides.
   b. $\sqrt{x} = 4$ Square both sides.

8. Simplify each expression.

a. $\left(\sqrt{x}\right)^2$ x **b.** $\left(\sqrt{x-1}\right)^2$ $x-1$

c. $\left(2\sqrt{x}\right)^2$ $4x$ **d.** $\left(2\sqrt{x-1}\right)^2$ $4x-4$

e. $\left(\sqrt{2x}\right)^2$ $2x$ **f.** $\left(\sqrt[3]{x}\right)^3$ x

In Exercises 9–12, an equation is incorrectly solved. Tell what is wrong with each solution.

9. $\sqrt{x-2}=3$

$\left(\sqrt{x-2}\right)^2=3$ On the second line, both sides of

$x-2=3$ the equation were not squared— only the left-hand side.

$x=5$

10. $2=\sqrt{x-9}$

$(2)^2=\left(\sqrt{x-9}\right)^2$ On the third line, 9 wasn't

$4=x-9$ added to *both* sides.

$-5=x$

$x=-5$

11. $\sqrt{a+2}-5=4$ On the second line,

$\left(\sqrt{a+2}-5\right)^2=4^2$ $\sqrt{a+2}$ wasn't isolated before squaring both sides.

$a+2-25=16$ Also, $\left(\sqrt{a+2}-5\right)^2\neq$

$a-23=16$ $a+2-25$.

$a=39$

12. $\sqrt[3]{x+1}=-2$

$\left(\sqrt[3]{x+1}\right)^2=(-2)^2$ On the second line, both sides should be cubed.

$x+1=4$

$x=3$

13. a. On the graph in Illustration 1, plot the points $A(-4,6)$, $B(4,0)$, $C(1,-4)$, and $D(-7,2)$.

b. Draw figure *ABCD*. What type of geometric figure is it?   rectangle

c. Find the length of each side of the figure.
AB: 10; *BC*: 5; *CD*: 10; *DA*: 5

d. Find the perimeter of the figure.   30 units

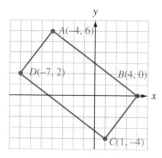

ILLUSTRATION 1

14. a. What type of geometric figure is figure *ABCD* shown in Illustration 2?   trapezoid

b. Give the coordinates of points *A*, *B*, *C*, and *D*.
$(-2,5)$, $(2,5)$, $(8,-3)$, $(-8,-3)$

c. Find the length of each side of the figure.
AB: 4; *BC*: 10; *CD*: 16; *DA*: 10

d. Find the area of the figure.   80 square units

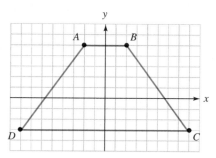

ILLUSTRATION 2

NOTATION   *Complete each solution to solve each equation.*

15. $\sqrt{x-3}=5$

$\left(\sqrt{x-3}\right)^2=5^2$

$x-3=25$

$x=28$

16. $\sqrt{2x-18}=\sqrt{x-1}$

$\left(\sqrt{2x-18}\right)^2=\left(\sqrt{x-1}\right)^2$

$2x-18=x-1$

$x-18=-1$

$x=17$

PRACTICE   *Solve each equation. Check all solutions. If an equation has no solutions, write "none."*

17. $\sqrt{x}=3$ 9   **18.** $\sqrt{x}=5$ 25

19. $\sqrt{2a}=4$ 8   **20.** $\sqrt{3a}=9$ 27

21. $\sqrt{r}+4=0$ none   **22.** $\sqrt{r}+1=0$ none

23. $-\sqrt{x}=-5$ 25   **24.** $-\sqrt{x}=-12$ 144

25. $10-\sqrt{s}=7$ 9   **26.** $-4=6-\sqrt{s}$ 100

27. $\sqrt{x+3}=2$ 1   **28.** $\sqrt{x-2}=3$ 11

29. $\sqrt{3-T}=-2$ none   **30.** $\sqrt{5-T}=10$ -95

31. $\sqrt{6+2x}=4$ 5   **32.** $\sqrt{7+2x}=-4$ none

33. $\sqrt{5x-5}-5=0$ 6   **34.** $\sqrt{6x+19}-7=0$ 5

35. $\sqrt{x+3}+5=12$ 46   **36.** $\sqrt{x-5}-3=4$ 54

37. $x-3=\sqrt{x^2-15}$ 4   **38.** $v-2=\sqrt{v^2-16}$ 5

39. $\sqrt{3t-9}=\sqrt{t+1}$ **40.** $\sqrt{a-3}=\sqrt{2a-8}$
5   5

41. $\sqrt{10-3x}=\sqrt{2x+20}$ -2

42. $\sqrt{1-2x}=\sqrt{x+10}$ -3

43. $\sqrt{3c-8}-\sqrt{c}=0$ 4

44. $\sqrt{2x}-\sqrt{x+8}=0$ 8

45. $x-1=\sqrt{x^2-4x+9}$ 4

46. $3d=\sqrt{9d^2-2d+8}$ 4

47. $\sqrt{4m^2 + 6m + 6} = -2m$ -1

48. $\sqrt{9t^2 + 4t + 20} = -3t$ -5

49. $\sqrt{3x + 3} = 3\sqrt{x - 1}$ 2

50. $2\sqrt{4x + 5} = 5\sqrt{x + 4}$ none

51. $2\sqrt{3x + 4} = \sqrt{5x + 9}$ -1

52. $\sqrt{3x + 6} = 2\sqrt{2x - 11}$ 10

53. $\sqrt[3]{x} = 7$ 343 **54.** $\sqrt[3]{x} = -9$ -729

55. $\sqrt[3]{x - 1} = 4$ 65 **56.** $\sqrt[3]{2x + 5} = 3$ 11

57. $\sqrt[3]{\frac{1}{2}x - 3} = 2$ 22 **58.** $\sqrt[3]{x + 4} = 1$ -3

59. $\sqrt[3]{7n - 1} + 1 = 4$ **60.** $\sqrt[3]{12m + 4} + 2 = 6$
4 5

Find the distance between points P and Q. If an answer is not exact, round to the nearest hundredth.

61. $P(3, -4)$ and $Q(0, 0)$ 5

62. $P(0, 0)$ and $Q(-6, 8)$ 10

63. $P(2, 4)$ and $Q(5, 9)$ 5.83

64. $P(5, 9)$ and $Q(9, 13)$ 5.66

65. $P(-2, -8)$ and $Q(3, 4)$ 13

66. $P(-5, -2)$ and $Q(7, 3)$ 13

67. $P(6, 8)$ and $Q(12, 16)$ 10

68. $P(10, 4)$ and $Q(2, -2)$ 10

▦ APPLICATIONS

69. NIAGARA FALLS   The distance s (in feet) that an object will fall in t seconds is given by the formula

$$t = \frac{\sqrt{s}}{4}$$

The time it took a stuntman to go over the Niagara Falls in a barrel was 3.25 seconds. Substitute 3.25 for t and solve the equation for s to find the height of the waterfall.   169 ft

70. WASHINGTON MONUMENT   Gabby Street, a professional baseball player of the 1920s, was known for once catching a ball dropped from the top of the Washington Monument in Washington, D.C. If the ball fell for slightly less than 6 seconds before it was caught, find the approximate height of the monument. (*Hint:* See Exercise 69.)   about 576 ft

71. FOUCAULT PENDULUM   The time t (in seconds) required for a pendulum of length L feet to swing through one back-and-forth cycle, called its period, is given by the formula

$$t = 1.11\sqrt{L}$$

The Foucault pendulum in Chicago's Museum of Science and Industry, shown in Illustration 3, is used to demonstrate the rotation of the earth. It completes one cycle in 8.91 seconds. To the nearest tenth of a foot, how long is the pendulum?   64.4 ft

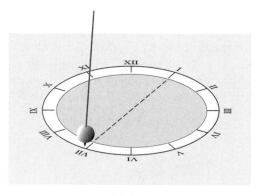

ILLUSTRATION 3

72. POWER USAGE   The current I (in amperes), the resistance R (in ohms), and the power P (in watts) are related by the formula

$$I = \sqrt{\frac{P}{R}}$$

Find the power (to the nearest watt) used by a space heater that draws 7 amps when the resistance is 10.2 ohms.   500 watts

73. ROAD SAFETY   The formula $s = k\sqrt{d}$ relates the speed s (in mph) of a car and the distance d of the skid when a driver hits the brakes. On wet pavement, $k = 3.24$. How far will a car skid if it is going 55 mph?   about 288 ft

74. ROAD SAFETY   How far will the car in Exercise 73 skid if it is traveling on dry pavement? On dry pavement, $k = 5.34$.   about 106 ft

75. SATELLITE ORBIT   The orbital speed s of an Earth satellite is related to its distance r from the Earth's center by the formula

$$\sqrt{r} = \frac{2.029 \times 10^7}{s}$$

If the satellite's orbital speed is 7×10^3 meters per second, find its altitude a (in meters) above the Earth's surface, as shown in Illustration 4.   about 2×10^6 m

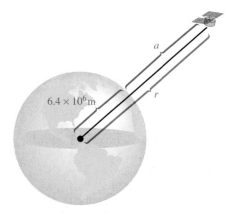

6.4×10^6 m

ILLUSTRATION 4

76. HIGHWAY DESIGN   A highway curve banked at 8° will accommodate traffic traveling at speed s (in mph) if the radius of the curve is r (feet), according to the equation $s = 1.45\sqrt{r}$. If highway engineers expect traffic to travel at 65 mph, to the nearest foot, what radius should they specify? (See Illustration 5.)
2,010 ft

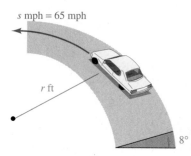

s mph = 65 mph

r ft

8°

ILLUSTRATION 5

77. GEOMETRY   The radius of a cone with volume V and height h is given by the formula

$$r = \sqrt{\frac{3V}{\pi h}}$$

Solve the equation for V. $V = \dfrac{\pi r^2 h}{3}$

78. WINDMILL   The power produced by a certain windmill is related to the speed of the wind by the formula

$$s = \sqrt[3]{\frac{P}{0.02}}$$

where P is the power (in watts) and s is the speed of the wind (in mph). How much power will the windmill produce if the wind is blowing at 30 mph?   540 watts

79. NAVIGATION   An oil tanker is to travel from Tunisia to Italy, as shown in Illustration 6. The captain wants to travel a course that is *always* the same distance from a point on the coast of Sardinia as it is from a point on the coast of Sicily (both denoted in red). How far will the tanker be from these points when it reaches
   a. position 1? $\sqrt{2} \approx 1.4$ units
   b. position 2? $\sqrt{10} \approx 3.2$ units

ILLUSTRATION 6

80. DECK DESIGN   The plans for a patio deck shown in Illustration 7 call for three redwood support braces directly under the hot tub. Find the length of each support. Round to the nearest tenth of a foot.
   brace 1: 4.2 units;
   brace 2: 6.7 units;
   brace 3: 2.2 units

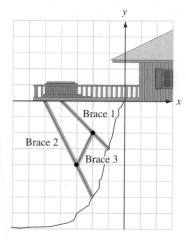

ILLUSTRATION 7

WRITING

81. Explain why a check is necessary when solving radical equations.

82. How would you know, without solving it, that the equation $\sqrt{x + 2} = -4$ has no solutions?

REVIEW   *Do the operations.*

83. $(3x^2 + 2x) + (5x^2 - 8x)$ $8x^2 - 6x$

84. $(7a^2 + 2a - 5) - (3a^2 - 2a + 1)$ $4a^2 + 4a - 6$

85. $(x + 3)(x + 3)$ $x^2 + 6x + 9$

86. $x - 1\overline{)x^2 - 6x + 5}$ $x - 5$

87. $(3y - 7)^2$ $9y^2 - 42y + 49$

88. $(3y + 7)^2$ $9y^2 + 42y + 49$

8.7 *Rational Exponents*

In this section, you will learn about

• Fractional exponents with numerators of 1
• Fractional exponents with numerators other than 1 • Rules for exponents

INTRODUCTION. We have seen that a positive integer exponent indicates the number of times that a base is to be used as a factor in a product. For example, x^4 means that x is to be used as a factor four times.

$$\overbrace{x^4 = x \cdot x \cdot x \cdot x}^{4 \text{ factors of } x}$$

Also, recall the following rules for exponents.

Rules for exponents

> If m and n represent natural numbers and there are no divisions by zero, then
>
> $$x^m x^n = x^{m+n} \qquad (x^m)^n = x^{m \cdot n} \qquad (xy)^n = x^n y^n \qquad \left(\frac{x}{y}\right)^n = \frac{x^n}{y^n}$$
>
> $$x^0 = 1 \qquad\qquad x^{-n} = \frac{1}{x^n} \qquad\qquad \frac{x^m}{x^n} = x^{m-n}$$

In this section, we will extend the definition and rules for exponents to cover fractional exponents.

Fractional exponents with numerators of 1

It is possible to raise numbers to fractional powers. To give meaning to rational (fractional) exponents, we consider $\sqrt{7}$. Because $\sqrt{7}$ is the positive number whose square is 7, we have

$$\left(\sqrt{7}\right)^2 = 7$$

We now consider the symbol $7^{1/2}$. If fractional exponents are to follow the same rules as integer exponents, the square of $7^{1/2}$ must be 7, because

$$\left(7^{1/2}\right)^2 = 7^{(1/2)2} \quad \text{Keep the base and multiply the exponents.}$$
$$= 7^1 \qquad \tfrac{1}{2} \cdot 2 = 1.$$
$$= 7$$

Since $(7^{1/2})^2$ and $\left(\sqrt{7}\right)^2$ are both equal to 7, we define $7^{1/2}$ to be $\sqrt{7}$. Similarly, we make these definitions.

$$7^{1/3} = \sqrt[3]{7}$$
$$7^{1/7} = \sqrt[7]{7}$$

and so on.

Rational exponents

> If n represents a positive integer greater than 1 and $\sqrt[n]{x}$ represents a real number, then
>
> $$x^{1/n} = \sqrt[n]{x}$$

EXAMPLE 1   *Rational exponents with numerators of 1.*
Simplify   **a.** $64^{1/2}$,   **b.** $64^{1/3}$,   and   **c.** $(-64)^{1/3}$

Solution

a. $64^{1/2} = \sqrt{64} = 8$ The denominator of the fractional exponent is 2. Therefore, we find the square root of the base.

b. $64^{1/3} = \sqrt[3]{64} = 4$ The denominator of the fractional exponent is 3. Therefore, we find the cube root of the base.

c. $(-64)^{1/3} = \sqrt[3]{-64} = -4$ The denominator of the fractional exponent is 3. Therefore, we find the cube root of the base.

Self Check

Simplify

a. $81^{1/2}$

b. $125^{1/3}$

c. $(-27)^{1/3}$

Answers: **a.** 9,   **b.** 5,   **c.** -3

Fractional exponents with numerators other than 1

We can extend the definition of $x^{1/n}$ to cover fractional exponents for which the numerator is not 1. For example, because $4^{3/2}$ can be written as $(4^{1/2})^3$, we have

$$4^{3/2} = (4^{1/2})^3 = \left(\sqrt{4}\right)^3 = 2^3 = 8$$

Because $4^{3/2}$ can also be written as $(4^3)^{1/2}$, we have

$$4^{3/2} = (4^3)^{1/2} = 64^{1/2} = \sqrt{64} = 8$$

In general, $x^{m/n}$ can be written as $(x^{1/n})^m$ or as $(x^m)^{1/n}$. Since $(x^{1/n})^m = \left(\sqrt[n]{x}\right)^m$ and $(x^m)^{1/n} = \sqrt[n]{x^m}$, we make the following definition.

Changing from rational exponents to radicals

If m and n represent positive integers ($n \neq 1$) and $\sqrt[n]{x}$ represents a real number, then

$$x^{m/n} = \sqrt[n]{x^m} = \left(\sqrt[n]{x}\right)^m$$

EXAMPLE 2   *Rational exponents with numerators other than 1.*
Simplify   **a.** $8^{2/3}$ and   **b.** $(-27)^{4/3}$.

Solution

These expressions can be simplified in two ways. Using the first method, we take the root of the base and then we find the power. The second method is to find the power first and then take the root.

a. $8^{2/3} = \left(\sqrt[3]{8}\right)^2$ or $8^{2/3} = \sqrt[3]{8^2}$
　　　　$= 2^2$　　　　　　　　　$= \sqrt[3]{64}$
　　　　$= 4$　　　　　　　　　　$= 4$

b. $(-27)^{4/3} = \left(\sqrt[3]{-27}\right)^4$ or $(-27)^{4/3} = \sqrt[3]{(-27)^4}$
　　　　　$= (-3)^4$　　　　　　　　$= \sqrt[3]{531{,}441}$
　　　　　$= 81$　　　　　　　　　　$= 81$

Self Check

Simplify

a. $16^{3/2}$

b. $(-8)^{4/3}$

Answers: a. 64,   **b.** 16   ■

The work in Example 2 suggests that in order to avoid large numbers, it is usually easier to take the root of the base first and then find the power.

EXAMPLE 3   *Rational exponents with numerators other than 1.*
Simplify   **a.** $125^{4/3}$,   **b.** $9^{5/2}$,   **c.** $-25^{3/2}$,   and   **d.** $(-27)^{2/3}$.

Solution

a. $125^{4/3} = \left(\sqrt[3]{125}\right)^4$　　　　　**b.** $9^{5/2} = \left(\sqrt{9}\right)^5$
　　　　$= (5)^4$　　　　　　　　　　　　$= (3)^5$
　　　　$= 625$　　　　　　　　　　　　$= 243$

c. $-25^{3/2} = -\left(\sqrt{25}\right)^3$　　　　**d.** $(-27)^{2/3} = \left(\sqrt[3]{-27}\right)^2$
　　　　$= -(5)^3$　　　　　　　　　　　$= (-3)^2$
　　　　$= -125$　　　　　　　　　　　$= 9$

Self Check

Simplify:

a. $100^{3/2}$

b. $(-8)^{2/3}$

Answers: a. 1,000,   **b.** 4   ■

Accent on Technology: *Fractional exponents*

To use a scientific calculator to evaluate an exponential expression containing a fractional exponent, we can use the $\boxed{y^x}$ key. For example, to evaluate $6^{-2/3}$, we enter these numbers and press these keys.

Keystrokes   6 y^x (2 +/− ÷ 3) =   ☐ 0.302853432

So $6^{-2/3} \approx 0.302853432$.

To use a graphing calculator to evaluate $6^{-2/3}$, we press the following keys.

Keystrokes   6 ^ ((−) 2 ÷ 3) ENTER   ☐ 6^(⁻2/3)
                                                    .3028534321

Rules for exponents

Because of the way in which $x^{1/n}$ and $x^{m/n}$ are defined, the familiar rules for exponents are valid for rational exponents. The following example illustrates the use of each rule.

EXAMPLE 4   *Using the rules for exponents.*   Simplify:

a. $4^{2/5}4^{1/5} = 4^{2/5+1/5} = 4^{3/5}$ $x^m x^n = x^{m+n}$.

b. $(5^{2/3})^{1/2} = 5^{(2/3)(1/2)} = 5^{1/3}$ $(x^m)^n = x^{m \cdot n}$.

c. $(3x)^{2/3} = 3^{2/3}x^{2/3}$ $(xy)^m = x^m y^m$.

d. $\dfrac{4^{3/5}}{4^{2/5}} = 4^{3/5-2/5} = 4^{1/5}$ $\dfrac{x^m}{x^n} = x^{m-n}$.

e. $\left(\dfrac{3}{2}\right)^{2/5} = \dfrac{3^{2/5}}{2^{2/5}}$ $\left(\dfrac{x}{y}\right)^n = \dfrac{x^n}{y^n}$.

f. $4^{-2/3} = \dfrac{1}{4^{2/3}}$ $x^{-n} = \dfrac{1}{x^n}$.

g. $(5^{1/3})^0 = 1$ $x^0 = 1$.

Self Check

Simplify:

a. $5^{1/3}5^{1/3}$

b. $(5^{1/3})^4$

c. $(3x)^{1/5}$

d. $\dfrac{5^{3/7}}{5^{2/7}}$

e. $\left(\dfrac{2}{3}\right)^{2/3}$

f. $5^{-2/7}$

g. $(12^{1/2})^0$

Answers: **a.** $5^{2/3}$,   **b.** $5^{4/3}$,
c. $3^{1/5}x^{1/5}$,   **d.** $5^{1/7}$,   **e.** $\dfrac{2^{2/3}}{3^{2/3}}$,
f. $\dfrac{1}{5^{2/7}}$,   **g.** 1 ∎

We can use the rules for exponents to simplify expressions containing rational exponents.

EXAMPLE 5   *Rational exponents.*   Simplify   **a.** $64^{-2/3}$,   **b.** $(x^2)^{1/2}$,
c. $(x^6y^4)^{1/2}$,   and   **d.** $(27x^{12})^{-1/3}$ ($x > 0$ and $y > 0$).

Solution

a. $64^{-2/3} = \dfrac{1}{64^{2/3}}$

$= \dfrac{1}{(64^{1/3})^2}$

$= \dfrac{1}{4^2}$

$= \dfrac{1}{16}$

b. $(x^2)^{1/2} = x^{2(1/2)}$

$= x^1$

$= x$

Self Check

Simplify:

a. $25^{-3/2}$

b. $(x^3)^{1/3}$

c. $(x^6y^9)^{-2/3}$

c. $(x^6 y^4)^{1/2} = x^{6(1/2)} y^{4(1/2)}$

$= x^3 y^2$

d. $(27x^{12})^{-1/3} = \dfrac{1}{(27x^{12})^{1/3}}$

$= \dfrac{1}{27^{1/3} x^{12(1/3)}}$

$= \dfrac{1}{3x^4}$

Answers: **a.** $\dfrac{1}{125}$,   **b.** x,

c. $\dfrac{1}{x^4 y^6}$

EXAMPLE 6   *Simplifying expressions containing rational*

exponents.   Simplify   **a.** $x^{1/3} x^{1/2}$,   **b.** $\dfrac{3x^{2/3}}{6x^{1/5}}$,   and   **c.** $\dfrac{2x^{-1/2}}{x^{3/4}}$ $(x > 0)$.

Solution

a. $x^{1/3} x^{1/2} = x^{2/6} x^{3/6}$ Get a common denominator for the fractional exponents.

$= x^{5/6}$ Keep the base and add the exponents.

b. $\dfrac{3x^{2/3}}{6x^{1/5}} = \dfrac{3x^{10/15}}{6x^{3/15}}$ Get a common denominator for the fractional exponents.

$= \dfrac{1}{2} x^{10/15 - 3/15}$ Simplify $\frac{3}{6}$. Keep the base and subtract the exponents.

$= \dfrac{1}{2} x^{7/15}$

c. $\dfrac{2x^{-1/2}}{x^{3/4}} = \dfrac{2x^{-2/4}}{x^{3/4}}$ Get a common denominator for the fractional exponents.

$= 2x^{-2/4 - 3/4}$ Keep the base and subtract the exponents.

$= 2x^{-5/4}$ Simplify.

$= \dfrac{2}{x^{5/4}}$ $x^{-5/4} = \dfrac{1}{x^{5/4}}$.

Self Check
Simplify:

a. $x^{2/3} x^{1/2}$

b. $\dfrac{x^{2/3}}{2x^{1/4}}$

Answers: **a.** $x^{7/6}$,   **b.** $\frac{1}{2} x^{5/12}$

STUDY SET   Section 8.7

VOCABULARY   *Fill in the blanks.*

1. A fractional exponent is also called a ___rational___ exponent.

2. In the expression $27^{1/3}$, 27 is called the ___base___ and the exponent is $\frac{1}{3}$.

CONCEPTS   *In Exercises 3–10, complete each rule for exponents.*

3. $x^m x^n =$ x^{m+n}

4. $(x^m)^n =$ $x^{m \cdot n}$

5. $\left(\dfrac{x}{y}\right)^n =$ $\dfrac{x^n}{y^n}$

6. $x^0 =$ 1

7. $x^{-n} =$ $\dfrac{1}{x^n}$

8. $\dfrac{x^m}{x^n} =$ x^{m-n}

9. $x^{1/n} =$ $\sqrt[n]{x}$

10. $x^{m/n} =$ $\sqrt[n]{x^m}$ or $\left(\sqrt[n]{x}\right)^m$

11. Write $\sqrt{5}$ using a fractional exponent. $5^{1/2}$

12. Write $5^{1/3}$ using a radical. $\sqrt[3]{5}$

13. Write $8^{4/3}$ using a radical. $\left(\sqrt[3]{8}\right)^4$

14. Write $\left(\sqrt{8}\right)^3$ using a fractional exponent. $8^{3/2}$

15. Complete the table of values.

x	$x^{1/2}$
0	0
1	1
4	2
9	3

16. Complete the table of values.

x	$x^{1/3}$
0	0
-1	-1
-8	-2
8	2

17. Graph each number on the number line.
$\{8^{1/3}, 17^{1/2}, 2^{3/2}, -5^{2/3}\}$

18. Graph each number on the number line.
$\{4^{-1/2}, 64^{-2/3}, (-8)^{-1/3}\}$

NOTATION *Complete each solution.*

19. Simplify $(-216)^{4/3}$.

$$(-216)^{4/3} = \left(\sqrt[3]{(-216)}\right)^4$$
$$= \left(-6\right)^4$$
$$= 1{,}296$$

20. Simplify $\dfrac{3x^{-2/3}}{x^{3/4}}$.

$$\frac{3x^{-2/3}}{x^{3/4}} = \frac{3x^{-8/12}}{x^{9/12}}$$
$$= 3x^{-8/12 - 9/12}$$
$$= 3x^{-17/12}$$

PRACTICE *Simplify each expression.*

21. $81^{1/2}$ 9

22. $100^{1/2}$ 10

23. $-144^{1/2}$ -12

24. $-400^{1/2}$ -20

25. $\left(\dfrac{1}{4}\right)^{1/2}$ $\frac{1}{2}$

26. $\left(\dfrac{1}{25}\right)^{1/2}$ $\frac{1}{5}$

27. $\left(\dfrac{4}{49}\right)^{1/2}$ $\frac{2}{7}$

28. $\left(\dfrac{9}{64}\right)^{1/2}$ $\frac{3}{8}$

29. $27^{1/3}$ 3

30. $8^{1/3}$ 2

31. $-125^{1/3}$ -5

32. $-1{,}000^{1/3}$ -10

33. $(-8)^{1/3}$ -2

34. $(-125)^{1/3}$ -5

35. $\left(\dfrac{27}{64}\right)^{1/3}$ $\frac{3}{4}$

36. $\left(\dfrac{64}{125}\right)^{1/3}$ $\frac{4}{5}$

37. $81^{3/2}$ 729

38. $16^{3/2}$ 64

39. $25^{3/2}$ 125

40. $4^{5/2}$ 32

41. $125^{2/3}$ 25

42. $8^{4/3}$ 16

43. $1{,}000^{2/3}$ 100

44. $27^{2/3}$ 9

45. $(-8)^{2/3}$ 4

46. $(-125)^{2/3}$ 25

47. $\left(\dfrac{8}{27}\right)^{2/3}$ $\frac{4}{9}$

48. $\left(\dfrac{49}{64}\right)^{3/2}$ $\frac{343}{512}$

Simplify each expression. Write your answers without using negative exponents.

49. $6^{3/5}6^{2/5}$ 6

50. $3^{4/7}3^{3/7}$ 3

51. $5^{2/3}5^{4/3}$ 25

52. $2^{7/8}2^{9/8}$ 4

53. $(7^{2/5})^{5/2}$ 7

54. $(8^{1/3})^3$ 8

55. $(5^{2/7})^7$ 25

56. $(3^{3/8})^8$ 27

57. $\dfrac{8^{3/2}}{8^{1/2}}$ 8

58. $\dfrac{11^{9/7}}{11^{2/7}}$ 11

59. $\dfrac{5^{11/3}}{5^{2/3}}$ 125

60. $\dfrac{27^{13/15}}{27^{8/15}}$ 3

61. $4^{-1/2}$ $\frac{1}{2}$

62. $8^{-1/3}$ $\frac{1}{2}$

63. $27^{-2/3}$ $\frac{1}{9}$

64. $36^{-3/2}$ $\frac{1}{216}$

65. $16^{-3/2}$ $\frac{1}{64}$

66. $100^{-5/2}$ $\frac{1}{100{,}000}$

67. $(-27)^{-4/3}$ $\frac{1}{81}$

68. $(-8)^{-4/3}$ $\frac{1}{16}$

Simplify each expression. Assume that all variables represent positive numbers.

69. $(x^{1/2})^2$ x

70. $(x^9)^{1/3}$ x^3

71. $(x^{12})^{1/6}$ x^2

72. $(x^{18})^{1/9}$ x^2

73. $x^{5/6}x^{7/6}$ x^2

74. $x^{2/3}x^{7/3}$ x^3

75. $y^{4/7}y^{10/7}$ y^2

76. $y^{5/11}y^{6/11}$ y

77. $\dfrac{x^{3/5}}{x^{1/5}}$ $x^{2/5}$

78. $\dfrac{x^{4/3}}{x^{2/3}}$ $x^{2/3}$

79. $\dfrac{x^{1/7}x^{3/7}}{x^{2/7}}$ $x^{2/7}$

80. $\dfrac{x^{5/6}x^{5/6}}{x^{7/6}}$ $x^{1/2}$

81. $x^{2/3}x^{3/4}$ $x^{17/12}$

82. $a^{3/5}a^{1/2}$ $a^{11/10}$

83. $(b^{1/2})^{3/5}$ $b^{3/10}$

84. $(x^{2/5})^{4/7}$ $x^{8/35}$

85. $\dfrac{t^{2/3}}{t^{2/5}}$ $t^{4/15}$

86. $\dfrac{p^{3/4}}{p^{1/3}}$ $p^{5/12}$

87. $\left(\dfrac{x^{4/5}}{x^{2/15}}\right)^3$ x^2

88. $\left(\dfrac{y^{2/3}}{y^{1/5}}\right)^{15}$ y^7

APPLICATIONS *If an answer is not exact, give it to the nearest tenth.*

89. SPEAKERS   The formula $A = V^{2/3}$ can be used to find the area A of one face of a cube if its volume V is known. Find the amount of floor space on the dance floor taken up by the speakers shown in Illustration 1 if each speaker is a cube with a volume of 2,744 cubic inches.   392 in.^{2}

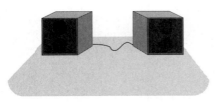

ILLUSTRATION 1

90. MEDICAL TESTS Before a series of X-rays are taken, a patient is injected with a special contrast mixture that highlights obstructions in his blood vessels. The amount of the original dose of contrast material remaining in the patient's bloodstream h hours after it is injected is given by $h^{-3/2}$. How much of the contrast material remains in the patient's bloodstream 4 hours after the injection? $\frac{1}{8}$ of the dose

91. HOLIDAY DECORATING Find the length s of each string of colored lights used to decorate an evergreen tree in the manner shown in Illustration 2 if $s = (r^2 + h^2)^{1/2}$. 26 ft

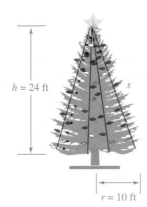

$h = 24$ ft s

$r = 10$ ft

ILLUSTRATION 2

92. VISIBILITY The distance d in miles a person in an airplane can see to the horizon on a clear day is given by the formula $d = 1.22a^{1/2}$, where a is the altitude of the plane in feet. Find d in Illustration 3. 231.5 mi

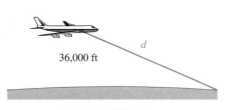

36,000 ft

d

ILLUSTRATION 3

93. TOY DESIGN Knowing the volume V of a sphere, we can find its radius r using the formula

$$r = \left(\frac{3V}{4\pi}\right)^{1/3}$$

If the volume occupied by a ball is 2π cubic inches, find its radius. 1.1 in.

94. EXERCISE EQUIPMENT Find the length l of the incline bench in Illustration 4, using the formula $l = (a^2 + b^2)^{1/2}$. 78.5 in.

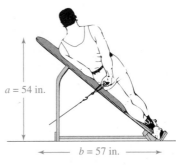

$a = 54$ in.

$b = 57$ in.

ILLUSTRATION 4

WRITING

95. What is a rational exponent? Give several examples.

96. Explain this statement: *In the expression $16^{3/2}$, the number 3/2 requires that two operations be performed on 16.*

REVIEW *Graph each equation.*

97. $x = 3$

98. $y = -3$

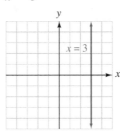

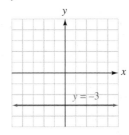

99. $-2x + y = 4$

100. $4x - y = 4$

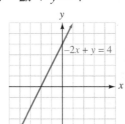

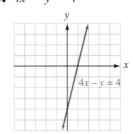

Inverse Operations

We have performed six operations with real numbers: addition, subtraction, multiplication, division, raising to a power, and finding a root. We have seen that there is a special relationship between *pairs* of operations. That is, subtraction does the opposite of addition, division does the opposite of multiplication, and finding a root does the opposite of raising to a power. Because of this, we call each pair **inverse operations.** Subtraction is the inverse operation of addition, division is the inverse operation of multiplication, and finding a root is the inverse operation of raising to a power.

Solving Equations

When solving equations, we use inverse operations to isolate the variable on one side of the equation.

Tell what operation is performed on the variable and what inverse operation should be used to isolate the variable; then solve the equation.

1. $x + 2 = -4$ addition, subtraction, -6

2. $x - 5 = 10$ subtraction, addition, 15

3. $-6x = 24$ multiplication, division, -4

4. $\dfrac{x}{2} = 40$ division, multiplication, 80

5. $\sqrt{x} = 7$ square root, square, 49

6. $x^2 = 169$ (assume $x > 0$)   squared, square root, 13

7. $\sqrt[3]{x} = -2$ cube root, cubed, -8

8. $x^3 = 64$ cubed, cube root, 4

When solving equations, we must often undo several operations to isolate the variable. Recall that these operations are undone in the *reverse* order of operations.

Solve each equation and check the result.

9. $-2x - 4 = 6$ -5

10. $\dfrac{3x}{5} + 3 = 9$ 10

11. $\sqrt{x + 1} = 4$
15

12. $x^2 = 9$ (assume $x > 0$)
3

13. $\sqrt{x} - 3 = 5$ 64

14. $\sqrt[3]{x} - 3 = 1$ 64

Applications

We can use the concept of inverse operation to find the length of a side of the cube in Illustration 1 if we know the area of a face or the volume of the cube.

15. To find the area of a face of the cube, we square the length of a side. How could we find the length of a side, knowing the area of a face?
Find the square root of the area.

16. To find the volume of the cube, we cube the length of a side. How could we find the length of a side if we knew the volume of the cube?
Find the cube root of the volume.

ILLUSTRATION 1

587

Section 8.1

THE PYTHAGOREAN THEOREM   Put 12 knots in a rope, each 1 foot apart, and connect the ends as shown in Illustration 1. Hammer three tent stakes in the ground so that the rope forms a triangle with sides of length 3, 4, and 5 spaces. Make some observations about the triangle. Use the Pythagorean theorem to prove one of your observations.

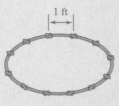

1 ft

ILLUSTRATION 1

A SPIRAL OF ROOTS   To do this project, you will need a piece of poster board, a protractor, a yardstick, and a pencil. Begin by drawing an isosceles right triangle near the right margin of the poster board. Label the length of each leg as 1 unit. (See Illustration 2.) Use the Pythagorean theorem to determine the length of the hypotenuse. Draw a second right triangle using the hypotenuse of the first triangle as one leg. Draw its second leg with a length of 1 unit. Find the length of the hypotenuse of triangle 2. Continue this process of creating right triangles, using the previous hypotenuse as one leg and drawing a new second leg of length 1 unit each time. Calculate the length of the resulting hypotenuse. What patterns, if any, do you see?

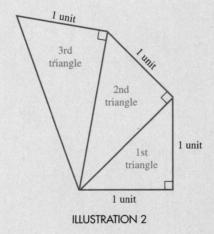

1 unit

3rd triangle

1 unit

2nd triangle

1 unit

1st triangle

1 unit

ILLUSTRATION 2

Section 8.2

nTH ROOTS   Use the $\boxed{\sqrt[x]{y}}$ key on a scientific calculator to approximate $\sqrt{2}$, $\sqrt[3]{2}$, $\sqrt[4]{2}$, $\sqrt[5]{2}$, and $\sqrt[6]{2}$. Do you see any pattern? Explain it in words.

Section 8.3

SIMPLIFYING RADICAL EXPRESSIONS   Suppose you are the algebra instructor of a student whose work is shown here. Write a note to the student explaining how she could save some steps in simplifying $\sqrt{72}$.

$$\sqrt{72} = \sqrt{4 \cdot 18}$$
$$= \sqrt{4}\sqrt{18}$$
$$= 2\sqrt{18}$$
$$= 2\sqrt{9 \cdot 2}$$
$$= 2\sqrt{9}\sqrt{2}$$
$$= 2(3)\sqrt{2}$$
$$= 6\sqrt{2}$$

Section 8.4

COMMON ERRORS   In each addition and subtraction problem below, tell what mistake was made. Compare each problem to a similar one involving variables to clarify your explanation. For example, compare Problem a to $2x + 3x$ to help you explain the correct procedure that should be used to simplify the expression.

a. $2\sqrt{5} + 3\sqrt{5} = 5\sqrt{10}$ **b.** $30 + 2\sqrt{2} = 32\sqrt{2}$

c. $7\sqrt{3} - 5\sqrt{3} = 2$ **d.** $6\sqrt{7} - 3\sqrt{2} = 3\sqrt{5}$

Section 8.5

RATIONALIZING NUMERATORS   Some problems in advanced mathematics require that the numerator of a fraction be rationalized. Extend the concepts studied in this section to develop a method to rationalize the numerators of

$$\frac{\sqrt{5}}{3}, \quad \frac{\sqrt{7}}{\sqrt{5}}, \quad \frac{\sqrt{y}}{6y}, \quad \text{and} \quad \frac{\sqrt{3} - \sqrt{2}}{12}$$

Section 8.6

SOLVING RADICAL EQUATIONS   In this chapter, we solved equations that contained two radicals. The radicals in those equations always had the same index. That is not the case for the following equation:

$$\sqrt{x} = \sqrt[3]{2x}$$

Brainstorm in your group to develop a procedure that can be used to solve this equation. What are its solutions?

Section 8.7

GRAPHING   Approximate the x- and y-coordinates of the following ordered pairs to the nearest tenth, then graph them on a rectangular coordinate system. (*Hint:* Each quadrant should contain only one point.)

$$A\left(\sqrt{2}, 3^{1/2}\right) \qquad B\left(-\sqrt{6}, 5^{3/2}\right)$$
$$C\left(-16^{2/3}, -\sqrt[3]{25}\right) \qquad D\left(9^{-1/2}, \sqrt[3]{-10}\right)$$

CHAPTER REVIEW

SECTION 8.1	*Square Roots*

CONCEPTS

The number b is a *square root* of a if $b^2 = a$.

The *principal square root* of a positive number a, denoted by $\sqrt{a}$, is the positive square root of a.

The expression within a *radical sign* $\sqrt{}$ is called the *radicand*.

Numbers that are not square roots of *integer squares* are *irrational numbers*. Square roots of negative numbers are called *imaginary numbers*.

The Pythagorean theorem: If the length of the hypotenuse of a right triangle is c and the lengths of the two legs are a and b, then $c^2 = a^2 + b^2$.

If a and b are positive numbers, and $a = b$, then $\sqrt{a} = \sqrt{b}$.

REVIEW EXERCISES

1. Fill in the blanks to make the statement true: The ___square___ of 4 is 16, because $4^2 = 16$; 4 is the ___square___ root of 16, because $4^2 = 16$.

2. Find each square root. Do not use a calculator.

a. $\sqrt{25}$ 5   **b.** $\sqrt{49}$ 7   **c.** $-\sqrt{144}$ -12 **d.** $-\sqrt{\dfrac{16}{81}}$ $-\frac{4}{9}$

e. $\sqrt{900}$ 30   **f.** $-\sqrt{0.64}$ -0.8 **g.** $\sqrt{1}$ 1   **h.** $\sqrt{0}$ 0

3. ▦ Use a calculator to approximate each expression to three decimal places.

a. $\sqrt{21}$ 4.583   **b.** $-\sqrt{15}$ -3.873 **c.** $2\sqrt{7}$ 5.292   **d.** $\sqrt{751.9}$ 27.421

4. Tell whether each number is rational, irrational, or imaginary. Which is not a real number? $\{\sqrt{-2}, \sqrt{68}, \sqrt{81}, \sqrt{3}\}$ imag, irr, rat, irr; $\sqrt{-2}$

5. Complete the table of values for each function and then graph it.

a. $f(x) = \sqrt{x}$ **b.** $f(x) = 2 - \sqrt{x}$

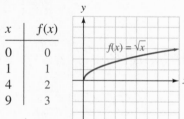

x	$f(x)$
0	0
1	1
4	2
9	3

x	$f(x)$
0	2
1	1
4	0
9	-1

6. Refer to the right triangle shown in Illustration 1.

a. Find c where $a = 21$ and $b = 28$.   35

b. Find b where $a = 1$ and $c = \sqrt{2}$.   1

c. Find a where $b = 5$ and $c = 7$. $2\sqrt{6}$

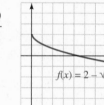

ILLUSTRATION 1

7. ▦ THEATER SEATING   For the theater seats shown in Illustration 2, how much higher is the seat at the top of the incline compared to the one at the bottom?   3.5 ft

ILLUSTRATION 2

8. ROAD SIGNS   To find the maximum velocity a car can safely travel around a curve without skidding, we can use the formula $v = \sqrt{2.5r}$, where v is the velocity in miles per hour and r is the radius of the curve in feet. How should the road sign in Illustration 3 be labeled if it is to be posted in front of a curve with a radius of 360 feet?   30 mph

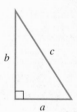

? mph

ILLUSTRATION 3

SECTION 8.2 — Higher-Order Roots; Radicands That Contain Variables

The number b is a *cube root* of a if $b^3 = a$.

The cube root of a is denoted by $\sqrt[3]{a}$. By definition, $\sqrt[3]{a} = b$ if $b^3 = a$.

The number b is an *nth root* of a if $b^n = a$.

In $\sqrt[n]{a}$, the number n is called the *index* of the radical.

When n is even, we say that the radical $\sqrt[n]{x}$ is an *even root*. When n is odd, $\sqrt[n]{x}$ is an *odd root*.

$$\sqrt{a} = \sqrt[2]{a}$$

9. Fill in the blanks to make the statement true: $\sqrt[3]{125} = 5$, because $5^3 = 125$; 5 is called the _____cube_____ root of 125.

10. Find each root. Do not use a calculator.

a. $\sqrt[3]{-27}$ -3 **b.** $-\sqrt[3]{125}$ -5 **c.** $\sqrt[4]{81}$ 3 **d.** $\sqrt[5]{32}$ 2

e. $\sqrt[3]{0}$ 0 **f.** $\sqrt[3]{-1}$ -1 **g.** $\sqrt[3]{\dfrac{1}{64}}$ $\frac{1}{4}$ **h.** $\sqrt[3]{1}$ 1

11.  Use a calculator to find each root to three decimal places.

a. $\sqrt[3]{16}$ **b.** $\sqrt[3]{-102.35}$ **c.** $\sqrt[4]{6}$ **d.** $\sqrt[5]{34,500}$
   2.520 -4.678 1.565   8.083

12. Find each root. Each variable represents a positive number.

a. $\sqrt{x^2}$ x **b.** $\sqrt{4b^4}$ $2b^2$ **c.** $\sqrt{x^4 y^4}$ $x^2 y^2$ **d.** $-\sqrt{y^{12}}$ $-y^6$

e. $\sqrt[3]{x^3}$ x **f.** $\sqrt[3]{y^6}$ y^2 **g.** $\sqrt[3]{27x^3}$ $3x$ **h.** $\sqrt[3]{-r^{12}}$ $-r^4$

13. DICE   Find the length of an edge of one of the dice shown in Illustration 4 if each one has a volume of 1,728 cubic millimeters.   12 mm

ILLUSTRATION 4

SECTION 8.3 — Simplifying Radical Expressions

The *multiplication property* of radicals: If a and b are positive or zero, then

$$\sqrt{ab} = \sqrt{a}\sqrt{b}$$

Simplified form of a radical:

1. Except for 1, the radicand has no perfect square factors.
2. No fraction appears in the radicand.
3. No radical appears in the denominator.

The *division property* of radicals:

$$\sqrt{\frac{a}{b}} = \frac{\sqrt{a}}{\sqrt{b}} \quad (b \neq 0)$$

14. Simplify each expression. All variables represent positive numbers.

a. $\sqrt{32}$ $4\sqrt{2}$ **b.** $\sqrt{500}$ $10\sqrt{5}$

c. $\sqrt{80x^2}$ $4x\sqrt{5}$ **d.** $-2\sqrt{63}$ $-6\sqrt{7}$

e. $-\sqrt{250t^3}$ $-5t\sqrt{10t}$ **f.** $-\sqrt{700z^5}$ $-10z^2\sqrt{7z}$

g. $\sqrt{200x^2y}$ $10x\sqrt{2y}$ **h.** $\dfrac{1}{5}\sqrt{75y^4}$ $y^2\sqrt{3}$

i. $\sqrt[3]{8x^2y^3}$ $2y\sqrt[3]{x^2}$ **j.** $\sqrt[3]{250x^4y^3}$ $5xy\sqrt[3]{2x}$

15. Simplify each expression. All variables represent positive numbers.

a. $\sqrt{\dfrac{16}{25}}$ $\frac{4}{5}$ **b.** $\sqrt{\dfrac{60}{49}}$ $\frac{2\sqrt{15}}{7}$

c. $\sqrt[3]{\dfrac{1,000}{27}}$ $\frac{10}{3}$ **d.** $\sqrt{\dfrac{242x^4}{169x^2}}$ $\frac{11x\sqrt{2}}{13}$

16. FITNESS EQUIPMENT   The length of the sit-up board in Illustration 5 can be found using the Pythagorean theorem.

a. Find its length. Express the answer in simplified radical form. $2\sqrt{10}$ ft

b. Express your result to part a as a decimal approximation rounded to the nearest tenth.   6.3 ft

ILLUSTRATION 5

SECTION 8.4	*Adding and Subtracting Radical Expressions*

Radical expressions can be added or subtracted if they contain like radicals.

Radicals are called *like* radicals when they have the same index and the same radicand.

17. Do the operations. All variables represent positive numbers.

a. $\sqrt{2} + \sqrt{8} - \sqrt{18}$ 0

b. $\sqrt{3} + 4 + \sqrt{27} - 7$ $-3 + 4\sqrt{3}$

c. $5\sqrt{28} - 3\sqrt{63}$ $\sqrt{7}$

d. $3y\sqrt{5xy^3} - y^2\sqrt{20xy}$ $y^2\sqrt{5xy}$

e. $\sqrt[3]{16} + \sqrt[3]{54}$ $5\sqrt[3]{2}$

f. $\sqrt[3]{2,000x^3} - \sqrt[3]{128x^3}$ $6x\sqrt[3]{2}$

18. Explain why we cannot add $3\sqrt{5}$ and $5\sqrt{3}$.
They do not contain like radicals—the radicands are different.

19. GARDENING   Find the difference in the lengths of the two wires used to secure the tree shown in Illustration 6. $13\sqrt{5}$ in.

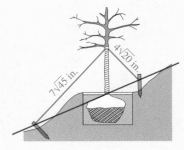

ILLUSTRATION 6

SECTION 8.5	*Multiplying and Dividing Radical Expressions*

The product of the square roots of two nonnegative numbers is equal to the square root of the product of those numbers.

To multiply radical expressions containing only one term, first multiply the coefficients, then multiply the radicals separately, and simplify the result.

Use the FOIL method to multiply two radical expressions, each having two terms.

If the denominator of a fraction is a square root, *rationalize* the denominator by multiplying the numerator and denominator by some appropriate square root.

If a two-term denominator of a fraction contains square roots, multiply the numerator and denominator by the *conjugate* of the denominator.

20. Do the operations.

a. $\sqrt{2}\sqrt{3}$ $\sqrt{6}$

b. $(-5\sqrt{5})(-2\sqrt{2})$ $10\sqrt{10}$

c. $(3\sqrt{3x})(4\sqrt{6x})$ $36x\sqrt{2}$

d. $(\sqrt{15} + 3x)^2$ $15 + 6x\sqrt{15} + 9x^2$

e. $\sqrt{2}(\sqrt{8} - \sqrt{18})$ -2

f. $(\sqrt{3} + \sqrt{5})(\sqrt{3} - \sqrt{5})$ -2

g. $(\sqrt[3]{4})(2\sqrt[3]{4})$
$4\sqrt[3]{2}$

h. $(\sqrt[3]{3} + 2)(\sqrt[3]{3} - 1)$
$\sqrt[3]{9} + \sqrt[3]{3} - 2$

21. VACUUM CLEANER NOZZLE   Illustration 7 shows the amount of surface area of a rug suctioned by a vacuum nozzle attachment.

a. Find the perimeter and area of this section of rug. Express the answers in simplified radical form. $(4\sqrt{6} + 10\sqrt{3})$ in.; $30\sqrt{2}$ in.^{2}

b. Express your results to part a as decimal approximations to the nearest tenth.   27.1 in.; 42.4 in.^{2}

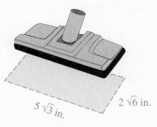

ILLUSTRATION 7

22. Rationalize each denominator.

a. $\dfrac{1}{\sqrt{7}}$ $\dfrac{\sqrt{7}}{7}$

b. $\sqrt{\dfrac{3}{7}}$ $\dfrac{\sqrt{21}}{7}$

c. $\dfrac{\sqrt{9}}{\sqrt{18}}$ $\dfrac{\sqrt{2}}{2}$

d. $\dfrac{\sqrt{c} - 4}{\sqrt{c} + 4}$ $\dfrac{c - 8\sqrt{c} + 16}{c - 16}$

e. $\dfrac{7}{\sqrt{2} + 1}$ $7\sqrt{2} - 7$

f. $\dfrac{8}{\sqrt[3]{16}}$ $2\sqrt[3]{4}$

| SECTION 8.6 | *Solving Radical Equations; the Distance Formula* |

To solve an equation containing square root radicals:

1. Isolate the radicals.
2. Square both sides and solve the resulting equation.
3. Check the solution. Discard any *extraneous* solutions.

Squaring property of equality:

If $a = b$, then $a^2 = b^2$.

The distance formula:

$$d = \sqrt{(x_2 - x_1)^2 + (y_2 - y_1)^2}$$

23. Simplify each expression. All variables represent positive numbers.

a. $\left(\sqrt{x}\right)^2$ x **b.** $\left(\sqrt[3]{x}\right)^3$ x **c.** $\left(2\sqrt{t}\right)^2$ $4t$ **d.** $\left(\sqrt{e-1}\right)^2$ $e - 1$

24. Solve each equation and check all solutions.

a. $\sqrt{x} = 9$ 81   **b.** $\sqrt{2x + 10} = 2$ -3

c. $\sqrt{3x + 4} + 5 = 3$ none   **d.** $\sqrt{2(r + 4)} = 2\sqrt{r}$ 4

e. $\sqrt{p^2 - 3} = p + 3$ -2 **f.** $\sqrt[3]{x - 1} = 3$ 28

25. FERRIS WHEEL   The distance d in feet that an object will fall in t seconds is given by the formula

$$t = \sqrt{\frac{d}{16}}$$

If a person drops a coin from the top of a Ferris wheel and it takes 2 seconds to hit the ground, how tall is the Ferris wheel?   64 ft

26. Find the distance between the points. If an answer is not exact, round to the nearest hundredth.

a. $(-7, 12), (-4, 8)$ 5   **b.** $(-15, -3), (-10, -16)$ 13.93

| SECTION 8.7 | *Rational Exponents* |

Real numbers can be raised to fractional powers.

Rational exponents:

$$x^{1/n} = \sqrt[n]{x}$$
$$x^{m/n} = \sqrt[n]{x^m} = \left(\sqrt[n]{x}\right)^m$$

The rules for exponents can be used to simplify expressions involving rational exponents.

27. Simplify each expression. Write answers without using negative exponents.

a. $49^{1/2}$ 7   **b.** $(-1,000)^{1/3}$ -10 **c.** $36^{3/2}$ 216   **d.** $\left(\dfrac{8}{27}\right)^{2/3}$ $\frac{4}{9}$

e. $4^{-3/2}$ $\frac{1}{8}$ **f.** $8^{2/3}8^{4/3}$ 64   **g.** $(3^{2/3})^3$ 9   **h.** $(a^4b^8)^{-1/2}$ $\dfrac{1}{a^2b^4}$

i. $x^{1/3}x^{2/5}$ $x^{11/15}$ **j.** $\dfrac{t^{3/4}}{t^{2/3}}$ $t^{1/12}$ **k.** $\dfrac{x^{2/5}x^{1/5}}{x^{-2/5}}$ x **l.** $\dfrac{x^{17/7}}{x^{3/7}}$ x^2

28. Graph each number on the number line: $\left\{4^{-1/2}, 12^{1/2}, 9^{1/3}, -2^{2/3}\right\}$.

29. DENTISTRY   The fractional amount of painkiller remaining in the system of a patient h hours after the original dose was injected into her gums is given by $h^{-3/2}$. How much of the original dose is in the patient's system 16 hours after the injection? $\frac{1}{64}$ of the original dose

30. Explain why $(-4)^{1/2}$ is not a real number.

$(-4)^{1/2} = \sqrt{-4}$; there is no real number that, when squared, gives -4.

Chapter 8 Test

In Problems 1–4, simplify each radical.

1. $\sqrt{100}$ 10

2. $-\sqrt{\dfrac{400}{9}}$ $-\frac{20}{3}$

3. $\sqrt[3]{-27}$ -3

4. $\sqrt{\dfrac{50}{49}}$ $\frac{5\sqrt{2}}{7}$

5. Evaluate $\sqrt{b^2 - 4ac}$ for $a = 2$, $b = 10$, and $c = 6$. Round to the nearest tenth.   7.2

6. A 26-foot ladder reaches a point on a wall 24 feet above the ground. How far from the wall is the ladder's base?   10 ft

In Problems 7–10, simplify each expression. Assume that x and y represent positive numbers.

7. $\sqrt{4x^2}$ $2x$

8. $\sqrt{54x^3}$ $3x\sqrt{6x}$

9. $\sqrt{\dfrac{18x^2y^3}{2xy}}$ $3y\sqrt{x}$

10. $\sqrt[3]{x^6y^3}$ x^2y

11. A square has an area of 24 square yards.
   a. Express the length of a side of the square in simplified radical form. $2\sqrt{6}$ yd
   b. Round the length of a side of the square to the nearest tenth.   4.9 yd

In Problems 12–18, do each operation and simplify.

12. $\sqrt{12} + \sqrt{27}$ $5\sqrt{3}$

13. $\sqrt{8x^3} - x\sqrt{18x}$ $-x\sqrt{2x}$

14. $\left(-2\sqrt{8x}\right)\left(3\sqrt{12x}\right)$ $-24x\sqrt{6}$

15. $\sqrt{3}\left(\sqrt{8} + \sqrt{6}\right)$ $2\sqrt{6} + 3\sqrt{2}$

16. $\left(\sqrt{2} + \sqrt{3}\right)\left(\sqrt{2} - \sqrt{3}\right)$ -1

17. $\left(2\sqrt{x} + 2\right)\left(\sqrt{x} - 3\right)$ $2x - 4\sqrt{x} - 6$

18. SEWING   A corner of fabric is folded over to form a collar and stitched down as shown in Illustration 1. From the dimensions given in the figure, determine the exact number of inches of stitching that must be made. Then give an approximation to one decimal place. (All measurements are in inches.) $\left(6\sqrt{2} + 2\sqrt{10}\right)$ in., 14.8 in.

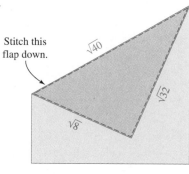

ILLUSTRATION 1

In Problems 19–20, rationalize each denominator.

19. $\dfrac{2}{\sqrt{2}}$ $\sqrt{2}$

20. $\dfrac{\sqrt{3x}}{\sqrt{x} + 2}$ $\dfrac{x\sqrt{3} - 2\sqrt{3x}}{x - 4}$

In Problems 21–24, solve each equation.

21. $\sqrt{x} = 15$ 225

22. $\sqrt{2 - x} - 2 = 6$ −62

23. $\sqrt{3x + 9} = 2\sqrt{x + 1}$ 5

24. $\sqrt[3]{x - 2} = 3$ 29

25. Find the distance between points $(-2, -3)$ and $(-8, 5)$.   10

26. 🖩 Complete the table and then graph the function. Round to the nearest tenth when necessary.

$f(x) = \sqrt{x}$

x	f(x)
0	0
1	1
2	1.4
3	1.7
4	2
5	2.2
6	2.4
7	2.6
8	2.8
9	3

$f(x) = \sqrt{x}$

27. Is $x = 0$ a solution of the radical equation $\sqrt{3x + 1} = x - 1$? Explain your answer.

No; when 0 is substituted for x, the result is not a true statement: $1 \neq -1$.

28. Explain why we cannot do the subtraction $4\sqrt{3} - 7\sqrt{2}$.

They do not contain like radicals—the radicands are different.

29. CARPENTRY   In Illustration 2, a carpenter is using a tape measure to see if the wall he just put up is perfectly "square" with the floor. Explain what mathematical concept he is applying. If the wall is positioned correctly, what should the measurement on the tape read?   the Pythagorean theorem; 5 ft

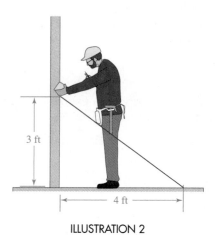

3 ft

4 ft

ILLUSTRATION 2

30. Explain why $\sqrt{-9}$ is not a real number.   There is no real number that, when squared, gives -9.

Simplify each expression.

31. $121^{1/2}$ 11

32. $p^{2/3}p^{4/3}$ p^2

Chapters 1–8 Cumulative Review Exercises

1. Tell whether each statement is true or false.
  a. All whole numbers are integers. true
  b. π is a rational number. false
  c. A real number is either rational or irrational. true

2. Find the value of the expression
$$\frac{-3(3 + 2)^2 - (-5)}{17 - 3|-4|} \quad -14$$

3. BACKPACK   Pediatricians advise that children should not carry more than 20% of their own body weight in a backpack. According to this warning, how much weight can a fifth-grade girl who weighs 85 pounds safely carry in her backpack?   17 lb

4. SCIENCE   Illustration 1 shows the recent budgets for the National Science Foundation. Determine the % change for the 1996 budget as compared to the 1995 budget. Round to the nearest tenth of a percent. -1.8%

In billions		% change
1992	$2.55	8.7%
1993	$2.75	8.0%
1994	$2.99	8.6%
1995	$3.27	9.5%
1996	$3.21	?
1997	$3.30	2.9%
1998	$3.43	3.9%
1999	$3.67	7.1%
2000	$3.91	6.5%

Based on data from the National Science Foundation

ILLUSTRATION 1

5. Simplify $3p - 6(p + z) + p$. $-2p - 6z$

6. Solve $2 - (4x + 7) = 3 + 2(x + 2)$. -2

7. Solve $3 - 3x \geq 6 + x$ and graph the solution. Then use interval notation to describe the solution.
$x \leq -\frac{3}{4}, \quad \left(-\infty, -\frac{3}{4}\right],$

8. Solve $0 \leq \dfrac{4 - x}{3} < 2$ and graph the solution. Then use interval notation to describe the solution.

$-2 < x \leq 4, \quad (-2, 4],$

9. SEARCH AND RESCUE   Two search and rescue teams leave base at the same time, looking for a lost boy. The first team, on foot, heads north at 2 mph and the other, on horseback, south at 4 mph. How long will it take them to search a distance of 21 miles between them?   3.5 hr

10. BLENDING COFFEE   A store sells regular coffee for $4 a pound and gourmet coffee for $7 a pound. Using 40 pounds of the gourmet coffee, the owner makes a blend to put on sale for $5 a pound. How many pounds of regular coffee should he use?   80

11. SURFACE AREA   The total surface area A of a box with dimensions l, w, and h (see Illustration 2) is given by the formula
$$A = 2lw + 2wh + 2lh$$
If $A = 202$ square inches, $l = 9$ inches, and $w = 5$ inches, find h.   4 in.

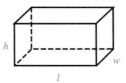

ILLUSTRATION 2

Graph each equation or inequality.

12. $3x - 4y = 12$

13. $y = \dfrac{1}{2}x$.

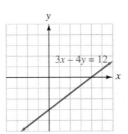

14. $x = 5$

15. $3x + 4y \leq 12$

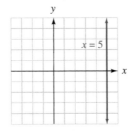

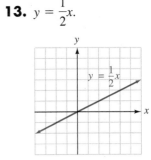

16. Write the equation of the line passing through $(-2, 5)$ and $(4, 8)$. $x - 2y = -12$

17. What is the slope of the line defined by each equation?
   a. $y = 3x - 7$ 3   **b.** $2x + 3y = -10$ $-\frac{2}{3}$

18. What is true about the slopes of two
   a. parallel lines?   they are the same
   b. perpendicular lines?   they are negative reciprocals

19. SHOPPING SURGE   On the graph in Illustration 3, draw a line through the points (1991, 724) and (1996, 974). The line approximates the total annual sales at U.S. shopping centers for the years 1991–1996. Find the rate of increase in sales over this period by finding the slope of the line. $50 billion/yr

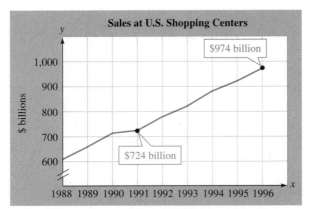

Based on data from International Council of Shopping Centers

ILLUSTRATION 3

20. If $f(x) = x^3 - x + 5$, find $f(-2)$. -1

21. Complete the table and graph the function. Then give the domain and range of the function.

$f(x) = |1 - x|$

x	$f(x)$
0	1
1	0
2	1
3	2
−1	2
−2	3

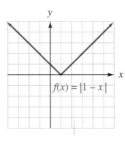

D: all reals; R: all real numbers greater than or equal to 0

22. BOATING   The graph in Illustration 4 shows the vertical distance from a point on the tip of a propeller to the centerline as the propeller spins. Is this the graph of a function?   yes

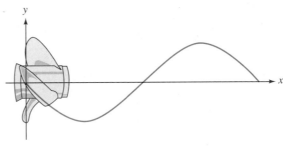

ILLUSTRATION 4

In Exercises 23–26, simplify each expression. Write each answer without using parentheses or negative exponents.

23. $(x^5)^2(x^7)^3$ x^{31}

24. $\left(\dfrac{a^3b}{c^4}\right)^5$ $\dfrac{a^{15}b^5}{c^{20}}$

25. $4^{-3} \cdot 4^{-2} \cdot 4^5$ 1

26. $(a^{-2}b^3)^{-4}$ $\dfrac{a^8}{b^{12}}$

27. ASTRONOMY   The **parsec**, a unit of distance used in astronomy, is 3×10^{16} meters. The distance to Betelgeuse, a star in the constellation Orion, is 1.6×10^2 parsecs. Use scientific notation to express this distance in meters. 4.8×10^{18} m

28. NCAA MEN'S BASKETBALL   The graph in Illustration 5 shows the University of Connecticut's lead or deficit during the second half of the 1999 championship game with Duke University.
   a. How many x-intercepts does the graph have? Explain their importance.

   3; they indicate that the game was tied 3 times in the second half.

   b. Give the coordinates of the highest point and the lowest point on the graph. What is the importance of each?

   (11, 6); in the second half, UConn had its largest lead (6 points) after 11 minutes had elapsed. (4, −5); in the second half, UConn faced its largest deficit (5 points) after 4 minutes had elapsed.

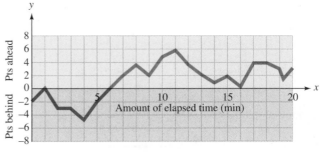

ILLUSTRATION 5

Do the indicated operations.

29. $(-r^4st^2)(2r^2st)(rst)$ $-2r^7s^3t^4$

30. $(-3t + 2s)(2t - 3s)$ $-6t^2 + 13st - 6s^2$

31. $(3a^2 - 2a + 4) - (a^2 - 3a + 7)$ $2a^2 + a - 3$

32. $(y - 6)^2$ $y^2 - 12y + 36$

33. $\dfrac{4x - 3y + 8z}{4xy}$ $\dfrac{1}{y} - \dfrac{3}{4x} + \dfrac{2z}{xy}$

34. $2 + x\overline{)3x + 2x^2 - 2}$ $2x - 1$

Factor each expression completely.

35. $3x^2y - 6xy^2$ $3xy(x - 2y)$

36. $2x^2 + 2xy - 3x - 3y$ $(x + y)(2x - 3)$

37. $25p^4 - 16q^2$ $(5p^2 + 4q)(5p^2 - 4q)$

38. $3x^3 - 243x$ $3x(x + 9)(x - 9)$

39. $x^2 - 11x - 12$ $(x - 12)(x + 1)$

40. $a^3 + 8b^3$ $(a + 2b)(a^2 - 2ab + 4b^2)$

41. $6a^2 - 7a - 20$ $(3a + 4)(2a - 5)$

42. $16m^2 - 20m - 6$ $2(4m + 1)(2m - 3)$

In Exercises 43–46, solve each equation.

43. $x^2 + 3x + 2 = 0$ $-1, -2$

44. $5x^2 = 10x$ $0, 2$

45. $6x^2 - x - 2 = 0$ $\frac{2}{3}, -\frac{1}{2}$

46. $2y^2 = 12 - 5y$ $\frac{3}{2}, -4$

47. CHILDREN'S STICKER   A rectangular-shaped sticker has an area of 20 cm². The width is 1 cm shorter than the length. (See Illustration 6.) Find the length of the sticker.   5 cm

(l – 1) cm

l cm

ILLUSTRATION 6

48. For what value of x is $\dfrac{4x}{x - 6}$ undefined?   6

Simplify each expression.

49. $\dfrac{x^2 + 2x + 1}{x^2 - 1}$ $\dfrac{x + 1}{x - 1}$

50. $-\dfrac{15a^2}{25a^3}$ $-\dfrac{3}{5a}$

Do the operation(s) and simplify when possible.

51. $\dfrac{p^2 - p - 6}{3p - 9} \div \dfrac{p^2 + 6p + 9}{p^2 - 9}$ $\dfrac{(p + 2)(p - 3)}{3(p + 3)}$

52. $\dfrac{x^2y^2}{cd} \cdot \dfrac{d^2}{c^2x}$ $\dfrac{xy^2d}{c^3}$

53. $\dfrac{x + 2}{x + 5} - \dfrac{x - 3}{x + 7}$ $\dfrac{7x + 29}{(x + 5)(x + 7)}$

54. $\dfrac{3x}{x + 2} + \dfrac{5x}{x + 2} - \dfrac{7x - 2}{x + 2}$ 1

55. $\dfrac{3a}{2b} - \dfrac{2b}{3a}$ $\dfrac{9a^2 - 4b^2}{6ab}$

56. $\dfrac{\dfrac{1}{x} + \dfrac{1}{y}}{\dfrac{1}{x} - \dfrac{1}{y}}$ $\dfrac{y + x}{y - x}$

In Exercises 57–58, solve each equation.

57. $\dfrac{4}{a} = \dfrac{6}{a} - 1$ 2

58. $\dfrac{a + 2}{a + 3} - 1 = \dfrac{-1}{a^2 + 2a - 3}$ 2

59. Solve the formula $\dfrac{1}{r} = \dfrac{1}{r_1} + \dfrac{1}{r_2}$ for r. $r = \dfrac{r_1r_2}{r_2 + r_1}$

60. ONLINE SALES   A company found that, on average, it made 9 online sales transactions for every 500 hits on its Internet Web site. If the company's Web site had 360,000 hits in one year, how many sales transactions did it have that year?   6,480

61. Assume that y varies inversely with x. If $y = 8$ when $x = 2$, find y when $x = 8$.   2

62. FILLING A POOL   An inlet pipe can fill an empty swimming pool in 5 hours, and another inlet pipe can fill the pool in 4 hours. How long will it take both pipes to fill the pool? $2\frac{2}{9}$ hr

In Exercises 63–64, solve each system of equations. If the equations of a system are dependent or if a system is inconsistent, so indicate.

63. $\begin{cases} x = y + 4 \\ 2x + y = 5 \end{cases}$ $(3, -1)$

64. $\begin{cases} \frac{3}{5}s + \frac{4}{5}t = 1 \\ -\frac{1}{4}s + \frac{3}{8}t = 1 \end{cases}$ $(-1, 2)$

65. FINANCIAL PLANNING   In investing \$6,000 of a couple's money, a financial planner put some of it into a savings account paying 6% annual interest. The rest was invested in a riskier mini-mall development plan paying 12% annually. The combined interest earned for the first year was \$540. How much money was invested at each rate? Use two variables to solve this problem.
6%: \$3,000; 12%: \$3,000

66. Graph the solution of $\begin{cases} 3x + 2y \geq 6 \\ x + 3y \leq 6 \end{cases}$

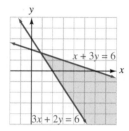

Simplify each expression. All variables represent positive numbers.

67. $\sqrt{\dfrac{49}{225}}$ $\frac{7}{15}$

68. $-\sqrt[3]{-27}$ 3

69. $-12x\sqrt{16x^2y^3}$ $-48x^2y\sqrt{y}$

70. $\sqrt{48} - \sqrt{8} + \sqrt{27} - \sqrt{32}$ $7\sqrt{3} - 6\sqrt{2}$

71. $\left(\sqrt{y} - 4\right)\left(\sqrt{y} - 5\right)$ $y - 9\sqrt{y} + 20$

72. $\left(-5\sqrt{6}\right)\left(4\sqrt{3}\right)$ $-60\sqrt{2}$

73. $\dfrac{4}{\sqrt{20}}$ $\frac{2\sqrt{5}}{5}$

74. $\dfrac{\sqrt{x} - 3}{\sqrt{x} + 3}$ $\dfrac{x - 6\sqrt{x} + 9}{x - 9}$

75. Solve $\sqrt{6x + 19} - 5 = 2$. 5

76. ▦ CARGO SPACE   How wide a piece of plywood can be stored diagonally in the back of the van shown in Illustration 7?   73 in.

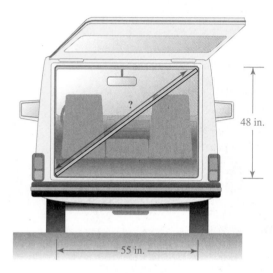

ILLUSTRATION 7

Quadratic Equations

9

WE HAVE PREVIOUSLY SOLVED QUADRATIC EQUATIONS BY FACTORING. IN THIS CHAPTER, WE WILL DISCUSS THREE OTHER METHODS THAT ARE USED TO SOLVE "QUADRATICS."

9.1 Completing the Square

In this section, you will learn about

- The square root method • Completing the square
- Solving equations with leading coefficients of 1
- Solving equations with leading coefficients other than 1

INTRODUCTION. Recall that equations that involve second-degree polynomials are called *quadratic equations.*

Quadratic equations

> A **quadratic equation** is an equation that can be written in the form
> $$ax^2 + bx + c = 0 \qquad (a \neq 0)$$
> where a, b, and c represent real numbers. This form is called **quadratic form.**

Some examples of quadratic equations are
$$x^2 + 12x - 13 = 0, \qquad 3q^2 = 3q + 2, \qquad a^2 - 5a = 0, \qquad \text{and} \qquad x^2 = 16.$$

In Chapter 5, we solved quadratic equations using the factoring method. In this section, we will discuss two new methods for solving quadratic equations. The first, called the *square root method,* is used when one side of the equation to solve is a quantity squared and the other side is a constant. The second method, called *completing the square,* involves the concept of perfect square trinomials.

The square root method

If $x^2 = 9$, x is a number whose square is 9. Since $3^2 = 9$ and $(-3)^2 = 9$, the equation $x^2 = 9$ has two solutions, $x = \sqrt{9} = 3$ and $x = -\sqrt{9} = -3$. In general, any equation of the form $x^2 = c$, where $c > 0$, has two solutions.

The square root method

> If c represents a positive real number, the equation $x^2 = c$ has two solutions:
> $$x = \sqrt{c} \qquad \text{or} \qquad x = -\sqrt{c}$$

We can write the previous result with **double-sign notation.** The statement
$$x = \pm\sqrt{c} \qquad \left(\text{read as "}x\text{ equals positive or negative } \sqrt{c}\text{"}\right)$$
means that $x = \sqrt{c}$ or $x = -\sqrt{c}$.

EXAMPLE 1   *Solving equations using the square root method.*
Solve $x^2 = 16$.

Solution

We use the square root method to find that the equation has two solutions.

$$x^2 = 16$$
$$x = \pm\sqrt{16} \quad \pm\sqrt{16} \text{ means that } x = \sqrt{16} \text{ or } x = -\sqrt{16}.$$
$$x = \pm 4 \qquad \text{Simplify: } \sqrt{16} = 4.$$

The solutions of $x^2 = 16$ are 4 and -4.

Check: **For $x = 4$**   **For $x = -4$**
$$x^2 = 16 \qquad\qquad x^2 = 16$$
$$4^2 \stackrel{?}{=} 16 \qquad\qquad (-4)^2 \stackrel{?}{=} 16$$
$$16 = 16 \qquad\qquad 16 = 16$$

Self Check
Solve $x^2 = 25$.

Answer: ± 5

The equation in Example 1 can also be solved by factoring.

$$x^2 = 16$$
$$x^2 - 16 = 0 \qquad \text{Subtract 16 from both sides.}$$
$$(x + 4)(x - 4) = 0 \qquad \text{Factor the difference of two squares.}$$
$$x + 4 = 0 \quad \text{or} \quad x - 4 = 0$$
$$x = -4 \qquad\qquad x = 4$$

COMMENT   When using the square root method to solve an equation, always write the $\pm$ symbol, or you will lose one of the solutions. For example, consider the equation from Example 1.

$$x^2 = 16$$
$$x = \pm\sqrt{16}$$

If you don't write this symbol, you will lose the solution $x = -\sqrt{16}$, which is $x = -4$.

EXAMPLE 2   *The square root method.*   Solve $3x^2 - 9 = 0$.

Solution

To solve the equation by the square root method, we first isolate x^2.

$$3x^2 - 9 = 0$$
$$3x^2 = 9 \qquad \text{Add 9 to both sides.}$$
$$x^2 = 3 \qquad \text{Divide both sides by 3.}$$
$$x = \pm\sqrt{3} \quad \text{Use the square root method.}$$

Check: **For $x = \sqrt{3}$**   **For $x = -\sqrt{3}$**
$$3x^2 - 9 = 0 \qquad\qquad 3x^2 - 9 = 0$$
$$3\left(\sqrt{3}\right)^2 - 9 \stackrel{?}{=} 0 \qquad 3\left(-\sqrt{3}\right)^2 - 9 = 0$$
$$3(3) - 9 \stackrel{?}{=} 0 \qquad\qquad 3(3) - 9 \stackrel{?}{=} 0$$
$$9 - 9 \stackrel{?}{=} 0 \qquad\qquad 9 - 9 \stackrel{?}{=} 0$$
$$0 = 0 \qquad\qquad 0 = 0$$

The solutions of $3x^2 - 9 = 0$ are $\sqrt{3}$ and $-\sqrt{3}$. Note that these are exact solutions. Using a calculator, we can approximate them to the nearest hundredth: $x \approx \pm 1.73$.

Self Check
Solve $2x^2 - 10 = 0$. Give the exact solutions and approximations to the nearest hundredth.

Answer: $\pm\sqrt{5}$; ± 2.24

EXAMPLE 3   *Hurricane.*   In 1998, Hurricane Mitch dumped heavy rains on Central America, causing extensive flooding in Honduras, Belize, and Guatemala. Figure 9-1 shows the position of the storm on October 26, at which time the weather service estimated that it covered an area of about 71,000 square miles. What was the diameter of the storm?

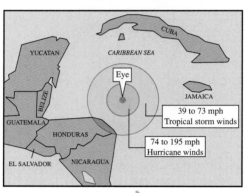

FIGURE 9-1

Solution   We can use the formula for the area of a circle to find the *radius* (in miles) of the circular-shaped storm.

$$A = \pi r^2$$

$\textbf{71,000} = \pi r^2$ Substitute 71,000 for the area A.

$\dfrac{71,000}{\pi} = r^2$ Divide both sides by π to isolate r^2.

Now we use the square root method to solve for r.

$$r = \sqrt{\frac{71,000}{\pi}} \qquad \text{or} \qquad r = -\sqrt{\frac{71,000}{\pi}}$$

Using a calculator to approximate the square root, we have

$r \approx 150.3329702$ The units are miles. The second solution is discarded, because the radius cannot be negative.

If we multiply the radius by 2, we find that the diameter of the storm was about 300 miles.   ■

EXAMPLE 4   *The square root method.*   Solve $(x - 1)^2 = 18$.

Solution

$(x - 1)^2 = 18$

$x - 1 = \pm\sqrt{18}$ Use the square root method to solve for $x - 1$.

To solve for x, we undo the subtraction of 1 on the left-hand side by adding 1 to both sides. In this case, when adding (or subtracting) a number on the right-hand side, we customarily write it *in front of* the radical expression.

$x - 1 = \pm\sqrt{18}$

$x - 1 + 1 = 1 \pm \sqrt{18}$ Add 1 to both sides, to isolate x.

$x = 1 \pm \sqrt{18}$ Simplify the left-hand side.

$x = 1 \pm 3\sqrt{2}$ Simplify the radical: $\sqrt{18} = \sqrt{9 \cdot 2} = 3\sqrt{2}$.

The solutions are $1 \pm 3\sqrt{2}$ (read as "1 plus or minus $3\sqrt{2}$"). We can approximate each of them to the nearest hundredth.

$1 + 3\sqrt{2} \approx 5.24$ $\qquad\qquad$ $1 - 3\sqrt{2} \approx -3.24$

Self Check
Solve $(x - 3)^2 = 8$.

Answer: $3 + 2\sqrt{2} \approx 5.83$,
$3 - 2\sqrt{2} \approx 0.17$ ■

Completing the square

In Section 5.5, we solved quadratic equations such as $x^2 + 12x - 13 = 0$ using the factoring method.

$$x^2 + 12x - 13 = 0$$

$$(x - 1)(x + 13) = 0 \qquad \text{Factor the trinomial } x^2 + 12x - 13.$$

$$x - 1 = 0 \quad \text{or} \quad x + 13 = 0 \qquad \text{Set each factor equal to 0.}$$

$$x = 1 \qquad\qquad x = -13 \quad \text{Solve each linear equation.}$$

The solutions of $x^2 + 12x - 13 = 0$ are $x = 1$ or $x = -13$.

Not every quadratic equation can be solved using the factoring method. For example, the trinomial in the equation $x^2 + 4x - 13 = 0$ cannot be factored using any of the techniques we have studied previously. To solve such equations, we can use another method called *completing the square*. It is based on the following **special products:**

$$x^2 + 2bx + b^2 = (x + b)^2 \qquad \text{and} \qquad x^2 - 2bx + b^2 = (x - b)^2$$

The trinomials $x^2 + 2bx + b^2$ and $x^2 - 2bx + b^2$ are both perfect square trinomials, since each one factors as the square of a binomial. In each trinomial, if we take one-half of the coefficient of the x and square it, we get the third term.

In $x^2 + 2bx + b^2$, if we take $\frac{1}{2}(2b)$, which is b, and square it, we get the third term, b^2.

In $x^2 - 2bx + b^2$, if we take $\frac{1}{2}(-2b) = -b$ and square it, we get $(-b)^2 = b^2$, which is the third term.

To change a binomial such as $x^2 + 12x$ into a perfect square trinomial, we take one-half of the coefficient of x (the 12), square it, and add it to $x^2 + 12x$.

$$x^2 + 12x + \left[\frac{1}{2}(12)\right]^2 = x^2 + 12x + (6)^2$$

$$= x^2 + 12x + 36$$

This result is a perfect square trinomial, because $x^2 + 12x + 36 = (x + 6)^2$.

EXAMPLE 5 *Completing the square.* Change each expression into a perfect square trinomial: **a.** $x^2 + 4x$, **b.** $x^2 - 6x$, and **c.** $x^2 - 5x$.

Solution

a. Since the coefficient of x is 4, we add the square of one-half of 4.

$$x^2 + 4x + \left[\frac{1}{2}(4)\right]^2 = x^2 + 4x + (2)^2 \quad \text{Simplify: } \tfrac{1}{2}(4) = 2.$$

$$= x^2 + 4x + 4 \qquad \text{This is } (x + 2)^2.$$

b. Since the coefficient of x is -6, we add the square of one-half of -6.

$$x^2 - 6x + \left[\frac{1}{2}(-6)\right]^2 = x^2 - 6x + (-3)^2 \quad \text{Simplify: } \tfrac{1}{2}(-6) = -3.$$

$$= x^2 - 6x + 9 \qquad \text{This is } (x - 3)^2.$$

c. Since the coefficient of x is -5, we add the square of one-half of -5.

$$x^2 - 5x + \left[\frac{1}{2}(-5)\right]^2 = x^2 - 5x + \left(-\frac{5}{2}\right)^2 \quad \text{Simplify: } \tfrac{1}{2}(-5) = -\tfrac{5}{2}.$$

$$= x^2 - 5x + \frac{25}{4} \qquad \text{This is } \left(x - \tfrac{5}{2}\right)^2.$$

Self Check

Change each expression into a perfect square trinomial:

a. $y^2 + 6y$

b. $y^2 - 8y$

c. $y^2 + 3y$

Answers: **a.** $y^2 + 6y + 9$,

b. $y^2 - 8y + 16$,

c. $y^2 + 3y + \dfrac{9}{4}$

Solving equations with leading coefficients of 1

If the quadratic equation $ax^2 + bx + c = 0$ has a leading coefficient of 1, it's easy to solve by completing the square.

EXAMPLE 6 *Completing the square.* Solve $x^2 + 4x - 13 = 0$. Give each answer to the nearest hundredth.

Solution

Since the coefficient of x^2 is 1, we can complete the square as follows:

$$x^2 + 4x - 13 = 0$$

$$x^2 + 4x = 13 \quad \text{Add 13 to both sides so that the constant term is on the right-hand side.}$$

We then find one-half of the coefficient of x, square it, and add the result to both sides to make the left-hand side a perfect square trinomial.

$$x^2 + 4x + \left[\frac{1}{2}(4)\right]^2 = 13 + \left[\frac{1}{2}(4)\right]^2 \quad \text{Since the coefficient of } x \text{ is 4, add the square of one-half of 4.}$$

$$x^2 + 4x + 4 = 13 + 4 \quad \text{Simplify: } \frac{1}{2}(4) = 2. \text{ Then square 2.}$$

$$(x + 2)^2 = 17 \quad \text{Factor } x^2 + 4x + 4 \text{ and simplify.}$$

$$x + 2 = \pm\sqrt{17} \quad \text{Use the square root method to solve for } x + 2.$$

$$x = -2 \pm \sqrt{17} \quad \text{Subtract 2 from both sides to isolate } x. \text{ Write } -2 \text{ in front of the radical.}$$

We can use a calculator to approximate each solution.

$$x = -2 + \sqrt{17} \qquad \text{or} \qquad x = -2 - \sqrt{17}$$

$$x \approx -2 + 4.123105626 \qquad\qquad x \approx 2 - 4.123105626$$

$$x \approx 2.12 \qquad\qquad\qquad\qquad x \approx -6.12$$

EXAMPLE 7 *Completing the square.* Solve $x^2 - 7x = 2$.

Solution

The constant term is already on the right-hand side. To complete the square on the left-hand side, we find one-half of the coefficient of x and add its square to both sides.

$$x^2 - 7x = 2$$

$$x^2 - 7x + \left[\frac{1}{2}(-7)\right]^2 = 2 + \left[\frac{1}{2}(-7)\right]^2 \quad \text{Since the coefficient of } x \text{ is } -7, \text{ add the square of one-half of } -7.$$

$$x^2 - 7x + \frac{49}{4} = 2 + \frac{49}{4} \quad \text{Simplify: } \frac{1}{2}(-7) = -\frac{7}{2}. \text{ Then square } -\frac{7}{2}.$$

$$\left(x - \frac{7}{2}\right)^2 = \frac{8}{4} + \frac{49}{4} \quad \text{Factor the left-hand side. Write 2 as } \frac{8}{4}.$$

$$\left(x - \frac{7}{2}\right)^2 = \frac{57}{4} \quad \text{The fractions have a common denominator. Add them.}$$

$$x - \frac{7}{2} = \pm\sqrt{\frac{57}{4}} \quad \text{Use the square root method to solve for } x - \frac{7}{2}.$$

$$x - \frac{7}{2} = \pm\frac{\sqrt{57}}{2} \quad \text{Simplify: } \sqrt{\frac{57}{4}} = \frac{\sqrt{57}}{\sqrt{4}} = \frac{\sqrt{57}}{2}.$$

Self Check

Solve $x^2 + 10x - 4 = 0$. Give the exact solutions and approximations to the nearest hundredth.

Answers: $-5 + \sqrt{29}$, $-5 - \sqrt{29}$; 0.39, -10.39 ■

Self Check

Solve $x^2 + 5x = 3$. Approximate the solutions to the nearest hundredth.

$$x = \frac{7}{2} \pm \frac{\sqrt{57}}{2} \qquad \text{Add } \tfrac{7}{2} \text{ to both sides.}$$

$$x = \frac{7 \pm \sqrt{57}}{2} \qquad \begin{array}{l}\text{Since the fractions have a common}\\ \text{denominator of 2, we can combine them.}\end{array}$$

If we approximate the solutions to the nearest hundredth, we have

$$\frac{7 + \sqrt{57}}{2} \approx 7.27 \qquad \text{and} \qquad \frac{7 - \sqrt{57}}{2} \approx -0.27$$

Answer: $\dfrac{-5 \pm \sqrt{37}}{2}$;

$0.54, -5.54$ ∎

Solving equations with leading coefficients other than 1

If the quadratic equation $ax^2 + bx + c = 0$ has a leading coefficient other than 1, we can make the leading coefficient 1 by dividing both sides of the equation by a.

EXAMPLE 8 *Completing the square.* Solve $4x^2 + 4x - 3 = 0$.

Solution

We divide both sides by 4 so that the coefficient of x^2 is 1. We then proceed as follows:

$$4x^2 + 4x - 3 = 0$$

$$x^2 + x - \frac{3}{4} = 0 \qquad \text{Divide both sides by 4: } \frac{4x^2}{4} + \frac{4x}{4} - \frac{3}{4} = \frac{0}{4}.$$

$$x^2 + x = \frac{3}{4} \qquad \begin{array}{l}\text{Add } \tfrac{3}{4} \text{ to both sides so that the constant term}\\ \text{is on the right-hand side.}\end{array}$$

$$x^2 + 1x + \left[\frac{1}{2}(1)\right]^2 = \frac{3}{4} + \left[\frac{1}{2}(1)\right]^2 \qquad \begin{array}{l}\text{Since the coefficient of } x \text{ is 1, add the square}\\ \text{of one-half of 1.}\end{array}$$

$$x^2 + x + \frac{1}{4} = \frac{3}{4} + \frac{1}{4} \qquad \text{Simplify: } \tfrac{1}{2}(1) = \tfrac{1}{2}. \text{ Then square } \tfrac{1}{2}.$$

$$\left(x + \frac{1}{2}\right)^2 = 1 \qquad \text{Factor and add.}$$

$$x + \frac{1}{2} = \pm 1 \qquad \begin{array}{l}\text{Solve for } x + \tfrac{1}{2} \text{ using the square root}\\ \text{method.}\end{array}$$

$$x = -\frac{1}{2} \pm 1 \qquad \text{Subtract } \tfrac{1}{2} \text{ from both sides to isolate } x.$$

$$x = -\frac{1}{2} + 1 \quad \text{or} \quad x = -\frac{1}{2} - 1$$

$$x = \frac{1}{2} \qquad\qquad x = -\frac{3}{2}$$

Self Check

Solve $2x^2 - 5x - 3 = 0$.

Answer: $3, -\frac{1}{2}$ ∎

COMMENT In Example 8, you may have noticed that $4x^2 + 4x - 3$ can be factored. Therefore, we could have solved $4x^2 + 4x - 3 = 0$ using the factoring method. This example illustrates an important fact: Completing the square can be used to solve *any* quadratic equation.

The previous examples illustrate that to solve a quadratic equation by completing the square, we follow these steps.

Completing the square to solve a quadratic equation

1. Write the equation in $ax^2 + bx + c = 0$ form. If the coefficient of x^2 is not 1, make it 1 by dividing both sides of the equation by the coefficient of x^2.

2. If necessary, add or subtract a number on both sides of the equation to get the constant term on the right-hand side.

3. Complete the square.
   a. Find half the coefficient of x and square it.
   b. Add that square to both sides of the equation.

4. Factor the perfect square trinomial and combine terms.

5. Solve the resulting quadratic equation using the square root method.

6. Check each solution.

EXAMPLE 9   *Solving equations by completing the square.*   Solve $2x^2 - 2 = 4x$.

Self Check

Solve $3x^2 - 18x = -12$.

Solution

We write the equation in $ax^2 + bx + c = 0$ form to see if it can be solved by factoring.

$2x^2 - 4x - 2 = 0$ Subtract $4x$ from both sides to get 0 on the right-hand side.

(1) $x^2 - 2x - 1 = 0$ Divide both sides by 2: $\dfrac{2x^2}{2} - \dfrac{4x}{2} - \dfrac{2}{2} = \dfrac{0}{2}$.

Since Equation 1 cannot be solved by factoring, we complete the square.

$$x^2 - 2x = 1 \qquad \text{Add 1 to both sides.}$$

$$x^2 - 2x + \left[\tfrac{1}{2}(-2)\right]^2 = 1 + \left[\tfrac{1}{2}(-2)\right]^2 \qquad \text{Since the coefficient of } x \text{ is } -2, \text{ add the square of one-half of } -2.$$

$$x^2 - 2x + 1 = 1 + 1 \qquad \text{Simplify: } \tfrac{1}{2}(-2) = -1. \text{ Then square } -1.$$

$$(x - 1)^2 = 2 \qquad \text{Factor and simplify.}$$

$$x - 1 = \pm\sqrt{2} \qquad \text{Use the square root method to solve for } x - 1.$$

$$x = 1 \pm \sqrt{2} \qquad \text{Add 1 to both sides.}$$

$$x = 1 + \sqrt{2} \quad \text{or} \quad x = 1 - \sqrt{2}$$

Answer: $3 \pm \sqrt{5}$ ∎

STUDY SET   Section 9.1

VOCABULARY   *Fill in the blanks.*

1. If the polynomial in the equation $ax^2 + bx + c = 0$ doesn't factor, we can solve the equation by ___completing___ the square.

2. Since $x^2 + 12x + 36 = (x + 6)^2$, we call the trinomial a perfect ___square___ trinomial.

3. In the equation $x^2 - 4x + 1 = 0$, the ___coefficient___ of x is -4.

4. A ___solution___ of an equation is a value of the variable that makes the equation true.

CONCEPTS   *In Exercises 5–8, fill in the blanks.*

5. The equation $x^2 = c$, where $c > 0$, has ___two___ solutions.

6. The solutions of $x^2 = c$, where $c > 0$, are $\sqrt{c}$ and $-\sqrt{c}$.

7. To complete the square on $x^2 + 8x$, we add the ___square___ of one-half of 8, which is 16.

8. To complete the square on $x^2 - 10x$, we add the square of ___one-half___ of -10, which is 25.

9. What is the first step if we solve $x^2 - 2x = 35$
   a. by the factoring method?
      Subtract 35 from both sides.
   b. by completing the square?   Add 1 to both sides.

10. The equation $n^2 - 4n + 6 = 0$ is written in $ax^2 + bx + c = 0$ form. What is b? -4

11. a. To solve $x^2 - 2x - 1 = 0$, we must complete the square. Why can't we use the factoring method?
because $x^2 - 2x - 1 = 0$ doesn't factor
  b. Can any quadratic equation be solved by completing the square? yes

12. Solve $x^2 - 81$ by using
  a. the square root method. ± 9
  b. the factoring method. ± 9

13. What is one-half of the given number?
  a. 4 $\quad 2$ **b.** -8 $\quad -4$
  c. 5 $\quad \frac{5}{2}$ **d.** -7 $\quad -\frac{7}{2}$

14. Find one-half of the given number and then square the result.
  a. 6 $\quad 9$ **b.** -12 $\quad 36$
  c. 3 $\quad \frac{9}{4}$ **d.** -5 $\quad \frac{25}{4}$

15. What is the result when both sides of $2x^2 + 4x - 8 = 0$ are divided by 2? $\quad x^2 + 2x - 4 = 0$

16. Write $3x^2 = -4x + 8$ in $ax^2 + bx + c = 0$ form. What is b? $\quad 3x^2 + 4x - 8 = 0;\ 4$

NOTATION *Complete each solution to solve the equation.*

17.
$$(y - 1)^2 = 9$$
$$y - 1 = \sqrt{9} \quad \text{or} \quad y - 1 = -\sqrt{9}$$
$$y - 1 = 3 \qquad\qquad y - 1 = -3$$
$$y = 4 \qquad\qquad\qquad y = -2$$

18.
$$y^2 + 2y - 3 = 0$$
$$y^2 + 2y = 3$$
$$y^2 + 2y + 1 = 3 + 1$$
$$(y + 1)^2 = 4$$
$$y + 1 = \sqrt{4} \quad \text{or} \quad y + 1 = -\sqrt{4}$$
$$y + 1 = 2 \qquad\qquad y + 1 = -2$$
$$y = 1 \qquad\qquad\qquad y = -3$$

19. a. In solving a quadratic equation, a student obtains $x = \pm\sqrt{10}$. How many solutions are represented by this notation? List them. two; $\sqrt{10}, -\sqrt{10}$
  b. In solving a quadratic equation, a student obtains $x = 8 \pm \sqrt{3}$. List each solution separately. Then round each one to the nearest hundredth.
  $8 + \sqrt{3}, 8 - \sqrt{3}; 9.73, 6.27$

20. Solve $x + 1 = \pm\sqrt{2}$ for x. $\quad -1 \pm \sqrt{2}$

PRACTICE *Use the square root method to solve each equation.*

21. $x^2 = 1$ $\quad \pm 1$ **22.** $r^2 = 4$ $\quad \pm 2$

23. $x^2 = 9$ $\quad \pm 3$ **24.** $x^2 = 32$ $\quad \pm 4\sqrt{2}$

25. $t^2 = 20$ $\quad \pm 2\sqrt{5}$ **26.** $x^2 = 0$ $\quad 0, 0$

27. $3m^2 = 27$ $\quad \pm 3$ **28.** $4x^2 = 64$ $\quad \pm 4$

29. $4x^2 = 16$ $\quad \pm 2$ **30.** $5x^2 = 125$ $\quad \pm 5$

31. $x^2 = \dfrac{9}{16}$ $\quad \pm\frac{3}{4}$ **32.** $x^2 = \dfrac{81}{25}$ $\quad \pm\frac{9}{5}$

33. $(x + 1)^2 = 25$ $\quad -6, 4$ **34.** $(x - 1)^2 = 49$ $\quad -6, 8$

35. $(x + 2)^2 = 81$ $\quad 7, -11$ **36.** $(x + 3)^2 = 16$ $\quad 1, -7$

37. $(x - 2)^2 = 8$
$2 \pm 2\sqrt{2}$
  38. $(x + 2)^2 = 50$
$-2 \pm 5\sqrt{2}$

Use the square root method to solve each equation. Use a calculator to approximate the solutions. Round to the nearest hundredth.

39. $x^2 = 45.82$ $\quad \pm 6.77$ **40.** $x^2 = 6.05$ $\quad \pm 2.46$

41. $(x + 2)^2 = 90.04$
$7.49, -11.49$
  42. $(x - 5)^2 = 33.31$
$10.77, -0.77$

Factor the trinomial square and use the square root method to solve each equation.

43. $y^2 + 4y + 4 = 4$ $\quad 0, -4$

44. $y^2 - 6y + 9 = 9$ $\quad 0, 6$

45. $9x^2 - 12x + 4 = 16$ $\quad 2, -\frac{2}{3}$

46. $4x^2 - 20x + 25 = 36$ $\quad \frac{11}{2}, -\frac{1}{2}$

Complete the square to make a perfect square trinomial.

47. $x^2 + 2x$ $\quad x^2 + 2x + 1$ **48.** $x^2 + 12x$
$x^2 + 12x + 36$

49. $x^2 - 4x$ $\quad x^2 - 4x + 4$ **50.** $x^2 - 14x$
$x^2 - 14x + 49$

51. $x^2 + 7x$ $\quad x^2 + 7x + \frac{49}{4}$ **52.** $x^2 + 21x$
$x^2 + 21x + \frac{441}{4}$

53. $a^2 - 3a$ $\quad a^2 - 3a + \frac{9}{4}$ **54.** $b^2 - 13b$
$b^2 - 13b + \frac{169}{4}$

55. $b^2 + \dfrac{2}{3}b$ $\quad b^2 + \frac{2}{3}b + \frac{1}{9}$ **56.** $c^2 - \dfrac{5}{2}c$ $\quad c^2 - \frac{5}{2}c + \frac{25}{16}$

Solve each equation by completing the square.

57. $x^2 + 6x + 8 = 0$
$-2, -4$
  58. $x^2 + 8x + 12 = 0$
$-2, -6$

59. $k^2 - 8k + 12 = 0$
$2, 6$
  60. $p^2 - 4p + 3 = 0$ $\quad 3, 1$

61. $x^2 - 2x = 15$ $\quad 5, -3$ **62.** $x^2 - 2x = 8$ $\quad 4, -2$

63. $g^2 + 5g - 6 = 0$
$1, -6$
  64. $s^2 = 14 - 5s$ $\quad 2, -7$

65. $2x^2 = 4 - 2x$ $\quad 1, -2$ **66.** $3q^2 = 3q + 6$ $\quad 2, -1$

67. $3x^2 + 9x + 6 = 0$
$-1, -2$
  68. $3d^2 + 48 = -24d$
$-4, -4$

69. $2x^2 = 3x + 2$ $\quad 2, -\frac{1}{2}$ **70.** $3x^2 = 2 - 5x$ $\quad -2, \frac{1}{3}$

71. $4x^2 = 2 - 7x$ $\quad -2, \frac{1}{4}$ **72.** $2x^2 = 5x + 3$ $\quad 3, -\frac{1}{2}$

Solve each equation. Give the exact solutions, and then give the solutions rounded to the nearest hundredth.

73. $x^2 + 4x + 1 = 0$
$-2 \pm \sqrt{3}; -0.27, -3.73$

74. $x^2 + 6x + 2 = 0$
$-3 \pm \sqrt{7}; -0.35, -5.65$

75. $x^2 - 2x - 4 = 0$
$1 \pm \sqrt{5}; 3.24, -1.24$

76. $x^2 - 4x = 2$
$2 \pm \sqrt{6}; 4.45, -0.45$

77. $x^2 = 4x + 3$
$2 \pm \sqrt{7}; 4.65, -0.65$

78. $x^2 = 6x - 3$
$3 \pm \sqrt{6}; 5.45, 0.55$

79. $4x^2 + 4x + 1 = 20$
$\dfrac{-1 \pm 2\sqrt{5}}{2}; -2.74, 1.74$

80. $9x^2 = 8 - 12x$
$\dfrac{-2 \pm 2\sqrt{3}}{3}; 0.49, -1.82$

Write each equation in the form $ax^2 + bx + c = 0$ and solve it by completing the square.

81. $2x(x + 3) = 8$ $1, -4$

82. $3x(x - 2) = 9$ $3, -1$

83. $6(x^2 - 1) = 5x$ $\frac{3}{2}, -\frac{2}{3}$

84. $2(3x^2 - 2) = 5x$ $\frac{4}{3}, -\frac{1}{2}$

85. $x(x + 3) - \dfrac{1}{2} = -2$ $\dfrac{-3 \pm \sqrt{3}}{2}$

86. $x[(x - 2) + 3] = 3\left(x - \dfrac{2}{9}\right)$ $\dfrac{3 \pm \sqrt{3}}{3}$

APPLICATIONS

87. CAROUSEL   In 1999, the city of Lancaster, Pennsylvania considered installing a classic Dentzel carousel in an abandoned downtown building. After learning that the circular-shaped carousel (like that shown in Illustration 1) would occupy 2,376 square feet of floor space and that it was 26 feet high, the proposal was determined to be impractical because of the large remodeling costs. Find the diameter of the carousel to the nearest foot.   55 ft

ILLUSTRATION 1

88. ESCAPE VELOCITY   The speed at which a rocket must be fired for it to leave the earth's gravitational attraction is called the *escape velocity*. See Illustration 2. If the escape velocity v_e, in miles per hour, is given by

$$\frac{v_e^2}{2g} = R$$

where $g = 78.545$ and $R = 3,960$, find v_e. Round to the nearest mi/hr.   24,941 mi/hr

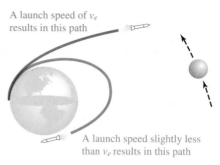

A launch speed of v_e results in this path

A launch speed slightly less than v_e results in this path

ILLUSTRATION 2

89. BICYCLE SAFETY   A bicycle training program for children uses a figure-8 course to help them improve their balance and steering. The course is laid out over a paved area covering 800 square feet, as shown in Illustration 3. Find its dimensions.   20 ft by 40 ft

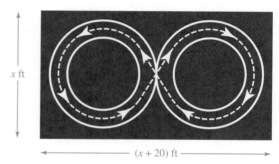

x ft

$(x + 20)$ ft

ILLUSTRATION 3

90. BADMINTON   The badminton court shown in Illustration 4 occupies 880 square feet of the floor space of a gymnasium. If its length is 4 feet more than twice its width, find its dimensions.   20 ft by 44 ft

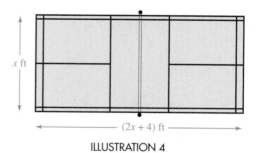

x ft

$(2x + 4)$ ft

ILLUSTRATION 4

WRITING

91. Explain how to complete the square on $x^2 - 5x$.

92. Explain the error in the following work.

Solve $x^2 = 28$.

$$x^2 = 28$$
$$x = \pm\sqrt{28}$$
$$x = 2 \pm \sqrt{7}$$

$\sqrt{28} = 2\sqrt{7}$. The 2 was incorrectly moved in front of the $\pm$ symbol. The correct answer is $\pm 2\sqrt{7}$.

93. Rounded to the nearest hundredth, one solution of the equation $x^2 + 4x + 1 = 0$ is -0.27. Use your calculator to check it. How could it be a solution if it doesn't make the left-hand side zero? Explain.

94. Give an example of a perfect square trinomial. Why do you think the word "perfect" is used to describe it?

REVIEW *Do each operation.*

95. $(y - 1)^2$
$y^2 - 2y + 1$

96. $(z + 2)^2$
$z^2 + 4z + 4$

97. $(x + y)^2$
$x^2 + 2xy + y^2$

98. $(a - b)^2$
$a^2 - 2ab + b^2$

99. $(2z)^2 \quad 4z^2$

100. $(xy)^2 \quad x^2y^2$

9.2 *The Quadratic Formula*

In this section, you will learn about

- The quadratic formula • Quadratic equations with no real solutions
- Applications

INTRODUCTION. We can solve any quadratic equation by completing the square, but the work is sometimes tedious. Fortunately, there is an easier way. In this section, we will develop a formula, called the *quadratic formula,* that will enable us to solve quadratic equations with much less effort.

The quadratic formula

We can solve the **general quadratic equation** $ax^2 + bx + c = 0$, where $a \neq 0$, by completing the square.

$$ax^2 + bx + c = 0$$

$$\frac{ax^2}{a} + \frac{bx}{a} + \frac{c}{a} = \frac{0}{a} \qquad \text{Divide both sides by } a \text{ so that the coefficient of } x^2 \text{ is 1.}$$

$$x^2 + \frac{b}{a}x + \frac{c}{a} = 0 \qquad \text{Simplify } \frac{\overset{1}{\cancel{a}}x^2}{\cancel{a}} = x^2. \text{ Write } \frac{bx}{a} \text{ as } \frac{b}{a}x.$$

$$x^2 + \frac{b}{a}x = -\frac{c}{a} \qquad \text{Subtract } \frac{c}{a} \text{ from both sides.}$$

Since the coefficient of x is $\frac{b}{a}$, we can complete the square on x by adding

$$\left(\frac{1}{2} \cdot \frac{b}{a}\right)^2 \qquad \text{or} \qquad \frac{b^2}{4a^2}$$

to both sides:

$$x^2 + \frac{b}{a}x + \frac{b^2}{4a^2} = \frac{b^2}{4a^2} - \frac{c}{a}$$

After factoring the perfect square trinomial on the left-hand side, we have

$$\left(x + \frac{b}{2a}\right)\left(x + \frac{b}{2a}\right) = \frac{b^2}{4a^2} - \frac{4ac}{4aa} \qquad \text{The lowest common denominator on the right-hand side is } 4a^2. \text{ Build the second fraction.}$$

(1)
$$\left(x + \frac{b}{2a}\right)^2 = \frac{b^2 - 4ac}{4a^2} \qquad \text{Subtract the numerators and write the difference over the common denominator.}$$

Equation 1 can be solved by the square root method to obtain

$$x + \frac{b}{2a} = \sqrt{\frac{b^2 - 4ac}{4a^2}} \qquad \text{or} \qquad x + \frac{b}{2a} = -\sqrt{\frac{b^2 - 4ac}{4a^2}}$$

$$x + \frac{b}{2a} = \frac{\sqrt{b^2 - 4ac}}{\sqrt{4a^2}} \qquad\qquad\qquad x + \frac{b}{2a} = -\frac{\sqrt{b^2 - 4ac}}{\sqrt{4a^2}}$$

$$x = -\frac{b}{2a} + \frac{\sqrt{b^2 - 4ac}}{2a} \qquad\qquad x = -\frac{b}{2a} - \frac{\sqrt{b^2 - 4ac}}{2a}$$

$$x = \frac{-b + \sqrt{b^2 - 4ac}}{2a} \qquad\qquad x = \frac{-b - \sqrt{b^2 - 4ac}}{2a}$$

These solutions are usually written in one formula called the **quadratic formula.**

Quadratic formula

The solutions of the quadratic equation $ax^2 + bx + c = 0$ are

$$x = \frac{-b \pm \sqrt{b^2 - 4ac}}{2a} \qquad (a \neq 0)$$

 COMMENT   When you write the quadratic formula, be careful to draw the fraction bar so that it includes the complete numerator. Do not write

$$x = -b \pm \frac{\sqrt{b^2 - 4ac}}{2a}$$

EXAMPLE 1   *The quadratic formula.*   Solve $x^2 + 5x + 6 = 0$.
Solution
The equation is written in $ax^2 + bx + c = 0$ form with $a = 1$, $b = 5$, and $c = 6$. We substitute these values into the quadratic formula and simplify.

$$x = \frac{-b \pm \sqrt{b^2 - 4ac}}{2a}$$ The quadratic formula.

$$= \frac{-5 \pm \sqrt{5^2 - 4(1)(6)}}{2(1)}$$ Substitute 1 for a, 5 for b, and 6 for c.

$$= \frac{-5 \pm \sqrt{25 - 24}}{2}$$ Evaluate the power and do the multiplication within the radical symbol.

$$= \frac{-5 \pm \sqrt{1}}{2}$$ Do the subtraction within the radical symbol.

$$x = \frac{-5 \pm 1}{2}$$ Simplify: $\sqrt{1} = 1$.

This notation represents two solutions. We simplify them separately, first using the $+$ sign and then using the $-$ sign.

$$x = \frac{-5 + 1}{2} \qquad \text{or} \qquad x = \frac{-5 - 1}{2}$$

$$x = \frac{-4}{2} \qquad\qquad\qquad x = \frac{-6}{2}$$

$$x = -2 \qquad\qquad\qquad x = -3$$

Self Check
Solve $x^2 + 6x + 5 = 0$.

Answer: $-1, -5$ ■

 COMMENT   In Example 1, you may have noticed that we could have solved $x^2 + 5x + 6 = 0$ using the factoring method. This example illustrates an important fact: The quadratic formula can be used to solve *any* quadratic equation.

EXAMPLE 2 *Writing equations in quadratic form.* Solve $2x^2 = 5x + 3$.

Self Check
Solve $4x^2 - 11x = 3$.

Solution
To identify a, b, and c, we must write the equation in quadratic form.

$$2x^2 = 5x + 3$$
$$2x^2 - 5x - 3 = 0 \qquad \text{Subtract } 5x \text{ and } 3 \text{ from both sides.}$$

In this equation, $a = 2$, $b = -5$, and $c = -3$. We substitute these values into the quadratic formula and simplify.

$$x = \frac{-b \pm \sqrt{b^2 - 4ac}}{2a} \qquad \text{The quadratic formula.}$$

$$= \frac{-(-5) \pm \sqrt{(-5)^2 - 4(2)(-3)}}{2(2)} \qquad \text{Substitute 2 for } a, -5 \text{ for } b, \text{ and } -3 \text{ for } c.$$

$$= \frac{5 \pm \sqrt{25 - (-24)}}{4} \qquad \begin{array}{l} -(-5) = 5. \text{ Evaluate the power and do the} \\ \text{multiplication within the radical symbol.} \end{array}$$

$$= \frac{5 \pm \sqrt{49}}{4} \qquad \begin{array}{l} \text{Do the subtraction within the radical symbol:} \\ 25 - (-24) = 25 + 24 = 49. \end{array}$$

$$= \frac{5 \pm 7}{4} \qquad \text{Simplify: } \sqrt{49} = 7.$$

Thus,

$$x = \frac{5 + 7}{4} \qquad \text{or} \qquad x = \frac{5 - 7}{4}$$

$$x = \frac{12}{4} \qquad\qquad\qquad x = \frac{-2}{4}$$

$$x = 3 \qquad\qquad\qquad x = -\frac{1}{2}$$

Answer: $3, -\dfrac{1}{4}$

∎

EXAMPLE 3 *Approximating solutions.* Solve $3x^2 = 2x + 4$. Round each solution to the nearest hundredth.

Self Check
Solve $2x^2 - 1 = 2x$. Round to the nearest hundredth.

Solution
We begin by writing the given equation in $ax^2 + bx + c = 0$ form.

$$3x^2 = 2x + 4$$
$$3x^2 - 2x - 4 = 0 \qquad \text{Subtract } 2x \text{ and } 4 \text{ from both sides.}$$

In this equation, $a = 3$, $b = -2$, and $c = -4$. We substitute these values into the quadratic formula and simplify.

$$x = \frac{-b \pm \sqrt{b^2 - 4ac}}{2a} \qquad \text{The quadratic formula.}$$

$$= \frac{-(-2) \pm \sqrt{(-2)^2 - 4(3)(-4)}}{2(3)} \qquad \text{Substitute 3 for } a, -2 \text{ for } b, \text{ and } -4 \text{ for } c.$$

$$= \frac{2 \pm \sqrt{4 + 48}}{6} \qquad \begin{array}{l} -(-2) = 2. \text{ Simplify within the radical} \\ \text{symbol.} \end{array}$$

$$= \frac{2 \pm \sqrt{52}}{6} \qquad \text{Do the addition within the radical symbol.}$$

$$= \frac{2 \pm 2\sqrt{13}}{6} \qquad \text{Simplify: } \sqrt{52} = \sqrt{4 \cdot 13} = 2\sqrt{13}.$$

$$= \frac{\overset{1}{\cancel{2}}\left(1 \pm \sqrt{13}\right)}{\underset{1}{\cancel{2} \cdot 3}}$$

In the numerator, factor out 2: $2 \pm 2\sqrt{13} = 2\left(1 \pm \sqrt{13}\right)$. Write 6 as $2 \cdot 3$. Then divide out the common factor of 2.

$$x = \frac{1 \pm \sqrt{13}}{3} \qquad \text{Simplify.}$$

Thus,

$$x = \frac{1 + \sqrt{13}}{3} \qquad \text{or} \qquad x = \frac{1 - \sqrt{13}}{3}$$

We can use a calculator to approximate each of these solutions. To the nearest hundredth,

$$\frac{1 + \sqrt{13}}{3} \approx 1.54 \qquad \text{and} \qquad \frac{1 - \sqrt{13}}{3} \approx -0.87$$

Answers: $\dfrac{1 + \sqrt{3}}{2} \approx 1.37,$

$\dfrac{1 - \sqrt{3}}{2} \approx -0.37$ ∎

Quadratic equations with no real solutions

The next example shows that some quadratic equations have no real-number solutions.

EXAMPLE 4 *An equation with no real-number solutions.* Solve $x^2 + 2x + 5 = 0$.

Solution

In this equation, $a = 1$, $b = 2$, and $c = 5$. We substitute these values into the quadratic formula.

$$x = \frac{-b \pm \sqrt{b^2 - 4ac}}{2a} \qquad \text{The quadratic formula.}$$

$$= \frac{-2 \pm \sqrt{2^2 - 4(1)(5)}}{2(1)} \qquad \text{Substitute 1 for } a, \text{ 2 for } b, \text{ and 5 for } c.$$

$$= \frac{-2 \pm \sqrt{4 - 20}}{2} \qquad \text{Evaluate the power and do the multiplication within the radical symbol.}$$

$$x = \frac{-2 \pm \sqrt{-16}}{2} \qquad \text{Do the subtraction within the radical symbol. The result is a negative number, } -16.$$

Since $\sqrt{-16}$ is not a real number, there are no real-number solutions.

Self Check

Does the equation

$$2x^2 + x + 1 = 0$$

have any real-number solutions?

Answer: no ∎

Applications

We have discussed several methods that are used to solve quadratic equations. To determine the most efficient method for a given equation, we can use the following strategy.

Strategy for solving quadratic equations

1. First, see whether the equation is in a form such that the **square root method** is easily applied.

2. If the square root method can't be used, write the equation in $ax^2 + bx + c = 0$ form.

3. Then see whether the equation can be solved using the **factoring method.**

4. If you can't factor the quadratic, solve the equation by **completing the square** or by the **quadratic formula.**

EXAMPLE 5   ***Nutrition.***   The poster in Figure 9-2 shows the six basic food groups, as established by the U.S. Department of Agriculture. If the area of the poster is 90 square inches and the base is 3 inches longer than the height, find the length of its base and its height.

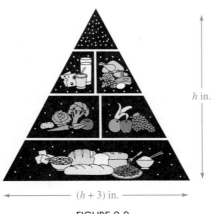

h in.

$(h + 3)$ in.

FIGURE 9-2

Analyze the problem   We are given the area of the triangular-shaped poster and asked to find the length of its base and its height.

Form an equation   Since the length of the base is related to the height, we let h represent the height of the triangle. Then $h + 3$ represents the length of the base. The area of a triangle is given by the formula $A = \frac{1}{2}bh$, which gives the equation

$\frac{1}{2}$	times	the length of the base	times	the height	equals	the area of the triangle.
$\frac{1}{2}$	$\cdot$	$(h + 3)$	$\cdot$	h	$=$	90

Solve the equation   To solve the equation $\frac{1}{2}(h + 3)h = 90$, we first write it in quadratic form.

$$\frac{1}{2}(h + 3)h = 90$$

$(h + 3)h = 180$ Multiply both sides by 2.

$h^2 + 3h = 180$ Distribute the multiplication by h.

$h^2 + 3h - 180 = 0$ Subtract 180 from both sides. The equation is now in quadratic form.

By inspection, we see that -180 has factors of -12 and 15 and that their sum is 3. Therefore, we can use the factoring method to solve the equation.

$(h - 12)(h + 15) = 0$ Factor $h^2 + 3h - 180$.

$h - 12 = 0$ or $h + 15 = 0$ Set each factor equal to 0.

$h = 12$ $h = -15$ Solve each linear equation.

State the conclusion   When $h = 12$, the length of the base, $h + 3$, is 15. We discard the solution $h = -15$, because the triangle cannot have a negative height. So the length of the base is 15 inches, and the height is 12 inches.

Check the result   With a base of 15 inches and a height of 12 inches, the base of the triangle is 3 inches longer than its height. Its area is $\frac{1}{2}(15)(12) = 90$ squaure inches. The solution checks.

EXAMPLE 6 *Movie stunt.* As part of an action scene in a movie, a stuntman is to fall from the top of a 95-foot-tall building into a large airbag directly below him on the ground, as shown in Figure 9-3. If an object falls s feet in t seconds, where $s = 16t^2$, and if the bag is inflated to a height of 10 feet, how long will the stuntman fall before making contact with the airbag?

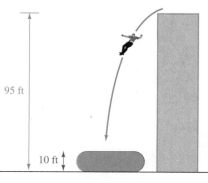

95 ft

10 ft

FIGURE 9-3

Solution If we subtract the height of the airbag from the height of the building, we find that the stuntman will fall $95 - 10 = 85$ feet. We substitute 85 for s in the formula and find that the equation is in a form that allows us to use the square root method.

$$s = 16t^2 \quad \text{The given formula.}$$

$$85 = 16t^2 \quad \text{Substitute 85 for } s.$$

$$\frac{85}{16} = t^2 \quad \text{Divide both sides by 16.}$$

$$\pm\sqrt{\frac{85}{16}} = t \quad \text{Use the square root method to solve the equation.}$$

$$\pm\frac{\sqrt{85}}{\sqrt{16}} = t \quad \text{The square root of a quotient is the quotient of the square roots.}$$

$$\pm\frac{\sqrt{85}}{4} = t \quad \sqrt{16} = 4.$$

The stuntman will fall for $\frac{\sqrt{85}}{4}$ seconds before making contact with the airbag. To the nearest tenth, this is 2.3 seconds. We discard the other solution, $-\frac{\sqrt{85}}{4}$, because a negative time does not make sense in this context. ∎

EXAMPLE 7 *Manufacturing.* A manufacturer of television parts receives an order for 52-inch picture tubes, measured along the diagonal as shown in Figure 9-4. The tubes are to be rectangular in shape and 4 inches wider than they are high. Find the dimensions of each tube.

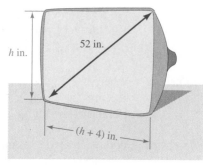

h in.

52 in.

$(h + 4)$ in.

FIGURE 9-4

Analyze the problem   We need to find the height and width of the rectangular picture tube. We note that two adjacent sides of the picture tube and a diagonal form a right triangle.

Form an equation   We can let h represent the height of the picture tube. Then $h + 4$ will represent the width. Since two adjacent sides and a diagonal of the tube form a right triangle, we can use the Pythagorean theorem to form the equation.

$$a^2 + b^2 = c^2 \qquad \text{The Pythagorean theorem.}$$
$$h^2 + (h + 4)^2 = 52^2 \qquad \text{Substitute } h \text{ for } a, (h + 4) \text{ for } b, \text{ and } 52 \text{ for } c.$$
$$h^2 + h^2 + 8h + 16 = 2{,}704 \qquad \text{Use the FOIL method: } (h + 4)^2 = h^2 + 8h + 16.$$
$$2h^2 + 8h - 2{,}688 = 0 \qquad \text{Subtract 2,704 from both sides and combine like terms.}$$
$$h^2 + 4h - 1{,}344 = 0 \qquad \text{Divide both sides by 2.}$$

Solve the equation   To solve $h^2 + 4h - 1{,}344 = 0$, we cannot use the square root method, and the factoring method looks difficult because of the cumbersome last term $(-1{,}344)$. We will use the quadratic formula.

$$h = \frac{-b \pm \sqrt{b^2 - 4ac}}{2a} \qquad \text{The quadratic formula.}$$

$$= \frac{-4 \pm \sqrt{(4)^2 - 4(1)(-1{,}344)}}{2(1)} \qquad \text{Substitute 1 for } a, 4 \text{ for } b, \text{ and } -1{,}344 \text{ for } c.$$

$$= \frac{-4 \pm \sqrt{16 + 5{,}376}}{2} \qquad \text{Find the power and do the multiplication within the radical symbol.}$$

$$= \frac{-4 \pm \sqrt{5{,}392}}{2} \qquad \text{Do the addition within the radical symbol.}$$

$$\approx \frac{-4 \pm 73.430239}{2} \qquad \text{Use a calculator to approximate } \sqrt{5{,}392}.$$

$$h \approx \frac{-4 + 73.430239}{2} \quad \text{or} \quad h \approx \frac{-4 - 73.430239}{2} \qquad \text{Use a calculator to approximate each solution.}$$

$$\approx \frac{69.430239}{2} \qquad\qquad \approx \frac{-77.430239}{2}$$

$$h \approx 34.7151195 \qquad\qquad h \approx -38.7151195$$

State the conclusion   The width of each tube will be approximately 34.7 inches, and the length will be approximately $34.7 + 4 = 38.7$ inches. We discard the second solution, because the diagonal measure of a TV picture tube cannot be negative.

Check the result   Check the solution by substituting 34.7, 38.7, and 52 into the Pythagorean theorem.   ∎

EXAMPLE 8   *Finance.*   If $\$P$ is invested at an annual rate r, it will grow to an amount of $\$A$ in n years according to the formula $A = P(1 + r)^n$. What interest rate is needed to make a \$5,000 investment grow to \$5,618 after 2 years?

Solution   We can substitute 5,000 for P, 5,618 for A, and 2 for n in the formula and solve for r.

$$A = P(1 + r)^n$$
$$5{,}618 = 5{,}000(1 + r)^2$$
$$5{,}618 = 5{,}000(1 + 2r + r^2) \qquad \text{Find } (1 + r)^2.$$
$$5{,}618 = 5{,}000 + 10{,}000r + 5{,}000r^2 \qquad \text{Distribute the multiplication by 5,000.}$$
$$0 = 5{,}000r^2 + 10{,}000r - 618 \qquad \text{Subtract 5,618 from both sides.}$$

We can use a calculator and solve this equation by the quadratic formula, where $a = 5,000$, $b = 10,000$, and $c = -618$.

$$r = \frac{-b \pm \sqrt{b^2 - 4ac}}{2a}$$

$$= \frac{-10,000 \pm \sqrt{10,000^2 - 4(5,000)(-618)}}{2(5,000)}$$

$$= \frac{-10,000 \pm \sqrt{100,000,000 + 12,360,000}}{10,000}$$

$$= \frac{-10,000 \pm \sqrt{112,360,000}}{10,000}$$

$$= \frac{-10,000 \pm 10,600}{10,000}$$

$$r = \frac{-10,000 + 10,600}{10,000} \quad \text{or} \quad r = \frac{-10,000 - 10,600}{10,000}$$

$$= \frac{600}{10,000} \qquad\qquad\qquad = \frac{-20,600}{10,000}$$

$$= 0.06 \qquad\qquad\qquad\quad = -2.06$$

$$r = 6\% \qquad\qquad\qquad\quad r = -206\%$$

The required rate is 6%. The rate of -206% has no meaning in this problem. ∎

STUDY SET Section 9.2 ⟨www⟩

VOCABULARY *Fill in the blanks.*

1. The general ___quadratic___ equation is $ax^2 + bx + c = 0$.

2. The formula
$$x = \frac{-b \pm \sqrt{b^2 - 4ac}}{2a}$$
is called the ___quadratic___ formula.

3. To ___solve___ a quadratic equation means to find all the values of the variable that make the equation true.

4. $\sqrt{-16}$ is not a ___real___ number.

CONCEPTS *In Exercises 5–10, fill in the blanks.*

5. In the quadratic equation $ax^2 + bx + c = 0$, a cannot equal 0 .

6. Before we can determine a, b, and c for $x = 3x^2 - 1$, we must write the equation in ___quadratic___ form.

7. In the quadratic equation $3x^2 - 5 = 0$, $a = $ 3 , $b = $ 0 , and $c = $ −5 .

8. In the quadratic equation $-4x^2 + 8x = 0$, $a = $ −4 , $b = $ 8 , and $c = $ 0 .

9. The formula for the area of a rectangle is $A = $ lw , and the formula for the area of a triangle is $A = $ $\frac{1}{2}bh$.

10. If a, b, and c are three sides of a right triangle and c is the hypotenuse, then $c^2 = $ $a^2 + b^2$.

11. In evaluating the numerator of
$$\frac{-5 \pm \sqrt{5^2 - 4(2)(1)}}{2(2)}$$
what operation should be performed first? Evaluate 5^2.

12. Consider the expression
$$\frac{3 \pm 6\sqrt{2}}{3}$$

a. How many terms does the numerator contain? 2
b. What common factor do the terms have? 3
c. Simplify the expression. $1 \pm 2\sqrt{2}$

13. A student used the quadratic formula to solve an equation and obtained
$$x = \frac{-3 \pm \sqrt{15}}{2}$$

a. How many solutions does the equation have? 2

b. What are they *exactly?*
$$\frac{-3 + \sqrt{15}}{2}, \frac{-3 - \sqrt{15}}{2}$$

c. Approximate them to the nearest hundredth. 0.44, −3.44

14. Write the following steps of the strategy for solving quadratic equations in the proper order.

- Use the quadratic formula.
- Write the equation in $ax^2 + bx + c = 0$ form.
- Use the factoring method.
- Use the square root method.

square root, write, factor, quadratic formula

15. The solutions of a quadratic equation are

$$x = 2 \pm \sqrt{3}$$

Graph them on a number line.

16. The solutions of a quadratic equation are

$$x = \frac{-1 \pm \sqrt{5}}{2}$$

Graph them on a number line.

NOTATION   *Complete each solution.*

17. Solve $x^2 - 5x - 6 = 0$.

$$x = \frac{-b \pm \sqrt{b^2 - 4ac}}{2a}$$

$$= \frac{-(-5) \pm \sqrt{(-5)^2 - 4(1)(-6)}}{2(1)}$$

$$= \frac{5 \pm \sqrt{25 + 24}}{2}$$

$$= \frac{5 \pm \sqrt{49}}{2}$$

$$x = \frac{5 \pm 7}{2}$$

$$x = \frac{5 + 7}{2} = 6 \quad \text{or} \quad x = \frac{5 - 7}{2} = -1$$

18. Solve $3x^2 + 2x - 2 = 0$.

$$x = \frac{-b \pm \sqrt{b^2 - 4ac}}{2a}$$

$$= \frac{-2 \pm \sqrt{2^2 - 4(3)(-2)}}{2(3)}$$

$$= \frac{-2 \pm \sqrt{4 + 24}}{6}$$

$$= \frac{-2 \pm \sqrt{28}}{6}$$

$$= \frac{-2 \pm 2\sqrt{7}}{6}$$

$$= \frac{2(-1 \pm \sqrt{7})}{2 \cdot 3}$$

$$x = \frac{-1 \pm \sqrt{7}}{3}$$

19. What is wrong with this student's work?

Solve $x^2 + 4x - 5 = 0$.

$$x = -4 \pm \frac{\sqrt{16 - 4(1)(-5)}}{2}$$

The student didn't extend the fraction bar so that it underlines the complete numerator.

20. In reading

$$\frac{-b \pm \sqrt{b^2 - 4ac}}{2a}$$

we say, "the __opposite (negative)__ of b, plus or __minus__ the __square__ root of b __squared__ minus 4 __times__ a times c, all __over__ $2a$."

PRACTICE   *Change each equation into quadratic form, if necessary, and find the values of a, b, and c. Do not solve the equation.*

21. $x^2 + 4x + 3 = 0$ $a = 1, b = 4, c = 3$

22. $x^2 - x - 4 = 0$ $a = 1, b = -1, c = -4$

23. $3x^2 - 2x + 7 = 0$ $a = 3, b = -2, c = 7$

24. $4x^2 + 7x - 3 = 0$ $a = 4, b = 7, c = -3$

25. $4y^2 = 2y - 1$ $a = 4, b = -2, c = 1$

26. $2x = 3x^2 + 4$ $a = 3, b = -2, c = 4$

27. $x(3x - 5) = 2$ $a = 3, b = -5, c = -2$

28. $y(5y + 10) = 8$ $a = 5, b = 10, c = -8$

29. $7(x^2 + 3) = -14x$ $a = 7, b = 14, c = 21$

30. $(2a + 3)(a - 2) = (a + 1)(a - 1)$
$a = 1, b = -1, c = -5$

Use the quadratic formula to find all real solutions.

31. $x^2 - 5x + 6 = 0$ $2, 3$

32. $x^2 + 5x + 4 = 0$ $-1, -4$

33. $x^2 + 7x + 12 = 0$ $-3, -4$

34. $x^2 - x - 12 = 0$ $-3, 4$

35. $2x^2 - x - 1 = 0$ $1, -\frac{1}{2}$

36. $2x^2 + 3x - 2 = 0$ $-2, \frac{1}{2}$

37. $3x^2 + 5x + 2 = 0$ $-1, -\frac{2}{3}$

38. $3x^2 - 4x + 1 = 0$ $1, \frac{1}{3}$

39. $4x^2 + 4x - 3 = 0$ $\frac{1}{2}, -\frac{3}{2}$

40. $4x^2 + 3x - 1 = 0$ $\frac{1}{4}, -1$

41. $x^2 + 3x + 1 = 0$ $\dfrac{-3 \pm \sqrt{5}}{2}$

42. $x^2 + 3x - 2 = 0$ $\dfrac{-3 \pm \sqrt{17}}{2}$

43. $3x^2 - x = 3$ $\dfrac{1 \pm \sqrt{37}}{6}$

44. $5x^2 = 3x + 1$ $\dfrac{3 \pm \sqrt{29}}{10}$

45. $x^2 + 5 = 2x$ no real solutions

46. $2x^2 + 3x = -3$ no real solutions

47. $x^2 = 1 - 2x$ $-1 \pm \sqrt{2}$

48. $x^2 = 4 + 2x$ $1 \pm \sqrt{5}$

49. $3x^2 = 6x + 2$ $\dfrac{3 \pm \sqrt{15}}{3}$

50. $3x^2 = -8x - 2$ $\dfrac{-4 \pm \sqrt{10}}{3}$

Use the most convenient method to find all real solutions. If a solution contains a radical, give the exact solution and then approximate it to the nearest hundredth.

51. $(2y - 1)^2 = 25$ $-2, 3$

52. $m^2 + 14m + 49 = 0$ $-7, -7$

53. $2x^2 + x = 5$ $\dfrac{-1 \pm \sqrt{41}}{4}$; $-1.85, 1.35$

54. $2x^2 - x + 2 = 0$ no real solutions

55. $x^2 - 2x - 1 = 0$ $1 \pm \sqrt{2}$; $-0.41; 2.41$

56. $b^2 = 18$ $\pm 3\sqrt{2}$; ± 4.24

57. $x^2 - 2x - 35 = 0$ $-5, 7$

58. $x^2 + 5x + 3 = 0$ $\dfrac{-5 \pm \sqrt{13}}{2}$; $-4.30, -0.70$

59. $x^2 + 2x + 7 = 0$ no real solutions

60. $3x^2 - x = 1$ $\dfrac{1 \pm \sqrt{13}}{6}$; $-0.43, 0.77$

61. $4c^2 + 16c = 0$ $-4, 0$

62. $t^2 - 1 = 0$ ± 1

63. $18 = 3y^2$ $\pm \sqrt{6}$; ± 2.45

64. $25x - 50x^2 = 0$ $0, \frac{1}{2}$

Solve each equation. Round each solution to the nearest tenth.

65. $2.4x^2 - 9.5x + 6.2 = 0$ $0.8, 3.1$

66. $-1.7x^2 + 0.5x + 0.9 = 0$ $-0.6, 0.9$

APPLICATIONS

67. HEIGHT OF A TRIANGLE   The triangle shown in Illustration 1 has an area of 30 square inches. Find its height.   6 in.

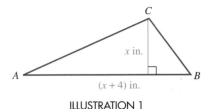

ILLUSTRATION 1

68. BOWLING   When the pins for a children's bowling game are set up, they occupy 418 cm^2 of floor space. See Illustration 2. If the base of the triangular-shaped region is 6 cm longer than twice the height, how wide is the last row of pins?   44 cm

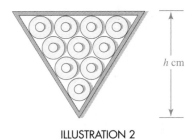

ILLUSTRATION 2

69. FLAG   According to the *Guinness Book of World Records 1998,* the largest flag flown from a flagpole was a Brazilian national flag, a rectangle having an area of 3,102 ft^2. If the flag is 19 feet longer than it is wide, find its width and length.   47 ft by 66 ft

70. COMICS   See Illustration 3. A comic strip occupies 96 square centimeters of space in a newspaper. The length of the rectangular space is 4 centimeters more than twice its width. Find its dimensions.
6 cm by 16 cm

ILLUSTRATION 3

71. COMMUNITY GARDEN   See Illustration 4. Residents of a community can work their own 16 ft $\times$ 24 ft plot of city-owned land if they agree to the following stipulations:

- The area of the garden cannot exceed 180 square feet.

- A path of uniform width must be maintained around the garden.

Find the dimensions of the largest possible garden.
10 ft by 18 ft

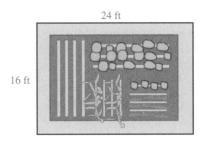

24 ft

16 ft

ILLUSTRATION 4

72. DECKING   The owner of the pool in Illustration 5 wants to surround it with a concrete deck of uniform width (shown in gray). If he can afford 368 square feet of decking, how wide can he make the deck?   4 ft

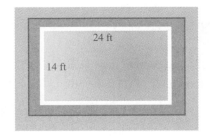

24 ft

14 ft

ILLUSTRATION 5

73. DAREDEVIL   In 1873, Henry Bellini combined a tightrope walk over the Niagara River with a leap into the churning river below, where he was picked up by a boat. If the rope was 200 feet above the water, for how many seconds did he fall before hitting the water? Round to the nearest tenth.   3.5 sec

74. FALLING OBJECT   A tourist drops a penny from the observation deck of the World Trade Center, 1,377 feet above the ground. How long will it take for the penny to hit the ground?   about 9.3 sec

75. ABACUS   The Chinese abacus shown in Illustration 6 consists of a frame, parallel wires, and beads that are moved to perform arithmetic computations. The frame is 21 centimeters wider than it is high. Find its dimensions.   15 cm by 36 cm

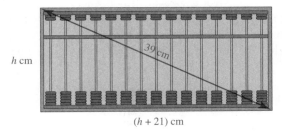

h cm

39 cm

$(h + 21)$ cm

ILLUSTRATION 6

76. INSTALLING A SIDEWALK   A 170-meter-long sidewalk from the mathematics building M to the

student center C is shown in red in Illustration 7. However, students prefer to walk directly from M to C. How long are the two segments of the existing sidewalk?   50 m and 120 m

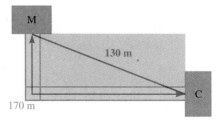

M

130 m

C

170 m

ILLUSTRATION 7

77. NAVIGATION   Two boats leave port at the same time, one sailing east and one sailing south. If one boat sails 10 nautical miles more than the other and they are then 50 nautical miles apart, how far does each boat sail? 30 and 40 nautical miles

78. NAVIGATION   One plane heads west from an airport, flying at 200 mph. One hour later, a second plane heads north from the same airport, flying at the same speed. When will the planes be 1,000 miles apart? 3 hr after the second plane takes off

79. INVESTING   We can use the formula $A = P(1 + r)^2$ to find the amount A that P will become when invested at an annual rate of $r\%$ for 2 years. What interest rate is needed to make $5,000 grow to $5,724.50 in 2 years?   7%

80. INVESTING   What interest rate is needed to make $7,000 grow to $8,470 in 2 years? See Exercise 79. 10%

81. MANUFACTURING   An electronics firm has found that its revenue for manufacturing and selling x television sets is given by the formula $R = -\frac{1}{6}x^2 + 450x$. How much revenue will be earned by manufacturing 600 television sets? (*Hint:* Multiply both sides of the equation by -6.) $210,000

82. RETAILING   When a wholesaler sells n CD players, his revenue R is given by the formula $R = 150n - \frac{1}{2}n^2$. How many players would he have to sell to receive $11,250? (*Hint:* Multiply both sides of the equation by -2.)   150

83. METAL FABRICATION   A square piece of tin, 12 inches on a side, is to have four equal squares cut from its corners, as shown in Illustration 8 on the next page. If the edges are then to be folded up to make a box with a floor area of 64 square inches, find the depth of the box.   2 in.

84. MAKING GUTTERS   A piece of sheet metal, 18 inches wide, is bent to form the gutter shown in Illustration 9 on the next page. If the cross-sectional area is 36 square inches, find the depth of the gutter. 3 in. or 6 in.

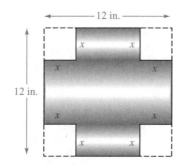

12 in.

12 in.

x x

x x

x x

x x

ILLUSTRATION 8

x

x

$18 - 2x$

ILLUSTRATION 9

WRITING

85. Do you agree or disagree with the following statement? Explain your answer.

The quadratic formula is the easiest method to use to solve quadratic equations.

86. Explain the meaning of the ± symbol.

87. Use the quadratic formula to solve $x^2 - 2x - 4 = 0$. What is an exact solution, and what is an approximate solution of this equation? Explain the difference.

88. Rewrite in words:
$$x = \frac{-b \pm 2\sqrt{b^2 - 4ac}}{2a}$$

REVIEW   *Solve each equation for the indicated variable.*

89. $A = p + prt$; for r $r = \dfrac{A - p}{pt}$

90. $F = \dfrac{GMm}{d^2}$, for M $M = \dfrac{Fd^2}{Gm}$

Write the equation of the line that has the given properties in general form.

91. Slope of $\frac{3}{5}$ and passing through $(0, 12)$ $3x - 5y = -60$

92. Passes through $(6, 8)$ and the origin $4x - 3y = 0$

Simplify each expression.

93. $2\sqrt{80}$ $42\sqrt{5}$ **94.** $22\sqrt{x^3 y^2}$ $2xy2\sqrt{x}$

Rationalize each denominator and simplify.

95. $\dfrac{x}{2\sqrt{7x}}$ $\dfrac{2\sqrt{7x}}{7}$ **96.** $\dfrac{2\sqrt{x} + 2}{2\sqrt{x} - 2}$ $\dfrac{x + 42\sqrt{x} + 4}{x - 4}$

9.3 *Graphing Quadratic Functions*

In this section, you will learn about

- Quadratic functions • Finding the vertex and the intercepts of a parabola
- A strategy for graphing quadratic functions • Finding a maximum value

INTRODUCTION. In this section, we consider a special type of function called a *quadratic function*. When graphing functions in Chapter 3, we constructed a table of values and plotted points. In this section, we will develop a more general strategy for graphing quadratic functions by analyzing the given function and determining the important characteristics of its graph.

Quadratic functions

Quadratic functions are defined by equations of the form $y = ax^2 + bx + c$ ($a \neq 0$), where the right-hand side is a second-degree polynomial in the variable x. Three examples of quadratic functions are

$$y = x^2 - 3 \qquad y = x^2 - 2x - 3 \qquad y = -2x^2 - 4x + 2$$

We can replace y with the function notation $f(x)$ to express the defining equation in the form $f(x) = ax^2 + bx + c$. For the functions just mentioned, we can write

$$f(x) = x^2 - 3 \qquad f(x) = x^2 - 2x - 3 \qquad f(x) = -2x^2 - 4x + 2$$

In Section 3.2, we constructed the graph of $y = x^2$ (a quadratic function) by plotting points. The result was the **parabola** shown in Figure 9-5.

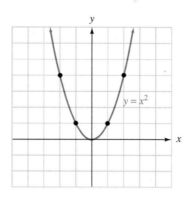

FIGURE 9-5

EXAMPLE 1   *Graphing quadratic functions.*   Graph $y = x^2 - 3$. Compare the graph to that of $y = x^2$.

Solution
The function is written in $y = ax^2 + bx + c$ form, where $a = 1$, $b = 0$, and $c = -3$. To find ordered pairs (x, y) that satisfy the equation, we pick several numbers x and find the corresponding values of y. If we let $x = 3$, we have

$$y = x^2 - 3$$
$$= 3^2 - 3 \quad \text{Substitute 3 for } x.$$
$$= 6$$

The ordered pair $(3, 6)$ and six others satisfying the equation appear in the table shown in Figure 9-6. To graph the equation, we plot each point and draw a smooth curve passing through them. The resulting parabola is the graph of $y = x^2 - 3$. The parabola opens upward, and the lowest point on the graph, called the **vertex of the parabola,** is the point $(0, -3)$.

Note that the graph of $y = x^2 - 3$ looks just like the graph of $y = x^2$, except that it is 3 units lower.

$y = x^2 - 3$

x	y	(x, y)
3	6	$(3, 6)$
2	1	$(2, 1)$
1	-2	$(1, -2)$
0	-3	$(0, -3)$
-1	-2	$(-1, -2)$
-2	1	$(-2, 1)$
-3	6	$(-3, 6)$

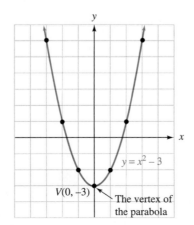

FIGURE 9-6

Self Check
Graph $y = x^2 + 2$. Compare the graph to that of $y = x^2$.

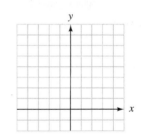

Answer: The graph has the same shape as the graph of $y = x^2$, but it is 2 units higher.

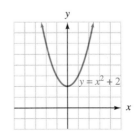

If we draw a vertical line through the vertex of a parabola and fold the graph on this line, the two sides of the graph will match. We call the vertical line the **axis of symmetry.**

EXAMPLE 2   *Graphing quadratic functions.*   Graph
$f(x) = -2x^2 - 4x + 2$, find its vertex, and draw its axis of symmetry.

Solution
The function is written in $f(x) = ax^2 + bx + c$ form, where $a = -2$, $b = -4$, and $c = 2$. We construct the table shown in Figure 9-7, plot the points, and draw the graph.

$$f(x) = -2x^2 - 4x + 2$$

x	$f(x)$	$(x, f(x))$
-3	-4	$(-3, -4)$
-2	2	$(-2, 2)$
-1	4	$(-1, 4)$
0	2	$(0, 2)$
1	-4	$(1, -4)$

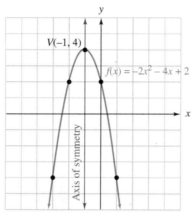

FIGURE 9-7

The parabola opens downward, so its vertex is its highest point, the point $(-1, 4)$.

Self Check
Graph $f(x) = -x^2 - 4x - 4$, find its vertex, and draw its axis of symmetry.

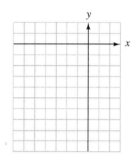

Answer: The vertex is at $(-2, 0)$.

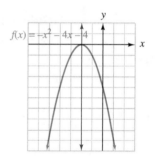

In Example 1, the coefficient of the x^2 term in $y = x^2 - 3$ is positive $(a = 1)$. In Example 2, the coefficient of the x^2 term in $f(x) = -2x^2 - 4x + 2$ is negative $(a = -2)$. The results of these first two examples illustrate the following fact.

Graphs of quadratic functions	The graph of the function $y = ax^2 + bx + c$ or $f(x) = ax^2 + bx + c$, where $a \neq 0$, is a parabola. It opens upward when $a > 0$ and downward when $a < 0$.

The cup-like shape of a parabola can be seen in a wide variety of real-world settings. Some examples are shown in Figure 9-8 (below and on the next page).

The path of a thrown object

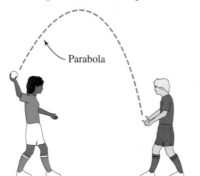

Parabola

The pursuit path of a shark seeking its prey

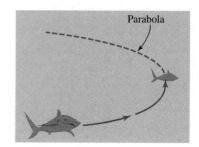

Parabola

FIGURE 9-8

The shape of a satellite antenna dish

The path of a stream of water

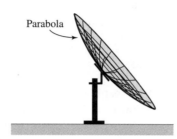

Parabola

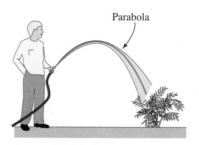

Parabola

FIGURE 9-8 (continued)

Finding the vertex and the intercepts of a parabola

It is easier to graph a quadratic function when we know the coordinates of the vertex of its parabolic graph. For a parabola defined by $y = ax^2 + bx + c$ or $f(x) = ax^2 + bx + c$, it can be shown that the x-coordinate of the vertex is given by $-\frac{b}{2a}$. This fact enables us to find the coordinates of its vertex.

Finding the vertex of a parabola

> The graph of the quadratic function $y = ax^2 + bx + c$ or $f(x) = ax^2 + bx + c$ is a parabola whose vertex has an x-coordinate of $-\frac{b}{2a}$. To find the y-coordinate of the vertex, substitute $-\frac{b}{2a}$ into the defining equation and find y.

EXAMPLE 3   *Finding the vertex of a parabola.*   Find the vertex of the parabola defined by $y = x^2 - 2x - 3$.

Solution

For $y = x^2 - 2x - 3$, we have $a = 1$, $b = -2$, and $c = -3$. To find the x-coordinate of the vertex, we substitute the values for a and b into the formula $x = -\frac{b}{2a}$.

$$x = -\frac{b}{2a}$$

$$x = -\frac{-2}{2(1)}$$

$$= 1$$

The x-coordinate of the vertex is $x = 1$. To find the y-coordinate, we substitute 1 for x:

$$y = x^2 - 2x - 3$$
$$y = 1^2 - 2(1) - 3$$
$$= 1 - 2 - 3$$
$$= -4$$

The vertex of the parabola is the point $(1, -4)$. See Figure 9-9(a) on the next page.

Self Check

Find the vertex of the parabola defined by $y = -x^2 + 6x - 8$.

Answer: $(3, 1)$ ∎

When graphing quadratic functions, it is often helpful to find the x- and y-intercepts of the parabola.

EXAMPLE 4   *Finding the intercepts of a parabola.*   Find the x- and y-intercepts of the parabola defined by $y = x^2 - 2x - 3$.

Self Check

Find the x- and y-intercepts of the parabola defined by $y = -x^2 + 6x - 8$.

Solution

To find the *y*-intercept of the parabola, we let $x = 0$ and solve for *y*.

$$y = x^2 - 2x - 3$$
$$y = 0^2 - 2(0) - 3$$
$$y = -3$$

The parabola passes through the point $(0, -3)$. We note that the *y*-coordinate of the *y*-intercept is the same as the value of the constant term *c* on the right-hand side of $y = x^2 - 2x - 3$.

To find the *x*-intercepts of the graph, we set *y* equal to 0 and solve the resulting quadratic equation.

$$y = x^2 - 2x - 3$$
$$0 = x^2 - 2x - 3 \qquad \text{Substitute 0 for } y.$$
$$0 = (x - 3)(x + 1) \qquad \text{Factor the trinomial.}$$
$$x - 3 = 0 \quad \text{or} \quad x + 1 = 0 \qquad \text{Set each factor equal to 0.}$$
$$x = 3 \qquad\qquad x = -1$$

Since there are two solutions, the graph has two *x*-intercepts: $(3, 0)$ and $(-1, 0)$. See Figure 9-9(a).

Answers: *y*-intercept: $(0, -8)$; *x*-intercepts: $(2, 0)$, $(4, 0)$ ∎

A strategy for graphing quadratic functions

We can use the characteristics of a parabola to draw its graph. For example, to graph $y = x^2 - 2x - 3$, we note that the coefficient of the x^2 term is positive ($a = 1$). Therefore, the parabola defined by this function opens upward. In Examples 3 and 4, we found that the vertex of the graph of $y = x^2 - 2x - 3$ is at $(1, -4)$ and that the graph has a *y*-intercept of $(0, -3)$ and *x*-intercepts of $(3, 0)$ and $(-1, 0)$. See Figure 9-9(a).

We can locate other points on the parabola by noting that the graph has the axis of symmetry shown in Figure 9-9(a). If the point $(0, -3)$, which is 1 unit to the left of the axis of symmetry, is on the graph, the point $(2, -3)$, which is 1 unit to the right of the axis of symmetry, is also on the graph.

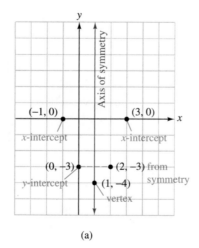

(a)

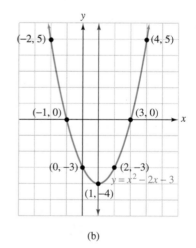

(b)

FIGURE 9-9

$$y = x^2 - 2x - 3$$

x	*y*	(*x*, *y*)
−2	5	(−2, 5)

We can complete the graph by plotting two more points. If $x = -2$, then $y = 5$, and the parabola passes through $(-2, 5)$. Again using symmetry, the parabola must also pass through $(4, 5)$. The completed graph of $y = x^2 - 2x - 3$ is shown in Figure 9-9(b).

Much can be determined about the graph of $y = ax^2 + bx + c$ from the coefficients a, b, and c. This information is summarized below.

Graphing a quadratic function
$y = ax^2 + bx + c$

Determine whether the parabola opens upward or downward by examining a.

The x-coordinate of the vertex of the parabola is $x = -\frac{b}{2a}$.

To find the y-coordinate of the vertex, substitute $-\frac{b}{2a}$ for x into the equation and find y.

The axis of symmetry is the vertical line passing through the vertex.

The y-intercept $(0, y)$ is determined by the value of y when $x = 0$: the y-intercept is $(0, c)$.

The x-intercepts (if any) are determined by the numbers x that make $y = 0$. To find them, solve the quadratic equation $ax^2 + bx + c = 0$.

EXAMPLE 5 *Graphing quadratic functions.* Graph $f(x) = -2x^2 - 8x - 8$.

Solution

Step 1 *Determine whether the parabola opens upward or downward.* The equation is in the form $f(x) = ax^2 + bx + c$, with $a = -2$, $b = -8$, and $c = -8$. Since $a < 0$, the parabola opens downward.

Step 2 *Find the vertex and draw the axis of symmetry.* To find the x-coordinate of the vertex, we substitute the values for a and b into the formula $x = -\frac{b}{2a}$.

$$x = -\frac{b}{2a}$$
$$x = -\frac{-8}{2(-2)}$$
$$= -2$$

The x-coordinate of the vertex is -2. To find the y-coordinate, we substitute -2 for x in the equation and find $f(-2)$.

$$f(x) = -2x^2 - 8x - 8$$
$$f(-2) = -2(-2)^2 - 8(-2) - 8$$
$$= -8 + 16 - 8$$
$$= 0 \qquad \text{If } f(-2) = 0, \text{ then } y = 0 \text{ for } x = -2.$$

The vertex of the parabola is the point $(-2, 0)$. This point is the blue dot in Figure 9-10 on the next page.

Step 3 *Find the x- and y-intercepts.* Since $c = -8$, the y-intercept of the parabola is $(0, -8)$. The point $(-4, -8)$, two units to the left of the axis of symmetry, must also be on the graph. We plot both points in black in Figure 9-10.

To find the x-intercepts, we set $f(x)$ equal to 0 and solve the resulting quadratic equation.

$$f(x) = -2x^2 - 8x - 8$$
$$0 = -2x^2 - 8x - 8 \qquad \text{Set } f(x) = 0.$$
$$0 = x^2 + 4x + 4 \qquad \text{Divide both sides by } -2.$$
$$= (x + 2)(x + 2) \qquad \text{Factor the trinomial.}$$
$$x + 2 = 0 \quad \text{or} \quad x + 2 = 0 \qquad \text{Set each factor equal to 0.}$$
$$x = -2 \qquad\qquad x = -2$$

Since the solutions are the same, the graph has only one x-intercept: $(-2, 0)$. This point is the vertex of the parabola and has already been plotted.

Self Check

Graph the function $y = -x^2 + 6x - 8$.

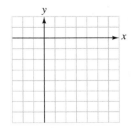

***Step 4** Plot another point.* Finally, we find another point on the parabola. If $x = -3$, then $y = -2$. We plot $(-3, -2)$ in Figure 9-10 and use symmetry to determine that $(-1, -2)$ is also on the graph. Both points are in green.

***Step 5** Draw a smooth curve through the points, as shown in Figure 9-10.*

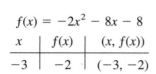

$$f(x) = -2x^2 - 8x - 8$$

x	$f(x)$	$(x, f(x))$
-3	-2	$(-3, -2)$

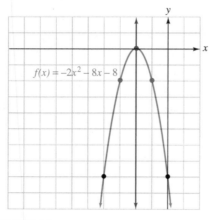

FIGURE 9-10

Answer:

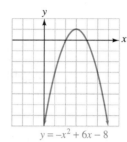

$$y = -x^2 + 6x - 8$$

COMMENT The number of x-intercepts of the graph of a quadratic function $y = ax^2 + bx + c$ is the same as the number of solutions of $ax^2 + bx + c = 0$. For example, the graph of $y = x^2 + x - 2$ in Figure 9-11(a) has two x-intercepts, and $x^2 + x - 2 = 0$ has two real-number solutions. In Figure 9-11(b), the graph has one x-intercept, and the corresponding equation has one real-number solution. In Figure 9-11(c), the graph does not have an x-intercept, and the corresponding equation does not have any real-number solutions. Note that the solutions of each equation are given by the x-coordinates of the x-intercepts of each respective graph.

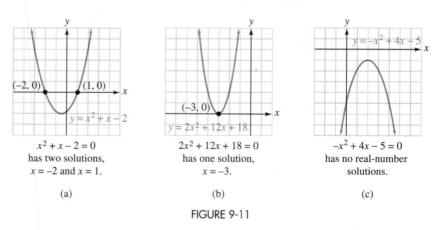

$x^2 + x - 2 = 0$ has two solutions, $x = -2$ and $x = 1$.	$2x^2 + 12x + 18 = 0$ has one solution, $x = -3$.	$-x^2 + 4x - 5 = 0$ has no real-number solutions.
(a)	(b)	(c)

FIGURE 9-11

Finding a maximum value

EXAMPLE 6 *Finding maximum revenue.* An electronics firm manufactures radios. Over the past 10 years, the firm has learned that it can sell x radios at a price of $200 - \frac{1}{5}x$ dollars. How many radios should the firm manufacture and sell to maximize its revenue? Find the maximum revenue.

Solution The revenue obtained is the product of the number of radios sold (x) and the price of each radio $200 - \frac{1}{5}x$. Thus, the revenue R is given by the function

$$R = x\left(200 - \frac{1}{5}x\right) \qquad \text{or} \qquad R = -\frac{1}{5}x^2 + 200x$$

Since the graph of this function is a parabola that opens downward, the *maximum* value of R will be the value of R determined by the vertex of the parabola. Because the x-coordinate of the vertex is at $x = -\frac{b}{2a}$, we have

$$x = -\frac{b}{2a}$$

$$= -\frac{200}{2\left(-\frac{1}{5}\right)} \qquad \text{Substitute 200 for } b \text{ and } -\frac{1}{5} \text{ for } a.$$

$$= -\frac{200}{-\frac{2}{5}} \qquad \text{Do the multiplication in the denominator.}$$

$$= (-200)\left(-\frac{5}{2}\right) \qquad \text{Division by } -\frac{2}{5} \text{ is the same as multiplication by its reciprocal, which is } -\frac{5}{2}.$$

$$= 500$$

If the firm manufactures 500 radios, the maximum revenue will be

$$R = -\frac{1}{5}x^2 + 200x \qquad \text{The revenue formula.}$$

$$= -\frac{1}{5}(500)^2 + 200(500) \qquad \text{Substitute 500 for } x, \text{ the number of radios.}$$

$$= 50,000$$

The firm should manufacture 500 radios to get a maximum revenue of $50,000. This fact is verified by examining the graph of $R = -\frac{1}{5}x^2 + 200x$, which appears in Figure 9-12.

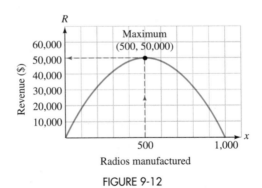

FIGURE 9-12

STUDY SET   Section 9.3

VOCABULARY   *Fill in the blanks.*

1. A function defined by the equation $y = ax^2 + bx + c \ (a \neq 0)$ is called a ___quadratic___ function.

2. The lowest (or highest) point on a parabola is called the ___vertex___ of the parabola.

3. The point where a parabola intersects the y-axis is called the ___y-intercept___.

4. The point (or points) where a parabola intersects the ___x-axis___ is (are) called the x-intercept(s).

5. For a parabola that opens upward or downward, the vertical line that passes through its vertex and splits the graph into two identical pieces is called the axis of ___symmetry___.

6. For the graph of $y = ax^2 + bx + c$, the ___coefficient___ of the x^2 term indicates whether the parabola opens upward or downward.

CONCEPTS   *In Exercises 7–10, fill in the blanks.*

7. The graph of $y = ax^2 + bx + c$, where $a \neq 0$, opens upward when $a > 0$.

8. The graph of $f(x) = ax^2 + bx + c$, where $a \neq 0$, opens downward when $a \, < \, 0$.

9. The y-intercept of the graph of $f(x) = ax^2 + bx + c$ is the point $(0, c)$.

10. The x-coordinate of the vertex of the parabola that results when we graph $y = ax^2 + bx + c$ is $x = \, -\frac{b}{2a}$.

11. Refer to the graph in Illustration 1.

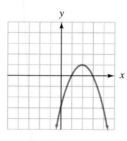

   a. What do we call the curve shown there?   a parabola

   b. What are the x-intercepts of the graph? $(1, 0), (3, 0)$

   c. What is the y-intercept of the graph? $(0, -3)$

   d. What is the vertex? $(2, 1)$

ILLUSTRATION 1

12. The vertex of a parabola is at $(1, -3)$, its y-intercept is $(0, -2)$, and it passes through the point $(3, 1)$, as shown in Illustration 2. Draw the axis of symmetry and use it to help determine two other points on the parabola. $(2, -2), (-1, 1)$

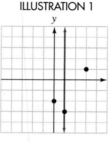

ILLUSTRATION 2

13. Sketch the graphs of parabolas with zero, one, and two x-intercepts.

14. Sketch the graph of a parabola that doesn't have a y-intercept, if possible.   not possible

15. HEALTH DEPARTMENT   The number of cases of flu seen by doctors at a county health clinic each week during a 10-week period is described by the quadratic function graphed in Illustration 3. Write a brief summary report about the flu outbreak. What important piece of information does the vertex give?

The most cases of flu (25) were reported the fifth week.

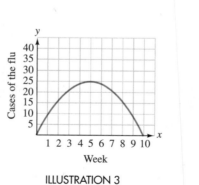

ILLUSTRATION 3

16. COST ANALYSIS   A company has found that when it assembles x carburetors in a production run, the manufacturing cost y per carburetor is given by the quad-

ratic function graphed in Illustration 4. What important piece of information does the vertex give?

The cost to manufacture a carburetor is lowest ($100) for a production run of 30 units.

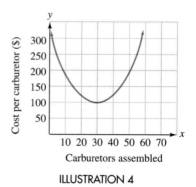

ILLUSTRATION 4

NOTATION

17. Tell whether this statement is true or false: The equations $y = 2x^2 - x - 2$ and $f(x) = 2x^2 - x - 2$ are the same.   true

18. The function $y = -x^2 + 3x - 5$ is written in $y = ax^2 + bx + c$ form. What are a, b, and c?
$-1, 3, -5$

19. Consider $y = 3x^2 + 3x - 8$. What is $-\dfrac{b}{2a}$? $-\frac{1}{2}$

20. Evaluate $\dfrac{-12}{2(-3)}$. -2

PRACTICE   *Graph each quadratic function and compare the graph to the graph of $y = x^2$.*

21. $y = x^2 + 1$
moved up 1

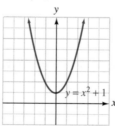

22. $y = x^2 - 4$
moved down 4

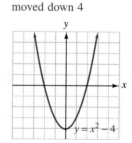

23. $f(x) = -x^2$
opens the opposite direction

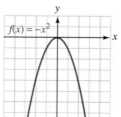

24. $f(x) = (x - 1)^2$
moved 1 to the right

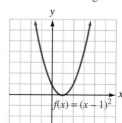
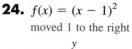

Find the vertex of the graph of each quadratic function.

25. $y = -x^2 + 6x - 8$ $(3, 1)$

26. $y = -x^2 - 2x - 1$ $(-1, 0)$

27. $f(x) = 2x^2 - 4x + 1$ $(1, -1)$

28. $f(x) = 2x^2 + 8x - 4$ $(-2, -12)$

Find the x- and y-intercepts of the graph of the quadratic function.

29. $f(x) = x^2 - 2x + 1$ $(1, 0); (0, 1)$

30. $f(x) = 2x^2 - 4x$ $(0, 0), (2, 0); (0, 0)$

31. $y = -x^2 - 10x - 21$ $(-3, 0), (-7, 0); (0, -21)$

32. $y = 3x^2 + 6x - 9$ $(-3, 0), (1, 0); (0, -9)$

Graph each quadratic function. Use the method discussed in Example 5.

33. $y = x^2 - 2x$

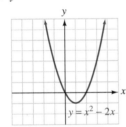

34. $f(x) = -x^2 - 4x$

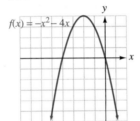

35. $f(x) = -x^2 + 2x$

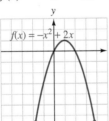

36. $y = x^2 + x$

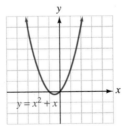

37. $f(x) = x^2 + 4x + 4$

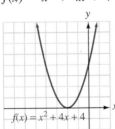

38. $f(x) = x^2 - 6x + 9$

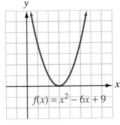

39. $y = -x^2 - 2x - 1$

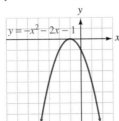

40. $y = -x^2 + 2x - 1$

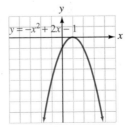

41. $y = x^2 + 2x - 3$

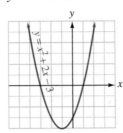

42. $y = x^2 + 6x + 5$

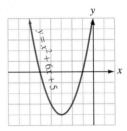

43. $f(x) = 2x^2 + 8x + 6$

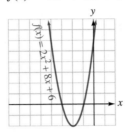

44. $f(x) = 3x^2 - 12x + 9$

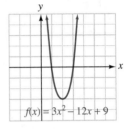

45. $y = x^2 - 2x - 8$

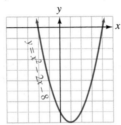

46. $y = -x^2 + 2x + 3$

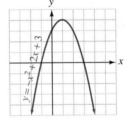

47. $y = x^2 - x - 2$

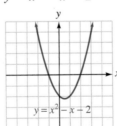

48. $y = -x^2 + 5x - 4$

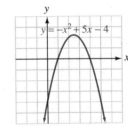

49. $f(x) = 2x^2 + 3x - 2$

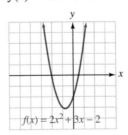

50. $f(x) = 3x^2 - 7x + 2$

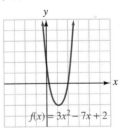

APPLICATIONS

51. TRAMPOLINE   Illustration 5 shows how far a trampolinist is from the ground (in relation to time) as she bounds into the air and then falls back down to the trampoline.

   a. How many feet above the ground is she $\frac{1}{2}$ second after bounding upward?   14 ft

b. When is she 9 feet above the ground?

0.25 sec and 1.75 sec

c. What is the maximum number of feet above the ground she gets? When does this occur?

18 ft; 1.0 sec

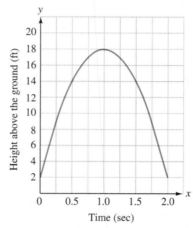

ILLUSTRATION 5

52. PROJECTILE   If we disregard air resistance and other outside factors, the path of a projectile, such as a kicked soccer ball, is parabolic. Suppose the path of the soccer ball after it is kicked is given by the quadratic function $y = -0.5x^2 + 2x$.

Use a calculator to complete the table of values in Illustration 6, and then plot the points and draw a smooth curve through them to depict the ball's path.

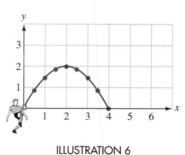

ILLUSTRATION 6

x	0	0.5	1	1.5	2	2.5	3	3.5	4
y	0	0.875	1.5	1.875	2	1.875	1.5	0.875	0

53. BRIDGE   The shapes of the suspension cables in certain types of bridges are parabolic. The suspension cable for the bridge shown in Illustration 7 is described by $y = 0.005x^2$. Finish the mathematical model of the bridge by completing the table of values using a calculator, plotting the points, and drawing a smooth curve through them to represent the cable. Finally, from each plotted point, draw a vertical support cable attached to the roadway.

x	−80	−60	−40	−20	0	20	40	60	80
y	32	18	8	2	0	2	8	18	32

54. SELLING TV SETS   A company has found that it can sell x TVs at a price of $\$\left(450 - \frac{1}{6}x\right)$

a. How many TVs must the company sell to maximize its revenue?   1,350

b. Find the maximum revenue. $303,750

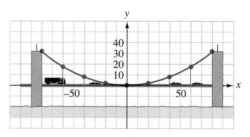

ILLUSTRATION 7

55. SELLING CD PLAYERS   A wholesaler sells CD players for $150 each. However, she gives volume discounts on purchases of 500 to 1,000 units according to the formula $\left(150 - \frac{1}{10}n\right)$ where n represents the number of units purchased.

a. How many units would a retailer have to buy for the wholesaler to obtain maximum revenue?   750

b. Find the maximum revenue. $56,250

56. TRACK AND FIELD   See Illustration 8. Sketch the parabolic path traveled by the long-jumper's center of gravity from the take-off board to the landing. Let the x-axis represent the ground.

ILLUSTRATION 8

WRITING

57. Explain why the y-intercept of the graph of $y = ax^2 + bx + c$, where $a \neq 0$, is $(0, c)$.

58. Use the example of a stream of water from a drinking fountain to explain the concept of the vertex of a parabola.

59. Explain why parabolas that open left or right are not graphs of functions.

60. Is it possible for the graph of a parabola not to have an x-intercept? Explain.

Is it possible for the graph of a parabola not to have a y-intercept? Explain.

REVIEW   *Simplify each expression.*

61. $2\sqrt{12} + 2\sqrt{27}$

$10\sqrt{3}$

62. $3\sqrt{2}\sqrt{6y} - 4\sqrt{2}\sqrt{3y}$

$-36y\sqrt{2}$

63. $\frac{1}{2}\sqrt{3} + 1\frac{1}{2}\sqrt{3} - 1\frac{1}{2}$

$2\sqrt{2}$

64. $\frac{1}{2}\sqrt{x} + 2\sqrt{2}$

$\frac{x + 4}{2\sqrt{x} + 4}$

Solve each equation.

65. $2\sqrt{6 + 2x} = 4$

5

66. $2\sqrt{1 - 2x} = 2\sqrt{x + 10}$

−3

Quadratic Equations

In this chapter, we have studied several ways to solve quadratic equations. We have also graphed quadratic functions and seen that their graphs are parabolas.

What Is a Quadratic Equation?

A quadratic equation can be written in the form $ax^2 + bx + c = 0$, where $a \neq 0$.
In Exercises 1–12, tell whether each item is a quadratic equation.

1. $y = 3x + 7$ no

2. $4(x + 5) = 2x$ no

3. $2x^2 - 3x + 4 = 0$ yes

4. $y(y - 6) = 0$ yes

5. $a^2 + 7a - 1 > 0$ no

6. $3y^2 - y + 4$ no

7. $5 = y - y^2$ yes

8. $x - 8 \ 0$ no

9. $2\overline{x + 7} = 4$ no

10. $x^2 = 16$ yes

11. $\dfrac{m}{2} - \dfrac{1}{3} = \dfrac{1}{4}$ no

12. $C = \dfrac{5}{9}(F - 32)$ no

Solving Quadratic Equations

The techniques we have used to solve linear equations cannot be used to solve a quadratic equation, because those techniques cannot isolate the variable on one side of the equation. Exercises 13–16 show examples of student work to solve quadratic equations. In each case, what did the student do wrong?

13. Solve $x^2 = 6$.

$\dfrac{x^2}{2} = \dfrac{6}{2}$ The student divided both sides by 2 and

$x = 3$ incorrectly thought that $\frac{x^2}{2}$ equals x. The square root method should be used.

14. Solve $x^2 - x = 10$.

$x(x - 1) = 10$

$x = 10$ or $x - 1 = 10$

$x = 11$

The student factored the left-hand side instead of first subtracting 10 from both sides and then factoring.

15. Solve $a^2 = 20$.

$a = 2\overline{\ 20\ }$ The student forgot to write the $\pm$ symbol when the square root method was used in

$a = 22\overline{\ 5\ }$ Step 2.

16. Solve $x^2 + 5x + 1 = 0$.

$a = 1 \quad b = 5 \quad c = 1$

$x = -5 \pm \dfrac{2\overline{\ 5^2\ } - 4\,(1)\,(1)}{2}$

$x = -5 \pm \dfrac{2\overline{\ 21\ }}{2}$

The student didn't draw the fraction bar so that it includes the complete numerator.

Solve each quadratic equation using the method listed.

17. $4x^2 - x = 0$; factoring method $0, \frac{1}{4}$

18. $x^2 + 3x + 1 = 0$; quadratic formula $\dfrac{-3 \pm \sqrt{5}}{2}$

19. $x^2 = 36$; square root method ± 6

20. $a^2 - a - 56 = 0$; factoring method $8, -7$

21. $x^2 + 4x + 1 = 0$; complete the square $-2 \pm \sqrt{3}$

22. $(x + 3)^2 = 16$; square root method $1, -7$

Quadratic Functions

The graph of the quadratic function $y = ax^2 + bx + c$ is a parabola. It opens upward when $a > 0$ and downward when $a < 0$.

23. The formula $R = 4x - x^2$ gives the revenue R (in tens of thousands of dollars) that a business obtains from the manufacture and sale of x patio chairs (in hundreds). Graph $R = 4x - x^2$ in Illustration 1.

24. Refer to Exercise 23. Find the vertex of the parabola. What is its significance concerning the revenue the business brings in?

Vertex (2, 4); the company should manufacture 200 chairs to get a maximum revenue of $40,000.

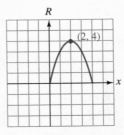

ILLUSTRATION 1

ACCENT ON TEAMWORK

Section 9.1

COMPLETING THE SQUARE Construct the model in Illustration 1. Label each piece of the model with its respective area. Show that the total area of the model is $(x^2 + 4x)$ square units. Next, add enough 1×1 squares to make the model a square. How many does it take to do this? Show that the area of the new figure can be expressed as $(x^2 + 4x + 4)$ or $(x + 2)(x + 2)$ square units Explain how this model demonstrates the process of completing the square on $x^2 + 4x$.

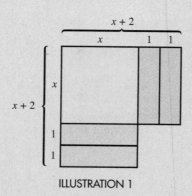

ILLUSTRATION 1

AUTHORING A TEXTBOOK Assign each of the nine examples in Section 9.1 to members of your group. Have them write a new but similar problem for each example, then write a solution complete with an explanation and author notes using the same format as this book. They should also create an accompanying Self Check problem and include the answer. Compile all nine examples into a booklet. Make copies of your booklet for the other members of the class.

Section 9.2

PREDICTING SOLUTIONS The expression $b^2 - 4ac$ is called the **discriminant** of the quadratic equation $ax^2 + bx + c = 0$. We can use the discriminant to predict the number of solutions a particular quadratic equation has.

If $b^2 - 4ac > 0$, the equation has two real solutions.
If $b^2 - 4ac = 0$, the equation has one real solution.
If $b^2 - 4ac < 0$, the equation has no real solutions.

For each quadratic equation, evaluate the discriminant to determine how many real-number solutions it has.

a. $4x^2 - 4x + 1 = 0$ **b.** $6x^2 - 5x - 6 = 0$
c. $5x^2 + x + 2 = 0$ **d.** $3x^2 + 10x - 2 = 0$
e. $2x^2 = 4x - 1$ **f.** $9x^2 = 12x - 4$

SOLVING QUADRATIC EQUATIONS Solve the quadratic equation $2x^2 - x - 1 = 0$ using these methods: factoring, completing the square, and the quadratic formula. Write each solution on a separate piece of paper. Under each solution, in two columns, list the advantages and the drawbacks of each method.

Section 9.3

PARABOLAS Use a home video camera to make a "documentary" showing examples of parabolic shapes you see in everyday life. Write a script for your video and have a narrator explain the setting, point out the vertex, and tell whether the parabola opens upward or downward in each case.

GRAPHING On one piece of graph paper, graph each of the following quadratic functions.

$$f(x) = x^2 \qquad g(x) = 2x^2 \qquad h(x) = \tfrac{1}{2}x^2$$

In general, what happens to the graph of $y = ax^2$ as a increases?

MINIMIZING/MAXIMIZING In the business world, it is good for a company to minimize its costs and to maximize its profits. In your group, make a list of quantities that are good to minimize and a list of quantities that are good to maximize.

SOLUTION AND GRAPH Write a quadratic function whose graph has the x-intercepts shown in Illustration 2. (*Hint:* Recall that there is a relation between the solution of a quadratic equation and the x-intercepts of the graph of the corresponding quadratic function.)

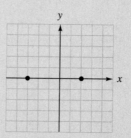

ILLUSTRATION 2

SECTION 9.1	*Completing the Square*

CONCEPTS

We can use the *square root method* to solve $x^2 = c$, where $c > 0$. The two solutions are

$x = 2\sqrt{c}$ and $x = -2\sqrt{c}$

[or $x = \pm 2\sqrt{c}$]

To make $x^2 + bx$ a trinomial square, add the square of one-half of the coefficient of x.

The factoring method doesn't always work in solving many quadratic equations. In these cases, we can use a method called *completing the square*.

To solve a quadratic equation by completing the square:

1. If necessary, divide both sides of the equation by the coefficient of x^2 to make its coefficient 1.

2. If necessary, get the constant on the right-hand side of the equation.

3. Complete the square and factor the resulting trinomial square.

4. Solve the quadratic equation using the square root method.

5. Check each solution.

REVIEW EXERCISES

1. Use the square root method to solve each quadratic equation.

   a. $x^2 = 25$ ± 5 **b.** $x^2 = 400$ ± 20

   c. $2x^2 = 18$ ± 3 **d.** $4y^2 = 9$ $\pm \frac{3}{2}$

   e. $t^2 = 8$ $\pm 2\sqrt{2}$ **f.** $2x^2 - 1 = 149$ $\pm 5\sqrt{3}$

2. Use the square root method to solve each equation.

   a. $(x - 1)^2 = 25$ $-4, 6$ **b.** $4(x - 2)^2 = 9$ $\frac{7}{2}, \frac{1}{2}$

   c. $(x - 8)^2 = 8$ $8 \pm 2\sqrt{2}$ **d.** $(x + 5)^2 = 75$ $-5 \pm 5\sqrt{3}$

3. Use the square root method to solve each equation. Round each solution to the nearest hundredth.

   a. $x^2 = 12$ ± 3.46 **b.** $(x - 1)^2 = 55$ $-6.42, 8.42$

4. Complete the square to make each expression a trinomial square.

   a. $x^2 + 4x$ $x^2 + 4x + 4$ **b.** $z^2 - 10z$ $z^2 - 10z + 25$

   c. $t^2 - 5t$ $t^2 - 5t + \frac{25}{4}$ **d.** $a^2 + \frac{3}{4}a$ $a^2 + \frac{3}{4}a + \frac{9}{64}$

5. Explain why the quadratic equation $x^2 + 4x + 1 = 0$ can't be solved by the factoring method. $x^2 + 4x + 1$ doesn't factor.

6. Solve each quadratic equation by completing the square.

   a. $x^2 - 8x + 15 = 0$ $3, 5$ **b.** $x^2 + 5x - 14 = 0$ $2, -7$

   c. $2x^2 + 5x - 3 = 0$ $\frac{1}{2}, -3$ **d.** $2x^2 - 2x - 1 = 0$ $\dfrac{1 \pm \sqrt{3}}{2}$

7. Solve $x^2 + 4x + 1 = 0$ by completing the square. Round each solution to the nearest hundredth. $-0.27, -3.73$

8. PLAYGROUND EQUIPMENT   The large tractor tire shown in Illustration 1 makes a good container for sand. If the circular area that the "sandbox" covers is 28.3 square feet, what is the radius of the tire? Round to the nearest tenth of a foot. 3.0 ft

ILLUSTRATION 1

SECTION 9.2   *The Quadratic Formula*

For the *general quadratic equation* $ax^2 + bx + c = 0$, where $a \neq 0$,

$$x = \frac{-b \pm 2\ \overline{b^2 - 4ac}}{2a}$$

This is called the *quadratic formula*.

9. Use the quadratic formula to solve each quadratic equation.
  a. $x^2 - 2x - 15 = 0$ $5, -3$ **b.** $x^2 - 6x - 7 = 0$ $7, -1$
  c. $6x^2 - 7x - 3 = 0$ $\frac{3}{2}, -\frac{1}{3}$ **d.** $x^2 - 6x + 7 = 0$ $3 \pm \sqrt{2}$

10. Use the quadratic formula to solve $3x^2 + 2x - 2 = 0$. Give the solutions in exact form and then rounded to the nearest hundredth. $\dfrac{-1 \pm \sqrt{7}}{3}, -1.22, 0.55$

11. Use the quadratic formula to solve $10x^2 + 2x + 1 = 0$.   no real solutions

12. SECURITY GATE   The length of the frame for the iron gate in Illustration 2 is 14 feet longer than the width. A diagonal crossbrace is 26 feet long. Find the width and length of the gate frame.   10 ft, 24 ft

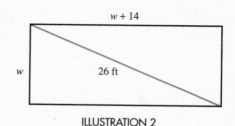

ILLUSTRATION 2

13. MILITARY   A pilot releases a bomb from an altitude of 3,000 feet. The bomb's height h above the target t seconds after its release is given by the formula

$$h = 3{,}000 + 40t - 16t^2$$

How long will it be until the bomb hits its target?   15 sec

Strategy for solving quadratic equations:

1. Try the square root method.
2. If it doesn't apply, write the equation in $ax^2 + bx + c = 0$ form.
3. Try the factoring method.
4. If it doesn't work, complete the square or use the quadratic formula.

14. Use the most convenient method to find all real solutions of each equation.
  a. $x^2 + 6x + 2 = 0$ $-3 \pm \sqrt{7}$ **b.** $(y + 3)^2 = 16$ $1, -7$
  c. $x^2 + 5x = 0$ $0, -5$ **d.** $2x^2 + x = 5$ $\dfrac{-1 \pm \sqrt{41}}{4}$
  e. $g^2 - 20 = 0$ $\pm 2\sqrt{5}$ **f.** $a^2 = 4a - 4$ $2, 2$
  g. $a^2 - 2a + 5 = 0$ no real solutions   **h.** $2c^2 = 800$ ± 20

SECTION 9.3   *Graphing Quadratic Functions*

The *vertex* of a parabola is the lowest (or highest) point on the parabola.

15. See the graph in Illustration 3.
  a. What are the x-intercepts of the parabola? $(-3, 0), (1, 0)$
  b. What is the y-intercept of the parabola? $(0, -3)$
  c. What is the vertex of the parabola? $(-1, -4)$
  d. Draw the axis of symmetry of the parabola on the graph.

A vertical line through the vertex of a parabola that opens upward or downward is its *axis of symmetry*.

16. What important information can be obtained from the vertex of the parabola in Illustration 4?   The maximum profit of $16,000 is obtained from the sale of 400 units.

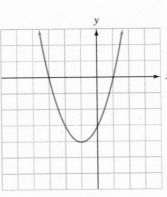

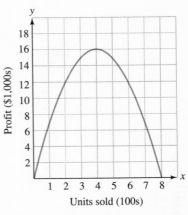

ILLUSTRATION 3   ILLUSTRATION 4

The graph of the quadratic function $y = ax^2 + bx + c$ is a parabola. It opens upward when $a > 0$ and downward when $a < 0$.

17. Find the vertex of the graph of each quadratic function and tell which direction the parabola opens. *Do not draw the graph.*

   a. $y = 2x^2 - 4x + 7$
      $(1, 5)$; upward

   b. $f(x) = -3x^2 + 18x - 11$
      $(3, 16)$; downward

The x-coordinate of the vertex of the parabola $y = ax^2 + bx + c$ is $x = -\frac{b}{2a}$. To find the y-coordinate of the vertex, substitute $-\frac{b}{2a}$ for x in the equation of the parabola and find y.

18. Find the x- and y-intercepts of the graph of $y = x^2 + 6x + 5$.
   $(-5, 0), (-1, 0); (0, 5)$

The x-intercepts of a parabola are determined by solving $ax^2 + bx + c = 0$. The y-intercept is $(0, c)$.

19. Graph each quadratic function by finding the vertex, x- and y-intercepts, and axis of symmetry of its graph.

   a. $y = x^2 + 2x - 3$

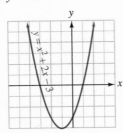

   b. $f(x) = -2x^2 + 4x - 2$

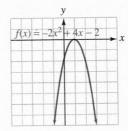

The number of x-intercepts of the graph of a quadratic function $y = ax^2 + bx + c$ is the same as the number of solutions of $ax^2 + bx + c = 0$.

20. The graphs of three quadratic functions are shown in Illustration 5. Fill in the blanks.

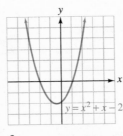

$x^2 + x - 2 = 0$ has 2 real-number solution(s).

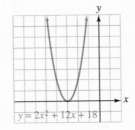

$2x^2 + 12x + 18 = 0$ has 1 real-number solution(s).

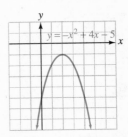

$-x^2 + 4x - 5 = 0$ has 0 real-number solution(s).

ILLUSTRATION 5

Solve each equation by the square root method.

1. $x^2 = 16$ ± 4

2. $u^2 = 24$ $\pm 2\sqrt{6}$

3. $4y^2 = 25$ $\pm\frac{5}{2}$

4. $(x - 2)^2 = 3$ $2 \pm \sqrt{3}$

5. ▦ ARCHERY   The area of the circular archery target shown in Illustration 1 is 5,026.5 cm². What is the radius of the target? Round to the nearest centimeter.   40 cm

ILLUSTRATION 1

6. Find the number required to complete the square on $x^2 - 14x$.   49

7. Complete the square to solve $a^2 + 2a - 4 = 0$. Give the exact solutions and then round them to the nearest hundredth. $-1 \pm \sqrt{5}$; $-3.24, 1.24$

8. Complete the square to solve $2x^2 = 3x + 2$. $2, -\frac{1}{2}$

In Problems 9–12, use the quadratic formula to find all real solutions of each equation.

9. $x^2 + 3x - 10 = 0$ $2, -5$

10. $2x^2 - 5x = 12$ $-\frac{3}{2}, 4$

11. $x^2 + 5 = 2x$ no real solutions

12. $x^2 = 4x - 2$ $2 \pm \sqrt{2}$

13. ▦ Solve $3x^2 - x - 1 = 0$ using the quadratic formula. Give the exact solutions, and then approximate them to the nearest hundredth.
$\dfrac{1 \pm \sqrt{13}}{6}$; $-0.43, 0.77$

14. 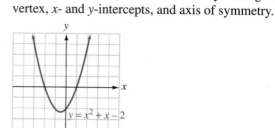 FLAG   According to the *Guinness Book of World Records 1998,* the largest flag in the world is the American "Superflag," which has an area of 128,775 ft². If its length is 5 feet less than twice its width, find its width and length.   255 ft, 505 ft

15. ADVERTISING   When a business runs x advertisements per week on television, the number y of air conditioners it sells is given by the quadratic function graphed in Illustration 2. What important information can be obtained from the vertex?

The most air conditioners sold in a week (18) occurred when 3 ads were run.

16. Graph the function $y = x^2 + x - 2$ by finding the vertex, x- and y-intercepts, and axis of symmetry.

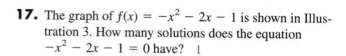

17. The graph of $f(x) = -x^2 - 2x - 1$ is shown in Illustration 3. How many solutions does the equation $-x^2 - 2x - 1 = 0$ have?   1

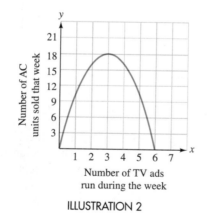

Number of TV ads run during the week

ILLUSTRATION 2

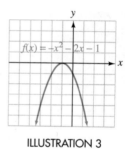

ILLUSTRATION 3

18. Explain the meaning of the $\pm$ symbol.   plus or minus

Chapters 1-9 Cumulative Review Exercises

1. Tell whether each statement is true or false.
   a. Every rational number can be written as a ratio of two integers. true
   b. The set of real numbers corresponds to all points on the number line. true
   c. The whole numbers and their opposites form the set of integers. true

2. Evaluate $-4 + 2[-7 - 3(-9)]$. 36

3. DRIVING SAFETY In cold weather climates, salt is spread on roads to keep snow and ice from bonding to the pavement. This allows snowplows to remove accumulated snow quickly. According to the graph in Illustration 1, when is the accident rate the worst?

2 hours before salt is spread

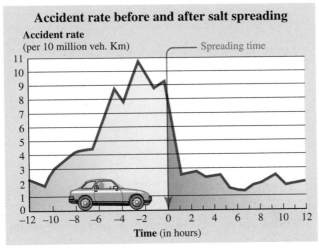

Accident rate before and after salt spreading

Based on data from the Salt Institute

ILLUSTRATION 1

4. EMPLOYMENT The following newspaper headline appeared in early 2000.

> **Xerox to Cut 5,200 Jobs, or 5.3% of Workforce, on Falling Profits**

How many employees did Xerox have at that time?
about 98,113

5. Simplify $3p - 6(p + z) + p$. $-2p - 6z$

6. Solve $\frac{5}{6}k = 10$. 12

7. Solve $-(3a + 1) + a = 2$. $-\frac{3}{2}$

8. Solve $5x + 7 < 2x + 1$ and graph the solution set. Then use interval notation to describe the solution.

$x < -2; (-\infty, -2)$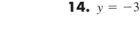

9. ENTREPRENEURS Last year, a women's professional organization made two small-business loans totaling $28,000 to young women beginning their own businesses. The money was lent at 7% and 10% simple interest rates. If the annual income the organization received from these loans was $2,560, what was each loan amount? $8,000 at 7%, $20,000 at 10%

10. Evaluate $(x - a)^2 + (y - b)^2$ for $x = -2$, $y = 1$, $a = 5$, and $b = -3$. 65

11. Evaluate $\frac{4}{5} \cdot 10 - 12$ @ 4

12. Find the slope of the line passing through $(-2, -2)$ and $(-12, -8)$. $\frac{3}{5}$

Graph each equation or inequality.

13. $2y - 2x = 6$

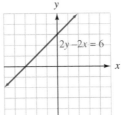

14. $y = -3$

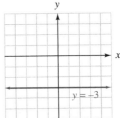

15. $y = -x + 2$

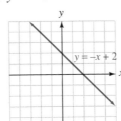

16. $y < 3x$

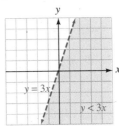

17. Graph the line passing through $(-2, -1)$ and having slope $\frac{4}{3}$

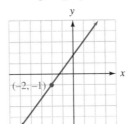

18. Graph $y = x^3 - 2$.

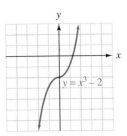

19. Write the equation of the line whose graph has slope $m = -2$ and y-intercept $(0, 1)$. $y = -2x + 1$

20. Write the equation of the line whose graph has slope $m = \frac{1}{4}$ and passes through the point $(8, 1)$. Answer in slope-intercept form. $y = \frac{1}{4}x - 1$

21. What is the slope of the line defined by $4x + 5y = 6$?
$-\frac{4}{5}$

22. If $f(x) = 3x^2 + 3x - 8$, find $f(-1)$. -8

23. Is the word *domain* associated with the input or the output of a function?   input

24. Is this the graph of a function?   yes

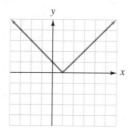

In Exercises 25–28, simplify each expression. Write each answer without using parentheses or negative exponents.

25. $y^3(y^2y^4)$ y^9

26. $\dfrac{b^2}{3a}b^{3}$ $\dfrac{b^6}{27a^3}$

27. $\dfrac{10a^4a^{-2}}{5a^2a^0}$ 2

28. $\dfrac{(r^2)^3}{(r^3)^4}$ $\dfrac{1}{r^6}$

29. FIVE-CARD POKER   The odds against being dealt the hand shown in Illustration 2 are about 2.6×10^6 to 1. Express the odds using standard notation.   2,600,000 to 1

ILLUSTRATION 2

30. PAIN RELIEVERS   See Illustration 3. Find the rate of change in the percent of individuals free of headache pain over the given time span after taking Acetaminophen.   16%/hr

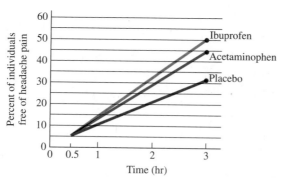

Based on data from *Health and Wellness*, Jones and Bartlett Publishers

ILLUSTRATION 3

Do the indicated operations.

31. $(-2a^3)(3a^2)$ $-6a^5$

32. $(2b - 1)(3b + 4)$ $6b^2 + 5b - 4$

33. $(2x + 5y)^2$ $4x^2 + 20xy + 25y^2$

34. $x - 3\overline{)2x^2 - 3 - 5x}$ $2x + 1$

Factor each expression completely.

35. $6a^2 - 12a^3b + 36ab$ $6a(a - 2a^2b + 6b)$

36. $2x + 2y + ax + ay$ $(x + y)(2 + a)$

37. $b^3 + 125$ $(b + 5)(b^2 - 5b + 25)$

38. $t^4 - 16$ $(t^2 + 4)(t + 2)(t - 2)$

Solve each equation.

39. $3x^2 + 8x = 0$ $0, -\frac{8}{3}$ **40.** $15x^2 - 2 = 7x$ $\frac{2}{3}, -\frac{1}{5}$

41. Write a polynomial that represents the perimeter of the rectangle shown in Illustration 4.
$6x^3 + 4x$

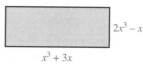

$2x^3 - x$

$x^3 + 3x$

ILLUSTRATION 4

42. HEIGHT OF A TRIANGLE   The triangle shown in Illustration 5 has an area of 22.5 square inches. Find its height. (*Hint:* Multiply both sides of the equation by 2.)   5 in.

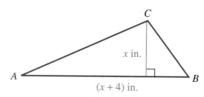

ILLUSTRATION 5

43. For what value $\dfrac{x}{x + 8}$ is undefined? -8

44. Simplify $\dfrac{3x^2 - 27}{x^2 + 3x - 18}$. $\dfrac{3(x + 3)}{x + 6}$

In Exercises 45–48, do the operations and simplify when possible.

45. $\dfrac{x^2 - x - 6}{2x^2 + 9x + 10} \div \dfrac{x^2 - 25}{2x^2 + 15x + 25}$ $\dfrac{x - 3}{x - 5}$

46. $\dfrac{x + 3}{x^2} + \dfrac{x + 5}{x^2}$ $\dfrac{2x + 8}{x^2}$

47. $\dfrac{x}{x - 2} + \dfrac{3x}{x^2 - 4}$ $\dfrac{x^2 + 5x}{x^2 - 4}$

48. $\dfrac{\dfrac{5}{y} + \dfrac{4}{y + 1}}{\dfrac{4}{y} - \dfrac{5}{y + 1}}$ $\dfrac{9y + 5}{4 - y}$

In Exercises 49–50, solve each equation.

49. $\dfrac{3r}{2} - \dfrac{3}{r} = \dfrac{3r}{2} + 3$ -1

50. $\dfrac{7}{q^2 - q - 2} + \dfrac{1}{q + 1} = \dfrac{3}{q - 2}$ 1

51. Solve the formula $\dfrac{1}{a} + \dfrac{1}{b} = 1$ for a. $a = \dfrac{b}{b - 1}$

52. ROOFING   A homeowner estimates that it will take him 7 days to roof his house. A professional roofer estimates that he could roof the house in 4 days. How long will it take if the homeowner helps the roofer? $2\frac{6}{11}$ days

53. LOSING WEIGHT   If a person cuts his or her daily calorie intake by 100, it will take 350 days for that person to lose 10 pounds. How long will it take for the person to lose 25 pounds?   875 days

54. GEAR   The speed of a gear varies inversely with the number of teeth. If a gear with 10 teeth makes 3 revolutions per second, how many revolutions per second will a gear with 25 teeth make?   1.2

55. Solve using the graphing method.
$$e\begin{cases} x + y = 1 \\ y = x + 5 \end{cases}$$

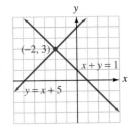

56. Solve using the substitution method.
$$e\begin{cases} y = 2x + 5 \\ x + 2y = -5 \end{cases} \quad (-3, -1)$$

57. Solve using the addition method.
$$\begin{cases} \dfrac{3}{5}s + \dfrac{4}{5}t = 1 \\ -\dfrac{1}{4}s + \dfrac{3}{8}t = 1 \end{cases} \quad (-1, 2)$$

58. MIXING CANDY   How many pounds of each candy shown in Illustration 6 must be mixed to obtain 60 pounds of candy that would be worth $3 per pound? Use two variables to solve this problem.   30 lb of each

ILLUSTRATION 6

59. Graph the solution set of
$$e\begin{cases} 3x + 4y \geq -7 \\ 2x - 3y \geq 1 \end{cases}$$

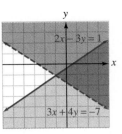

60. DEMOGRAPHICS   Refer to the graph in Illustration 7. To which stage does each of the following descriptions apply?

Stage 2 : Rapidly growing population: Births far outnumber deaths.

Stage 3 : Stable population: Birth rate drops; births and deaths are more or less equal.

Stage 1 : Stable population: Births and deaths are more or less equal.

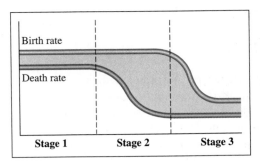

ILLUSTRATION 7

Simplify each expression. All variables represent positive numbers.

61. $2\sqrt{50x^2}$ $5x2\sqrt{2}$

62. $2\sqrt[3]{-27y^3}$ $-3y$

63. $32\sqrt{24} + 2\sqrt{54}$ $92\sqrt{6}$

64. $12\sqrt{2} + 1212\sqrt{2} - 32$ $-1 - 22\sqrt{2}$

65. B$\sqrt{\dfrac{72x^3}{y^2}}$ $\dfrac{6x2\sqrt{2x}}{y}$

66. $\dfrac{8}{2\sqrt{10}}$ $\dfrac{42\sqrt{10}}{5}$

67. Solve $2\sqrt{6x + 1} + 2 = 7$.   4

68. Solve $x^2 + 8x + 12 = 0$ by completing the square $-2, -6$

69. Solve $t^2 = 75$. $\pm 52\sqrt{3}$

70. 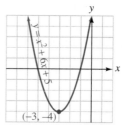 STORAGE CUBES   The diagonal distance across the face of each of the stacking cubes shown in Illustration 8 is 15 inches. What is the height of the entire storage arrangement? Round to the nearest tenth of an inch.   21.2 in.

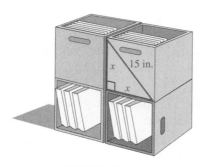

ILLUSTRATION 8

71. Solve $3x^2 - x - 1 = 0$ using the quadratic formula. Give the exact solutions, and then approximate each to the nearest hundredth.
$\dfrac{1 \pm 2\sqrt{13}}{6}$; $-0.43, 0.77$

72. QUILT   According to the *Guinness Book of World Records 1998,* the world's largest quilt was made by the Seniors' Association of Saskatchewan, Canada, in 1994. If the length of the rectangular quilt is 11 feet less than twice its width and it has an area of 12,865 ft², find its width and length.   83 ft × 155 ft

73. Find the vertex and the *x*- and *y*-intercepts of the graph of $y = x^2 + 6x + 5$. Then graph the function.

(graph with $y = x^2 + 6x + 5$, point $(-3, -4)$)

74. POWER OUTPUT   The graph in Illustration 9 shows the power output (in horsepower, hp) of a certain engine for various engine speeds (in revolutions per minute, rpm).
a. At an engine speed of 3,000 rpm, what is the power output?   150 hp
b. For what engine speed(s) is the power output 125 hp?   2,000 rpm and 5,000 rpm
c. For what engine speed does the power output reach a maximum?   4,000 rpm

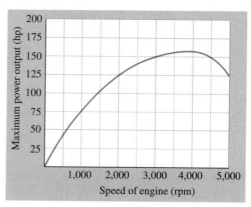

ILLUSTRATION 9

In this appendix, you will learn about

• The mean • The median • The mode

INTRODUCTION. Statistics is a branch of mathematics that deals with the analysis of numerical data. In statistics, three types of averages are commonly used as measures of central tendency of a distribution of numbers: the *mean,* the *median,* and the *mode.*

The mean

We have previously discussed the mean of a distribution.

The mean

> The **mean** of several values is the sum of those values divided by the number of values.
>
> $$\text{Mean} = \frac{\text{sum of the values}}{\text{number of values}}$$

EXAMPLE 1 *Physiology.* As part of a class project, a student measured ten people's reaction time to a visual stimulus. Their reaction times (in hundredths of a second) were

0.36, 0.24, 0.23, 0.41, 0.28, 0.25, 0.20, 0.28, 0.39, 0.26

Find the mean reaction time.

Solution

To find the mean, we add the values and divide by the number of values.

$$\text{Mean} = \frac{0.36 + 0.24 + 0.23 + 0.41 + 0.28 + 0.25 + 0.20 + 0.28 + 0.39 + 0.26}{10}$$

$$= \frac{2.9}{10}$$

$$= 0.29$$

The mean reaction time is 0.29 second. ■

EXAMPLE 2 *Banking.* When the mean (average) daily balance of a checking account falls below $500 in any week, the customer must pay a $20 service charge. What minimum balance must a customer have on Friday to avoid a service charge? See Figure I-1.

SECURITY SAVINGS BANK		
Day	**Date**	**Daily balance**
Mon	5/09	$670.70
Tues	5/10	$540.19
Wed	5/11	−$60.39
Thurs	5/12	$475.65
Fri	5/13	

FIGURE I-1

Analyze the problem   We can find the mean (average) daily balance for the week by adding the daily balances and dividing by 5. If the mean is $500 or more, there will be no service charge.

Form an equation   We can let x = the minimum balance needed on Friday and translate the words into mathematical symbols.

The sum of the five daily balances	divided by	5	is	$500.

$$\frac{670.70 + 540.19 + (-60.39) + 475.65 + x}{5} = 500$$

Solve the equation

$$\frac{670.70 + 540.19 + (-60.39) + 475.65 + x}{5} = 500$$

$$\frac{1{,}626.15 + x}{5} = 500 \qquad \text{Simplify the numerator.}$$

$$5\left(\frac{1{,}626.15 + x}{5}\right) = 5(500) \qquad \text{Multiply both sides by 5.}$$

$$1{,}626.15 + x = 2{,}500$$

$$x = 873.85 \qquad \text{Subtract 1,626.15 from both sides.}$$

State the conclusion   On Friday, the account balance must be at least $873.85 to avoid a service charge.

Check the result   Check the result by adding the five daily balances and dividing by 5.   ■

The median

The median   The **median** of several values is the middle value. To find the median of several values,

1. Arrange the values in increasing order.
2. If there is an odd number of values, choose the middle value.
3. If there is an even number of values, add the middle two values and divide by 2.

EXAMPLE 3   *Finding the median.*   In Example 1, the following values were the reaction times of ten people to a visual stimulus.

0.36, 0.24, 0.23, 0.41, 0.28, 0.25, 0.20, 0.28, 0.39, 0.26

Find the median of these values.

Solution

To find the median, we first arrange the values in increasing order:

$$0.20, 0.23, 0.24, 0.25, \; 0.26 \;, \; 0.28 \;, 0.28, 0.36, 0.39, 0.41$$

Because there is an even number of values, the median will be the sum of the middle two values, 0.26 and 0.28, divided by 2. Thus, the median is

$$\text{Median} = \frac{0.26 + 0.28}{2} = 0.27$$

The median reaction time is 0.27 second. ■

The mode

The mode	The **mode** of several values is the value that occurs most often.

EXAMPLE 4   *Finding the mode.*   Find the mode of the following values.

$$0.36, 0.24, 0.23, 0.41, 0.28, 0.25, 0.20, 0.28, 0.39, 0.26$$

Solution   Since the value 0.28 occurs most often, it is the mode. ■

If two different numbers in a distribution tie for occuring most often, there are two modes, and the distribution is called **bimodal**.

Although the mean is probably the most common measure of average, the median and the mode are frequently used. For example, workers' salaries are usually compared to the median (average) salary. To say that the modal (average) shoe size is 10 means that a shoe size of 10 occurs more often than any other shoe size.

STUDY SET   Appendix I

PRACTICE   *In Exercises 1–3, use the following distribution of values: 7, 5, 9, 10, 8, 6, 6, 7, 9, 12, 9.*

1. Find the mean.   8

2. Find the median.   8

3. Find the mode.   9

In Exercises 4–6, use the following distribution of values: 8, 12, 23, 12, 10, 16, 26, 12, 14, 8, 16, 23.

4. Find the median.   13

5. Find the mode.   12

6. Find the mean.   15

7. Find the mean, median, and mode of the following values: 24, 27, 30, 27, 31, 30, and 27.   28, 27, 27

8. Find the mean, median, and mode of the following golf scores: 85, 87, 88, 82, 85, 91, 88, and 88.
86.75, 87.5, 88

APPLICATIONS

9. FOOTBALL   The gains and losses made by a running back on seven plays were −8 yd, 2 yd, −6 yd, 6 yd, 4 yd, −7 yd, and −5 yd. Find his average (mean) yards per carry.   −2 yd

10. SALES   If a clerk had the sales shown in Illustration 1 for one week, find the mean of her daily sales. $1,211

Monday	$1,525
Tuesday	$ 785
Wednesday	$1,628
Thursday	$1,214
Friday	$ 917
Saturday	$1,197

ILLUSTRATION 1

11. VIRUSES   Illustration 2 gives the approximate lengths (in centimicrons) of the viruses that cause five common diseases. Find the mean length of the viruses.
74.5 centimicrons

Polio	2.5
Influenza	105.1
Pharyngitis	74.9
Chicken pox	137.4
Yellow fever	52.6

ILLUSTRATION 2

12. SALARIES   Ten workers in a small business have monthly salaries of $2,500, $1,750, $2,415, $3,240, $2,790, $3,240, $2,650, $2,415, $2,415, and $2,650. Find the average (mean) salary. $2,606.50

13. JOB TESTING   To be accepted into a police training program, a recruit must have an average (mean) score of 85 on a battery of four tests. If a candidate scored 78 on the oral test, 91 on the physical test, and 87 on the psychological test, what is the lowest score she can obtain on the written test and be accepted into the program?   84

14. GAS MILEAGE   Mileage estimates for four cars owned by a small business are shown in Illustration 3. If the business buys a fifth car, what must its mileage average be so that the five-car fleet averages 20.8 mpg?
24.5 mpg

Model	City mileage (mpg)
Chevrolet Lumina	20.3
Jeep Cherokee	14.1
Ford Contour	28.2
Dodge Caravan	16.9

ILLUSTRATION 3

15. SPORT FISHING   The weights (in pounds) of the trophy fish caught one week in Catfish Lake were 4, 7, 4, 3, 3, 5, 6, 9, 4, 5, 8, 13, 4, 5, 4, 6, and 9. Find the median and modal averages of the fish caught.
5 lb, 4 lb

16. SALARIES   Find the median and mode of the ten salaries given in Exercise 12. $2,575, $2,415

17. FUEL EFFICIENCY   The ten most fuel-efficient cars in 1997, based on manufacturer's estimates, are shown in Illustration 4. Find the median and mode of the city mileage estimates.   median: 29.5, mode: 29

18. FUEL EFFICIENCY   Use the data in Illustration 4 to find the median and mode of the highway mileage estimates.   median 38; mode: 38

Model	mpg city/hwy
Geo Metro LSi	39/43
Honda Civic HX coupe	35/41
Honda Civic LX sedan	33/38
Mazda Protégé	31/35
Nissan Sentra GXE	30/40
Toyota Paseo	29/37
Saturn SL1	29/40
Dodge Neon Sport Coupe	29/38
Hyundai Accent	29/38
Toyota Tercel DX	28/38

ILLUSTRATION 4

WRITING

19. Explain why the mean of two numbers is halfway between the numbers.

20. Can the mean, median, and mode of a distribution be the same number? Explain.

21. Must the mean, median, and mode of a distribution be the same number? Explain.

22. Can the mode of a distribution be greater than the mean? Explain.

APPENDIX II ROOTS AND POWERS

n	n^2	$\sqrt{n}$	n^3	$\sqrt[3]{n}$	n	n^2	$\sqrt{n}$	n^3	$\sqrt[3]{n}$
1	1	1.000	1	1.000	51	2,601	7.141	132,651	3.708
2	4	1.414	8	1.260	52	2,704	7.211	140,608	3.733
3	9	1.732	27	1.442	53	2,809	7.280	148,877	3.756
4	16	2.000	64	1.587	54	2,916	7.348	157,464	3.780
5	25	2.236	125	1.710	55	3,025	7.416	166,375	3.803
6	36	2.449	216	1.817	56	3,136	7.483	175,616	3.826
7	49	2.646	343	1.913	57	3,249	7.550	185,193	3.849
8	64	2.828	512	2.000	58	3,364	7.616	195,112	3.871
9	81	3.000	729	2.080	59	3,481	7.681	205,379	3.893
10	100	3.162	1,000	2.154	60	3,600	7.746	216,000	3.915
11	121	3.317	1,331	2.224	61	3,721	7.810	226,981	3.936
12	144	3.464	1,728	2.289	62	3,844	7.874	238,328	3.958
13	169	3.606	2,197	2.351	63	3,969	7.937	250,047	3.979
14	196	3.742	2,744	2.410	64	4,096	8.000	262,144	4.000
15	225	3.873	3,375	2.466	65	4,225	8.062	274,625	4.021
16	256	4.000	4,096	2.520	66	4,356	8.124	287,496	4.041
17	289	4.123	4,913	2.571	67	4,489	8.185	300,763	4.062
18	324	4.243	5,832	2.621	68	4,624	8.246	314,432	4.082
19	361	4.359	6,859	2.668	69	4,761	8.307	328,509	4.102
20	400	4.472	8,000	2.714	70	4,900	8.367	343,000	4.121
21	441	4.583	9,261	2.759	71	5,041	8.426	357,911	4.141
22	484	4.690	10,648	2.802	72	5,184	8.485	373,248	4.160
23	529	4.796	12,167	2.844	73	5,329	8.544	389,017	4.179
24	576	4.899	13,824	2.884	74	5,476	8.602	405,224	4.198
25	625	5.000	15,625	2.924	75	5,625	8.660	421,875	4.217
26	676	5.099	17,576	2.962	76	5,776	8.718	438,976	4.236
27	729	5.196	19,683	3.000	77	5,929	8.775	456,533	4.254
28	784	5.292	21,952	3.037	78	6,084	8.832	474,552	4.273
29	841	5.385	24,389	3.072	79	6,241	8.888	493,039	4.291
30	900	5.477	27,000	3.107	80	6,400	8.944	512,000	4.309
31	961	5.568	29,791	3.141	81	6,561	9.000	531,441	4.327
32	1,024	5.657	32,768	3.175	82	6,724	9.055	551,368	4.344
33	1,089	5.745	35,937	3.208	83	6,889	9.110	571,787	4.362
34	1,156	5.831	39,304	3.240	84	7,056	9.165	592,704	4.380
35	1,225	5.916	42,875	3.271	85	7,225	9.220	614,125	4.397
36	1,296	6.000	46,656	3.302	86	7,396	9.274	636,056	4.414
37	1,369	6.083	50,653	3.332	87	7,569	9.327	658,503	4.431
38	1,444	6.164	54,872	3.362	88	7,744	9.381	681,472	4.448
39	1,521	6.245	59,319	3.391	89	7,921	9.434	704,969	4.465
40	1,600	6.325	64,000	3.420	90	8,100	9.487	729,000	4.481
41	1,681	6.403	68,921	3.448	91	8,281	9.539	753,571	4.498
42	1,764	6.481	74,088	3.476	92	8,464	9.592	778,688	4.514
43	1,849	6.557	79,507	3.503	93	8,649	9.644	804,357	4.531
44	1,936	6.633	85,184	3.530	94	8,836	9.695	830,584	4.547
45	2,025	6.708	91,125	3.557	95	9,025	9.747	857,375	4.563
46	2,116	6.782	97,336	3.583	96	9,216	9.798	884,736	4.579
47	2,209	6.856	103,823	3.609	97	9,409	9.849	912,673	4.595
48	2,304	6.928	110,592	3.634	98	9,604	9.899	941,192	4.610
49	2,401	7.000	117,649	3.659	99	9,801	9.950	970,299	4.626
50	2,500	7.071	125,000	3.684	100	10,000	10.000	1,000,000	4.642

Index

I-2

I-3